Complete Solutions Manual

College Algebra

ELEVENTH EDITION

R. David Gustafson
Rock Valley College

Jeffrey D. Hughes
Hinds Community College

Prepared by

Michael G. Welden

Australia • Brazil • Japan • Korea • Mexico • Singapore • Spain • United Kingdom • United States

For product information and technology assistance, contact us at
Cengage Learning Customer & Sales Support,
1-800-354-9706

For permission to use material from this text or product, submit all requests online at **www.cengage.com/permissions**
Further permissions questions can be emailed to
permissionrequest@cengage.com

ISBN-13: 978-1-133-10342-4
ISBN-10: 1-133-10342-1

Brooks/Cole
20 Davis Drive
Belmont, CA 94002-3098
USA

Cengage Learning is a leading provider of customized learning solutions with office locations around the globe, including Singapore, the United Kingdom, Australia, Mexico, Brazil, and Japan. Locate your local office at: **www.cengage.com/global**

Cengage Learning products are represented in Canada by Nelson Education, Ltd.

To learn more about Brooks/Cole, visit **www.cengage.com/brookscole**

Purchase any of our products at your local college store or at our preferred online store **www.cengagebrain.com**

Printed in the United States of America
1 2 3 4 5 17 16 15 14 13

Contents

Preface

This manual contains detailed solutions to all of the exercises of the text *College Algebra*, eleventh edition, by R. David Gustafson and Jeff Hughes.

Many of the exercises in the text may be solved using more than one method, but it is not feasible to list all possible solutions in this manual. Also, some of the exercises may have been solved in this manual using a method that differs slightly from that presented in the text. There are a few exercises in the text whose solutions may vary from person to person. Some of these solutions may not have been included in this manual. For the solution to an exercise like this, the notation "answers may vary" has been included.

If you are a student using this manual, please remember that only reading a solution does not teach you how to solve a problem. To repeat a commonly used phrase, mathematics is not a spectator sport. You MUST make an honest attempt to solve each exercise in the text without using this manual first. This manual should be viewed more or less as a last resort. Above all, DO NOT simply copy the solution from this manual onto your own paper. Doing so will not help you learn how to do the exercise, nor will it help you to do better on quizzes or tests.

I would like to thank Paul McCombs from Rock Valley College and Cynthia Ashton of Brooks/Cole Publishing Company for their help and support. This solutions manual was prepared using EXP 5.1.

This book is dedicated to John, who helps me to realize that mathematics cannot describe everything in life.

May your study of this material be successful and rewarding.

Michael G. Welden

Exercises 0.1 (page 13)

1. set **2.** subset **3.** union **4.** intersection

5. decimal **6.** variable **7.** 2 **8.** even

9. composite **10.** rational **11.** decimals **12.** $\leq$

13. negative **14.** 0 **15.** $x + (y + z)$ **16.** yx

17. $5m + 5 \cdot 2$ **18.** commutative, multiplication **19.** interval **20.** no

21. two **22.** half-open **23.** positive **24.** distance

25. Every natural number is a whole number, so $\mathbf{N} \subset \mathbf{W}$. **TRUE**

26. Every rational number is a real number, so $\mathbf{Q} \subset \mathbf{R}$. **TRUE**

27. The rational number $\frac{1}{2}$ is **not** a natural number, so $\mathbf{Q} \not\subset \mathbf{N}$. **FALSE**

28. Every integer is a rational number, so $\mathbf{Z} \subset \mathbf{Q}$. **TRUE**

29. Every whole number is an integer, so $\mathbf{W} \subset \mathbf{Z}$. **TRUE**

30. The real number $\sqrt{2}$ is **not** an integer, so $\mathbf{R} \not\subset \mathbf{Z}$. **FALSE**

31. $A \cup B = \{$a, b, c, d, e, f, g$\}$

32. $A \cap B = \{$d, e$\}$

33. $A \cap C = \{$a, c, e$\}$

34. $B \cup C = \{$a, c, d, e, f, g$\}$

35. $\frac{9}{16} = 0.5625$; terminates

36. $\frac{3}{8} = 0.375$; terminates

37. $\frac{3}{11} = 0.272727...$; repeats

38. $\frac{5}{12} = 0.416666...$; repeats

39. natural: 1, 2, 6, 7

40. whole: 0, 1, 2, 6, 7

41. integers: $-5, -4, 0, 1, 2, 6, 7$

42. rational: $-5, -4, -\frac{2}{3}, 0, 1, 2, 2.75, 6, 7$

43. irrational: $\sqrt{2}$ **44.** prime: 2, 7 **45.** composite: 6

46. even: $-4, 0, 2, 6$ **47.** odd: $-5, 1, 7$ **48.** negative: $-5, -4, -\frac{2}{3}$

49. 

50. 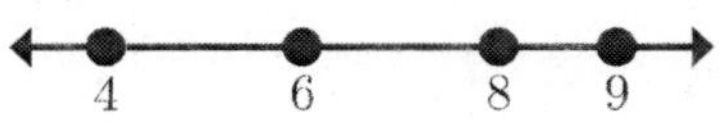

51. 11 13 17 19

52. −2 −1 0 1 2 3 4

53. −4 −3 −2 −1

54. −8 −6 −4 −2

55. −5 −3 −1 1 3

56. −0.7 1.75 $3\frac{7}{8}$

57. $x > 2 \rightarrow (2, \infty)$

2

58. $x < 4 \rightarrow (-\infty, 4)$

4

59. $0 < x < 5 \rightarrow (0, 5)$

0 5

60. $-2 < x < 3 \rightarrow (-2, 3)$

−2 3

61. $x > -4 \rightarrow (-4, \infty)$

−4

62. $x < 3 \rightarrow (-\infty, 3)$

3

63. $-2 \le x < 2 \rightarrow [-2, 2)$

−2 2

64. $-4 < x \le 1 \rightarrow (-4, 1]$

−4 1

65. $x \le 5 \rightarrow (-\infty, 5]$

5

66. $x \ge -1 \rightarrow [-1, \infty)$

−1

67. $-5 < x \le 0 \rightarrow (-5, 0]$

−5 0

68. $-3 \le x < 4 \rightarrow [-3, 4)$

−3 4

69. $-2 \le x \le 3 \rightarrow [-2, 3]$

−2 3

70. $-4 \le x \le 4 \rightarrow [-4, 4]$

−4 4

71. $6 \ge x \ge 2 \rightarrow 2 \le x \le 6 \rightarrow [2, 6]$

2 6

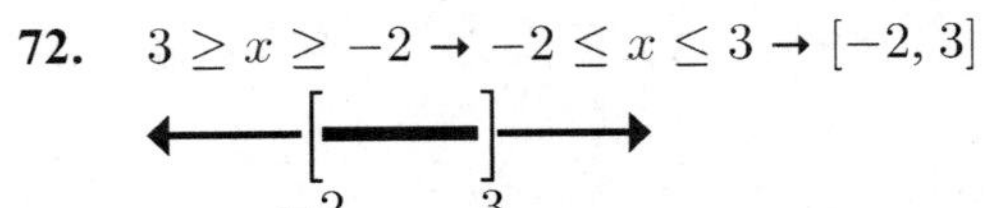

72. $3 \ge x \ge -2 \rightarrow -2 \le x \le 3 \rightarrow [-2, 3]$

−2 3

73. $x > -5$ and $x < 4 \rightarrow (-5, \infty) \cap (-\infty, 4)$

$(-5, \infty)$ −5

$(-\infty, 4)$ 4

$(-5, \infty) \cap (-\infty, 4)$ −5 4

74. $x \geq -3$ and $x < 6 \rightarrow [-3, \infty) \cap (-\infty, 6)$

$[-3, \infty)$; -3

$(-\infty, 6)$; 6

$[-3, \infty) \cap (-\infty, 6)$; -3 6

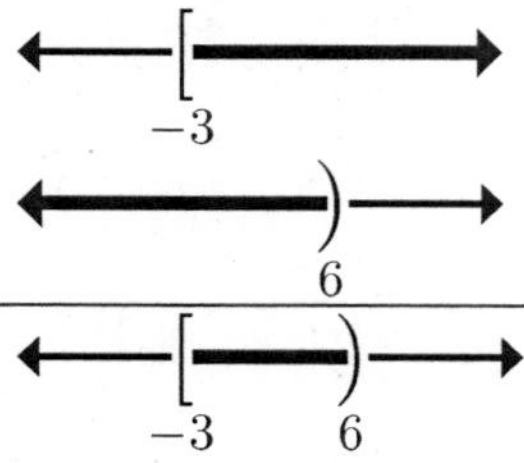

75. $x \geq -8$ and $x \leq -3 \rightarrow [-8, \infty) \cap (-\infty, -3]$

$[-8, \infty)$; -8

$(-\infty, -3]$; -3

$[-8, \infty) \cap (-\infty, -3]$; -8 -3

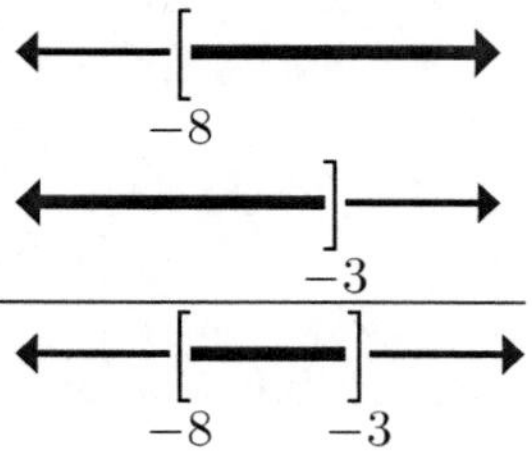

76. $x > 1$ and $x \leq 7 \rightarrow (1, \infty) \cap (-\infty, 7]$

$(1, \infty)$; 1

$(-\infty, 7]$; 7

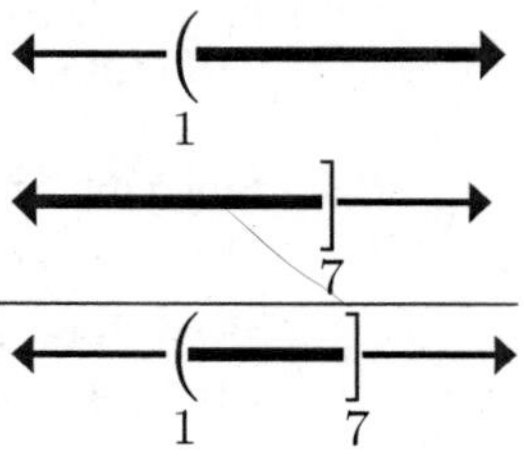

$(1, \infty) \cap (-\infty, 7]$; 1 7

77. $x < -2$ or $x > 2 \rightarrow (-\infty, -2) \cup (2, \infty)$

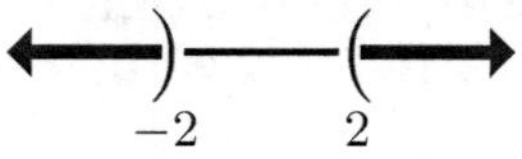

-2 2

78. $x \leq -5$ or $x > 0 \rightarrow (-\infty, -5] \cup (0, \infty)$

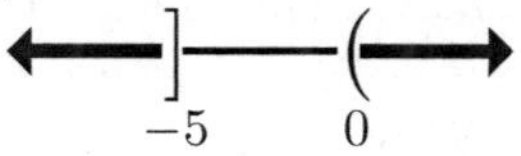

-5 0

79. $x \leq -1$ or $x \geq 3 \rightarrow (-\infty, -1] \cup [3, \infty)$

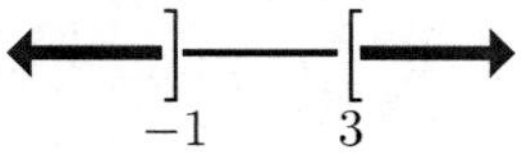

-1 3

80. $x < -3$ or $x \geq 2 \rightarrow (-\infty, -3) \cup [2, \infty)$

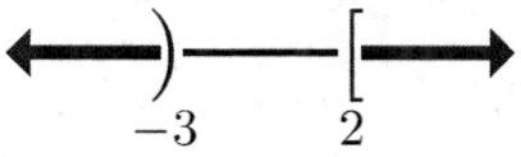

-3 2

81. Since $13 \geq 0$, $|13| = 13$.

82. Since $-17 < 0$, $|-17| = -(-17) = 17$.

83. Since $0 \geq 0$, $|0| = 0$.

84. Since $63 \geq 0$, $|63| = 63$.
$-|63| = -(63) = -63$

85. Since $-8 < 0$, $|-8| = -(-8) = 8$.
$-|-8| = -(8) = -8$

86. Since $-25 < 0$, $|-25| = -(-25) = 25$.

87. Since $32 \geq 0$, $|32| = 32$.
$-|32| = -(32) = -32$

88. Since $-6 < 0$, $|-6| = -(-6) = 6$.
$-|-6| = -(6) = -6$

89. Since $\pi - 5 < 0$,
$|\pi - 5| = -(\pi - 5) = -\pi + 5 = 5 - \pi$.

90. Since $8 - \pi \geq 0$, $|8 - \pi| = 8 - \pi$.

91. $|\pi - \pi| = |0| = 0$

92. Since $2\pi \geq 0$, $|2\pi| = 2\pi$.

93. If $x \geq 2$, then $x + 1 \geq 0$. Then
$|x + 1| = x + 1$.

94. If $x \leq -2$, then $x + 1 < 0$. Then
$|x + 1| = -(x + 1)$.

95. If $x < 0$, then $x - 4 < 0$. Then
$|x - 4| = -(x - 4)$.

96. If $x > 10$, then $x - 7 \geq 0$. Then
$|x - 7| = x - 7$.

97. distance $= |8 - 3| = |5| = 5$

98. distance $= |12 - (-5)| = |17| = 17$

99. distance $= |-3 - (-8)| = |5| = 5$

100. distance $= |-20 - 6| = |-26| = 26$

101. Since population must be positive and never has a fractional part, the set of **natural numbers** should be used.

102. Since the subdivisions on a ruler are measured in fractions of an inch, the set of **rational numbers** should be used.

103. Since temperatures are usually reported without fractional parts and may be either positive or negative (or zero), the set of **integers** should be used.

104. Since the financial condition of a business is usually described in terms of dollars and cents (fractional parts of a dollar), the set of **rational numbers** should be used.

105. $-x$ will represent a positive number if x itself is negative. For instance, if $x = -3$, then $-x = -(-3) = 3$, which is a positive number.

106. Every integer is a rational number because every integer is equal to itself over 1.

107. The statement is always true.

108. The statement is always true.

109. The statement is not always true.
(For example, let $a = 5$ and $b = -2$.)

110. The statement will be true if
$a \geq 0$ and $b \geq 0$, or if $a \leq 0$ and $b \leq 0$.

111. The statement $a < b > c$ could be interpreted to mean that $a > c$, when this is not necessarily true.

112. $|b - a| = |-1(a - b)| = |-1| \cdot |a - b|$
$= |a - b|$

Exercises 0.2 (page 24)

1. factor

2. natural

3. 3, $2x$

4. exponential

5. scientific, integer

6. **Answers may vary.**

7. $x^m x^n = x^{m+n}$

8. $(x^m)^n = x^{mn}$

9. $(xy)^n = x^n y^n$

10. $\frac{x^m}{x^n} = x^{m-n}$

11. $x^0 = 1$

12. $x^{-n} = \frac{1}{x^n}$

13. $13^2 = 13 \cdot 13 = 169$

14. $10^3 = 10 \cdot 10 \cdot 10 = 1{,}000$

15. $-5^2 = -1 \cdot 5 \cdot 5 = -25$

16. $(-5)^2 = (-5)(-5) = 25$

17. $4x^3 = 4 \cdot x \cdot x \cdot x$

18. $(4x)^3 = (4x)(4x)(4x)$

19. $(-5x)^4 = (-5x)(-5x)(-5x)(-5x)$

20. $-6x^2 = -6 \cdot x \cdot x$

21. $-8x^4 = -8 \cdot x \cdot x \cdot x \cdot x$

22. $(-8x)^4 = (-8x)(-8x)(-8x)(-8x)$

23. $7xxx = 7x^3$

24. $-8yyyy = -8y^4$

25. $(-x)(-x) = (-1)(-1)x^2 = x^2$

26. $(2a)(2a)(2a) = 2 \cdot 2 \cdot 2 \cdot a^3 = 8a^3$

27. $(3t)(3t)(-3t) = (3)(3)(-3)t^3 = -27t^3$

28. $-(2b)(2b)(2b)(2b) = -1 \cdot 2 \cdot 2 \cdot 2 \cdot 2 \cdot b^4 = -16b^4$

29. $xxxyy = x^3y^2$

30. $aaabbbb = a^3b^4$

31. $2.2^3 = 10.648$

32. $7.1^4 = 2541.1681$

33. $-0.5^4 = -0.0625$

34. $(-0.2)^4 = 0.0016$

35. $x^2x^3 = x^{2+3} = x^5$

36. $y^3y^4 = y^{3+4} = y^7$

37. $(z^2)^3 = z^{2 \cdot 3} = z^6$

38. $(t^6)^7 = t^{6 \cdot 7} = t^{42}$

39. $(y^5y^2)^3 = (y^7)^3 = y^{21}$

40. $(a^3a^6)a^4 = a^9a^4 = a^{13}$

41. $(z^2)^3(z^4)^5 = z^6z^{20} = z^{26}$

42. $(t^3)^4(t^5)^2 = t^{12}t^{10} = t^{22}$

43. $(a^2)^3(a^4)^2 = a^6a^8 = a^{14}$

44. $(a^2)^4(a^3)^3 = a^8a^9 = a^{17}$

45. $(3x)^3 = 3^3x^3 = 27x^3$

46. $(-2y)^4 = (-2)^4y^4 = 16y^4$

47. $(x^2y)^3 = (x^2)^3y^3 = x^6y^3$

48. $(x^3z^4)^6 = (x^3)^6(z^4)^6 = x^{18}z^{24}$

49. $\left(\frac{a^2}{b}\right)^3 = \frac{(a^2)^3}{b^3} = \frac{a^6}{b^3}$

50. $\left(\frac{x}{y^3}\right)^4 = \frac{x^4}{(y^3)^4} = \frac{x^4}{y^{12}}$

51. $(-x)^0 = 1$

52. $4x^0 = 4 \cdot 1 = 4$

53. $(4x)^0 = 1$

SECTION 0.2

54. $-2x^0 = -2 \cdot 1 = -2$

55. $z^{-4} = \dfrac{1}{z^4}$

56. $\dfrac{1}{t^{-2}} = t^2$

57. $y^{-2}y^{-3} = y^{-5} = \dfrac{1}{y^5}$

58. $-m^{-2}m^3 = -m^1 = -m$

59. $\left(x^3x^{-4}\right)^{-2} = \left(x^{-1}\right)^{-2} = x^2$

60. $\left(y^{-2}y^3\right)^{-4} = \left(y^1\right)^{-4} = y^{-4} = \dfrac{1}{y^4}$

61. $\dfrac{x^7}{x^3} = x^{7-3} = x^4$

62. $\dfrac{r^5}{r^2} = r^{5-2} = r^3$

63. $\dfrac{a^{21}}{a^{17}} = a^{21-17} = a^4$

64. $\dfrac{t^{13}}{t^4} = t^{13-4} = t^9$

65. $\dfrac{\left(x^2\right)^2}{x^2x} = \dfrac{x^4}{x^3} = x^{4-3} = x^1 = x$

66. $\dfrac{s^9s^3}{\left(s^2\right)^2} = \dfrac{s^{12}}{s^4} = s^{12-4} = s^8$

67. $\left(\dfrac{m^3}{n^2}\right)^3 = \dfrac{\left(m^3\right)^3}{\left(n^2\right)^3} = \dfrac{m^9}{n^6}$

68. $\left(\dfrac{t^4}{t^3}\right)^3 = \left(t^{4-3}\right)^3 = \left(t^1\right)^3 = t^3$

69. $\dfrac{\left(a^3\right)^{-2}}{aa^2} = \dfrac{a^{-6}}{a^3} = a^{-6-3} = a^{-9} = \dfrac{1}{a^9}$

70. $\dfrac{r^9r^{-3}}{\left(r^{-2}\right)^3} = \dfrac{r^6}{r^{-6}} = r^{6-(-6)} = r^{12}$

71. $\left(\dfrac{a^{-3}}{b^{-1}}\right)^{-4} = \dfrac{\left(a^{-3}\right)^{-4}}{\left(b^{-1}\right)^{-4}} = \dfrac{a^{12}}{b^4}$

72. $\left(\dfrac{t^{-4}}{t^{-3}}\right)^{-2} = \dfrac{\left(t^{-4}\right)^{-2}}{\left(t^{-3}\right)^{-2}} = \dfrac{t^8}{t^6} = t^2$

73. $\left(\dfrac{r^4r^{-6}}{r^3r^{-3}}\right)^2 = \left(\dfrac{r^{-2}}{r^0}\right)^2 = \left(r^{-2}\right)^2 = r^{-4}$
$= \dfrac{1}{r^4}$

74. $\dfrac{\left(x^{-3}x^2\right)^2}{\left(x^2x^{-5}\right)^{-3}} = \dfrac{\left(x^{-1}\right)^2}{\left(x^{-3}\right)^{-3}} = \dfrac{x^{-2}}{x^9} = x^{-11} = \dfrac{1}{x^{11}}$

75. $\left(\dfrac{x^5y^{-2}}{x^{-3}y^2}\right)^4 = \left(\dfrac{x^5x^3}{y^2y^2}\right)^4 = \left(\dfrac{x^8}{y^4}\right)^4 = \dfrac{x^{32}}{y^{16}}$

76. $\left(\dfrac{x^{-7}y^5}{x^7y^{-4}}\right)^3 = \left(\dfrac{y^5y^4}{x^7x^7}\right)^3 = \left(\dfrac{y^9}{x^{14}}\right)^3 = \dfrac{y^{27}}{x^{42}}$

77. $\left(\dfrac{5x^{-3}y^{-2}}{3x^2y^{-3}}\right)^{-2} = \left(\dfrac{3x^2y^{-3}}{5x^{-3}y^{-2}}\right)^2 = \left(\dfrac{3x^2x^3y^2}{5y^3}\right)^2 = \left(\dfrac{3x^5}{5y}\right)^2 = \dfrac{9x^{10}}{25y^2}$

78. $\left(\dfrac{3x^2y^{-5}}{2x^{-2}y^{-6}}\right)^{-3} = \left(\dfrac{2x^{-2}y^{-6}}{3x^2y^{-5}}\right)^3 = \left(\dfrac{2y^5}{3x^2x^2y^6}\right)^3 = \left(\dfrac{2}{3x^4y}\right)^3 = \dfrac{8}{27x^{12}y^3}$

79. $\left(\dfrac{3x^5y^{-3}}{6x^{-5}y^3}\right)^{-2} = \left(\dfrac{6x^{-5}y^3}{3x^5y^{-3}}\right)^2 = \left(\dfrac{2y^3y^3}{1x^5x^5}\right)^2 = \left(\dfrac{2y^6}{x^{10}}\right)^2 = \dfrac{4y^{12}}{x^{20}}$

80. $\left(\frac{12x^{-4}y^3z^{-5}}{4x^4y^{-3}z^5}\right)^3 = \left(\frac{3y^3y^3}{1x^4x^4z^5z^5}\right)^3 = \left(\frac{3y^6}{x^8z^{10}}\right)^3 = \frac{27y^{18}}{x^{24}z^{30}}$

81. $\frac{(8^{-2}z^{-3}y)^{-1}}{(5y^2z^{-2})^3(5yz^{-2})^{-1}} = \frac{8^2z^3y^{-1}}{5^3y^6z^{-6}\cdot 5^{-1}y^{-1}z^2} = \frac{64z^3y^{-1}}{5^2y^5z^{-4}} = \frac{64z^3z^4}{25y^5y^1} = \frac{64z^7}{25y^6}$

82. $\frac{(m^{-2}n^3p^4)^{-2}(mn^{-2}p^3)^4}{(mn^{-2}p^3)^{-4}(mn^2p)^{-1}} = \frac{m^4n^{-6}p^{-8}\cdot m^4n^{-8}p^{12}}{m^{-4}n^8p^{-12}\cdot m^{-1}n^{-2}p^{-1}} = \frac{m^8n^{-14}p^4}{m^{-5}n^6p^{-13}} = \frac{m^8m^5p^4p^{13}}{n^6n^{14}} = \frac{m^{13}p^{17}}{n^{20}}$

83. $-\frac{5[6^2+(9-5)]}{4(2-3)^2} = -\frac{5[36+4]}{4(-1)^2} = -\frac{5[40]}{4(1)} = -\frac{200}{4} = -50$

84. $\frac{6[3-(4-7)^2]}{-5(2-4^2)} = \frac{6[3-(-3)^2]}{-5(2-16)} = \frac{6[3-9]}{-5(-14)} = \frac{6[-6]}{70} = \frac{-36}{70} = -\frac{18}{35}$

85. $x^2 = (-2)^2 = 4$

86. $-x^2 = -(-2)^2 = -1\cdot 4 = -4$

87. $x^3 = (-2)^3 = -8$

88. $-x^3 = -(-2)^3 = -1\cdot(-8) = 8$

89. $(-xz)^3 = [-1\cdot(-2)\cdot 3]^3 = 6^3 = 216$

90. $-xz^3 = -1\cdot(-2)\cdot 3^3 = 2\cdot 27 = 54$

91. $\frac{-(x^2z^3)}{z^2-y^2} = \frac{-[(-2)^2\cdot 3^3]}{3^2-0^2} = \frac{-[4\cdot 27]}{9-0} = \frac{-108}{9} = -12$

92. $\frac{z^2(x^2-y^2)}{x^3z} = \frac{3^2[(-2)^2-0^2]}{(-2)^3(3)} = \frac{9(4-0)}{(-8)(3)} = \frac{9(4)}{-24} = \frac{36}{-24} = -\frac{3}{2}$

93. $5x^2 - 3y^3z = 5(-2)^2 - 3(0)^3(3) = 5(4) - 3(0)(3) = 20 - 0 = 20$

94. $3(x-z)^2 + 2(y-z)^3 = 3(-2-3)^2 + 2(0-3)^3 = 3(-5)^2 + 2(-3)^3 = 3(25) + 2(-27)$
$= 75 + (-54) = 21$

95. $\frac{-3x^{-3}z^{-2}}{6x^2z^{-3}} = \frac{-1z^3}{2x^2x^3z^2} = \frac{-z}{2x^5} = \frac{-3}{2(-2)^5} = \frac{-3}{2(-32)} = \frac{-3}{-64} = \frac{3}{64}$

96. $\frac{(-5x^2z^{-3})^2}{5xz^{-2}} = \frac{25x^4z^{-6}}{5xz^{-2}} = \frac{5x^4}{xz^{-2}z^6} = \frac{5x^3}{z^4} = \frac{5(-2)^3}{3^4} = \frac{5(-8)}{81} = \frac{-40}{81} = -\frac{40}{81}$

97. $372{,}000 = 3.72\times 10^5$

98. $89{,}500 = 8.95\times 10^4$

99. $-177{,}000{,}000 = -1.77\times 10^8$

100. $-23{,}470{,}000{,}000 = -2.347\times 10^{10}$

101. $0.007 = 7\times 10^{-3}$

102. $0.00052 = 5.2\times 10^{-4}$

103. $-0.000000693 = -6.93 \times 10^{-7}$

104. $-0.000000089 = -8.9 \times 10^{-8}$

105. $1{,}000{,}000{,}000{,}000 = 1 \times 10^{12}$

106. $0.000001 = 1 \times 10^{-6}$

107. $9.37 \times 10^{5} = 937{,}000$

108. $4.26 \times 10^{9} = 4{,}260{,}000{,}000$

109. $2.21 \times 10^{-5} = 0.0000221$

110. $2.774 \times 10^{-2} = 0.02774$

111. $0.00032 \times 10^{4} = 3.2$

112. $9{,}300.0 \times 10^{-4} = 0.93$

113. $-3.2 \times 10^{-3} = -0.0032$

114. $-7.25 \times 10^{3} = -7{,}250$

115. $$\frac{(65{,}000)(45{,}000)}{250{,}000} = \frac{(6.5 \times 10^4)(4.5 \times 10^4)}{2.5 \times 10^5} = \frac{(6.5)(4.5)}{2.5} \times 10^{4+4-5} = 11.7 \times 10^3$$
$$= 1.17 \times 10^1 \times 10^3$$
$$= 1.17 \times 10^4$$

116. $$\frac{(0.000000045)(0.00000012)}{45{,}000{,}000} = \frac{(4.5 \times 10^{-8})(1.2 \times 10^{-7})}{4.5 \times 10^7} = \frac{(4.5)(1.2)}{4.5} \times 10^{(-8)+(-7)-7}$$
$$= 1.2 \times 10^{-22}$$

117. $$\frac{(0.00000035)(170{,}000)}{0.00000085} = \frac{(3.5 \times 10^{-7})(1.7 \times 10^5)}{8.5 \times 10^{-7}} = \frac{(3.5)(1.7)}{8.5} \times 10^{(-7)+5-(-7)}$$
$$= 0.7 \times 10^5$$
$$= 7 \times 10^{-1} \times 10^5 = 7 \times 10^4$$

118. $$\frac{(0.0000000144)(12{,}000)}{600{,}000} = \frac{(1.44 \times 10^{-8})(1.2 \times 10^4)}{6 \times 10^5} = \frac{(1.44)(1.2)}{6} \times 10^{(-8)+4-5}$$
$$= 0.288 \times 10^{-9}$$
$$= 2.88 \times 10^{-1} \times 10^{-9} = 2.88 \times 10^{-10}$$

119. $$\frac{(45{,}000{,}000{,}000)(212{,}000)}{0.00018} = \frac{(4.5 \times 10^{10})(2.12 \times 10^5)}{1.8 \times 10^{-4}} = \frac{(4.5)(2.12)}{1.8} \times 10^{10+5-(-4)}$$
$$= 5.3 \times 10^{19}$$

120. $$\frac{(0.00000000275)(4{,}750)}{500{,}000{,}000{,}000} = \frac{(2.75 \times 10^{-9})(4.75 \times 10^3)}{5 \times 10^{11}} = \frac{(2.75)(4.75)}{5} \times 10^{(-9)+3-11}$$
$$= 2.6125 \times 10^{-17}$$

121. $$3.31 \times 10^4 \text{ cm/sec} = \frac{3.31 \times 10^4 \text{ cm}}{1 \text{ sec}} \cdot \frac{1 \text{ m}}{100 \text{ cm}} \cdot \frac{60 \text{ sec}}{1 \text{ min}} = \frac{(3.31 \times 10^4)(6 \times 10^1)}{1 \times 10^2} \text{ m/min}$$
$$= \frac{(3.31)(6)}{1} \times 10^{4+1-2} \text{ m/min}$$
$$= 19.86 \times 10^3 \text{ m/min}$$
$$= 1.986 \times 10^4 \text{ m/min}$$

122. $V = lwh = (6{,}000\text{ mm})(9{,}700\text{ mm})(4{,}700\text{ mm}) = (6 \times 10^3)(9.7 \times 10^3)(4.7 \times 10^3)\text{ mm}^3$
$= (6)(9.7)(4.7) \times 10^{3+3+3}\text{ mm}^3$
$= 273.54 \times 10^9\text{ mm}^3$
$= 2.7354 \times 10^{11}\text{ mm}^3$

123. $\text{mass} = 1{,}000{,}000{,}000(0.00000000000000000000000167248\text{ g})$
$= (1 \times 10^9)(1.67248 \times 10^{-24}\text{ g}) = 1.67248 \times 10^{-15}\text{ g}$

124. $30{,}000{,}000{,}000\text{ cm/sec} = \dfrac{30{,}000{,}000{,}000\text{ cm}}{1\text{ sec}} \cdot \dfrac{1\text{ mile}}{160{,}934.4\text{ cm}} \cdot \dfrac{60\text{ sec}}{1\text{ min}} \cdot \dfrac{60\text{ min}}{1\text{ hr}}$
$= \dfrac{(3 \times 10^{10})(6 \times 10^1)(6 \times 10^1)}{1.609344 \times 10^5}\text{ mile/hr}$
$= \dfrac{(3)(6)(6)}{1.609344} \times 10^{10+1+1-5}\text{ mile/hr}$
$\approx 67.11 \times 10^7\text{ mile/hr} = 6.711 \times 10^8\text{ mile/hr}$

125. Earth: $n = 3$
$d = 9{,}275{,}200[3(2^{n-2}) + 4]$
$= 9{,}275{,}200[3(2^{3-2}) + 4]$
$= 9{,}275{,}200[3(2^1) + 4]$
$= 9{,}275{,}200[10]$
$= 92{,}752{,}000 \approx 93{,}000{,}000$
9.3×10^7 mi

Mars: $n = 4$
$d = 9{,}275{,}200[3(2^{n-2}) + 4]$
$= 9{,}275{,}200[3(2^{4-2}) + 4]$
$= 9{,}275{,}200[3(2^2) + 4]$
$= 9{,}275{,}200[16]$
$= 148{,}403{,}200 \approx 148{,}000{,}000$
1.48×10^8 mi

126. $10 \cdot 10 \cdot 10 \cdot 26 \cdot 26 \cdot 26 = 10^3 \cdot 26^3$; $10^3 \cdot 26^3 = 17{,}576{,}000 = 1.7576 \times 10^7$

127. polar radius $= 6.3567505 \times 10^3$ km
equatorial radius $= 6.378135 \times 10^3$ km

128. polar radius $= 3.941185 \times 10^3$ mi
equatorial radius $= 3.9544437 \times 10^3$ mi

129. $x^n x^2 = x^{n+2}$

130. $\dfrac{x^m}{x^3} = x^{m-3}$

131. $\dfrac{x^m x^2}{x^3} = \dfrac{x^{m+2}}{x^3} = x^{m+2-3} = x^{m-1}$

132. $\dfrac{x^{3m+5}}{x^2} = x^{3m+5-2} = x^{3m+3}$

133. $x^{m+1}x^3 = x^{m+1+3} = x^{m+4}$

134. $a^{n-3}a^3 = a^{n-3+3} = a^n$

135. In the expression $-x^4$, the base of the exponent is x, while in the expression $(-x)^4$, the base of the exponent is $-x$.

136. 32×10^2 is not in scientific notation because 32 is not a number between 1 and 10.

137. $(-2, 4) \Rightarrow$ 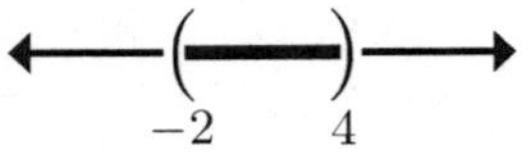

138. $(-\infty, -3] \cup [3, \infty) \Rightarrow$
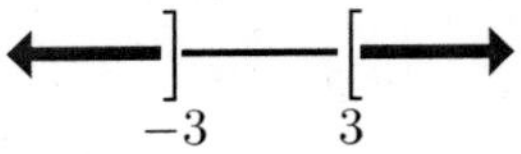

139. Since $\pi - 5 < 0$,
$|\pi - 5| = -(\pi - 5) = -\pi + 5 = 5 - \pi$.

140. distance $= |-5 - (-7)| = |2| = 2$

Exercises 0.3 (page 38)

1. 0

2. positive

3. not

4. $(6^2)^{1/3}$, $(6^{1/3})^2$

5. $a^{1/n}$

6. $|a|$

7. $\sqrt[n]{ab}$

8. $\dfrac{\sqrt[n]{a}}{\sqrt[n]{b}}$

9. $\neq$

10. $\sqrt[mn]{x}$

11. $9^{1/2} = (3^2)^{1/2} = 3$

12. $8^{1/3} = (2^3)^{1/3} = 2$

13. $\left(\frac{1}{25}\right)^{1/2} = \left[\left(\frac{1}{5}\right)^2\right]^{1/2} = \frac{1}{5}$

14. $\left(\frac{16}{625}\right)^{1/4} = \left[\left(\frac{2}{5}\right)^4\right]^{1/4} = \frac{2}{5}$

15. $-81^{1/4} = -(3^4)^{1/4} = -3$

16. $-\left(\frac{8}{27}\right)^{1/3} = -\left[\left(\frac{2}{3}\right)^3\right]^{1/3} = -\frac{2}{3}$

17. $(10{,}000)^{1/4} = (10^4)^{1/4} = 10$

18. $(1{,}024)^{1/5} = (4^5)^{1/5} = 4$

19. $\left(-\frac{27}{8}\right)^{1/3} = \left[\left(-\frac{3}{2}\right)^3\right]^{1/3} = -\frac{3}{2}$

20. $-64^{1/3} = -(4^3)^{1/3} = -4$

21. $(-64)^{1/2} \Rightarrow$ not a real number

22. $(-125)^{1/3} = [(-5)^3]^{1/3} = -5$

23. $(16a^2)^{1/2} = [(4a)^2]^{1/2} = 4|a|$

24. $(25a^4)^{1/2} = \left[(5a^2)^2\right]^{1/2} = 5|a^2| = 5a^2$

25. $(16a^4)^{1/4} = \left[(2a)^4\right]^{1/4} = 2|a|$

26. $(-64a^3)^{1/3} = [(-4a)^3]^{1/3} = -4a$

27. $(-32a^5)^{1/5} = [(-2a)^5]^{1/5} = -2a$

28. $(64a^6)^{1/6} = [(2a)^6]^{1/6} = 2|a|$

29. $(-216b^6)^{1/3} = \left[(-6b^2)^3\right]^{1/3} = -6b^2$

30. $(256t^8)^{1/4} = \left[(4t^2)^4\right]^{1/4} = 4|t^2| = 4t^2$

31. $\left(\frac{16a^4}{25b^2}\right)^{1/2} = \left[\left(\frac{4a^2}{5b}\right)^2\right]^{1/2} = \left|\frac{4a^2}{5b}\right| = \frac{4a^2}{5|b|}$

32. $\left(-\frac{a^5}{32b^{10}}\right)^{1/5} = \left[\left(-\frac{a}{2b^2}\right)^5\right]^{1/5} = -\frac{a}{2b^2}$

33. $\left(-\frac{1{,}000x^6}{27y^3}\right)^{1/3} = \left[\left(-\frac{10x^2}{3y}\right)^3\right]^{1/3} = -\frac{10x^2}{3y}$

34. $\left(\frac{49t^2}{100z^4}\right)^{1/2} = \left[\left(\frac{7t}{10z^2}\right)^2\right]^{1/2} = \left|\frac{7t}{10z^2}\right| = \frac{7|t|}{10z^2}$

35. $4^{3/2} = \left(4^{1/2}\right)^3 = 2^3 = 8$

36. $8^{2/3} = \left(8^{1/3}\right)^2 = 2^2 = 4$

37. $-16^{3/2} = -\left(16^{1/2}\right)^3 = -(4)^3 = -64$

38. $(-8)^{2/3} = \left[(-8)^{1/3}\right]^2 = (-2)^2 = 4$

39. $-1{,}000^{2/3} = -\left(1{,}000^{1/3}\right)^2 = -(10)^2 = -100$

40. $100^{3/2} = \left(100^{1/2}\right)^3 = 10^3 = 1{,}000$

41. $64^{-1/2} = \frac{1}{64^{1/2}} = \frac{1}{8}$

42. $25^{-1/2} = \frac{1}{25^{1/2}} = \frac{1}{5}$

43. $64^{-3/2} = \frac{1}{64^{3/2}} = \frac{1}{\left(64^{1/2}\right)^3} = \frac{1}{8^3} = \frac{1}{512}$

44. $49^{-3/2} = \frac{1}{49^{3/2}} = \frac{1}{\left(49^{1/2}\right)^3} = \frac{1}{7^3} = \frac{1}{343}$

45. $-9^{-3/2} = -\frac{1}{9^{3/2}} = -\frac{1}{\left(9^{1/2}\right)^3} = -\frac{1}{3^3} = -\frac{1}{27}$

46. $(-27)^{-2/3} = \frac{1}{(-27)^{2/3}} = \frac{1}{\left[(-27)^{1/3}\right]^2} = \frac{1}{(-3)^2} = \frac{1}{9}$

47. $\left(\frac{4}{9}\right)^{5/2} = \left[\left(\frac{4}{9}\right)^{1/2}\right]^5 = \left(\frac{2}{3}\right)^5 = \frac{32}{243}$

48. $\left(\frac{25}{81}\right)^{3/2} = \left[\left(\frac{25}{81}\right)^{1/2}\right]^3 = \left(\frac{5}{9}\right)^3 = \frac{125}{729}$

49. $\left(-\frac{27}{64}\right)^{-2/3} = \left(-\frac{64}{27}\right)^{2/3} = \left[\left(-\frac{64}{27}\right)^{1/3}\right]^2 = \left(-\frac{4}{3}\right)^2 = \frac{16}{9}$

50. $\left(\frac{125}{8}\right)^{-4/3} = \left(\frac{8}{125}\right)^{4/3} = \left[\left(\frac{8}{125}\right)^{1/3}\right]^4 = \left(\frac{2}{5}\right)^4 = \frac{16}{625}$

51. $\left(100s^4\right)^{1/2} = 100^{1/2}\left(s^4\right)^{1/2} = 10s^2$

52. $\left(64u^6v^3\right)^{1/3} = 64^{1/3}\left(u^6\right)^{1/3}\left(v^3\right)^{1/3} = 4u^2v$

53. $(32y^{10}z^5)^{-1/5} = \dfrac{1}{(32y^{10}z^5)^{1/5}} = \dfrac{1}{32^{1/5}(y^{10})^{1/5}(z^5)^{1/5}} = \dfrac{1}{2y^2z}$

54. $(625a^4b^8)^{-1/4} = \dfrac{1}{(625a^4b^8)^{1/4}} = \dfrac{1}{625^{1/4}(a^4)^{1/4}(b^8)^{1/4}} = \dfrac{1}{5ab^2}$

55. $(x^{10}y^5)^{3/5} = x^{30/5}y^{15/5} = x^6y^3$

56. $(64a^6b^{12})^{5/6} = 64^{5/6}a^{30/6}b^{60/6} = (64^{1/6})^5a^5b^{10} = 2^5a^5b^{10} = 32a^5b^{10}$

57. $(r^8s^{16})^{-3/4} = r^{-24/4}s^{-48/4} = r^{-6}s^{-12} = \dfrac{1}{r^6s^{12}}$

58. $(-8x^9y^{12})^{-2/3} = (-8)^{-2/3}x^{-18/3}y^{-24/3} = \dfrac{1}{(-8)^{2/3}}x^{-6}y^{-8} = \dfrac{1}{(-2)^2x^6y^8} = \dfrac{1}{4x^6y^8}$

59. $\left(-\dfrac{8a^6}{125b^9}\right)^{2/3} = \dfrac{(-8)^{2/3}a^{12/3}}{125^{2/3}b^{18/3}} = \dfrac{(-2)^2a^4}{5^2b^6} = \dfrac{4a^4}{25b^6}$

60. $\left(\dfrac{16x^4}{625y^8}\right)^{3/4} = \dfrac{16^{3/4}x^{12/4}}{625^{3/4}y^{24/4}} = \dfrac{2^3x^3}{5^3y^6} = \dfrac{8x^3}{125y^6}$

61. $\left(\dfrac{27r^6}{1{,}000s^{12}}\right)^{-2/3} = \left(\dfrac{1{,}000s^{12}}{27r^6}\right)^{2/3} = \dfrac{1{,}000^{2/3}s^{24/3}}{27^{2/3}r^{12/3}} = \dfrac{10^2s^8}{3^2r^4} = \dfrac{100s^8}{9r^4}$

62. $\left(-\dfrac{32m^{10}}{243n^{15}}\right)^{-2/5} = \left(\dfrac{-243n^{15}}{32m^{10}}\right)^{2/5} = \dfrac{(-243)^{2/5}n^{30/5}}{32^{2/5}m^{20/5}} = \dfrac{(-3)^2n^6}{2^2m^4} = \dfrac{9n^6}{4m^4}$

63. $\dfrac{a^{2/5}a^{4/5}}{a^{1/5}} = \dfrac{a^{6/5}}{a^{1/5}} = a^{5/5} = a$

64. $\dfrac{x^{6/7}x^{3/7}}{x^{2/7}x^{5/7}} = \dfrac{x^{9/7}}{x^{7/7}} = x^{2/7}$

65. $\sqrt{49} = \sqrt{7^2} = 7$

66. $\sqrt{81} = \sqrt{9^2} = 9$

67. $\sqrt[3]{125} = \sqrt[3]{5^3} = 5$

68. $\sqrt[3]{-64} = \sqrt[3]{(-4)^3} = -4$

69. $\sqrt[3]{-125} = \sqrt[3]{(-5)^3} = -5$

70. $\sqrt[5]{-243} = \sqrt[5]{(-3)^5} = -3$

71. $\sqrt[5]{-\dfrac{32}{100{,}000}} = \sqrt[5]{\left(-\dfrac{2}{10}\right)^5} = -\dfrac{2}{10} = -\dfrac{1}{5}$

72. $\sqrt[4]{\dfrac{256}{625}} = \sqrt[4]{\left(\dfrac{4}{5}\right)^4} = \dfrac{4}{5}$

73. $\sqrt{36x^2} = \sqrt{(6x)^2} = |6x| = 6|x|$

74. $-\sqrt{25y^2} = -\sqrt{(5y)^2} = -|5y| = -5|y|$

75. $\sqrt{9y^4} = \sqrt{(3y^2)^2} = |3y^2| = 3y^2$

76. $\sqrt{a^4b^8} = \sqrt{(a^2b^4)^2} = |a^2b^4| = a^2b^4$

77. $\sqrt[3]{8y^3} = \sqrt[3]{(2y)^3} = 2y$

78. $\sqrt[3]{-27z^9} = \sqrt[3]{(-3z^3)^3} = -3z^3$

79. $\sqrt[4]{\dfrac{x^4y^8}{z^{12}}} = \sqrt[4]{\left(\dfrac{xy^2}{z^3}\right)^4} = \left|\dfrac{xy^2}{z^3}\right| = \dfrac{|x|y^2}{|z^3|}$

80. $\sqrt[5]{\dfrac{a^{10}b^5}{c^{15}}} = \sqrt[5]{\left(\dfrac{a^2b}{c^3}\right)^5} = \dfrac{a^2b}{c^3}$

81. $\sqrt{8} - \sqrt{2} = \sqrt{4}\sqrt{2} - \sqrt{2} = 2\sqrt{2} - \sqrt{2} = \sqrt{2}$

82. $\sqrt{75} - 2\sqrt{27} = \sqrt{25}\sqrt{3} - 2\sqrt{9}\sqrt{3} = 5\sqrt{3} - 2(3)\sqrt{3} = 5\sqrt{3} - 6\sqrt{3} = -\sqrt{3}$

83. $\sqrt{200x^2} + \sqrt{98x^2} = \sqrt{100x^2}\sqrt{2} + \sqrt{49x^2}\sqrt{2} = 10x\sqrt{2} + 7x\sqrt{2} = 17x\sqrt{2}$

84. $\sqrt{128a^3} - a\sqrt{162a} = \sqrt{64a^2}\sqrt{2a} - a\sqrt{81}\sqrt{2a} = 8a\sqrt{2a} - 9a\sqrt{2a} = -a\sqrt{2a}$

85. $2\sqrt{48y^5} - 3y\sqrt{12y^3} = 2\sqrt{16y^4}\sqrt{3y} - 3y\sqrt{4y^2}\sqrt{3y} = 2(4y^2)\sqrt{3y} - 3y(2y)\sqrt{3y}$
$= 8y^2\sqrt{3y} - 6y^2\sqrt{3y} = 2y^2\sqrt{3y}$

86. $y\sqrt{112y} + 4\sqrt{175y^3} = y\sqrt{16}\sqrt{7y} + 4\sqrt{25y^2}\sqrt{7y} = y(4)\sqrt{7y} + 4(5y)\sqrt{7y}$
$= 4y\sqrt{7y} + 20y\sqrt{7y} = 24y\sqrt{7y}$

87. $2\sqrt[3]{81} + 3\sqrt[3]{24} = 2\sqrt[3]{27}\sqrt[3]{3} + 3\sqrt[3]{8}\sqrt[3]{3} = 2(3)\sqrt[3]{3} + 3(2)\sqrt[3]{3} = 6\sqrt[3]{3} + 6\sqrt[3]{3} = 12\sqrt[3]{3}$

88. $3\sqrt[4]{32} - 2\sqrt[4]{162} = 3\sqrt[4]{16}\sqrt[4]{2} - 2\sqrt[4]{81}\sqrt[4]{2} = 3(2)\sqrt[4]{2} - 2(3)\sqrt[4]{2} = 6\sqrt[4]{2} - 6\sqrt[4]{2} = 0$

89. $\sqrt[4]{768z^5} + \sqrt[4]{48z^5} = \sqrt[4]{256z^4}\sqrt[4]{3z} + \sqrt[4]{16z^4}\sqrt[4]{3z} = 4z\sqrt[4]{3z} + 2z\sqrt[4]{3z} = 6z\sqrt[4]{3z}$

90. $-2\sqrt[5]{64y^2} + 3\sqrt[5]{486y^2} = -2\sqrt[5]{32}\sqrt[5]{2y^2} + 3\sqrt[5]{243}\sqrt[5]{2y^2} = -2(2)\sqrt[5]{2y^2} + 3(3)\sqrt[5]{2y^2}$
$= -4\sqrt[5]{2y^2} + 9\sqrt[5]{2y^2} = 5\sqrt[5]{2y^2}$

91. $\sqrt{8x^2y} - x\sqrt{2y} + \sqrt{50x^2y} = \sqrt{4x^2}\sqrt{2y} - x\sqrt{2y} + \sqrt{25x^2}\sqrt{2y}$
$= 2x\sqrt{2y} - x\sqrt{2y} + 5x\sqrt{2y} = 6x\sqrt{2y}$

92. $3x\sqrt{18x} + 2\sqrt{2x^3} - \sqrt{72x^3} = 3x\sqrt{9}\sqrt{2x} + 2\sqrt{x^2}\sqrt{2x} - \sqrt{36x^2}\sqrt{2x}$
$= 3x(3)\sqrt{2x} + 2x\sqrt{2x} - 6x\sqrt{2x}$
$= 9x\sqrt{2x} + 2x\sqrt{2x} - 6x\sqrt{2x} = 5x\sqrt{2x}$

93. $\sqrt[3]{16xy^4} + y\sqrt[3]{2xy} - \sqrt[3]{54xy^4} = \sqrt[3]{8y^3}\sqrt[3]{2xy} + y\sqrt[3]{2xy} - \sqrt[3]{27y^3}\sqrt[3]{2xy}$
$= 2y\sqrt[3]{2xy} + y\sqrt[3]{2xy} - 3y\sqrt[3]{2xy} = 0$

94. $\sqrt[4]{512x^5} - \sqrt[4]{32x^5} + \sqrt[4]{1{,}250x^5} = \sqrt[4]{256x^4}\sqrt[4]{2x} - \sqrt[4]{16x^4}\sqrt[4]{2x} + \sqrt[4]{625x^4}\sqrt[4]{2x}$
$= 4x\sqrt[4]{2x} - 2x\sqrt[4]{2x} + 5x\sqrt[4]{2x} = 7x\sqrt[4]{2x}$

95. $\dfrac{3}{\sqrt{3}} = \dfrac{3}{\sqrt{3}} \cdot \dfrac{\sqrt{3}}{\sqrt{3}} = \dfrac{3\sqrt{3}}{3} = \sqrt{3}$

96. $\dfrac{6}{\sqrt{5}} = \dfrac{6}{\sqrt{5}} \cdot \dfrac{\sqrt{5}}{\sqrt{5}} = \dfrac{6\sqrt{5}}{5}$

97. $\dfrac{2}{\sqrt{x}} = \dfrac{2}{\sqrt{x}} \cdot \dfrac{\sqrt{x}}{\sqrt{x}} = \dfrac{2\sqrt{x}}{x}$

98. $\dfrac{8}{\sqrt{y}} = \dfrac{8}{\sqrt{y}} \cdot \dfrac{\sqrt{y}}{\sqrt{y}} = \dfrac{8\sqrt{y}}{y}$

99. $\dfrac{2}{\sqrt[3]{2}} = \dfrac{2}{\sqrt[3]{2}} \cdot \dfrac{\sqrt[3]{4}}{\sqrt[3]{4}} = \dfrac{2\sqrt[3]{4}}{\sqrt[3]{8}} = \dfrac{2\sqrt[3]{4}}{2} = \sqrt[3]{4}$

100. $\dfrac{4d}{\sqrt[3]{9}} = \dfrac{4d}{\sqrt[3]{9}} \cdot \dfrac{\sqrt[3]{3}}{\sqrt[3]{3}} = \dfrac{4d\sqrt[3]{3}}{\sqrt[3]{27}} = \dfrac{4d\sqrt[3]{3}}{3}$

101. $\dfrac{5a}{\sqrt[3]{25a}} = \dfrac{5a}{\sqrt[3]{25a}} \cdot \dfrac{\sqrt[3]{5a^2}}{\sqrt[3]{5a^2}} = \dfrac{5a\sqrt[3]{5a^2}}{\sqrt[3]{125a^3}} = \dfrac{5a\sqrt[3]{5a^2}}{5a} = \sqrt[3]{5a^2}$

102. $\dfrac{7}{\sqrt[3]{36c}} = \dfrac{7}{\sqrt[3]{36c}} \cdot \dfrac{\sqrt[3]{6c^2}}{\sqrt[3]{6c^2}} = \dfrac{7\sqrt[3]{6c^2}}{\sqrt[3]{216c^3}} = \dfrac{7\sqrt[3]{6c^2}}{6c}$

103. $\dfrac{2b}{\sqrt[4]{3a^2}} = \dfrac{2b}{\sqrt[4]{3a^2}} \cdot \dfrac{\sqrt[4]{27a^2}}{\sqrt[4]{27a^2}} = \dfrac{2b\sqrt[4]{27a^2}}{\sqrt[4]{81a^4}} = \dfrac{2b\sqrt[4]{27a^2}}{3a}$

104. $\sqrt{\dfrac{x}{2y}} = \dfrac{\sqrt{x}}{\sqrt{2y}} = \dfrac{\sqrt{x}}{\sqrt{2y}} \cdot \dfrac{\sqrt{2y}}{\sqrt{2y}} = \dfrac{\sqrt{2xy}}{2y}$

105. $\sqrt[3]{\dfrac{2u^4}{9v}} = \dfrac{\sqrt[3]{2u^4}}{\sqrt[3]{9v}} = \dfrac{\sqrt[3]{u^3}\sqrt[3]{2u}}{\sqrt[3]{9v}} \cdot \dfrac{\sqrt[3]{3v^2}}{\sqrt[3]{3v^2}} = \dfrac{u\sqrt[3]{6uv^2}}{\sqrt[3]{27v^3}} = \dfrac{u\sqrt[3]{6uv^2}}{3v}$

106. $\sqrt[3]{-\dfrac{3s^5}{4r^2}} = \dfrac{\sqrt[3]{-3s^5}}{\sqrt[3]{4r^2}} = \dfrac{\sqrt[3]{-s^3}\sqrt[3]{3s^2}}{\sqrt[3]{4r^2}} \cdot \dfrac{\sqrt[3]{2r}}{\sqrt[3]{2r}} = \dfrac{-s\sqrt[3]{6rs^2}}{\sqrt[3]{8r^3}} = -\dfrac{s\sqrt[3]{6rs^2}}{2r}$

107. $\dfrac{\sqrt{5}}{10} = \dfrac{\sqrt{5}}{10} \cdot \dfrac{\sqrt{5}}{\sqrt{5}} = \dfrac{5}{10\sqrt{5}} = \dfrac{1}{2\sqrt{5}}$

108. $\dfrac{\sqrt{y}}{3} = \dfrac{\sqrt{y}}{3} \cdot \dfrac{\sqrt{y}}{\sqrt{y}} = \dfrac{y}{3\sqrt{y}}$

109. $\dfrac{\sqrt[3]{9}}{3} = \dfrac{\sqrt[3]{9}}{3} \cdot \dfrac{\sqrt[3]{3}}{\sqrt[3]{3}} = \dfrac{\sqrt[3]{27}}{3\sqrt[3]{3}} = \dfrac{3}{3\sqrt[3]{3}} = \dfrac{1}{\sqrt[3]{3}}$

110. $\dfrac{\sqrt[3]{16b^2}}{16} = \dfrac{\sqrt[3]{16b^2}}{16} \cdot \dfrac{\sqrt[3]{4b}}{\sqrt[3]{4b}} = \dfrac{\sqrt[3]{64b^3}}{16\sqrt[3]{4b}} = \dfrac{4b}{16\sqrt[3]{4b}} = \dfrac{b}{4\sqrt[3]{4b}}$

111. $\dfrac{\sqrt[5]{16b^3}}{64a} = \dfrac{\sqrt[5]{16b^3}}{64a} \cdot \dfrac{\sqrt[5]{2b^2}}{\sqrt[5]{2b^2}} = \dfrac{\sqrt[5]{32b^5}}{64a\sqrt[5]{2b^2}} = \dfrac{2b}{64a\sqrt[5]{2b^2}} = \dfrac{b}{32a\sqrt[5]{2b^2}}$

112. $\sqrt{\frac{3x}{57}} = \frac{\sqrt{3x}}{\sqrt{57}} = \frac{\sqrt{3x}}{\sqrt{57}} \cdot \frac{\sqrt{3x}}{\sqrt{3x}} = \frac{3x}{\sqrt{171x}} = \frac{3x}{\sqrt{9}\sqrt{19x}} = \frac{3x}{3\sqrt{19x}} = \frac{x}{\sqrt{19x}}$

113. $\sqrt{\frac{1}{3}} - \sqrt{\frac{1}{27}} = \frac{\sqrt{1}}{\sqrt{3}} - \frac{\sqrt{1}}{\sqrt{27}} = \frac{1}{\sqrt{3}} \cdot \frac{\sqrt{3}}{\sqrt{3}} - \frac{1}{\sqrt{27}} \cdot \frac{\sqrt{3}}{\sqrt{3}} = \frac{\sqrt{3}}{3} - \frac{\sqrt{3}}{\sqrt{81}} = \frac{\sqrt{3}}{3} - \frac{\sqrt{3}}{9}$

$= \frac{3\sqrt{3}}{9} - \frac{\sqrt{3}}{9} = \frac{2\sqrt{3}}{9}$

114. $\sqrt[3]{\frac{1}{2}} + \sqrt[3]{\frac{1}{16}} = \frac{\sqrt[3]{1}}{\sqrt[3]{2}} + \frac{\sqrt[3]{1}}{\sqrt[3]{16}} = \frac{1}{\sqrt[3]{2}} \cdot \frac{\sqrt[3]{4}}{\sqrt[3]{4}} + \frac{1}{\sqrt[3]{16}} \cdot \frac{\sqrt[3]{4}}{\sqrt[3]{4}} = \frac{\sqrt[3]{4}}{\sqrt[3]{8}} + \frac{\sqrt[3]{4}}{\sqrt[3]{64}} = \frac{\sqrt[3]{4}}{2} + \frac{\sqrt[3]{4}}{4}$

$= \frac{2\sqrt[3]{4}}{4} + \frac{\sqrt[3]{4}}{4} = \frac{3\sqrt[3]{4}}{4}$

115. $\sqrt{\frac{x}{8}} - \sqrt{\frac{x}{2}} + \sqrt{\frac{x}{32}} = \frac{\sqrt{x}}{\sqrt{8}} - \frac{\sqrt{x}}{\sqrt{2}} + \frac{\sqrt{x}}{\sqrt{32}} = \frac{\sqrt{x}}{\sqrt{8}} \cdot \frac{\sqrt{2}}{\sqrt{2}} - \frac{\sqrt{x}}{\sqrt{2}} \cdot \frac{\sqrt{2}}{\sqrt{2}} + \frac{\sqrt{x}}{\sqrt{32}} \cdot \frac{\sqrt{2}}{\sqrt{2}}$

$= \frac{\sqrt{2x}}{\sqrt{16}} - \frac{\sqrt{2x}}{\sqrt{4}} + \frac{\sqrt{2x}}{\sqrt{64}}$

$= \frac{\sqrt{2x}}{4} - \frac{\sqrt{2x}}{2} + \frac{\sqrt{2x}}{8}$

$= \frac{2\sqrt{2x}}{8} - \frac{4\sqrt{2x}}{8} + \frac{\sqrt{2x}}{8} = -\frac{\sqrt{2x}}{8}$

116. $\sqrt[3]{\frac{y}{4}} + \sqrt[3]{\frac{y}{32}} - \sqrt[3]{\frac{y}{500}} = \frac{\sqrt[3]{y}}{\sqrt[3]{4}} + \frac{\sqrt[3]{y}}{\sqrt[3]{32}} - \frac{\sqrt[3]{y}}{\sqrt[3]{500}} = \frac{\sqrt[3]{y}}{\sqrt[3]{4}} \cdot \frac{\sqrt[3]{2}}{\sqrt[3]{2}} + \frac{\sqrt[3]{y}}{\sqrt[3]{32}} \cdot \frac{\sqrt[3]{2}}{\sqrt[3]{2}} - \frac{\sqrt[3]{y}}{\sqrt[3]{500}} \cdot \frac{\sqrt[3]{2}}{\sqrt[3]{2}}$

$= \frac{\sqrt[3]{2y}}{\sqrt[3]{8}} + \frac{\sqrt[3]{2y}}{\sqrt[3]{64}} - \frac{\sqrt[3]{2y}}{\sqrt[3]{1{,}000}}$

$= \frac{\sqrt[3]{2y}}{2} + \frac{\sqrt[3]{2y}}{4} - \frac{\sqrt[3]{2y}}{10}$

$= \frac{10\sqrt[3]{2y}}{20} + \frac{5\sqrt[3]{2y}}{20} - \frac{2\sqrt[3]{2y}}{20} = \frac{13\sqrt[3]{2y}}{20}$

117. $\sqrt[4]{9} = 9^{1/4} = (3^2)^{1/4} = 3^{2/4} = 3^{1/2} = \sqrt{3}$

118. $\sqrt[6]{27} = 27^{1/6} = (3^3)^{1/6} = 3^{3/6} = 3^{1/2} = \sqrt{3}$

119. $\sqrt[10]{16x^6} = (16x^6)^{1/10} = (2^4x^6)^{1/10} = 2^{4/10}x^{6/10} = 2^{2/5}x^{3/5} = (2^2x^3)^{1/5} = \sqrt[5]{4x^3}$

120. $\sqrt[6]{27x^9} = (27x^9)^{1/6} = (3^3x^9)^{1/6} = 3^{3/6}x^{9/6} = 3^{1/2}x^{3/2} = (3x^3)^{1/2} = \sqrt{3x^3} = x\sqrt{3x}$

121. $\sqrt{2}\sqrt[3]{2} = 2^{1/2} \cdot 2^{1/3} = 2^{3/6} \cdot 2^{2/6} = \sqrt[6]{2^3}\sqrt[6]{2^2} = \sqrt[6]{8}\sqrt[6]{4} = \sqrt[6]{32}$

122. $\sqrt{3}\sqrt[3]{5} = 3^{1/2}5^{1/3} = 3^{3/6}5^{2/6} = \sqrt[6]{3^3}\sqrt[6]{5^2} = \sqrt[6]{27}\sqrt[6]{25} = \sqrt[6]{675}$

123. $\dfrac{\sqrt[4]{3}}{\sqrt{2}}=\dfrac{3^{1/4}}{2^{1/2}}=\dfrac{3^{1/4}}{2^{2/4}}=\dfrac{\sqrt[4]{3}}{\sqrt[4]{2^2}}=\dfrac{\sqrt[4]{3}}{\sqrt[4]{4}}=\dfrac{\sqrt[4]{3}}{\sqrt[4]{4}}\cdot\dfrac{\sqrt[4]{4}}{\sqrt[4]{4}}=\dfrac{\sqrt[4]{12}}{\sqrt[4]{16}}=\dfrac{\sqrt[4]{12}}{2}$

124. $\dfrac{\sqrt[3]{2}}{\sqrt{5}}=\dfrac{2^{1/3}}{5^{1/2}}=\dfrac{2^{2/6}}{5^{3/6}}=\dfrac{\sqrt[6]{2^2}}{\sqrt[6]{5^3}}=\dfrac{\sqrt[6]{4}}{\sqrt[6]{125}}=\dfrac{\sqrt[6]{4}}{\sqrt[6]{125}}\cdot\dfrac{\sqrt[6]{125}}{\sqrt[6]{125}}=\dfrac{\sqrt[6]{500}}{\sqrt[6]{15{,}625}}=\dfrac{\sqrt[6]{500}}{5}$

125. $\sqrt[4]{x^4}=|x|$. Since $|x|=x$ if $x\geq 0$, then $\sqrt[4]{x^4}=x$ if $x\geq 0$.

126. $\sqrt[n]{\dfrac{x}{y}}=\left(\dfrac{x}{y}\right)^{1/n}=\dfrac{x^{1/n}}{y^{1/n}}=\dfrac{\sqrt[n]{x}}{\sqrt[n]{y}}$

127. $\left(\dfrac{x}{y}\right)^{-m/n}=\dfrac{x^{-m/n}}{y^{-m/n}}=\dfrac{x^{-m/n}}{y^{-m/n}}\cdot\dfrac{x^{m/n}y^{m/n}}{x^{m/n}y^{m/n}}=\dfrac{y^{m/n}}{x^{m/n}}=\dfrac{(y^m)^{1/n}}{(x^m)^{1/n}}=\left(\dfrac{y^m}{x^m}\right)^{1/n}=\sqrt[n]{\dfrac{y^m}{x^m}}$

128. Consider the case when n is even, m is odd and x is negative. Then $x^{m/n}=\left(x^{1/n}\right)^m=\left(\sqrt[n]{x}\right)^m$. Thus, $\sqrt[n]{x}$ must be a real number for the expression to be defined.

129. $-2<x\leq 5\Rightarrow(-2,5]$

130. If $x>4$, then $3-x<0$. Then $|3-x|=-(3-x)=-3+x=x-3$.

131. $x^2-y^2=(-2)^2-3^2=4-9=-5$

132. $\dfrac{xy+4y}{x}=\dfrac{-2(3)+4(3)}{-2}=\dfrac{-6+12}{-2}=\dfrac{6}{-2}=-3$

133. $617{,}000{,}000=6.17\times10^8$

134. $0.00235\times10^4=23.5$

Exercises 0.4 (page 50)

1. monomial, variables

2. degree, variables

3. trinomial

4. binomial

5. one

6. zero

7. like

8. degree

9. coefficients, variables

10. $3\sqrt{x}-2$

11. yes, trinomial, 2nd degree

12. yes, binomial, 3rd degree

13. no

14. no

15. yes, binomial, 3rd degree

16. yes, monomial, 5th degree

17. yes, monomial, 0th degree

18. no

19. yes, monomial, no degree

20. yes, none, 3rd degree

21. $(x^3-3x^2)+(5x^3-8x)=x^3-3x^2+5x^3-8x=x^3+5x^3-3x^2-8x=6x^3-3x^2-8x$

22. $(2x^4 - 5x^3) + (7x^3 - x^4 + 2x) = 2x^4 - 5x^3 + 7x^3 - x^4 + 2x$
$= 2x^4 - x^4 - 5x^3 + 7x^3 + 2x = x^4 + 2x^3 + 2x$

23. $(y^5 + 2y^3 + 7) - (y^5 - 2y^3 - 7) = y^5 + 2y^3 + 7 - y^5 + 2y^3 + 7$
$= y^5 - y^5 + 2y^3 + 2y^3 + 7 + 7 = 4y^3 + 14$

24. $(3t^7 - 7t^3 + 3) - (7t^7 - 3t^3 + 7) = 3t^7 - 7t^3 + 3 - 7t^7 + 3t^3 - 7$
$= 3t^7 - 7t^7 - 7t^3 + 3t^3 + 3 - 7 = -4t^7 - 4t^3 - 4$

25. $2(x^2 + 3x - 1) - 3(x^2 + 2x - 4) + 4 = 2(x^2) + 2(3x) + 2(-1) - 3(x^2) - 3(2x) - 3(-4) + 4$
$= 2x^2 + 6x - 2 - 3x^2 - 6x + 12 + 4$
$= 2x^2 - 3x^2 + 6x - 6x - 2 + 12 + 4 = -x^2 + 14$

26. $5(x^3 - 8x + 3) + 2(3x^2 + 5x) - 7 = 5(x^3) + 5(-8x) + 5(3) + 2(3x^2) + 2(5x) - 7$
$= 5x^3 - 40x + 15 + 6x^2 + 10x - 7$
$= 5x^3 + 6x^2 - 40x + 10x + 15 - 7 = 5x^3 + 6x^2 - 30x + 8$

27. $8(t^2 - 2t + 5) + 4(t^2 - 3t + 2) - 6(2t^2 - 8)$
$= 8(t^2) + 8(-2t) + 8(5) + 4(t^2) + 4(-3t) + 4(2) - 6(2t^2) - 6(-8)$
$= 8t^2 - 16t + 40 + 4t^2 - 12t + 8 - 12t^2 + 48$
$= 8t^2 + 4t^2 - 12t^2 - 16t - 12t + 40 + 8 + 48 = -28t + 96$

28. $-3(x^3 - x) + 2(x^2 + x) + 3(x^3 - 2x) = -3(x^3) - 3(-x) + 2(x^2) + 2(x) + 3(x^3) + 3(-2x)$
$= -3x^3 + 3x + 2x^2 + 2x + 3x^3 - 6x$
$= -3x^3 + 3x^3 + 2x^2 + 3x + 2x - 6x = 2x^2 - x$

29. $y(y^2 - 1) - y^2(y + 2) - y(2y - 2) = y(y^2) + y(-1) - y^2(y) - y^2(2) - y(2y) - y(-2)$
$= y^3 - y - y^3 - 2y^2 - 2y^2 + 2y$
$= y^3 - y^3 - 2y^2 - 2y^2 - y + 2y = -4y^2 + y$

30. $-4a^2(a + 1) + 3a(a^2 - 4) - a^2(a + 2)$
$= -4a^2(a) - 4a^2(1) + 3a(a^2) + 3a(-4) - a^2(a) - a^2(2)$
$= -4a^3 - 4a^2 + 3a^3 - 12a - a^3 - 2a^2$
$= -4a^3 + 3a^3 - a^3 - 4a^2 - 2a^2 - 12a = -2a^3 - 6a^2 - 12a$

31. $xy(x - 4y) - y(x^2 + 3xy) + xy(2x + 3y)$
$= xy(x) + xy(-4y) - y(x^2) - y(3xy) + xy(2x) + xy(3y)$
$= x^2y - 4xy^2 - x^2y - 3xy^2 + 2x^2y + 3xy^2$
$= x^2y - x^2y + 2x^2y - 4xy^2 - 3xy^2 + 3xy^2 = 2x^2y - 4xy^2$

32. $3mn(m+2n) - 6m(3mn+1) - 2n(4mn-1)$
$= 3mn(m) + 3mn(2n) - 6m(3mn) - 6m(1) - 2n(4mn) - 2n(-1)$
$= 3m^2n + 6mn^2 - 18m^2n - 6m - 8mn^2 + 2n$
$= 3m^2n - 18m^2n + 6mn^2 - 8mn^2 - 6m + 2n = -15m^2n - 2mn^2 - 6m + 2n$

33. $2x^2y^3(4xy^4) = 2(4)x^2xy^3y^4 = 8x^3y^7$

34. $-15a^3b(-2a^2b^3) = -15(-2)a^3a^2bb^3$
$= 30a^5b^4$

35. $-3m^2n(2mn^2)\left(-\frac{mn}{12}\right) = (-3)(2)\left(-\frac{1}{12}\right)m^2mmnn^2n = \frac{6}{12}m^4n^4 = \frac{m^4n^4}{2}$

36. $-\frac{3r^2s^3}{5}\left(\frac{2r^2s}{3}\right)\left(\frac{15rs^2}{2}\right) = \left(-\frac{3}{5}\right)\left(\frac{2}{3}\right)\left(\frac{15}{2}\right)r^2r^2rs^3ss^2 = -3r^5s^6$

37. $-4rs(r^2+s^2) = -4rs(r^2) - 4rs(s^2) = -4r^3s - 4rs^3$

38. $6u^2v(2uv^2 - y) = 6u^2v(2uv^2) + 6u^2v(-y) = 12u^3v^3 - 6u^2vy$

39. $6ab^2c(2ac + 3bc^2 - 4ab^2c) = 6ab^2c(2ac) + 6ab^2c(3bc^2) + 6ab^2c(-4ab^2c)$
$= 12a^2b^2c^2 + 18ab^3c^3 - 24a^2b^4c^2$

40. $-\frac{mn^2}{2}(4mn - 6m^2 - 8) = -\frac{mn^2}{2}(4mn) - \frac{mn^2}{2}(-6m^2) - \frac{mn^2}{2}(-8)$
$= -2m^2n^3 + 3m^3n^2 + 4mn^2$

41. $(a+2)(a+2) = a^2 + 2a + 2a + 4$
$= a^2 + 4a + 4$

42. $(y-5)(y-5) = y^2 - 5y - 5y + 25$
$= y^2 - 10y + 25$

43. $(a-6)^2 = (a-6)(a-6)$
$= a^2 - 6a - 6a + 36$
$= a^2 - 12a + 36$

44. $(t+9)^2 = (t+9)(t+9)$
$= t^2 + 9t + 9t + 81$
$= t^2 + 18t + 81$

45. $(x+4)(x-4) = x^2 - 4x + 4x - 16$
$= x^2 - 16$

46. $(z+7)(z-7) = z^2 - 7z + 7z - 49$
$= z^2 - 49$

47. $(x-3)(x+5) = x^2 + 5x - 3x - 15$
$= x^2 + 2x - 15$

48. $(z+4)(z-6) = z^2 - 6z + 4z - 24$
$= z^2 - 2z - 24$

49. $(u+2)(3u-2) = 3u^2 - 2u + 6u - 4$
$= 3u^2 + 4u - 4$

50. $(4x+1)(2x-3) = 8x^2 - 12x + 2x - 3$
$= 8x^2 - 10x - 3$

51. $(5x-1)(2x+3) = 10x^2 + 15x - 2x - 3$
$= 10x^2 + 13x - 3$

52. $(4x-1)(2x-7) = 8x^2 - 28x - 2x + 7$
$= 8x^2 - 30x + 7$

53. $(3a-2b)^2=(3a-2b)(3a-2b)=9a^2-6ab-6ab+4b^2=9a^2-12ab+4b^2$

54. $(4a+5b)(4a-5b)=16a^2-20ab+20ab-25b^2=16a^2-25b^2$

55. $(3m+4n)(3m-4n)=9m^2-12mn+12mn-16n^2=9m^2-16n^2$

56. $(4r+3s)^2=(4r+3s)(4r+3s)=16r^2+12rs+12rs+9s^2=16r^2+24rs+9s^2$

57. $(2y-4x)(3y-2x)=6y^2-4xy-12xy+8x^2=6y^2-16xy+8x^2$

58. $(-2x+3y)(3x+y)=-6x^2-2xy+9xy+3y^2=-6x^2+7xy+3y^2$

59. $(9x-y)(x^2-3y)=9x^3-27xy-x^2y+3y^2=9x^3-x^2y-27xy+3y^2$

60. $(8a^2+b)(a+2b)=8a^3+16a^2b+ab+2b^2$

61. $(5z+2t)(z^2-t)=5z^3-5tz+2tz^2-2t^2=5z^3+2tz^2-5tz-2t^2$

62. $(y-2x^2)(x^2+3y)=x^2y+3y^2-2x^4-6x^2y=-2x^4-5x^2y+3y^2$

63. $\left(\sqrt{5}+3x\right)\left(2-\sqrt{5}x\right)=2\sqrt{5}-5x+6x-3\sqrt{5}x^2=-3\sqrt{5}\,x^2+x+2\sqrt{5}$

64. $\left(\sqrt{2}+x\right)\left(3+\sqrt{2}x\right)=3\sqrt{2}+2x+3x+\sqrt{2}x^2=\sqrt{2}\,x^2+5x+3\sqrt{2}$

65.
$$\begin{aligned}(3x-1)^3&=(3x-1)(3x-1)(3x-1)\\&=\left(9x^2-3x-3x+1\right)(3x-1)\\&=\left(9x^2-6x+1\right)(3x-1)\\&=9x^2(3x)+9x^2(-1)-6x(3x)-6x(-1)+1(3x)+1(-1)\\&=27x^3-9x^2-18x^2+6x+3x-1=27x^3-27x^2+9x-1\end{aligned}$$

66.
$$\begin{aligned}(2x-3)^3&=(2x-3)(2x-3)(2x-3)\\&=\left(4x^2-6x-6x+9\right)(2x-3)\\&=\left(4x^2-12x+9\right)(2x-3)\\&=4x^2(2x)+4x^2(-3)-12x(2x)-12x(-3)+9(2x)+9(-3)\\&=8x^3-12x^2-24x^2+36x+18x-27=8x^3-36x^2+54x-27\end{aligned}$$

67.
$$\begin{aligned}(3x+1)\left(2x^2+4x-3\right)&=3x\left(2x^2\right)+3x(4x)+3x(-3)+1\left(2x^2\right)+1(4x)+1(-3)\\&=6x^3+12x^2-9x+2x^2+4x-3=6x^3+14x^2-5x-3\end{aligned}$$

68.
$$\begin{aligned}(2x-5)\left(x^2-3x+2\right)&=2x\left(x^2\right)+2x(-3x)+2x(2)-5\left(x^2\right)-5(-3x)-5(2)\\&=2x^3-6x^2+4x-5x^2+15x-10=2x^3-11x^2+19x-10\end{aligned}$$

69. $(3x+2y)(2x^2-3xy+4y^2)$
$$= 3x(2x^2)+3x(-3xy)+3x(4y^2)+2y(2x^2)+2y(-3xy)+2y(4y^2)$$
$$= 6x^3-9x^2y+12xy^2+4x^2y-6xy^2+8y^3 = 6x^3-5x^2y+6xy^2+8y^3$$

70. $(4r-3s)(2r^2+4rs-2s^2)$
$$= 4r(2r^2)+4r(4rs)+4r(-2s^2)-3s(2r^2)-3s(4rs)-3s(-2s^2)$$
$$= 8r^3+16r^2s-8rs^2-6r^2s-12rs^2+6s^3 = 8r^3+10r^2s-20rs^2+6s^3$$

71. $2y^n(3y^n+y^{-n}) = 2y^n(3y^n)+2y^n(y^{-n}) = 6y^{n+n}+2y^{n+(-n)} = 6y^{2n}+2y^0 = 6y^{2n}+2$

72. $3a^{-n}(2a^n+3a^{n-1}) = 3a^{-n}(2a^n)+3a^{-n}(3a^{n-1}) = 6a^{-n+n}+9a^{-n+n-1} = 6a^0+9a^{-1}$
$$= 6+\frac{9}{a}$$

73. $-5x^{2n}y^n(2x^{2n}y^{-n}+3x^{-2n}y^n) = -5x^{2n}y^n(2x^{2n}y^{-n}) - 5x^{2n}y^n(3x^{-2n}y^n)$
$$= -10x^{2n+2n}y^{n+(-n)} - 15x^{2n+(-2n)}y^{n+n}$$
$$= -10x^{4n}y^0 - 15x^0y^{2n} = -10x^{4n}-15y^{2n}$$

74. $-2a^{3n}b^{2n}(5a^{-3n}b-ab^{-2n}) = -2a^{3n}b^{2n}(5a^{-3n}b) - 2a^{3n}b^{2n}(-ab^{-2n})$
$$= -10a^{3n+(-3n)}b^{2n+1} + 2a^{3n+1}b^{2n+(-2n)}$$
$$= -10a^0b^{2n+1}+2a^{3n+1}b^0 = -10b^{2n+1}+2a^{3n+1}$$

75. $(x^n+3)(x^n-4) = x^nx^n-4x^n+3x^n-12 = x^{2n}-x^n-12$

76. $(a^n-5)(a^n-3) = a^na^n-3a^n-5a^n+15 = a^{2n}-8a^n+15$

77. $(2r^n-7)(3r^n-2) = 2r^n(3r^n)-2r^n(2)-7(3r^n)+14$
$$= 6r^{2n}-4r^n-21r^n+14 = 6r^{2n}-25r^n+14$$

78. $(4z^n+3)(3z^n+1) = 4z^n(3z^n)+4z^n(1)+3(3z^n)+3$
$$= 12z^{2n}+4z^n+9z^n+3 = 12z^{2n}+13z^n+3$$

79. $x^{1/2}(x^{1/2}y+xy^{1/2}) = x^{1/2}x^{1/2}y+x^{1/2}xy^{1/2} = x^{2/2}y+x^{3/2}y^{1/2} = xy+x^{3/2}y^{1/2}$

80. $ab^{1/2}(a^{1/2}b^{1/2}+b^{1/2}) = ab^{1/2}a^{1/2}b^{1/2}+ab^{1/2}b^{1/2} = a^{3/2}b^{2/2}+ab^{2/2} = a^{3/2}b+ab$

81. $(a^{1/2}+b^{1/2})(a^{1/2}-b^{1/2}) = a^{1/2}a^{1/2}-a^{1/2}b^{1/2}+a^{1/2}b^{1/2}-b^{1/2}b^{1/2}$
$$= a^{2/2}-b^{2/2} = a-b$$

82. $(x^{3/2}+y^{1/2})^2 = (x^{3/2}+y^{1/2})(x^{3/2}+y^{1/2}) = x^{3/2}x^{3/2}+x^{3/2}y^{1/2}+x^{3/2}y^{1/2}+y^{1/2}y^{1/2}$
$$= x^{6/2}+2x^{3/2}y^{1/2}+y^{2/2}$$
$$= x^3+2x^{3/2}y^{1/2}+y$$

83. $\dfrac{2}{\sqrt{3}-1} = \dfrac{2}{\sqrt{3}-1} \cdot \dfrac{\sqrt{3}+1}{\sqrt{3}+1} = \dfrac{2\left(\sqrt{3}+1\right)}{\left(\sqrt{3}\right)^2 - 1^2} = \dfrac{2\left(\sqrt{3}+1\right)}{3-1} = \dfrac{2\left(\sqrt{3}+1\right)}{2} = \sqrt{3}+1$

84. $\dfrac{1}{\sqrt{5}+2} = \dfrac{1}{\sqrt{5}+2} \cdot \dfrac{\sqrt{5}-2}{\sqrt{5}-2} = \dfrac{1\left(\sqrt{5}-2\right)}{\left(\sqrt{5}\right)^2 - 2^2} = \dfrac{\sqrt{5}-2}{5-4} = \dfrac{\sqrt{5}-2}{1} = \sqrt{5}-2$

85. $\dfrac{3x}{\sqrt{7}+2} = \dfrac{3x}{\sqrt{7}+2} \cdot \dfrac{\sqrt{7}-2}{\sqrt{7}-2} = \dfrac{3x\left(\sqrt{7}-2\right)}{\left(\sqrt{7}\right)^2 - 2^2} = \dfrac{3x\left(\sqrt{7}-2\right)}{7-4} = \dfrac{3x\left(\sqrt{7}-2\right)}{3} = x\left(\sqrt{7}-2\right)$

86. $\dfrac{14y}{\sqrt{2}-3} = \dfrac{14y}{\sqrt{2}-3} \cdot \dfrac{\sqrt{2}+3}{\sqrt{2}+3} = \dfrac{14y\left(\sqrt{2}+3\right)}{\left(\sqrt{2}\right)^2 - 3^2} = \dfrac{14y\left(\sqrt{2}+3\right)}{2-9} = -2y\left(\sqrt{2}+3\right)$

87. $\dfrac{x}{x-\sqrt{3}} = \dfrac{x}{x-\sqrt{3}} \cdot \dfrac{x+\sqrt{3}}{x+\sqrt{3}} = \dfrac{x\left(x+\sqrt{3}\right)}{x^2 - \left(\sqrt{3}\right)^2} = \dfrac{x\left(x+\sqrt{3}\right)}{x^2-3}$

88. $\dfrac{y}{2y+\sqrt{7}} = \dfrac{y}{2y+\sqrt{7}} \cdot \dfrac{2y-\sqrt{7}}{2y-\sqrt{7}} = \dfrac{y\left(2y-\sqrt{7}\right)}{(2y)^2 - \left(\sqrt{7}\right)^2} = \dfrac{y\left(2y-\sqrt{7}\right)}{4y^2-7}$

89. $\dfrac{y+\sqrt{2}}{y-\sqrt{2}} = \dfrac{y+\sqrt{2}}{y-\sqrt{2}} \cdot \dfrac{y+\sqrt{2}}{y+\sqrt{2}} = \dfrac{\left(y+\sqrt{2}\right)\left(y+\sqrt{2}\right)}{y^2 - \left(\sqrt{2}\right)^2} = \dfrac{y^2+2y\sqrt{2}+2}{y^2-2}$

90. $\dfrac{x-\sqrt{3}}{x+\sqrt{3}} = \dfrac{x-\sqrt{3}}{x+\sqrt{3}} \cdot \dfrac{x-\sqrt{3}}{x-\sqrt{3}} = \dfrac{\left(x-\sqrt{3}\right)\left(x-\sqrt{3}\right)}{x^2 - \left(\sqrt{3}\right)^2} = \dfrac{x^2-2x\sqrt{3}+3}{x^2-3}$

91. $\dfrac{\sqrt{2}-\sqrt{3}}{1-\sqrt{3}} = \dfrac{\sqrt{2}-\sqrt{3}}{1-\sqrt{3}} \cdot \dfrac{1+\sqrt{3}}{1+\sqrt{3}} = \dfrac{\sqrt{2}+\sqrt{6}-\sqrt{3}-\left(\sqrt{3}\right)^2}{1^2-\left(\sqrt{3}\right)^2} = \dfrac{\sqrt{2}+\sqrt{6}-\sqrt{3}-3}{1-3}$

$= \dfrac{\sqrt{2}+\sqrt{6}-\sqrt{3}-3}{-2}$

$= \dfrac{-\left(\sqrt{2}+\sqrt{6}-\sqrt{3}-3\right)}{2}$

$= \dfrac{\sqrt{3}+3-\sqrt{2}-\sqrt{6}}{2}$

92. $$\frac{\sqrt{3}-\sqrt{2}}{1+\sqrt{2}} = \frac{\sqrt{3}-\sqrt{2}}{1+\sqrt{2}} \cdot \frac{1-\sqrt{2}}{1-\sqrt{2}} = \frac{\sqrt{3}-\sqrt{6}-\sqrt{2}+\left(\sqrt{2}\right)^2}{1^2-\left(\sqrt{2}\right)^2} = \frac{\sqrt{3}-\sqrt{6}-\sqrt{2}+2}{1-2}$$
$$= \frac{\sqrt{3}-\sqrt{6}-\sqrt{2}+2}{-1}$$
$$= -\left(\sqrt{3}-\sqrt{6}-\sqrt{2}+2\right)$$
$$= \sqrt{6}+\sqrt{2}-\sqrt{3}-2$$

93. $$\frac{\sqrt{x}-\sqrt{y}}{\sqrt{x}+\sqrt{y}} = \frac{\sqrt{x}-\sqrt{y}}{\sqrt{x}+\sqrt{y}} \cdot \frac{\sqrt{x}-\sqrt{y}}{\sqrt{x}-\sqrt{y}} = \frac{\sqrt{x^2}-\sqrt{xy}-\sqrt{xy}+\sqrt{y^2}}{\left(\sqrt{x}\right)^2-\left(\sqrt{y}\right)^2} = \frac{x-2\sqrt{xy}+y}{x-y}$$

94. $$\frac{\sqrt{2x}+y}{\sqrt{2x}-y} = \frac{\sqrt{2x}+y}{\sqrt{2x}-y} \cdot \frac{\sqrt{2x}+y}{\sqrt{2x}+y} = \frac{\sqrt{4x^2}+y\sqrt{2x}+y\sqrt{2x}+y^2}{\left(\sqrt{2x}\right)^2-y^2} = \frac{2x+2y\sqrt{2x}+y^2}{2x-y^2}$$

95. $$\frac{\sqrt{2}+1}{2} = \frac{\sqrt{2}+1}{2} \cdot \frac{\sqrt{2}-1}{\sqrt{2}-1} = \frac{\left(\sqrt{2}\right)^2-1^2}{2\left(\sqrt{2}-1\right)} = \frac{2-1}{2\left(\sqrt{2}-1\right)} = \frac{1}{2\left(\sqrt{2}-1\right)}$$

96. $$\frac{\sqrt{x}-3}{3} = \frac{\sqrt{x}-3}{3} \cdot \frac{\sqrt{x}+3}{\sqrt{x}+3} = \frac{\left(\sqrt{x}\right)^2-3^2}{3(\sqrt{x}+3)} = \frac{x-9}{3(\sqrt{x}+3)}$$

97. $$\frac{y-\sqrt{3}}{y+\sqrt{3}} = \frac{y-\sqrt{3}}{y+\sqrt{3}} \cdot \frac{y+\sqrt{3}}{y+\sqrt{3}} = \frac{y^2-\left(\sqrt{3}\right)^2}{y^2+y\sqrt{3}+y\sqrt{3}+\sqrt{9}} = \frac{y^2-3}{y^2+2y\sqrt{3}+3}$$

98. $$\frac{\sqrt{a}-\sqrt{b}}{\sqrt{a}+\sqrt{b}} = \frac{\sqrt{a}-\sqrt{b}}{\sqrt{a}+\sqrt{b}} \cdot \frac{\sqrt{a}+\sqrt{b}}{\sqrt{a}+\sqrt{b}} = \frac{\left(\sqrt{a}\right)^2-\left(\sqrt{b}\right)^2}{\sqrt{a^2}+\sqrt{ab}+\sqrt{ab}+\sqrt{b^2}} = \frac{a-b}{a+2\sqrt{ab}+b}$$

99. $$\frac{\sqrt{x+3}-\sqrt{x}}{3} = \frac{\sqrt{x+3}-\sqrt{x}}{3} \cdot \frac{\sqrt{x+3}+\sqrt{x}}{\sqrt{x+3}+\sqrt{x}} = \frac{\left(\sqrt{x+3}\right)^2-\left(\sqrt{x}\right)^2}{3(\sqrt{x+3}+\sqrt{x})}$$
$$= \frac{x+3-x}{3(\sqrt{x+3}+\sqrt{x})}$$
$$= \frac{3}{3(\sqrt{x+3}+\sqrt{x})} = \frac{1}{\sqrt{x+3}+\sqrt{x}}$$

100. $$\frac{\sqrt{2+h}-\sqrt{2}}{h}=\frac{\sqrt{2+h}-\sqrt{2}}{h}\cdot\frac{\sqrt{2+h}+\sqrt{2}}{\sqrt{2+h}+\sqrt{2}}=\frac{\left(\sqrt{2+h}\right)^2-\left(\sqrt{2}\right)^2}{h\left(\sqrt{2+h}+\sqrt{2}\right)}$$
$$=\frac{2+h-2}{h\left(\sqrt{2+h}+\sqrt{2}\right)}$$
$$=\frac{h}{h\left(\sqrt{2+h}+\sqrt{2}\right)}=\frac{1}{\sqrt{2+h}+\sqrt{2}}$$

101. $$\frac{36a^2b^3}{18ab^6}=2a^{2-1}b^{3-6}=2a^1b^{-3}=\frac{2a}{b^3}$$

102. $$\frac{-45r^2s^5t^3}{27r^6s^2t^8}=-\frac{5}{3}r^{2-6}s^{5-2}t^{3-8}=-\frac{5}{3}r^{-4}s^3t^{-5}=-\frac{5s^3}{3r^4t^5}$$

103. $$\frac{16x^6y^4z^9}{-24x^9y^6z^0}=-\frac{2}{3}x^{6-9}y^{4-6}z^{9-0}=-\frac{2}{3}x^{-3}y^{-2}z^9=-\frac{2z^9}{3x^3y^2}$$

104. $$\frac{32m^6n^4p^2}{26m^6n^7p^2}=\frac{16}{13}m^{6-6}n^{4-7}p^{2-2}=\frac{16}{13}m^0n^{-3}p^0=\frac{16}{13n^3}$$

105. $$\frac{5x^3y^2+15x^3y^4}{10x^2y^3}=\frac{5x^3y^2}{10x^2y^3}+\frac{15x^3y^4}{10x^2y^3}$$
$$=\frac{x}{2y}+\frac{3xy}{2}$$

106. $$\frac{9m^4n^9-6m^3n^4}{12m^3n^3}=\frac{9m^4n^9}{12m^3n^3}-\frac{6m^3n^4}{12m^3n^3}$$
$$=\frac{3mn^6}{4}-\frac{n}{2}$$

107. $$\frac{24x^5y^7-36x^2y^5+12xy}{60x^5y^4}=\frac{24x^5y^7}{60x^5y^4}-\frac{36x^2y^5}{60x^5y^4}+\frac{12xy}{60x^5y^4}=\frac{2y^3}{5}-\frac{3y}{5x^3}+\frac{1}{5x^4y^3}$$

108. $$\frac{9a^3b^4+27a^2b^4-18a^2b^3}{18a^2b^7}=\frac{9a^3b^4}{18a^2b^7}+\frac{27a^2b^4}{18a^2b^7}-\frac{18a^2b^3}{18a^2b^7}=\frac{a}{2b^3}+\frac{3}{2b^3}-\frac{1}{b^4}$$

109.
$$\begin{array}{r}
3x+2\\
x+3\,\big)\overline{3x^2+11x+6}\\
\underline{3x^2+9x}\\
2x+6\\
\underline{2x+6}\\
0
\end{array}$$

110.
$$\begin{array}{r}
x+3\\
3x+2\,\big)\overline{3x^2+11x+6}\\
\underline{3x^2+2x}\\
9x+6\\
\underline{9x+6}\\
0
\end{array}$$

111.
$$\begin{array}{r}
x-7+\frac{2}{2x-5}\\
2x-5\,\big)\overline{2x^2-19x+37}\\
\underline{2x^2-5x\phantom{+37}}\\
-14x+37\\
\underline{-14x+35}\\
2
\end{array}$$

112.
$$\begin{array}{r}
2x-5\\
x-7\,\big)\overline{2x^2-19x+35}\\
\underline{2x^2-14x}\\
-5x+35\\
\underline{-5x+35}\\
0
\end{array}$$

113.

$$\begin{array}{r l}
 & 2x^2 + 2x + 2 + \frac{3}{x-1} \\
x-1 & \overline{)\,2x^3 + 0x^2 + 0x + 1} \\
 & \underline{2x^3 - 2x^2} \\
 & \quad 2x^2 + 0x + 1 \\
 & \quad \underline{2x^2 - 2x} \\
 & \qquad 2x + 1 \\
 & \qquad \underline{2x - 2} \\
 & \qquad\qquad 3
\end{array}$$

114.

$$\begin{array}{r l}
 & x^2 - x + 3 + \frac{1}{2x-7} \\
2x-7 & \overline{)\,2x^3 - 9x^2 + 13x - 20} \\
 & \underline{2x^3 - 7x^2} \\
 & \quad -2x^2 + 13x - 20 \\
 & \quad \underline{-2x^2 + 7x} \\
 & \qquad 6x - 20 \\
 & \qquad \underline{6x - 21} \\
 & \qquad\qquad 1
\end{array}$$

115.

$$\begin{array}{r l}
 & x - 3 \\
x^2 + x - 1 & \overline{)\,x^3 - 2x^2 - 4x + 3} \\
 & \underline{x^3 + x^2 - x} \\
 & \quad -3x^2 - 3x + 3 \\
 & \quad \underline{-3x^2 - 3x + 3} \\
 & \qquad\qquad 0
\end{array}$$

116.

$$\begin{array}{r l}
 & x - 2 + \frac{-x-1}{x^2-3} \\
x^2 - 3 & \overline{)\,x^3 - 2x^2 - 4x + 5} \\
 & \underline{x^3 \qquad - 3x} \\
 & \quad -2x^2 - x + 5 \\
 & \quad \underline{-2x^2 \qquad + 6} \\
 & \qquad -x - 1
\end{array}$$

117.

$$\begin{array}{r l}
 & x^2 - 2 + \frac{-x^2+5}{x^3-2} \\
x^3 - 2 & \overline{)\,x^5 + 0x^4 - 2x^3 - 3x^2 + 0x + 9} \\
 & \underline{x^5 \qquad\qquad - 2x^2} \\
 & \quad -2x^3 - x^2 + 0x + 9 \\
 & \quad \underline{-2x^3 \qquad\qquad + 4} \\
 & \qquad -x^2 \qquad + 5
\end{array}$$

118.

$$\begin{array}{r l}
 & x^2 - 2 + \frac{3}{x^3-3} \\
x^3 - 3 & \overline{)\,x^5 + 0x^4 - 2x^3 - 3x^2 + 0x + 9} \\
 & \underline{x^5 \qquad\qquad - 3x^2} \\
 & \quad -2x^3 \qquad + 0x + 9 \\
 & \quad \underline{-2x^3 \qquad\qquad + 6} \\
 & \qquad\qquad\qquad 3
\end{array}$$

119.

$$\begin{array}{r l}
 & x^4 + 2x^3 + 4x^2 + 8x + 16 \\
x - 2 & \overline{)\,x^5 + 0x^4 + 0x^3 + 0x^2 + 0x - 32} \\
 & \underline{x^5 - 2x^4} \\
 & \quad 2x^4 + 0x^3 \\
 & \quad \underline{2x^4 - 4x^3} \\
 & \qquad 4x^3 + 0x^2 \\
 & \qquad \underline{4x^3 - 8x^2} \\
 & \qquad\quad 8x^2 + 0x \\
 & \qquad\quad \underline{8x^2 - 16x} \\
 & \qquad\qquad 16x - 32 \\
 & \qquad\qquad \underline{16x - 32} \\
 & \qquad\qquad\qquad 0
\end{array}$$

120.

$$\begin{array}{r l}
 & x^3 - x^2 + x - 1 \\
x + 1 & \overline{)\,x^4 + 0x^3 + 0x^2 + 0x - 1} \\
 & \underline{x^4 + x^3} \\
 & \quad -x^3 + 0x^2 \\
 & \quad \underline{-x^3 - x^2} \\
 & \qquad x^2 + 0x \\
 & \qquad \underline{x^2 + x} \\
 & \qquad\quad -x - 1 \\
 & \qquad\quad \underline{-x - 1} \\
 & \qquad\qquad 0
\end{array}$$

121.

$$\begin{array}{r l}
 & 6x^2 + x - 12 \\
6x^2 + 11x - 10 & \overline{)\,36x^4 + 72x^3 - 121x^2 - 142x + 120} \\
 & \underline{36x^4 + 66x^3 - 60x^2} \\
 & \quad 6x^3 - 61x^2 - 142x \\
 & \quad \underline{6x^3 + 11x^2 - 10x} \\
 & \qquad -72x^2 - 132x + 120 \\
 & \qquad \underline{-72x^2 - 132x + 120} \\
 & \qquad\qquad\qquad 0
\end{array}$$

122.
$$
\begin{array}{r|l}
 & 6x^2 + 11x - 10 \\
\hline
6x^2 + x - 12 & 36x^4 + 72x^3 - 121x^2 - 142x + 120 \\
 & \underline{36x^4 + 6x^3 - 72x^2} \\
 & \quad 66x^3 - 49x^2 - 142x \\
 & \quad \underline{66x^3 + 11x^2 - 132x} \\
 & \qquad -60x^2 - 10x + 120 \\
 & \qquad \underline{-60x^2 - 10x + 120} \\
 & \qquad\qquad 0
\end{array}
$$

123. Area = length · width = $(x+5)(x-2)$ ft^2 = $(x^2 - 2x + 5x - 10)$ ft^2 = $(x^2 + 3x - 10)$ ft^2

124.
$$
\begin{aligned}
\text{Area} &= \frac{1}{2} \cdot \text{base} \cdot \text{height} \\
x^2 + 3x - 40 &= \frac{1}{2}(x+8) \cdot \text{height} \\
2(x^2 + 3x - 40) &= (x+8) \cdot \text{height} \\
2x^2 + 6x - 80 &= (x+8) \cdot \text{height} \\
\frac{2x^2 + 6x - 80}{x+8} &= \text{height}
\end{aligned}
$$

$$
\begin{array}{r|l}
 & 2x - 10 \\
\hline
x + 8 & 2x^2 + 6x - 80 \\
 & \underline{2x^2 + 16x} \\
 & \quad -10x - 80 \\
 & \quad \underline{-10x - 80} \\
 & \qquad 0
\end{array}
$$

The height is $(2x - 10)$ ft.

125.
$$
\begin{aligned}
\text{Volume} &= l \cdot w \cdot h \\
&= (12 - 2x)(12 - 2x)x \text{ in.}^3 \\
&= (144 - 48x + 4x^2)x \text{ in.}^3 \\
&= (144x - 48x^2 + 4x^3) \text{ in.}^3
\end{aligned}
$$

126. $t = \dfrac{d}{r} = \dfrac{3x^2 + 19x + 20}{3x + 4}$

$$
\begin{array}{r|l}
 & x + 5 \\
\hline
3x + 4 & 3x^2 + 19x + 20 \\
 & \underline{3x^2 + 4x} \\
 & \quad 15x + 20 \\
 & \quad \underline{15x + 20} \\
 & \qquad 0
\end{array}
$$

$t = x + 5$

127.
$$
\begin{aligned}
(a+b+c)^2 = (a+b+c)(a+b+c) &= a(a+b+c) + b(a+b+c) + c(a+b+c) \\
&= a^2 + ab + ac + ab + b^2 + bc + ac + bc + c^2 \\
&= a^2 + b^2 + c^2 + 2ab + 2bc + 2ac
\end{aligned}
$$

128.
$$
\begin{aligned}
(a+b+c+d)^2 &= (a+b+c+d)(a+b+c+d) \\
&= a(a+b+c+d) + b(a+b+c+d) + c(a+b+c+d) + d(a+b+c+d) \\
&= a^2 + ab + ac + ad + ab + b^2 + bc + bd + ac + bc + c^2 + cd + ad + bd + cd + d^2 \\
&= a^2 + b^2 + c^2 + d^2 + 2ab + 2ac + 2ad + 2bc + 2bd + 2cd
\end{aligned}
$$

129. Answers may vary.

130. Multiply the numeratior and denominator by the conjugate of the numerator $(\sqrt{x} - 2)$.

131. Check the formula with $a = 1$ and $b = 2$.

132. Check the formula with $a = 3$ and $b = 4$.

133. $9^{3/2} = (9^{1/2})^3 = 3^3 = 27$

134. $\left(\frac{8}{125}\right)^{-2/3} = \left(\frac{125}{8}\right)^{2/3} = \left(\left(\frac{125}{8}\right)^{1/3}\right)^2 = \left(\frac{5}{2}\right)^2 = \frac{25}{4}$

135. $\left(\frac{625x^4}{16y^8}\right)^{3/4} = \frac{625^{3/4}(x^4)^{3/4}}{16^{3/4}(y^8)^{3/4}} = \frac{125x^3}{8y^6}$

136. $\sqrt{80x^4} = \sqrt{16x^4}\sqrt{5} = 4x^2\sqrt{5}$

137. $\sqrt[3]{16ab^4} - b\sqrt[3]{54ab} = \sqrt[3]{8b^3}\sqrt[3]{2ab} - b\sqrt[3]{27}\sqrt[3]{2ab} = 2b\sqrt[3]{2ab} - b(3)\sqrt[3]{2ab} = 2b\sqrt[3]{2ab} - 3b\sqrt[3]{2ab} = -b\sqrt[3]{2ab}$

138. $x\sqrt[4]{1{,}280x} + \sqrt[4]{80x^5} = x\sqrt[4]{256}\sqrt[4]{5x} + \sqrt[4]{16x^4}\sqrt[4]{5x} = 4x\sqrt[4]{5x} + 2x\sqrt[4]{5x} = 6x\sqrt[4]{5x}$

Exercises 0.5 (page 61)

1. factor

2. integer, prime

3. $ax + bx = x(a+b)$

4. $x^2 - y^2 = (x+y)(x-y)$

5. $x^2 + 2xy + y^2 = (x+y)(x+y) = (x+y)^2$

6. $x^2 - 2xy + y^2 = (x-y)(x-y) = (x-y)^2$

7. $x^3 + y^3 = (x+y)(x^2 - xy + y^2)$

8. $x^3 - y^3 = (x-y)(x^2 + xy + y^2)$

9. $3x - 6 = 3(x-2)$

10. $5y - 15 = 5(y-3)$

11. $8x^2 + 4x^3 = 4x^2(2+x)$

12. $9y^3 + 6y^2 = 3y^2(3y+2)$

13. $7x^2y^2 + 14x^3y^2 = 7x^2y^2(1+2x)$

14. $25y^2z - 15yz^2 = 5yz(5y - 3z)$

15. $a(x+y) + b(x+y) = (x+y)(a+b)$

16. $b(x-y) + a(x-y) = (x-y)(b+a)$

17. $4a + b - 12a^2 - 3ab = 4a + b - 3a(4a+b) = 1(4a+b) - 3a(4a+b) = (4a+b)(1-3a)$

18. $x^2 + 4x + xy + 4y = x(x+4) + y(x+4) = (x+4)(x+y)$

19. $4x^2 - 9 = (2x)^2 - 3^2 = (2x+3)(2x-3)$

20. $36z^2 - 49 = (6z)^2 - 7^2 = (6z+7)(6z-7)$

21. $4 - 9r^2 = 2^2 - (3r)^2 = (2+3r)(2-3r)$

22. $16 - 49x^2 = 4^2 - (7x)^2 = (4+7x)(4-7x)$

23. $81x^4 - 1 = (9x^2)^2 - 1^2 = (9x^2+1)(9x^2-1) = (9x^2+1)(3x+1)(3x-1)$

24. $81 - x^4 = 9^2 - (x^2)^2 = (9+x^2)(9-x^2) = (9+x^2)(3+x)(3-x)$

25. $(x+z)^2 - 25 = (x+z)^2 - 5^2 = (x+z+5)(x+z-5)$

26. $(x-y)^2 - 9 = (x-y)^2 - 3^2 = (x-y+3)(x-y-3)$

27. $x^2 + 8x + 16 = (x+4)(x+4) = (x+4)^2$

28. $a^2 - 12a + 36 = (a-6)(a-6) = (a-6)^2$

29. $b^2 - 10b + 25 = (b-5)(b-5) = (b-5)^2$

30. $y^2 + 14y + 49 = (y+7)(y+7) = (y+7)^2$

31. $m^2 + 4mn + 4n^2 = (m+2n)(m+2n)$
$= (m+2n)^2$

32. $r^2 - 8rs + 16s^2 = (r-4s)(r-4s)$
$= (r-4s)^2$

33. $12x^2 - xy - 6y^2 = (4x-3y)(3x+2y)$

34. $8x^2 - 10xy - 3y^2 = (4x+y)(2x-3y)$

35. $x^2 + 10x + 21$: $a = 1$, $b = 10$, $c = 21$
key number $= ac = 1(21) = 21$
$x^2 + 10x + 21 = x^2 + 7x + 3x + 21$
$= x(x+7) + 3(x+7)$
$= (x+7)(x+3)$

36. $x^2 + 7x + 10$: $a = 1$, $b = 7$, $c = 10$
key number $= ac = 1(10) = 10$
$x^2 + 7x + 10 = x^2 + 5x + 2x + 10$
$= x(x+5) + 2(x+5)$
$= (x+5)(x+2)$

37. $x^2 - 4x - 12$: $a = 1$, $b = -4$, $c = -12$
key number $= ac = 1(-12) = -12$
$x^2 - 4x - 12 = x^2 - 6x + 2x - 12$
$= x(x-6) + 2(x-6)$
$= (x-6)(x+2)$

38. $x^2 - 2x - 63$: $a = 1$, $b = -2$, $c = -63$
key number $= ac = 1(-63) = -63$
$x^2 - 2x - 63 = x^2 - 9x + 7x - 63$
$= x(x-9) + 7(x-9)$
$= (x-9)(x+7)$

39. $6p^2 + 7p - 3$: $a = 6$, $b = 7$, $c = -3$
key number $= ac = 6(-3) = -18$
$6p^2 + 7p - 3 = 6p^2 + 9p - 2p - 3$
$= 3p(2p+3) - (2p+3)$
$= (2p+3)(3p-1)$

40. $4q^2 - 19q + 12$: $a = 4$, $b = -19$, $c = 12$
key number $= ac = 4(12) = 48$
$4q^2 - 19q + 12 = 4q^2 - 3q - 16q + 12$
$= q(4q-3) - 4(4q-3)$
$= (4q-3)(q-4)$

41. $t^3 + 343 = t^3 + 7^3 = (t+7)[t^2 - (t)(7) + 7^2] = (t+7)(t^2 - 7t + 49)$

42. $r^3 + 8s^3 = r^3 + (2s)^3 = (r+2s)\left[r^2 - (r)(2s) + (2s)^2\right] = (r+2s)(r^2 - 2rs + 4s^2)$

43. $8z^3 - 27 = (2z)^3 - 3^3 = (2z-3)\left[(2z)^2 + (2z)(3) + 3^2\right] = (2z-3)(4z^2 + 6z + 9)$

44. $125a^3 - 64 = (5a)^3 - 4^3 = (5a-4)\left[(5a)^2 + (5a)(4) + 4^2\right] = (5a-4)(25a^2 + 20a + 16)$

45. $3a^2bc + 6ab^2c + 9abc^2 = 3abc(a + 2b + 3c)$

46. $5x^3y^3z^3 + 25x^2y^2z^2 - 125xyz = 5xyz(x^2y^2z^2 + 5xyz - 25)$

47. $3x^3 + 3x^2 - x - 1 = 3x^2(x+1) - 1(x+1) = (x+1)(3x^2 - 1)$

48. $4x + 6xy - 9y - 6 = 2x(2+3y) - 3(3y+2) = (3y+2)(2x-3)$

49. $2txy + 2ctx - 3ty - 3ct = t(2xy + 2cx - 3y - 3c) = t[2x(y+c) - 3(y+c)] = t(y+c)(2x-3)$

50. $2ax + 4ay - bx - 2by = 2a(x + 2y) - b(x + 2y) = (x + 2y)(2a - b)$

51. $ax + bx + ay + by + az + bz = x(a + b) + y(a + b) + z(a + b) = (a + b)(x + y + z)$

52. $$6x^2y^3 + 18xy + 3x^2y^2 + 9x = 3x(2xy^3 + 6y + xy^2 + 3) = 3x[2y(xy^2 + 3) + 1(xy^2 + 3)] = 3x(xy^2 + 3)(2y + 1)$$

53. $$x^2 - (y - z)^2 = [x + (y - z)][x - (y - z)] = (x + y - z)(x - y + z)$$

54. $$z^2 - (y + 3)^2 = [z + (y + 3)][z - (y + 3)] = (z + y + 3)(z - y - 3)$$

55. $$(x - y)^2 - (x + y)^2 = [(x - y) + (x + y)][(x - y) - (x + y)] = (x - y + x + y)(x - y - x - y) = (2x)(-2y) = -4xy$$

56. $$(2a + 3)^2 - (2a - 3)^2 = [(2a + 3) + (2a - 3)][(2a + 3) - (2a - 3)] = (2a + 3 + 2a - 3)(2a + 3 - 2a + 3) = (4a)(6) = 24a$$

57. $x^4 - y^4 = (x^2)^2 - (y^2)^2 = (x^2 + y^2)(x^2 - y^2) = (x^2 + y^2)(x + y)(x - y)$

58. $z^4 - 81 = (z^2)^2 - 9^2 = (z^2 + 9)(z^2 - 9) = (z^2 + 9)(z^2 - 3^2) = (z^2 + 9)(z + 3)(z - 3)$

59. $3x^2 - 12 = 3(x^2 - 4) = 3(x + 2)(x - 2)$

60. $$3x^3y - 3xy = 3xy(x^2 - 1) = 3xy(x + 1)(x - 1)$$

61. $$18xy^2 - 8x = 2x(9y^2 - 4) = 2x(3y + 2)(3y - 2)$$

62. $$27x^2 - 12 = 3(9x^2 - 4) = 3(3x + 2)(3x - 2)$$

63. $x^2 - 2x + 15 \Rightarrow$ prime

64. $x^2 + x + 2 \Rightarrow$ prime

65. $$-15 + 2a + 24a^2 = 24a^2 + 2a - 15 = (6a + 5)(4a - 3)$$

66. $$-32 - 68x + 9x^2 = 9x^2 - 68x - 32 = (9x + 4)(x - 8)$$

67. $6x^2 + 29xy + 35y^2 = (3x + 7y)(2x + 5y)$

68. $10x^2 - 17xy + 6y^2 = (5x - 6y)(2x - y)$

69. $12p^2 - 58pq - 70q^2 = 2(6p^2 - 29pq - 35q^2) = 2(6p - 35q)(p + q)$

70. $3x^2 - 6xy - 9y^2 = 3(x^2 - 2xy - 3y^2) = 3(x - 3y)(x + y)$

71. $-6m^2 + 47mn - 35n^2 = -(6m^2 - 47mn + 35n^2) = -(6m - 5n)(m - 7n)$

72. $-14r^2 - 11rs + 15s^2 = -(14r^2 + 11rs - 15s^2) = -(7r - 5s)(2r + 3s)$

73. $-6x^3 + 23x^2 + 35x = -x(6x^2 - 23x - 35) = -x(6x + 7)(x - 5)$

74. $-y^3 - y^2 + 90y = -y(y^2 + y - 90) = -y(y + 10)(y - 9)$

75. $6x^4 - 11x^3 - 35x^2 = x^2(6x^2 - 11x - 35) = x^2(2x-7)(3x+5)$

76. $12x + 17x^2 - 7x^3 = -7x^3 + 17x^2 + 12x = -x(7x^2 - 17x - 12) = -x(x-3)(7x+4)$

77. $x^4 + 2x^2 - 15 = (x^2+5)(x^2-3)$

78. $x^4 - x^2 - 6 = (x^2-3)(x^2+2)$

79. $a^{2n} - 2a^n - 3 = (a^n - 3)(a^n + 1)$

80. $a^{2n} + 6a^n + 8 = (a^n+4)(a^n+2)$

81. $6x^{2n} - 7x^n + 2 = (3x^n - 2)(2x^n - 1)$

82. $9x^{2n} + 9x^n + 2 = (3x^n+2)(3x^n+1)$

83. $$\begin{aligned} 4x^{2n} - 9y^{2n} &= (2x^n)^2 - (3y^n)^2 \\ &= (2x^n + 3y^n)(2x^n - 3y^n) \end{aligned}$$

84. $8x^{2n} - 2x^n - 3 = (4x^n - 3)(2x^n + 1)$

85. $10y^{2n} - 11y^n - 6 = (5y^n + 2)(2y^n - 3)$

86. $$\begin{aligned} 16y^{4n} - 25y^{2n} &= y^{2n}(16y^{2n} - 25) \\ &= y^{2n}\left[(4y^n)^2 - 5^2\right] \\ &= y^{2n}(4y^n+5)(4y^n-5) \end{aligned}$$

87. $2x^3 + 2{,}000 = 2(x^3 + 1{,}000) = 2(x^3 + 10^3) = 2(x+10)(x^2 - 10x + 100)$

88. $3y^3 + 648 = 3(y^3 + 216) = 3(y^3 + 6^3) = 3(y+6)(y^2 - 6y + 36)$

89. $$\begin{aligned} (x+y)^3 - 64 = (x+y)^3 - 4^3 &= [(x+y)-4]\left[(x+y)^2 + 4(x+y) + 4^2\right] \\ &= (x+y-4)(x^2 + 2xy + y^2 + 4x + 4y + 16) \end{aligned}$$

90. $$\begin{aligned} (x-y)^3 + 27 = (x-y)^3 + 3^3 &= [(x-y)+3]\left[(x-y)^2 - 3(x-y) + 3^2\right] \\ &= (x-y+3)(x^2 - 2xy + y^2 - 3x + 3y + 9) \end{aligned}$$

91. $$\begin{aligned} 64a^6 - y^6 = (8a^3)^2 - (y^3)^2 &= (8a^3 + y^3)(8a^3 - y^3) \\ &= (2a+y)(4a^2 - 2ay + y^2)(2a-y)(4a^2 + 2ay + y^2) \\ &= (2a+y)(2a-y)(4a^2 - 2ay + y^2)(4a^2 + 2ay + y^2) \end{aligned}$$

92. $a^6 + b^6 = (a^2)^3 + (b^2)^3 = (a^2+b^2)\left((a^2)^2 - a^2b^2 + (b^2)^2\right) = (a^2+b^2)(a^4 - a^2b^2 + b^4)$

93. $a^3 - b^3 + a - b = (a-b)(a^2 + ab + b^2) + (a-b)1 = (a-b)(a^2 + ab + b^2 + 1)$

94. $(a^2 - y^2) - 5(a+y) = (a+y)(a-y) - 5(a+y) = (a+y)(a-y-5)$

95. $$\begin{aligned} 64x^6 + y^6 = (4x^2)^3 + (y^2)^3 &= (4x^2 + y^2)\left((4x^2)^2 - 4x^2y^2 + (y^2)^2\right) \\ &= (4x^2 + y^2)(16x^4 - 4x^2y^2 + y^4) \end{aligned}$$

96. $$\begin{aligned} z^2 + 6z + 9 - 225y^2 = (z+3)(z+3) - 225y^2 &= (z+3)^2 - (15y)^2 \\ &= (z+3+15y)(z+3-15y) \end{aligned}$$

97. $x^2 - 6x + 9 - 144y^2 = (x-3)(x-3) - 144y^2 = (x-3)^2 - (12y)^2$
$= (x - 3 + 12y)(x - 3 - 12y)$

98. $x^2 + 2x - 9y^2 + 1 = x^2 + 2x + 1 - 9y^2 = (x+1)(x+1) - 9y^2$
$= (x+1)^2 - (3y)^2 = (x + 1 + 3y)(x + 1 - 3y)$

99. $(a+b)^2 - 3(a+b) - 10 = [(a+b) - 5][(a+b) + 2] = (a + b - 5)(a + b + 2)$

100. $2(a+b)^2 - 5(a+b) - 3 = [2(a+b) + 1][(a+b) - 3] = (2a + 2b + 1)(a + b - 3)$

101. $x^6 + 7x^3 - 8 = (x^3 + 8)(x^3 - 1) = (x+2)(x^2 - 2x + 4)(x-1)(x^2 + x + 1)$

102. $x^6 - 13x^4 + 36x^2 = x^2(x^4 - 13x^2 + 36) = x^2(x^2 - 9)(x^2 - 4) = x^2(x+3)(x-3)(x+2)(x-2)$

103. $x^4 + x^2 + 1 = x^4 + 2x^2 + 1 - x^2$
$= (x^2+1)(x^2+1) - x^2$
$= (x^2+1)^2 - x^2$
$= (x^2 + 1 + x)(x^2 + 1 - x)$

104. $x^4 + 3x^2 + 4 = x^4 + 4x^2 + 4 - x^2$
$= (x^2+2)(x^2+2) - x^2$
$= (x^2+2)^2 - x^2$
$= (x^2 + 2 + x)(x^2 + 2 - x)$

105. $x^4 + 7x^2 + 16 = x^4 + 8x^2 + 16 - x^2$
$= (x^2+4)(x^2+4) - x^2$
$= (x^2+4)^2 - x^2$
$= (x^2 + 4 + x)(x^2 + 4 - x)$

106. $y^4 + 2y^2 + 9 = y^4 + 6y^2 + 9 - 4y^2$
$= (y^2+3)(y^2+3) - 4y^2$
$= (y^2+3)^2 - (2y)^2$
$= (y^2 + 3 + 2y)(y^2 + 3 - 2y)$

107. $4a^4 + 1 + 3a^2 = 4a^4 + 4a^2 + 1 - a^2 = (2a^2+1)(2a^2+1) - a^2 = (2a^2+1)^2 - a^2$
$= (2a^2 + 1 + a)(2a^2 + 1 - a)$

108. $x^4 + 25 + 6x^2 = x^4 + 10x^2 + 25 - 4x^2 = (x^2+5)(x^2+5) - 4x^2$
$= (x^2+5)^2 - (2x)^2 = (x^2 + 5 + 2x)(x^2 + 5 - 2x)$

109. $V = \frac{4}{3}\pi r_1^3 - \frac{4}{3}\pi r_2^3$
$= \frac{4}{3}\pi(r_1^3 - r_2^3)$
$= \frac{4}{3}\pi(r_1 - r_2)(r_1^2 + r_1 r_2 + r_2^2)$

110. $f = 144 - 16t^2$
$= 16(9 - t^2)$
$= 16(3+t)(3-t)$

111-114. Answers may vary.

115. $3x + 2 = 2\left(\frac{3x}{2} + \frac{2}{2}\right) = 2\left(\frac{3}{2}x + 1\right)$

116. $5x - 3 = 5\left(\frac{5x}{5} - \frac{3}{5}\right) = 5\left(x - \frac{3}{5}\right)$

117. $x^2 + 2x + 4 = 2\left(\frac{x^2}{2} + \frac{2x}{2} + \frac{4}{2}\right)$
$= 2\left(\frac{1}{2}x^2 + x + 2\right)$

118. $3x^2 - 2x - 5 = 3\left(\frac{3x^2}{3} - \frac{2x}{3} - \frac{5}{3}\right)$
$= 3\left(x^2 - \frac{2}{3}x - \frac{5}{3}\right)$

119. $a + b = a\left(\frac{a}{a} + \frac{b}{a}\right) = a\left(1 + \frac{b}{a}\right)$

120. $a - b = b\left(\frac{a}{b} - \frac{b}{b}\right) = b\left(\frac{a}{b} - 1\right)$

121. $x + x^{1/2} = x^{1/2}\left(x^{1-1/2} + x^{1/2-1/2}\right) = x^{1/2}\left(x^{1/2} + 1\right)$

122. $x^{3/2} - x^{1/2} = x^{1/2}\left(x^{3/2-1/2} - x^{1/2-1/2}\right) = x^{1/2}(x - 1)$

123. $2x + \sqrt{2}y = \sqrt{2}\left(\frac{2x}{\sqrt{2}} + \frac{\sqrt{2}y}{\sqrt{2}}\right) = \sqrt{2}\left(\sqrt{2}x + y\right)$

124. $\sqrt{3}a - 3b = \sqrt{3}\left(\frac{\sqrt{3}a}{\sqrt{3}} - \frac{3b}{\sqrt{3}}\right) = \sqrt{3}\left(a - \sqrt{3}b\right)$

125. $ab^{3/2} - a^{3/2}b = ab\left(\frac{ab^{3/2}}{ab} - \frac{a^{3/2}b}{ab}\right) = ab\left(b^{1/2} - a^{1/2}\right)$

126. $ab^2 + b = b^{-1}\left(\frac{ab^2}{b^{-1}} + \frac{b}{b^{-1}}\right) = b^{-1}\left(ab^3 + b^2\right)$

127. $x^2 + x - 6 + xy - 2y = (x + 3)(x - 2) + y(x - 2) = (x - 2)(x + 3 + y)$

128. $2x^2 + 5x + 2 - xy - 2y = (2x + 1)(x + 2) - y(x + 2) = (x + 2)(2x + 1 - y)$

129. $a^4 + 2a^3 + a^2 + a + 1 = a^2\left(a^2 + 2a + 1\right) + a + 1 = a^2(a + 1)(a + 1) + 1(a + 1)$
$= (a + 1)\left[a^2(a + 1) + 1\right]$
$= (a + 1)\left(a^3 + a^2 + 1\right)$

130. $a^4 + a^3 - 2a^2 + a - 1 = a^2\left(a^2 + a - 2\right) + a - 1 = a^2(a + 2)(a - 1) + 1(a - 1)$
$= (a - 1)\left[a^2(a + 2) + 1\right]$
$= (a - 1)\left(a^3 + 2a^2 + 1\right)$

131. The number 1 is neither prime nor composite.

132. $[-2, 3) \Rightarrow$ 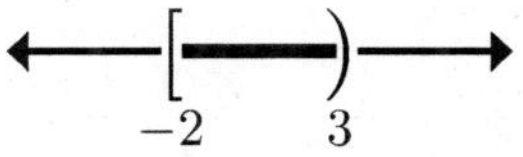

133. $\left(x^3x^2\right)^4 = \left(x^5\right)^4 = x^{20}$

134. $\frac{\left(a^3\right)^3\left(a^2\right)^4}{\left(a^2a^3\right)^3} = \frac{a^9a^8}{\left(a^5\right)^3} = \frac{a^{17}}{a^{15}} = a^2$

135. $\left(\frac{3x^4x^3}{6x^{-2}x^4}\right)^0 = 1$

136. $\sqrt{20x^5} = \sqrt{4x^4}\sqrt{5x} = 2x^2\sqrt{5x}$

137. $\sqrt{20x} - \sqrt{125x} = \sqrt{4}\sqrt{5x} - \sqrt{25}\sqrt{5x} = 2\sqrt{5x} - 5\sqrt{5x} = -3\sqrt{5x}$

138. $\frac{3}{\sqrt[3]{3}} = \frac{3}{\sqrt[3]{3}} \cdot \frac{\sqrt[3]{9}}{\sqrt[3]{9}} = \frac{3\sqrt[3]{9}}{\sqrt[3]{27}} = \frac{3\sqrt[3]{9}}{3} = \sqrt[3]{9}$

Exercises 0.6 (page 71)

1. numerator

2. denominator

3. $ad = bc$

4. zero

5. $\frac{ac}{bd}$

6. $\frac{ad}{bc}$

7. $\frac{a+c}{b}$

8. $\frac{a-c}{b}$

9. $$\frac{8x}{3y} \stackrel{?}{=} \frac{16x}{6y}$$
$$8x \cdot 6y \stackrel{?}{=} 3y \cdot 16x$$
$$48xy = 48xy$$
EQUAL

10. $$\frac{3x^2}{4y^2} \stackrel{?}{=} \frac{12y^2}{16x^2}$$
$$3x^2 \cdot 16x^2 \stackrel{?}{=} 4y^2 \cdot 12y^2$$
$$48x^4 \neq 48y^4$$
NOT EQUAL

11. $$\frac{25xyz}{12ab^2c} \stackrel{?}{=} \frac{50a^2bc}{24xyz}$$
$$25xyz \cdot 24xyz \stackrel{?}{=} 12ab^2c \cdot 50a^2bc$$
$$600x^2y^2z^2 \neq 600a^3b^3c^2$$
NOT EQUAL

12. $$\frac{15rs^2}{4rs^2} \stackrel{?}{=} \frac{37.5a^3}{10a^3}$$
$$15rs^2 \cdot 10a^3 \stackrel{?}{=} 4rs^2 \cdot 37.5a^3$$
$$150rs^2a^3 = 150rs^2a^3$$
EQUAL

13. $\frac{7a^2b}{21ab^2} = \frac{a \cdot 7ab}{3b \cdot 7ab} = \frac{a}{3b} \cdot \frac{7ab}{7ab} = \frac{a}{3b}$

14. $\frac{35p^3q^2}{49p^4q} = \frac{5q \cdot 7p^3q}{7p \cdot 7p^3q} = \frac{5q}{7p} \cdot \frac{7p^3q}{7p^3q} = \frac{5q}{7p}$

15. $\frac{4x}{7} \cdot \frac{2}{5a} = \frac{4x \cdot 2}{7 \cdot 5a} = \frac{8x}{35a}$

16. $\frac{-5y}{2z} \cdot \frac{4}{y^2} = \frac{-5y \cdot 4}{2z \cdot y^2} = \frac{-20y}{2y^2z} = -\frac{10}{yz}$

17. $\frac{8m}{5n} \div \frac{3m}{10n} = \frac{8m}{5n} \cdot \frac{10n}{3m} = \frac{80mn}{15mn} = \frac{16}{3}$

18. $\frac{15p}{8q} \div \frac{-5p}{16q^2} = \frac{15p}{8q} \cdot \frac{16q^2}{-5p} = \frac{240pq^2}{-40pq} = -6q$

19. $\frac{3z}{5c} + \frac{2z}{5c} = \frac{3z+2z}{5c} = \frac{5z}{5c} = \frac{z}{c}$

20. $\frac{7a}{4b} - \frac{3a}{4b} = \frac{7a-3a}{4b} = \frac{4a}{4b} = \frac{a}{b}$

21. $\frac{15x^2y}{7a^2b^3} - \frac{x^2y}{7a^2b^3} = \frac{14x^2y}{7a^2b^3} = \frac{2x^2y}{a^2b^3}$

22. $\frac{8rst^2}{15m^4t^2} + \frac{7rst^2}{15m^4t^2} = \frac{15rst^2}{15m^4t^2} = \frac{rs}{m^4}$

23. $\frac{2x-4}{x^2-4} = \frac{2(x-2)}{(x+2)(x-2)} = \frac{2}{x+2}$

24. $\frac{x^2-16}{x^2-8x+16} = \frac{(x+4)(x-4)}{(x-4)(x-4)} = \frac{x+4}{x-4}$

25. $\frac{4-x^2}{x^2-5x+6} = \frac{(2+x)(2-x)}{(x-3)(x-2)} = -\frac{x+2}{x-3}$

26. $$\frac{25-x^2}{x^2+10x+25} = \frac{(5+x)(5-x)}{(x+5)(x+5)} = \frac{5-x}{x+5} = -\frac{x-5}{x+5}$$

27. $\frac{6x^3+x^2-12x}{4x^3+4x^2-3x} = \frac{x(6x^2+x-12)}{x(4x^2+4x-3)} = \frac{x(2x+3)(3x-4)}{x(2x+3)(2x-1)} = \frac{3x-4}{2x-1}$

28. $\dfrac{6x^4-5x^3-6x^2}{2x^3-7x^2-15x}=\dfrac{x^2(6x^2-5x-6)}{x(2x^2-7x-15)}=\dfrac{x^2(2x-3)(3x+2)}{x(2x+3)(x-5)}=\dfrac{x(2x-3)(3x+2)}{(2x+3)(x-5)}$

29. $\dfrac{x^3-8}{x^2+ax-2x-2a}=\dfrac{x^3-2^3}{x(x+a)-2(x+a)}=\dfrac{(x-2)(x^2+2x+4)}{(x+a)(x-2)}=\dfrac{x^2+2x+4}{x+a}$

30. $\dfrac{xy+2x+3y+6}{x^3+27}=\dfrac{x(y+2)+3(y+2)}{x^3+3^3}=\dfrac{(y+2)(x+3)}{(x+3)(x^2-3x+9)}=\dfrac{y+2}{x^2-3x+9}$

31. $\dfrac{x^2-1}{x}\cdot\dfrac{x^2}{x^2+2x+1}=\dfrac{(x+1)(x-1)}{x}\cdot\dfrac{x^2}{(x+1)(x+1)}=\dfrac{x(x-1)}{x+1}$

32. $\dfrac{y^2-2y+1}{y}\cdot\dfrac{y+2}{y^2+y-2}=\dfrac{(y-1)(y-1)}{y}\cdot\dfrac{y+2}{(y+2)(y-1)}=\dfrac{y-1}{y}$

33. $\dfrac{3x^2+7x+2}{x^2+2x}\cdot\dfrac{x^2-x}{3x^2+x}=\dfrac{(3x+1)(x+2)}{x(x+2)}\cdot\dfrac{x(x-1)}{x(3x+1)}=\dfrac{x-1}{x}$

34. $\dfrac{x^2+x}{2x^2+3x}\cdot\dfrac{2x^2+x-3}{x^2-1}=\dfrac{x(x+1)}{x(2x+3)}\cdot\dfrac{(2x+3)(x-1)}{(x+1)(x-1)}=1$

35. $\dfrac{x^2+x}{x-1}\cdot\dfrac{x^2-1}{x+2}=\dfrac{x(x+1)}{x-1}\cdot\dfrac{(x+1)(x-1)}{x+2}=\dfrac{x(x+1)^2}{x+2}$

36. $\dfrac{x^2+5x+6}{x^2+6x+9}\cdot\dfrac{x+2}{x^2-4}=\dfrac{(x+2)(x+3)}{(x+3)(x+3)}\cdot\dfrac{x+2}{(x+2)(x-2)}=\dfrac{x+2}{(x+3)(x-2)}$

37. $\dfrac{2x^2+32}{8}\div\dfrac{x^2+16}{2}=\dfrac{2x^2+32}{8}\cdot\dfrac{2}{x^2+16}=\dfrac{2(x^2+16)}{8}\cdot\dfrac{2}{x^2+16}=\dfrac{1}{2}$

38. $\dfrac{x^2+x-6}{x^2-6x+9}\div\dfrac{x^2-4}{x^2-9}=\dfrac{x^2+x-6}{x^2-6x+9}\cdot\dfrac{x^2-9}{x^2-4}=\dfrac{(x+3)(x-2)}{(x-3)(x-3)}\cdot\dfrac{(x+3)(x-3)}{(x+2)(x-2)}$

$=\dfrac{(x+3)^2}{(x-3)(x+2)}$

39. $\dfrac{z^2+z-20}{z^2-4}\div\dfrac{z^2-25}{z-5}=\dfrac{z^2+z-20}{z^2-4}\cdot\dfrac{z-5}{z^2-25}=\dfrac{(z+5)(z-4)}{(z+2)(z-2)}\cdot\dfrac{z-5}{(z+5)(z-5)}$

$=\dfrac{z-4}{(z+2)(z-2)}$

40. $$\frac{ax+bx+a+b}{a^2+2ab+b^2} \div \frac{x^2-1}{x^2-2x+1} = \frac{ax+bx+a+b}{a^2+2ab+b^2} \cdot \frac{x^2-2x+1}{x^2-1}$$
$$= \frac{x(a+b)+1(a+b)}{(a+b)(a+b)} \cdot \frac{(x-1)(x-1)}{(x+1)(x-1)}$$
$$= \frac{(a+b)(x+1)}{(a+b)(a+b)} \cdot \frac{(x-1)(x-1)}{(x+1)(x-1)} = \frac{x-1}{a+b}$$

41. $$\frac{3x^2+5x-2}{x^3+2x^2} \div \frac{6x^2+13x-5}{2x^3+5x^2} = \frac{3x^2+5x-2}{x^3+2x^2} \cdot \frac{2x^3+5x^2}{6x^2+13x-5}$$
$$= \frac{(3x-1)(x+2)}{x^2(x+2)} \cdot \frac{x^2(2x+5)}{(3x-1)(2x+5)} = 1$$

42. $$\frac{x^2+13x+12}{8x^2-6x-5} \div \frac{2x^2-x-3}{8x^2-14x+5} = \frac{x^2+13x+12}{8x^2-6x-5} \cdot \frac{8x^2-14x+5}{2x^2-x-3}$$
$$= \frac{(x+12)(x+1)}{(4x-5)(2x+1)} \cdot \frac{(4x-5)(2x-1)}{(2x-3)(x+1)} = \frac{(x+12)(2x-1)}{(2x+1)(2x-3)}$$

43. $$\frac{x^2+7x+12}{x^3-x^2-6x} \cdot \frac{x^2-3x-10}{x^2+2x-3} \cdot \frac{x^3-4x^2+3x}{x^2-x-20}$$
$$= \frac{(x+3)(x+4)}{x(x-3)(x+2)} \cdot \frac{(x-5)(x+2)}{(x+3)(x-1)} \cdot \frac{x(x-3)(x-1)}{(x-5)(x+4)} = 1$$

44. $$\frac{x(x-2)-3}{x(x+7)-3(x-1)} \cdot \frac{x(x+1)-2}{x(x-7)+3(x+1)} = \frac{x^2-2x-3}{x^2+7x-3x+3} \cdot \frac{x^2+x-2}{x^2-7x+3x+3}$$
$$= \frac{x^2-2x-3}{x^2+4x+3} \cdot \frac{x^2+x-2}{x^2-4x+3}$$
$$= \frac{(x-3)(x+1)}{(x+3)(x+1)} \cdot \frac{(x+2)(x-1)}{(x-3)(x-1)} = \frac{x+2}{x+3}$$

45. $$\frac{x^2-2x-3}{21x^2-50x-16} \cdot \frac{3x-8}{x-3} \div \frac{x^2+6x+5}{7x^2-33x-10} = \frac{x^2-2x-3}{21x^2-50x-16} \cdot \frac{3x-8}{x-3} \cdot \frac{7x^2-33x-10}{x^2+6x+5}$$
$$= \frac{(x-3)(x+1)}{(7x+2)(3x-8)} \cdot \frac{3x-8}{x-3} \cdot \frac{(7x+2)(x-5)}{(x+5)(x+1)}$$
$$= \frac{x-5}{x+5}$$

46. $$\frac{x^3+27}{x^2-4} \div \left(\frac{x^2+4x+3}{x^2+2x} \div \frac{x^2+x-6}{x^2-3x+9}\right) = \frac{x^3+27}{x^2-4} \div \left(\frac{x^2+4x+3}{x^2+2x} \cdot \frac{x^2-3x+9}{x^2+x-6}\right)$$
$$= \frac{x^3+27}{x^2-4} \div \left(\frac{(x+3)(x+1)}{x(x+2)} \cdot \frac{x^2-3x+9}{(x+3)(x-2)}\right)$$
$$= \frac{x^3+27}{x^2-4} \div \frac{(x+1)(x^2-3x+9)}{x(x+2)(x-2)}$$
$$= \frac{(x+3)(x^2-3x+9)}{(x+2)(x-2)} \cdot \frac{x(x+2)(x-2)}{(x+1)(x^2-3x+9)}$$
$$= \frac{x(x+3)}{x+1}$$

47. $$\frac{3}{x+3} + \frac{x+2}{x+3} = \frac{3+x+2}{x+3} = \frac{x+5}{x+3}$$

48. $$\frac{3}{x+1} + \frac{x+2}{x+1} = \frac{3+x+2}{x+1} = \frac{x+5}{x+1}$$

49. $$\frac{4x}{x-1} - \frac{4}{x-1} = \frac{4x-4}{x-1} = \frac{4(x-1)}{x-1} = 4$$

50. $$\frac{6x}{x-2} - \frac{3}{x-2} = \frac{6x-3}{x-2} = \frac{3(2x-1)}{x-2}$$

51. $$\frac{2}{5-x} + \frac{1}{x-5} = \frac{-2}{x-5} + \frac{1}{x-5} = \frac{-1}{x-5}$$

52. $$\frac{3}{x-6} - \frac{2}{6-x} = \frac{3}{x-6} - \frac{-2}{x-6} = \frac{5}{x-6}$$

53. $$\frac{3}{x+1} + \frac{2}{x-1} = \frac{3(x-1)}{(x+1)(x-1)} + \frac{2(x+1)}{(x-1)(x+1)} = \frac{3x-3}{(x+1)(x-1)} + \frac{2x+2}{(x-1)(x+1)}$$
$$= \frac{5x-1}{(x+1)(x-1)}$$

54. $$\frac{3}{x+4} + \frac{x}{x-4} = \frac{3(x-4)}{(x+4)(x-4)} + \frac{x(x+4)}{(x-4)(x+4)} = \frac{3x-12}{(x+4)(x-4)} + \frac{x^2+4x}{(x-4)(x+4)}$$
$$= \frac{x^2+7x-12}{(x+4)(x-4)}$$

55. $$\frac{a+3}{a^2+7a+12} + \frac{a}{a^2-16} = \frac{a+3}{(a+3)(a+4)} + \frac{a}{(a+4)(a-4)}$$
$$= \frac{1}{a+4} + \frac{a}{(a+4)(a-4)}$$
$$= \frac{1(a-4)}{(a+4)(a-4)} + \frac{a}{(a+4)(a-4)}$$
$$= \frac{a-4}{(a+4)(a-4)} + \frac{a}{(a+4)(a-4)}$$
$$= \frac{2a-4}{(a+4)(a-4)} = \frac{2(a-2)}{(a+4)(a-4)}$$

56. $$\frac{a}{a^2+a-2}+\frac{2}{a^2-5a+4}=\frac{a}{(a+2)(a-1)}+\frac{2}{(a-4)(a-1)}$$
$$=\frac{a(a-4)}{(a+2)(a-1)(a-4)}+\frac{2(a+2)}{(a-4)(a-1)(a+2)}$$
$$=\frac{a^2-4a}{(a+2)(a-1)(a-4)}+\frac{2a+4}{(a+2)(a-1)(a-4)}$$
$$=\frac{a^2-2a+4}{(a+2)(a-1)(a-4)}$$

57. $$\frac{x}{x^2-4}-\frac{1}{x+2}=\frac{x}{(x+2)(x-2)}-\frac{1}{x+2}=\frac{x}{(x+2)(x-2)}-\frac{1(x-2)}{(x+2)(x-2)}$$
$$=\frac{x}{(x+2)(x-2)}-\frac{x-2}{(x+2)(x-2)}$$
$$=\frac{2}{(x+2)(x-2)}$$

58. $$\frac{b^2}{b^2-4}-\frac{4}{b^2+2b}=\frac{b^2}{(b+2)(b-2)}-\frac{4}{b(b+2)}=\frac{b^2(b)}{b(b+2)(b-2)}-\frac{4(b-2)}{b(b+2)(b-2)}$$
$$=\frac{b^3}{b(b+2)(b-2)}-\frac{4b-8}{b(b+2)(b-2)}$$
$$=\frac{b^3-4b+8}{b(b+2)(b-2)}$$

59. $$\frac{3x-2}{x^2+2x+1}-\frac{x}{x^2-1}=\frac{3x-2}{(x+1)(x+1)}-\frac{x}{(x+1)(x-1)}$$
$$=\frac{(3x-2)(x-1)}{(x+1)(x+1)(x-1)}-\frac{x(x+1)}{(x+1)(x-1)(x+1)}$$
$$=\frac{3x^2-5x+2}{(x+1)(x+1)(x-1)}-\frac{x^2+x}{(x+1)(x+1)(x-1)}$$
$$=\frac{2x^2-6x+2}{(x+1)(x+1)(x-1)}=\frac{2(x^2-3x+1)}{(x+1)^2(x-1)}$$

60. $$\frac{2t}{t^2-25}-\frac{t+1}{t^2+5t}=\frac{2t}{(t+5)(t-5)}-\frac{t+1}{t(t+5)}=\frac{2t(t)}{t(t+5)(t-5)}-\frac{(t+1)(t-5)}{t(t+5)(t-5)}$$
$$=\frac{2t^2}{t(t+5)(t-5)}-\frac{t^2-4t-5}{t(t+5)(t-5)}$$
$$=\frac{t^2+4t+5}{t(t+5)(t-5)}$$

61. $$\frac{2}{y^2-1}+3+\frac{1}{y+1}=\frac{2}{(y+1)(y-1)}+\frac{3}{1}+\frac{1}{y+1}$$
$$=\frac{2}{(y+1)(y-1)}+\frac{3(y+1)(y-1)}{1(y+1)(y-1)}+\frac{1(y-1)}{(y+1)(y-1)}$$
$$=\frac{2}{(y+1)(y-1)}+\frac{3y^2-3}{(y+1)(y-1)}+\frac{y-1}{(y+1)(y-1)}$$
$$=\frac{3y^2+y-2}{(y+1)(y-1)}=\frac{(3y-2)(y+1)}{(y+1)(y-1)}=\frac{3y-2}{y-1}$$

62. $$2+\frac{4}{t^2-4}-\frac{1}{t-2}=\frac{2}{1}+\frac{4}{(t+2)(t-2)}-\frac{1}{t-2}$$
$$=\frac{2(t+2)(t-2)}{1(t+2)(t-2)}+\frac{4}{(t+2)(t-2)}-\frac{1(t+2)}{(t+2)(t-2)}$$
$$=\frac{2t^2-8}{(t+2)(t-2)}+\frac{4}{(t+2)(t-2)}-\frac{t+2}{(t+2)(t-2)}$$
$$=\frac{2t^2-t-6}{(t+2)(t-2)}=\frac{(2t+3)(t-2)}{(t+2)(t-2)}=\frac{2t+3}{t+2}$$

63. $$\frac{1}{x-2}+\frac{3}{x+2}-\frac{3x-2}{x^2-4}=\frac{1}{x-2}+\frac{3}{x+2}-\frac{3x-2}{(x+2)(x-2)}$$
$$=\frac{1(x+2)}{(x-2)(x+2)}+\frac{3(x-2)}{(x+2)(x-2)}-\frac{3x-2}{(x+2)(x-2)}$$
$$=\frac{x+2}{(x+2)(x-2)}+\frac{3x-6}{(x+2)(x-2)}-\frac{3x-2}{(x+2)(x-2)}$$
$$=\frac{x-2}{(x+2)(x-2)}=\frac{1}{x+2}$$

64. $$\frac{x}{x-3}-\frac{5}{x+3}+\frac{3(3x-1)}{x^2-9}=\frac{x}{x-3}-\frac{5}{x+3}+\frac{9x-3}{(x+3)(x-3)}$$
$$=\frac{x(x+3)}{(x-3)(x+3)}-\frac{5(x-3)}{(x+3)(x-3)}+\frac{9x-3}{(x+3)(x-3)}$$
$$=\frac{x^2+3x}{(x+3)(x-3)}-\frac{5x-15}{(x+3)(x-3)}+\frac{9x-3}{(x+3)(x-3)}$$
$$=\frac{x^2+7x+12}{(x+3)(x-3)}=\frac{(x+3)(x+4)}{(x+3)(x-3)}=\frac{x+4}{x-3}$$

65. $$\left(\frac{1}{x-2}+\frac{1}{x-3}\right)\cdot\frac{x-3}{2x}=\left(\frac{1(x-3)}{(x-2)(x-3)}+\frac{1(x-2)}{(x-3)(x-2)}\right)\cdot\frac{x-3}{2x}$$
$$=\left(\frac{x-3}{(x-2)(x-3)}+\frac{x-2}{(x-2)(x-3)}\right)\cdot\frac{x-3}{2x}$$
$$=\frac{2x-5}{(x-2)(x-3)}\cdot\frac{x-3}{2x}=\frac{2x-5}{2x(x-2)}$$

66. $$\left(\frac{1}{x+1}-\frac{1}{x-2}\right)\div\frac{1}{x-2}=\left(\frac{1(x-2)}{(x+1)(x-2)}-\frac{1(x+1)}{(x-2)(x+1)}\right)\cdot\frac{x-2}{1}$$
$$=\left(\frac{x-2}{(x+1)(x-2)}-\frac{x+1}{(x+1)(x-2)}\right)\cdot\frac{x-2}{1}$$
$$=\frac{-3}{(x+1)(x-2)}\cdot\frac{x-2}{1}=\frac{-3}{x+1}$$

67. $$\frac{3x}{x-4}-\frac{x}{x+4}-\frac{3x+1}{16-x^2}=\frac{3x}{x-4}-\frac{x}{x+4}-\frac{3x+1}{(4+x)(4-x)}$$
$$=\frac{3x}{x-4}-\frac{x}{x+4}+\frac{3x+1}{(x+4)(x-4)}$$
$$=\frac{3x(x+4)}{(x-4)(x+4)}-\frac{x(x-4)}{(x+4)(x-4)}+\frac{3x+1}{(x+4)(x-4)}$$
$$=\frac{3x^2+12x}{(x+4)(x-4)}-\frac{x^2-4x}{(x+4)(x-4)}+\frac{3x+1}{(x+4)(x-4)}$$
$$=\frac{2x^2+19x+1}{(x+4)(x-4)}$$

68. $$\frac{7x}{x-5}+\frac{3x}{5-x}+\frac{3x-1}{x^2-25}=\frac{7x}{x-5}+\frac{-3x}{x-5}+\frac{3x-1}{(x+5)(x-5)}$$
$$=\frac{4x}{x-5}+\frac{3x-1}{(x+5)(x-5)}$$
$$=\frac{4x(x+5)}{(x-5)(x+5)}+\frac{3x-1}{(x+5)(x-5)}$$
$$=\frac{4x^2+20x}{(x+5)(x-5)}+\frac{3x-1}{(x+5)(x-5)}=\frac{4x^2+23x-1}{(x+5)(x-5)}$$

69. $$\frac{1}{x^2+3x+2}-\frac{2}{x^2+4x+3}+\frac{1}{x^2+5x+6}$$
$$=\frac{1}{(x+2)(x+1)}-\frac{2}{(x+3)(x+1)}+\frac{1}{(x+2)(x+3)}$$
$$=\frac{1(x+3)}{(x+2)(x+1)(x+3)}-\frac{2(x+2)}{(x+3)(x+1)(x+2)}+\frac{1(x+1)}{(x+2)(x+3)(x+1)}$$
$$=\frac{x+3}{(x+2)(x+1)(x+3)}-\frac{2x+4}{(x+2)(x+1)(x+3)}+\frac{x+1}{(x+2)(x+1)(x+3)}$$
$$=\frac{x+3-2x-4+x+1}{(x+2)(x+1)(x+3)}=\frac{0}{(x+2)(x+1)(x+3)}=0$$

70. $$\frac{-2}{x-y}+\frac{2}{x-z}-\frac{2z-2y}{(y-x)(z-x)}=\frac{2}{y-x}+\frac{-2}{z-x}-\frac{2z-2y}{(y-x)(z-x)}$$
$$=\frac{2(z-x)}{(y-x)(z-x)}+\frac{-2(y-x)}{(z-x)(y-x)}-\frac{2z-2y}{(y-x)(z-x)}$$
$$=\frac{2z-2x}{(y-x)(z-x)}+\frac{-2y+2x}{(y-x)(z-x)}-\frac{2z-2y}{(y-x)(z-x)}$$
$$=\frac{2z-2x-2y+2x-2z+2y}{(y-x)(z-x)}=\frac{0}{(y-x)(z-x)}=0$$

71. $$\frac{3x-2}{x^2+x-20}-\frac{4x^2+2}{x^2-25}+\frac{3x^2-25}{x^2-16}$$
$$=\frac{3x-2}{(x+5)(x-4)}-\frac{4x^2+2}{(x+5)(x-5)}+\frac{3x^2-25}{(x+4)(x-4)}$$
$$=\frac{(3x-2)(x-5)(x+4)}{(x+5)(x-4)(x-5)(x+4)}-\frac{(4x^2+2)(x-4)(x+4)}{(x+5)(x-5)(x-4)(x+4)}\cdots$$
$$+\frac{(3x^2-25)(x+5)(x-5)}{(x+4)(x-4)(x+5)(x-5)}$$
$$=\frac{3x^3-5x^2-58x+40}{(x+5)(x-4)(x-5)(x+4)}-\frac{4x^4-62x^2-32}{(x+5)(x-4)(x-5)(x+4)}\cdots$$
$$+\frac{3x^4-100x^2+625}{(x+5)(x-4)(x-5)(x+4)}$$
$$=\frac{3x^3-5x^2-58x+40-4x^4+62x^2+32+3x^4-100x^2+625}{(x+5)(x-4)(x-5)(x+4)}$$
$$=\frac{-x^4+3x^3-43x^2-58x+697}{(x+5)(x-4)(x-5)(x+4)}$$

72. $$\frac{3x+2}{8x^2-10x-3}+\frac{x+4}{6x^2-11x+3}-\frac{1}{4x+1}$$
$$=\frac{3x+2}{(4x+1)(2x-3)}+\frac{x+4}{(3x-1)(2x-3)}-\frac{1}{4x+1}$$
$$=\frac{(3x+2)(3x-1)}{(4x+1)(2x-3)(3x-1)}+\frac{(x+4)(4x+1)}{(3x-1)(2x-3)(4x+1)}-\frac{1(2x-3)(3x-1)}{(4x+1)(2x-3)(3x-1)}$$
$$=\frac{9x^2+3x-2}{(4x+1)(2x-3)(3x-1)}+\frac{4x^2+17x+4}{(4x+1)(2x-3)(3x-1)}-\frac{6x^2-11x+3}{(4x+1)(2x-3)(3x-1)}$$
$$=\frac{9x^2+3x-2+4x^2+17x+4-6x^2+11x-3}{(4x+1)(2x-3)(3x-1)}=\frac{7x^2+31x-1}{(4x+1)(2x-3)(3x-1)}$$

73. $$\frac{\frac{3a}{b}}{\frac{6ac}{b^2}}=\frac{3a}{b}\div\frac{6ac}{b^2}=\frac{3a}{b}\cdot\frac{b^2}{6ac}=\frac{b}{2c}$$

74. $$\frac{\frac{3t^2}{9x}}{\frac{t}{18x}}=\frac{3t^2}{9x}\div\frac{t}{18x}=\frac{3t^2}{9x}\cdot\frac{18x}{t}=6t$$

75. $$\frac{3a^2b}{\frac{ab}{27}}=\frac{3a^2b}{1}\div\frac{ab}{27}=\frac{3a^2b}{1}\cdot\frac{27}{ab}=81a$$

76. $$\frac{\frac{3u^2v}{4t}}{3uv}=\frac{3u^2v}{4t}\div\frac{3uv}{1}=\frac{3u^2v}{4t}\cdot\frac{1}{3uv}=\frac{u}{4t}$$

77. $\dfrac{\frac{x-y}{ab}}{\frac{y-x}{ab}} = \dfrac{x-y}{ab} \div \dfrac{y-x}{ab} = \dfrac{x-y}{ab} \cdot \dfrac{ab}{y-x} = -1$

78. $\dfrac{\frac{x^2-5x+6}{2x^2y}}{\frac{x^2-9}{2x^2y}} = \dfrac{x^2-5x+6}{2x^2y} \div \dfrac{x^2-9}{2x^2y} = \dfrac{x^2-5x+6}{2x^2y} \cdot \dfrac{2x^2y}{x^2-9}$
$= \dfrac{(x-3)(x-2)}{2x^2y} \cdot \dfrac{2x^2y}{(x+3)(x-3)} = \dfrac{x-2}{x+3}$

79. $\dfrac{\frac{1}{x}+\frac{1}{y}}{xy} = \dfrac{xy\left(\frac{1}{x}+\frac{1}{y}\right)}{xy(xy)} = \dfrac{xy\left(\frac{1}{x}\right)+xy\left(\frac{1}{y}\right)}{x^2y^2} = \dfrac{y+x}{x^2y^2}$

80. $\dfrac{xy}{\frac{11}{x}+\frac{11}{y}} = \dfrac{xy(xy)}{xy\left(\frac{11}{x}+\frac{11}{y}\right)} = \dfrac{x^2y^2}{xy\left(\frac{11}{x}\right)+xy\left(\frac{11}{y}\right)} = \dfrac{x^2y^2}{11y+11x} = \dfrac{x^2y^2}{11(y+x)}$

81. $\dfrac{\frac{1}{x}+\frac{1}{y}}{\frac{1}{x}-\frac{1}{y}} = \dfrac{xy\left(\frac{1}{x}+\frac{1}{y}\right)}{xy\left(\frac{1}{x}-\frac{1}{y}\right)} = \dfrac{xy\left(\frac{1}{x}\right)+xy\left(\frac{1}{y}\right)}{xy\left(\frac{1}{x}\right)-xy\left(\frac{1}{y}\right)}$
$= \dfrac{y+x}{y-x}$

82. $\dfrac{\frac{1}{x}-\frac{1}{y}}{\frac{1}{x}+\frac{1}{y}} = \dfrac{xy\left(\frac{1}{x}-\frac{1}{y}\right)}{xy\left(\frac{1}{x}+\frac{1}{y}\right)} = \dfrac{xy\left(\frac{1}{x}\right)-xy\left(\frac{1}{y}\right)}{xy\left(\frac{1}{x}\right)+xy\left(\frac{1}{y}\right)}$
$= \dfrac{y-x}{y+x}$

83. $\dfrac{\frac{3a}{b}-\frac{4a^2}{x}}{\frac{1}{b}+\frac{1}{ax}} = \dfrac{abx\left(\frac{3a}{b}-\frac{4a^2}{x}\right)}{abx\left(\frac{1}{b}+\frac{1}{ax}\right)} = \dfrac{abx\left(\frac{3a}{b}\right)-abx\left(\frac{4a^2}{x}\right)}{abx\left(\frac{1}{b}\right)+abx\left(\frac{1}{ax}\right)} = \dfrac{3a^2x-4a^3b}{ax+b} = \dfrac{a^2(3x-4ab)}{ax+b}$

84. $\dfrac{1-\frac{x}{y}}{\frac{x^2}{y^2}-1} = \dfrac{y^2\left(1-\frac{x}{y}\right)}{y^2\left(\frac{x^2}{y^2}-1\right)} = \dfrac{y^2(1)-y^2\left(\frac{x}{y}\right)}{y^2\left(\frac{x^2}{y^2}\right)-y^2(1)} = \dfrac{y^2-xy}{x^2-y^2} = \dfrac{y(y-x)}{(x+y)(x-y)} = \dfrac{-y}{x+y}$

85. $\dfrac{x+1-\frac{6}{x}}{x+5+\frac{6}{x}} = \dfrac{x\left(x+1-\frac{6}{x}\right)}{x\left(x+5+\frac{6}{x}\right)} = \dfrac{x(x)+x(1)-x\left(\frac{6}{x}\right)}{x(x)+x(5)+x\left(\frac{6}{x}\right)} = \dfrac{x^2+x-6}{x^2+5x+6} = \dfrac{(x+3)(x-2)}{(x+2)(x+3)} = \dfrac{x-2}{x+2}$

86. $\dfrac{2z}{1-\frac{3}{z}} = \dfrac{z(2z)}{z\left(1-\frac{3}{z}\right)} = \dfrac{2z^2}{z(1)-z\left(\frac{3}{z}\right)}$
$= \dfrac{2z^2}{z-3}$

87. $\dfrac{3xy}{1-\frac{1}{xy}} = \dfrac{xy(3xy)}{xy\left(1-\frac{1}{xy}\right)} = \dfrac{3x^2y^2}{xy(1)-xy\left(\frac{1}{xy}\right)}$
$= \dfrac{3x^2y^2}{xy-1}$

88. $\dfrac{x-3+\frac{1}{x}}{-\frac{1}{x}-x+3} = \dfrac{x\left(x-3+\frac{1}{x}\right)}{x\left(-\frac{1}{x}-x+3\right)} = \dfrac{x^2-3x+1}{-1-x^2+3x} = \dfrac{x^2-3x+1}{-(x^2-3x+1)} = -1$

89. $\dfrac{3x}{x+\frac{1}{x}} = \dfrac{x(3x)}{x\left(x+\frac{1}{x}\right)} = \dfrac{3x^2}{x^2+1}$

90. $$\frac{2x^2+4}{2+\frac{4x}{5}}=\frac{5(2x^2+4)}{5\left(2+\frac{4x}{5}\right)}=\frac{10x^2+20}{10+4x}=\frac{2(5x^2+10)}{2(5+2x)}=\frac{5x^2+10}{5+2x}$$

91. $$\frac{\frac{x}{x+2}-\frac{2}{x-1}}{\frac{3}{x+2}+\frac{x}{x-1}}=\frac{(x+2)(x-1)\left(\frac{x}{x+2}-\frac{2}{x-1}\right)}{(x+2)(x-1)\left(\frac{3}{x+2}+\frac{x}{x-1}\right)}=\frac{(x+2)(x-1)\left(\frac{x}{x+2}\right)-(x+2)(x-1)\left(\frac{2}{x-1}\right)}{(x+2)(x-1)\left(\frac{3}{x+2}\right)+(x+2)(x-1)\left(\frac{x}{x-1}\right)}$$
$$=\frac{(x-1)(x)-(x+2)(2)}{(x-1)(3)+(x+2)(x)}$$
$$=\frac{x^2-x-2x-4}{3x-3+x^2+2x}=\frac{x^2-3x-4}{x^2+5x-3}$$

92. $$\frac{\frac{2x}{x-3}+\frac{1}{x-2}}{\frac{3}{x-3}-\frac{x}{x-2}}=\frac{(x-3)(x-2)\left(\frac{2x}{x-3}+\frac{1}{x-2}\right)}{(x-3)(x-2)\left(\frac{3}{x-3}-\frac{x}{x-2}\right)}=\frac{(x-3)(x-2)\left(\frac{2x}{x-3}\right)+(x-3)(x-2)\left(\frac{1}{x-2}\right)}{(x-3)(x-2)\left(\frac{3}{x-3}\right)-(x-3)(x-2)\left(\frac{x}{x-2}\right)}$$
$$=\frac{(x-2)(2x)+(x-3)(1)}{(x-2)(3)-(x-3)(x)}$$
$$=\frac{2x^2-4x+x-3}{3x-6-x^2+3x}$$
$$=\frac{2x^2-3x-3}{-x^2+6x-6}=-\frac{2x^2-3x-3}{x^2-6x+6}$$

93. $$\frac{1}{1+x^{-1}}=\frac{1}{1+\frac{1}{x}}=\frac{x(1)}{x\left(1+\frac{1}{x}\right)}=\frac{x}{x+1}$$

94. $$\frac{y^{-1}}{x^{-1}+y^{-1}}=\frac{\frac{1}{y}}{\frac{1}{x}+\frac{1}{y}}=\frac{xy\left(\frac{1}{y}\right)}{xy\left(\frac{1}{x}+\frac{1}{y}\right)}=\frac{x}{y+x}$$

95. $$\frac{3(x+2)^{-1}+2(x-1)^{-1}}{(x+2)^{-1}}=\frac{\frac{3}{x+2}+\frac{2}{x-1}}{\frac{1}{x+2}}=\frac{(x+2)(x-1)\left(\frac{3}{x+2}+\frac{2}{x-1}\right)}{(x+2)(x-1)\left(\frac{1}{x+2}\right)}$$
$$=\frac{(x+2)(x-1)\left(\frac{3}{x+2}\right)+(x+2)(x-1)\left(\frac{2}{x-1}\right)}{x-1}$$
$$=\frac{(x-1)(3)+(x+2)(2)}{x-1}$$
$$=\frac{3x-3+2x+4}{x-1}=\frac{5x+1}{x-1}$$

96. $$\frac{2x(x-3)^{-1}-3(x+2)^{-1}}{(x-3)^{-1}(x+2)^{-1}}=\frac{\frac{2x}{x-3}-\frac{3}{x+2}}{\frac{1}{(x-3)(x+2)}}=\frac{(x-3)(x+2)\left(\frac{2x}{x-3}-\frac{3}{x+2}\right)}{(x-3)(x+2)\left(\frac{1}{(x-3)(x+2)}\right)}$$
$$=\frac{(x+2)(2x)-(x-3)(3)}{1}$$
$$=2x^2+4x-3x+9=2x^2+x+9$$

97. $$\frac{1}{\frac{1}{k_1}+\frac{1}{k_2}}=\frac{k_1k_2(1)}{k_1k_2\left(\frac{1}{k_1}+\frac{1}{k_2}\right)}=\frac{k_1k_2}{k_1k_2\left(\frac{1}{k_1}\right)+k_1k_2\left(\frac{1}{k_2}\right)}=\frac{k_1k_2}{k_2+k_1}$$

98. $\dfrac{1}{\frac{1}{R_1}+\frac{1}{R_2}+\frac{1}{R_3}} = \dfrac{R_1R_2R_3(1)}{R_1R_2R_3\left(\frac{1}{R_1}+\frac{1}{R_2}+\frac{1}{R_3}\right)} = \dfrac{R_1R_2R_3}{R_1R_2R_3\left(\frac{1}{R_1}\right)+R_1R_2R_3\left(\frac{1}{R_2}\right)+R_1R_2R_3\left(\frac{1}{R_3}\right)}$

$= \dfrac{R_1R_2R_3}{R_2R_3+R_1R_3+R_1R_2}$

99. $\dfrac{x}{1+\frac{1}{3x^{-1}}} = \dfrac{x}{1+\frac{1}{\frac{3}{x}}} = \dfrac{x}{1+\frac{x(1)}{x\left(\frac{3}{x}\right)}} = \dfrac{x}{1+\frac{x}{3}} = \dfrac{3x}{3\left(1+\frac{x}{3}\right)} = \dfrac{3x}{3+x}$

100. $\dfrac{ab}{2+\frac{3}{2a^{-1}}} = \dfrac{ab}{2+\frac{3}{\frac{2}{a}}} = \dfrac{ab}{2+\frac{a(3)}{a\left(\frac{2}{a}\right)}} = \dfrac{ab}{2+\frac{3a}{2}} = \dfrac{2ab}{2\left(2+\frac{3a}{2}\right)} = \dfrac{2ab}{4+3a}$

101. $\dfrac{1}{1+\frac{1}{1+\frac{1}{x}}} = \dfrac{1}{1+\frac{x(1)}{x\left(1+\frac{1}{x}\right)}} = \dfrac{1}{1+\frac{x}{x+1}} = \dfrac{(x+1)1}{(x+1)\left(1+\frac{x}{x+1}\right)} = \dfrac{x+1}{x+1+x} = \dfrac{x+1}{2x+1}$

102. $\dfrac{y}{2+\frac{2}{2+\frac{2}{y}}} = \dfrac{y}{2+\frac{y(2)}{y\left(2+\frac{2}{y}\right)}} = \dfrac{y}{2+\frac{2y}{2y+2}} = \dfrac{(2y+2)(y)}{(2y+2)\left(2+\frac{2y}{2y+2}\right)} = \dfrac{2y^2+2y}{(2y+2)(2)+2y}$

$= \dfrac{2y(y+1)}{4y+4+2y}$

$= \dfrac{2y(y+1)}{2(3y+2)} = \dfrac{y(y+1)}{3y+2}$

103-106. Answers may vary.

107. Since $-6<0$, $|-6| = -(-6) = 6$.

108. If $x<0$, then $5-x \geq 0$. Then $|5-x| = 5-x$.

109. $\left(\dfrac{x^3y^{-2}}{x^{-1}y}\right)^{-3} = \left(\dfrac{x^{-1}y}{x^3y^{-2}}\right)^3 = \left(\dfrac{y^2y}{x^3x}\right)^3 = \left(\dfrac{y^3}{x^4}\right)^3 = \dfrac{y^9}{x^{12}}$

110. $(27x^6)^{2/3} = 27^{2/3}(x^6)^{2/3} = (27^{1/3})^2x^{12/3} = 3^2x^4 = 9x^4$

111. $\sqrt{20}-\sqrt{45} = \sqrt{4}\sqrt{5}-\sqrt{9}\sqrt{5} = 2\sqrt{5}-3\sqrt{5} = -\sqrt{5}$

112. $2(x^2+4)-3(2x^2+5) = 2(x^2)+2(4)-3(2x^2)-3(5) = 2x^2+8-6x^2-15 = -4x^2-7$

Chapter 0 Review (page 75)

1. natural: 3, 6, 8

2. whole: 0, 3, 6, 8

3. integers: $-6, -3, 0, 3, 6, 8$

4. rational: $-6, -3, 0, \frac{1}{2}, 3, 6, 8$

CHAPTER 0 REVIEW

5. irrational: π, $\sqrt{5}$

6. real: $-6, -3, 0, \frac{1}{2}, 3, \pi, \sqrt{5}, 6, 8$

7. prime: 3

8. composite: 6, 8

9. even integers: $-6, 0, 6, 8$

10. odd integers: $-3, 3$

11. associative property of addition

12. commutative property of addition

13. associative property of multiplication

14. distributive property

15. commutative property of multiplication

16. commutative property of addition

17. double negative rule

18. 11 13 17 19

19. 6 8 10 12 14

20. $-3 < x \le 5$

-3 5

21. $x \ge 0$ or $x < -1$

-1 0

22. $(-2, 4]$

-2 4

23. $(-\infty, 2) \cap (-5, \infty)$

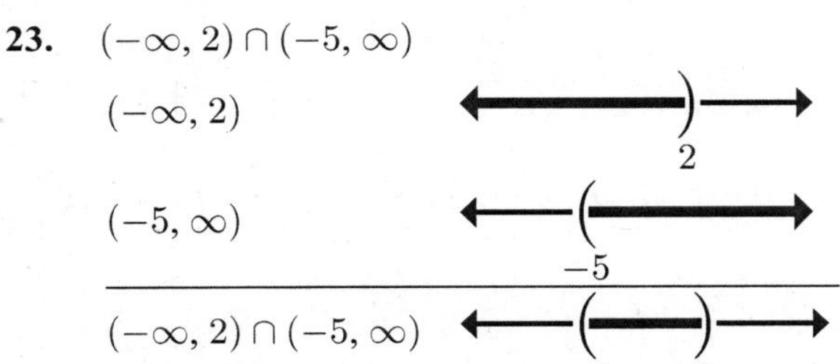

24. $(-\infty, -4) \cup [6, \infty)$

-4 6

25. Since $6 \ge 0$, $|6| = 6$.

26. Since $-25 < 0$, $|-25| = -(-25) = 25$.

27. Since $1 - \sqrt{2} < 0$,
$\left|1 - \sqrt{2}\right| = -\left(1 - \sqrt{2}\right) = \sqrt{2} - 1$.

28. Since $\sqrt{3} - 1 \ge 0$,
$\left|\sqrt{3} - 1\right| = \sqrt{3} - 1$.

29. distance $= |7 - (-5)| = |12| = 12$

CHAPTER 0 REVIEW

30. $-5a^3 = -5aaa$

31. $(-5a)^2 = (-5a)(-5a)$

32. $3ttt = 3t^3$

33. $(-2b)(3b) = (-2)(3)bb = -6b^2$

34. $n^2n^4 = n^{2+4} = n^6$

35. $(p^3)^2 = p^{3\cdot 2} = p^6$

36. $(x^3y^2)^4 = (x^3)^4(y^2)^4 = x^{12}y^8$

37. $\left(\frac{a^4}{b^2}\right)^3 = \frac{(a^4)^3}{(b^2)^3} = \frac{a^{12}}{b^6}$

38. $(m^{-3}n^0)^2 = (m^{-3}\cdot 1)^2 = m^{-6} = \frac{1}{m^6}$

39. $\left(\frac{p^{-2}q^2}{2}\right)^3 = \left(\frac{q^2}{2p^2}\right)^3 = \frac{(q^2)^3}{(2p^2)^3} = \frac{q^6}{8p^6}$

40. $\frac{a^5}{a^8} = a^{5-8} = a^{-3} = \frac{1}{a^3}$

41. $\left(\frac{a^2}{b^3}\right)^{-2} = \left(\frac{b^3}{a^2}\right)^2 = \frac{b^6}{a^4}$

42. $\left(\frac{3x^2y^{-2}}{x^2y^2}\right)^{-2} = \left(\frac{x^2y^2}{3x^2y^{-2}}\right)^2 = \left(\frac{x^2y^2y^2}{3x^2}\right)^2 = \left(\frac{y^4}{3}\right)^2 = \frac{y^8}{9}$

43. $\left(\frac{a^{-3}b^2}{ab^{-3}}\right)^{-2} = \left(\frac{ab^{-3}}{a^{-3}b^2}\right)^2 = \left(\frac{aa^3}{b^2b^3}\right)^2 = \left(\frac{a^4}{b^5}\right)^2 = \frac{a^8}{b^{10}}$

44. $\left(\frac{-3x^3y}{xy^3}\right)^{-2} = \left(\frac{xy^3}{-3x^3y}\right)^2 = \left(\frac{y^2}{-3x^2}\right)^2 = \frac{y^4}{9x^4}$

45. $\left(-\frac{2m^{-2}n^0}{4m^2n^{-1}}\right)^{-3} = \left(-\frac{4m^2n^{-1}}{2m^{-2}n^0}\right)^3 = \left(-\frac{2m^2m^2}{n^1n^0}\right)^3 = \left(-\frac{2m^4}{n}\right)^3 = -\frac{8m^{12}}{n^3}$

46. $-x^2 - xy^2 = -(-3)^2 - (-3)(3)^2 = -(+9) - (-3)(9) = -9 - (-27) = -9 + 27 = 18$

47. $6{,}750 = 6.750 \times 10^3$

48. $0.00023 = 2.3 \times 10^{-4}$

49. $4.8 \times 10^2 = 480$

50. $0.25 \times 10^{-3} = 0.00025$

51. $\frac{(45{,}000)(350{,}000)}{0.000105} = \frac{(4.5 \times 10^4)(3.5 \times 10^5)}{1.05 \times 10^{-4}} = \frac{4.5 \times 3.5 \times 10^4 \times 10^5}{1.05 \times 10^{-4}} = \frac{15.75 \times 10^9}{1.05 \times 10^{-4}}$
$= 15 \times 10^{13}$
$= 1.5 \times 10^{14}$

52. $121^{1/2} = (11^2)^{1/2} = 11$

53. $\left(\frac{27}{125}\right)^{1/3} = \left[\left(\frac{3}{5}\right)^3\right]^{1/3} = \frac{3}{5}$

54. $(32x^5)^{1/5} = 32^{1/5}(x^5)^{1/5} = 2x$

55. $(81a^4)^{1/4} = 81^{1/4}(a^4)^{1/4} = 3|a|$

56. $(-1{,}000x^6)^{1/3} = (-1{,}000)^{1/3}(x^6)^{1/3} = -10x^2$

57. $(-25x^2)^{1/2} = (-25)^{1/2}(x^2)^{1/2}$ $\Rightarrow$ not a real number

58. $(x^{12}y^2)^{1/2} = (x^{12})^{1/2}(y^2)^{1/2} = x^6|y|$

59. $\left(\dfrac{x^{12}}{y^4}\right)^{-1/2} = \left(\dfrac{y^4}{x^{12}}\right)^{1/2} = \dfrac{y^2}{x^6}$

60. $\left(\dfrac{-c^{2/3}c^{5/3}}{c^{-2/3}}\right)^{1/3} = \left(\dfrac{-c^{7/3}}{c^{-2/3}}\right)^{1/3} = (-c^{9/3})^{1/3} = (-c^3)^{1/3} = -c$

61. $\left(\dfrac{a^{-1/4}a^{3/4}}{a^{9/2}}\right)^{-1/2} = \left(\dfrac{a^{9/2}}{a^{-1/4}a^{3/4}}\right)^{1/2} = \left(\dfrac{a^{9/2}}{a^{2/4}}\right)^{1/2} = \left(\dfrac{a^{9/2}}{a^{1/2}}\right)^{1/2} = (a^{8/2})^{1/2} = (a^4)^{1/2} = a^2$

62. $64^{2/3} = (64^{1/3})^2 = 4^2 = 16$

63. $32^{-3/5} = \dfrac{1}{32^{3/5}} = \dfrac{1}{(32^{1/5})^3} = \dfrac{1}{2^3} = \dfrac{1}{8}$

64. $\left(\dfrac{16}{81}\right)^{3/4} = \dfrac{16^{3/4}}{81^{3/4}} = \dfrac{(16^{1/4})^3}{(81^{1/4})^3} = \dfrac{2^3}{3^3} = \dfrac{8}{27}$

65. $\left(\dfrac{32}{243}\right)^{2/5} = \dfrac{32^{2/5}}{243^{2/5}} = \dfrac{(32^{1/5})^2}{(243^{1/5})^2} = \dfrac{2^2}{3^2} = \dfrac{4}{9}$

66. $\left(\dfrac{8}{27}\right)^{-2/3} = \left(\dfrac{27}{8}\right)^{2/3} = \dfrac{27^{2/3}}{8^{2/3}} = \dfrac{(27^{1/3})^2}{(8^{1/3})^2} = \dfrac{3^2}{2^2} = \dfrac{9}{4}$

67. $\left(\dfrac{16}{625}\right)^{-3/4} = \left(\dfrac{625}{16}\right)^{3/4} = \dfrac{625^{3/4}}{16^{3/4}} = \dfrac{(625^{1/4})^3}{(16^{1/4})^3} = \dfrac{5^3}{2^3} = \dfrac{125}{8}$

68. $(-216x^3)^{2/3} = (-216)^{2/3}(x^3)^{2/3} = 36x^2$

69. $\dfrac{p^{a/2}p^{a/3}}{p^{a/6}} = \dfrac{p^{3a/6}p^{2a/6}}{p^{a/6}} = \dfrac{p^{5a/6}}{p^{a/6}} = p^{4a/6} = p^{2a/3}$

70. $\sqrt{36} = 6$

71. $-\sqrt{49} = -7$

72. $\sqrt{\dfrac{9}{25}} = \dfrac{\sqrt{9}}{\sqrt{25}} = \dfrac{3}{5}$

73. $\sqrt[3]{\dfrac{27}{125}} = \dfrac{\sqrt[3]{27}}{\sqrt[3]{125}} = \dfrac{3}{5}$

74. $\sqrt{x^2y^4} = \sqrt{x^2}\sqrt{y^4} = |x|y^2$

75. $\sqrt[3]{x^3} = x$

76. $\sqrt[4]{\dfrac{m^8n^4}{p^{16}}} = \dfrac{\sqrt[4]{m^8}\sqrt[4]{n^4}}{\sqrt[4]{p^{16}}} = \dfrac{m^2|n|}{p^4}$

77. $\sqrt[5]{\dfrac{a^{15}b^{10}}{c^5}} = \dfrac{\sqrt[5]{a^{15}}\sqrt[5]{b^{10}}}{\sqrt[5]{c^5}} = \dfrac{a^3b^2}{c}$

78. $\sqrt{50} + \sqrt{8} = \sqrt{25}\sqrt{2} + \sqrt{4}\sqrt{2} = 5\sqrt{2} + 2\sqrt{2} = 7\sqrt{2}$

79. $\sqrt{12} + \sqrt{3} - \sqrt{27} = \sqrt{4}\sqrt{3} + \sqrt{3} - \sqrt{9}\sqrt{3} = 2\sqrt{3} + \sqrt{3} - 3\sqrt{3} = 3\sqrt{3} - 3\sqrt{3} = 0$

80. $\sqrt[3]{24x^4} - \sqrt[3]{3x^4} = \sqrt[3]{8x^3}\sqrt[3]{3x} - \sqrt[3]{x^3}\sqrt[3]{3x} = 2x\sqrt[3]{3x} - x\sqrt[3]{3x} = x\sqrt[3]{3x}$

81. $\dfrac{\sqrt{7}}{\sqrt{5}} = \dfrac{\sqrt{7}}{\sqrt{5}} \cdot \dfrac{\sqrt{5}}{\sqrt{5}} = \dfrac{\sqrt{35}}{5}$

82. $\dfrac{8}{\sqrt{8}} = \dfrac{8}{\sqrt{8}} \cdot \dfrac{\sqrt{2}}{\sqrt{2}} = \dfrac{8\sqrt{2}}{\sqrt{16}} = \dfrac{8\sqrt{2}}{4} = 2\sqrt{2}$

83. $\dfrac{1}{\sqrt[3]{2}} = \dfrac{1}{\sqrt[3]{2}} \cdot \dfrac{\sqrt[3]{4}}{\sqrt[3]{4}} = \dfrac{\sqrt[3]{4}}{\sqrt[3]{8}} = \dfrac{\sqrt[3]{4}}{2}$

84. $\dfrac{2}{\sqrt[3]{25}} = \dfrac{2}{\sqrt[3]{25}} \cdot \dfrac{\sqrt[3]{5}}{\sqrt[3]{5}} = \dfrac{2\sqrt[3]{5}}{\sqrt[3]{125}} = \dfrac{2\sqrt[3]{5}}{5}$

85. $\dfrac{\sqrt{2}}{5} = \dfrac{\sqrt{2}}{5} \cdot \dfrac{\sqrt{2}}{\sqrt{2}} = \dfrac{2}{5\sqrt{2}}$

86. $\dfrac{\sqrt{5}}{5} = \dfrac{\sqrt{5}}{5} \cdot \dfrac{\sqrt{5}}{\sqrt{5}} = \dfrac{5}{5\sqrt{5}} = \dfrac{1}{\sqrt{5}}$

87. $\dfrac{\sqrt{2x}}{3} = \dfrac{\sqrt{2x}}{3} \cdot \dfrac{\sqrt{2x}}{\sqrt{2x}} = \dfrac{2x}{3\sqrt{2x}}$

88. $\dfrac{3\sqrt[3]{7x}}{2} = \dfrac{3\sqrt[3]{7x}}{2} \cdot \dfrac{\sqrt[3]{49x^2}}{\sqrt[3]{49x^2}} = \dfrac{3\sqrt[3]{343x^3}}{2\sqrt[3]{49x^2}} = \dfrac{21x}{2\sqrt[3]{49x^2}}$

89. 3rd degree, binomial

90. 2nd degree, trinomial

91. 2nd degree, monomial

92. 4th degree, trinomial

93. $2(x+3) + 3(x-4) = 2x + 6 + 3x - 12 = 5x - 6$

94. $3x^2(x-1) - 2x(x+3) - x^2(x+2) = 3x^3 - 3x^2 - 2x^2 - 6x - x^3 - 2x^2 = 2x^3 - 7x^2 - 6x$

95. $(3x+2)(3x+2) = 9x^2 + 6x + 6x + 4 = 9x^2 + 12x + 4$

96. $(3x+y)(2x-3y) = 6x^2 - 9xy + 2xy - 3y^2 = 6x^2 - 7xy - 3y^2$

97. $(4a+2b)(2a-3b) = 8a^2 - 12ab + 4ab - 6b^2 = 8a^2 - 8ab - 6b^2$

98. $(z+3)(3z^2+z-1) = 3z^3 + z^2 - z + 9z^2 + 3z - 3 = 3z^3 + 10z^2 + 2z - 3$

99. $(a^n+2)(a^n-1) = a^{2n} - a^n + 2a^n - 2 = a^{2n} + a^n - 2$

100. $\left(\sqrt{2}+x\right)^2 = \left(\sqrt{2}+x\right)\left(\sqrt{2}+x\right) = \left(\sqrt{2}\right)^2 + x\sqrt{2} + x\sqrt{2} + x^2 = 2 + 2x\sqrt{2} + x^2$

101. $\left(\sqrt{2}+1\right)\left(\sqrt{3}+1\right) = \sqrt{6} + \sqrt{2} + \sqrt{3} + 1$

102. $\left(\sqrt[3]{3}-2\right)\left(\sqrt[3]{9}+2\sqrt[3]{3}+4\right) = \sqrt[3]{27} + 2\sqrt[3]{9} + 4\sqrt[3]{3} - 2\sqrt[3]{9} - 4\sqrt[3]{3} - 8 = 3 - 8 = -5$

103. $\dfrac{2}{\sqrt{3}-1} = \dfrac{2}{\sqrt{3}-1} \cdot \dfrac{\sqrt{3}+1}{\sqrt{3}+1} = \dfrac{2\left(\sqrt{3}+1\right)}{\left(\sqrt{3}\right)^2 - 1^2} = \dfrac{2\left(\sqrt{3}+1\right)}{3-1} = \dfrac{2\left(\sqrt{3}+1\right)}{2} = \sqrt{3}+1$

104. $\dfrac{-2}{\sqrt{3}-\sqrt{2}} = \dfrac{-2}{\sqrt{3}-\sqrt{2}} \cdot \dfrac{\sqrt{3}+\sqrt{2}}{\sqrt{3}+\sqrt{2}} = \dfrac{-2\left(\sqrt{3}+\sqrt{2}\right)}{\left(\sqrt{3}\right)^2 - \left(\sqrt{2}\right)^2} = \dfrac{-2\left(\sqrt{3}+\sqrt{2}\right)}{3-2}$

$= \dfrac{-2\left(\sqrt{3}+\sqrt{2}\right)}{1}$

$= -2\left(\sqrt{3}+\sqrt{2}\right)$

105. $\dfrac{2x}{\sqrt{x}-2} = \dfrac{2x}{\sqrt{x}-2} \cdot \dfrac{\sqrt{x}+2}{\sqrt{x}+2} = \dfrac{2x\left(\sqrt{x}+2\right)}{\left(\sqrt{x}\right)^2 - 2^2} = \dfrac{2x\left(\sqrt{x}+2\right)}{x-4}$

106. $\dfrac{\sqrt{x}-\sqrt{y}}{\sqrt{x}+\sqrt{y}} = \dfrac{\sqrt{x}-\sqrt{y}}{\sqrt{x}+\sqrt{y}} \cdot \dfrac{\sqrt{x}-\sqrt{y}}{\sqrt{x}-\sqrt{y}} = \dfrac{\sqrt{x^2}-\sqrt{xy}-\sqrt{xy}+y}{\left(\sqrt{x}\right)^2 - \left(\sqrt{y}\right)^2} = \dfrac{x-2\sqrt{xy}+y}{x-y}$

107. $\dfrac{\sqrt{x}+2}{5} = \dfrac{\sqrt{x}+2}{5} \cdot \dfrac{\sqrt{x}-2}{\sqrt{x}-2} = \dfrac{\left(\sqrt{x}\right)^2 - 2^2}{5\left(\sqrt{x}-2\right)} = \dfrac{x-4}{5\left(\sqrt{x}-2\right)}$

108. $\dfrac{1-\sqrt{a}}{a} = \dfrac{1-\sqrt{a}}{a} \cdot \dfrac{1+\sqrt{a}}{1+\sqrt{a}} = \dfrac{1^2 - \left(\sqrt{a}\right)^2}{a\left(1+\sqrt{a}\right)} = \dfrac{1-a}{a\left(1+\sqrt{a}\right)}$

109. $\dfrac{3x^2y^2}{6x^3y} = \dfrac{y}{2x}$

110. $\dfrac{4a^2b^3+6ab^4}{2b^2} = \dfrac{4a^2b^3}{2b^2} + \dfrac{6ab^4}{2b^2}$

$= 2a^2b + 3ab^2$

111.

$$
\begin{array}{r|l}
 & x^2 + 2x + 1 \\
\hline
2x+3 & 2x^3 + 7x^2 + 8x + 3 \\
 & \underline{2x^3 + 3x^2} \\
 & \quad 4x^2 + 8x \\
 & \quad \underline{4x^2 + 6x} \\
 & \qquad 2x + 3 \\
 & \qquad \underline{2x + 3} \\
 & \qquad\quad 0
\end{array}
$$

112.

$$
\begin{array}{r|l}
 & x^3 + 2x - 3 + \frac{-6}{x^2-1} \\
\hline
x^2-1 & x^5 + 0x^4 + x^3 - 3x^2 - 2x - 3 \\
 & \underline{x^5 \qquad - x^3} \\
 & \quad 2x^3 - 3x^2 - 2x \\
 & \quad \underline{2x^3 \qquad - 2x} \\
 & \qquad -3x^2 \qquad - 3 \\
 & \qquad \underline{-3x^2 \qquad + 3} \\
 & \qquad\qquad -6
\end{array}
$$

113. $3t^3 - 3t = 3t(t^2-1) = 3t(t+1)(t-1)$

114. $5r^3 - 5 = 5(r^3-1) = 5(r^3-1^3) = 5(r-1)(r^2+r+1)$

115. $6x^2 + 7x - 24 = (3x+8)(2x-3)$

116. $3a^2 + ax - 3a - x = a(3a+x) - 1(3a+x) = (3a+x)(a-1)$

117. $8x^3 - 125 = (2x)^3 - 5^3 = (2x-5)\left[(2x)^2 + (2x)(5) + 5^2\right] = (2x-5)(4x^2 + 10x + 25)$

118. $6x^2 - 20x - 16 = 2(3x^2 - 10x - 8) = 2(3x+2)(x-4)$

119. $x^2 + 6x + 9 - t^2 = (x+3)(x+3) - t^2 = (x+3)^2 - t^2 = (x+3+t)(x+3-t)$

120. $3x^2 - 1 + 5x = 3x^2 + 5x - 1 \Rightarrow$ prime

121. $8z^3 + 343 = (2z)^3 + 7^3 = (2z+7)\left[(2z)^2 - (2z)(7) + 7^2\right] = (2z+7)(4z^2 - 14z + 49)$

122. $1 + 14b + 49b^2 = 49b^2 + 14b + 1 = (7b+1)(7b+1) = (7b+1)^2$

123. $121z^2 + 4 - 44z = 121z^2 - 44z + 4 = (11z-2)(11z-2) = (11z-2)^2$

124. $64y^3 - 1{,}000 = 8(8y^3 - 125) = 8\left[(2y)^3 - 5^3\right] = 8(2y-5)(4y^2 + 10y + 25)$

125. $2xy - 4zx - wy + 2zw = 2x(y-2z) - w(y-2z) = (y-2z)(2x-w)$

126.
$$\begin{aligned} x^8 + x^4 + 1 = x^8 + 2x^4 + 1 - x^4 &= (x^4+1)(x^4+1) - x^4 \\ &= (x^4+1)^2 - (x^2)^2 \\ &= (x^4+1+x^2)(x^4+1-x^2) \\ &= (x^4+2x^2+1-x^2)(x^4-x^2+1) \\ &= \left[(x^2+1)(x^2+1) - x^2\right](x^4-x^2+1) \\ &= (x^2+1+x)(x^2+1-x)(x^4-x^2+1) \end{aligned}$$

127. $\dfrac{2-x}{x^2-4x+4} = \dfrac{-(x-2)}{(x-2)(x-2)} = \dfrac{-1}{x-2}$

128. $\dfrac{a^2-9}{a^2-6a+9} = \dfrac{(a+3)(a-3)}{(a-3)(a-3)} = \dfrac{a+3}{a-3}$

129. $\dfrac{x^2-4x+4}{x+2} \cdot \dfrac{x^2+5x+6}{x-2} = \dfrac{(x-2)(x-2)}{x+2} \cdot \dfrac{(x+2)(x+3)}{x-2} = (x-2)(x+3)$

130. $\dfrac{2y^2-11y+15}{y^2-6y+8} \cdot \dfrac{y^2-2y-8}{y^2-y-6} = \dfrac{(2y-5)(y-3)}{(y-4)(y-2)} \cdot \dfrac{(y-4)(y+2)}{(y-3)(y+2)} = \dfrac{2y-5}{y-2}$

131.
$$\begin{aligned} \frac{2t^2+t-3}{3t^2-7t+4} \div \frac{10t+15}{3t^2-t-4} &= \frac{2t^2+t-3}{3t^2-7t+4} \cdot \frac{3t^2-t-4}{10t+15} \\ &= \frac{(2t+3)(t-1)}{(3t-4)(t-1)} \cdot \frac{(3t-4)(t+1)}{5(2t+3)} = \frac{t+1}{5} \end{aligned}$$

132.
$$\begin{aligned} \frac{p^2+7p+12}{p^3+8p^2+4p} \div \frac{p^2-9}{p^2} = \frac{p^2+7p+12}{p^3+8p^2+4p} \cdot \frac{p^2}{p^2-9} &= \frac{(p+3)(p+4)}{p(p^2+8p+4)} \cdot \frac{p^2}{(p+3)(p-3)} \\ &= \frac{p(p+4)}{(p^2+8p+4)(p-3)} \end{aligned}$$

133. $\dfrac{x^2+x-6}{x^2-x-6}\cdot\dfrac{x^2-x-6}{x^2+x-2}\div\dfrac{x^2-4}{x^2-5x+6}$

$$=\frac{x^2+x-6}{x^2-x-6}\cdot\frac{x^2-x-6}{x^2+x-2}\cdot\frac{x^2-5x+6}{x^2-4}$$

$$=\frac{(x+3)(x-2)}{(x-3)(x+2)}\cdot\frac{(x-3)(x+2)}{(x+2)(x-1)}\cdot\frac{(x-2)(x-3)}{(x+2)(x-2)}=\frac{(x+3)(x-2)(x-3)}{(x+2)^2(x-1)}$$

134. $\left(\dfrac{2x+6}{x+5}\div\dfrac{2x^2-2x-4}{x^2-25}\right)\dfrac{x^2-x-2}{x^2-2x-15}=\dfrac{2x+6}{x+5}\cdot\dfrac{x^2-25}{2(x^2-x-2)}\cdot\dfrac{x^2-x-2}{x^2-2x-15}$

$$=\frac{2(x+3)}{x+5}\cdot\frac{(x+5)(x-5)}{2(x-2)(x+1)}\cdot\frac{(x-2)(x+1)}{(x-5)(x+3)}=1$$

135. $\dfrac{2}{x-4}+\dfrac{3x}{x+5}=\dfrac{2(x+5)}{(x-4)(x+5)}+\dfrac{3x(x-4)}{(x+5)(x-4)}=\dfrac{2x+10}{(x-4)(x+5)}+\dfrac{3x^2-12x}{(x-4)(x+5)}$

$$=\frac{3x^2-10x+10}{(x-4)(x+5)}$$

136. $\dfrac{5x}{x-2}-\dfrac{3x+7}{x+2}+\dfrac{2x+1}{x+2}=\dfrac{5x}{x-2}+\dfrac{-x-6}{x+2}=\dfrac{5x(x+2)}{(x-2)(x+2)}+\dfrac{(-x-6)(x-2)}{(x+2)(x-2)}$

$$=\frac{5x^2+10x}{(x-2)(x+2)}+\frac{-x^2-4x+12}{(x-2)(x+2)}$$

$$=\frac{4x^2+6x+12}{(x-2)(x+2)}=\frac{2(2x^2+3x+6)}{(x-2)(x+2)}$$

137. $\dfrac{x}{x-1}+\dfrac{x}{x-2}+\dfrac{x}{x-3}$

$$=\frac{x(x-2)(x-3)}{(x-1)(x-2)(x-3)}+\frac{x(x-1)(x-3)}{(x-2)(x-1)(x-3)}+\frac{x(x-1)(x-2)}{(x-3)(x-1)(x-2)}$$

$$=\frac{x^3-5x^2+6x}{(x-1)(x-2)(x-3)}+\frac{x^3-4x^2+3x}{(x-1)(x-2)(x-3)}+\frac{x^3-3x^2+2x}{(x-1)(x-2)(x-3)}$$

$$=\frac{3x^3-12x^2+11x}{(x-1)(x-2)(x-3)}=\frac{x(3x^2-12x+11)}{(x-1)(x-2)(x-3)}$$

138. $\dfrac{x}{x+1}-\dfrac{3x+7}{x+2}+\dfrac{2x+1}{x+2}=\dfrac{x}{x+1}+\dfrac{-3x-7}{x+2}+\dfrac{2x+1}{x+2}$

$$=\frac{x}{x+1}+\frac{-x-6}{x+2}$$

$$=\frac{x(x+2)}{(x+1)(x+2)}+\frac{(-x-6)(x+1)}{(x+2)(x+1)}$$

$$=\frac{x^2+2x}{(x+1)(x+2)}+\frac{-x^2-7x-6}{(x+1)(x+2)}=\frac{-5x-6}{(x+1)(x+2)}$$

139. $\dfrac{3(x+1)}{x} - \dfrac{5(x^2+3)}{x^2} + \dfrac{x}{x+1} = \dfrac{3x(x+1)(x+1)}{x^2(x+1)} - \dfrac{5(x^2+3)(x+1)}{x^2(x+1)} + \dfrac{x(x^2)}{x^2(x+1)}$

$= \dfrac{3x^3+6x^2+3x}{x^2(x+1)} - \dfrac{5x^3+5x^2+15x+15}{x^2(x+1)} + \dfrac{x^3}{x^2(x+1)}$

$= \dfrac{-x^3+x^2-12x-15}{x^2(x+1)}$

140. $\dfrac{3x}{x+1} + \dfrac{x^2+4x+3}{x^2+3x+2} - \dfrac{x^2+x-6}{x^2-4} = \dfrac{3x}{x+1} + \dfrac{(x+3)(x+1)}{(x+1)(x+2)} - \dfrac{(x+3)(x-2)}{(x+2)(x-2)}$

$= \dfrac{3x}{x+1} + \dfrac{x+3}{x+2} - \dfrac{x+3}{x+2} = \dfrac{3x}{x+1}$

141. $\dfrac{\frac{5x}{2}}{\frac{3x^2}{8}} = \dfrac{5x}{2} \div \dfrac{3x^2}{8} = \dfrac{5x}{2} \cdot \dfrac{8}{3x^2} = \dfrac{20}{3x}$

142. $\dfrac{\frac{3x}{y}}{\frac{6x}{y^2}} = \dfrac{3x}{y} \div \dfrac{6x}{y^2} = \dfrac{3x}{y} \cdot \dfrac{y^2}{6x} = \dfrac{y}{2}$

143. $\dfrac{\frac{1}{x}+\frac{1}{y}}{x-y} = \dfrac{xy\left(\frac{1}{x}+\frac{1}{y}\right)}{xy(x-y)} = \dfrac{xy\left(\frac{1}{x}\right)+xy\left(\frac{1}{y}\right)}{xy(x-y)} = \dfrac{y+x}{xy(x-y)}$

144. $\dfrac{x^{-1}+y^{-1}}{y^{-1}-x^{-1}} = \dfrac{\frac{1}{x}+\frac{1}{y}}{\frac{1}{y}-\frac{1}{x}} = \dfrac{xy\left(\frac{1}{x}+\frac{1}{y}\right)}{xy\left(\frac{1}{y}-\frac{1}{x}\right)} = \dfrac{xy\left(\frac{1}{x}\right)+xy\left(\frac{1}{y}\right)}{xy\left(\frac{1}{y}\right)-xy\left(\frac{1}{x}\right)} = \dfrac{y+x}{x-y}$

Chapter 0 Test (page 82)

1. odd integers: $-7, 1, 3$

2. prime numbers: 3

3. commutative property of addition

4. distributive property

5. $-4 < x \leq 2 \Rightarrow$ 

6. $(-\infty, -3) \cup [6, \infty) \Rightarrow$ 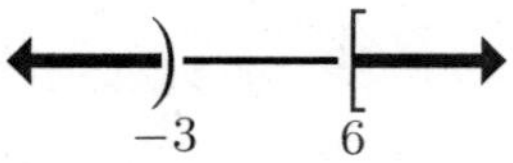

7. Since $-17 < 0$, $|-17| = -(-17) = 17$

8. If $x < 0$, then $x - 7 < 0$. Then $|x-7| = -(x-7)$.

9. distance $= |12-(-4)| = |16| = 16$

10. distance $= |-12-(-20)| = |8| = 8$

11. $x^4x^5x^2 = x^{4+5+2} = x^{11}$

12. $\dfrac{r^2r^3s}{r^4s^2} = \dfrac{r^5s}{r^4s^2} = \dfrac{r}{s}$

13. $\dfrac{(a^{-1}a^2)^{-2}}{a^{-3}} = \dfrac{(a^1)^{-2}}{a^{-3}} = \dfrac{a^{-2}}{a^{-3}} = a$

14. $\left(\dfrac{x^0x^2}{x^{-2}}\right)^6 = \left(\dfrac{x^2}{x^{-2}}\right)^6 = (x^4)^6 = x^{24}$

15. $450{,}000 = 4.5 \times 10^5$

16. $0.000345 = 3.45 \times 10^{-4}$

17. $3.7 \times 10^3 = 3{,}700$

18. $1.2 \times 10^{-3} = 0.0012$

19. $(25a^4)^{1/2} = 25^{1/2}(a^4)^{1/2} = 5a^2$

20. $\left(\frac{36}{81}\right)^{3/2} = \frac{36^{3/2}}{81^{3/2}} = \frac{(36^{1/2})^3}{(81^{1/2})^3} = \frac{216}{729}$

21. $\left(\frac{8t^6}{27s^9}\right)^{-2/3} = \left(\frac{27s^9}{8t^6}\right)^{2/3} = \frac{27^{2/3}(s^9)^{2/3}}{8^{2/3}(t^6)^{2/3}} = \frac{(27^{1/3})^2 s^6}{(8^{1/3})^2 t^4} = \frac{9s^6}{4t^4}$

22. $\sqrt[3]{27a^6} = \sqrt[3]{27}\sqrt[3]{a^6} = 3a^2$

23. $\sqrt{12} + \sqrt{27} = \sqrt{4}\sqrt{3} + \sqrt{9}\sqrt{3}$
$= 2\sqrt{3} + 3\sqrt{3} = 5\sqrt{3}$

24. $2\sqrt[3]{3x^4} - 3x\sqrt[3]{24x} = 2\sqrt[3]{x^3}\sqrt[3]{3x} - 3x\sqrt[3]{8}\sqrt[3]{3x} = 2x\sqrt[3]{3x} - 3x(2)\sqrt[3]{3x} = 2x\sqrt[3]{3x} - 6x\sqrt[3]{3x}$
$= -4x\sqrt[3]{3x}$

25. $\frac{x}{\sqrt{x}-2} = \frac{x}{\sqrt{x}-2} \cdot \frac{\sqrt{x}+2}{\sqrt{x}+2} = \frac{x(\sqrt{x}+2)}{(\sqrt{x})^2 - 2^2} = \frac{x(\sqrt{x}+2)}{x-4}$

26. $\frac{\sqrt{x}-\sqrt{y}}{\sqrt{x}+\sqrt{y}} = \frac{\sqrt{x}-\sqrt{y}}{\sqrt{x}+\sqrt{y}} \cdot \frac{\sqrt{x}+\sqrt{y}}{\sqrt{x}+\sqrt{y}} = \frac{(\sqrt{x})^2 - (\sqrt{y})^2}{\sqrt{x^2} + \sqrt{xy} + \sqrt{xy} + \sqrt{y^2}} = \frac{x-y}{x + 2\sqrt{xy} + y}$

27. $(a^2+3) - (2a^2-4) = a^2 + 3 - 2a^2 + 4$
$= -a^2 + 7$

28. $(3a^3b^2)(-2a^3b^4) = -6a^6b^6$

29. $(3x-4)(2x+7) = 6x^2 + 21x - 8x - 28$
$= 6x^2 + 13x - 28$

30. $(a^n+2)(a^n-3) = a^{2n} - 3a^n + 2a^n - 6$
$= a^{2n} - a^n - 6$

31. $(x^2+4)(x^2-4) = x^4 - 4x^2 + 4x^2 - 16 = x^4 - 16$

32. $(x^2 - x + 2)(2x - 3) = 2x^3 - 3x^2 - 2x^2 + 3x + 4x - 6 = 2x^3 - 5x^2 + 7x - 6$

33.
$$\begin{array}{r|l} & 6x + 19 + \frac{34}{x-3} \\ \hline x-3 & 6x^2 + x - 23 \\ & \underline{6x^2 - 18x} \\ & 19x - 23 \\ & \underline{19x - 57} \\ & 34 \end{array}$$

34.
$$\begin{array}{r|l} & x^2 + 2x + 1 \\ \hline 2x-1 & 2x^3 + 3x^2 + 0x - 1 \\ & \underline{2x^3 - x^2} \\ & 4x^2 + 0x \\ & \underline{4x^2 - 2x} \\ & 2x - 1 \\ & \underline{2x - 1} \\ & 0 \end{array}$$

35. $3x + 6y = 3(x + 2y)$

36. $x^2 - 100 = x^2 - 10^2 = (x+10)(x-10)$

37. $10t^2 - 19tw + 6w^2 = (5t - 2w)(2t - 3w)$

38. $3a^3 - 648 = 3(a^3 - 216)$
$= 3(a-6)(a^2 + 6a + 36)$

39. $x^4 - x^2 - 12 = (x^2 - 4)(x^2 + 3)$
$= (x + 2)(x - 2)(x^2 + 3)$

40. $6x^4 + 11x^2 - 10 = (3x^2 - 2)(2x^2 + 5)$

41. $\dfrac{x}{x+2} + \dfrac{2}{x+2} = \dfrac{x+2}{x+2} = 1$

42. $\dfrac{x}{x+1} - \dfrac{x}{x-1} = \dfrac{x(x-1)}{(x+1)(x-1)} - \dfrac{x(x+1)}{(x+1)(x-1)} = \dfrac{x^2 - x - x^2 - x}{(x+1)(x-1)} = \dfrac{-2x}{(x+1)(x-1)}$

43. $\dfrac{x^2 + x - 20}{x^2 - 16} \cdot \dfrac{x^2 - 25}{x - 5} = \dfrac{(x+5)(x-4)}{(x+4)(x-4)} \cdot \dfrac{(x+5)(x-5)}{x-5} = \dfrac{(x+5)^2}{x+4}$

44. $\dfrac{x+2}{x^2 + 2x + 1} \div \dfrac{x^2 - 4}{x + 1} = \dfrac{x+2}{(x+1)(x+1)} \cdot \dfrac{x+1}{(x+2)(x-2)} = \dfrac{1}{(x+1)(x-2)}$

45. $\dfrac{\frac{1}{a} + \frac{1}{b}}{\frac{1}{b}} = \dfrac{ab\left(\frac{1}{a} + \frac{1}{b}\right)}{ab\left(\frac{1}{b}\right)} = \dfrac{ab\left(\frac{1}{a}\right) + ab\left(\frac{1}{b}\right)}{a} = \dfrac{b+a}{a}$

46. $\dfrac{x^{-1}}{x^{-1} + y^{-1}} = \dfrac{\frac{1}{x}}{\frac{1}{x} + \frac{1}{y}} = \dfrac{xy\left(\frac{1}{x}\right)}{xy\left(\frac{1}{x} + \frac{1}{y}\right)} = \dfrac{y}{xy\left(\frac{1}{x}\right) + xy\left(\frac{1}{y}\right)} = \dfrac{y}{y+x}$

Exercises 1.1 (page 93)

1. root, solution

2. identity

3. no

4. conditional

5. linear

6. rational

7. one

8. denominator

9. $x + 3 = 1$
no restrictions

10. $\dfrac{1}{2}x - 7 = 14$
no restrictions

11. $\dfrac{1}{x} = 12$
$x \neq 0$

12. $\dfrac{3}{x-2} = 9x$
$x \neq 2$

13. $\dfrac{8}{x-3} = \dfrac{5}{x+2}$
$x - 3 \neq 0 \quad x + 2 \neq 0$
$x \neq 3 \quad x \neq -2$
$x \neq 3, x \neq -2$

14. $\dfrac{x}{x-3} = -\dfrac{4}{x+4}$
$x - 3 \neq 0 \quad x + 4 \neq 0$
$x \neq 3 \quad x \neq -4$
$x \neq 3, x \neq -4$

15. $\dfrac{1}{x-3} = \dfrac{5x}{x^2 - 16}$
$\dfrac{1}{x-3} = \dfrac{5x}{(x+4)(x-4)}$
$x - 3 \neq 0 \quad x + 4 \neq 0 \quad x - 4 \neq 0$
$x \neq 3 \quad x \neq -4 \quad x \neq 4$
$x \neq 3, x \neq -4, x \neq 4$

16. $\dfrac{1}{x^2 - 3x - 4} = \dfrac{5}{x} + 2$
$\dfrac{1}{(x+1)(x-4)} = \dfrac{5}{x} + 2$
$x + 1 \neq 0 \quad x - 4 \neq 0 \quad x \neq 0$
$x \neq -1 \quad x \neq 4$
$x \neq -1, x \neq 4, x \neq 0$

17.
$$\begin{aligned} 2x + 5 &= 15 \\ 2x + 5 - 5 &= 15 - 5 \\ 2x &= 10 \\ \frac{2x}{2} &= \frac{10}{2} \\ x &= 5 \end{aligned}$$
conditional equation

18.
$$\begin{aligned} 3x + 2 &= x + 8 \\ 3x - x + 2 &= x - x + 8 \\ 2x + 2 &= 8 \\ 2x + 2 - 2 &= 8 - 2 \\ 2x &= 6 \\ \frac{2x}{2} &= \frac{6}{2} \\ x &= 3 \end{aligned}$$
conditional equation

19.
$$\begin{aligned} 2(n + 2) - 5 &= 2n \\ 2n + 4 - 5 &= 2n \\ 2n - 1 &= 2n \\ 2n - 2n - 1 &= 2n - 2n \\ -1 &\neq 0 \end{aligned}$$
contradiction

20.
$$\begin{aligned} 3(m + 2) &= 2(m + 3) + m \\ 3m + 6 &= 2m + 6 + m \\ 3m + 6 &= 3m + 6 \end{aligned}$$
identity

21.
$$\begin{aligned} \frac{x + 7}{2} &= 7 \\ 2 \cdot \frac{x + 7}{2} &= 2(7) \\ x + 7 &= 14 \\ x + 7 - 7 &= 14 - 7 \\ x &= 7 \end{aligned}$$
conditional equation

22.
$$\begin{aligned} \frac{x}{2} - 7 &= 14 \\ \frac{x}{2} - 7 + 7 &= 14 + 7 \\ \frac{x}{2} &= 21 \\ 2 \cdot \frac{x}{2} &= 2(21) \\ x &= 42 \end{aligned}$$
conditional equation

23.
$$\begin{aligned} 2(a + 1) &= 3(a - 2) - a \\ 2a + 2 &= 3a - 6 - a \\ 2a + 2 &= 2a - 6 \\ 2a - 2a + 2 &= 2a - 2a - 6 \\ 2 &\neq -6 \end{aligned}$$
contradiction

24.
$$\begin{aligned} x^2 &= (x + 4)(x - 4) + 16 \\ x^2 &= x^2 - 16 + 16 \\ x^2 &= x^2 \end{aligned}$$
identity

25.
$$\begin{aligned} 3(x - 3) &= \frac{6x - 18}{2} \\ 3x - 9 &= \frac{6x - 18}{2} \\ 2(3x - 9) &= 2 \cdot \frac{6x - 18}{2} \\ 6x - 18 &= 6x - 18 \end{aligned}$$
identity

26.
$$\begin{aligned} x(x + 2) &= (x + 1)^2 \\ x^2 + 2x &= (x + 1)(x + 1) \\ x^2 + 2x &= x^2 + 2x + 1 \\ x^2 - x^2 + 2x &= x^2 - x^2 + 2x + 1 \\ 2x &= 2x + 1 \\ 2x - 2x &= 2x - 2x + 1 \\ 0 &\neq 1 \end{aligned}$$
contradiction

27.
$$\begin{aligned} \frac{3}{b-3} &= 1 \\ (b-3)\cdot\frac{3}{b-3} &= (b-3)(1) \\ 3 &= b-3 \\ 3+3 &= b-3+3 \\ 6 &= b \end{aligned}$$
conditional equation

28.
$$\begin{aligned} x^2-8x+15 &= (x-3)(x+5) \\ x^2-8x+15 &= x^2+2x-15 \\ x^2-x^2-8x+15 &= x^2-x^2+2x-15 \\ -8x+15 &= 2x-15 \\ -8x+8x+15 &= 2x+8x-15 \\ 15 &= 10x-15 \\ 15+15 &= 10x-15+15 \\ 30 &= 10x \\ \frac{30}{10} &= \frac{10x}{10} \\ 3 &= x \end{aligned}$$
conditional equation

29.
$$\begin{aligned} 2x^2+5x-3 &= (2x-1)(x+3) \\ 2x^2+5x-3 &= 2x^2+5x-3 \end{aligned}$$
identity

30.
$$\begin{aligned} 2x^2+5x-3 &= 2x\left(x+\frac{19}{2}\right) \\ 2x^2+5x-3 &= 2x^2+19x \\ 2x^2-2x^2+5x-3 &= 2x^2-2x^2+19x \\ 5x-3 &= 19x \\ 5x-5x-3 &= 19x-5x \\ -3 &= 14x \\ \frac{-3}{14} &= \frac{14x}{14} \\ -\frac{3}{14} &= x \end{aligned}$$
conditional equation

31.
$$\begin{aligned} 2x+7 &= 10-x \\ 3x+7 &= 10 \\ 3x &= 3 \\ x &= 1 \end{aligned}$$

32.
$$\begin{aligned} 9a-3 &= 15+3a \\ 6a-3 &= 15 \\ 6a &= 18 \\ a &= 3 \end{aligned}$$

33.
$$\begin{aligned} 5(x-2) &= 2(x+4) \\ 5x-10 &= 2x+8 \\ 3x-10 &= 8 \\ 3x &= 18 \\ x &= 6 \end{aligned}$$

34.
$$\begin{aligned} 5(r-4) &= -5(r-4) \\ 5r-20 &= -5r+20 \\ 10r-20 &= 20 \\ 10r &= 40 \\ r &= 4 \end{aligned}$$

35.
$$\begin{aligned} 7(2x+5)-6(x+8) &= 7 \\ 14x+35-6x-48 &= 7 \\ 8x-13 &= 7 \\ 8x &= 20 \\ x &= \frac{20}{8} = \frac{5}{2} \end{aligned}$$

36.
$$\begin{aligned} 6(x-5)-4(x+2) &= -1 \\ 6x-30-4x-8 &= -1 \\ 2x-38 &= -1 \\ 2x &= 37 \\ x &= \frac{37}{2} \end{aligned}$$

37.
$$\begin{aligned} \frac{5}{3}z - 8 &= 7 \\ \frac{5}{3}z &= 15 \\ 3 \cdot \frac{5}{3}z &= 3(15) \\ 5z &= 45 \\ z &= 9 \end{aligned}$$

38.
$$\begin{aligned} \frac{4}{3}y + 12 &= -4 \\ \frac{4}{3}y &= -16 \\ 3 \cdot \frac{4}{3}y &= 3(-16) \\ 4y &= -48 \\ y &= -12 \end{aligned}$$

39.
$$\begin{aligned} \frac{z}{5} + 2 &= 4 \\ \frac{z}{5} &= 2 \\ 5 \cdot \frac{z}{5} &= 5(2) \\ z &= 10 \end{aligned}$$

40.
$$\begin{aligned} \frac{3p}{7} - p &= -4 \\ 7\left(\frac{3p}{7} - p\right) &= 7(-4) \\ 3p - 7p &= -28 \\ -4p &= -28 \\ p &= 7 \end{aligned}$$

41.
$$\begin{aligned} \frac{3x-2}{3} &= 2x + \frac{7}{3} \\ 3 \cdot \frac{3x-2}{3} &= 3\left(2x + \frac{7}{3}\right) \\ 3x - 2 &= 6x + 7 \\ -3x - 2 &= 7 \\ -3x &= 9 \\ x &= -3 \end{aligned}$$

42.
$$\begin{aligned} \frac{7}{2}x + 5 &= x + \frac{15}{2} \\ 2\left(\frac{7}{2}x + 5\right) &= 2\left(x + \frac{15}{2}\right) \\ 7x + 10 &= 2x + 15 \\ 5x + 10 &= 15 \\ 5x &= 5 \\ x &= 1 \end{aligned}$$

43.
$$\begin{aligned} \frac{3x+1}{20} &= \frac{1}{2} \\ 20 \cdot \frac{3x+1}{20} &= 20 \cdot \frac{1}{2} \\ 3x + 1 &= 10 \\ 3x &= 9 \\ x &= 3 \end{aligned}$$

44.
$$\begin{aligned} 2x - \frac{7}{6} + \frac{x}{6} &= \frac{4x+3}{6} \\ 6\left(2x - \frac{7}{6} + \frac{x}{6}\right) &= 6 \cdot \frac{4x+3}{6} \\ 12x - 7 + x &= 4x + 3 \\ 13x - 7 &= 4x + 3 \\ 9x - 7 &= 3 \\ 9x &= 10 \\ x &= \frac{10}{9} \end{aligned}$$

45.
$$\begin{aligned} \frac{3+x}{3} + \frac{x+7}{2} &= 4x + 1 \\ 6\left(\frac{3+x}{3} + \frac{x+7}{2}\right) &= 6(4x+1) \\ 2(3+x) + 3(x+7) &= 24x + 6 \\ 6 + 2x + 3x + 21 &= 24x + 6 \\ 5x + 27 &= 24x + 6 \\ -19x + 27 &= 6 \\ -19x &= -21 \\ x &= \frac{21}{19} \end{aligned}$$

46.
$$\begin{aligned} 2(2x+1) - \frac{3x}{2} &= \frac{-3(4+x)}{2} \\ 2\left[2(2x+1) - \frac{3x}{2}\right] &= 2 \cdot \frac{-3(4+x)}{2} \\ 4(2x+1) - 3x &= -3(4+x) \\ 8x + 4 - 3x &= -12 - 3x \\ 5x + 4 &= -12 - 3x \\ 8x + 4 &= -12 \\ 8x &= -16 \\ x &= -2 \end{aligned}$$

47.
$$\begin{aligned}\frac{3}{2}(3x-2)-10x-4&=0\\2\left[\frac{3}{2}(3x-2)-10x-4\right]&=2(0)\\3(3x-2)-20x-8&=0\\9x-6-20x-8&=0\\-11x-14&=0\\-11x&=14\\x&=-\frac{14}{11}\end{aligned}$$

48.
$$\begin{aligned}\frac{a(a-3)+5}{7}&=\frac{(a-1)^2}{7}\\7\left[\frac{a(a-3)+5}{7}\right]&=7\left[\frac{(a-1)^2}{7}\right]\\a(a-3)+5&=(a-1)(a-1)\\a^2-3a+5&=a^2-2a+1\\-3a+5&=-2a+1\\5&=a+1\\4&=a\end{aligned}$$

49.
$$\begin{aligned}\frac{(y+2)^2}{3}&=y+2+\frac{y^2}{3}\\3\left[\frac{(y+2)^2}{3}\right]&=3\left(y+2+\frac{y^2}{3}\right)\\(y+2)^2&=3y+6+y^2\\y^2+4y+4&=y^2+3y+6\\4y+4&=3y+6\\y+4&=6\\y&=2\end{aligned}$$

50.
$$\begin{aligned}(t+1)(t-1)&=(t+2)(t-3)+4\\t^2-1&=t^2-t-6+4\\-1&=-t-2\\t-1&=-2\\t&=-1\end{aligned}$$

51.
$$\begin{aligned}x(x+2)&=(x+1)^2-1\\x^2+2x&=(x+1)(x+1)-1\\x^2+2x&=x^2+2x+1-1\\x^2+2x&=x^2+2x\\0&=0\Rightarrow\text{identity}\end{aligned}$$

52.
$$\begin{aligned}(x-2)(x-3)&=(x+3)(x+4)\\x^2-5x+6&=x^2+7x+12\\-5x+6&=7x+12\\-12x+6&=12\\-12x&=6\\x&=-\frac{6}{12}=-\frac{1}{2}\end{aligned}$$

53.
$$\begin{aligned}2(s+2)+(s+3)^2&=s(s+5)+2\left(\frac{17}{2}+s\right)\\2s+4+s^2+6s+9&=s^2+5s+17+2s\\s^2+8s+13&=s^2+7s+17\\8s+13&=7s+17\\s&=4\end{aligned}$$

54.
$$\begin{aligned} \frac{3}{x}+\frac{1}{2}&=\frac{4}{x}\\ 2x\left(\frac{3}{x}+\frac{1}{2}\right)&=2x\cdot\frac{4}{x}\\ 6+x&=8\\ x&=2 \end{aligned}$$

55.
$$\begin{aligned} \frac{2}{x+1}+\frac{1}{3}&=\frac{1}{x+1}\\ 3(x+1)\left(\frac{2}{x+1}+\frac{1}{3}\right)&=3(x+1)\cdot\frac{1}{x+1}\\ 6+1(x+1)&=3(1)\\ 6+x+1&=3\\ x+7&=3\\ x&=-4 \end{aligned}$$

56.
$$\begin{aligned} \frac{3}{x-2}+\frac{1}{x}&=\frac{3}{x-2}\\ x(x-2)\left(\frac{3}{x-2}+\frac{1}{x}\right)&=x(x-2)\cdot\frac{3}{x-2}\\ 3x+1(x-2)&=3x\\ 3x+x-2&=3x\\ 4x-2&=3x\\ x&=2 \end{aligned}$$

The answer does not check. ⇒ no solution

57.
$$\begin{aligned} \frac{9t+6}{t(t+3)}&=\frac{7}{t+3}\\ t(t+3)\left[\frac{9t+6}{t(t+3)}\right]&=t(t+3)\cdot\frac{7}{t+3}\\ 9t+6&=7t\\ 2t+6&=0\\ 2t&=-6\\ t&=-3 \end{aligned}$$

The answer does not check. ⇒ no solution

58.
$$\begin{aligned} x+\frac{2(-2x+1)}{3x+5}&=\frac{3x^2}{3x+5}\\ (3x+5)\left[x+\frac{2(-2x+1)}{3x+5}\right]&=(3x+5)\cdot\frac{3x^2}{3x+5}\\ x(3x+5)+2(-2x+1)&=3x^2\\ 3x^2+5x-4x+2&=3x^2\\ x+2&=0\\ x&=-2 \end{aligned}$$

59.
$$\begin{aligned} \frac{2}{(a-7)(a+2)}&=\frac{4}{(a+3)(a+2)}\\ (a-7)(a+2)(a+3)\cdot\frac{2}{(a-7)(a+2)}&=(a-7)(a+2)(a+3)\cdot\frac{4}{(a+3)(a+2)}\\ 2(a+3)&=4(a-7)\\ 2a+6&=4a-28\\ -2a&=-34\\ a&=17 \end{aligned}$$

60.

$$\begin{aligned}
\frac{2}{n-2}+\frac{1}{n+1}&=\frac{1}{n^2-n-2}\\
\frac{2}{n-2}+\frac{1}{n+1}&=\frac{1}{(n-2)(n+1)}\\
(n-2)(n+1)\left(\frac{2}{n-2}+\frac{1}{n+1}\right)&=(n-2)(n+1)\cdot\frac{1}{(n-2)(n+1)}\\
2(n+1)+1(n-2)&=1\\
2n+2+n-2&=1\\
3n&=1\\
n&=\frac{1}{3}
\end{aligned}$$

61.

$$\begin{aligned}
\frac{2x+3}{x^2+5x+6}+\frac{3x-2}{x^2+x-6}&=\frac{5x-2}{x^2-4}\\
\frac{2x+3}{(x+3)(x+2)}+\frac{3x-2}{(x+3)(x-2)}&=\frac{5x-2}{(x+2)(x-2)}\\
(x-2)(2x+3)+(x+2)(3x-2)&=(x+3)(5x-2) \quad \{\text{multiply by common denominator}\}\\
2x^2-x-6+3x^2+4x-4&=5x^2+13x-6\\
5x^2+3x-10&=5x^2+13x-6\\
3x-10&=13x-6\\
-10x&=4\\
x&=-\frac{4}{10}=-\frac{2}{5}
\end{aligned}$$

62.

$$\begin{aligned}
\frac{3x}{x^2+x}-\frac{2x}{x^2+5x}&=\frac{x+2}{x^2+6x+5}\\
\frac{3x}{x(x+1)}-\frac{2x}{x(x+5)}&=\frac{x+2}{(x+5)(x+1)}\\
\frac{3}{x+1}-\frac{2}{x+5}&=\frac{x+2}{(x+5)(x+1)}\\
3(x+5)-2(x+1)&=x+2 \quad \{\text{multiply by common denominator}\}\\
3x+15-2x-2&=x+2\\
x+13&=x+2\\
13&\neq 2 \Rightarrow \text{no solution}
\end{aligned}$$

63.

$$\frac{3x+5}{x^3+8}+\frac{3}{x^2-4}=\frac{2(3x-2)}{(x-2)(x^2-2x+4)}$$

$$\frac{3x+5}{(x+2)(x^2-2x+4)}+\frac{3}{(x+2)(x-2)}=\frac{2(3x-2)}{(x-2)(x^2-2x+4)}$$

$$(x-2)(3x+5)+\left(x^2-2x+4\right)(3)=2(x+2)(3x-2)\quad \{\text{multiply by common denominator}\}$$

$$3x^2-x-10+3x^2-6x+12=6x^2+8x-8$$

$$6x^2-7x+2=6x^2+8x-8$$

$$-15x=-10$$

$$x=\frac{-10}{-15}=\frac{2}{3}$$

64.

$$\frac{1}{n+8}-\frac{3n-4}{5n^2+42n+16}=\frac{1}{5n+2}$$

$$\frac{1}{n+8}-\frac{3n-4}{(5n+2)(n+8)}=\frac{1}{5n+2}$$

$$(5n+2)(1)-(3n-4)=n+8\quad \{\text{multiply by common denominator}\}$$

$$5n+2-3n+4=n+8$$

$$2n+6=n+8$$

$$n=2$$

65.

$$\frac{1}{11-n}-\frac{2(3n-1)}{-7n^2+74n+33}=\frac{1}{7n+3}$$

$$\frac{-1}{n-11}+\frac{2(3n-1)}{7n^2-74n-33}=\frac{1}{7n+3}$$

$$\frac{-1}{n-11}+\frac{6n-2}{(7n+3)(n-11)}=\frac{1}{7n+3}$$

$$-(7n+3)+6n-2=(n-11)1\quad \{\text{multiply by common denominator}\}$$

$$-7n-3+6n-2=n-11$$

$$-n-5=n-11$$

$$-2n=-6$$

$$n=3$$

66.

$$\frac{4}{a^2-13a-48}-\frac{2}{a^2-18a+32}=\frac{1}{a^2+a-6}$$

$$\frac{4}{(a-16)(a+3)}-\frac{2}{(a-16)(a-2)}=\frac{1}{(a+3)(a-2)}$$

$$4(a-2)-2(a+3)=1(a-16)\quad \{\text{multiply by common denominator}\}$$

$$4a-8-2a-6=a-16$$

$$2a-14=a-16$$

$$a=-2$$

67. $$\begin{aligned} \frac{5}{y+4}+\frac{2}{y+2}&=\frac{6}{y+2}-\frac{1}{y^2+6y+8}\\ \frac{5}{y+4}&=\frac{4}{y+2}-\frac{1}{(y+2)(y+4)}\\ 5(y+2)&=4(y+4)-1 \quad \{\text{multiply by common denominator}\}\\ 5y+10&=4y+16-1\\ 5y+10&=4y+15\\ y&=5 \end{aligned}$$

68. $$\begin{aligned} \frac{6}{2a-6}-\frac{3}{3-3a}&=\frac{1}{a^2-4a+3}\\ \frac{6}{2(a-3)}-\frac{3}{3(1-a)}&=\frac{1}{(a-3)(a-1)}\\ \frac{3}{a-3}+\frac{1}{a-1}&=\frac{1}{(a-3)(a-1)}\\ 3(a-1)+1(a-3)&=1 \quad \{\text{multiply by common denominator}\}\\ 3a-3+a-3&=1\\ 4a-6&=1\\ 4a&=7\\ a&=\frac{7}{4} \end{aligned}$$

69. $$\begin{aligned} \frac{3y}{6-3y}+\frac{2y}{2y+4}&=\frac{8}{4-y^2}\\ \frac{3y}{3(2-y)}+\frac{2y}{2(y+2)}&=\frac{8}{(2+y)(2-y)}\\ \frac{y}{2-y}+\frac{y}{2+y}&=\frac{8}{(2+y)(2-y)}\\ y(2+y)+y(2-y)&=8 \quad \{\text{multiply by common denominator}\}\\ 2y+y^2+2y-y^2&=8\\ 4y&=8\\ y&=2 \Rightarrow \text{The solution does not check, so the equation has no solution.} \end{aligned}$$

70. $$\begin{aligned} \frac{3+2a}{a^2+6+5a}-\frac{2-3a}{a^2-6+a}&=\frac{5a-2}{a^2-4}\\ \frac{2a+3}{(a+2)(a+3)}+\frac{3a-2}{(a+3)(a-2)}&=\frac{5a-2}{(a+2)(a-2)}\\ (a-2)(2a+3)+(a+2)(3a-2)&=(a+3)(5a-2) \quad \{\text{multiply by common denominator}\}\\ 2a^2-a-6+3a^2+4a-4&=5a^2+13a-6\\ 5a^2+3a-10&=5a^2+13a-6\\ -10a&=4\\ a&=\frac{4}{-10}=-\frac{2}{5} \end{aligned}$$

71.

$$\frac{a}{a+2} - 1 = -\frac{3a+2}{a^2+4a+4}$$
$$\frac{a}{a+2} - \frac{1}{1} = -\frac{3a+2}{(a+2)(a+2)}$$
$$(a+2)(a+2)\left[\frac{a}{a+2} - 1\right] = (a+2)(a+2)\cdot\left[-\frac{3a+2}{(a+2)(a+2)}\right]$$
$$a(a+2) - (a+2)(a+2) = -(3a+2)$$
$$a^2 + 2a - \left(a^2+4a+4\right) = -3a - 2$$
$$a^2 + 2a - a^2 - 4a - 4 = -3a - 2$$
$$-2a - 4 = -3a - 2$$
$$a = 2$$

72.

$$\frac{x-1}{x+3} + \frac{x-2}{x-3} = \frac{1-2x}{3-x}$$
$$\frac{x-1}{x+3} + \frac{x-2}{x-3} = \frac{2x-1}{x-3}$$
$$(x-3)(x-1) + (x+3)(x-2) = (x+3)(2x-1) \quad \{\text{multiply by common denominator}\}$$
$$x^2 - 4x + 3 + x^2 + x - 6 = 2x^2 + 5x - 3$$
$$2x^2 - 3x - 3 = 2x^2 + 5x - 3$$
$$-8x = 0$$
$$x = \frac{0}{-8} = 0$$

73.

$$k = 2.2p$$
$$\frac{k}{2.2} = \frac{2.2p}{2.2}$$
$$\frac{k}{2.2} = p$$

74.

$$ax + b = 0$$
$$ax = -b$$
$$x = -\frac{b}{a}$$

75.

$$p = 2l + 2w$$
$$p - 2l = 2w$$
$$\frac{p-2l}{2} = \frac{2w}{2}$$
$$\frac{p-2l}{2} = w$$

76.

$$V = \frac{1}{3}\pi r^2 h$$
$$3V = 3\cdot\frac{1}{3}\pi r^2 h$$
$$3V = \pi r^2 h$$
$$\frac{3V}{\pi r^2} = \frac{\pi r^2 h}{\pi r^2}$$
$$\frac{3V}{\pi r^2} = h$$

77.

$$V = \frac{1}{3}\pi r^2 h$$
$$3V = 3\cdot\frac{1}{3}\pi r^2 h$$
$$3V = \pi r^2 h$$
$$\frac{3V}{\pi h} = \frac{\pi r^2 h}{\pi h}$$
$$\frac{3V}{\pi h} = r^2$$

78.

$$z = \frac{x-\mu}{\sigma}$$
$$z\sigma = \frac{x-\mu}{\sigma}\cdot\sigma$$
$$z\sigma = x - \mu$$
$$\mu + z\sigma = x$$
$$\mu = x - z\sigma$$

79.

$$\begin{aligned} P_n &= L + \frac{si}{f} \\ P_n - L &= \frac{si}{f} \\ f(P_n - L) &= f \cdot \frac{si}{f} \\ f(P_n - L) &= si \\ \frac{f(P_n - L)}{i} &= \frac{si}{i} \\ \frac{f(P_n - L)}{i} &= s \end{aligned}$$

80.

$$\begin{aligned} P_n &= L + \frac{si}{f} \\ P_n - L &= \frac{si}{f} \\ f(P_n - L) &= f \cdot \frac{si}{f} \\ f(P_n - L) &= si \\ \frac{f(P_n - L)}{P_n - L} &= \frac{si}{P_n - L} \\ f &= \frac{si}{P_n - L} \end{aligned}$$

81.

$$\begin{aligned} F &= \frac{mMg}{r^2} \\ Fr^2 &= \frac{mMg}{r^2} \cdot r^2 \\ Fr^2 &= mMg \\ \frac{Fr^2}{Mg} &= \frac{mMg}{Mg} \\ \frac{Fr^2}{Mg} &= m \end{aligned}$$

82.

$$\begin{aligned} \frac{1}{f} &= \frac{1}{p} + \frac{1}{q} \\ fpq \cdot \frac{1}{f} &= fpq\left(\frac{1}{p} + \frac{1}{q}\right) \\ pq &= fq + fp \\ pq &= f(q + p) \\ \frac{pq}{q + p} &= \frac{f(q + p)}{q + p} \\ \frac{pq}{q + p} &= f \end{aligned}$$

83.

$$\begin{aligned} \frac{x}{a} + \frac{y}{b} &= 1 \\ \frac{y}{b} &= 1 - \frac{x}{a} \\ b \cdot \frac{y}{b} &= b\left(1 - \frac{x}{a}\right) \\ y &= b\left(1 - \frac{x}{a}\right) \end{aligned}$$

84.

$$\begin{aligned} \frac{x}{a} - \frac{y}{b} &= 1 \\ ab\left(\frac{x}{a} - \frac{y}{b}\right) &= ab \cdot 1 \\ bx - ay &= ab \\ bx &= ab + ay \\ bx &= a(b + y) \\ \frac{bx}{b + y} &= \frac{a(b + y)}{b + y} \\ \frac{bx}{b + y} &= a \end{aligned}$$

85.

$$\begin{aligned} \frac{1}{r} &= \frac{1}{r_1} + \frac{1}{r_2} \\ rr_1r_2 \cdot \frac{1}{r} &= rr_1r_2\left(\frac{1}{r_1} + \frac{1}{r_2}\right) \\ r_1r_2 &= rr_2 + rr_1 \\ r_1r_2 &= r(r_2 + r_1) \\ \frac{r_1r_2}{r_2 + r_1} &= \frac{r(r_2 + r_1)}{r_2 + r_1} \\ \frac{r_1r_2}{r_2 + r_1} &= r \end{aligned}$$

86.

$$\begin{aligned} \frac{1}{r} &= \frac{1}{r_1} + \frac{1}{r_2} \\ rr_1r_2 \cdot \frac{1}{r} &= rr_1r_2\left(\frac{1}{r_1} + \frac{1}{r_2}\right) \\ r_1r_2 &= rr_2 + rr_1 \\ r_1r_2 - rr_1 &= rr_2 \\ r_1(r_2 - r) &= rr_2 \\ \frac{r_1(r_2 - r)}{r_2 - r} &= \frac{rr_2}{r_2 - r} \\ r_1 &= \frac{rr_2}{r_2 - r} \end{aligned}$$

87.

$$\begin{aligned} l &= a + (n - 1)d \\ l &= a + nd - d \\ l - a + d &= nd \\ \frac{l - a + d}{d} &= \frac{nd}{d} \\ \frac{l - a + d}{d} &= n \end{aligned}$$

88.

$$\begin{aligned} l &= a + (n - 1)d \\ l - a &= (n - 1)d \\ \frac{l - a}{n - 1} &= \frac{(n - 1)d}{n - 1} \\ \frac{l - a}{n - 1} &= d \end{aligned}$$

89.
$$\begin{aligned} a &= (n-2)\frac{180}{n} \\ an &= (n-2)\frac{180}{n}\cdot n \\ an &= (n-2)180 \\ an &= 180n - 360 \\ 360 &= 180n - an \\ 360 &= n(180-a) \\ \frac{360}{180-a} &= n \end{aligned}$$

90.
$$\begin{aligned} S &= \frac{a-lr}{1-r} \\ S(1-r) &= \frac{a-lr}{1-r}(1-r) \\ S(1-r) &= a-lr \\ S - Sr + lr &= a \end{aligned}$$

91.
$$\begin{aligned} R &= \frac{1}{\frac{1}{r_1}+\frac{1}{r_2}+\frac{1}{r_3}} \\ R &= \frac{r_1r_2r_3(1)}{r_1r_2r_3\left(\frac{1}{r_1}+\frac{1}{r_2}+\frac{1}{r_3}\right)} \\ R &= \frac{r_1r_2r_3}{r_2r_3+r_1r_3+r_1r_2} \\ R(r_2r_3+r_1r_3+r_1r_2) &= r_1r_2r_3 \\ Rr_2r_3+Rr_1r_3+Rr_1r_2 &= r_1r_2r_3 \\ Rr_1r_3+Rr_1r_2-r_1r_2r_3 &= -Rr_2r_3 \\ r_1(Rr_3+Rr_2-r_2r_3) &= -Rr_2r_3 \\ r_1 &= \frac{-Rr_2r_3}{Rr_3+Rr_2-r_2r_3} \end{aligned}$$

92.
$$\begin{aligned} R &= \frac{1}{\frac{1}{r_1}+\frac{1}{r_2}+\frac{1}{r_3}} \\ R &= \frac{r_1r_2r_3(1)}{r_1r_2r_3\left(\frac{1}{r_1}+\frac{1}{r_2}+\frac{1}{r_3}\right)} \\ R &= \frac{r_1r_2r_3}{r_2r_3+r_1r_3+r_1r_2} \\ R(r_2r_3+r_1r_3+r_1r_2) &= r_1r_2r_3 \\ Rr_2r_3+Rr_1r_3+Rr_1r_2 &= r_1r_2r_3 \\ Rr_2r_3+Rr_1r_3-r_1r_2r_3 &= -Rr_1r_2 \\ r_3(Rr_2+Rr_1-r_1r_2) &= -Rr_1r_2 \\ r_3 &= \frac{-Rr_1r_2}{Rr_2+Rr_1-r_1r_2} \end{aligned}$$

93. Answers may vary.

94. Answers may vary.

95. $(25x^2)^{1/2} = \left[(5x)^2\right]^{1/2} = 5|x|$

96. $\left(\dfrac{25p^2}{16q^4}\right)^{1/2} = \left[\left(\dfrac{5p}{4q^2}\right)^2\right]^{1/2} = \dfrac{5|p|}{4q^2}$

97. $\left(\frac{125x^3}{8y^6}\right)^{-2/3} = \left(\frac{8y^6}{125x^3}\right)^{2/3}$
$= \frac{8^{2/3}(y^6)^{2/3}}{125^{2/3}(x^3)^{2/3}} = \frac{4y^4}{25x^2}$

98. $\left(-\frac{27y^3}{1{,}000x^6}\right)^{1/3} = \frac{(-27)^{1/3}(y^3)^{1/3}}{1{,}000^{1/3}(x^6)^{1/3}}$
$= \frac{-3y}{10x^2} = -\frac{3y}{10x^2}$

99. $\sqrt{25y^2} = \sqrt{(5y)^2} = 5|y|$

100. $\sqrt[3]{-125y^9} = \sqrt[3]{(-5y^3)^3} = -5y^3$

101. $\sqrt[4]{\frac{a^4b^{12}}{z^8}} = \sqrt[4]{\left(\frac{ab^3}{z^2}\right)^4} = \frac{|ab^3|}{z^2}$

102. $\sqrt[5]{\frac{x^{10}y^5}{z^{15}}} = \sqrt[5]{\left(\frac{x^2y}{z^3}\right)^5} = \frac{x^2y}{z^3}$

Exercises 1.2 (page 101)

1. add

2. perimeter

3. amount

4. break point

5. rate, time

6. $0.05(30) = 1.5$

7. Let x = the score on the first exam.
Then $x + 5$ = the score on the midterm,
and $x + 13$ = the score on the final.

$$\frac{\boxed{\text{Sum of scores}}}{3} = 90$$
$$\frac{x + x + 5 + x + 13}{3} = 90$$
$$\frac{3x + 18}{3} = 90$$
$$3x + 18 = 270$$
$$3x = 252$$
$$x = 84$$

His score on the first exam was 84.

8. Let x = the score on the first exam. Then her scores on the following tests were $x + 3$, $x + 6$ and $x + 9$.

$$\frac{\boxed{\text{Sum of scores}}}{4} = 69.5$$
$$\frac{x + x + 3 + x + 6 + x + 9}{4} = 69.5$$
$$\frac{4x + 18}{4} = 69.5$$
$$4x + 18 = 278$$
$$4x = 260$$
$$x = 65$$

Her score on the first exam was 65%.

9. Let x = the program development score.

$$\frac{\boxed{\text{Sum of scores}}}{4} = 86$$
$$\frac{82 + 90 + x + 78}{4} = 86$$
$$\frac{x + 250}{4} = 86$$
$$x + 250 = 344$$
$$x = 94$$

The program development score was 94.

10. Let x = the score on the final round.

$$\frac{\boxed{\text{Sum of scores}}}{4} = 72$$
$$\frac{76 + 68 + 70 + x}{4} = 72$$
$$\frac{x + 214}{4} = 72$$
$$x + 214 = 288$$
$$x = 74$$

She needs to shoot 74 on the final round.

11. Let $x =$ the number of locks replaced.

$$40 + 28 \cdot \boxed{\text{Number of locks}} = 236$$
$$40 + 28x = 236$$
$$28x = 196$$
$$x = 7$$

7 locks can be changed for $236.

12. Let $x =$ the number of interviews.

$$20 + 0.75 \cdot \boxed{\text{Number of interviews}} = 56$$
$$20 + 0.75x = 56$$
$$0.75x = 36$$
$$x = 48$$

He interviewed 48 people.

13. Let $x =$ the width.
Then $x + 26 =$ the height.

$$\boxed{\text{Perimeter}} = 92$$
$$2x + 2(x + 26) = 92$$
$$2x + 2x + 52 = 92$$
$$4x = 40$$
$$x = 10$$

The dimensions are 10 ft by 36 ft.

14. Let $x =$ the width.
Then $x + 115 =$ the length.

$$\boxed{\text{Perimeter}} = 570$$
$$2x + 2(x + 115) = 570$$
$$2x + 2x + 230 = 570$$
$$4x = 340$$
$$x = 85$$

The dimensions are 85 ft by 200 ft.

15.

$$\boxed{\text{Perimeter}} = 14$$
$$x + (x + 2) + x + (x + 2) = 14$$
$$4x + 4 = 14$$
$$4x = 10$$
$$x = \frac{5}{2} = 2\frac{1}{2} \Rightarrow \text{The width is } 2\frac{1}{2} \text{ feet.}$$

16.

$$\boxed{\text{Total Fence Length}} = 2 \cdot \boxed{\text{Square Fence Length}}$$
$$x + (x + 24) + x + (x + 24) = 2 \cdot (x + x + x + x)$$
$$4x + 48 = 8x$$
$$48 = 4x$$
$$x = 12$$

The total fencing required is $4x + 48 = 4(12) + 48 = 96$ feet.

17.

$$\boxed{\text{Total Area}} = 2 \cdot \boxed{\text{Triangular Area}}$$
$$20x + \frac{1}{2}(16)(20) = 2 \cdot \frac{1}{2}(16)(20)$$
$$20x + 160 = 320$$
$$20x = 160$$
$$x = 8$$

The dimensions are 8 feet by 20 feet.

18.

$$\boxed{\text{Sum of angles}} = 180$$
$$x + x + 30 + x + 30 = 180$$
$$3x + 60 = 180$$
$$3x = 120$$
$$x = 40$$

The angles measure 40°, 70° and 70°.

19.

$$\boxed{\begin{matrix}\text{New}\\\text{Area}\end{matrix}} = \boxed{\begin{matrix}\text{Old}\\\text{Area}\end{matrix}} + 0.50 \cdot \boxed{\begin{matrix}\text{Old}\\\text{Area}\end{matrix}}$$

$$\begin{aligned}12(x+10)+12x &= 12(x+10)+0.50\cdot 12(x+10)\\ 12x+120+12x &= 12x+120+6x+60\\ 24x+120 &= 18x+180\\ 6x &= 60\\ x &= 10 \Rightarrow \text{The length of the living room is } x+10=20 \text{ feet.}\end{aligned}$$

20.

$$\begin{aligned}\boxed{\text{Area}} &= 54\\ \frac{1}{2}d(12+8) &= 54\\ 10d &= 54\\ d &= 5.4 \Rightarrow \text{The depth is 5.4 inches}\end{aligned}$$

21. Let $x =$ the amount invested at 7%. Then $22000 - x =$ the amount invested at 6%.

$$\boxed{\text{Interest at 7\%}} + \boxed{\text{Interest at 6\%}} = \boxed{\text{Total interest}}$$

$$\begin{aligned}0.07x + 0.06(22000-x) &= 1420\\ 0.07x + 1320 - 0.06x &= 1420\\ 0.01x &= 100\\ x &= 10000\end{aligned}$$

\$10,000 was invested at 7% and \$12,000 was invested at 6%.

22. Let $x =$ the amount invested at 7%.

$$\boxed{\text{Interest at 7\%}} + \boxed{\text{Interest at 9\%}} = \boxed{\text{Total interest}}$$

$$\begin{aligned}0.07x + 0.09(20000) &= 5000\\ 0.07x + 1800 &= 5000\\ 0.07x &= 3200\\ x &\approx 45714.29\end{aligned}$$

She needs to invest \$45,714.29 at 7% to reach her goal.

23. Let $x =$ the amount invested at each rate.

$$\boxed{\text{Interest at 6\%}} + \boxed{\text{Interest at 7\%}} + \boxed{\text{Interest at 8\%}} = \boxed{\text{Total interest}}$$

$$\begin{aligned}0.06x + 0.07x + 0.08x &= 2037\\ 0.21x &= 2037\\ x &= 9700\end{aligned}$$

\$9,700 was invested at each rate, for a total investment of \$29,100.

24. Let $x =$ the amount invested at 8%. Then $37{,}000 - x =$ the amount invested at $9\frac{1}{2}$%.

$$\boxed{\text{Interest at } 9\tfrac{1}{2}\%} = \boxed{\text{Interest at } 8\%} + 452.50$$
$$0.095(37{,}000 - x) = 0.08x + 452.50$$
$$3515 - 0.095x = 0.08x + 452.50$$
$$3062.50 = 0.175x$$
$$17500 = x$$

\$17,500 is invested at 8% and \$19,500 is invested at $9\frac{1}{2}$%.

25. Let $x =$ the number of full-price tickets sold. Then $585 - x =$ the number of student tickets sold.

$$2.50 \cdot \boxed{\#\text{ of full-price}} + 1.75 \cdot \boxed{\#\text{ of student}} = 1217.25$$
$$2.50x + 1.75(585 - x) = 1217.25$$
$$2.50x + 1023.75 - 1.75x = 1217.25$$
$$0.75x = 193.50$$
$x = 258 \Rightarrow$ There were 327 student tickets sold.

26. Let $x =$ the cost of a student ticket.

$$\boxed{\text{Cost of full-price}} \cdot \boxed{\#\text{ of full-price}} + \boxed{\text{Cost of student}} \cdot \boxed{\#\text{ of student}} = 4960$$
$$480(7) + x(800 - 480) = 4960$$
$$3360 + 320x = 4960$$
$$320x = 1600$$
$x = 5 \Rightarrow$ A student ticket cost \$5.

27. Let $p =$ the original price.

$$\boxed{\text{Original price}} - \boxed{\text{Discount}} = \boxed{\text{New price}}$$
$$p - 0.20p = 63.96$$
$$0.80p = 63.96$$
$$p = 79.95$$

The original price was \$79.95.

28. Let $w =$ the wholesale cost.

$$\boxed{\text{Wholesale cost}} + \boxed{\text{Markup}} = \boxed{\text{Selling price}}$$
$$w + 0.30w = 588.90$$
$$1.30w = 588.90$$
$$w = 453$$

The wholesale cost is \$453.

29. Let $x =$ # of plates for equal costs.

$$\boxed{\text{Cost of 1st machine}} = \boxed{\text{Cost of 2nd machine}}$$
$$600 + 3x = 800 + 2x$$
$$x = 200$$

The break point is 200 plates.

30. Let $x =$ # of fasteners for equal costs.

$$\boxed{\text{Cost of 1st machine}} = \boxed{\text{Cost of 2nd machine}}$$
$$1200 + 0.005x = 1500 + 0.0015x$$
$$0.0035x = 300$$
$$x \approx 85714$$

The break point is about 85,714 fasteners.

31. Let x = # of computers to break even.

$\boxed{\text{Income}} = \boxed{\text{Expenses}}$

$$\begin{aligned} 1275x &= 8925 + 850x \\ 425x &= 8925 \\ x &= 21 \end{aligned}$$

21 computers need to be sold to break even.

32. Let x = # of meals to break even.

$\boxed{\text{Income}} = \boxed{\text{Expenses}}$

$$\begin{aligned} 6x &= 137.50 + 4.75x \\ 1.25x &= 137.50 \\ x &= 110 \end{aligned}$$

More than 110 meals need to be sold to make a profit.

33. Let x = days for both working together.

$\boxed{\text{Man in 1 day}} + \boxed{\text{Roofer in 1 day}} = \boxed{\text{Total in 1 day}}$

$$\begin{aligned} \frac{1}{7} + \frac{1}{4} &= \frac{1}{x} \\ 28x\left(\frac{1}{7} + \frac{1}{4}\right) &= 28x\left(\frac{1}{x}\right) \\ 4x + 7x &= 28 \\ 11x &= 28 \\ x &= \frac{28}{11} = 2\frac{6}{11} \end{aligned}$$

They can roof the house in $2\frac{6}{11}$ days.

34. Let x = hours for both working together.

$\boxed{\text{Crew 1 in 1 hour}} + \boxed{\text{Crew 2 in 1 hour}} = \boxed{\text{Total in 1 hour}}$

$$\begin{aligned} \frac{1}{8} + \frac{1}{10} &= \frac{1}{x} \\ 40x\left(\frac{1}{8} + \frac{1}{10}\right) &= 40x\left(\frac{1}{x}\right) \\ 5x + 4x &= 40 \\ 9x &= 40 \\ x &= \frac{40}{9} = 4\frac{4}{9} \end{aligned}$$

They can seal the parking lot in $4\frac{4}{9}$ hours.

35. Let x = hours for both working together.

$\boxed{\text{Woman in 1 hour}} + \boxed{\text{Man in 1 hour}} = \boxed{\text{Total in 1 hour}}$

$$\begin{aligned} \frac{1}{2} + \frac{1}{4} &= \frac{1}{x} \\ 4x\left(\frac{1}{2} + \frac{1}{4}\right) &= 4x\left(\frac{1}{x}\right) \\ 2x + x &= 4 \\ 3x &= 4 \\ x &= \frac{4}{3} = 1\frac{1}{3} \end{aligned}$$

They can mow the lawn in $1\frac{1}{3}$ hours.

36. Let x = days for both hoses to fill the pool.

$\boxed{\text{1st hose in 1 day}} + \boxed{\text{2nd hose in 1 day}} = \boxed{\text{Total in 1 day}}$

$$\begin{aligned} \frac{1}{3} + \frac{1}{2} &= \frac{1}{x} \\ 6x\left(\frac{1}{3} + \frac{1}{2}\right) &= 6x\left(\frac{1}{x}\right) \\ 2x + 3x &= 6 \\ 5x &= 6 \\ x &= \frac{6}{5} = 1\frac{1}{5} \end{aligned}$$

The pool can be filled in $1\frac{1}{5}$ days.

37. Let x = hours for pool to fill with drain open.

$\boxed{\text{Pipe in 1 hour}} - \boxed{\text{Drain in 1 hour}} = \boxed{\text{Total in 1 hour}}$

$$\frac{1}{10} - \frac{1}{19} = \frac{1}{x}$$
$$190x\left(\frac{1}{10} - \frac{1}{19}\right) = 190x\left(\frac{1}{x}\right)$$
$$19x - 10x = 190$$
$$9x = 190$$
$$x = \frac{190}{9} = 21\frac{1}{9}$$

The pool can be filled in $21\frac{1}{9}$ hours.

38. Let x = hours for sister to stuff 1000 shrimp.

$\boxed{\text{Sam in 1 hour}} + \boxed{\text{Sister in 1 hour}} = \boxed{\text{Total in 1 hour}}$

$$\frac{1}{6} + \frac{1}{x} = \frac{1}{4}$$
$$24x\left(\frac{1}{6} + \frac{1}{x}\right) = 24x\left(\frac{1}{4}\right)$$
$$4x + 24 = 6x$$
$$24 = 2x$$
$$12 = x$$

She can stuff 1,000 shrimp in 12 hours, so she can stuff 500 shrimp in 6 hours.

39. Let x = the ounces of water added.

$\boxed{\text{Oz of alc. at start}} + \boxed{\text{Oz of alc. added}} = \boxed{\text{Oz of alc. at end}}$

$$0.15(20) + 0(x) = 0.10(20 + x)$$
$$3 = 2 + 0.1x$$
$$1 = 0.1x$$
$$\frac{1}{0.1} = x$$
$$10 = x$$

10 oz of water should be added.

40. Let x = the ml of water removed.

$\boxed{\text{ml of salt at start}} - \boxed{\text{ml of salt removed}} = \boxed{\text{ml of salt at end}}$

$$0.02(300) - 0(x) = 0.03(300 - x)$$
$$6 = 9 - 0.03x$$
$$0.03x = 3$$
$$x = \frac{3}{0.03}$$
$$x = 100$$

a. 100 ml of water should be boiled away.

b. The new level will be at the 200-ml mark.

41. Let x = the liters of liquid replaced with pure antifreeze.

$\boxed{\text{Liters of a.f. at start}} - \boxed{\text{Liters of a.f. removed}} + \boxed{\text{Liters of a.f. replaced}} = \boxed{\text{Liters of a.f. at end}}$

$$0.40(6) - 0.40x + x = 0.50(6)$$
$$2.4 + 0.6x = 3$$
$$0.6x = 0.6$$
$$x = 1 \Rightarrow \text{1 liter should be replaced with pure antifreeze.}$$

42. Let x = the liters of skimmed milk added.

$\boxed{\text{Liters of butterfat at start}} + \boxed{\text{Liters of butterfat added}} = \boxed{\text{Liters of butterfat at end}}$

$$0.035(3) + 0(x) = 0.02(3 + x)$$
$$0.105 + 0 = 0.06 + 0.02x$$
$$0.045 = 0.02x$$
$$2.25 = x \Rightarrow \text{2.25 liters of skimmed milk should be added.}$$

43. Let $x =$ the liters of pure alcohol added.

$$\boxed{\text{Liters of alcohol at start}} + \boxed{\text{Liters of alcohol added}} = \boxed{\text{Liters of alcohol at end}}$$

$$\begin{aligned} 0.20(1) + x &= 0.25(1 + x) \\ 0.20 + x &= 0.25 + 0.25x \\ 0.75x &= 0.05 \\ x &= \frac{0.05}{0.75} = \frac{1}{15} \Rightarrow \frac{1}{15} \text{ of a liter of pure alcohol should be added.} \end{aligned}$$

44. Let $x =$ the cubic centimeters of water added.

$$\boxed{\text{Cubic centimeters of chemical at start}} + \boxed{\text{Cubic centimeters of chemical added}} = \boxed{\text{Cubic centimeters of chemical at end}}$$

$$\begin{aligned} 400 + 0 &= 0.25(1000 + x) \\ 400 &= 250 + 0.25x \\ 150 &= 0.25x \\ 600 &= x \Rightarrow 600 \text{ cubic centimeters of water should be added.} \end{aligned}$$

45. Let $x =$ the gallons of pure chlorine added.

$$\boxed{\text{Gallons of chlorine at start}} + \boxed{\text{Gallons of chlorine added}} = \boxed{\text{Gallons of chlorine at end}}$$

$$\begin{aligned} 0(15000) + x &= 0.0003(15000 + x) \\ x &= 4.5 + 0.0003x \\ 0.9997x &= 4.5 \\ x &\approx 4.5 \Rightarrow \text{About 4.5 gallons of pure chlorine should be added.} \end{aligned}$$

46. Let $x =$ the percentage of substitute fuel used. Then $1 - x =$ the percentage of gasoline used.

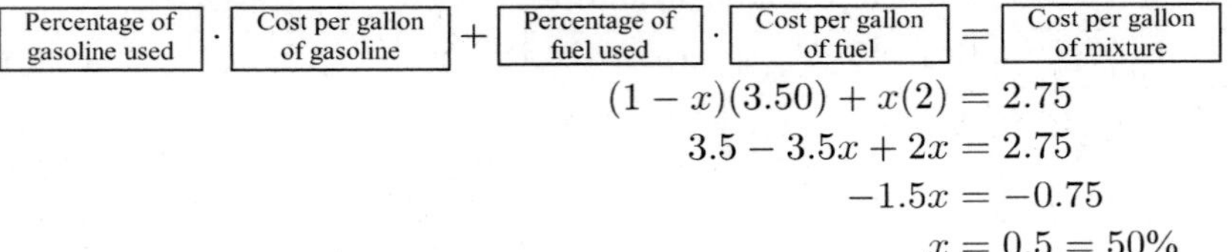

$$\boxed{\text{Percentage of gasoline used}} \cdot \boxed{\text{Cost per gallon of gasoline}} + \boxed{\text{Percentage of fuel used}} \cdot \boxed{\text{Cost per gallon of fuel}} = \boxed{\text{Cost per gallon of mixture}}$$

$$\begin{aligned} (1 - x)(3.50) + x(2) &= 2.75 \\ 3.5 - 3.5x + 2x &= 2.75 \\ -1.5x &= -0.75 \\ x &= 0.5 = 50\% \end{aligned}$$

The substitute fuel should be 25% of the mixture.

47. Let $x =$ the liters of water evaporated.

$$\boxed{\text{Liters of salt at start}} - \boxed{\text{Liters of salt evaporated}} = \boxed{\text{Liters of salt at end}}$$

$$\begin{aligned} 0.24(12) - 0(x) &= 0.36(12 - x) \\ 2.88 - 0 &= 4.32 - 0.36x \\ 0.36x &= 1.44 \\ x &= 4 \Rightarrow 4 \text{ liters of water should be evaporated.} \end{aligned}$$

48. Let $x =$ the ml of water boiled away.

$$\boxed{\text{ml of salt at start}} - \boxed{\text{ml of salt removed}} = \boxed{\text{ml of salt at end}}$$

$$\begin{aligned} 0.05(320) - 0(x) &= 0.06(320 - x) \\ 16 - 0 &= 19.2 - 0.06x \\ 0.06x &= 3.2 \\ x &= \frac{3.2}{0.06} = \frac{320}{6} = \frac{160}{3} = 53\frac{1}{3} \Rightarrow 53\frac{1}{3} \text{ ml of water should be boiled away.} \end{aligned}$$

49. Let $x =$ the pounds of extra-lean hamburger used.

$$\boxed{\text{Pounds of fat in hamburger}} + \boxed{\text{Pounds of fat in lean hamburger}} = \boxed{\text{Pounds of fat in mixture}}$$

$$\begin{aligned} 0.15(30) + 0.07(x) &= 0.10(30 + x) \\ 4.5 + 0.07x &= 3 + 0.1x \\ 1.5 &= 0.03x \\ 50 &= x \end{aligned}$$

50 pounds of the extra-lean hamburger should be used.

50. Let $x =$ the gallons of cream used. Then $20 - x =$ the gallons of milk used

$$\boxed{\text{Gallons of fat in cream}} + \boxed{\text{Gallons of fat in milk}} = \boxed{\text{Gallons of fat in mixture}}$$

$$\begin{aligned} 0.22(x) + 0.02(20 - x) &= 0.04(20) \\ 0.22x + 0.4 - 0.02x &= 0.8 \\ 0.2x &= 0.4 \\ x &= 2 \end{aligned}$$

2 gallons of cream should be used.

51. Let $x =$ the gallons of 5% solution used.

$$\boxed{\text{Gallons of alc. in 5\% solution}} + \boxed{\text{Gallons of alc. in 1\% solution}} = \boxed{\text{Gallons of alc. in 2\% solution}}$$

$$\begin{aligned} 0.05(x) + 0.01(90) &= 0.02(x + 90) \\ 0.05x + 0.9 &= 0.02x + 1.8 \\ 0.03x &= 0.9 \\ x &= 30 \end{aligned}$$

30 gallons of the 5% solution should be used.

52. Let $x =$ the ounces of 1% cream used. Then $1 - x =$ the ounces of 5% cream used.

$$\boxed{\text{Ounces of h.c. in 1\% cream}} + \boxed{\text{Ounces of h.c. in 5\% cream}} = \boxed{\text{Ounces of h.c. in final cream}}$$

$$\begin{aligned} 0.01x + 0.05(1 - x) &= 0.02(1) \\ 0.01x + 0.05 - 0.05x &= 0.02 \\ -0.04x &= -0.03 \\ x &= 0.75 \end{aligned}$$

0.75 ounces of the 1% cream should be used with 0.25 ounces of the 5% cream.

53. Let r = his first rate. Then $r + 26$ = his return rate.

$$\boxed{\text{Distance to city}} = \boxed{\text{Return distance}}$$
$$5r = 3(r + 26)$$
$$5r = 3r + 78$$
$$2r = 78$$
$r = 39 \Rightarrow$ He drove 39 mph going and 65 mph returning.

54. Let t = the time Allison and Austin travel.

$$\boxed{\text{Distance Suzi travels}} = \boxed{\text{Distance Jim travels}} + 60$$
$$60t = 48t + 60$$
$$12t = 60$$
$t = 5 \Rightarrow$ They traveled for 5 hours, so Allison traveled 300 miles.

55. Let t = the time the cars travel.

$$\boxed{\text{Distance 1st car travels}} + \boxed{\text{Distance 2nd car travels}} = \boxed{\text{Total distance}}$$
$$60t + 64t = 310$$
$$124t = 310$$
$t = 2.5 \Rightarrow$ They will be 310 miles apart after 2.5 hours.

56. Let t = the hours the robbers travel. Then $t - \frac{10}{60} = t - \frac{1}{6}$ = the hours the police travel.

$$\boxed{\text{Distance robbers travel}} = \boxed{\text{Distance police travel}}$$
$$70t = 78\left(t - \frac{1}{6}\right)$$
$$70t = 78t - 13$$
$$-8t = -13$$
$$t = \frac{13}{8} = 1\frac{5}{8} = 1.625$$
$t - \frac{1}{6} = 1.625 - \frac{1}{6} \approx 1.458 \Rightarrow$ The police will catch up after about 1.458 hours.

57. Let t = the time the runners run.

$$\boxed{\text{Distance 1st runs}} + \boxed{\text{Distance 2nd runs}} = \boxed{\text{Distance between them (in miles)}}$$
$$8t + 10t = \frac{440}{1760}$$
$$18t = \frac{1}{4}$$
$$t = \frac{1}{72}\text{ hour} = \frac{1}{72}(60\text{ minutes}) = \frac{5}{6}\text{ minute} = 50\text{ seconds}$$
They will meet after 50 seconds.

58. Let $r =$ the rate before lunch. Then $r + 10 =$ the rate after lunch.

$$\boxed{\text{Distance before lunch}} + \boxed{\text{Distance after lunch}} = \boxed{\text{Total distance}}$$

$$\begin{aligned} 5r + 3(r+10) &= 430 \\ 5r + 3r + 30 &= 430 \\ 8r &= 400 \\ r &= 50 \Rightarrow \text{He drove 50 mph before lunch.} \end{aligned}$$

59. Let $r =$ the speed of the boat in still water.
Then the speed of the boat is $r + 2$ downstream and $r - 2$ upstream.

$$\boxed{\text{Time upstream}} = \boxed{\text{Time downstream}} \qquad \{\text{Note: Time} = \text{Distance} \div \text{Rate}\}$$

$$\begin{aligned} \frac{5}{r-2} &= \frac{7}{r+2} \\ (r+2)(r-2)\frac{5}{r-2} &= (r+2)(r-2)\frac{7}{r+2} \\ 5(r+2) &= 7(r-2) \\ 5r + 10 &= 7r - 14 \\ 24 &= 2r \\ 12 &= r \Rightarrow \text{The speed of the boat is 12 mph.} \end{aligned}$$

60. Let $w =$ the speed of the wind.
Then the speed of the plane is $340 + w$ downwind and $340 - w$ upwind.

$$\boxed{\text{Time upwind}} = \boxed{\text{Time downwind}}$$

$$\begin{aligned} \frac{140}{340-w} &= \frac{200}{340+w} \\ (340+w)(340-w)\frac{140}{340-w} &= (340+w)(340-w)\frac{200}{340+w} \\ 140(340+w) &= 200(340-w) \\ 47{,}600 + 140w &= 68{,}000 - 200w \\ 340w &= 20{,}400 \\ w &= 60 \Rightarrow \text{The speed of the wind is 60 mph.} \end{aligned}$$

61. Since the mixture is to be 25% barley, there will be $0.25(2400) = 600$ pounds of barley used.
Thus, the other 1800 pounds will be either oats or soybean meal.
Let $x =$ the number of pounds of oats used. Then $1800 - x =$ the number of pounds of meal used.

$$\boxed{\text{Pounds of protein from barley}} + \boxed{\text{Pounds of protein from oats}} + \boxed{\text{Pounds of protein from soybean meal}} = \boxed{\text{Total pounds of protein}}$$

$$\begin{aligned} 0.117(600) + 0.118x + 0.445(1800 - x) &= 0.14(2400) \\ 70.2 + 0.118x + 801 - 0.445x &= 336 \\ 871.2 - 0.327x &= 336 \\ -0.327x &= -535.2 \\ x &\approx 1637 \end{aligned}$$

The farmer should use 600 pounds of barley, 1,637 pounds of oats and 163 pounds of soybean meal.

62. Since the mixture is to be 20% barley, there will be $0.20(2400) = 480$ pounds of barley used. Thus, the other 1920 pounds will be either oats or soybean meal.
Let $x =$ the number of pounds of oats used. Then $1920 - x =$ the number of pounds of meal used.

$$\boxed{\text{Pounds of protein from barley}} + \boxed{\text{Pounds of protein from oats}} + \boxed{\text{Pounds of protein from soybean meal}} = \boxed{\text{Total pounds of protein}}$$

$$\begin{aligned} 0.117(480) + 0.118x + 0.445(1920 - x) &= 0.14(2400) \\ 56.16 + 0.118x + 854.4 - 0.445x &= 336 \\ 910.56 - 0.327x &= 336 \\ -0.327x &= -574.56 \\ x &\approx 1757 \end{aligned}$$

The farmer should use 480 pounds of barley, 1,757 pounds of oats and 163 pounds of soybean meal.

63.
$$\begin{aligned} V &= \pi r^2 h \\ 712.51 &= \pi(4.5)^2 d \\ \frac{712.51}{\pi(4.5)^2} &= d \\ 11.2 &\approx d \end{aligned}$$

The hole is about 11.2 millimeters deep.

64. Since the diameter of the semicircle is 6 feet, the radius of the semicircle is 3 feet.

$$\boxed{\text{Area of rectangle}} + \boxed{\text{Area of semicircle}} = \boxed{\text{Total area}}$$

$$\begin{aligned} 6(h - 3) + \tfrac{1}{2}\pi(3)^2 &= 68.2 \\ 6h - 18 + 4.5\pi &= 68.2 \\ 6h &= 68.2 + 18 - 4.5\pi \\ 6h &\approx 72.0628 \\ h &\approx 12 \end{aligned}$$

The height of the window is about 12 feet.

65. **Answers may vary.**

66. **Answers may vary.**

67. $x^2 - 2x - 63 = (x - 9)(x + 7)$

68. $2x^2 + 11x - 21 = (2x - 3)(x + 7)$

69. $9x^2 - 12x - 5 = (3x + 1)(3x - 5)$

70. $9x^2 - 2x - 7 = (x - 1)(9x + 7)$

71. $x^2 + 6x + 9 = (x + 3)(x + 3) = (x + 3)^2$

72. $x^2 - 10x + 25 = (x - 5)(x - 5) = (x - 5)^2$

73.
$$\begin{aligned} x^3 + 8 &= (x + 2)(x^2 - 2x + 2^2) \\ &= (x + 2)(x^2 - 2x + 4) \end{aligned}$$

74.
$$\begin{aligned} 27a^3 - 64 &= (3a - 4)\left[(3a)^2 + (3a)(4) + 4^2\right] \\ &= (3a - 4)(9a^2 + 12a + 16) \end{aligned}$$

Exercises 1.3 (page 116)

1. $ax^2 + bx + c = 0$

2. $ab = 0$

3. $\sqrt{c}, -\sqrt{c}$

4. $x = \dfrac{-b \pm \sqrt{b^2 - 4ac}}{2a}$

5. rational numbers

6. not real numbers

7.
$$\begin{aligned} x^2 - x - 6 &= 0 \\ (x+2)(x-3) &= 0 \\ x+2 = 0 \quad &\textbf{or} \quad x-3=0 \\ x=-2 \quad & \quad x=3 \end{aligned}$$

8.
$$\begin{aligned} x^2 + 8x + 15 &= 0 \\ (x+5)(x+3) &= 0 \\ x+5 = 0 \quad &\textbf{or} \quad x+3=0 \\ x=-5 \quad & \quad x=-3 \end{aligned}$$

9.
$$\begin{aligned} x^2 - 144 &= 0 \\ (x+12)(x-12) &= 0 \\ x+12 = 0 \quad &\textbf{or} \quad x-12=0 \\ x=-12 \quad & \quad x=12 \end{aligned}$$

10.
$$\begin{aligned} x^2 + 4x &= 0 \\ x(x+4) &= 0 \\ x = 0 \quad &\textbf{or} \quad x+4=0 \\ x=0 \quad & \quad x=-4 \end{aligned}$$

11.
$$\begin{aligned} 2x^2 + x - 10 &= 0 \\ (2x+5)(x-2) &= 0 \\ 2x+5 = 0 \quad &\textbf{or} \quad x-2=0 \\ 2x=-5 \quad & \quad x=2 \\ x=-\tfrac{5}{2} \quad & \quad x=2 \end{aligned}$$

12.
$$\begin{aligned} 3x^2 + 4x - 4 &= 0 \\ (3x-2)(x+2) &= 0 \\ 3x-2 = 0 \quad &\textbf{or} \quad x+2=0 \\ 3x=2 \quad & \quad x=-2 \\ x=\tfrac{2}{3} \quad & \quad x=-2 \end{aligned}$$

13.
$$\begin{aligned} 5x^2 - 13x + 6 &= 0 \\ (5x-3)(x-2) &= 0 \\ 5x-3 = 0 \quad &\textbf{or} \quad x-2=0 \\ 5x=3 \quad & \quad x=2 \\ x=\tfrac{3}{5} \quad & \quad x=2 \end{aligned}$$

14.
$$\begin{aligned} 2x^2 + 5x - 12 &= 0 \\ (2x-3)(x+4) &= 0 \\ 2x-3 = 0 \quad &\textbf{or} \quad x+4=0 \\ 2x=3 \quad & \quad x=-4 \\ x=\tfrac{3}{2} \quad & \quad x=-4 \end{aligned}$$

15.
$$\begin{aligned} 15x^2 + 16x &= 15 \\ 15x^2 + 16x - 15 &= 0 \\ (3x+5)(5x-3) &= 0 \\ 3x+5 = 0 \quad &\textbf{or} \quad 5x-3=0 \\ 3x=-5 \quad & \quad 5x=3 \\ x=-\tfrac{5}{3} \quad & \quad x=\tfrac{3}{5} \end{aligned}$$

16.
$$\begin{aligned} 6x^2 - 25x &= -25 \\ 6x^2 - 25x + 25 &= 0 \\ (3x-5)(2x-5) &= 0 \\ 3x-5 = 0 \quad &\textbf{or} \quad 2x-5=0 \\ 3x=5 \quad & \quad 2x=5 \\ x=\tfrac{5}{3} \quad & \quad x=\tfrac{5}{2} \end{aligned}$$

17.
$$\begin{aligned} 12x^2 + 9 &= 24x \\ 12x^2 - 24x + 9 &= 0 \\ 3(4x^2 - 8x + 3) &= 0 \\ (2x-1)(2x-3) &= 0 \\ 2x-1 = 0 \quad &\textbf{or} \quad 2x-3=0 \\ 2x=1 \quad & \quad 2x=3 \\ x=\tfrac{1}{2} \quad & \quad x=\tfrac{3}{2} \end{aligned}$$

18.
$$\begin{aligned} 24x^2 + 6 &= 24x \\ 24x^2 - 24x + 6 &= 0 \\ 6(4x^2 - 4x + 1) &= 0 \\ (2x-1)(2x-1) &= 0 \\ 2x-1 = 0 \quad &\textbf{or} \quad 2x-1=0 \\ 2x=1 \quad & \quad 2x=1 \\ x=\tfrac{1}{2} \quad & \quad x=\tfrac{1}{2} \end{aligned}$$

19.
$$\begin{aligned} x^2 &= 9 \\ x=\sqrt{9} \quad &\textbf{or} \quad x=-\sqrt{9} \\ x=3 \quad & \quad x=-3 \end{aligned}$$

20.
$$\begin{aligned} x^2 &= 64 \\ x=\sqrt{64} \quad &\textbf{or} \quad x=-\sqrt{64} \\ x=8 \quad & \quad x=-8 \end{aligned}$$

21.
$$\begin{aligned} y^2 - 50 &= 0 \\ y^2 &= 50 \end{aligned}$$
$$y = \sqrt{50} \quad \textbf{or} \quad y = -\sqrt{50}$$
$$y = 5\sqrt{2} \qquad y = -5\sqrt{2}$$

22.
$$\begin{aligned} x^2 - 75 &= 0 \\ x^2 &= 75 \end{aligned}$$
$$x = \sqrt{75} \quad \textbf{or} \quad x = -\sqrt{75}$$
$$x = 5\sqrt{3} \qquad x = -5\sqrt{3}$$

23.
$$\begin{aligned} 2x^2 &= 40 \\ x^2 &= 20 \end{aligned}$$
$$x = \sqrt{20} \quad \textbf{or} \quad x = -\sqrt{20}$$
$$x = 2\sqrt{5} \qquad x = -2\sqrt{5}$$

24.
$$\begin{aligned} 5x^2 &= 400 \\ x^2 &= 80 \end{aligned}$$
$$x = \sqrt{80} \quad \textbf{or} \quad x = -\sqrt{80}$$
$$x = 4\sqrt{5} \qquad x = -4\sqrt{5}$$

25.
$$\begin{aligned} 4x^2 &= 7 \\ x^2 &= \tfrac{7}{4} \end{aligned}$$
$$x = \sqrt{\tfrac{7}{4}} \quad \textbf{or} \quad x = -\sqrt{\tfrac{7}{4}}$$
$$x = \tfrac{\sqrt{7}}{2} \qquad x = -\tfrac{\sqrt{7}}{2}$$

26.
$$\begin{aligned} 16x^2 &= 11 \\ x^2 &= \tfrac{11}{16} \end{aligned}$$
$$x = \sqrt{\tfrac{11}{16}} \quad \textbf{or} \quad x = -\sqrt{\tfrac{11}{16}}$$
$$x = \tfrac{\sqrt{11}}{4} \qquad x = -\tfrac{\sqrt{11}}{4}$$

27.
$$\begin{aligned} 2x^2 - 13 &= 0 \\ 2x^2 &= 13 \\ x^2 &= \tfrac{13}{2} \end{aligned}$$
$$x = \sqrt{\tfrac{13}{2}} \quad \textbf{or} \quad x = -\sqrt{\tfrac{13}{2}}$$
$$x = \tfrac{\sqrt{13}}{\sqrt{2}} \cdot \tfrac{\sqrt{2}}{\sqrt{2}} \qquad x = -\tfrac{\sqrt{13}}{\sqrt{2}} \cdot \tfrac{\sqrt{2}}{\sqrt{2}}$$
$$x = \tfrac{\sqrt{26}}{2} \qquad x = -\tfrac{\sqrt{26}}{2}$$

28.
$$\begin{aligned} -3x^2 &= -11 \\ x^2 &= \tfrac{11}{3} \end{aligned}$$
$$x = \sqrt{\tfrac{11}{3}} \quad \textbf{or} \quad x = -\sqrt{\tfrac{11}{3}}$$
$$x = \tfrac{\sqrt{11}}{\sqrt{3}} \cdot \tfrac{\sqrt{3}}{\sqrt{3}} \qquad x = -\tfrac{\sqrt{11}}{\sqrt{3}} \cdot \tfrac{\sqrt{3}}{\sqrt{3}}$$
$$x = \tfrac{\sqrt{33}}{3} \qquad x = -\tfrac{\sqrt{33}}{3}$$

29.
$$(x-1)^2 = 4$$
$$x - 1 = \sqrt{4} \quad \textbf{or} \quad x - 1 = -\sqrt{4}$$
$$x - 1 = 2 \qquad x - 1 = -2$$
$$x = 3 \qquad x = -1$$

30.
$$\begin{aligned} (y+2)^2 - 49 &= 0 \\ (y+2)^2 &= 49 \end{aligned}$$
$$y + 2 = \sqrt{49} \quad \textbf{or} \quad y + 2 = -\sqrt{49}$$
$$y + 2 = 7 \qquad y + 2 = -7$$
$$y = 5 \qquad y = -9$$

31.
$$\begin{aligned} (x+1)^2 - 8 &= 0 \\ (x+1)^2 &= 8 \end{aligned}$$
$$x + 1 = \sqrt{8} \quad \textbf{or} \quad x + 1 = -\sqrt{8}$$
$$x + 1 = 2\sqrt{2} \qquad x + 1 = -2\sqrt{2}$$
$$x = -1 + 2\sqrt{2} \qquad x = -1 - 2\sqrt{2}$$

32.
$$(y+2)^2-98=0$$
$$(y+2)^2=98$$
$$y+2=\sqrt{98} \quad \textbf{or} \quad y+2=-\sqrt{98}$$
$$y+2=7\sqrt{2} \qquad y+2=-7\sqrt{2}$$
$$y=-2+7\sqrt{2} \qquad y=-2-7\sqrt{2}$$

33.
$$(2x+1)^2=27$$
$$2x+1=\sqrt{27} \quad \textbf{or} \quad 2x+1=-\sqrt{27}$$
$$2x+1=3\sqrt{3} \qquad 2x+1=-3\sqrt{3}$$
$$2x=-1+3\sqrt{3} \qquad 2x=-1-3\sqrt{3}$$
$$x=\tfrac{-1+3\sqrt{3}}{2} \qquad x=\tfrac{-1-3\sqrt{3}}{2}$$

34.
$$(5y+2)^2-48=0$$
$$(5y+2)^2=48$$
$$5y+2=\sqrt{48} \quad \textbf{or} \quad 5y+2=-\sqrt{48}$$
$$5y+2=4\sqrt{3} \qquad 5y+2=-4\sqrt{3}$$
$$5y=-2+4\sqrt{3} \qquad 5y=-2-4\sqrt{3}$$
$$y=\tfrac{-2+4\sqrt{3}}{5} \qquad y=\tfrac{-2-4\sqrt{3}}{5}$$

35. $x^2+6x+\left[\tfrac{1}{2}(6)\right]^2=x^2+6x+3^2$
$=x^2+6x+9$

36. $x^2+8x+\left[\tfrac{1}{2}(8)\right]^2=x^2+8x+4^2$
$=x^2+8x+16$

37. $x^2-4x+\left[\tfrac{1}{2}(-4)\right]^2=x^2-4x+(-2)^2$
$=x^2-4x+4$

38. $x^2-12x+\left[\tfrac{1}{2}(-12)\right]^2=x^2-12x+(-6)^2$
$=x^2-12x+36$

39. $a^2+5a+\left[\tfrac{1}{2}(5)\right]^2=a^2+5a+\left(\dfrac{5}{2}\right)^2$
$=a^2+5a+\dfrac{25}{4}$

40. $t^2+9t+\left[\tfrac{1}{2}(9)\right]^2=t^2+9t+\left(\dfrac{9}{2}\right)^2$
$=t^2+9t+\dfrac{81}{4}$

41. $r^2-11r+\left[\tfrac{1}{2}(-11)\right]^2=r^2-11r+\left(\dfrac{-11}{2}\right)^2=r^2-11r+\dfrac{121}{4}$

42. $s^2-7s+\left[\tfrac{1}{2}(-7)\right]^2=s^2-7s+\left(\tfrac{-7}{2}\right)^2=s^2-7s+\tfrac{49}{4}$

43. $y^2+\dfrac{3}{4}y+\left[\dfrac{1}{2}\left(\dfrac{3}{4}\right)\right]^2=y^2+\dfrac{3}{4}y+\left(\dfrac{3}{8}\right)^2$
$=y^2+\dfrac{3}{4}y+\dfrac{9}{64}$

44. $p^2+\dfrac{3}{2}p+\left[\dfrac{1}{2}\left(\dfrac{3}{2}\right)\right]^2=p^2+\dfrac{3}{2}p+\left(\dfrac{3}{4}\right)^2$
$=p^2+\dfrac{3}{2}p+\dfrac{9}{16}$

45. $q^2 - \frac{1}{5}q + \left[\frac{1}{2}\left(-\frac{1}{5}\right)\right]^2 = q^2 - \frac{1}{5}q + \left(\frac{-1}{10}\right)^2 = q^2 - \frac{1}{5}q + \frac{1}{100}$

46. $m^2 - \frac{2}{3}m + \left[\frac{1}{2}\left(-\frac{2}{3}\right)\right]^2 = m^2 - \frac{2}{3}m + \left(\frac{-1}{3}\right)^2 = m^2 - \frac{2}{3}m + \frac{1}{9}$

47.
$$x^2 - 8x + 15 = 0$$
$$x^2 - 8x = -15$$
$$x^2 - 8x + 16 = -15 + 16$$
$$(x-4)^2 = 1$$
$x - 4 = \sqrt{1}$ **or** $x - 4 = -\sqrt{1}$
$x - 4 = 1$ $\quad$ $x - 4 = -1$
$x = 5$ $\quad$ $x = 3$

48.
$$x^2 + 10x + 21 = 0$$
$$x^2 + 10x = -21$$
$$x^2 + 10x + 25 = -21 + 25$$
$$(x+5)^2 = 4$$
$x + 5 = \sqrt{4}$ **or** $x + 5 = -\sqrt{4}$
$x + 5 = 2$ $\quad$ $x + 5 = -2$
$x = -3$ $\quad$ $x = -7$

49.
$$x^2 + 12x = -8$$
$$x^2 + 12x + 36 = -8 + 36$$
$$(x+6)^2 = 28$$
$x + 6 = \sqrt{28}$ **or** $x + 6 = -\sqrt{28}$
$x + 6 = 2\sqrt{7}$ $\quad$ $x + 6 = -2\sqrt{7}$
$x = -6 + 2\sqrt{7}$ $\quad$ $x = -6 - 2\sqrt{7}$

50.
$$x^2 - 6x = -1$$
$$x^2 - 6x + 9 = -1 + 9$$
$$(x-3)^2 = 8$$
$x - 3 = \sqrt{8}$ **or** $x - 3 = -\sqrt{8}$
$x - 3 = 2\sqrt{2}$ $\quad$ $x - 3 = -2\sqrt{2}$
$x = 3 + 2\sqrt{2}$ $\quad$ $x = 3 - 2\sqrt{2}$

51.
$$x^2 + 5 = -5x$$
$$x^2 + 5x = -5$$
$$x^2 + 5x + \frac{25}{4} = -5 + \frac{25}{4}$$
$$\left(x + \frac{5}{2}\right)^2 = \frac{5}{4}$$
$x + \frac{5}{2} = \sqrt{\frac{5}{4}}$ **or** $x + \frac{5}{2} = -\sqrt{\frac{5}{4}}$
$x + \frac{5}{2} = \frac{\sqrt{5}}{2}$ $\quad$ $x + \frac{5}{2} = -\frac{\sqrt{5}}{2}$
$x = \frac{-5 + \sqrt{5}}{2}$ $\quad$ $x = \frac{-5 - \sqrt{5}}{2}$

52.

$$x^2 + 1 = -4x$$
$$x^2 + 4x = -1$$
$$x^2 + 4x + 4 = -1 + 4$$
$$(x + 2)^2 = 3$$

$$x + 2 = \sqrt{3} \quad \textbf{or} \quad x + 2 = -\sqrt{3}$$
$$x = -2 + \sqrt{3} \qquad x = -2 - \sqrt{3}$$

53.

$$2x^2 - 20x = -49$$
$$x^2 - 10x = -\frac{49}{2}$$
$$x^2 - 10x + 25 = -\frac{49}{2} + \frac{50}{2}$$
$$(x - 5)^2 = \frac{1}{2}$$

$$x - 5 = \sqrt{\frac{1}{2}} \quad \textbf{or} \quad x - 5 = -\sqrt{\frac{1}{2}}$$
$$x - 5 = \frac{1}{\sqrt{2}} \qquad x - 5 = -\frac{1}{\sqrt{2}}$$
$$x - \frac{10}{2} = \frac{\sqrt{2}}{2} \qquad x - \frac{10}{2} = -\frac{\sqrt{2}}{2}$$
$$x = \frac{10+\sqrt{2}}{2} \qquad x = \frac{10-\sqrt{2}}{2}$$

54.

$$4x^2 + 8x = 7$$
$$x^2 + 2x = \frac{7}{4}$$
$$x^2 + 2x + 1 = \frac{7}{4} + \frac{4}{4}$$
$$(x + 1)^2 = \frac{11}{4}$$

$$x + 1 = \sqrt{\frac{11}{4}} \quad \textbf{or} \quad x + 1 = -\sqrt{\frac{11}{4}}$$
$$x + 1 = \frac{\sqrt{11}}{2} \qquad x + 1 = -\frac{\sqrt{11}}{2}$$
$$x + \frac{2}{2} = \frac{\sqrt{11}}{2} \qquad x + \frac{2}{2} = -\frac{\sqrt{11}}{2}$$
$$x = \frac{-2+\sqrt{11}}{2} \qquad x = \frac{-2-\sqrt{11}}{2}$$

55.

$$\begin{aligned} 3x^2 &= 1 - 4x \\ 3x^2 + 4x &= 1 \\ x^2 + \frac{4}{3}x &= \frac{1}{3} \\ x^2 + \frac{4}{3}x + \frac{4}{9} &= \frac{1}{3} + \frac{4}{9} \\ \left(x + \frac{2}{3}\right)^2 &= \frac{7}{9} \end{aligned}$$

$$x + \frac{2}{3} = \sqrt{\frac{7}{9}} \quad \textbf{or} \quad x + \frac{2}{3} = -\sqrt{\frac{7}{9}}$$

$$x + \frac{2}{3} = \frac{\sqrt{7}}{3} \qquad x + \frac{2}{3} = -\frac{\sqrt{7}}{3}$$

$$x = \frac{-2 + \sqrt{7}}{3} \qquad x = \frac{-2 - \sqrt{7}}{3}$$

56.

$$\begin{aligned} 3x^2 + 4x &= 5 \\ x^2 + \frac{4}{3}x &= \frac{5}{3} \\ x^2 + \frac{4}{3}x + \frac{4}{9} &= \frac{5}{3} + \frac{4}{9} \\ \left(x + \frac{2}{3}\right)^2 &= \frac{19}{9} \end{aligned}$$

$$x + \frac{2}{3} = \sqrt{\frac{19}{9}} \quad \textbf{or} \quad x + \frac{2}{3} = -\sqrt{\frac{19}{9}}$$

$$x + \frac{2}{3} = \frac{\sqrt{19}}{3} \qquad x + \frac{2}{3} = -\frac{\sqrt{19}}{3}$$

$$x = \frac{-2 + \sqrt{19}}{3} \qquad x = \frac{-2 - \sqrt{19}}{3}$$

57.

$$\begin{aligned} 2x^2 &= 3x + 1 \\ 2x^2 - 3x &= 1 \\ x^2 - \frac{3}{2}x &= \frac{1}{2} \\ x^2 - \frac{3}{2}x + \frac{9}{16} &= \frac{1}{2} + \frac{9}{16} \\ \left(x - \frac{3}{4}\right)^2 &= \frac{17}{16} \end{aligned}$$

$$x - \frac{3}{4} = \sqrt{\frac{17}{16}} \quad \textbf{or} \quad x - \frac{3}{4} = -\sqrt{\frac{17}{16}}$$

$$x - \frac{3}{4} = \frac{\sqrt{17}}{4} \qquad x - \frac{3}{4} = -\frac{\sqrt{17}}{4}$$

$$x = \frac{3 + \sqrt{17}}{4} \qquad x = \frac{3 - \sqrt{17}}{4}$$

58.

$$2x^2 + 5x = 14$$
$$x^2 + \frac{5}{2}x = 7$$
$$x^2 + \frac{5}{2}x + \frac{25}{16} = \frac{112}{16} + \frac{25}{16}$$
$$\left(x + \frac{5}{4}\right)^2 = \frac{137}{16}$$

$$x + \frac{5}{4} = \sqrt{\frac{137}{16}} \quad \textbf{or} \quad x + \frac{5}{4} = -\sqrt{\frac{137}{16}}$$
$$x + \frac{5}{4} = \frac{\sqrt{137}}{4} \qquad x + \frac{5}{4} = -\frac{\sqrt{137}}{4}$$
$$x = \frac{-5 + \sqrt{137}}{4} \qquad x = \frac{-5 - \sqrt{137}}{4}$$

59. $x^2 - 12 = 0 \Rightarrow a = 1, b = 0, c = -12$

$$x = \frac{-b \pm \sqrt{b^2 - 4ac}}{2a} = \frac{-(0) \pm \sqrt{(0)^2 - 4(1)(-12)}}{2(1)} = \frac{0 \pm \sqrt{0 + 48}}{2} = \frac{0 \pm \sqrt{48}}{2} = \frac{\pm\sqrt{48}}{2}$$
$$x = \frac{\sqrt{48}}{2} = \frac{4\sqrt{3}}{2} = 2\sqrt{3} \text{ or } x = \frac{-\sqrt{48}}{2} = \frac{-4\sqrt{3}}{2} = -2\sqrt{3}$$

60. $x^2 - 60 = 0 \Rightarrow a = 1, b = 0, c = -60$

$$x = \frac{-b \pm \sqrt{b^2 - 4ac}}{2a} = \frac{-(0) \pm \sqrt{(0)^2 - 4(1)(-60)}}{2(1)} = \frac{0 \pm \sqrt{0 + 240}}{2} = \frac{0 \pm \sqrt{240}}{2}$$
$$x = \frac{\sqrt{240}}{2} = \frac{4\sqrt{15}}{2} = 2\sqrt{15} \text{ or } x = \frac{-\sqrt{240}}{2} = \frac{-4\sqrt{15}}{2} = -2\sqrt{15}$$

61. $x^2 - 25x = 0 \Rightarrow a = 1, b = -25, c = 0$

$$x = \frac{-b \pm \sqrt{b^2 - 4ac}}{2a} = \frac{-(-25) \pm \sqrt{(-25)^2 - 4(1)(0)}}{2(1)} = \frac{25 \pm \sqrt{625 - 0}}{2} = \frac{25 \pm \sqrt{625}}{2}$$
$$x = \frac{25 + 25}{2} = \frac{50}{2} = 25 \text{ or } x = \frac{25 - 25}{2} = \frac{0}{2} = 0$$

62. $x^2 + x = 0 \Rightarrow a = 1, b = 1, c = 0$

$$x = \frac{-b \pm \sqrt{b^2 - 4ac}}{2a} = \frac{-(1) \pm \sqrt{(1)^2 - 4(1)(0)}}{2(1)} = \frac{-1 \pm \sqrt{1 - 0}}{2} = \frac{-1 \pm \sqrt{1}}{2}$$
$$x = \frac{-1 + 1}{2} = \frac{0}{2} = 0 \text{ or } x = \frac{-1 - 1}{2} = \frac{-2}{2} = -1$$

63. $2x^2 - x - 15 = 0 \Rightarrow a = 2, b = -1, c = -15$

$$x = \frac{-b \pm \sqrt{b^2 - 4ac}}{2a} = \frac{-(-1) \pm \sqrt{(-1)^2 - 4(2)(-15)}}{2(2)} = \frac{1 \pm \sqrt{1 + 120}}{4} = \frac{1 \pm \sqrt{121}}{4}$$

$$= \frac{1 \pm 11}{4}$$

$$x = \frac{1 + 11}{4} = \frac{12}{4} = 3 \text{ or } x = \frac{1 - 11}{4} = \frac{-10}{4} = -\frac{5}{2}$$

64. $6x^2 + x - 2 = 0 \Rightarrow a = 6, b = 1, c = -2$

$$x = \frac{-b \pm \sqrt{b^2 - 4ac}}{2a} = \frac{-(1) \pm \sqrt{(1)^2 - 4(6)(-2)}}{2(6)} = \frac{-1 \pm \sqrt{1 + 48}}{12} = \frac{-1 \pm \sqrt{49}}{12} = \frac{-1 \pm 7}{12}$$

$$x = \frac{-1 + 7}{12} = \frac{6}{12} = \frac{1}{2} \text{ or } x = \frac{-1 - 7}{12} = \frac{-8}{12} = -\frac{2}{3}$$

65. $3x^2 = -5x - 1 \Rightarrow 3x^2 + 5x + 1 = 0 \Rightarrow a = 3, b = 5, c = 1$

$$x = \frac{-b \pm \sqrt{b^2 - 4ac}}{2a} = \frac{-(5) \pm \sqrt{(5)^2 - 4(3)(1)}}{2(3)} = \frac{-5 \pm \sqrt{25 - 12}}{6} = \frac{-5 \pm \sqrt{13}}{6}$$

66. $2x^2 = 5x + 11 \Rightarrow 2x^2 - 5x - 11 = 0 \Rightarrow a = 2, b = -5, c = -11$

$$x = \frac{-b \pm \sqrt{b^2 - 4ac}}{2a} = \frac{-(-5) \pm \sqrt{(-5)^2 - 4(2)(-11)}}{2(2)} = \frac{5 \pm \sqrt{25 + 88}}{4} = \frac{5 \pm \sqrt{113}}{4}$$

67. $x^2 + 1 = -7x \Rightarrow x^2 + 7x + 1 = 0 \Rightarrow a = 1, b = 7, c = 1$

$$x = \frac{-b \pm \sqrt{b^2 - 4ac}}{2a} = \frac{-(7) \pm \sqrt{(7)^2 - 4(1)(1)}}{2(1)} = \frac{-7 \pm \sqrt{49 - 4}}{2} = \frac{-7 \pm \sqrt{45}}{2}$$

$$= \frac{-7 \pm 3\sqrt{5}}{2}$$

68. $13x^2 + 1 = -10x \Rightarrow 13x^2 + 10x + 1 = 0 \Rightarrow a = 13, b = 10, c = 1$

$$x = \frac{-b \pm \sqrt{b^2 - 4ac}}{2a} = \frac{-(10) \pm \sqrt{(10)^2 - 4(13)(1)}}{2(13)} = \frac{-10 \pm \sqrt{100 - 52}}{26} = \frac{-10 \pm \sqrt{48}}{26}$$

$$x = = \frac{-10 \pm \sqrt{48}}{26} = = \frac{-10 \pm 4\sqrt{3}}{26} = \frac{2\left(-5 \pm 2\sqrt{3}\right)}{26} = \frac{-5 \pm 2\sqrt{3}}{13}$$

69. $3x^2 + 6x = -1 \Rightarrow 3x^2 + 6x + 1 = 0 \Rightarrow a = 3, b = 6, c = 1$

$$x = \frac{-b \pm \sqrt{b^2 - 4ac}}{2a} = \frac{-(6) \pm \sqrt{(6)^2 - 4(3)(1)}}{2(3)} = \frac{-6 \pm \sqrt{36 - 12}}{6} = \frac{-6 \pm \sqrt{24}}{6}$$

$$x = \frac{-6 \pm \sqrt{24}}{6} = \frac{-6 \pm 2\sqrt{6}}{6} = \frac{2\left(-3 \pm \sqrt{6}\right)}{6} = \frac{-3 \pm \sqrt{6}}{3}$$

70. $2x(x+3)=-1 \Rightarrow 2x^2+6x+1=0 \Rightarrow a=2, b=6, c=1$

$$x=\frac{-b\pm\sqrt{b^2-4ac}}{2a}=\frac{-(6)\pm\sqrt{(6)^2-4(2)(1)}}{2(2)}=\frac{-6\pm\sqrt{36-8}}{4}=\frac{-6\pm\sqrt{28}}{4}$$

$$x=\frac{-6\pm\sqrt{28}}{4}=\frac{-6\pm2\sqrt{7}}{4}=\frac{-3\pm\sqrt{7}}{2}$$

71. $5x\left(x+\frac{1}{5}\right)=3 \Rightarrow 5x^2+x-3=0 \Rightarrow a=5, b=1, c=-3$

$$x=\frac{-b\pm\sqrt{b^2-4ac}}{2a}=\frac{-(1)\pm\sqrt{(1)^2-4(5)(-3)}}{2(5)}=\frac{-1\pm\sqrt{1+60}}{10}=\frac{-1\pm\sqrt{61}}{10}$$

72. $7x^2=2x+2 \Rightarrow 7x^2-2x-2=0 \Rightarrow a=7, b=-2, c=-2$

$$x=\frac{-b\pm\sqrt{b^2-4ac}}{2a}=\frac{-(-2)\pm\sqrt{(-2)^2-4(7)(-2)}}{2(7)}=\frac{2\pm\sqrt{4+56}}{14}=\frac{2\pm\sqrt{60}}{14}$$

$$x=\frac{2\pm\sqrt{60}}{14}=\frac{2\pm2\sqrt{15}}{14}=\frac{1\pm\sqrt{15}}{7}$$

73.

$$h=\tfrac{1}{2}gt^2$$
$$2h=gt^2$$
$$\tfrac{2h}{g}=t^2$$
$$\pm\sqrt{\frac{2h}{g}}=t$$

74.

$$x^2+y^2=r^2$$
$$x^2=r^2-y^2$$
$$x=\pm\sqrt{r^2-y^2}$$

75.

$$h=64t-16t^2$$
$$16t^2-64t+h=0;\ a=16,\ b=-64,\ c=h$$
$$t=\frac{-b\pm\sqrt{b^2-4ac}}{2a}$$
$$=\frac{-(-64)\pm\sqrt{(-64)^2-4(16)h}}{2(16)}$$
$$=\frac{64\pm\sqrt{4096-64h}}{32}$$
$$=\frac{64\pm\sqrt{64(64-h)}}{32}$$
$$=\frac{64\pm8\sqrt{64-h}}{32}=\frac{8\pm\sqrt{64-h}}{4}$$

76.

$$y=16x^2-4$$
$$y+4=16x^2$$
$$\frac{y+4}{16}=x^2$$
$$\pm\sqrt{\frac{y+4}{16}}=x$$
$$\frac{\pm\sqrt{y+4}}{4}=x$$

77. $\frac{x^2}{a^2}+\frac{y^2}{b^2}=1$

$$\frac{y^2}{b^2}=1-\frac{x^2}{a^2}$$
$$\frac{y^2}{b^2}=\frac{a^2-x^2}{a^2}$$
$$y^2=\frac{b^2(a^2-x^2)}{a^2}$$
$$y=\pm\sqrt{\frac{b^2(a^2-x^2)}{a^2}}$$
$$y=\pm\frac{b\sqrt{a^2-x^2}}{a}$$

78. $\frac{x^2}{a^2}-\frac{y^2}{b^2}=1$

$$\frac{x^2}{a^2}=1+\frac{y^2}{b^2}$$
$$\frac{x^2}{a^2}=\frac{b^2+y^2}{b^2}$$
$$x^2=\frac{a^2(b^2+y^2)}{b^2}$$
$$x=\pm\sqrt{\frac{a^2(b^2+y^2)}{b^2}}$$
$$x=\pm\frac{a\sqrt{b^2+y^2}}{b}$$

79. $\frac{x^2}{a^2}-\frac{y^2}{b^2}=1$

$$a^2b^2\left(\frac{x^2}{a^2}-\frac{y^2}{b^2}\right)=a^2b^2(1)$$
$$b^2x^2-a^2y^2=a^2b^2$$
$$b^2x^2=a^2b^2+a^2y^2$$
$$b^2x^2=a^2(b^2+y^2)$$
$$\frac{b^2x^2}{b^2+y^2}=a^2$$
$$\pm\sqrt{\frac{b^2x^2}{b^2+y^2}}=a$$
$$\pm\frac{bx\sqrt{b^2+y^2}}{b^2+y^2}=a$$

80. $\frac{x^2}{a^2}-\frac{y^2}{b^2}=1$

$$a^2b^2\left(\frac{x^2}{a^2}-\frac{y^2}{b^2}\right)=a^2b^2(1)$$
$$b^2x^2-a^2y^2=a^2b^2$$
$$b^2x^2-a^2b^2=a^2y^2$$
$$b^2(x^2-a^2)=a^2y^2$$
$$b^2=\frac{a^2y^2}{x^2-a^2}$$
$$b=\pm\sqrt{\frac{a^2y^2}{x^2-a^2}}$$
$$b=\pm\frac{ay\sqrt{x^2-a^2}}{x^2-a^2}$$

81. $x^2+xy-y^2=0\Rightarrow a=1, b=y, c=-y^2$

$$x=\frac{-b\pm\sqrt{b^2-4ac}}{2a}$$
$$=\frac{-(y)\pm\sqrt{(y)^2-4(1)(-y^2)}}{2(1)}$$
$$=\frac{-y\pm\sqrt{y^2+4y^2}}{2}$$
$$=\frac{-y\pm\sqrt{5y^2}}{2}=\frac{-y\pm y\sqrt{5}}{2}$$

82. $x^2-3xy+y^2=0\Rightarrow y^2-3xy+x^2=0$

$a=1, b=-3x, c=x^2$

$$y=\frac{-b\pm\sqrt{b^2-4ac}}{2a}$$
$$=\frac{-(-3x)\pm\sqrt{(-3x)^2-4(1)(x^2)}}{2(1)}$$
$$=\frac{3x\pm\sqrt{9x^2-4x^2}}{2}$$
$$=\frac{3x\pm\sqrt{5x^2}}{2}=\frac{3x\pm x\sqrt{5}}{2}$$

83. $x^2 + 6x + 9 = 0 \Rightarrow a = 1, b = 6, c = 9$
$b^2 - 4ac = 6^2 - 4(1)(9) = 36 - 36 = 0$
one repeated rational root

84. $-3x^2 + 2x = 21 \Rightarrow -3x^2 + 2x - 21 = 0$
$a = -3, b = 2, c = -21$
$b^2 - 4ac = (2)^2 - 4(-3)(-21)$
$= 4 - 252 = -248$
no real roots

85. $3x^2 - 2x + 5 = 0 \Rightarrow a = 3, b = -2, c = 5$
$b^2 - 4ac = (-2)^2 - 4(3)(5)$
$= 4 - 60 = -56$
no real roots

86. $9x^2 + 42x + 49 = 0$
$a = 9, b = 42, c = 49$
$b^2 - 4ac = (42)^2 - 4(9)(49)$
$= 1764 - 1764 = 0$
one repeated rational root

87. $10x^2 + 29x = 21 \Rightarrow 10x^2 + 29x - 21 = 0$
$a = 10, b = 29, c = -21$
$b^2 - 4ac = (29)^2 - 4(10)(-21)$
$= 841 + 840 = 1681$
two different rational roots

88. $10x^2 + x = 21 \Rightarrow 10x^2 + x - 21 = 0$
$a = 10, b = 1, c = -21$
$b^2 - 4ac = (1)^2 - 4(10)(-21)$
$= 1 + 840 = 841$
two different rational roots

89. $x^2 - 5x + 2 = 0 \Rightarrow a = 1, b = -5, c = 2$
$b^2 - 4ac = (-5)^2 - 4(1)(2) = 25 - 8 = 17$
two different irrational roots

90. $-8x^2 - 2x = 13 \Rightarrow -8x^2 - 2x - 13 = 0$
$a = -8, b = -2, c = -13$
$b^2 - 4ac = (-2)^2 - 4(-8)(-13)$
$= 4 - 416 = -412$
no real roots

91. $1492x^2 + 1984x - 1776 = 0$
$a = 1492, b = 1984, c = -1776$
$b^2 - 4ac = (1984)^2 - 4(1492)(-1776)$
$= 3{,}936{,}256 + 10{,}599{,}168$
$= 14{,}535{,}424$
The solutions are real numbers.

92. $2004x^2 + 10x + 1994 = 0$
$a = 2004, b = 10, c = 1994$
$b^2 - 4ac = (10)^2 - 4(2004)(1994)$
$= 100 - 15{,}983{,}904$
$= -15{,}983{,}804$
The solutions are not real numbers.

93. $x^2 + kx + 3k - 5 = 0$
$a = 1, b = k, c = 3k - 5$
Set the discriminant equal to 0:
$$b^2 - 4ac = 0$$
$$k^2 - 4(1)(3k - 5) = 0$$
$$k^2 - 4(3k - 5) = 0$$
$$k^2 - 12k + 20 = 0$$
$$(k - 2)(k - 10) = 0$$
$$k = 2 \text{ or } k = 10$$

94. $x^2 - 2bx + b^2 = 0$
$a = 1, b = -2b, c = b^2$
Set the discriminant equal to 0:
$$b^2 - 4ac = 0$$
$$(-2b)^2 - 4(1)(b^2) = 0$$
$$4b^2 - 4b^2 = 0$$
$$0 = 0$$
True for all values of b

95.
$$\begin{aligned} x+1 &= \frac{12}{x} \\ x(x+1) &= x\left(\frac{12}{x}\right) \\ x^2+x &= 12 \\ x^2+x-12 &= 0 \\ (x+4)(x-3) &= 0 \end{aligned}$$
$$x+4=0 \quad \textbf{or} \quad x-3=0$$
$$x=-4 \qquad\qquad x=3$$

96.
$$\begin{aligned} x-2 &= \frac{15}{x} \\ x(x-2) &= x\left(\frac{15}{x}\right) \\ x^2-2x &= 15 \\ x^2-2x-15 &= 0 \\ (x+3)(x-5) &= 0 \end{aligned}$$
$$x+3=0 \quad \textbf{or} \quad x-5=0$$
$$x=-3 \qquad\qquad x=5$$

97.
$$\begin{aligned} 8x-\frac{3}{x} &= 10 \\ x\left(8x-\frac{3}{x}\right) &= x(10) \\ 8x^2-3 &= 10x \\ 8x^2-10x-3 &= 0 \\ (4x+1)(2x-3) &= 0 \end{aligned}$$
$$4x+1=0 \quad \textbf{or} \quad 2x-3=0$$
$$4x=-1 \qquad\qquad 2x=3$$
$$x=-\tfrac{1}{4} \qquad\qquad x=\tfrac{3}{2}$$

98.
$$\begin{aligned} 15x-\frac{4}{x} &= 4 \\ x\left(15x-\frac{4}{x}\right) &= x(4) \\ 15x^2-4 &= 4x \\ 15x^2-4x-4 &= 0 \\ (5x+2)(3x-2) &= 0 \end{aligned}$$
$$5x+2=0 \quad \textbf{or} \quad 3x-2=0$$
$$5x=-2 \qquad\qquad 3x=2$$
$$x=-\tfrac{2}{5} \qquad\qquad x=\tfrac{2}{3}$$

99.
$$\begin{aligned} \frac{5}{x} &= \frac{4}{x^2}-6 \\ x^2\left(\frac{5}{x}\right) &= x^2\left(\frac{4}{x^2}-6\right) \\ 5x &= 4-6x^2 \\ 6x^2+5x-4 &= 0 \\ (3x+4)(2x-1) &= 0 \end{aligned}$$
$$3x+4=0 \quad \textbf{or} \quad 2x-1=0$$
$$3x=-4 \qquad\qquad 2x=1$$
$$x=-\tfrac{4}{3} \qquad\qquad x=\tfrac{1}{2}$$

100.
$$\begin{aligned} \frac{6}{x^2}+\frac{1}{x} &= 12 \\ x^2\left(\frac{6}{x^2}+\frac{1}{x}\right) &= x^2(12) \\ 6+x &= 12x^2 \\ 0 &= 12x^2-x-6 \\ 0 &= (3x+2)(4x-3) \end{aligned}$$
$$3x+2=0 \quad \textbf{or} \quad 4x-3=0$$
$$3x=-2 \qquad\qquad 4x=3$$
$$x=-\tfrac{2}{3} \qquad\qquad x=\tfrac{3}{4}$$

101.
$$\begin{aligned} x\left(30-\frac{13}{x}\right) &= \frac{10}{x} \\ 30x-13 &= \frac{10}{x} \\ x(30x-13) &= x\left(\frac{10}{x}\right) \\ 30x^2-13x &= 10 \end{aligned}$$
$$\begin{aligned} 30x^2-13x &= 10 \\ 30x^2-13x-10 &= 0 \\ (5x+2)(6x-5) &= 0 \end{aligned}$$
$$5x+2=0 \quad \textbf{or} \quad 6x-5=0$$
$$5x=-2 \qquad\qquad 6x=5$$
$$x=-\tfrac{2}{5} \qquad\qquad x=\tfrac{5}{6}$$

102.
$$\begin{aligned} x\left(20-\frac{17}{x}\right) &= \frac{10}{x} \\ 20x-17 &= \frac{10}{x} \\ x(20x-17) &= x\left(\frac{10}{x}\right) \\ 20x^2-17x &= 10 \\ 20x^2-17x-10 &= 0 \\ (5x+2)(4x-5) &= 0 \end{aligned}$$
$$\begin{aligned} 5x+2=0 \quad &\textbf{or} \quad 4x-5=0 \\ 5x=-2 \quad &\quad\quad 4x=5 \\ x=-\tfrac{2}{5} \quad &\quad\quad x=\tfrac{5}{4} \end{aligned}$$

103.
$$\begin{aligned} \frac{1}{x}+\frac{3}{x+2} &= 2 \\ x(x+2)\left(\frac{1}{x}+\frac{3}{x+2}\right) &= x(x+2)(2) \\ 1(x+2)+3x &= 2x(x+2) \\ x+2+3x &= 2x^2+4x \\ 0 &= 2x^2-2 \\ 0 &= 2(x+1)(x-1) \end{aligned}$$
$$\begin{aligned} x+1=0 \quad &\textbf{or} \quad x-1=0 \\ x=-1 \quad &\quad\quad x=1 \end{aligned}$$

104.
$$\begin{aligned} \frac{1}{x-1}+\frac{1}{x-4} &= \frac{5}{4} \\ 4(x-1)(x-4)\left(\frac{1}{x-1}+\frac{1}{x-4}\right) &= 4(x-1)(x-4)\frac{5}{4} \\ 4(x-4)+4(x-1) &= 5(x-1)(x-4) \\ 4x-16+4x-4 &= 5x^2-25x+20 \\ 0 &= 5x^2-33x+40 \\ 0 &= (5x-8)(x-5) \end{aligned}$$
$$\begin{aligned} 5x-8=0 \quad &\textbf{or} \quad x-5=0 \\ 5x=8 \quad &\quad\quad x=5 \\ x=\tfrac{8}{5} \quad &\quad\quad x=5 \end{aligned}$$

105.
$$\begin{aligned} \frac{1}{x+1}+\frac{5}{2x-4} &= 1 \\ (x+1)(2x-4)\left(\frac{1}{x+1}+\frac{5}{2x-4}\right) &= (x+1)(2x-4)1 \\ 1(2x-4)+5(x+1) &= (x+1)(2x-4) \\ 2x-4+5x+5 &= 2x^2-2x-4 \\ 0 &= 2x^2-9x-5 \\ 0 &= (2x+1)(x-5) \end{aligned}$$
$$\begin{aligned} 2x+1=0 \quad &\textbf{or} \quad x-5=0 \\ 2x=-1 \quad &\quad\quad x=5 \\ x=-\tfrac{1}{2} \quad &\quad\quad x=5 \end{aligned}$$

106.

$$\frac{x(2x+1)}{x-2} = \frac{10}{x-2}$$
$$(x-2)\frac{x(2x+1)}{x-2} = (x-2)\frac{10}{x-2}$$
$$x(2x+1) = 10$$
$$2x^2 + x = 10$$
$$2x^2 + x - 10 = 0$$
$$(2x+5)(x-2) = 0$$
$$2x+5 = 0 \quad \textbf{or} \quad x-2 = 0$$
$$2x = -5 \qquad x = 2$$
$$x = -\tfrac{5}{2} \qquad x = 2$$

Since $x = 2$ does not check, the only solution is $x = -\frac{5}{2}$.

107.

$$x + 1 + \frac{x+2}{x-1} = \frac{3}{x-1}$$
$$(x-1)\left(\frac{x+1}{1} + \frac{x+2}{x-1}\right) = (x-1)\frac{3}{x-1}$$
$$(x-1)(x+1) + x + 2 = 3$$
$$x^2 - 1 + x + 2 = 3$$
$$x^2 + x - 2 = 0$$
$$(x+2)(x-1) = 0$$
$$x+2 = 0 \quad \textbf{or} \quad x-1 = 0$$
$$x = -2 \qquad x = 1$$

Since $x = 1$ does not check, the only solution is $x = -2$.

108.

$$\frac{1}{4-y} = \frac{1}{4} + \frac{1}{y+2}$$
$$4(4-y)(y+2)\left(\frac{1}{4-y}\right) = 4(4-y)(y+2)\left(\frac{1}{4} + \frac{1}{y+2}\right)$$
$$4(y+2)(1) = (4-y)(y+2)(1) + 4(4-y)(1)$$
$$4y + 8 = -y^2 + 2y + 8 + 16 - 4y$$
$$y^2 + 6y - 16 = 0$$
$$(y+8)(y-2) = 0$$
$$y+8 = 0 \quad \textbf{or} \quad y-2 = 0$$
$$y = -8 \qquad y = 2$$

109.

$$\frac{24}{a} - 11 = \frac{-12}{a+1}$$
$$a(a+1)\left(\frac{24}{a} - 11\right) = a(a+1)\frac{-12}{a+1}$$
$$24(a+1) - 11a(a+1) = a(-12)$$
$$24a + 24 - 11a^2 - 11a = -12a$$
$$0 = 11a^2 - 25a - 24$$
$$0 = (11a+8)(a-3)$$
$$11a + 8 = 0 \quad \textbf{or} \quad a-3 = 0$$
$$11a = -8 \qquad a = 3$$
$$a = -\tfrac{8}{11} \qquad a = 3$$

110. $$\frac{(a-2)(a+4)}{10} = \frac{a(a-3)}{5}$$

$$10\left[\frac{(a-2)(a+4)}{10}\right] = 10\left[\frac{a(a-3)}{5}\right]$$

$$(a-2)(a+4) = 2a(a-3)$$

$$a^2 + 2a - 8 = 2a^2 - 6a$$

$$0 = a^2 - 8a + 8$$

$a = 1, b = -8, c = 8$

$$a = \frac{-b \pm \sqrt{b^2 - 4ac}}{2a} = \frac{-(-8) \pm \sqrt{(-8)^2 - 4(1)(8)}}{2(1)} = \frac{8 \pm \sqrt{32}}{2} = \frac{8 \pm 4\sqrt{2}}{2} = 4 \pm 2\sqrt{2}$$

111. $$\frac{4+a}{2a} = \frac{a-2}{3}$$

$$6a\left(\frac{4+a}{2a}\right) = 6a\left(\frac{a-2}{3}\right)$$

$$12 + 3a = 2a^2 - 4a$$

$$0 = 2a^2 - 7a - 12$$

$a = 2, b = -7, c = -12$

$$a = \frac{-b \pm \sqrt{b^2 - 4ac}}{2a} = \frac{-(-7) \pm \sqrt{(-7)^2 - 4(2)(-12)}}{2(2)} = \frac{7 \pm \sqrt{145}}{4}$$

112. $$\frac{36}{b} - 17 = \frac{-24}{b+1}$$

$$b(b+1)\left(\frac{36}{b} - 17\right) = b(b+1)\frac{-24}{b+1}$$

$$36(b+1) - 17b(b+1) = b(-24)$$

$$36b + 36 - 17b^2 - 17b = -24b$$

$$0 = 17b^2 - 43b - 36 \Rightarrow a = 17, b = -43, c = -36$$

$$b = \frac{-b \pm \sqrt{b^2 - 4ac}}{2a} = \frac{-(-43) \pm \sqrt{(-43)^2 - 4(17)(-36)}}{2(17)} = \frac{43 \pm \sqrt{4297}}{34}$$

113. If r_1 and r_2 are the roots of $ax^2 + bx + c = 0$, then their values are

$$r_1 = \frac{-b + \sqrt{b^2 - 4ac}}{2a} \text{ and } r_2 = \frac{-b - \sqrt{b^2 - 4ac}}{2a}.$$

$$r_1 + r_2 = \frac{-b + \sqrt{b^2 - 4ac}}{2a} + \frac{-b - \sqrt{b^2 - 4ac}}{2a} = \frac{-2b}{2a} = -\frac{b}{a}$$

114. If r_1 and r_2 are the roots of $ax^2+bx+c=0$, then their values are

$$r_1=\frac{-b+\sqrt{b^2-4ac}}{2a} \text{ and } r_2=\frac{-b-\sqrt{b^2-4ac}}{2a}.$$

$$r_1r_2=\frac{-b+\sqrt{b^2-4ac}}{2a}\cdot\frac{-b-\sqrt{b^2-4ac}}{2a}$$

$$=\frac{\left(-b+\sqrt{b^2-4ac}\right)\left(-b-\sqrt{b^2-4ac}\right)}{4a^2}$$

$$=\frac{(-b)^2-\left(\sqrt{b^2-4ac}\right)^2}{4a^2}=\frac{b^2-(b^2-4ac)}{4a^2}=\frac{b^2-b^2+4ac}{4a^2}=\frac{4ac}{4a^2}=\frac{c}{a}$$

115. Rewrite the equation as $16t^2-v_0t+h=0$ and solve for t using the quadratic formula.
$a=16, b=-v_0, c=h$

$$t=\frac{-b\pm\sqrt{b^2-4ac}}{2a}=\frac{-(-v_0)\pm\sqrt{(-v_0)^2-4(16)(h)}}{2(16)}=\frac{v_0\pm\sqrt{v_0^2-64h}}{32}$$

Since t_1 and t_2 are the solutions to the equation, we have

$t_1=\dfrac{v_0-\sqrt{v_0^2-64h}}{32}$ and $t_2=\dfrac{v_0+\sqrt{v_0^2-64h}}{32}$. Calculate $16t_1t_2$:

$$16t_1t_2=16\cdot\frac{v_0-\sqrt{v_0^2-64h}}{32}\cdot\frac{v_0+\sqrt{v_0^2-64h}}{32}=16\cdot\frac{v_0^2-(v_0^2-64h)}{1024}$$

$$=\frac{16\cdot 64h}{1024}=\frac{1024h}{1024}=h$$

Thus, $h=16t_1t_2$.

116. Proceed as in **#115** to calculate t_1 and t_2. Then

$$16(t_1+t_2)=16\left(\frac{v_0-\sqrt{v_0^2-64h}}{32}+\frac{v_0+\sqrt{v_0^2-64h}}{32}\right)=16\left(\frac{2v_0}{32}\right)=\frac{32v_0}{32}=v_0.$$

Thus $v_0=16(t_1+t_2)$.

117-120. Answers may vary.

121. $5x(x-2)-x(3x-2)=5x^2-10x-3x^2+2x=2x^2-8x$

122. $(x+3)(x-9)-x(x-5)=x^2-6x-27-x^2+5x=-x-27$

123. $(m+3)^2-(m-3)^2=(m+3)(m+3)-(m-3)(m-3)$
$=m^2+6m+9-\left(m^2-6m+9\right)$
$=m^2+6m+9-m^2+6m-9=12m$

124. $[(y+z)(y-z)]^2=[y^2-z^2]^2=(y^2-z^2)(y^2-z^2)=y^4-2y^2z^2+z^4$

125. $\sqrt{50x^3}-x\sqrt{8x}=\sqrt{25x^2}\sqrt{2x}-x\sqrt{4}\sqrt{2x}=5x\sqrt{2x}-2x\sqrt{2x}=3x\sqrt{2x}$

126. $\frac{2x}{\sqrt{5}-2}=\frac{2x}{\sqrt{5}-2}\cdot\frac{\sqrt{5}+2}{\sqrt{5}+2}=\frac{2x(\sqrt{5}+2)}{(\sqrt{5})^2-2^2}=\frac{2x(\sqrt{5}+2)}{5-4}=\frac{2x(\sqrt{5}+2)}{1}=2x\left(\sqrt{5}+2\right)$

Exercises 1.4 (page 125)

1. $A = lw$

2. $d = rt$

3. Let $w =$ the width of the rectangle.
Then $w + 4 =$ the length.

$$\boxed{\text{Width}} \cdot \boxed{\text{Length}} = \boxed{\text{Area}}$$
$$w(w+4) = 32$$
$$w^2 + 4w = 32$$
$$w^2 + 4w - 32 = 0$$
$$(w+8)(w-4) = 0$$
$$w + 8 = 0 \quad \textbf{or} \quad w - 4 = 0$$
$$w = -8 \qquad\qquad w = 4$$

Since the width cannot be negative, the only reasonable solution is $w = 4$.
The dimensions are 4 feet by 8 feet.

4. Let $w =$ the width of the rectangle.
Then $5w =$ the length.

$$\boxed{\text{Width}} \cdot \boxed{\text{Length}} = \boxed{\text{Area}}$$
$$w \cdot 5w = 125$$
$$5w^2 = 125$$
$$w^2 = 25$$
$$w = \sqrt{25} \quad \textbf{or} \quad w = -\sqrt{25}$$
$$w = 5 \qquad\qquad w = -5$$

Since the width cannot be negative, the only reasonable solution is $w = 5$.
The dimensions are 5 feet by 25 feet, and the perimeter is 60 feet.

5. Let $w =$ the width of the screen. Then $w + 88 =$ the length.

$$\boxed{\text{Width}} \cdot \boxed{\text{Length}} = \boxed{\text{Area}}$$
$$w(w+88) = 11520$$
$$w^2 + 88w = 11520$$
$$w^2 + 88w - 11520 = 0 \Rightarrow a = 1, b = 88, c = -11520$$
$$w = \frac{-b \pm \sqrt{b^2 - 4ac}}{2a} = \frac{-(88) \pm \sqrt{(88)^2 - 4(1)(-11520)}}{2(1)} = \frac{-88 \pm \sqrt{53824}}{2}$$

$w = 72$ or $w = -160$; Since the screen cannot have a negative width, the solution is $w = 72$ and the dimensions of the screen are 160 ft by 72 ft.

6. Let $w =$ the width of the screen. Then $w + 20 =$ the length.

$$\boxed{\text{Width}} \cdot \boxed{\text{Length}} = \boxed{\text{Area}}$$
$$w(w+20) = 11349$$
$$w^2 + 20w = 11349$$
$$w^2 + 20w - 11349 = 0 \Rightarrow a = 1, b = 20, c = -11349$$
$$w = \frac{-b \pm \sqrt{b^2 - 4ac}}{2a} = \frac{-(20) \pm \sqrt{(20)^2 - 4(1)(-11349)}}{2(1)} = \frac{-20 \pm \sqrt{45796}}{2}$$

$w = 97$ or $w = -117$; Since the screen cannot have a negative width, the solution is $w = 97$ and the dimensions of the screen are 117 ft by 97 ft.

7. Let $s =$ the side of the second square. Then $s - 4 =$ the side of the first square.

$$\boxed{\text{Area of first}} + \boxed{\text{Area of second}} = 106$$
$$(s-4)^2 + s^2 = 106$$
$$s^2 - 8s + 16 + s^2 = 106$$
$$2s^2 - 8s - 90 = 0$$
$$2(s^2 - 4s - 45) = 0$$
$$2(s+5)(s-9) = 0$$
$$s + 5 = 0 \quad \textbf{or} \quad s - 9 = 0$$
$$s = -5 \qquad s = 9$$

Since the side cannot be negative, the only reasonable solution is $s = 9$. The larger square has a side of length 9 cm.

8. Let $s =$ the side of the original square. Then the new rectangle has dimensions of $s + 10$ and $s - 8$.

$$\boxed{\text{Length}} \cdot \boxed{\text{Width}} = \boxed{\text{Area}}$$
$$(s+10)(s-8) = 63$$
$$s^2 + 2s - 80 = 63$$
$$s^2 + 2s - 143 = 0$$
$$(s+13)(s-11) = 0$$
$$s + 13 = 0 \quad \textbf{or} \quad s - 11 = 0$$
$$s = -13 \qquad s = 11$$

Since the side cannot be negative, the only reasonable solution is $s = 11$. The original area was $11^2 = 121\text{ m}^2$.

9. Let the dimensions be x and $1.9x$.

$$\boxed{\text{Width}} \cdot \boxed{\text{Length}} = \boxed{\text{Area}}$$
$$x(1.9x) = 100$$
$$1.9x^2 = 100$$
$$x^2 = \frac{100}{1.9}$$
$$x = \pm\sqrt{\frac{100}{1.9}}$$
$$x \approx \pm 7.25$$

$1.9x \approx 1.9(7.25) \approx 13.75$

Since the dimensions cannot be negative, the only reasonable solution $7\frac{1}{4}$ ft by $13\frac{3}{4}$ ft.

10. $P = 2l + 2w$, so $l = \dfrac{P - 2w}{2} = \dfrac{54 - 2w}{2}$.

$$\boxed{\text{Length}} \cdot \boxed{\text{Width}} = \boxed{\text{Area}}$$
$$\frac{54 - 2w}{2} \cdot w = 180$$
$$(54 - 2w)w = 360$$
$$54w - 2w^2 = 360$$
$$0 = 2w^2 - 54w + 360$$
$$0 = 2(w^2 - 27w + 180)$$
$$0 = 2(w - 12)(w - 15)$$
$$w - 12 = 0 \quad \textbf{or} \quad w - 15 = 0$$
$$w = 12 \qquad w = 15$$

The dimensions are 12 cm by 15 cm.

11. The floor area of the box is a square with a side of length $12 - 2x$.

$$\boxed{\text{Floor area}} = 64$$
$$(12 - 2x)^2 = 64$$
$$144 - 48x + 4x^2 = 64$$
$$4x^2 - 48x + 80 = 0$$
$$4(x^2 - 12x + 20) = 0$$
$$4(x-2)(x-10) = 0$$
$$x - 2 = 0 \quad \textbf{or} \quad x - 10 = 0$$
$$x = 2 \qquad x = 10$$

The solution $x = 10$ does not make sense in the problem, so the depth is 2 inches.

12. $$\boxed{\text{Cross-sectional area}} = 36$$
$$x(18 - 2x) = 36$$
$$18x - 2x^2 = 36$$
$$0 = 2x^2 - 18x + 36$$
$$0 = 2(x^2 - 9x + 18)$$
$$0 = 2(x-3)(x-6)$$
$$x - 3 = 0 \quad \textbf{or} \quad x - 6 = 0$$
$$x = 3 \qquad x = 6$$

Both solutions are valid, so the depth of the gutter is either 3 inches or 6 inches.

13. Let $h =$ the height of the triangle.
Then $\frac{1}{3}h =$ the base of the triangle.

$\frac{1}{2} \cdot \boxed{\text{Base}} \cdot \boxed{\text{Height}} = \boxed{\text{Area}}$

$$\frac{1}{2} \cdot \frac{1}{3}h \cdot h = 24$$
$$\frac{1}{6}h^2 = 24$$
$$h^2 = 144$$
$$h = \sqrt{144} \quad \textbf{or} \quad h = -\sqrt{144}$$
$$h = 12 \qquad\qquad h = -12$$

Since the height cannot be negative, the only reasonable solution is $h = 12$.
The base has a length of 4 meters.

14. Let $h =$ the height of the triangle.
Then $\frac{1}{2}h =$ the base of the triangle.

$\frac{1}{2} \cdot \boxed{\text{Base}} \cdot \boxed{\text{Height}} = \boxed{\text{Area}}$

$$\frac{1}{2} \cdot \frac{1}{2}h \cdot h = 100$$
$$\frac{1}{4}h^2 = 100$$
$$h^2 = 400$$
$$h = \sqrt{400} \quad \textbf{or} \quad h = -\sqrt{400}$$
$$h = 20 \qquad\qquad h = -20$$

Since the height cannot be negative, the only reasonable solution is $h = 20$.
The base has a height of 20 yards.

15. Let the legs have lengths x and $x - 14$.

$$x^2 + (x - 14)^2 = 26^2$$
$$x^2 + x^2 - 28x + 196 = 676$$
$$2x^2 - 28x - 480 = 0$$
$$2(x^2 - 14x - 240) = 0$$
$$2(x - 24)(x + 10) = 0$$
$$x - 24 = 0 \quad \textbf{or} \quad x + 10 = 0$$
$$x = 24 \qquad\qquad x = -10$$

Since lengths are positive, the answer is $x = 24$, and the legs have length 10 meters and 24 meters.

16. Let the legs have lengths x and $5x$.

$$x^2 + (5x)^2 = \left(10\sqrt{26}\right)^2$$
$$x^2 + 25x^2 = 2600$$
$$26x^2 = 2600$$
$$x^2 = 100$$
$$x = \sqrt{100} \quad \textbf{or} \quad x = -\sqrt{100}$$
$$x = 10 \qquad\qquad x = -10$$

Since lengths are positive, the answer is $x = 10$, and the legs have length 10 cm and 50 cm.

17. Let $x =$ the height of the screen. Then $x + 17.5 =$ the width. Use the Pythagorean Theorem:

$$\text{height}^2 + \text{width}^2 = \text{diagonal}^2$$
$$x^2 + (x + 17.5)^2 = 46^2$$
$$x^2 + x^2 + 35x + 306.25 = 2116$$
$$2x^2 + 35x - 1809.75 = 0$$
$$a = 2,\ b = 35,\ c = -1809.75$$

$$x = \frac{-b \pm \sqrt{b^2 - 4ac}}{2a}$$
$$= \frac{-35 \pm \sqrt{35^2 - 4(2)(-1809.75)}}{2(2)}$$
$$= \frac{-35 \pm \sqrt{15703}}{4} \approx \frac{-35 \pm 125.312}{4}$$

The only positive solution is 22.6. The dimensions are 22.6 inches by 40.1 inches.

18. Let $x =$ the width of the rug. Then $x + 2 =$ the length. Use the Pythagorean Theorem:

$$\text{width}^2 + \text{length}^2 = \text{diagonal}^2$$
$$x^2 + (x+2)^2 = 12^2$$
$$x^2 + x^2 + 4x + 4 = 144$$
$$2x^2 + 4x - 140 = 0$$
$$a = 2,\ b = 4,\ c = -140$$

$$x = \frac{-b \pm \sqrt{b^2 - 4ac}}{2a} = \frac{-4 \pm \sqrt{4^2 - 4(2)(-140)}}{2(2)} = \frac{-4 \pm \sqrt{1136}}{4} \approx \frac{-4 \pm 33.705}{4}$$

The only positive solution is 7.4. The dimensions are 7.4 feet by 9.4 feet.

19. Let $r =$ the cyclist's rate from DeKalb to Rockford. Then his return rate is $r - 10$.

	Rate	Time	Dist.
First trip	r	$\frac{40}{r}$	40
Return trip	$r-10$	$\frac{40}{r-10}$	40

$$\boxed{\text{Return time}} = \boxed{\text{First time}} + 2$$
$$\frac{40}{r-10} = \frac{40}{r} + 2$$
$$r(r-10)\frac{40}{r-10} = r(r-10)\left(\frac{40}{r} + 2\right)$$
$$40r = 40(r-10) + 2r(r-10)$$
$$40r = 40r - 400 + 2r^2 - 20r$$
$$0 = 2r^2 - 20r - 400$$
$$0 = 2(r-20)(r+10)$$
$$r - 20 = 0 \quad \textbf{or} \quad r + 10 = 0$$
$$r = 20 \qquad\qquad r = -10$$

Since $r = -10$ does not make sense, the solution is $r = 20$. The cyclist rides 20 mph going and 10 mph returning.

20. Let $r =$ the farmer's first rate. Then his return rate is $r + 10$.

	Rate	Time	Dist.
First trip	r	$\frac{120}{r}$	120
Return trip	$r+10$	$\frac{120}{r+10}$	120

$$\boxed{\text{Return time}} = \boxed{\text{First time}} - 1$$
$$\frac{120}{r+10} = \frac{120}{r} - 1$$
$$r(r+10)\frac{120}{r+10} = r(r+10)\left(\frac{120}{r} - 1\right)$$
$$120r = 120(r+10) - r(r+10)$$
$$120r = 120r + 1200 - r^2 - 10r$$
$$r^2 + 10r - 1200 = 0$$
$$(r-30)(r+40) = 0$$
$$r - 30 = 0 \quad \textbf{or} \quad r + 40 = 0$$
$$r = 30 \qquad\qquad r = -40$$

Since $r = -40$ does not make sense, the solution is $r = 30$. The farmer drives 30 kph going and 40 kph returning.

21. Let $r =$ the slower rate. Then the faster rate is $r + 10$.

$$\boxed{\text{Faster time}} = \boxed{\text{Slower time}} - 1$$

	Rate	Time	Dist.
Slower trip	r	$\frac{420}{r}$	420
Faster trip	$r + 10$	$\frac{420}{r+10}$	420

$$\frac{420}{r+10} = \frac{420}{r} - 1$$
$$r(r+10)\frac{420}{r+10} = r(r+10)\left(\frac{420}{r} - 1\right)$$
$$420r = 420(r+10) - r(r+10)$$
$$420r = 420r + 4200 - r^2 - 10r$$
$$r^2 + 10r - 4200 = 0$$
$$(r-60)(r+70) = 0$$
$$r - 60 = 0 \quad \textbf{or} \quad r + 70 = 0$$
$$r = 60 \qquad\qquad r = -70$$

Since $r = -70$ does not make sense, the solution is $r = 60$. The slower speed results in a trip of length 7 hours.

22. Let $r =$ the driver's slower rate. Then her faster rate is $r + 25$.

$$\boxed{\text{Faster time}} = \boxed{\text{Slower time}} - \frac{10}{60}$$

	Rate	Time	Dist.
Slower trip	r	$\frac{25}{r}$	25
Faster trip	$r + 25$	$\frac{25}{r+25}$	25

$$\frac{25}{r+25} = \frac{25}{r} - \frac{1}{6}$$
$$6r(r+25)\frac{25}{r+25} = 6r(r+25)\left(\frac{25}{r} - \frac{1}{6}\right)$$
$$150r = 150(r+25) - r(r+25)$$
$$150r = 150r + 3750 - r^2 - 25r$$
$$r^2 + 25r - 3750 = 0$$
$$(r-50)(r+75) = 0$$
$$r - 50 = 0 \quad \textbf{or} \quad r + 75 = 0$$
$$r = 50 \qquad\qquad r = -75$$

Since $r = -75$ does not make sense, the solution is $r = 50$. The driver's usual speed is 50 kph.

23. Set $h = 0$:

$$h = -16t^2 + 400t$$
$$0 = -16t^2 + 400t$$
$$16t^2 - 400t = 0$$
$$16t(t-25) = 0$$
$$16t = 0 \quad \textbf{or} \quad t - 25 = 0$$
$$t = 0 \qquad\qquad t = 25$$

$t = 0$ represents when the projectile was fired, so it returns to earth after 25 seconds.

24. Set $h = 0$:

$$h = -16t^2 + 104t$$
$$0 = -16t^2 + 104t$$
$$16t^2 - 104t = 0$$
$$8t(2t-13) = 0$$
$$8t = 0 \quad \textbf{or} \quad 2t - 13 = 0$$
$$t = 0 \qquad\qquad t = \tfrac{13}{2} = 6.5$$

$t = 0$ represents when the projectile was fired, so it returns after 6.5 seconds.

25. Set $s = 1454$:

$$s = 16t^2$$
$$1454 = 16t^2$$
$$\frac{1454}{16} = t^2$$
$$t = \sqrt{\frac{1454}{16}} \quad \textbf{or} \quad t = -\sqrt{\frac{1454}{16}}$$
$$t \approx 9.5 \qquad t \approx -9.5$$

$t = -9.5$ does not make sense, so it takes it about 9.5 seconds to hit the ground.

26. Set $d = 312$:

$$d = 16t^2$$
$$312 = 16t^2$$
$$\frac{312}{16} = t^2$$
$$t = \sqrt{\frac{312}{16}} \quad \textbf{or} \quad t = -\sqrt{\frac{312}{16}}$$
$$t \approx 4.4 \qquad t \approx -4.4$$

$t = -4.4$ does not make sense, so the fall lasted about 4.4 seconds.

27. Set $h = 5$ and $s = 48$.

$$h = s - 16t^2$$
$$5 = 48 - 16t^2$$
$$16t^2 = 43$$
$$t = \sqrt{\frac{43}{16}} \quad \textbf{or} \quad t = -\sqrt{\frac{43}{16}}$$
$$t \approx 1.6 \qquad t \approx -1.6$$

$t = -1.6$ does not make sense, so she has about 1.6 seconds to get out of the way.

28. Set $h = 16$:

$$h = -16t^2 + 32t$$
$$16 = -16t^2 + 32t$$
$$16t^2 - 32t + 16 = 0$$
$$16(t-1)(t-1) = 0$$
$$t - 1 = 0 \quad \textbf{or} \quad t - 1 = 0$$
$$t = 1 \qquad t = 1$$

It takes the object 1 second to reach a height of 16 feet.

29. Let $x =$ the number of nickel increases. The new fare $= 25 + 5x$ (in cents), while the number of passengers $= 3000 - 80x$.

$$\boxed{\text{Number of passengers}} \cdot \boxed{\text{Fare}} = \boxed{\text{Revenue}}$$
$$(3000 - 80x)(25 + 5x) = 99400$$
$$75000 + 13000x - 400x^2 = 99400$$
$$400x^2 - 13000x + 24400 = 0$$
$$200(2x^2 - 65x + 122) = 0$$
$$200(2x - 61)(x - 2) = 0$$
$$2x - 61 = 0 \quad \textbf{or} \quad x - 2 = 0$$
$$x = 30.5 \qquad x = 2$$

Since you cannot have half of a nickel increase, $x = 30.5$ does not make sense. Thus, there should be 2 nickel increases, for a fare increase of 10 cents.

30. Let $x =$ the number of dollar increases. The new price $= 12 + x$, while the number attending $= 500 - 50x$.

$$\boxed{\text{Number attending}} \cdot \boxed{\text{Price}} = \boxed{\text{Revenue}}$$
$$(500 - 50x)(12 + x) = 5600$$
$$6000 - 100x - 50x^2 = 5600$$
$$50x^2 + 100x - 400 = 0$$
$$50(x^2 + 2x - 8) = 0$$
$$50(x + 4)(x - 2) = 0$$
$$x + 4 = 0 \quad \textbf{or} \quad x - 2 = 0$$
$$x = -4 \qquad x = 2$$

Since you cannot have a negative number of increases, $x = -4$ does not make sense. Thus, there should be an increase of 2 dollars, for a ticket price of \$14.

31. Let x = the number of \$0.50 decreases. The new price = $15 - 0.5x$, while the number attending = $1200 + 40x$.

$\boxed{\text{Number attending}} \cdot \boxed{\text{Price}} = \boxed{\text{Revenue}}$

$$(1200 + 40x)(15 - 0.5x) = 17280$$
$$18000 - 20x^2 = 17280$$
$$20x^2 = 720$$
$$x^2 = 36$$

$x = \sqrt{36}$ **or** $x = -\sqrt{36}$

$x = 6$ $\quad$ $x = -6$

$x = -6$ does not make sense. Thus, there should be six 50-cent decreases, for a ticket price of \$12 and an attendance of 1440 people.

32. Let x = the number of subscribers over 3000. The new profit = $20 + 0.01x$, while the number subscribing = $3000 + x$.

$\boxed{\text{Number subscribing}} \cdot \boxed{\text{Profit}} = \boxed{\text{Total profit}}$

$$(3000 + x)(20 + 0.01x) = 120000$$
$$60000 + 50x + 0.01x^2 = 120000$$
$$0.01x^2 + 50x - 60000 = 0$$
$$x^2 + 5000x - 6000000 = 0$$
$$(x + 6000)(x - 1000) = 0$$

$x + 6000 = 0$ **or** $x - 1000 = 0$

$x = -6000$ $\quad$ $x = 1000$

$x = -6000$ does not make sense. The increase should be 1000, for a total of 4000.

33. Let x = Chloe's principal.

	I	P	r
Chloe	240	x	$\frac{240}{x}$
Morgan	280	$x + 1000$	$\frac{280}{x+1000}$

$\boxed{\text{Morgan's rate}} = \boxed{\text{Chloe's rate}} - 0.01$

$$\frac{280}{x + 1000} = \frac{240}{x} - 0.01$$
$$x(x + 1000)\frac{280}{x + 1000} = x(x + 1000)\left(\frac{240}{x} - 0.01\right)$$
$$280x = 240(x + 1000) - 0.01x(x + 1000)$$
$$0.01x^2 + 50x - 240{,}000 = 0$$
$$x^2 + 5000x - 24{,}000{,}000 = 0$$
$$(x - 3000)(x + 8000) = 0$$

$x - 3000 = 0$ **or** $x + 8000 = 0$

$x = 3000$ $\quad$ $x = -8000 \Rightarrow$ $x = -8000$ does not make sense. The principal amounts were \$3000 and \$4000. The interest rates were 8% for Chloe and 7% for Morgan.

34. Let x = Laura's principal.

	I	P	r
Laura	400	x	$\frac{400}{x}$
Scott	800	$x + 3000$	$\frac{800}{x+3000}$

$\boxed{\text{Scott's rate}} = \boxed{\text{Laura's rate}} + 0.02$

$$\frac{800}{x + 3000} = \frac{400}{x} + 0.02$$
$$x(x + 3000)\frac{800}{x + 3000} = x(x + 3000)\left(\frac{400}{x} + 0.02\right)$$
$$800x = 400(x + 3000) + 0.02x(x + 3000)$$
$$800x = 400x + 1{,}200{,}000 + 0.02x^2 + 60x$$
$$0.02x^2 - 340x + 1{,}200{,}000 = 0$$
$$x^2 - 17{,}000x + 60{,}000{,}000 = 0$$
$$(x - 5000)(x - 12{,}000) = 0$$

$x - 5000 = 0$ **or** $x - 12{,}000 = 0$

$x = 5000$ $\quad$ $x = 12{,}000 \Rightarrow$ Laura invested either \$5000 or \$12,000, so Scott invested either \$8000 or \$15,000.

35. Let $x =$ the total number of professors.

$$\boxed{\text{New share with lower number}} = \boxed{\text{Original share}} + 10$$

$$\frac{150}{x-4} = \frac{150}{x} + 10$$

$$x(x-4)\frac{150}{x-4} = x(x-4)\left(\frac{150}{x} + 10\right)$$

$$150x = 150(x-4) + 10x(x-4)$$

$$150x = 150x - 600 + 10x^2 - 40x$$

$$0 = 10x^2 - 40x - 600$$

$$0 = x^2 - 4x - 60$$

$$0 = (x-10)(x+6)$$

$$x - 10 = 0 \quad \textbf{or} \quad x + 6 = 0$$

$$x = 10 \qquad\qquad x = -6$$

$x = -6$ does not make sense, so there are 10 professors in the department.

36. Let $x =$ the actual number of cameras.

$$\boxed{\text{Actual price per camera}} - 10 = \boxed{\text{New price per camera}}$$

$$\frac{180}{x} - 10 = \frac{180}{x+3}$$

$$x(x+3)\left(\frac{180}{x} - 10\right) = x(x+3)\frac{180}{x+3}$$

$$180(x+3) - 10x(x+3) = 180x$$

$$10x^2 + 30x - 540 = 0$$

$$x^2 + 3x - 54 = 0$$

$$(x-6)(x+9) = 0$$

$$x - 6 = 0 \quad \textbf{or} \quad x + 9 = 0$$

$$x = 6 \qquad\qquad x = -9$$

$x = -9$ does not make sense, so there are 6 cameras, with each costing \$30.

37. Let $x =$ time for the second pipe to fill tank.

$$\boxed{\text{First in 1 hour}} + \boxed{\text{Second in 1 hour}} = \boxed{\text{Total in 1 hour}}$$

$$\frac{1}{4} + \frac{1}{x} = \frac{1}{x-2}$$

$$4x(x-2)\left(\frac{1}{4} + \frac{1}{x}\right) = 4x(x-2) \cdot \frac{1}{x-2}$$

$$x(x-2) + 4(x-2) = 4x$$

$$x^2 - 2x + 4x - 8 = 4x$$

$$x^2 - 2x - 8 = 0$$

$$(x-4)(x+2) = 0$$

$$x - 4 = 0 \quad \textbf{or} \quad x + 2 = 0$$

$$x = 4 \qquad\qquad x = -2$$

Since $x = -2$ does not make sense, the solution is $x = 4$. It takes the second pipe 4 hours to fill the tank alone.

38. Let $x =$ time for the both hoses to fill pool.

$$\boxed{\text{First in 1 hour}} + \boxed{\text{Second in 1 hour}} = \boxed{\text{Total in 1 hour}}$$

$$\frac{1}{6} + \frac{1}{x+3} = \frac{1}{x}$$

$$6x(x+3)\left(\frac{1}{6} + \frac{1}{x+3}\right) = 6x(x+3) \cdot \frac{1}{x}$$

$$x(x+3) + 6x = 6(x+3)$$

$$x^2 + 3x + 6x = 6x + 18$$

$$x^2 + 3x - 18 = 0$$

$$(x-3)(x+6) = 0$$

$$x - 3 = 0 \quad \textbf{or} \quad x + 6 = 0$$

$$x = 3 \qquad\qquad x = -6$$

Since $x = -6$ does not make sense, the solution is $x = 3$. It takes the second hose 6 hours to fill the pool alone.

39. Let $x =$ time for the Steven to mow lawn.

$$\boxed{\text{Steven in 1 hour}} + \boxed{\text{Kristy in 1 hour}} = \boxed{\text{Total in 1 hour}}$$

$$\frac{1}{x} + \frac{1}{x-1} = \frac{1}{5}$$

$$5x(x-1)\left(\frac{1}{x} + \frac{1}{x-1}\right) = 5x(x-1) \cdot \frac{1}{5}$$

$$5(x-1) + 5x = x(x-1)$$

$$5x - 5 + 5x = x^2 - x$$

$$0 = x^2 - 11x + 5$$

$a = 1, b = -11, c = 5$

$$x = \frac{-b \pm \sqrt{b^2 - 4ac}}{2a}$$

$$= \frac{-(-11) \pm \sqrt{(-11)^2 - 4(1)(5)}}{2(1)}$$

$$= \frac{11 \pm \sqrt{101}}{2} \approx 10.5 \text{ or } 0.5$$

$x = 0.5$ does not make sense, so Kristy could mow the lawn in about 9.5 hours alone.

40. Let $x =$ time for the Sarah to clean it.

$$\boxed{\text{Sarah in 1 hour}} + \boxed{\text{Heidi in 1 hour}} = \boxed{\text{Total in 1 hour}}$$

$$\begin{aligned}
\frac{1}{x} + \frac{1}{x+3} &= \frac{1}{2} \\
2x(x+3)\left(\frac{1}{x} + \frac{1}{x+3}\right) &= 2x(x+3)\cdot\frac{1}{2} \\
2(x+3) + 2x &= x(x+3) \\
2x + 6 + 2x &= x^2 + 3x \\
0 &= x^2 - x - 6 \\
0 &= (x-3)(x+2)
\end{aligned}$$

$$x - 3 = 0 \quad \textbf{or} \quad x + 2 = 0$$
$$x = 3 \qquad\qquad x = -2$$

$x = -2$ does not make sense. It would take Heidi 6 hours to clean the garage alone.

41. The number of trees is the length of the row divided by the space between the trees, plus 1. Let $x =$ the original spacing.

$$\boxed{\text{Original number}} - 44 = \boxed{\text{New number}}$$

$$\begin{aligned}
\frac{1320}{x} + 1 - 44 &= \frac{1320}{x+1} + 1 \\
\frac{1320}{x} - 44 &= \frac{1320}{x+1} \\
x(x+1)\left(\frac{1320}{x} - 44\right) &= x(x+1)\frac{1320}{x+1} \\
1320(x+1) - 44x(x+1) &= 1320x \\
44x^2 + 44x - 1320 &= 0 \\
x^2 + x - 30 &= 0 \\
(x-5)(x+6) &= 0
\end{aligned}$$

$$x - 5 = 0 \quad \textbf{or} \quad x + 6 = 0$$
$$x = 5 \qquad\qquad x = -6$$

$x = -6$ does not make sense. The original spacing was 5 feet, resulting in 265 trees, so the new spacing will require 221 trees.

42. Let $x =$ the actual number of spokes.

$$\boxed{\text{Actual angles between spokes}} - 6 = \boxed{\text{New angle between spokes}}$$

$$\begin{aligned}
\frac{360}{x} - 6 &= \frac{360}{x+10} \\
x(x+10)\left(\frac{360}{x} - 6\right) &= x(x+10)\frac{360}{x+10} \\
360(x+10) - 6x(x+10) &= 360x \\
6x^2 + 60x - 3600 &= 0 \\
x^2 + 10x - 600 &= 0 \\
(x-20)(x+30) &= 0
\end{aligned}$$

$$x - 20 = 0 \quad \textbf{or} \quad x + 30 = 0$$
$$x = 20 \qquad\qquad x = -30$$

$x = -30$ does not make sense, so there are 20 spokes.

43. Let $h = 15$:

$$\begin{aligned}
\frac{l}{h} &= \frac{h}{l-h} \\
\frac{l}{15} &= \frac{15}{l-15} \\
15(l-15)\cdot\frac{l}{15} &= 15(l-15)\cdot\frac{15}{l-15} \\
l(l-15) &= 15^2 \\
l^2 - 15l - 225 &= 0
\end{aligned}$$

$a = 1, b = -15, c = -225$

$$\begin{aligned}
l &= \frac{-b \pm \sqrt{b^2 - 4ac}}{2a} \\
&= \frac{-(-15) \pm \sqrt{(-15)^2 - 4(1)(-225)}}{2(1)} \\
&= \frac{15 \pm \sqrt{1125}}{2} \approx \frac{15 \pm 33.541}{2}
\end{aligned}$$

The only positive solution is $l = 24.3$ ft.

44. If $AE = 1$, then $AD = BC = 1$ and $BE = x - 1$.

$$\frac{AB}{AD} = \frac{BC}{BE}$$
$$\frac{x}{1} = \frac{1}{x-1}$$
$$(x-1)\cdot\frac{x}{1} = (x-1)\cdot\frac{1}{x-1}$$
$$x^2 - x = 1$$
$$x^2 - x - 1 = 0$$

$a = 1, b = -1, c = -1$

$$x = \frac{-b \pm \sqrt{b^2 - 4ac}}{2a}$$
$$= \frac{-(-1) \pm \sqrt{(-1)^2 - 4(1)(-1)}}{2(1)}$$
$$= \frac{1 \pm \sqrt{5}}{2} \approx \frac{1 \pm 2.236}{2}$$

The only positive solution is $x = 1.618$.

The ratio is about $\frac{1.618}{1}$, or 1.618 to 1.

45.
$$V = \pi r^2 h$$
$$47.75 = \pi r^2 (5.25)$$
$$\frac{47.75}{5.25\pi} = r^2$$
$$\pm\sqrt{\frac{47.75}{5.25\pi}} = r$$
$$\pm 1.70 \approx r$$

The radius is about 1.70 in.

46. Let $x =$ the length of a side of the city.

$$\boxed{\text{Area}} = \boxed{\text{Perimeter}} + 124$$
$$x^2 = 4x + 124$$
$$x^2 - 4x - 124 = 0$$

$a = 1, b = -4, c = -124$

$$x = \frac{-b \pm \sqrt{b^2 - 4ac}}{2a}$$
$$= \frac{-(-4) \pm \sqrt{(-4)^2 - 4(1)(-124)}}{2(1)}$$
$$= \frac{4 \pm \sqrt{512}}{2} \approx 13.3 \text{ or } -9.3$$

The dimensions were 13.3 mi by 13.3 mi.

47. Let $x =$ the length of the diagonal.

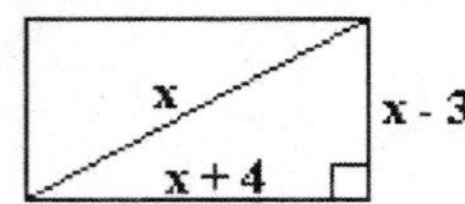

Using the Pythagorean Theorem:

$$(x+4)^2 + (x-3)^2 = x^2$$
$$x^2 + 8x + 16 + x^2 - 6x + 9 = x^2$$
$$x^2 + 2x + 25 = 0$$

$a = 1, b = 2, c = 25$

$$x = \frac{-b \pm \sqrt{b^2 - 4ac}}{2a}$$
$$= \frac{-2 \pm \sqrt{2^2 - 4(1)(25)}}{2(1)} = \frac{-2 \pm \sqrt{-96}}{2}$$

This does not equal a real number, so it is not possible.

48. **Answers may vary.**

49. $\frac{2}{x} - \frac{1}{x-3} = \frac{2(x-3)}{x(x-3)} - \frac{1(x)}{(x-3)(x)} = \frac{2x-6}{x(x-3)} - \frac{x}{x(x-3)} = \frac{x-6}{x(x-3)}$

50. $\frac{1}{x} \cdot \frac{x^2-5x}{x-3} = \frac{1}{x} \cdot \frac{x(x-5)}{x-3} = \frac{x-5}{x-3}$

51. $\frac{x+3}{x^2-x-6} \div \frac{x^2+3x}{x^2-9} = \frac{x+3}{x^2-x-6} \cdot \frac{x^2-9}{x^2+3x} = \frac{x+3}{(x-3)(x+2)} \cdot \frac{(x+3)(x-3)}{x(x+3)} = \frac{x+3}{x(x+2)}$

52. $\frac{\frac{1}{x}-\frac{1}{2}}{x-2} = \frac{(\frac{1}{x}-\frac{1}{2})2x}{(x-2)2x} = \frac{2-x}{2x(x-2)} = -\frac{1}{2x}$

53. $\frac{\frac{1}{x}+\frac{1}{y}}{\frac{1}{x}-\frac{1}{y}} = \frac{xy\left(\frac{1}{x}+\frac{1}{y}\right)}{xy\left(\frac{1}{x}-\frac{1}{y}\right)} = \frac{xy(\frac{1}{x})+xy\left(\frac{1}{y}\right)}{xy(\frac{1}{x})-xy\left(\frac{1}{y}\right)} = \frac{y+x}{y-x}$

54.
$$\begin{aligned}\frac{x}{x+1} + \frac{x+1}{x} \cdot \frac{x^2-x}{3} = \frac{x}{x+1} + \frac{x+1}{x} \cdot \frac{x(x-1)}{3} &= \frac{x}{x+1} + \frac{(x+1)(x-1)}{3} \\ &= \frac{x(3)}{(x+1)(3)} + \frac{(x+1)(x-1)(x+1)}{3(x+1)} \\ &= \frac{3x}{3(x+1)} + \frac{x^3+x^2-x-1}{3(x+1)} \\ &= \frac{x^3+x^2+2x-1}{3(x+1)}\end{aligned}$$

Exercises 1.5 (page 138)

1. imaginary

2. real, imaginary

3. imaginary

4. real

5. $2-5i$

6. $\sqrt{a^2+b^2}$

7. real

8. real

9. $\sqrt{-144} = \sqrt{-1}\sqrt{144} = 12i$

10. $-\sqrt{-225} = -\sqrt{-1}\sqrt{225} = -15i$

11. $-2\sqrt{-24} = -2\sqrt{-1}\sqrt{24} = -2i \cdot 2\sqrt{6} = -4i\sqrt{6}$

12. $7\sqrt{-48} = 7\sqrt{-1}\sqrt{48} = 7i \cdot 4\sqrt{3} = 28i\sqrt{3}$

13. $\sqrt{-\frac{50}{9}} = \sqrt{-1} \cdot \frac{\sqrt{50}}{\sqrt{9}} = i \cdot \frac{5\sqrt{2}}{3} = \frac{5}{3}i\sqrt{2}$

14. $-\sqrt{-\frac{72}{25}} = -\sqrt{-1} \cdot \frac{\sqrt{72}}{\sqrt{25}} = -i \cdot \frac{6\sqrt{2}}{5} = -\frac{6}{5}i\sqrt{2}$

15. $-7\sqrt{-\frac{3}{8}} = -7\sqrt{-1} \cdot \frac{\sqrt{3}}{\sqrt{8}} = -7i \cdot \frac{\sqrt{3}}{\sqrt{8}} \cdot \frac{\sqrt{2}}{\sqrt{2}} = -7i \cdot \frac{\sqrt{6}}{\sqrt{16}} = -\frac{7}{4}i\sqrt{6}$

16. $5\sqrt{-\frac{5}{27}} = 5\sqrt{-1}\cdot\frac{\sqrt{5}}{\sqrt{27}} = 5i\cdot\frac{\sqrt{5}}{\sqrt{27}}\cdot\frac{\sqrt{3}}{\sqrt{3}} = 5i\cdot\frac{\sqrt{15}}{\sqrt{81}} = \frac{5}{9}i\sqrt{15}$

17. Equate real parts: $\boxed{x = 3}$
Equate imaginary parts: $x + y = 8$
$3 + y = 8$
$\boxed{y = 5}$

18. Equate imaginary parts: $5 = -y$
$\boxed{-5 = y}$
Equate real parts: $x = y$
$\boxed{x = -5}$

19. Equate real parts: $3x = 2$
$\boxed{x = \frac{2}{3}}$
Equate imaginary parts: $-2y = x + y$
$-3y = x$
$y = -\frac{1}{3}x$
$y = -\frac{1}{3}\cdot\frac{2}{3}$
$\boxed{y = -\frac{2}{9}}$

20. Equate real parts: $\boxed{x = 2}$ Equate imaginary parts: $x + y = -1$
$2 + y = -1$
$\boxed{y = -3}$

21. $(2 - 7i) + (3 + i) = 2 - 7i + 3 + i$
$= 5 - 6i$

22. $(-7 + 2i) + (2 - 8i) = -7 + 2i + 2 - 8i$
$= -5 - 6i$

23. $(5 - 6i) - (7 + 4i) = 5 - 6i - 7 - 4i$
$= -2 - 10i$

24. $(11 + 2i) - (13 - 5i) = 11 + 2i - 13 + 5i$
$= -2 + 7i$

25. $(14i + 2) + \left(2 - \sqrt{-16}\right) = (14i + 2) + (2 - 4i) = 14i + 2 + 2 - 4i = 4 + 10i$

26. $\left(5 + \sqrt{-64}\right) - (23i - 32) = (5 + 8i) - (23i - 32) = 5 + 8i - 23i + 32 = 37 - 15i$

27. $\left(3 + \sqrt{-4}\right) - \left(2 + \sqrt{-9}\right) = (3 + 2i) - (2 + 3i) = 3 + 2i - 2 - 3i = 1 - i$

28. $\left(7 - \sqrt{-25}\right) + \left(-8 + \sqrt{-1}\right) = (7 - 5i) + (-8 + i) = 7 - 5i - 8 + i = -1 - 4i$

29. $-5(3 + 5i) = -15 - 25i$

30. $5(2 - i) = 10 - 5i$

31. $7i(4 - 8i) = 28i - 56i^2 = 28i - 56(-1) = 28i + 56 = 56 + 28i$

32. $-2i(3 - 7i) = -6i + 14i^2 = -6i + 14(-1) = -6i - 14 = -14 - 6i$

33. $(2 + 3i)(3 + 5i) = 6 + 19i + 15(-1) = 6 + 19i - 15 = -9 + 19i$

34. $(5 - 7i)(2 + i) = 10 - 9i - 7i^2 = 10 - 9i - 7(-1) = 10 - 9i + 7 = 17 - 9i$

35. $(2+3i)^2 = (2+3i)(2+3i) = 4+12i+9i^2 = 4+12i+9(-1) = 4+12i-9 = -5+12i$

36. $(3-4i)^2 = (3-4i)(3-4i) = 9-24i+16i^2 = 9-24i+16(-1) = 9-24i-16 = -7-24i$

37. $\left(11+\sqrt{-25}\right)\left(2-\sqrt{-36}\right) = (11+5i)(2-6i) = 22-56i-30i^2 = 22-56i-30(-1)$
$= 22-56i+30 = 52-56i$

38. $\left(6+\sqrt{-49}\right)\left(6-\sqrt{-49}\right) = (6+7i)(6-7i) = 36-49i^2 = 36-49(-1) = 36+49 = 85+0i$

39. $\left(\sqrt{-16}+3\right)\left(2+\sqrt{-9}\right) = (4i+3)(2+3i) = 6+17i+12i^2 = 6+17i+12(-1)$
$= 6+17i-12 = -6+17i$

40. $\left(12-\sqrt{-4}\right)\left(-7+\sqrt{-25}\right) = (12-2i)(-7+5i) = -84+74i-10i^2 = -84+74i-10(-1)$
$= -84+74i+10$
$= -74+74i$

41. $\dfrac{1}{-i} = \dfrac{1}{-i}\cdot\dfrac{i}{i} = \dfrac{i}{-i^2} = \dfrac{i}{1} = 0+i$

42. $\dfrac{3}{i} = \dfrac{3}{i}\cdot\dfrac{i}{i} = \dfrac{3i}{i^2} = \dfrac{3i}{-1} = 0-3i$

43. $\dfrac{-4}{3i} = \dfrac{-4}{3i}\cdot\dfrac{i}{i} = \dfrac{-4i}{3i^2} = \dfrac{-4i}{-3} = 0+\dfrac{4}{3}i$

44. $\dfrac{10}{7i} = \dfrac{10}{7i}\cdot\dfrac{i}{i} = \dfrac{10i}{7i^2} = \dfrac{10i}{-7} = 0-\dfrac{10}{7}i$

45. $\dfrac{1}{2+i} = \dfrac{1(2-i)}{(2+i)(2-i)} = \dfrac{2-i}{2^2-i^2} = \dfrac{2-i}{4-(-1)} = \dfrac{2-i}{5} = \dfrac{2}{5}-\dfrac{1}{5}i$

46. $\dfrac{-2}{3-i} = \dfrac{-2(3+i)}{(3-i)(3+i)} = \dfrac{-2(3+i)}{3^2-i^2} = \dfrac{-2(3+i)}{9-(-1)} = \dfrac{-2(3+i)}{10} = \dfrac{-(3+i)}{5} = -\dfrac{3}{5}-\dfrac{1}{5}i$

47. $\dfrac{2i}{7+i} = \dfrac{2i(7-i)}{(7+i)(7-i)} = \dfrac{14i-2i^2}{7^2-i^2} = \dfrac{14i-2(-1)}{49-(-1)} = \dfrac{14i+2}{50} = \dfrac{7i+1}{25} = \dfrac{1}{25}+\dfrac{7}{25}i$

48. $\dfrac{-3i}{2+5i} = \dfrac{-3i(2-5i)}{(2+5i)(2-5i)} = \dfrac{-6i+15i^2}{2^2-(5i)^2} = \dfrac{-6i-15}{4-25i^2} = \dfrac{-6i-15}{29} = -\dfrac{15}{29}-\dfrac{6}{29}i$

49. $\dfrac{2+i}{3-i} = \dfrac{(2+i)(3+i)}{(3-i)(3+i)} = \dfrac{6+5i+i^2}{9-i^2} = \dfrac{5+5i}{10} = \dfrac{5}{10}+\dfrac{5}{10}i = \dfrac{1}{2}+\dfrac{1}{2}i$

50. $\dfrac{3-i}{1+i} = \dfrac{(3-i)(1-i)}{(1+i)(1-i)} = \dfrac{3-4i+i^2}{1-i^2} = \dfrac{2-4i}{2} = \dfrac{2}{2}-\dfrac{4}{2}i = 1-2i$

51. $\dfrac{4-5i}{2+3i} = \dfrac{(4-5i)(2-3i)}{(2+3i)(2-3i)} = \dfrac{8-22i+15i^2}{4-9i^2} = \dfrac{-7-22i}{13} = -\dfrac{7}{13}-\dfrac{22}{13}i$

52. $\dfrac{34+2i}{2-4i} = \dfrac{(34+2i)(2+4i)}{(2-4i)(2+4i)} = \dfrac{68+140i+8i^2}{4-16i^2} = \dfrac{60+140i}{20} = \dfrac{60}{20} + \dfrac{140}{20}i = 3+7i$

53. $\dfrac{5-\sqrt{-16}}{-8+\sqrt{-4}} = \dfrac{5-4i}{-8+2i} = \dfrac{(5-4i)(-8-2i)}{(-8+2i)(-8-2i)} = \dfrac{-40+22i+8i^2}{64-4i^2} = \dfrac{-48+22i}{68} = -\dfrac{48}{68} + \dfrac{22}{68}i$

$= -\dfrac{12}{17} + \dfrac{11}{34}i$

54. $\dfrac{3-\sqrt{-9}}{2-\sqrt{-1}} = \dfrac{3-3i}{2-i} = \dfrac{(3-3i)(2+i)}{(2-i)(2+i)} = \dfrac{6-3i-3i^2}{4-i^2} = \dfrac{9-3i}{5} = \dfrac{9}{5} - \dfrac{3}{5}i$

55. $\dfrac{2+i\sqrt{3}}{3+i} = \dfrac{\left(2+i\sqrt{3}\right)(3-i)}{(3+i)(3-i)} = \dfrac{6-2i+3i\sqrt{3}-i^2\sqrt{3}}{9-i^2} = \dfrac{6+\sqrt{3}+\left(3\sqrt{3}-2\right)i}{10}$

$= \dfrac{6+\sqrt{3}}{10} + \dfrac{3\sqrt{3}-2}{10}i$

56. $\dfrac{3+i}{4-i\sqrt{2}} = \dfrac{(3+i)\left(4+i\sqrt{2}\right)}{\left(4-i\sqrt{2}\right)\left(4+i\sqrt{2}\right)} = \dfrac{12+3i\sqrt{2}+4i+i^2\sqrt{2}}{16-2i^2} = \dfrac{12-\sqrt{2}+\left(3\sqrt{2}+4\right)i}{18}$

$= \dfrac{12-\sqrt{2}}{18} + \dfrac{4+3\sqrt{2}}{18}i$

57. $i^9 = i^8 i = \left(i^4\right)^2 i = 1^2 i = i$

58. $i^{26} = i^{24}i^2 = \left(i^4\right)^6 i^2 = 1^6 i^2 = 1(-1) = -1$

59. $i^{38} = i^{36}i^2 = \left(i^4\right)^9 i^2 = 1^9 i^2 = i^2 = -1$

60. $i^{99} = i^{96}i^3 = \left(i^4\right)^{24} i^3 = 1^{24} i^3 = i^3 = -i$

61. $i^{87} = i^{84}i^3 = \left(i^4\right)^{21} i^3 = 1^{21} i^3 = i^3 = -i$

62. $i^{44} = \left(i^4\right)^{11} = 1^{11} = 1$

63. $i^{100} = \left(i^4\right)^{25} = 1^{25} = 1$

64. $i^{201} = i^{200}i = \left(i^4\right)^{50} i = 1^{50} i = i$

65. $i^{-6} = \dfrac{1}{i^6} = \dfrac{1 \cdot i^2}{i^6 \cdot i^2} = \dfrac{i^2}{i^8} = \dfrac{i^2}{1} = i^2 = -1$

66. $i^0 = 1$

67. $i^{-10} = \dfrac{1}{i^{10}} = \dfrac{1 \cdot i^2}{i^{10} \cdot i^2} = \dfrac{i^2}{i^{12}} = \dfrac{i^2}{1} = i^2$

$= -1$

68. $i^{-31} = \dfrac{1}{i^{31}} = \dfrac{1 \cdot i}{i^{31} \cdot i} = \dfrac{i}{i^{32}} = \dfrac{i}{1} = i$

69. $\dfrac{1}{i^3} = \dfrac{1 \cdot i}{i^3 \cdot i} = \dfrac{i}{i^4} = \dfrac{i}{1} = i = i$

70. $\dfrac{3}{i^5} = \dfrac{3 \cdot i^3}{i^5 \cdot i^3} = \dfrac{3i^3}{i^8} = \dfrac{3i^3}{1} = 3i^3 = -3i$

71. $\dfrac{-4}{i^{10}} = \dfrac{-4 \cdot i^2}{i^{10} \cdot i^2} = \dfrac{-4i^2}{i^{12}} = \dfrac{-4i^2}{1} = -4(-1)$

$= 4$

72. $\dfrac{-10}{i^{24}} = \dfrac{-10}{1} = -10$

73. $|3+4i| = \sqrt{3^2+4^2} = \sqrt{9+16}$
$= \sqrt{25} = 5$

74. $|5+12i| = \sqrt{5^2+12^2} = \sqrt{25+144}$
$= \sqrt{169} = 13$

75. $|2+3i| = \sqrt{2^2+3^2} = \sqrt{4+9} = \sqrt{13}$

76. $|5-i| = \sqrt{5^2+(-1)^2} = \sqrt{25+1} = \sqrt{26}$

77. $\left|-7+\sqrt{-49}\right| = |-7+7i| = \sqrt{(-7)^2+7^2} = \sqrt{49+49} = \sqrt{98} = 7\sqrt{2}$

78. $\left|-2-\sqrt{-16}\right| = |-2-4i| = \sqrt{(-2)^2+(-4)^2} = \sqrt{4+16} = \sqrt{20} = 2\sqrt{5}$

79. $\left|\frac{1}{2}+\frac{1}{2}i\right| = \sqrt{\left(\frac{1}{2}\right)^2+\left(\frac{1}{2}\right)^2} = \sqrt{\frac{1}{4}+\frac{1}{4}} = \sqrt{\frac{1}{2}} = \frac{\sqrt{2}}{2}$

80. $\left|\frac{1}{2}-\frac{1}{4}i\right| = \sqrt{\left(\frac{1}{2}\right)^2+\left(-\frac{1}{4}\right)^2} = \sqrt{\frac{1}{4}+\frac{1}{16}} = \sqrt{\frac{5}{16}} = \frac{\sqrt{5}}{4}$

81. $|-6i| = |0-6i| = \sqrt{0^2+(-6)^2} = \sqrt{0+36} = \sqrt{36} = 6$

82. $|5i| = |0+5i| = \sqrt{0^2+5^2} = \sqrt{0+25} = \sqrt{25} = 5$

83. $\left|\frac{2}{1+i}\right| = \left|\frac{2(1-i)}{(1+i)(1-i)}\right| = \left|\frac{2(1-i)}{1-i^2}\right| = \left|\frac{2(1-i)}{2}\right| = |1-i| = \sqrt{1^2+(-1)^2} = \sqrt{2}$

84. $\left|\frac{3}{3+i}\right| = \left|\frac{3(3-i)}{(3+i)(3-i)}\right| = \left|\frac{3(3-i)}{9-i^2}\right| = \left|\frac{3(3-i)}{10}\right| = \left|\frac{9-3i}{10}\right| = \sqrt{\left(\frac{9}{10}\right)^2+\left(-\frac{3}{10}\right)^2}$
$= \sqrt{\frac{81}{100}+\frac{9}{100}}$
$= \sqrt{\frac{90}{100}} = \sqrt{\frac{9}{10}} = \frac{3\sqrt{10}}{10}$

85. $\left|\frac{-3i}{2+i}\right| = \left|\frac{-3i(2-i)}{(2+i)(2-i)}\right| = \left|\frac{-3i(2-i)}{4-i^2}\right| = \left|\frac{-3i(2-i)}{5}\right| = \left|\frac{-6i+3i^2}{5}\right|$
$= \left|-\frac{3}{5}-\frac{6}{5}i\right|$
$= \sqrt{\left(-\frac{3}{5}\right)^2+\left(-\frac{6}{5}\right)^2}$
$= \sqrt{\frac{9}{25}+\frac{36}{25}}$
$= \sqrt{\frac{45}{25}} = \frac{\sqrt{45}}{5} = \frac{3\sqrt{5}}{5}$

86. $$\left|\frac{5i}{i-2}\right| = \left|\frac{5i}{-2+i}\right| = \left|\frac{5i(-2-i)}{(-2+i)(-2-i)}\right|\left|\frac{5i(-2-i)}{4-i^2}\right| = \left|\frac{5i(-2-i)}{5}\right| = \left|\frac{-10i-5i^2}{5}\right|$$
$$= |1-2i|$$
$$= \sqrt{1^2+(-2)^2}$$
$$= \sqrt{1+4} = \sqrt{5}$$

87. $$\left|\frac{i+2}{i-2}\right| = \left|\frac{(i+2)(i+2)}{(i-2)(i+2)}\right| = \left|\frac{i^2+4i+4}{i^2-4}\right| = \left|\frac{3+4i}{5}\right| = \left|\frac{3}{5}+\frac{4}{5}i\right| = \sqrt{\left(\frac{3}{5}\right)^2+\left(\frac{4}{5}\right)^2}$$
$$= \sqrt{\frac{9}{25}+\frac{16}{25}}$$
$$= \sqrt{\frac{25}{25}} = \sqrt{1} = 1$$

88. $$\left|\frac{2+i}{2-i}\right| = \left|\frac{(2+i)(2+i)}{(2-i)(2+i)}\right| = \left|\frac{4+4i+i^2}{4^2-i^2}\right| = \left|\frac{3+4i}{5}\right| = \left|\frac{3}{5}+\frac{4}{5}i\right| = \sqrt{\left(\frac{3}{5}\right)^2+\left(\frac{4}{5}\right)^2}$$
$$= \sqrt{\frac{9}{25}+\frac{16}{25}}$$
$$= \sqrt{\frac{25}{25}} = \sqrt{1} = 1$$

89. $x^2 = -169$

$x = \sqrt{-169}$ **or** $x = -\sqrt{-169}$

$x = 13i$ $\quad x = -13i$

90. $x^2 = -81$

$x = \sqrt{-81}$ **or** $x = -\sqrt{-81}$

$x = 9i$ $\quad x = -9i$

91. $y^2 + 54 = 0$

$y^2 = -54$

$y = \sqrt{-54}$ **or** $y = -\sqrt{-54}$

$y = i\sqrt{9}\sqrt{6}$ $\quad y = -i\sqrt{9}\sqrt{6}$

$y = 3i\sqrt{6}$ $\quad y = -3i\sqrt{6}$

92. $x^2 + 125 = 0$

$x^2 = -125$

$x = \sqrt{-125}$ **or** $x = -\sqrt{-125}$

$x = i\sqrt{25}\sqrt{5}$ $\quad x = -i\sqrt{25}\sqrt{5}$

$x = 5i\sqrt{5}$ $\quad x = -5i\sqrt{5}$

93. $2x^2 = -90$

$x^2 = -45$

$x = \sqrt{-45}$ **or** $x = -\sqrt{-45}$

$x = i\sqrt{9}\sqrt{5}$ $\quad x = -i\sqrt{9}\sqrt{5}$

$x = 3i\sqrt{5}$ $\quad x = -3i\sqrt{5}$

94. $5x^2 = -400$

$x^2 = -80$

$x = \sqrt{-80}$ **or** $x = -\sqrt{-80}$

$x = i\sqrt{16}\sqrt{5}$ $\quad x = -i\sqrt{16}\sqrt{5}$

$x = 4i\sqrt{5}$ $\quad x = -4i\sqrt{5}$

95.
$$9x^2 = -7$$
$$x^2 = -\frac{7}{9}$$
$$x = \sqrt{-\frac{7}{9}} \quad \textbf{or} \quad x = -\sqrt{-\frac{7}{9}}$$
$$x = i\frac{\sqrt{7}}{\sqrt{9}} \qquad x = -i\frac{\sqrt{7}}{\sqrt{9}}$$
$$x = \frac{\sqrt{7}}{3}i \qquad x = -\frac{\sqrt{7}}{3}i$$

96.
$$25x^2 = -11$$
$$x^2 = -\frac{11}{25}$$
$$x = \sqrt{-\frac{11}{25}} \quad \textbf{or} \quad x = -\sqrt{-\frac{11}{25}}$$
$$x = i\frac{\sqrt{11}}{\sqrt{25}} \qquad x = -i\frac{\sqrt{11}}{\sqrt{25}}$$
$$x = \frac{\sqrt{11}}{5}i \qquad x = -\frac{\sqrt{11}}{5}i$$

97.
$$2x^2 + 15 = 0$$
$$2x^2 = -15$$
$$x^2 = -\frac{15}{2}$$
$$x = \sqrt{-\frac{15}{2}} \quad \textbf{or} \quad x = -\sqrt{-\frac{15}{2}}$$
$$x = i\frac{\sqrt{15}}{\sqrt{2}} \cdot \frac{\sqrt{2}}{\sqrt{2}} \qquad x = -i\frac{\sqrt{15}}{\sqrt{2}} \cdot \frac{\sqrt{2}}{\sqrt{2}}$$
$$x = \frac{\sqrt{30}}{2}i \qquad x = -\frac{\sqrt{30}}{2}i$$

98.
$$-5x^2 = 11$$
$$x^2 = -\frac{11}{5}$$
$$x = \sqrt{-\frac{11}{5}} \quad \textbf{or} \quad x = -\sqrt{-\frac{11}{2}}$$
$$x = i\frac{\sqrt{11}}{\sqrt{5}} \cdot \frac{\sqrt{5}}{\sqrt{5}} \qquad x = -i\frac{\sqrt{11}}{\sqrt{5}} \cdot \frac{\sqrt{5}}{\sqrt{5}}$$
$$x = \frac{\sqrt{55}}{5}i \qquad x = -\frac{\sqrt{55}}{5}i$$

99.
$$(x+1)^2 + 12 = 0$$
$$(x+1)^2 = -12$$
$$x + 1 = \sqrt{-12} \quad \textbf{or} \quad x + 1 = -\sqrt{-12}$$
$$x = -1 + i\sqrt{4}\sqrt{3} \qquad x = -1 - i\sqrt{4}\sqrt{3}$$
$$x = -1 + 2i\sqrt{3} \qquad x = -1 - 2i\sqrt{3}$$

100.
$$(y+2)^2 + 120 = 0$$
$$(y+2)^2 = -120$$
$$y + 2 = \sqrt{-120} \quad \textbf{or} \quad y + 2 = -\sqrt{-120}$$
$$y = -2 + i\sqrt{4}\sqrt{30} \qquad y = -2 - i\sqrt{4}\sqrt{30}$$
$$y = -2 + 2i\sqrt{30} \qquad y = -2 - 2i\sqrt{30}$$

101.
$$(5x+1)^2 = -8$$
$$5x + 1 = \sqrt{-8} \quad \textbf{or} \quad 5x + 1 = -\sqrt{-8}$$
$$5x = -1 + i\sqrt{4}\sqrt{2} \qquad 5x = -1 - i\sqrt{4}\sqrt{2}$$
$$x = -\frac{1}{5} + \frac{2i\sqrt{2}}{5} \qquad x = -\frac{1}{5} - \frac{2i\sqrt{2}}{5}$$

102.

$$(7y+2)^2+48=0$$
$$(7y+2)^2=-48$$

$$7y+2=\sqrt{-48} \quad \textbf{or} \quad 7y+2=-\sqrt{-48}$$
$$7y=-2+i\sqrt{16}\sqrt{3} \qquad 7y=-2-i\sqrt{16}\sqrt{3}$$
$$y=-\frac{2}{7}+\frac{4i\sqrt{3}}{7} \qquad y=-\frac{2}{7}-\frac{4i\sqrt{3}}{7}$$

103.

$$x^2-10x+37=0$$
$$x^2-10x=-37$$
$$x^2-10x+25=-37+25$$
$$(x-5)^2=-12$$

$$x-5=\sqrt{-12} \quad \textbf{or} \quad x-5=-\sqrt{-12}$$
$$x=5+i\sqrt{4}\sqrt{3} \qquad x=5-i\sqrt{4}\sqrt{3}$$
$$x=5+2i\sqrt{3} \qquad x=5-2i\sqrt{3}$$

104.

$$a^2+16a+82=0$$
$$a^2+16a=-82$$
$$a^2+16a+64=-82+64$$
$$(a+8)^2=-18$$

$$a+8=\sqrt{-18} \quad \textbf{or} \quad a+8=-\sqrt{-18}$$
$$a=-8+i\sqrt{9}\sqrt{2} \qquad a=-8-i\sqrt{9}\sqrt{2}$$
$$a=-8+3i\sqrt{2} \qquad a=-8-3i\sqrt{2}$$

105.

$$y^2+11y=-49$$
$$y^2+11y+\frac{121}{4}=-\frac{196}{4}+\frac{121}{4}$$
$$\left(y+\frac{11}{2}\right)^2=-\frac{75}{4}$$

$$y+\frac{11}{2}=\sqrt{-\frac{75}{4}} \quad \textbf{or} \quad y+\frac{11}{2}=-\sqrt{-\frac{75}{4}}$$
$$y=-\frac{11}{2}+i\frac{\sqrt{75}}{\sqrt{4}} \qquad y=-\frac{11}{2}-i\frac{\sqrt{75}}{\sqrt{4}}$$
$$y=-\frac{11}{2}+\frac{5\sqrt{3}}{2}i \qquad y=-\frac{11}{2}-\frac{5\sqrt{3}}{2}i$$

106.

$$x^2 - 5x = -22$$
$$x^2 - 5x + \frac{25}{4} = -\frac{88}{4} + \frac{25}{4}$$
$$\left(x - \frac{5}{2}\right)^2 = -\frac{63}{4}$$

$$x - \frac{5}{2} = \sqrt{-\frac{63}{4}} \quad \textbf{or} \quad x - \frac{5}{2} = -\sqrt{-\frac{63}{4}}$$
$$x = \frac{5}{2} + i\frac{\sqrt{63}}{\sqrt{4}} \qquad x = \frac{5}{2} - i\frac{\sqrt{63}}{\sqrt{4}}$$
$$x = \frac{5}{2} + \frac{3\sqrt{7}}{2}i \qquad x = \frac{5}{2} - \frac{3\sqrt{7}}{2}i$$

107.

$$9x^2 = 18x - 14$$
$$9x^2 - 18x = -14$$
$$x^2 - 2x = -\frac{14}{9}$$
$$x^2 - 2x + 1 = -\frac{14}{9} + \frac{9}{9}$$
$$(x-1)^2 = -\frac{5}{9}$$

$$x - 1 = \sqrt{-\frac{5}{9}} \quad \textbf{or} \quad x - 1 = -\sqrt{-\frac{5}{9}}$$
$$x = 1 + i\frac{\sqrt{5}}{\sqrt{9}} \qquad x = 1 - i\frac{\sqrt{5}}{\sqrt{9}}$$
$$x = 1 + \frac{\sqrt{5}}{3}i \qquad x = 1 - \frac{\sqrt{5}}{3}i$$

108.

$$7z^2 = -14z - 13$$
$$7z^2 + 14z = -13$$
$$z^2 + 2z = -\frac{13}{7}$$
$$z^2 + 2z + 1 = -\frac{13}{7} + \frac{7}{7}$$
$$(z+1)^2 = -\frac{6}{7}$$

$$z + 1 = \sqrt{-\frac{6}{7}} \quad \textbf{or} \quad z + 1 = -\sqrt{-\frac{6}{7}}$$
$$z = -1 + i\frac{\sqrt{6}}{\sqrt{7}} \qquad z = -1 - i\frac{\sqrt{6}}{\sqrt{7}}$$
$$z = -1 + \frac{\sqrt{42}}{7}i \qquad z = -1 - \frac{\sqrt{42}}{7}i$$

109.

$$\begin{aligned} 2x^2 &= 14x - 30 \\ 2x^2 - 14x &= -30 \\ x^2 - 7x &= -15 \\ x^2 - 7x + \frac{49}{4} &= -\frac{60}{4} + \frac{49}{4} \\ \left(x - \frac{7}{2}\right)^2 &= -\frac{11}{4} \end{aligned}$$

$$x - \frac{7}{2} = \sqrt{-\frac{11}{4}} \quad \textbf{or} \quad x - \frac{7}{2} = -\sqrt{-\frac{11}{4}}$$

$$x = \frac{7}{2} + i\frac{\sqrt{11}}{\sqrt{4}} \qquad x = \frac{7}{2} - i\frac{\sqrt{11}}{\sqrt{4}}$$

$$x = \frac{7}{2} + \frac{\sqrt{11}}{2}i \qquad x = \frac{7}{2} - \frac{\sqrt{11}}{2}i$$

110.

$$\begin{aligned} 5x^2 + x &= -5 \\ x^2 + \frac{1}{5}x &= -1 \\ x^2 + \frac{1}{5}x + \frac{1}{100} &= -\frac{100}{100} + \frac{1}{100} \\ \left(x + \frac{1}{10}\right)^2 &= -\frac{99}{100} \end{aligned}$$

$$x + \frac{1}{10} = \sqrt{-\frac{99}{100}} \quad \textbf{or} \quad x + \frac{1}{10} = -\sqrt{-\frac{99}{100}}$$

$$x = -\frac{1}{10} + i\frac{\sqrt{99}}{\sqrt{100}} \qquad x = -\frac{1}{10} - i\frac{\sqrt{99}}{\sqrt{100}}$$

$$x = -\frac{1}{10} + \frac{3\sqrt{11}}{10}i \qquad x = -\frac{1}{10} - \frac{3\sqrt{11}}{10}i$$

111. $x^2 + 2x + 2 = 0 \Rightarrow a = 1, b = 2, c = 2$

$$x = \frac{-b \pm \sqrt{b^2 - 4ac}}{2a} = \frac{-2 \pm \sqrt{2^2 - 4(1)(2)}}{2(1)} = \frac{-2 \pm \sqrt{4 - 8}}{2} = \frac{-2 \pm \sqrt{-4}}{2} = \frac{-2 \pm 2i}{2} = -1 \pm i$$

112. $a^2 + 4a + 8 = 0 \Rightarrow a = 1, b = 4, c = 8$

$$a = \frac{-b \pm \sqrt{b^2 - 4ac}}{2a} = \frac{-4 \pm \sqrt{4^2 - 4(1)(8)}}{2(1)} = \frac{-4 \pm \sqrt{16 - 32}}{2} = \frac{-4 \pm \sqrt{-16}}{2} = \frac{-4 \pm 4i}{2} = -2 \pm 2i$$

113. $y^2 + 4y + 5 = 0 \Rightarrow a = 1, b = 4, c = 5$

$$y = \frac{-b \pm \sqrt{b^2 - 4ac}}{2a} = \frac{-4 \pm \sqrt{4^2 - 4(1)(5)}}{2(1)} = \frac{-4 \pm \sqrt{16 - 20}}{2} = \frac{-4 \pm \sqrt{-4}}{2} = \frac{-4 \pm 2i}{2} = -2 \pm i$$

114. $x^2 + 2x + 5 = 0 \Rightarrow a = 1, b = 2, c = 5$

$$x = \frac{-b \pm \sqrt{b^2 - 4ac}}{2a} = \frac{-2 \pm \sqrt{2^2 - 4(1)(5)}}{2(1)} = \frac{-2 \pm \sqrt{4 - 20}}{2} = \frac{-2 \pm \sqrt{-16}}{2} = \frac{-2 \pm 4i}{2} = -1 \pm 2i$$

115. $x^2 - 2x = -5 \Rightarrow x^2 - 2x + 5 = 0 \Rightarrow a = 1, b = -2, c = 5$

$$x = \frac{-b \pm \sqrt{b^2 - 4ac}}{2a} = \frac{-(-2) \pm \sqrt{(-2)^2 - 4(1)(5)}}{2(1)} = \frac{2 \pm \sqrt{4 - 20}}{2} = \frac{2 \pm \sqrt{-16}}{2} = \frac{2 \pm 4i}{2} = 1 \pm 2i$$

116. $z^2 - 3z = -8 \Rightarrow z^2 - 3z + 8 = 0 \Rightarrow a = 1, b = -3, c = 8$

$$z = \frac{-b \pm \sqrt{b^2 - 4ac}}{2a} = \frac{-(-3) \pm \sqrt{(-3)^2 - 4(1)(8)}}{2(1)} = \frac{3 \pm \sqrt{9 - 32}}{2} = \frac{3 \pm \sqrt{-23}}{2} = \frac{3}{2} \pm \frac{\sqrt{23}}{2}i$$

117. $x^2 - \frac{2}{3}x = -\frac{2}{9} \Rightarrow x^2 - \frac{2}{3}x + \frac{2}{9} = 0 \Rightarrow 9x^2 - 6x + 2 = 0 \Rightarrow a = 9, b = -6, c = 2$

$$x = \frac{-b \pm \sqrt{b^2 - 4ac}}{2a} = \frac{-(-6) \pm \sqrt{(-6)^2 - 4(9)(2)}}{2(9)} = \frac{6 \pm \sqrt{36 - 72}}{18} = \frac{6 \pm \sqrt{-36}}{18} = \frac{6 \pm 6i}{18} = \frac{1}{3} \pm \frac{1}{3}i$$

118. $x^2 + \frac{5}{4} = x \Rightarrow x^2 - x + \frac{5}{4} = 0 \Rightarrow 4x^2 - 4x + 5 = 0 \Rightarrow a = 4, b = -4, c = 5$

$$x = \frac{-b \pm \sqrt{b^2 - 4ac}}{2a} = \frac{-(-4) \pm \sqrt{(-4)^2 - 4(4)(5)}}{2(4)} = \frac{4 \pm \sqrt{16 - 80}}{8} = \frac{4 \pm \sqrt{-64}}{8} = \frac{4 \pm 8i}{8} = \frac{1}{2} \pm i$$

119. $x^2 + 4 = x^2 - (-4) = x^2 - (2i)^2 = (x + 2i)(x - 2i)$

120. $16a^2 + 9 = (4a)^2 - (-9) = (4a)^2 - (3i)^2 = (4a + 3i)(4a - 3i)$

121. $25p^2 + 36q^2 = (5p)^2 - (-36q^2) = (5p)^2 - (6qi)^2 = (5p + 6qi)(5p - 6qi)$

122. $100r^2 + 49s^2 = (10r)^2 - (-49s^2) = (10r)^2 - (7si)^2 = (10r + 7si)(10r - 7si)$

123. $2y^2 + 8z^2 = 2(y^2 + 4z^2) = 2[y^2 - (-4z^2)] = 2\left[y^2 - (2zi)^2\right] = 2(y + 2zi)(y - 2zi)$

124. $12b^2 + 75c^2 = 3(4b^2 + 25c^2) = 3\left[(2b)^2 - (-25c^2)\right] = 3\left[(2b)^2 - (5ci)^2\right] = 3(2b + 5ci)(2b - 5ci)$

125. $50m^2 + 2n^2 = 2(25m^2 + n^2) = 2\left[(5m)^2 - (-n^2)\right] = 2\left[(5m)^2 - (ni)^2\right] = 2(5m + ni)(5m - ni)$

126. $64a^4 + 4b^2 = 4(16a^4 + b^2) = 4\left[(4a^2)^2 - (-b^2)\right] = 4\left[(4a^2)^2 - (bi)^2\right] = 4(4a^2 + bi)(4a^2 - bi)$

127. $V = IR = (3 - 2i)(3 + 6i) = 9 + 18i - 6i - 12i^2 = 9 + 12i + 12 = 21 + 12i$

128. $R = \frac{V}{I} = \frac{21 + i}{2 - 3i} = \frac{(21 + i)(2 + 3i)}{(2 - 3i)(2 + 3i)} = \frac{42 + 63i + 2i + 3i^2}{4 - 9i^2} = \frac{39 + 65i}{13} = 3 + 5i$

129. $V = IZ = (0.5 + 2.0i)(0.4 - 3.0i) = 0.2 - 1.5i + 0.8i - 6i^2 = 0.2 - 0.7i + 6 = 6.2 - 0.7i$

130. **1.** $i^2 + i = -1 + i$
2. $(-1 + i)^2 + i = (-1 + i)(-1 + i) + i = 1 - i - i + i^2 + i = -i$
3. $(-i)^2 + i = i^2 + i = -1 + i$

131.
$$\begin{aligned}(a + bi) + (c + di) &= a + bi + c + di\\ &= a + c + bi + di\\ &= (a + c) + (b + d)i\end{aligned}$$
$$\begin{aligned}(c + di) + (a + bi) &= c + di + a + bi\\ &= c + a + di + bi\\ &= (c + a) + (d + b)i\\ &= (a + c) + (b + d)i\end{aligned}$$

132.
$$\begin{aligned}(a + bi)(c + di) &= ac + adi + bci + bdi^2\\ &= ac + (ad + bc)i - bd\\ &= (ac - bd) + (ad + bc)i\end{aligned}$$
$$\begin{aligned}(c + di)(a + bi) &= ac + bci + adi + bdi^2\\ &= ac + (bc + ad)i - bd\\ &= (ac - bd) + (ad + bc)i\end{aligned}$$

133.
$$\begin{aligned}[(a + bi) + (c + di)] + (e + fi) &= a + bi + c + di + e + fi\\ &= a + c + e + bi + di + fi\\ &= (a + c + e) + (b + d + f)i\end{aligned}$$
$$\begin{aligned}(a + bi) + [(c + di) + (e + fi)] &= a + bi + c + di + e + fi\\ &= a + c + e + bi + di + fi\\ &= (a + c + e) + (b + d + f)i\end{aligned}$$

134.
$$\begin{aligned}a + bi &= \frac{1}{a - bi}\\ &= \frac{1(a + bi)}{(a - bi)(a + bi)}\\ &= \frac{a + bi}{a^2 - b^2 i^2}\\ &= \frac{a + bi}{a^2 + b^2}\\ &= \frac{a}{a^2 + b^2} + \frac{b}{a^2 + b^2}i\end{aligned}$$

Thus, a must equal $\frac{a}{a^2 + b^2}$ and b must equal $\frac{b}{a^2 + b^2}$.
If $a^2 + b^2 = 1$, then this will certainly be true.
Some solutions to $a^2 + b^2 = 1$ are below:
$\begin{cases} a = 1 \\ b = 0 \end{cases}$ $\begin{cases} a = -1 \\ b = 0 \end{cases}$ $\begin{cases} a = 0 \\ b = 1 \end{cases}$ $\begin{cases} a = 0 \\ b = -1 \end{cases}$
Some complex numbers with the described property are then:
$1 + 0i,\ -1 + 0i,\ 0 + i,\ 0 - i$

There are many other possible solutions.

135. Answers may vary.

136. Answers may vary.

137. $\sqrt{8x^3}\sqrt{4x} = \sqrt{32x^4} = \sqrt{16x^4}\sqrt{2} = 4x^2\sqrt{2}$

138. $\left(\sqrt{x}-5\right)^2 = \left(\sqrt{x}-5\right)\left(\sqrt{x}-5\right) = x - 10\sqrt{x} + 25$

139. $\left(\sqrt{x+1}-2\right)^2 = \left(\sqrt{x+1}-2\right)\left(\sqrt{x+1}-2\right) = x+1-4\sqrt{x+1}+4 = x-4\sqrt{x+1}+5$

140. $\left(-3\sqrt{2x+1}\right)^2 = (-3)^2\left(\sqrt{2x+1}\right)^2 = 9(2x+1) = 18x+9$

141. $\dfrac{4}{\sqrt{5}-1} = \dfrac{4}{\sqrt{5}-1}\cdot\dfrac{\sqrt{5}+1}{\sqrt{5}+1} = \dfrac{4\left(\sqrt{5}+1\right)}{\left(\sqrt{5}\right)^2-1^2} = \dfrac{4\left(\sqrt{5}+1\right)}{5-1} = \dfrac{4\left(\sqrt{5}+1\right)}{4} = \sqrt{5}+1$

142. $\dfrac{x-4}{\sqrt{x}+2} = \dfrac{x-4}{\sqrt{x}+2}\cdot\dfrac{\sqrt{x}-2}{\sqrt{x}-2} = \dfrac{(x-4)\left(\sqrt{x}-2\right)}{\left(\sqrt{x}\right)^2-(2)^2} = \dfrac{(x-4)\left(\sqrt{x}-2\right)}{x-4} = \sqrt{x}-2$

Exercises 1.6 (page 147)

1. equal

2. b^2

3. extraneous

4. radicands

5.
$$\begin{aligned} x^3+9x^2+20x &= 0 \\ x\left(x^2+9x+20\right) &= 0 \\ x(x+5)(x+4) &= 0 \end{aligned}$$
$x=0$ **or** $x+5=0$ **or** $x+4=0$
$x=0$ $\quad x=-5$ $\quad x=-4$

6.
$$\begin{aligned} x^3+4x^2-21x &= 0 \\ x\left(x^2+4x-21\right) &= 0 \\ x(x+7)(x-3) &= 0 \end{aligned}$$
$x=0$ **or** $x+7=0$ **or** $x-3=0$
$x=0$ $\quad x=-7$ $\quad x=3$

7.
$$\begin{aligned} 6a^3-5a^2-4a &= 0 \\ a\left(6a^2-5a-4\right) &= 0 \\ a(2a+1)(3a-4) &= 0 \end{aligned}$$
$a=0$ **or** $2a+1=0$ **or** $3a-4=0$
$a=0$ $\quad 2a=-1$ $\quad 3a=4$
$a=0$ $\quad a=-\frac{1}{2}$ $\quad a=\frac{4}{3}$

8.
$$\begin{aligned} 8b^3-10b^2+3b &= 0 \\ b\left(8b^2-10b+3\right) &= 0 \\ b(4b-3)(2b-1) &= 0 \end{aligned}$$
$b=0$ **or** $4b-3=0$ **or** $2b-1=0$
$b=0$ $\quad 4b=3$ $\quad 2b=1$
$b=0$ $\quad b=\frac{3}{4}$ $\quad b=\frac{1}{2}$

9.
$$\begin{aligned} y^4-26y^2+25 &= 0 \\ \left(y^2-25\right)\left(y^2-1\right) &= 0 \end{aligned}$$
$y^2-25=0$ **or** $y^2-1=0$
$y^2=25$ $\quad y^2=1$
$y=\pm 5$ $\quad y=\pm 1$

10.
$$\begin{aligned} y^4-13y^2+36 &= 0 \\ \left(y^2-4\right)\left(y^2-9\right) &= 0 \end{aligned}$$
$y^2-4=0$ **or** $y^2-9=0$
$y^2=4$ $\quad y^2=9$
$y=\pm 2$ $\quad y=\pm 3$

11.
$$\begin{aligned} x^4 - 37x^2 + 36 &= 0 \\ (x^2 - 36)(x^2 - 1) &= 0 \end{aligned}$$
$$\begin{array}{lcl} x^2 - 36 = 0 & \textbf{or} & x^2 - 1 = 0 \\ x^2 = 36 & & x^2 = 1 \\ x = \pm 6 & & x = \pm 1 \end{array}$$

12.
$$\begin{aligned} x^4 - 50x^2 + 49 &= 0 \\ (x^2 - 49)(x^2 - 1) &= 0 \end{aligned}$$
$$\begin{array}{lcl} x^2 - 49 = 0 & \textbf{or} & x^2 - 1 = 0 \\ x^2 = 49 & & x^2 = 1 \\ x = \pm 7 & & x = \pm 1 \end{array}$$

13.
$$\begin{aligned} 2y^4 - 46y^2 &= -180 \\ 2(y^4 - 23y^2 + 90) &= 0 \\ 2(y^2 - 18)(y^2 - 5) &= 0 \end{aligned}$$
$$\begin{array}{lcl} y^2 - 18 = 0 & \textbf{or} & y^2 - 5 = 0 \\ y^2 = 18 & & y^2 = 5 \\ y = \pm\sqrt{18} & & y = \pm\sqrt{5} \\ y = \pm 3\sqrt{2} & & y = \pm\sqrt{5} \end{array}$$

14.
$$\begin{aligned} 2x^4 - 102x^2 &= -196 \\ 2(x^4 - 51x^2 + 98) &= 0 \\ 2(x^2 - 49)(x^2 - 2) &= 0 \end{aligned}$$
$$\begin{array}{lcl} x^2 - 49 = 0 & \textbf{or} & x^2 - 2 = 0 \\ x^2 = 49 & & x^2 = 2 \\ x = \pm 7 & & x = \pm\sqrt{2} \end{array}$$

15.
$$\begin{aligned} z^{3/2} - z^{1/2} &= 0 \\ z^{1/2}(z^{2/2} - 1) &= 0 \\ z^{1/2}(z - 1) &= 0 \end{aligned}$$
$$\begin{array}{lcl} z^{1/2} = 0 & \textbf{or} & z - 1 = 0 \\ (z^{1/2})^2 = 0^2 & & z = 1 \\ z = 0 & & z = 1 \end{array}$$
Both answers check.

16.
$$\begin{aligned} r^{5/2} - r^{3/2} &= 0 \\ r^{3/2}(r^{2/2} - 1) &= 0 \\ r^{3/2}(r - 1) &= 0 \end{aligned}$$
$$\begin{array}{lcl} r^{3/2} = 0 & \textbf{or} & r - 1 = 0 \\ (r^{3/2})^2 = 0^2 & & r = 1 \\ r^3 = 0 & & r = 1 \\ r = 0 & & r = 1 \end{array}$$
Both answers check.

17.
$$\begin{aligned} 2m^{2/3} + 3m^{1/3} - 2 &= 0 \\ (2m^{1/3} - 1)(m^{1/3} + 2) &= 0 \end{aligned}$$
$$\begin{array}{lcl} 2m^{1/3} - 1 = 0 & \textbf{or} & m^{1/3} + 2 = 0 \\ m^{1/3} = \frac{1}{2} & & m^{1/3} = -2 \\ (m^{1/3})^3 = \left(\frac{1}{2}\right)^3 & & (m^{1/3})^3 = (-2)^3 \\ m = \frac{1}{8} & & m = -8 \end{array}$$
Both answers check.

18.
$$\begin{aligned} 6t^{2/5} + 11t^{1/5} + 3 &= 0 \\ (2t^{1/5} + 3)(3t^{1/5} + 1) &= 0 \end{aligned}$$
$$\begin{array}{lcl} 2t^{1/5} + 3 = 0 & \textbf{or} & 3t^{1/5} + 1 = 0 \\ t^{1/5} = -\frac{3}{2} & & t^{1/5} = -\frac{1}{3} \\ (t^{1/5})^5 = \left(-\frac{3}{2}\right)^5 & & (t^{1/5})^5 = \left(-\frac{1}{3}\right)^5 \\ t = -\frac{243}{32} & & t = -\frac{1}{243} \end{array}$$
Both answers check.

19.
$$x - 13x^{1/2} + 12 = 0$$
$$(x^{1/2} - 12)(x^{1/2} - 1) = 0$$
$$x^{1/2} - 12 = 0 \quad \textbf{or} \quad x^{1/2} - 1 = 0$$
$$x^{1/2} = 12 \qquad x^{1/2} = 1$$
$$(x^{1/2})^2 = (12)^2 \qquad (x^{1/2})^2 = (1)^2$$
$$x = 144 \qquad x = 1$$
Both answers check.

20.
$$p + p^{1/2} - 20 = 0$$
$$(p^{1/2} + 5)(p^{1/2} - 4) = 0$$
$$p^{1/2} + 5 = 0 \quad \textbf{or} \quad p^{1/2} - 4 = 0$$
$$p^{1/2} = -5 \qquad p^{1/2} = 4$$
$$(p^{1/2})^2 = (-5)^2 \qquad (p^{1/2})^2 = (4)^2$$
$$p = 25 \qquad p = 16$$
$p = 25$ does not check and is extraneous.

21.
$$2t^{1/3} + 3t^{1/6} - 2 = 0$$
$$(2t^{1/6} - 1)(t^{1/6} + 2) = 0$$
$$2t^{1/6} - 1 = 0 \quad \textbf{or} \quad t^{1/6} + 2 = 0$$
$$t^{1/6} = \tfrac{1}{2} \qquad t^{1/6} = -2$$
$$(t^{1/6})^6 = (\tfrac{1}{2})^6 \qquad (t^{1/6})^6 = (-2)^6$$
$$t = \tfrac{1}{64} \qquad t = 64$$
$t = 64$ does not check and is extraneous.

22.
$$z^3 - 7z^{3/2} - 8 = 0$$
$$(z^{3/2} + 1)(z^{3/2} - 8) = 0$$
$$z^{3/2} + 1 = 0 \quad \textbf{or} \quad z^{3/2} - 8 = 0$$
$$z^{3/2} = -1 \qquad z^{3/2} = 8$$
$$(z^{3/2})^2 = (-1)^2 \qquad (z^{3/2})^2 = (8)^2$$
$$z^3 = 1 \qquad z^3 = 64$$
$$z = 1 \qquad z = 4$$
$z = 1$ does not check and is extraneous.

23.
$$6p + p^{1/2} - 1 = 0$$
$$(2p^{1/2} + 1)(3p^{1/2} - 1) = 0$$
$$2p^{1/2} + 1 = 0 \quad \textbf{or} \quad 3p^{1/2} - 1 = 0$$
$$p^{1/2} = -\tfrac{1}{2} \qquad p^{1/2} = \tfrac{1}{3}$$
$$(p^{1/2})^2 = (-\tfrac{1}{2})^2 \qquad (p^{1/2})^2 = (\tfrac{1}{3})^2$$
$$p = \tfrac{1}{4} \qquad p = \tfrac{1}{9}$$
$p = \frac{1}{4}$ does not check and is extraneous.

24.
$$3r - r^{1/2} - 2 = 0$$
$$(3r^{1/2} + 2)(r^{1/2} - 1) = 0$$
$$3r^{1/2} + 2 = 0 \quad \textbf{or} \quad r^{1/2} - 1 = 0$$
$$r^{1/2} = -\tfrac{2}{3} \qquad r^{1/2} = 1$$
$$(r^{1/2})^2 = (-\tfrac{2}{3})^2 \qquad (r^{1/2})^2 = (1)^2$$
$$r = \tfrac{4}{9} \qquad r = 1$$
$r = \frac{4}{9}$ does not check and is extraneous.

25.
$$\begin{aligned}\sqrt{x-2}-3&=2\\ \sqrt{x-2}&=5\\ \left(\sqrt{x-2}\right)^2&=5^2\\ x-2&=25\\ x&=27\end{aligned}$$
The solution checks.

26.
$$\begin{aligned}\sqrt{a-3}-5&=0\\ \sqrt{a-3}&=5\\ \left(\sqrt{a-3}\right)^2&=5^2\\ a-3&=25\\ a&=28\end{aligned}$$
The solution checks.

27.
$$\begin{aligned}3\sqrt{x+1}&=\sqrt{6}\\ \left(3\sqrt{x+1}\right)^2&=\left(\sqrt{6}\right)^2\\ 9(x+1)&=6\\ 9x+9&=6\\ 9x&=-3\\ x&=-\tfrac{1}{3}\end{aligned}$$
The solution checks.

28.
$$\begin{aligned}\sqrt{x+3}&=2\sqrt{x}\\ \left(\sqrt{x+3}\right)^2&=\left(2\sqrt{x}\right)^2\\ x+3&=4x\\ 3&=3x\\ 1&=x\end{aligned}$$
The solution checks.

29.
$$\begin{aligned}\sqrt{5a-2}&=\sqrt{a+6}\\ \left(\sqrt{5a-2}\right)^2&=\left(\sqrt{a+6}\right)^2\\ 5a-2&=a+6\\ 4a&=8\\ a&=2\end{aligned}$$
The solution checks.

30.
$$\begin{aligned}\sqrt{16x+4}&=\sqrt{x+4}\\ \left(\sqrt{16x+4}\right)^2&=\left(\sqrt{x+4}\right)^2\\ 16x+4&=x+4\\ 15x&=0\\ x&=0\end{aligned}$$
The solution checks.

31.
$$\begin{aligned}2\sqrt{x^2+3}&=\sqrt{-16x-3}\\ \left(2\sqrt{x^2+3}\right)^2&=\left(\sqrt{-16x-3}\right)^2\\ 4(x^2+3)&=-16x-3\\ 4x^2+12&=-16x-3\\ 4x^2+16x+15&=0\\ (2x+3)(2x+5)&=0\end{aligned}$$
$$2x+3=0 \quad \textbf{or} \quad 2x+5=0$$
$$x=-\tfrac{3}{2} \qquad\qquad x=-\tfrac{5}{2}$$
Both solutions check.

32.
$$\begin{aligned}\sqrt{x^2+1}&=\frac{\sqrt{-7x+11}}{\sqrt{6}}\\ \left(\sqrt{x^2+1}\right)^2&=\left(\frac{\sqrt{-7x+11}}{\sqrt{6}}\right)^2\\ x^2+1&=\frac{-7x+11}{6}\\ 6x^2+6&=-7x+11\\ 6x^2+7x-5&=0\\ (2x-1)(3x+5)&=0\end{aligned}$$
$$2x-1=0 \quad \textbf{or} \quad 3x+5=0$$
$$x=\tfrac{1}{2} \qquad\qquad x=-\tfrac{5}{3}$$
Both solutions check.

33.
$$\begin{aligned}\sqrt[3]{7x+1} &= 4\\ \left(\sqrt[3]{7x+1}\right)^3 &= 4^3\\ 7x+1 &= 64\\ 7x &= 63\\ x &= 9\end{aligned}$$
The solution checks.

34.
$$\begin{aligned}\sqrt[3]{11a-40} &= 5\\ \left(\sqrt[3]{11a-40}\right)^3 &= 5^3\\ 11a-40 &= 125\\ 11a &= 165\\ a &= 15\end{aligned}$$
The solution checks.

35.
$$\begin{aligned}\sqrt[4]{30t+25} &= 5\\ \left(\sqrt[4]{30t+25}\right)^4 &= 5^4\\ 30t+25 &= 625\\ 30t &= 600\\ t &= 20\end{aligned}$$
The solution checks.

36.
$$\begin{aligned}\sqrt[4]{3z+1} &= 2\\ \left(\sqrt[4]{3z+1}\right)^4 &= 2^4\\ 3z+1 &= 16\\ 3z &= 15\\ z &= 5\end{aligned}$$
The solution checks.

37.
$$\begin{aligned}\sqrt{x^2+21} &= x+3\\ \left(\sqrt{x^2+21}\right)^2 &= (x+3)^2\\ x^2+21 &= x^2+6x+9\\ 21 &= 6x+9\\ 12 &= 6x\\ 2 &= x\end{aligned}$$
The solution checks.

38.
$$\begin{aligned}\sqrt{5-x^2} &= -(x+1)\\ \left(\sqrt{5-x^2}\right)^2 &= [-(x+1)]^2\\ 5-x^2 &= (x+1)^2\\ 5-x^2 &= x^2+2x+1\\ 0 &= 2x^2+2x-4\\ 0 &= 2(x+2)(x-1)\end{aligned}$$
$$x+2=0 \quad \textbf{or} \quad x-1=0$$
$$x=-2 \qquad\qquad x=1$$
$x=1$ does not check and is extraneous.

39.
$$\begin{aligned}\sqrt{y+2} &= 4-y\\ \left(\sqrt{y+2}\right)^2 &= (4-y)^2\\ y+2 &= 16-8y+y^2\\ 0 &= y^2-9y+14\\ 0 &= (y-2)(y-7)\end{aligned}$$
$$y-2=0 \quad \textbf{or} \quad y-7=0$$
$$y=2 \qquad\qquad y=7$$
$y=7$ does not check and is extraneous.

40.
$$\begin{aligned}\sqrt{3z+1} &= z-1\\ \left(\sqrt{3z+1}\right)^2 &= (z-1)^2\\ 3z+1 &= z^2-2z+1\\ 0 &= z^2-5z\\ 0 &= z(z-5)\end{aligned}$$
$$z=0 \quad \textbf{or} \quad z-5=0$$
$$z=0 \qquad\qquad z=5$$
$z=0$ does not check and is extraneous.

41.
$$\begin{aligned} x - \sqrt{7x-12} &= 0 \\ x &= \sqrt{7x-12} \\ x^2 &= \left(\sqrt{7x-12}\right)^2 \\ x^2 &= 7x - 12 \\ x^2 - 7x + 12 &= 0 \\ (x-4)(x-3) &= 0 \end{aligned}$$
$x - 4 = 0$ **or** $x - 3 = 0$
$x = 4$ $\quad x = 3$

Both solutions check.

42.
$$\begin{aligned} x - \sqrt{4x-4} &= 0 \\ x &= \sqrt{4x-4} \\ x^2 &= \left(\sqrt{4x-4}\right)^2 \\ x^2 &= 4x - 4 \\ x^2 - 4x + 4 &= 0 \\ (x-2)(x-2) &= 0 \end{aligned}$$
$x - 2 = 0$ **or** $x - 2 = 0$
$x = 2$ $\quad x = 2$

The solution checks.

43.
$$\begin{aligned} x + 4 &= \sqrt{\frac{6x+6}{5}} + 3 \\ x + 1 &= \sqrt{\frac{6x+6}{5}} \\ (x+1)^2 &= \left(\sqrt{\frac{6x+6}{5}}\right)^2 \\ x^2 + 2x + 1 &= \frac{6x+6}{5} \\ 5x^2 + 10x + 5 &= 6x + 6 \\ 5x^2 + 4x - 1 &= 0 \\ (5x-1)(x+1) &= 0 \end{aligned}$$
$5x - 1 = 0$ **or** $x + 1 = 0$
$x = \frac{1}{5}$ $\quad x = -1$

Both solutions check.

44.
$$\begin{aligned} \sqrt{\frac{8x+43}{3}} - 1 &= x \\ \sqrt{\frac{8x+43}{3}} &= x + 1 \\ \left(\sqrt{\frac{8x+43}{3}}\right)^2 &= (x+1)^2 \\ \frac{8x+43}{3} &= x^2 + 2x + 1 \\ 8x + 43 &= 3x^2 + 6x + 3 \\ 0 &= 3x^2 - 2x - 40 \\ 0 &= (3x+10)(x-4) \end{aligned}$$
$3x + 10 = 0$ **or** $x - 4 = 0$
$x = -\frac{10}{3}$ $\quad x = 4$

$x = -\frac{10}{3}$ does not check and is extraneous.

45.
$$\begin{aligned} \sqrt{\frac{x^2-1}{x-2}} &= 2\sqrt{2} \\ \left(\sqrt{\frac{x^2-1}{x-2}}\right)^2 &= \left(2\sqrt{2}\right)^2 \\ \frac{x^2-1}{x-2} &= 8 \\ x^2 - 1 &= 8x - 16 \\ x^2 - 8x + 15 &= 0 \\ (x-3)(x-5) &= 0 \end{aligned}$$
$x - 3 = 0$ **or** $x - 5 = 0$
$x = 3$ $\quad x = 5$

Both solutions check.

46.
$$\begin{aligned} \frac{\sqrt{x^2-1}}{\sqrt{3x-5}} &= \sqrt{2} \\ \left(\frac{\sqrt{x^2-1}}{\sqrt{3x-5}}\right)^2 &= \left(\sqrt{2}\right)^2 \\ \frac{x^2-1}{3x-5} &= 2 \\ x^2 - 1 &= 6x - 10 \\ x^2 - 6x + 9 &= 0 \\ (x-3)(x-3) &= 0 \end{aligned}$$
$x - 3 = 0$ **or** $x - 3 = 0$
$x = 3$ $\quad x = 3$

The solution checks.

47.

$$\begin{aligned} \sqrt[3]{x^3+7} &= x+1 \\ \left(\sqrt[3]{x^3+7}\right)^3 &= (x+1)^3 \\ x^3+7 &= x^3+3x^2+3x+1 \\ 0 &= 3x^2+3x-6 \\ 0 &= 3(x+2)(x-1) \end{aligned}$$

$x+2=0$ **or** $x-1=0$

$x=-2$ $\quad$ $x=1$

Both solutions check.

48.

$$\begin{aligned} \sqrt[3]{x^3-7}+1 &= x \\ \sqrt[3]{x^3-7} &= x-1 \\ \left(\sqrt[3]{x^3-7}\right)^3 &= (x-1)^3 \\ x^3-7 &= x^3-3x^2+3x-1 \\ 3x^2-3x-6 &= 0 \\ 3(x-2)(x+1) &= 0 \end{aligned}$$

$x-2=0$ **or** $x+1=0$

$x=2$ $\quad$ $x=-1$

Both solutions check.

49.

$$\begin{aligned} \sqrt[3]{8x^3+61} &= 2x+1 \\ \left(\sqrt[3]{8x^3+61}\right)^3 &= (2x+1)^3 \\ 8x^3+61 &= 8x^3+12x^2+6x+1 \\ 0 &= 12x^2+6x-60 \\ 0 &= 6(2x+5)(x-2) \end{aligned}$$

$2x+5=0$ **or** $x-2=0$

$x=-\frac{5}{2}$ $\quad$ $x=2$

Both solutions check.

50.

$$\begin{aligned} \sqrt[3]{8x^3-37} &= 2x-1 \\ \left(\sqrt[3]{8x^3-37}\right)^3 &= (2x-1)^3 \\ 8x^3-37 &= 8x^3-12x^2+6x-1 \\ 12x^2-6x-36 &= 0 \\ 6(2x+3)(x-2) &= 0 \end{aligned}$$

$2x+3=0$ **or** $x-2=0$

$x=-\frac{3}{2}$ $\quad$ $x=2$

Both solutions check.

51.

$$\begin{aligned} \sqrt{2p+1}-1 &= \sqrt{p} \\ \left(\sqrt{2p+1}-1\right)^2 &= \left(\sqrt{p}\right)^2 \\ 2p+1-2\sqrt{2p+1}+1 &= p \\ p+2 &= 2\sqrt{2p+1} \\ (p+2)^2 &= \left(2\sqrt{2p+1}\right)^2 \\ p^2+4p+4 &= 4(2p+1) \\ p^2+4p+4 &= 8p+4 \\ p^2-4p &= 0 \\ p(p-4) &= 0 \end{aligned}$$

$p=0$ **or** $p-4=0$

$p=0$ $\quad$ $p=4$

Both solutions check.

52.

$$\begin{aligned} \sqrt{r}+\sqrt{r+2} &= 2 \\ \sqrt{r} &= 2-\sqrt{r+2} \\ \left(\sqrt{r}\right)^2 &= \left(2-\sqrt{r+2}\right)^2 \\ r &= 4-4\sqrt{r+2}+r+2 \\ 4\sqrt{r+2} &= 6 \\ \left(4\sqrt{r+2}\right)^2 &= 6^2 \\ 16(r+2) &= 36 \\ 16r+32 &= 36 \\ 16r &= 4 \\ r &= \tfrac{4}{16}=\tfrac{1}{4} \end{aligned}$$

The solution checks.

53.
$$\begin{aligned}
\sqrt{x+3} &= \sqrt{2x+8}-1\\
\left(\sqrt{x+3}\right)^2 &= \left(\sqrt{2x+8}-1\right)^2\\
x+3 &= 2x+8-2\sqrt{2x+8}+1\\
2\sqrt{2x+8} &= x+6\\
\left(2\sqrt{2x+8}\right)^2 &= (x+6)^2\\
4(2x+8) &= x^2+12x+36\\
8x+32 &= x^2+12x+36\\
0 &= x^2+4x+4\\
0 &= (x+2)(x+2)\\
x+2=0 \quad &\textbf{or} \quad x+2=0\\
x=-2 \quad & \quad\quad x=-2
\end{aligned}$$
The solution checks.

54.
$$\begin{aligned}
\sqrt{x+2}+1 &= \sqrt{2x+5}\\
\left(\sqrt{x+2}+1\right)^2 &= \left(\sqrt{2x+5}\right)^2\\
x+2+2\sqrt{x+2}+1 &= 2x+5\\
2\sqrt{x+2} &= x+2\\
\left(2\sqrt{x+2}\right)^2 &= (x+2)^2\\
4(x+2) &= x^2+4x+4\\
4x+8 &= x^2+4x+4\\
0 &= x^2-4\\
0 &= (x+2)(x-2)\\
x+2=0 \quad &\textbf{or} \quad x-2=0\\
x=-2 \quad & \quad\quad x=2
\end{aligned}$$
Both solutions check.

55.
$$\begin{aligned}
\sqrt{y+8}-\sqrt{y-4} &= -2\\
\sqrt{y+8} &= \sqrt{y-4}-2\\
(\sqrt{y+8})^2 &= (\sqrt{y-4}-2)^2\\
y+8 &= y-4-4\sqrt{y-4}+4\\
4\sqrt{y-4} &= -8\\
(4\sqrt{y-4})^2 &= (-8)^2\\
16(y-4) &= 64\\
16y-64 &= 64\\
16y &= 128\\
y &= 8
\end{aligned}$$
The solution does not check. $\Rightarrow$ No solution.

56.
$$\begin{aligned}
\sqrt{z+5}-2 &= \sqrt{z-3}\\
\left(\sqrt{z+5}-2\right)^2 &= \left(\sqrt{z-3}\right)^2\\
z+5-2(2)\sqrt{z+5}+4 &= z-3\\
12 &= 4\sqrt{z+5}\\
12^2 &= \left(4\sqrt{z+5}\right)^2\\
144 &= 16(z+5)\\
144 &= 16z+80\\
64 &= 16z\\
4 &= z
\end{aligned}$$
The solution checks.

57.
$$\begin{aligned}
\sqrt{2b+3}-\sqrt{b+1} &= \sqrt{b-2}\\
\left(\sqrt{2b+3}-\sqrt{b+1}\right)^2 &= \left(\sqrt{b-2}\right)^2\\
2b+3-2\sqrt{(2b+3)(b+1)}+b+1 &= b-2\\
3b+4-2\sqrt{2b^2+5b+3} &= b-2\\
2b+6 &= 2\sqrt{2b^2+5b+3}\\
(2b+6)^2 &= \left(2\sqrt{2b^2+5b+3}\right)^2\\
4b^2+24b+36 &= 4\left(2b^2+5b+3\right)\\
4b^2+24b+36 &= 8b^2+20b+12\\
0 &= 4b^2-4b-24\\
0 &= 4(b-3)(b+2)\\
b-3=0 \quad &\textbf{or} \quad b+2=0\\
b=3 \quad & \quad\quad b=-2
\end{aligned}$$
$b=-2$ does not check, so it is an extraneous solution.

58.

$$\begin{aligned}
\sqrt{a+1}+\sqrt{3a} &= \sqrt{5a+1} \\
\left(\sqrt{a+1}+\sqrt{3a}\right)^2 &= \left(\sqrt{5a+1}\right)^2 \\
a+1+2\sqrt{3a(a+1)}+3a &= 5a+1 \\
4a+1+2\sqrt{3a^2+3a} &= 5a+1 \\
2\sqrt{3a^2+3a} &= a \\
\left(2\sqrt{3a^2+3a}\right)^2 &= a^2 \\
4\left(3a^2+3a\right) &= a^2 \\
12a^2+12a &= a^2 \\
11a^2+12a &= 0 \\
a(11a+12) &= 0
\end{aligned}$$

$a=0$ **or** $11a+12=0$ $\quad$ $a=-\frac{12}{11}$ does not check, so it

$a=0$ $\qquad\qquad a=-\frac{12}{11}$ $\quad$ is an extraneous solution.

59.

$$\begin{aligned}
\sqrt{\sqrt{b}+\sqrt{b+8}} &= 2 \\
\left(\sqrt{\sqrt{b}+\sqrt{b+8}}\right)^2 &= 2^2 \\
\sqrt{b}+\sqrt{b+8} &= 4 \\
\sqrt{b+8} &= 4-\sqrt{b} \\
\left(\sqrt{b+8}\right)^2 &= \left(4-\sqrt{b}\right)^2 \\
b+8 &= 16-8\sqrt{b}+b \\
8\sqrt{b} &= 8 \\
\sqrt{b} &= 1 \\
\left(\sqrt{b}\right)^2 &= 1^2 \\
b &= 1 \Rightarrow \text{The solution checks.}
\end{aligned}$$

60.
$$
\begin{aligned}
\sqrt{\sqrt{x+19}-\sqrt{x-2}} &= \sqrt{3} \\
\left(\sqrt{\sqrt{x+19}-\sqrt{x-2}}\right)^2 &= \left(\sqrt{3}\right)^2 \\
\sqrt{x+19}-\sqrt{x-2} &= 3 \\
\sqrt{x+19} &= 3+\sqrt{x-2} \\
\left(\sqrt{x+19}\right)^2 &= \left(3+\sqrt{x-2}\right)^2 \\
x+19 &= 9+6\sqrt{x-2}+x-2 \\
12 &= 6\sqrt{x-2} \\
2 &= \sqrt{x-2} \\
2^2 &= \left(\sqrt{x-2}\right)^2 \\
4 &= x-2 \\
6 &= x \Rightarrow \text{The solutions checks.}
\end{aligned}
$$

61.
$$
\begin{aligned}
t &= \sqrt{\frac{d}{16}} \\
5 &= \sqrt{\frac{d}{16}} \\
5^2 &= \left(\sqrt{\frac{d}{16}}\right)^2 \\
25 &= \frac{d}{16} \\
400 &= d \Rightarrow \text{The bridge is 400 feet high.}
\end{aligned}
$$

62.
$$
\begin{aligned}
d &= \sqrt{1.5h} \\
30 &= \sqrt{1.5h} \\
30^2 &= \left(\sqrt{1.5h}\right)^2 \\
900 &= 1.5h \\
600 &= h
\end{aligned}
$$
The tower must be 600 feet tall.

63.
$$
\begin{aligned}
l &= \sqrt{f^2+h^2} \\
10 &= \sqrt{f^2+6^2} \\
10^2 &= \left(\sqrt{f^2+36}\right)^2 \\
100 &= f^2+36 \\
64 &= f^2 \\
\pm 8 &= f
\end{aligned}
$$
He should nail the brace to the floor 8 feet from the wall.

64.
$$
\begin{aligned}
v &= \sqrt[3]{\frac{P}{0.02}} \\
31 &= \sqrt[3]{\frac{P}{0.02}} \\
31^3 &= \left(\sqrt[3]{\frac{P}{0.02}}\right)^3 \\
29791 &= \frac{P}{0.02} \\
29791(0.02) &= P \\
600 &\approx P
\end{aligned}
$$
The power generated is about 600 watts.

65.
$$r = \sqrt[n]{\frac{A}{P}} - 1$$
$$0.065 = \sqrt[4]{\frac{4000}{P}} - 1$$
$$1.065 = \sqrt[4]{\frac{4000}{P}}$$
$$(1.065)^4 = \left(\sqrt[4]{\frac{4000}{P}}\right)^4$$
$$1.286466 \approx \frac{4000}{P}$$
$$1.286466P \approx 4000$$
$$P \approx 3109$$
The original price was about $3109.

66.
$$w_2 = \sqrt{w_1^2 + w_3^2}$$
$$12.5 = \sqrt{w_1^2 + (7.5)^2}$$
$$(12.5)^2 = \left(\sqrt{w_1^2 + 56.25}\right)^2$$
$$156.25 = w_1^2 + 56.25$$
$$100 = w_1^2$$
$$\pm\sqrt{100} = w_1$$
$$w_1 = 10 \text{ lb}$$

67. **Answers may vary.**

68. **Answers may vary.**

69. Natural numbers between -4 and 4:

70. Integers between -4 and 4:

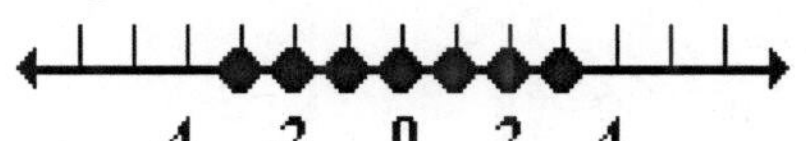

71. $x \geq 3 \Rightarrow [3, \infty)$

72. $x < -5 \Rightarrow (-\infty, -5)$

73. $-2 \leq x < 1 \Rightarrow [-2, 1)$

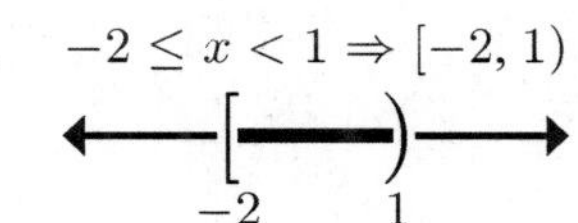

74. $-3 \leq x \leq 3 \Rightarrow [-3, 3]$

75. $x < 1$ or $x \geq 2$
$(-\infty, 1) \cup [2, \infty)$

76. $x \leq 1$ or $x > 2$
$(-\infty, 1] \cup (2, \infty)$

Exercises 1.7 (page 162)

1. right

2. $a = b$

3. $a < c$

4. $b + c$

5. $b - c$

6. $<$

7. $>$

8. $>$

9. linear

10. quadratic

11. equivalent

12. rational

13.
$$3x + 2 < 5$$
$$3x < 3$$
$$x < 1 \Rightarrow (-\infty, 1)$$

14.
$$-2x + 4 < 6$$
$$-2x < 2$$
$$x > -1 \Rightarrow (-1, \infty)$$

15. $3x + 2 \geq 5$
$3x \geq 3$
$x \geq 1 \Rightarrow [1, \infty)$

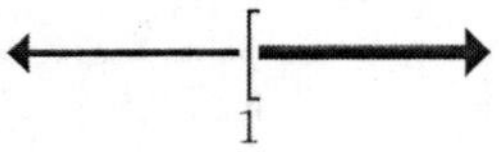

1

16. $-2x + 4 \geq 6$
$-2x \geq 2$
$x \leq -1 \Rightarrow (-\infty, -1]$

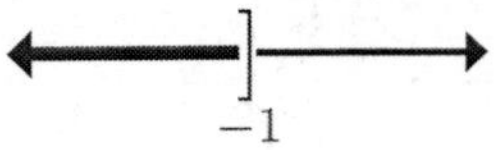

-1

17. $-5x + 3 > -2$
$-5x > -5$
$x < 1 \Rightarrow (-\infty, 1)$

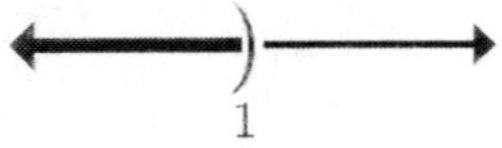

1

18. $4x - 3 > -4$
$4x > -1$
$x > -\frac{1}{4} \Rightarrow (-\frac{1}{4}, \infty)$

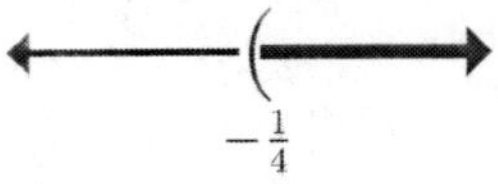

$-\frac{1}{4}$

19. $-5x + 3 \leq -2$
$-5x \leq -5$
$x \geq 1 \Rightarrow [1, \infty)$

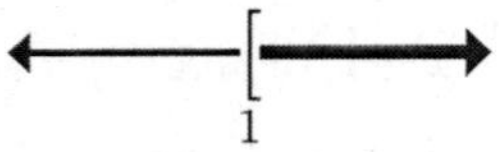

1

20. $4x - 3 \leq -4$
$4x \leq -1$
$x \leq -\frac{1}{4} \Rightarrow (-\infty, -\frac{1}{4}]$

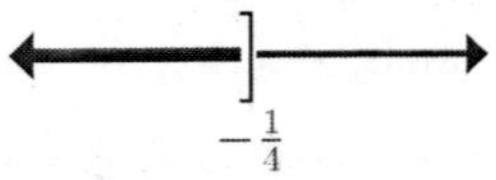

$-\frac{1}{4}$

21. $2(x - 3) \leq -2(x - 3)$
$2x - 6 \leq -2x + 6$
$4x \leq 12$
$x \leq 3 \Rightarrow (-\infty, 3]$

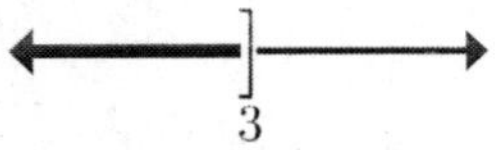

3

22. $3(x + 2) \leq 2(x + 5)$
$3x + 6 \leq 2x + 10$
$x \leq 4 \Rightarrow (-\infty, 4]$

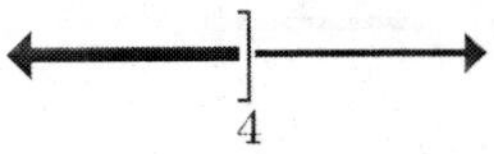

4

23. $\frac{3}{5}x + 4 > 2$
$5\left(\frac{3}{5}x + 4\right) > 5(2)$
$3x + 20 > 10$
$3x > -10$
$x > -\frac{10}{3} \Rightarrow (-\frac{10}{3}, \infty)$

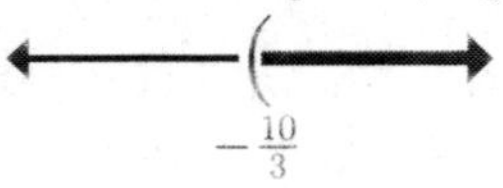

$-\frac{10}{3}$

24. $\frac{1}{4}x - 3 > 5$
$4\left(\frac{1}{4}x - 3\right) > 4(5)$
$x - 12 > 20$
$x > 32 \Rightarrow (32, \infty)$

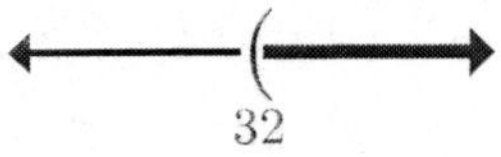

32

25.
$$\begin{aligned}\frac{x+3}{4} &< \frac{2x-4}{3}\\ 12\cdot\frac{x+3}{4} &< 12\cdot\frac{2x-4}{3}\\ 3(x+3) &< 4(2x-4)\\ 3x+9 &< 8x-16\\ -5x &< -25\\ x &> 5 \Rightarrow (5,\infty)\end{aligned}$$

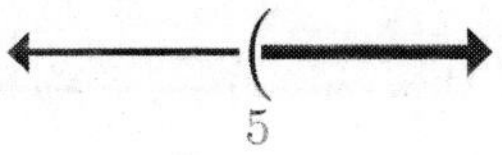

26.
$$\begin{aligned}\frac{x+2}{5} &> \frac{x-1}{2}\\ 10\cdot\frac{x+2}{5} &> 10\cdot\frac{x-1}{2}\\ 2(x+2) &> 5(x-1)\\ 2x+4 &> 5x-5\\ -3x &> -9\\ x &< 3 \Rightarrow (-\infty,3)\end{aligned}$$

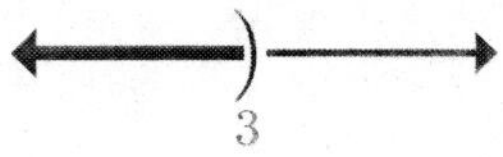

27.
$$\begin{aligned}\frac{6(x-4)}{5} &\geq \frac{3(x+2)}{4}\\ 20\cdot\frac{6x-24}{5} &\geq 20\cdot\frac{3x+6}{4}\\ 4(6x-24) &\geq 5(3x+6)\\ 24x-96 &\geq 15x+30\\ 9x &\geq 126\\ x &\geq 14 \Rightarrow [14,\infty)\end{aligned}$$

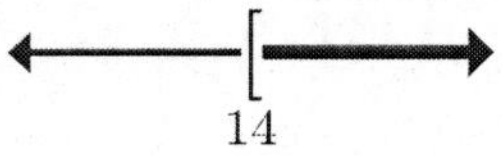

28.
$$\begin{aligned}\frac{3(x+3)}{2} &< \frac{2(x+7)}{3}\\ 6\cdot\frac{3x+9}{2} &< 6\cdot\frac{2x+14}{3}\\ 3(3x+9) &< 2(2x+14)\\ 9x+27 &< 4x+28\\ 5x &< 1\\ x &< \tfrac{1}{5} \Rightarrow (-\infty,\tfrac{1}{5})\end{aligned}$$

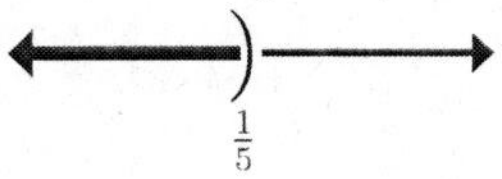

29.
$$\begin{aligned}\frac{5}{9}(a+3)-a &\geq \frac{4}{3}(a-3)-1\\ 9\left[\frac{5}{9}(a+3)-a\right] &\geq 9\left[\frac{4}{3}(a-3)-1\right]\\ 5(a+3)-9a &\geq 12(a-3)-9\\ 5a+15-9a &\geq 12a-36-9\\ -16a &\geq -60\\ a &\leq \frac{-60}{-16}\\ a &\leq \tfrac{15}{4} \Rightarrow (-\infty,\tfrac{15}{4}]\end{aligned}$$

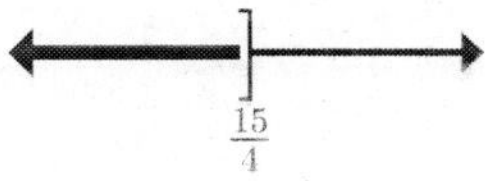

30.
$$\begin{aligned}\frac{2}{3}y-y &\leq -\frac{3}{2}(y-5)\\ 6\left(\frac{2}{3}y-y\right) &\leq 6\left[-\frac{3}{2}(y-5)\right]\\ 4y-6y &\leq -9(y-5)\\ -2y &\leq -9y+45\\ 7y &\leq 45\\ y &\leq \tfrac{45}{7} \Rightarrow (-\infty,\tfrac{45}{7}]\end{aligned}$$

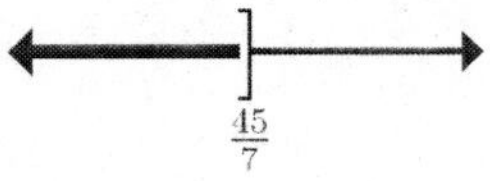

31.

$$\frac{2}{3}a - \frac{3}{4}a < \frac{3}{5}\left(a + \frac{2}{3}\right) + \frac{1}{3}$$
$$60\left(\frac{2}{3}a - \frac{3}{4}a\right) < 60\left[\frac{3}{5}\left(a + \frac{2}{3}\right) + \frac{1}{3}\right]$$
$$40a - 45a < 36\left(a + \frac{2}{3}\right) + 20$$
$$-5a < 36a + 24 + 20$$
$$-41a < 44$$
$$a > -\tfrac{44}{41} \Rightarrow \left(-\tfrac{44}{41}, \infty\right)$$

$-\frac{44}{41}$

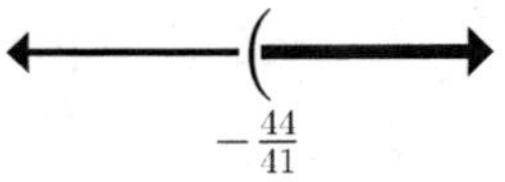

32.

$$\frac{1}{4}b + \frac{2}{3}b - \frac{1}{2} > \frac{1}{2}(b+1) + b$$
$$12\left(\frac{1}{4}b + \frac{2}{3}b - \frac{1}{2}\right) > 12\left[\frac{1}{2}(b+1) + b\right]$$
$$3b + 8b - 6 > 6(b+1) + 12b$$
$$11b - 6 > 6b + 6 + 12b$$
$$-7b > 12$$
$$b < -\tfrac{12}{7} \Rightarrow \left(-\infty, -\tfrac{12}{7}\right)$$

$-\frac{12}{7}$

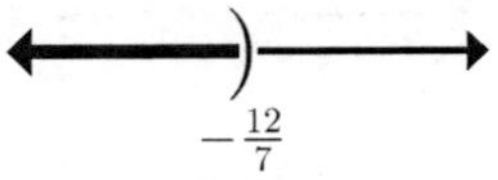

33.

$$4 < 2x - 8 \le 10$$
$$12 < 2x \le 18$$
$$6 < x \le 9 \Rightarrow (6, 9]$$

6 9

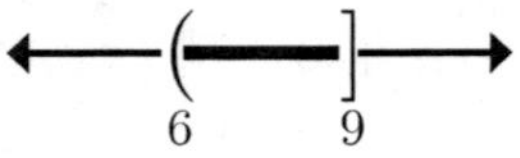

34.

$$3 \le 2x + 2 < 6$$
$$1 \le 2x < 4$$
$$\tfrac{1}{2} \le x < 2 \Rightarrow \left[\tfrac{1}{2}, 2\right)$$

$\frac{1}{2}$ 2

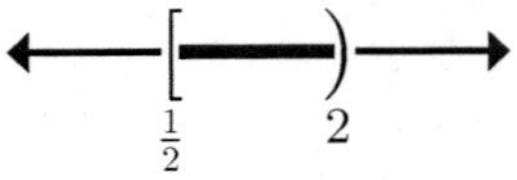

35.

$$9 \ge \frac{x-4}{2} > 2$$
$$18 \ge x - 4 > 4$$
$$22 \ge x > 8$$
$$8 < x \le 22 \Rightarrow (8, 22]$$

8 22

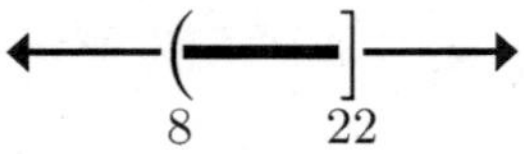

36.

$$5 < \frac{x-2}{6} < 6$$
$$30 < x - 2 < 36$$
$$32 < x < 38 \Rightarrow (32, 38)$$

32 38

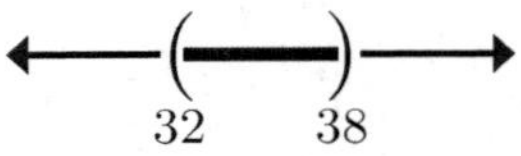

37.

$$0 \le \frac{4-x}{3} \le 5$$
$$0 \le 4 - x \le 15$$
$$-4 \le -x \le 11$$
$$4 \ge x \ge -11$$
$$-11 \le x \le 4 \Rightarrow [-11, 4]$$

−11 4

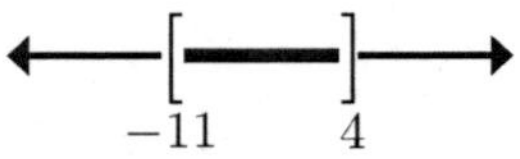

38.

$$0 \ge \frac{5-x}{2} \ge -10$$
$$0 \ge 5 - x \ge -20$$
$$-5 \ge -x \ge -25$$
$$5 \le x \le 25 \Rightarrow [5, 25]$$

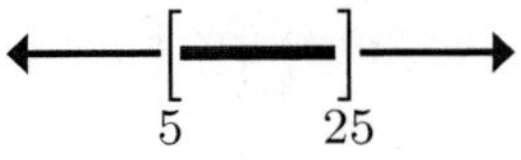

5 25

39.
$$\begin{aligned}
-2 \geq &\frac{1-x}{2} \geq -10 \\
-4 \geq &\ 1-x \geq -20 \\
-5 \geq &\ -x \geq -21 \\
5 \leq &\ x \leq 21 \Rightarrow [5, 21]
\end{aligned}$$

40.
$$\begin{aligned}
-2 \leq &\frac{1-x}{2} < 10 \\
-4 \leq &\ 1-x < 20 \\
-5 \leq &\ -x < 19 \\
5 \geq &\ x > -19 \\
-19 < &\ x \leq 5 \Rightarrow (-19, 5]
\end{aligned}$$

41. $-3x > -2x > -x$

$-3x > -2x$ **and** $-2x > -x$

$-x > 0$ $\quad$ $-x > 0$

$x < 0$ $\quad$ $x < 0$

$x < 0 \Rightarrow (-\infty, 0)$

42. $-3x < -2x < -x$

$-3x < -2x$ **and** $-2x < -x$

$-x < 0$ $\quad$ $-x < 0$

$x > 0$ $\quad$ $x > 0$

$x > 0 \Rightarrow (0, \infty)$

43. $x < 2x < 3x$

$x < 2x$ **and** $2x < 3x$

$-x < 0$ $\quad$ $-x < 0$

$x > 0$ $\quad$ $x > 0$

$x > 0 \Rightarrow (0, \infty)$

44. $x > 2x > 3x$

$x > 2x$ **and** $2x > 3x$

$-x > 0$ $\quad$ $-x > 0$

$x < 0$ $\quad$ $x < 0$

$x < 0 \Rightarrow (-\infty, 0)$

45. $2x + 1 < 3x - 2 < 12$

$2x + 1 < 3x - 2$ **and** $3x - 2 < 12$

$-x < -3$ $\quad$ $3x < 14$

$x > 3$ $\quad$ $x < \frac{14}{3}$

$x > 3$

$x < \frac{14}{3}$

$x > 3$ **and** $x < \frac{14}{3}$

Solution set: $\left(3, \frac{14}{3}\right)$

46. $2 - x < 3x + 5 < 18$

$2 - x < 3x + 5$ **and** $3x + 5 < 18$

$-4x < 3$ $\quad$ $3x < 13$

$x > -\frac{3}{4}$ $\quad$ $x < \frac{13}{3}$

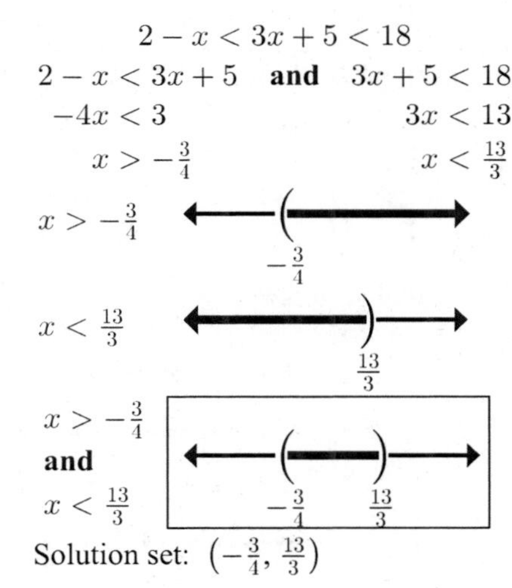

$x > -\frac{3}{4}$ **and** $x < \frac{13}{3}$

Solution set: $\left(-\frac{3}{4}, \frac{13}{3}\right)$

47. $2 + x < 3x - 2 < 5x + 2$

$2 + x < 3x - 2$ **and** $3x - 2 < 5x + 2$

$-2x < -4$ $\quad$ $-2x < 4$

$x > 2$ $\quad$ $x > -2$

$x > 2$ (2)

$x > -2$ (−2)

$x > 2$ **and** $x > -2$ (2)

Solution set: $(2, \infty)$

48. $x > 2x + 3 > 4x - 7$

$x > 2x + 3$ **and** $2x + 3 > 4x - 7$

$-x > 3$ $\quad$ $-2x > -10$

$x < -3$ $\quad$ $x < 5$

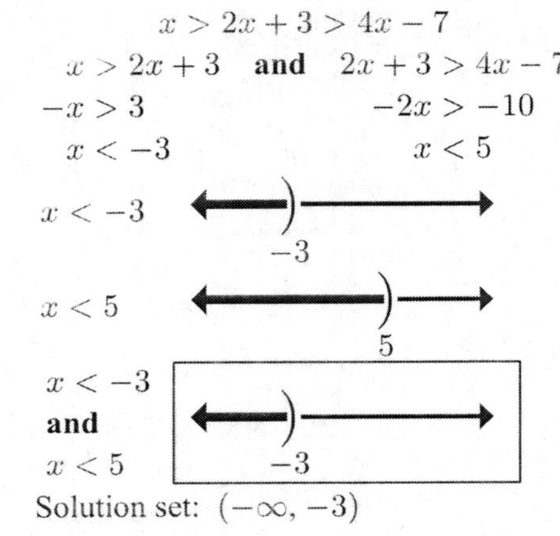

Solution set: $(-\infty, -3)$

49. $3 + x > 7x - 2 > 5x - 10$

$3 + x > 7x - 2$ **and** $7x - 2 > 5x - 10$

$-6x > -5$ $\quad$ $2x > -8$

$x < \frac{5}{6}$ $\quad$ $x > -4$

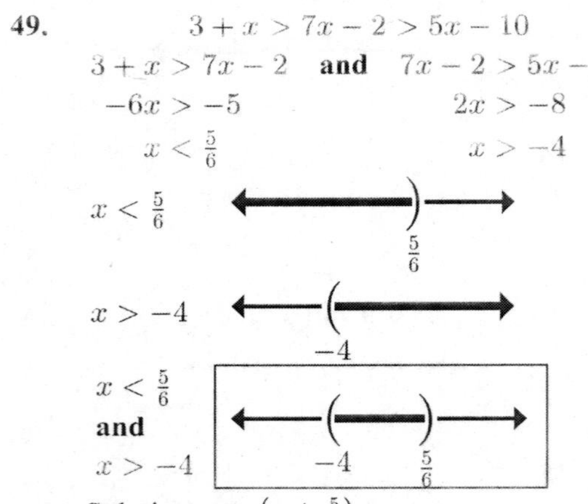

Solution set: $\left(-4, \frac{5}{6}\right)$

50. $2 - x < 3x + 1 < 10x$

$2 - x < 3x + 1$ **and** $3x + 1 < 10x$

$-4x < -1$ $\quad$ $-7x < -1$

$x > \frac{1}{4}$ $\quad$ $x > \frac{1}{7}$

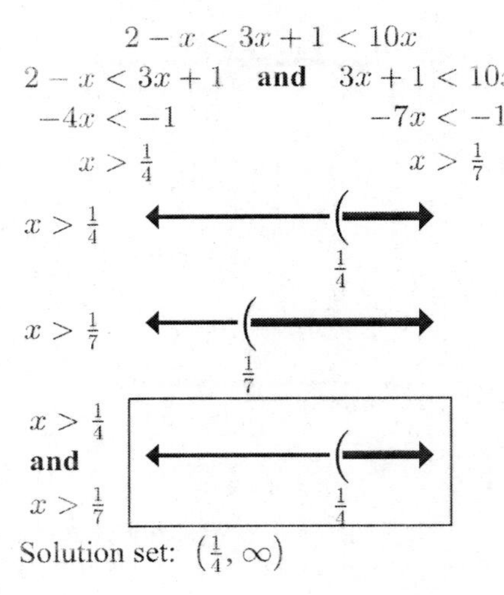

Solution set: $\left(\frac{1}{4}, \infty\right)$

51. $x \le x + 1 \le 2x + 3$

$x \le x + 1$ **and** $x + 1 \le 2x + 3$

$0 \le 1$ $\quad$ $-x \le 2$

true for all real numbers x $\quad$ $x \ge -2$

$0 \le 1$

$x \ge -2$ [−2

$0 \le 1$ **and** $x \ge -2$ [−2

Solution set: $[-2, \infty)$

52. $-x \ge -2x + 1 \ge -3x + 1$

$-x \ge -2x + 1$ **and** $-2x + 1 \ge -3x + 1$

$x \ge 1$ $\quad$ $x \ge 0$

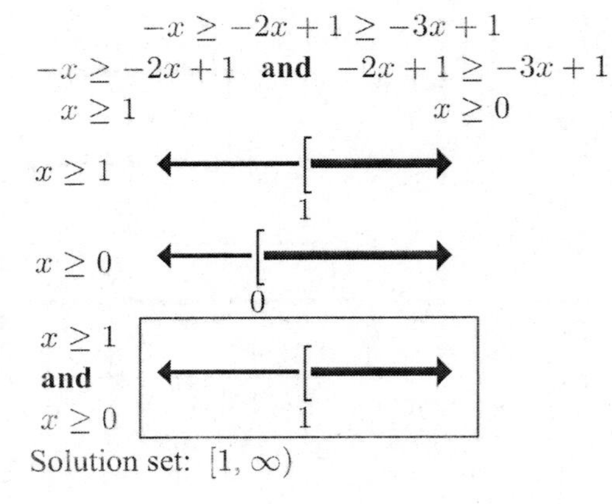

Solution set: $[1, \infty)$

53. $x^2 + 7x + 12 < 0$
$(x+3)(x+4) < 0$
factors $= 0$: $x = -3$, $x = -4$
intervals: $(-\infty, -4)$, $(-4, -3)$, $(-3, \infty)$

interval	test number	value of $x^2+7x+12$
$(-\infty, -4)$	-5	$+2$
$(-4, -3)$	-3.5	-0.25
$(-3, \infty)$	0	$+12$

Solution: $(-4, -3)$

-4 -3

54. $x^2 - 13x + 12 \le 0$
$(x-12)(x-1) \le 0$
factors $= 0$: $x = 12$, $x = 1$
intervals: $(-\infty, 1)$, $(1, 12)$, $(12, \infty)$

interval	test number	value of $x^2-13x+12$
$(-\infty, 1)$	0	$+12$
$(1, 12)$	2	-10
$(12, \infty)$	13	$+12$

Solution: $[1, 12]$

1 12

55. $x^2 - 5x + 6 \ge 0$
$(x-3)(x-2) \ge 0$
factors $= 0$: $x = 3$, $x = 2$
intervals: $(-\infty, 2)$, $(2, 3)$, $(3, \infty)$

interval	test number	value of x^2-5x+6
$(-\infty, 2)$	0	$+6$
$(2, 3)$	2.5	-0.25
$(3, \infty)$	4	$+2$

Solution: $(-\infty, 2] \cup [3, \infty)$

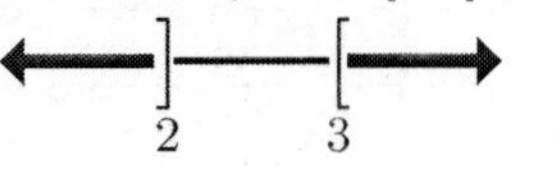

56. $6x^2 + 5x - 6 > 0$
$(2x+3)(3x-2) > 0$
factors $= 0$: $x = -\frac{3}{2}$, $x = \frac{2}{3}$
intervals: $\left(-\infty, -\frac{3}{2}\right)$, $\left(-\frac{3}{2}, \frac{2}{3}\right)$, $\left(\frac{2}{3}, \infty\right)$

interval	test number	value of $6x^2+5x-6$
$\left(-\infty, -\frac{3}{2}\right)$	-2	$+8$
$\left(-\frac{3}{2}, \frac{2}{3}\right)$	0	-6
$\left(\frac{2}{3}, \infty\right)$	1	$+5$

Solution: $\left(-\infty, -\frac{3}{2}\right) \cup \left(\frac{2}{3}, \infty\right)$

$-\frac{3}{2}$ $\frac{2}{3}$

57. $x^2 + 5x + 6 < 0$
$(x+3)(x+2) < 0$
factors $= 0$: $x = -3$, $x = -2$
intervals: $(-\infty, -3)$, $(-3, -2)$, $(-2, \infty)$

interval	test number	value of x^2+5x+6
$(-\infty, -3)$	-4	$+2$
$(-3, -2)$	-2.5	-0.25
$(-2, \infty)$	0	$+6$

Solution: $(-3, -2)$

-3 -2

58. $x^2 + 9x + 20 \ge 0$
$(x+4)(x+5) \ge 0$
factors $= 0$: $x = -4$, $x = -5$
intervals: $(-\infty, -5)$, $(-5, -4)$, $(-4, \infty)$

interval	test number	value of $x^2+9x+20$
$(-\infty, -5)$	-6	$+2$
$(-5, -4)$	-4.5	-0.25
$(-4, \infty)$	0	$+20$

Solution: $(-\infty, -5] \cup [-4, \infty)$

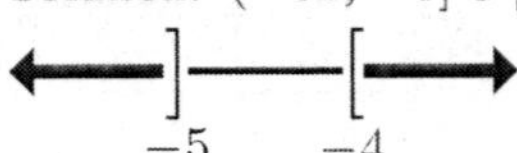

59. $6x^2 + 5x + 1 \geq 0$

$(2x+1)(3x+1) \geq 0$

factors $= 0$: $x = -\frac{1}{2}$, $x = -\frac{1}{3}$

intervals: $\left(-\infty, -\frac{1}{2}\right)$, $\left(-\frac{1}{2}, -\frac{1}{3}\right)$, $\left(-\frac{1}{3}, \infty\right)$

interval	test number	value of $6x^2+5x+1$
$\left(-\infty, -\frac{1}{2}\right)$	-1	$+2$
$\left(-\frac{1}{2}, -\frac{1}{3}\right)$	-0.4	-0.04
$\left(-\frac{1}{3}, \infty\right)$	0	$+1$

Solution: $\left(-\infty, -\frac{1}{2}\right] \cup \left[-\frac{1}{3}, \infty\right)$

60. $x^2 + 9x + 20 < 0$

$(x+5)(x+4) < 0$

factors $= 0$: $x = -5$, $x = -4$

intervals: $(-\infty, -5)$, $(-5, -4)$, $(-4, \infty)$

interval	test number	value of $x^2+9x+20$
$(-\infty, -5)$	-6	$+2$
$(-5, -4)$	-4.5	-0.25
$(-4, \infty)$	0	$+20$

Solution: $(-5, -4)$

61. $6x^2 - 5x < -1$

$6x^2 - 5x + 1 < 0$

$(2x-1)(3x-1) < 0$

factors $= 0$: $x = \frac{1}{2}$, $x = \frac{1}{3}$

intervals: $\left(-\infty, \frac{1}{3}\right)$, $\left(\frac{1}{3}, \frac{1}{2}\right)$, $\left(\frac{1}{2}, \infty\right)$

interval	test number	value of $6x^2-5x+1$
$\left(-\infty, \frac{1}{3}\right)$	0	$+1$
$\left(\frac{1}{3}, \frac{1}{2}\right)$	0.4	-0.04
$\left(\frac{1}{2}, \infty\right)$	1	$+2$

Solution: $\left(\frac{1}{3}, \frac{1}{2}\right)$

62. $9x^2 + 24x > -16$

$9x^2 + 24x + 16 > 0$

$(3x+4)(3x+4) > 0$

factors $= 0$: $x = -\frac{4}{3}$, $x = -\frac{4}{3}$

intervals: $\left(-\infty, -\frac{4}{3}\right)$, $\left(-\frac{4}{3}, \infty\right)$

interval	test number	value of $9x^2+24x+16$
$\left(-\infty, -\frac{4}{3}\right)$	-2	$+4$
$\left(-\frac{4}{3}, \infty\right)$	0	$+16$

Solution: $\left(-\infty, -\frac{4}{3}\right) \cup \left(-\frac{4}{3}, \infty\right)$

63. $2x^2 \geq 3 - x$

$2x^2 + x - 3 \geq 0$

$(2x+3)(x-1) \geq 0$

factors $= 0$: $x = -\frac{3}{2}$, $x = 1$

intervals: $\left(-\infty, -\frac{3}{2}\right)$, $\left(-\frac{3}{2}, 1\right)$, $(1, \infty)$

interval	test number	value of $2x^2+x-3$
$\left(-\infty, -\frac{3}{2}\right)$	-2	$+3$
$\left(-\frac{3}{2}, 1\right)$	0	-3
$(1, \infty)$	2	$+7$

Solution: $\left(-\infty, -\frac{3}{2}\right] \cup [1, \infty)$

64. $9x^2 \leq 24x - 16$

$9x^2 - 24x + 16 \leq 0$

$(3x-4)(3x-4) \leq 0$

factors $= 0$: $x = \frac{4}{3}$, $x = \frac{4}{3}$

intervals: $\left(-\infty, \frac{4}{3}\right)$, $\left(\frac{4}{3}, \infty\right)$

interval	test number	value of $9x^2-24x+16$
$\left(-\infty, \frac{4}{3}\right)$	0	$+16$
$\left(\frac{4}{3}, \infty\right)$	2	$+4$

Solution: $x = \frac{4}{3}$, or $\left[\frac{4}{3}, \frac{4}{3}\right]$

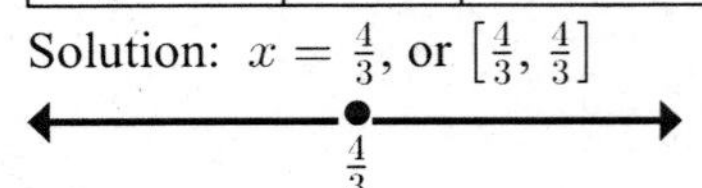

65. $x^2 - 3 \geq 0$

$x^2 - 3 = 0$

$x^2 = 3$

$x = \pm\sqrt{3}$

intervals: $\left(-\infty, -\sqrt{3}\right), \left(-\sqrt{3}, \sqrt{3}\right), \left(\sqrt{3}, \infty\right)$

interval	test number	value of x^2-3
$\left(-\infty, -\sqrt{3}\right)$	-2	$+1$
$\left(-\sqrt{3}, \sqrt{3}\right)$	0	-3
$\left(\sqrt{3}, \infty\right)$	2	$+1$

Solution: $\left(-\infty, -\sqrt{3}\right] \cup \left[\sqrt{3}, \infty\right)$

$-\sqrt{3}$ $\sqrt{3}$

66. $x^2 - 7 \leq 0$

$x^2 - 7 = 0$

$x^2 = 7$

$x = \pm\sqrt{7}$

intervals: $\left(-\infty, -\sqrt{7}\right), \left(-\sqrt{7}, \sqrt{7}\right), \left(\sqrt{7}, \infty\right)$

interval	test number	value of x^2-7
$\left(-\infty, -\sqrt{7}\right)$	-3	$+2$
$\left(-\sqrt{7}, \sqrt{7}\right)$	0	-7
$\left(\sqrt{7}, \infty\right)$	3	$+2$

Solution: $\left[-\sqrt{7}, \sqrt{7}\right]$

$-\sqrt{7}$ $\sqrt{7}$

67. $x^2 - 11 < 0$

$x^2 - 11 = 0$

$x^2 = 11$

$x = \pm\sqrt{11}$

intervals: $\left(-\infty, -\sqrt{11}\right), \left(-\sqrt{11}, \sqrt{11}\right), \left(\sqrt{11}, \infty\right)$

interval	test number	value of x^2-11
$\left(-\infty, -\sqrt{11}\right)$	-4	$+5$
$\left(-\sqrt{11}, \sqrt{11}\right)$	0	-11
$\left(\sqrt{11}, \infty\right)$	4	$+5$

Solution: $\left(-\sqrt{11}, \sqrt{11}\right)$

$-\sqrt{11}$ $\sqrt{11}$

68. $x^2 - 20 > 0$

$x^2 - 20 = 0$

$x^2 = 20$

$x = \pm\sqrt{20} = \pm 2\sqrt{5}$

intervals: $\left(-\infty, -2\sqrt{5}\right)$, $\left(-2\sqrt{5}, 2\sqrt{5}\right)$, $\left(2\sqrt{5}, \infty\right)$

interval	test number	value of x^2-20
$\left(-\infty, -2\sqrt{5}\right)$	-5	$+5$
$\left(-2\sqrt{5}, 2\sqrt{5}\right)$	0	-20
$\left(2\sqrt{5}, \infty\right)$	5	$+5$

Solution: $\left(-\infty, -2\sqrt{5}\right) \cup \left(2\sqrt{5}, \infty\right)$

$-2\sqrt{5}$ $2\sqrt{5}$

69. $\dfrac{x+3}{x-2} < 0$

factors $= 0$: $x = -3, x = 2$

intervals: $(-\infty, -3), (-3, 2), (2, \infty)$

interval	test number	sign of $\frac{x+3}{x-2}$
$(-\infty, -3)$	-4	$+$
$(-3, 2)$	0	$-$
$(2, \infty)$	3	$+$

Solution: $(-3, 2)$

-3 2

70. $\dfrac{x+3}{x-2} > 0$

factors $= 0$: $x = -3, x = 2$

intervals: $(-\infty, -3), (-3, 2), (2, \infty)$

interval	test number	sign of $\frac{x+3}{x-2}$
$(-\infty, -3)$	-4	$+$
$(-3, 2)$	0	$-$
$(2, \infty)$	3	$+$

Solution: $(-\infty, -3) \cup (2, \infty)$

-3 2

71. $\dfrac{x^2+x}{x^2-1} > 0$

$\dfrac{x(x+1)}{(x+1)(x-1)} > 0$

factors $= 0$: $x = 0, x = -1, x = 1$

intervals: $(-\infty, -1), (-1, 0), (0, 1), (1, \infty)$

interval	test number	sign of $\frac{x^2+x}{x^2-1}$
$(-\infty, -1)$	-2	$+$
$(-1, 0)$	$-\frac{1}{2}$	$+$
$(0, 1)$	$\frac{1}{2}$	$-$
$(1, \infty)$	2	$+$

Solution: $(-\infty, -1) \cup (-1, 0) \cup (1, \infty)$

-1 0 1

72. $\dfrac{x^2-4}{x^2-9} < 0 \Rightarrow \dfrac{(x+2)(x-2)}{(x+3)(x-3)} < 0$

factors $= 0$: $x = \pm 2, x = \pm 3$

intervals: $(-\infty, -3), (-3, -2), (-2, 2), (2, 3), (3, \infty)$

interval	test number	sign of $\frac{x^2-4}{x^2-9}$
$(-\infty, -3)$	-4	$+$
$(-3, -2)$	-2.5	$-$
$(-2, 2)$	0	$+$
$(2, 3)$	2.5	$-$
$(3, \infty)$	4	$+$

Solution: $(-3, -2) \cup (2, 3)$

-3 -2 2 3

73. $\dfrac{x^2+5x+6}{x^2+x-6} \geq 0 \Rightarrow \dfrac{(x+3)(x+2)}{(x+3)(x-2)} \geq 0$

factors $= 0$: $x = -3$, $x = \pm 2$

intervals: $(-\infty, -3)$, $(-3, -2)$, $(-2, 2)$, $(2, \infty)$

interval	test number	sign of $\frac{x^2+5x+6}{x^2+x-6}$
$(-\infty, -3)$	-4	$+$
$(-3, -2)$	-2.5	$+$
$(-2, 2)$	0	$-$
$(2, \infty)$	3	$+$

Include endpoints which make the numerator equal to 0. Do not include endpoints which make the denominator equal to 0.

Solution: $(-\infty, -3) \cup (-3, -2] \cup (2, \infty)$

74. $\dfrac{x^2+10x+25}{x^2-x-12} \leq 0 \Rightarrow \dfrac{(x+5)(x+5)}{(x+3)(x-4)} \leq 0$

factors $= 0$: $x = -3$, $x = 4$, $x = -5$

intervals: $(-\infty, -5)$, $(-5, -3)$, $(-3, 4)$, $(4, \infty)$

interval	test number	sign of $\frac{x^2+10x+25}{x^2-x-12}$
$(-\infty, -5)$	-6	$+$
$(-5, -3)$	-4	$+$
$(-3, 4)$	0	$-$
$(4, \infty)$	5	$+$

Include endpoints which make the numerator equal to 0. Do not include endpoints which make the denominator equal to 0.

Solution: $[-5, -5] \cup (-3, 4)$

75. $\dfrac{6x^2-x-1}{x^2+4x+4} > 0 \Rightarrow \dfrac{(2x-1)(3x+1)}{(x+2)(x+2)} > 0$

factors $= 0$: $x = \frac{1}{2}$, $x = -\frac{1}{3}$, $x = -2$

intervals: $(-\infty, -2)$, $(-2, -\frac{1}{3})$, $(-\frac{1}{3}, \frac{1}{2})$, $(\frac{1}{2}, \infty)$

interval	test number	sign of $\frac{6x^2-x-1}{x^2+4x+4}$
$(-\infty, -2)$	-3	$+$
$(-2, -\frac{1}{3})$	-1	$+$
$(-\frac{1}{3}, \frac{1}{2})$	0	$-$
$(\frac{1}{2}, \infty)$	1	$+$

Solution: $(-\infty, -2) \cup (-2, -\frac{1}{3}) \cup (\frac{1}{2}, \infty)$

76. $\dfrac{6x^2-3x-3}{x^2-2x-8} < 0 \Rightarrow \dfrac{3(2x+1)(x-1)}{(x+2)(x-4)} < 0$

factors $= 0$: $x = -\frac{1}{2}$, $x = 1$, $x = -2$, $x = 4$

intervals: $(-\infty, -2)$, $(-2, -\frac{1}{2})$, $(-\frac{1}{2}, 1)$, $(1, 4)$, $(4, \infty)$

interval	test number	sign of $\frac{6x^2-3x-3}{x^2-2x-8}$
$(-\infty, -2)$	-3	$+$
$(-2, -\frac{1}{2})$	-1	$-$
$(-\frac{1}{2}, 1)$	0	$+$
$(1, 4)$	2	$-$
$(4, \infty)$	5	$+$

Solution: $(-2, -\frac{1}{2}) \cup (1, 4)$

77. $\dfrac{3}{x} > 2$

$\dfrac{3}{x} - 2 > 0$

$\dfrac{3-2x}{x} > 0$

factors $= 0$: $x = \frac{3}{2}$, $x = 0$

intervals: $(-\infty, 0)$, $(0, \frac{3}{2})$, $(\frac{3}{2}, \infty)$

interval	test number	sign of $\frac{3-2x}{x}$
$(-\infty, 0)$	-1	$-$
$(0, \frac{3}{2})$	1	$+$
$(\frac{3}{2}, \infty)$	2	$-$

Solution: $(0, \frac{3}{2})$

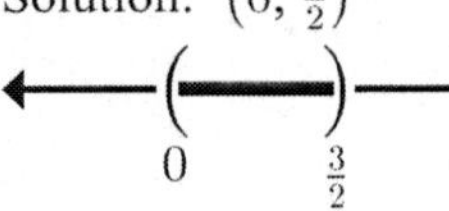

78.

$$\frac{3}{x} < 2$$
$$\frac{3}{x} - 2 < 0$$
$$\frac{3 - 2x}{x} < 0$$

factors $= 0$: $x = \frac{3}{2}, x = 0$

intervals: $(-\infty, 0), \left(0, \frac{3}{2}\right), \left(\frac{3}{2}, \infty\right)$

interval	test number	sign of $\frac{3-2x}{x}$
$(-\infty, 0)$	-1	$-$
$\left(0, \frac{3}{2}\right)$	1	$+$
$\left(\frac{3}{2}, \infty\right)$	2	$-$

Solution: $(-\infty, 0) \cup \left(\frac{3}{2}, \infty\right)$

79.

$$\frac{6}{x} < 4$$
$$\frac{6}{x} - 4 < 0$$
$$\frac{6 - 4x}{x} < 0$$

factors $= 0$: $x = \frac{3}{2}, x = 0$

intervals: $(-\infty, 0), \left(0, \frac{3}{2}\right), \left(\frac{3}{2}, \infty\right)$

interval	test number	sign of $\frac{6-4x}{x}$
$(-\infty, 0)$	-1	$-$
$\left(0, \frac{3}{2}\right)$	1	$+$
$\left(\frac{3}{2}, \infty\right)$	2	$-$

Solution: $(-\infty, 0) \cup \left(\frac{3}{2}, \infty\right)$

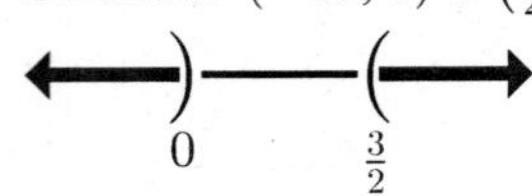

80.

$$\frac{6}{x} > 4$$
$$\frac{6}{x} - 4 > 0$$
$$\frac{6 - 4x}{x} > 0$$

factors $= 0$: $x = \frac{3}{2}, x = 0$

intervals: $(-\infty, 0), \left(0, \frac{3}{2}\right), \left(\frac{3}{2}, \infty\right)$

interval	test number	sign of $\frac{6-4x}{x}$
$(-\infty, 0)$	-1	$-$
$\left(0, \frac{3}{2}\right)$	1	$+$
$\left(\frac{3}{2}, \infty\right)$	2	$-$

Solution: $\left(0, \frac{3}{2}\right)$

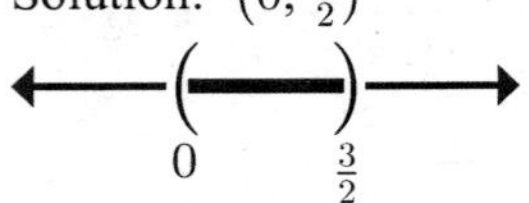

81.

$$\frac{3}{x-2} \le 5$$
$$\frac{3}{x-2} - 5 \le 0$$
$$\frac{3}{x-2} - \frac{5(x-2)}{x-2} \le 0$$
$$\frac{3 - 5x + 10}{x-2} \le 0$$
$$\frac{13 - 5x}{x-2} \le 0$$

factors $= 0$: $x = \frac{13}{5}, x = 2$

intervals: $(-\infty, 2), \left(2, \frac{13}{5}\right), \left(\frac{13}{5}, \infty\right)$

interval	test number	sign of $\frac{13-5x}{x-2}$
$(-\infty, 2)$	0	$-$
$\left(2, \frac{13}{5}\right)$	$\frac{11}{5}$	$+$
$\left(\frac{13}{5}, \infty\right)$	3	$-$

Solution: $(-\infty, 2) \cup \left[\frac{13}{5}, \infty\right)$

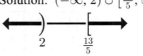

Include endpoints which make the numerator equal to 0. Do not include endpoints which make the denominator equal to 0.

82.

$$\frac{3}{x+2} \le 4$$
$$\frac{3}{x+2} - 4 \le 0$$
$$\frac{3}{x+2} - \frac{4(x+2)}{x+2} \le 0$$
$$\frac{3-4x-8}{x+2} \le 0$$
$$\frac{-4x-5}{x+2} \le 0$$

factors $= 0$: $x = -2, x = -\frac{5}{4}$

intervals: $(-\infty, -2), \left(-2, -\frac{5}{4}\right), \left(-\frac{5}{4}, \infty\right)$

interval	test number	sign of $\frac{-4x-5}{x+2}$
$(-\infty, -2)$	-3	$-$
$\left(-2, -\frac{5}{4}\right)$	$-\frac{7}{4}$	$+$
$\left(-\frac{5}{4}, \infty\right)$	0	$-$

Solution: $(-\infty, -2) \cup \left[-\frac{5}{4}, \infty\right)$

-2 $\quad -\frac{5}{4}$

Include endpoints which make the the numerator equal to 0. Do not include endpoints which make the denominator equal to 0.

83.

$$\frac{6}{x^2-1} < 1$$
$$\frac{6}{x^2-1} - 1 < 0$$
$$\frac{6}{x^2-1} - \frac{x^2-1}{x^2-1} < 0$$
$$\frac{7-x^2}{x^2-1} < 0$$
$$\frac{7-x^2}{(x+1)(x-1)} < 0$$

factors $= 0$: $x = \pm\sqrt{7}, x = \pm 1$

intervals: $\left(-\infty, -\sqrt{7}\right), \left(-\sqrt{7}, -1\right), (-1, 1), \left(1, \sqrt{7}\right), \left(\sqrt{7}, \infty\right)$

interval	test number	sign of $\frac{7-x^2}{x^2-1}$
$\left(-\infty, -\sqrt{7}\right)$	-3	$-$
$\left(-\sqrt{7}, -1\right)$	-2	$+$
$(-1, 1)$	0	$-$
$\left(1, \sqrt{7}\right)$	2	$+$
$\left(\sqrt{7}, \infty\right)$	3	$-$

Sol'n: $\left(-\infty, -\sqrt{7}\right) \cup (-1, 1) \cup \left(\sqrt{7}, \infty\right)$

$-\sqrt{7}$ $\quad -1$ $\quad 1$ $\quad \sqrt{7}$

84.

$$\frac{6}{x^2-1} > 1$$
$$\frac{6}{x^2-1} - 1 > 0$$
$$\frac{6}{x^2-1} - \frac{x^2-1}{x^2-1} > 0$$
$$\frac{7-x^2}{x^2-1} > 0$$
$$\frac{7-x^2}{(x+1)(x-1)} > 0$$

factors $= 0$: $x = \pm\sqrt{7}, x = \pm 1$

intervals: $\left(-\infty, -\sqrt{7}\right), \left(-\sqrt{7}, -1\right), (-1, 1), \left(1, \sqrt{7}\right), \left(\sqrt{7}, \infty\right)$

interval	test number	sign of $\frac{7-x^2}{x^2-1}$
$\left(-\infty, -\sqrt{7}\right)$	-3	$-$
$\left(-\sqrt{7}, -1\right)$	-2	$+$
$(-1, 1)$	0	$-$
$\left(1, \sqrt{7}\right)$	2	$+$
$\left(\sqrt{7}, \infty\right)$	3	$-$

Sol'n: $\left(-\sqrt{7}, -1\right) \cup \left(1, \sqrt{7}\right)$

$-\sqrt{7}$ $\quad -1$ $\quad 1$ $\quad \sqrt{7}$

85. Let $x =$ the number of minutes after 3 minutes. The total cost $= 40 + 10x$ cents.

$$\boxed{\text{Total cost}} < 200$$
$$40 + 10x < 200$$
$$10x < 160$$
$$x < 16$$

A person can talk for up to 16 minutes after the initial 3 minutes, for a total of up to 19 minutes for less than $2.

86. Let $x =$ the number of games. Then the total cost $= 1695.95 + 19.95x$.

$$\boxed{\text{Total cost}} < 2000$$
$$1695.95 + 19.95x < 2000$$
$$19.95x < 304.05$$
$$x < 15.2$$

She can buy up to 15 games.

87. Let $x =$ the number of CDs. Then the total cost $= 150 + 9.75x$.

$$\boxed{\text{Total cost}} < 275$$
$$150 + 9.75x < 275$$
$$9.75x < 125$$
$$x < 12.8$$

He can buy up to 12 disks.

88. Let $x =$ the number of disks. Then the total cost $= 425 + 7.50x$.

$$\boxed{\text{Total cost}} < 600$$
$$425 + 7.50x < 600$$
$$7.50x < 175$$
$$x < 23.3$$

She can buy up to 23 disks.

89. Let $p =$ the price of the refrigerator. Then the total cost $= p + 0.065p + 0.0025p$.

$$\boxed{\text{Total cost}} < 1200$$
$$p + 0.065p + 0.0025p < 1200$$
$$1.0675p < 1200$$
$$p < 1124.122$$
$$p \leq \$1124.12$$

90. Let $x =$ the number of hours after the first. Then the total cost $= 17.50 + 8.95x$.

$$\boxed{\text{Total cost}} < 75$$
$$17.50 + 8.95x < 75$$
$$8.95x < 57.50$$
$$x < 6.4$$

A person could have the rototiller for up to 6 hours after the first hour, for a total of up to 7 hours.

91. Let $a =$ the assessed value. Find when Method 1 < Method 2:

$$2200 + 0.04a < 1200 + 0.06a$$
$$1000 < 0.02a$$
$$50000 < a$$

The first method will benefit the taxpayer when $a > \$50,000$.

92. Let $b =$ the hospital bill. Find when Cost of Plan 1 > Cost of Plan 2:

$$100 + 0.30(b - 100) > 200 + 0.20(b - 200)$$
$$100 + 0.30b - 30 > 200 + 0.20b - 40$$
$$0.1b > 90$$
$$b > 900$$

Plan 2 is better for bills over $900.

93. Let $b =$ the hospital bill. Find when Cost of Plan 1 > Cost of Plan 2:

$$\begin{aligned} 200 + 0.30(b - 200) &> 400 + 0.20(b - 400) \\ 200 + 0.30b - 60 &> 400 + 0.20b - 80 \\ 0.1b &> 180 \\ b &> 1800 \end{aligned}$$

Plan 2 is better for bills over \$1,800.

94. Let $P =$ the perimeter. Then the length is equal to $\frac{P - 2w}{2}$, or $\frac{P - 80}{2}$.

$$\begin{array}{ccccc} 180 & < & P & < & 200 \\ 180 - 80 & < & P - 80 & < & 200 - 80 \\ 100 & < & P - 80 & < & 120 \\ \frac{100}{2} & < & \frac{P-80}{2} & < & \frac{120}{2} \\ 50 & < & \text{length} & < & 60 \end{array}$$

The length is between 50 and 60 inches.

95. Let $P =$ the perimeter. Then the length of one side is equal to $\frac{P}{3}$.

$$\begin{array}{ccccc} 50 & < & P & < & 60 \\ \frac{50}{3} & < & \frac{P}{3} & < & \frac{60}{3} \\ 16\frac{2}{3} & < & \text{length} & < & 20 \end{array}$$

The length of a side is between $16\frac{2}{3}$ and 20 cm.

96. Let $P =$ the perimeter. Then the length of one side is equal to $\frac{P}{4}$, so the area is equal to

$$A = s^2 = \left(\frac{P}{4}\right)^2$$

$$\begin{array}{ccccc} 25 & < & P & < & 60 \\ \frac{25}{4} & < & \frac{P}{4} & < & \frac{60}{4} \\ \left(\frac{25}{4}\right)^2 & < & \left(\frac{P}{4}\right)^2 & < & 15^2 \\ \frac{625}{16} & < & \text{Area} & < & 225 \end{array}$$

The area is between $\frac{625}{16}$ m^2 and 225 m^2.

97.

$$\begin{array}{ccccc} 20 & < & l & < & 30 \\ 40 & < & 2l & < & 60 \\ 40 + 2w & < & 2l + 2w & < & 60 + 2w \\ 40 + 2w & < & P & < & 60 + 2w \end{array}$$

98.

$$\begin{array}{ccccc} 10 & < & C & < & 20 \\ \frac{9}{5}(10) & < & \frac{9}{5}C & < & \frac{9}{5}(20) \\ 18 + 32 & < & \frac{9}{5}C + 32 & < & 36 + 32 \\ 50 & < & F & < & 68 \end{array}$$

99. **Answers may vary.**

100. **Answers may vary.**

101. even integers: $0, -2, 2$

102. natural numbers: $1, 2$

103. prime numbers: 2

104. irrational numbers: $-\pi, \sqrt{7}$

105. real numbers: all in the list

106. rational numbers: $-9, -2, -\frac{1}{2}, 0, 1, 2, \frac{21}{2}$

Exercises 1.8 (page 171)

1. x

2. $-x$

3. $x = k$ or $x = -k$

4. $a = -b$

5. $-k < x < k$

6. $x < -k$ or $x > k$

7. $x \leq -k$ or $x \geq k$

8. $|a|$

9. $|7| = 7$

10. $|-9| = 9$

11. $|0| = 0$

12. $|3 - 5| = |-2| = 2$

13. $|5| - |-3| = 5 - 3 = 2$

14. $|-3| + |5| = 3 + 5 = 8$

15. $|\pi - 2| = +(\pi - 2) = \pi - 2$

16. $|\pi - 4| = -(\pi - 4) = 4 - \pi$

17. $x \geq 5 \Rightarrow |x-5| = x-5$

18. $x \leq 5 \Rightarrow |x-5| = -(x-5) = 5-x$

19. $|x^3| = \begin{cases} x^3 & \text{if } x \geq 0 \\ -x^3 & \text{if } x < 0 \end{cases}$

20. $|2x| = \begin{cases} 2x & \text{if } x \geq 0 \\ -2x & \text{if } x < 0 \end{cases}$

21. $|x+2| = 2$

$x+2=2$ **or** $x+2=-2$

$x=0$ $\quad x=-4$

22. $|2x+5| = 3$

$2x+5=3$ **or** $2x+5=-3$

$2x=-2$ $\quad 2x=-8$

$x=-1$ $\quad x=-4$

23. $|3x-1|-7=-2$

$|3x-1|=5$

$3x-1=5$ **or** $3x-1=-5$

$3x=6$ $\quad 3x=-4$

$x=2$ $\quad x=-\frac{4}{3}$

24. $|7x-5|+5=8$

$|7x-5|=3$

$7x-5=3$ **or** $7x-5=-3$

$7x=8$ $\quad 7x=2$

$x=\frac{8}{7}$ $\quad x=\frac{2}{7}$

25. $\left|\frac{3x-4}{2}\right| = 5$

$\frac{3x-4}{2}=5$ **or** $\frac{3x-4}{2}=-5$

$3x-4=10$ $\quad 3x-4=-10$

$3x=14$ $\quad 3x=-6$

$x=\frac{14}{3}$ $\quad x=-2$

26. $\left|\frac{10x+1}{2}\right| = \frac{9}{2}$

$\frac{10x+1}{2}=\frac{9}{2}$ **or** $\frac{10x+1}{2}=-\frac{9}{2}$

$10x+1=9$ $\quad 10x+1=-9$

$10x=8$ $\quad 10x=-10$

$x=\frac{8}{10}=\frac{4}{5}$ $\quad x=-1$

27. $\left|\frac{2x-4}{5}\right|+6=8$

$\left|\frac{2x-4}{5}\right|=2$

$\frac{2x-4}{5}=2$ **or** $\frac{2x-4}{5}=-2$

$2x-4=10$ $\quad 2x-4=-10$

$2x=14$ $\quad 2x=-6$

$x=7$ $\quad x=-3$

28. $\left|\frac{3x+11}{7}\right|-15=-14$

$\left|\frac{3x+11}{7}\right|=1$

$\frac{3x+11}{7}=1$ **or** $\frac{3x+11}{7}=-1$

$3x+11=7$ $\quad 3x+11=-7$

$3x=-4$ $\quad 3x=-18$

$x=-\frac{4}{3}$ $\quad x=-6$

29. $\left|\frac{x-3}{4}\right| = -2$

An absolute value can never equal a negative number.
no solution

30. $\left|\frac{x+5}{2}\right|+3=2$

$\left|\frac{x+5}{2}\right|=-1$

An absolute value can never equal a negative number.
no solution

31. $$\left|\frac{x-5}{3}\right| = 0$$

$$\frac{x-5}{3} = 0 \quad \textbf{or} \quad \frac{x-5}{3} = -0$$
$$x-5 = 0 \qquad x-5=0$$
$$x = 5 \qquad x = 5$$

32. $$\left|\frac{x+7}{9}\right| = 0$$

$$\frac{x+7}{9} = 0 \quad \textbf{or} \quad \frac{x+7}{9} = -0$$
$$x+7 = 0 \qquad x+7=0$$
$$x = -7 \qquad x = -7$$

33. $$\left|\frac{4x-2}{x}\right| = 3$$

$$\frac{4x-2}{x} = 3 \quad \textbf{or} \quad \frac{4x-2}{x} = -3$$
$$4x-2 = 3x \qquad 4x-2 = -3x$$
$$x = 2 \qquad 7x = 2$$
$$x = 2 \qquad x = \tfrac{2}{7}$$

34. $$\left|\frac{2(x-3)}{3x}\right| = 6$$

$$\frac{2x-6}{3x} = 6 \quad \textbf{or} \quad \frac{2x-6}{3x} = -6$$
$$2x-6 = 18x \qquad 2x-6 = -18x$$
$$-16x = 6 \qquad 20x = 6$$
$$x = -\tfrac{3}{8} \qquad x = \tfrac{3}{10}$$

35. $|x| = x$

True for all $x \geq 0$.

36. $$|x| + x = 2$$
$$|x| = -x+2$$

$$x = -x+2 \quad \textbf{or} \quad x = -(-x+2)$$
$$2x = 2 \qquad x = x-2$$
$$x = 1 \qquad 0 = -2 \Rightarrow \text{not true}$$

37. $$|x+3| = |x|$$

$$x+3 = x \quad \textbf{or} \quad x+3 = -x$$
$$0 = 3 \qquad 2x = -3$$
$$\text{not true} \qquad x = -\tfrac{3}{2}$$

38. $$|x+5| = |5-x|$$

$$x+5 = 5-x \quad \textbf{or} \quad x+5 = -(5-x)$$
$$2x = 0 \qquad x+5 = -5+x$$
$$x = 0 \qquad 0 = -10$$
$$\text{not true}$$

39. $$|x-3| = |2x+3|$$

$$x-3 = 2x+3 \quad \textbf{or} \quad x-3 = -(2x+3)$$
$$-x = 6 \qquad x-3 = -2x-3$$
$$x = -6 \qquad 3x = 0$$
$$x = 0$$

40. $$|x-2| = |3x+8|$$

$$x-2 = 3x+8 \quad \textbf{or} \quad x-2 = -(3x+8)$$
$$-2x = 10 \qquad x-2 = -3x-8$$
$$x = -5 \qquad 4x = -6$$
$$x = -\tfrac{3}{2}$$

41. $$|x+2| = |x-2|$$

$$x+2 = x-2 \quad \textbf{or} \quad x+2 = -(x-2)$$
$$0 = -4 \qquad x+2 = -x+2$$
$$\text{not true} \qquad 2x = 0$$
$$x = 0$$

42. $$|2x-3| = |3x-5|$$

$$2x-3 = 3x-5 \quad \textbf{or} \quad 2x-3 = -(3x-5)$$
$$-x = -2 \qquad 2x-3 = -3x+5$$
$$x = 2 \qquad 5x = 8$$
$$x = \tfrac{8}{5}$$

43.

$$\left|\frac{x+3}{2}\right| = |2x-3|$$

$$\frac{x+3}{2} = 2x-3 \quad \textbf{or} \quad \frac{x+3}{2} = -(2x-3)$$

$$x+3 = 4x-6 \qquad \frac{x+3}{2} = -2x+3$$

$$-3x = -9 \qquad x+3 = -4x+6$$

$$x = 3 \qquad 5x = 3$$

$$x = \tfrac{3}{5}$$

44.

$$\left|\frac{x-2}{3}\right| = |6-x|$$

$$\frac{x-2}{3} = 6-x \quad \textbf{or} \quad \frac{x-2}{3} = -(6-x)$$

$$\frac{x-2}{3} = 6-x \qquad \frac{x-2}{3} = -6+x$$

$$x-2 = 18-3x \qquad x-2 = -18+3x$$

$$4x = 20 \qquad -2x = -16$$

$$x = 5 \qquad x = 8$$

45.

$$\left|\frac{3x-1}{2}\right| = \left|\frac{2x+3}{3}\right|$$

$$\frac{3x-1}{2} = \frac{2x+3}{3} \quad \textbf{or} \quad \frac{3x-1}{2} = -\frac{2x+3}{3}$$

$$6\left(\frac{3x-1}{2} = \frac{2x+3}{3}\right) \qquad 6\left(\frac{3x-1}{2} = -\frac{2x+3}{3}\right)$$

$$3(3x-1) = 2(2x+3) \qquad 3(3x-1) = -2(2x+3)$$

$$9x-3 = 4x+6 \qquad 9x-3 = -4x-6$$

$$5x = 9 \qquad 13x = -3$$

$$x = \tfrac{9}{5} \qquad x = -\tfrac{3}{13}$$

46.

$$\left|\frac{5x+2}{3}\right| = \left|\frac{x-1}{4}\right|$$

$$\frac{5x+2}{3} = \frac{x-1}{4} \quad \textbf{or} \quad \frac{5x+2}{3} = -\frac{x-1}{4}$$

$$12\left(\frac{5x+2}{3} = \frac{x-1}{4}\right) \qquad 12\left(\frac{5x+2}{3} = -\frac{x-1}{4}\right)$$

$$4(5x+2) = 3(x-1) \qquad 4(5x+2) = -3(x-1)$$

$$20x+8 = 3x-3 \qquad 20x+8 = -3x+3$$

$$17x = -11 \qquad 23x = -5$$

$$x = -\tfrac{11}{17} \qquad x = -\tfrac{5}{23}$$

47.

$$|x-3| < 6$$

$$-6 < x-3 < 6$$

$$-3 < x < 9$$

$$(-3, 9)$$

−3 9

48.

$$|x-2| \geq 4$$

$$x-2 \geq 4 \quad \textbf{or} \quad x-2 \leq -4$$

$$x \geq 6 \qquad x \leq -2$$

$$(-\infty, -2] \cup [6, \infty)$$

−2 6

49.
$$|x+3|>6$$
$$x+3>6 \quad \textbf{or} \quad x+3<-6$$
$$x>3 \qquad\qquad x<-9$$
$$(-\infty,-9)\cup(3,\infty)$$

−9 3

50.
$$|x+2|\le 4$$
$$-4\le x+2\le 4$$
$$-6\le x \le 2$$
$$[-6,2]$$

−6 2

51.
$$|2x+4|\ge 10$$
$$2x+4\ge 10 \quad \textbf{or} \quad 2x+4\le -10$$
$$2x\ge 6 \qquad\qquad 2x\le -14$$
$$x\ge 3 \qquad\qquad x\le -7$$
$$(-\infty,-7]\cup[3,\infty)$$

−7 3

52.
$$|5x-2|<7$$
$$-7<5x-2<7$$
$$-5<5x<9$$
$$-1<x<\tfrac{9}{5}$$
$$\left(-1,\tfrac{9}{5}\right)$$

−1 $\frac{9}{5}$

53.
$$|3x+5|+1\le 9$$
$$|3x+5|\le 8$$
$$-8\le 3x+5\le 8$$
$$-13\le 3x\le 3$$
$$-\tfrac{13}{3}\le x\le 1$$
$$\left[-\tfrac{13}{3},1\right]$$

$-\frac{13}{3}$ 1

54.
$$|2x-7|-3>2$$
$$|2x-7|>5$$
$$2x-7>5 \quad \textbf{or} \quad 2x-7<-5$$
$$2x>12 \qquad\qquad 2x<2$$
$$x>6 \qquad\qquad x<1$$
$$(-\infty,1)\cup(6,\infty)$$

1 6

55.
$$|x+3|>0$$
$$x+3>0 \quad \textbf{or} \quad x+3<-0$$
$$x>-3 \qquad\qquad x<-3$$
$$(-\infty,-3)\cup(-3,\infty)$$

−3

56.
$$|x-3|\le 0$$
$$-0\le x-3\le 0$$
$$3\le x\le 3$$
$$[3,3]$$

3

57.
$$\left|\tfrac{5x+2}{3}\right|<1$$
$$-1<\tfrac{5x+2}{3}<1$$
$$-3<5x+2<3$$
$$-5<5x<1$$
$$-1<x<\tfrac{1}{5}$$
$$\left(-1,\tfrac{1}{5}\right)$$

−1 $\frac{1}{5}$

58.
$$\left|\tfrac{3x+2}{4}\right|>2$$
$$\tfrac{3x+2}{4}>2 \quad \textbf{or} \quad \tfrac{3x+2}{4}<-2$$
$$3x+2>8 \qquad\qquad 3x+2<-8$$
$$3x>6 \qquad\qquad 3x<-10$$
$$x>2 \qquad\qquad x<-\tfrac{10}{3}$$
$$\left(-\infty,-\tfrac{10}{3}\right)\cup(2,\infty)$$

$-\frac{10}{3}$ 2

59.

$$3\left|\frac{3x-1}{2}\right| > 5$$
$$\left|\frac{3x-1}{2}\right| > \frac{5}{3}$$

$$\frac{3x-1}{2} > \frac{5}{3} \quad \textbf{or} \quad \frac{3x-1}{2} < -\frac{5}{3}$$
$$6 \cdot \frac{3x-1}{2} > 6 \cdot \frac{5}{3} \qquad 6 \cdot \frac{3x-1}{2} < 6\left(-\frac{5}{3}\right)$$
$$9x - 3 > 10 \qquad 9x - 3 < -10$$
$$9x > 13 \qquad 9x < -7$$
$$x > \frac{13}{9} \qquad x < -\frac{7}{9}$$
$$\left(-\infty, -\frac{7}{9}\right) \cup \left(\frac{13}{9}, \infty\right)$$

$-\frac{7}{9}$ $\frac{13}{9}$

60.

$$2\left|\frac{8x+2}{5}\right| \le 1$$
$$\left|\frac{8x+2}{5}\right| \le \frac{1}{2}$$
$$-\frac{1}{2} \le \frac{8x+2}{5} \le \frac{1}{2}$$
$$10\left(-\frac{1}{2}\right) \le 10 \cdot \frac{8x+2}{5} \le 10 \cdot \frac{1}{2}$$
$$-5 \le 16x + 4 \le 5$$
$$-9 \le 16x \le 1$$
$$-\frac{9}{16} \le x \le \frac{1}{16}$$
$$\left[-\frac{9}{16}, \frac{1}{16}\right]$$

$-\frac{9}{16}$ $\frac{1}{16}$

61.

$$\frac{|x-1|}{-2} > -3$$
$$|x-1| < 6$$
$$-6 < x - 1 < 6$$
$$-5 < x < 7$$
$$(-5, 7)$$

-5 7

62.

$$\frac{|2x-3|}{-3} < -1$$
$$|2x-3| > 3$$
$$2x - 3 > 3 \quad \textbf{or} \quad 2x - 3 < -3$$
$$2x > 6 \qquad 2x < 0$$
$$x > 3 \qquad x < 0$$
$$(-\infty, 0) \cup (3, \infty)$$

0 3

63. $$0 < |2x+1| < 3$$

$0 < |2x+1|$ **and** $|2x+1| < 3$

(1) $|2x+1| > 0$

$2x+1 > 0$ **or** $2x+1 < -0$

$2x > -1$ $\quad$ $2x < -1$

$x > -\frac{1}{2}$ $\quad$ $x < -\frac{1}{2}$

(2) $|2x+1| < 3$

$-3 < 2x+1 < 3$

$-4 < 2x < 2$

$-2 < x < 1$

(1) 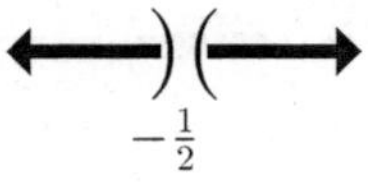 $-\frac{1}{2}$

(2) -2 $\quad$ 1

(1) $-\frac{1}{2}$

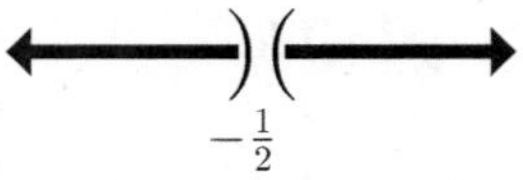

(2) -2 $\quad$ 1

(1) and (2) 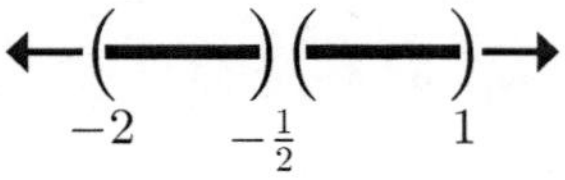 -2 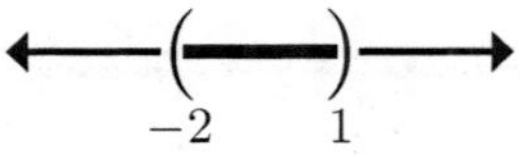 $\quad$ $-\frac{1}{2}$ 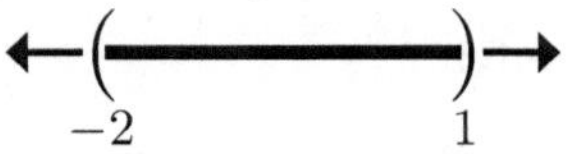 $\quad$ 1 $\Rightarrow (-2, -\frac{1}{2}) \cup (-\frac{1}{2}, 1)$

64. $$0 < |2x-3| < 1$$

$0 < |2x-3|$ **and** $|2x-3| < 1$

(1) $|2x-3| > 0$

$2x-3 > 0$ **or** $2x-3 < -0$

$2x > 3$ $\quad$ $2x < 3$

$x > \frac{3}{2}$ $\quad$ $x < \frac{3}{2}$

(2) $|2x-3| < 1$

$-1 < 2x-3 < 1$

$2 < 2x < 4$

$1 < x < 2$

(1) 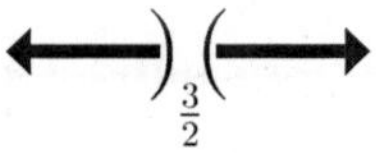 $\frac{3}{2}$

(2) 1 $\quad$ 2

(1) $\frac{3}{2}$

(2) 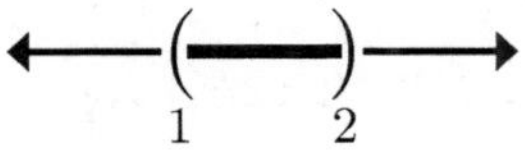 1 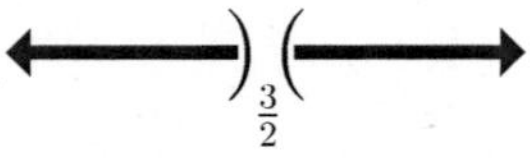 $\quad$ 2

(1) and (2) 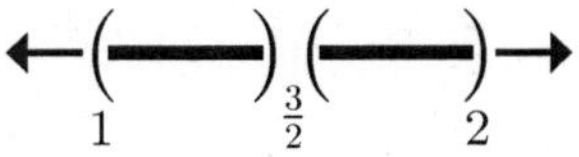 1 $\quad$ $\frac{3}{2}$ $\quad$ 2 $\Rightarrow (1, \frac{3}{2}) \cup (\frac{3}{2}, 2)$

65.

$$8 > |3x - 1| > 3$$

$|3x - 1| > 3$ **and** $8 > |3x - 1|$

(1) $|3x - 1| > 3$

$3x - 1 > 3$ **or** $3x - 1 < -3$

$3x > 4 \qquad 3x < -2$

$x > \frac{4}{3} \qquad x < -\frac{2}{3}$

(2) $|3x - 1| < 8$

$-8 < 3x - 1 < 8$

$-7 < 3x < 9$

$-\frac{7}{3} < x < 3$

(1) $-\frac{2}{3}$, $\frac{4}{3}$ **(2)** $-\frac{7}{3}$, 3

(1) $-\frac{2}{3}$, $\frac{4}{3}$

(2) $-\frac{7}{3}$, 3

(1) and (2) $-\frac{7}{3}$, $-\frac{2}{3}$, $\frac{4}{3}$, 3 $\Rightarrow \left(-\frac{7}{3}, -\frac{2}{3}\right) \cup \left(\frac{4}{3}, 3\right)$

66.

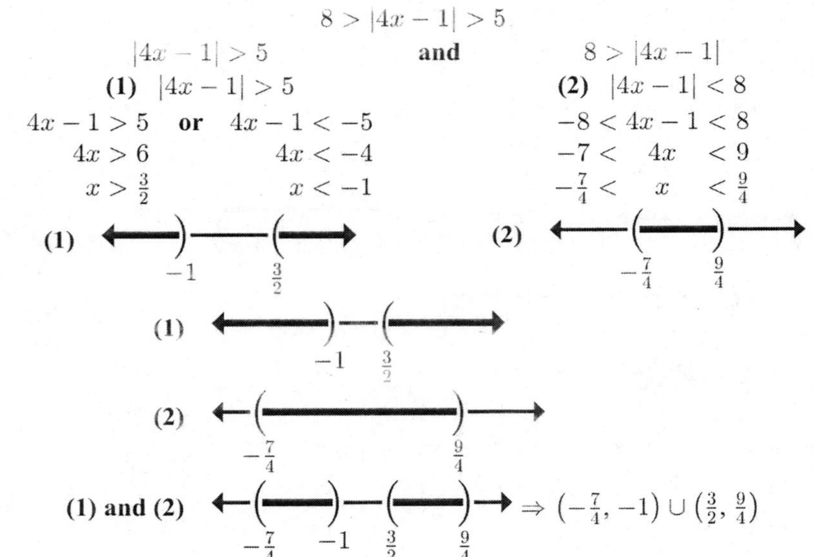

$$8 > |4x - 1| > 5$$

$|4x - 1| > 5$ **and** $8 > |4x - 1|$

(1) $|4x - 1| > 5$

$4x - 1 > 5$ **or** $4x - 1 < -5$

$4x > 6 \qquad 4x < -4$

$x > \frac{3}{2} \qquad x < -1$

(2) $|4x - 1| < 8$

$-8 < 4x - 1 < 8$

$-7 < 4x < 9$

$-\frac{7}{4} < x < \frac{9}{4}$

(1) -1, $\frac{3}{2}$ **(2)** $-\frac{7}{4}$, $\frac{9}{4}$

(1) -1, $\frac{3}{2}$

(2) $-\frac{7}{4}$, $\frac{9}{4}$

(1) and (2) $-\frac{7}{4}$, -1, $\frac{3}{2}$, $\frac{9}{4}$ $\Rightarrow \left(-\frac{7}{4}, -1\right) \cup \left(\frac{3}{2}, \frac{9}{4}\right)$

67. $$2 < \left|\frac{x-5}{3}\right| < 4$$

$$2 < \left|\frac{x-5}{3}\right| \quad \textbf{and} \quad \left|\frac{x-5}{3}\right| < 4$$

(1) $\left|\frac{x-5}{3}\right| > 2$ **(2)** $\left|\frac{x-5}{3}\right| < 4$

$$\begin{array}{lll} \frac{x-5}{3} > 2 & \textbf{or} \quad \frac{x-5}{3} < -2 & \quad -4 < \frac{x-5}{3} < 4 \\ x-5 > 6 & \quad x-5 < -6 & \quad -12 < x-5 < 12 \\ x > 11 & \quad x < -1 & \quad -7 < x < 17 \end{array}$$

(1) 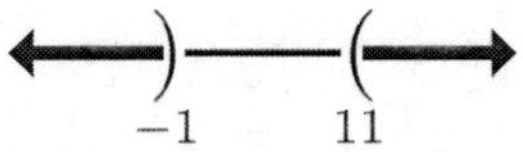

(2) 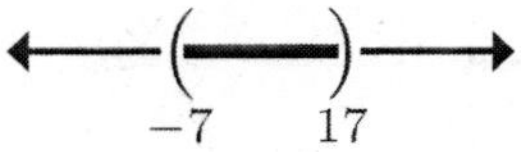

(1) 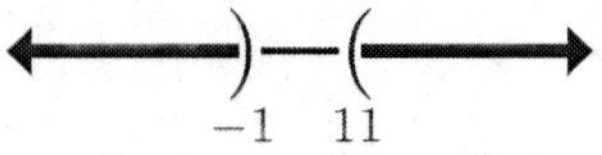

(2) 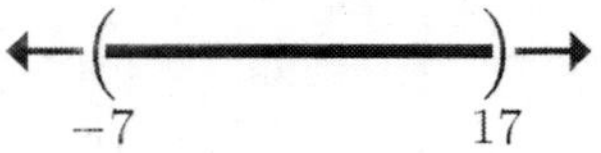

(1) and (2) 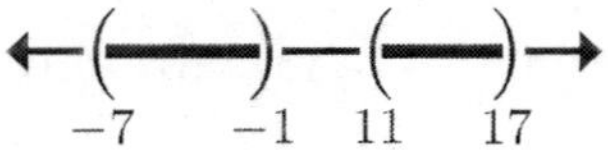

$\Rightarrow (-7, -1) \cup (11, 17)$

68. $$3 < \left|\frac{x-3}{2}\right| < 5$$

$$3 < \left|\frac{x-3}{2}\right| \quad \textbf{and} \quad \left|\frac{x-3}{2}\right| < 5$$

(1) $\left|\frac{x-3}{2}\right| > 3$ **(2)** $\left|\frac{x-3}{2}\right| < 5$

$$\begin{array}{lll} \frac{x-3}{2} > 3 & \textbf{or} \quad \frac{x-3}{2} < -3 & \quad -5 < \frac{x-3}{2} < 5 \\ x-3 > 6 & \quad x-3 < -6 & \quad -10 < x-3 < 10 \\ x > 9 & \quad x < -3 & \quad -7 < x < 13 \end{array}$$

(1) 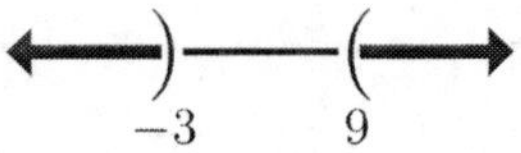

(2) 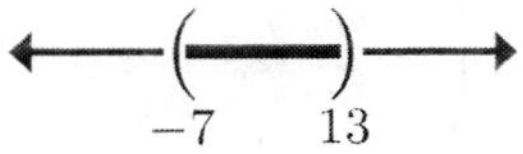

(1) 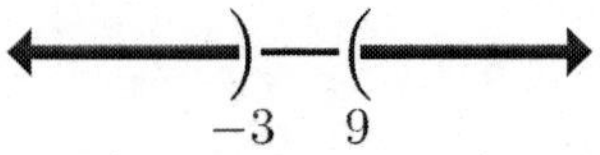

(2) 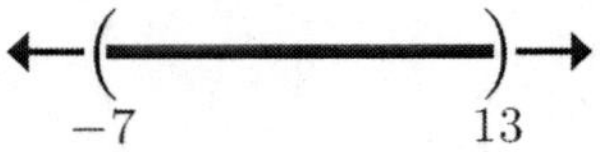

(1) and (2) 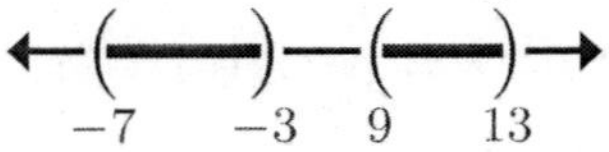

$\Rightarrow (-7, -3) \cup (9, 13)$

69.

$$10 > \left|\frac{x-2}{2}\right| > 4$$

$\left|\frac{x-2}{2}\right| > 4$ **and** $10 > \left|\frac{x-2}{2}\right|$

(1) $\left|\frac{x-2}{2}\right| > 4$ **(2)** $\left|\frac{x-2}{2}\right| < 10$

$\frac{x-2}{2} > 4$ **or** $\frac{x-2}{2} < -4$

$x-2>8$ $\quad x-2<-8$

$x>10$ $\quad x<-6$

$-10 < \frac{x-2}{2} < 10$

$-20 < x-2 < 20$

$-18 < x < 22$

(1) 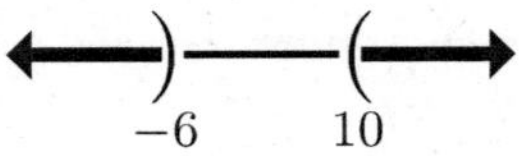 ←—) —— (—→ with -6, 10

(2) 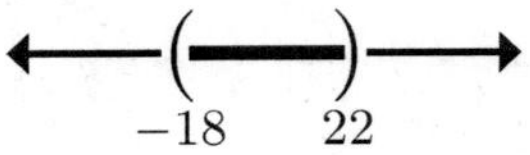 ←—(——)—→ with -18, 22

(1) 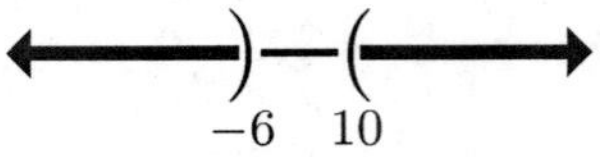 ←—)—(—→ with -6, 10

(2) 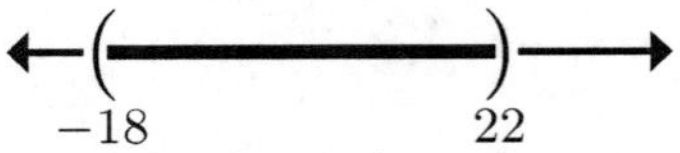 ←(——)→ with -18, 22

(1) and (2) 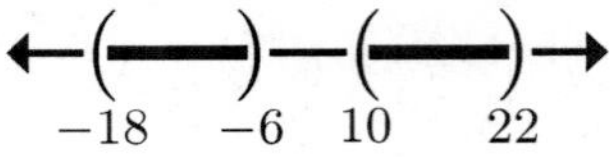 ←(—)—(—)→ with -18, -6, 10, 22 $\Rightarrow (-18, -6) \cup (10, 22)$

70.

$$5 \geq \left|\frac{x+2}{3}\right| > 1$$

$\left|\frac{x+2}{3}\right| > 1$ **and** $5 \geq \left|\frac{x+2}{3}\right|$

(1) $\left|\frac{x+2}{3}\right| > 1$ **(2)** $\left|\frac{x+2}{3}\right| \leq 5$

$\frac{x+2}{3} > 1$ **or** $\frac{x+2}{3} < -1$

$x+2>3$ $\quad x+2<-3$

$x>1$ $\quad x<-5$

$-5 \leq \frac{x+2}{3} \leq 5$

$-15 \leq x+2 \leq 15$

$-17 \leq x \leq 13$

(1) 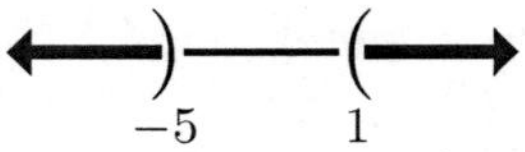 ←—) —— (—→ with -5, 1

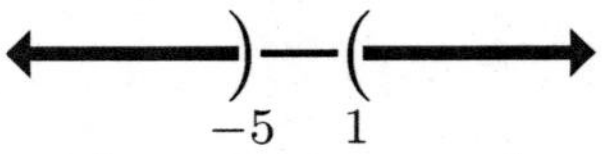

(2) 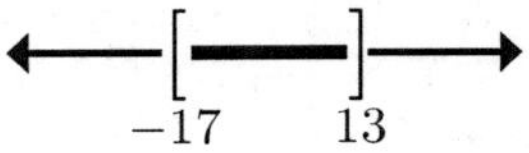 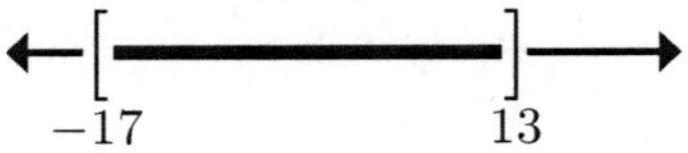 ←—[——]—→ with -17, 13

(1) ←—)—(—→ with -5, 1

(2) ←[——]→ with -17, 13

(1) and (2) 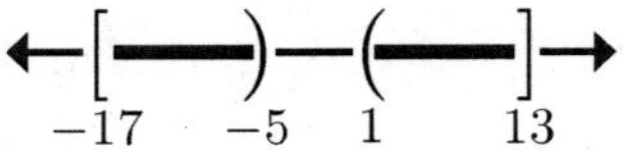 ←[—)—(—]→ with -17, -5, 1, 13 $\Rightarrow [-17, -5) \cup (1, 13]$

71. $$2 \le \left|\frac{x+1}{3}\right| < 3$$

$$2 \le \left|\frac{x+1}{3}\right| \quad \textbf{and} \quad \left|\frac{x+1}{3}\right| < 3$$

(1) $\left|\frac{x+1}{3}\right| \ge 2$ **(2)** $\left|\frac{x+1}{3}\right| < 3$

$$\frac{x+1}{3} \ge 2 \quad \textbf{or} \quad \frac{x+1}{3} \le -2 \qquad -3 < \frac{x+1}{3} < 3$$

$$x+1 \ge 6 \qquad x+1 \le -6 \qquad -9 < x+1 < 9$$

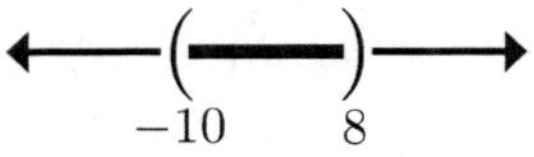

$$x \ge 5 \qquad x \le -7 \qquad -10 < x < 8$$

(1) 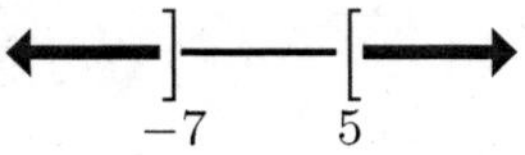 ⟵] ——[⟶ at -7, 5 **(2)** ⟵(——)⟶ at -10, 8

(1) 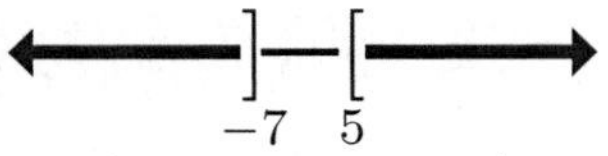 ⟵]—[⟶ at -7, 5

(2) 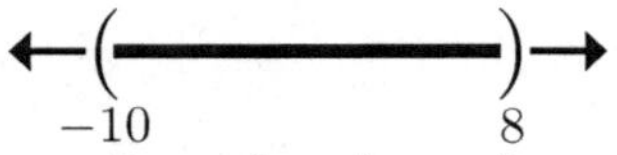 ⟵(——)⟶ at -10, 8

(1) and (2) 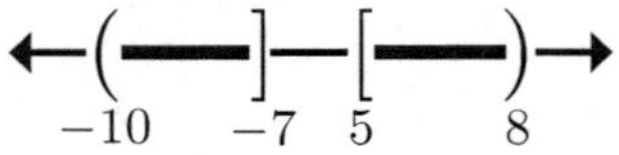 ⟵(—]—[—)⟶ at -10, -7, 5, 8 $\Rightarrow (-10, -7] \cup [5, 8)$

72. $$8 > \left|\frac{3x+1}{2}\right| > 2$$

$$\left|\frac{3x+1}{2}\right| > 2 \quad \textbf{and} \quad 8 > \left|\frac{3x+1}{2}\right|$$

(1) $\left|\frac{3x+1}{2}\right| > 2$ **(2)** $\left|\frac{3x+1}{2}\right| < 8$

$$\frac{3x+1}{2} > 2 \quad \textbf{or} \quad \frac{3x+1}{2} < -2 \qquad -8 < \frac{3x+1}{2} < 8$$

$$3x+1 > 4 \qquad 3x+1 < -4 \qquad -16 < 3x+1 < 16$$

$$3x > 3 \qquad 3x < -5 \qquad -17 < 3x < 15$$

$$x > 1 \qquad x < -\tfrac{5}{3} \qquad -\tfrac{17}{3} < x < 5$$

(1) 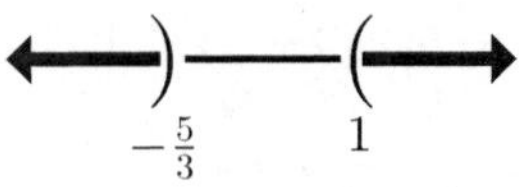 ⟵) ——(⟶ at $-\frac{5}{3}$, 1 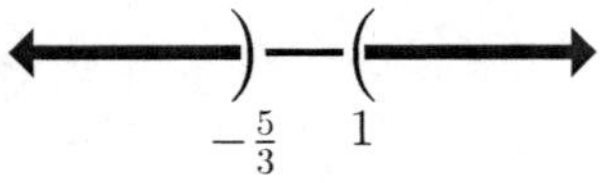 **(2)** 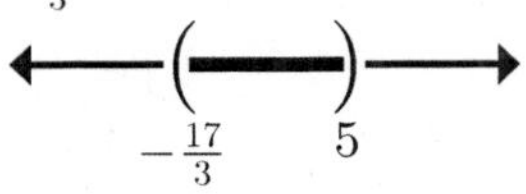 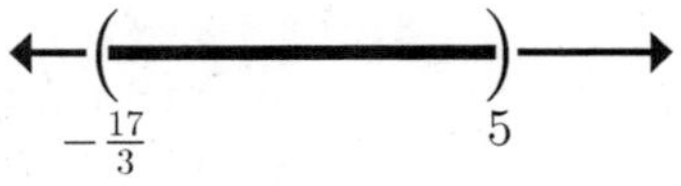 ⟵(——)⟶ at $-\frac{17}{3}$, 5

(1) ⟵)—(⟶ at $-\frac{5}{3}$, 1

(2) ⟵(——)⟶ at $-\frac{17}{3}$, 5

(1) and (2) 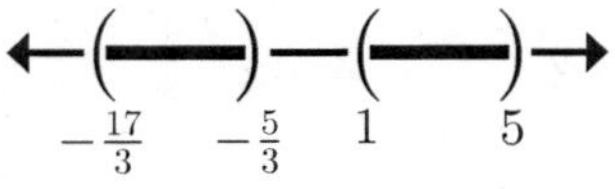 ⟵(—)—(—)⟶ at $-\frac{17}{3}$, $-\frac{5}{3}$, 1, 5 $\Rightarrow \left(-\frac{17}{3}, -\frac{5}{3}\right) \cup (1, 5)$

73.
$$|x+1| \geq |x|$$
$$\sqrt{(x+1)^2} \geq \sqrt{x^2}$$
$$(x+1)^2 \geq x^2$$
$$x^2+2x+1 \geq x^2$$
$$2x \geq -1$$
$$x \geq -\tfrac{1}{2}$$
Solution: $\left[-\frac{1}{2}, \infty\right)$

74.
$$|x+1| < |x+2|$$
$$\sqrt{(x+1)^2} < \sqrt{(x+2)^2}$$
$$(x+1)^2 < (x+2)^2$$
$$x^2+2x+1 < x^2+4x+4$$
$$-2x < 3$$
$$x > -\tfrac{3}{2}$$
Solution: $\left(-\frac{3}{2}, \infty\right)$

75.
$$|2x+1| < |2x-1|$$
$$\sqrt{(2x+1)^2} < \sqrt{(2x-1)^2}$$
$$(2x+1)^2 < (2x-1)^2$$
$$4x^2+4x+1 < 4x^2-4x+1$$
$$8x < 0$$
$$x < 0$$
Solution: $(-\infty, 0)$

76.
$$|3x-2| \geq |3x+1|$$
$$\sqrt{(3x-2)^2} \geq \sqrt{(3x+1)^2}$$
$$(3x-2)^2 \geq (3x+1)^2$$
$$9x^2-12x+4 \geq 9x^2+6x+1$$
$$-18x \geq -3$$
$$x \leq \tfrac{1}{6}$$
Solution: $\left(-\infty, \frac{1}{6}\right]$

77.
$$|x+1| < |x|$$
$$\sqrt{(x+1)^2} < \sqrt{x^2}$$
$$(x+1)^2 < x^2$$
$$x^2+2x+1 < x^2$$
$$2x < -1$$
$$x < -\tfrac{1}{2}$$
Solution: $\left(-\infty, -\frac{1}{2}\right)$

78.
$$|x+2| \leq |x+1|$$
$$\sqrt{(x+2)^2} \leq \sqrt{(x+1)^2}$$
$$(x+2)^2 \leq (x+1)^2$$
$$x^2+4x+4 \leq x^2+2x+1$$
$$2x \leq -3$$
$$x \leq -\tfrac{3}{2}$$
Solution: $\left(-\infty, -\frac{3}{2}\right]$

79.
$$|2x+1| \geq |2x-1|$$
$$\sqrt{(2x+1)^2} \geq \sqrt{(2x-1)^2}$$
$$(2x+1)^2 \geq (2x-1)^2$$
$$4x^2+4x+1 \geq 4x^2-4x+1$$
$$8x \geq 0$$
$$x \geq 0$$
Solution: $[0, \infty)$

80.
$$|3x-2| < |3x+1|$$
$$\sqrt{(3x-2)^2} < \sqrt{(3x+1)^2}$$
$$(3x-2)^2 < (3x+1)^2$$
$$9x^2-12x+4 < 9x^2+6x+1$$
$$-18x < -3$$
$$x > \tfrac{1}{6}$$
Solution: $\left(\frac{1}{6}, \infty\right)$

81.
$$|t-78°| \leq 8°$$
$$-8° \leq t-78° \leq 8°$$
$$70° \leq t \leq 86°$$

82.
$$|t-40°| \leq 80°$$
$$-80° \leq t-40° \leq 80°$$
$$-40° \leq t \leq 120°$$

83.
$$\begin{aligned} 0.6° + 0.5° &= 1.1° \\ 0.6° - 0.5° &= 0.1° \end{aligned}$$
$$\begin{aligned} 0.1° \le\ & c \le 1.1° \\ 0.6° - 0.5° \le\ & c \le 0.6° + 0.5° \\ -0.5° \le\ & c - 0.6° \le 0.5° \\ & |c - 0.6°| \le 0.5° \end{aligned}$$

84.
$$\begin{aligned} 0.25 + 0.015 &= 0.265 \\ 0.25 - 0.015 &= 0.235 \end{aligned}$$
$$\begin{aligned} 0.235 \le\ & x \le 0.265 \\ 0.25 - 0.015 \le\ & x \le 0.25 + 0.015 \\ -0.015 \le\ & x - 0.25 \le 0.015 \\ & |x - 0.25| \le 0.015 \text{ in.} \end{aligned}$$

85.
$$\frac{38 + 72}{2} = \frac{110}{2} = 55$$
$$\begin{aligned} 38 &= 55 - 17 \\ 72 &= 55 + 17 \end{aligned}$$
$$\begin{aligned} 38 <\ & h < 72 \\ 55 - 17 <\ & h < 55 + 17 \\ -17 <\ & h - 55 < 17 \\ & |h - 55| < 17 \end{aligned}$$

86.
$$\begin{aligned} & |h - 1500| \le 200 \\ -200 \le\ & h - 1500 \le 200 \\ 1300 \le\ & h \le 1700 \end{aligned}$$

87.
$$\begin{aligned} & |p - 25.46| \le 1.00 \\ -1.00 \le\ & p - 25.46 \le 1.00 \\ 24.46 \le\ & p \le 26.46 \end{aligned}$$

a. 24.76% and 26.45% are within the range. **b.** The error is less than 1%.

88.
$$|p - 25.46| > 1.00$$
$$p - 25.46 > 1.00 \quad \textbf{or} \quad p - 25.46 < -1.00$$
$$p > 26.46 \qquad\qquad p < 24.46$$

a. 22.91% and 26.49% are within the range. **b.** The error is more than 1%.

89. **Answers may vary.**

90. $|x| + 9 = 0$

$|x| = -9$

Since the absolute value of x can never equal a negative number, the equation has no solution.

91-94. Answers may vary.

95. $37{,}250 = 3.725 \times 10^4$

96. $0.0003725 = 3.725 \times 10^{-4}$

97. $5.23 \times 10^5 = 523{,}000$

98. $7.9 \times 10^{-4} = 0.00079$

99.
$$\begin{aligned} (x - y)^2 - (x + y)^2 = [(x - y)(x - y)] - [(x + y)(x + y)] &= [x^2 - 2xy + y^2] - [x^2 + 2xy + y^2] \\ &= x^2 - 2xy + y^2 - x^2 - 2xy - y^2 \\ &= -4xy \end{aligned}$$

100.
$$\begin{aligned} (p + q)^2 + (p - q)^2 = [(p + q)(p + q)] + [(p - q)(p - q)] &= [p^2 + 2pq + q^2] + [p^2 - 2pq + q^2] \\ &= p^2 + 2pq + q^2 + p^2 - 2pq + q^2 \\ &= 2p^2 + 2q^2 \end{aligned}$$

Chapter 1 Review (page 175)

1. $3x + 7 = 4$
no restrictions on x

2. $x + \frac{1}{x} = 2$
restriction: $x \neq 0$

3. $\frac{1}{x-1} = 4$
restriction: $x \neq 1$

4. $\frac{1}{x-2} = \frac{2}{x-3}$
restriction: $x \neq 2, x \neq 3$

5.
$$\begin{aligned} 3(9x+4) &= 28 \\ 27x + 12 &= 28 \\ 27x &= 16 \\ x &= \tfrac{16}{27} \end{aligned}$$
conditional equation

6.
$$\begin{aligned} \tfrac{3}{2}a &= 7(a+11) \\ 2 \cdot \tfrac{3}{2}a &= 2 \cdot 7(a+11) \\ 3a &= 14a + 154 \\ -11a &= 154 \\ a &= -\tfrac{154}{11} = -14 \end{aligned}$$
conditional equation

7.
$$\begin{aligned} 8(3x-5) - 4(x+3) &= 12 \\ 24x - 40 - 4x - 12 &= 12 \\ 20x - 52 &= 12 \\ 20x &= 64 \\ x &= \tfrac{64}{20} = \tfrac{16}{5} \Rightarrow \text{conditional equation} \end{aligned}$$

8.
$$\begin{aligned} \frac{x+3}{x+4} + \frac{x+3}{x+2} &= 2 \\ (x+4)(x+2)\left(\frac{x+3}{x+4} + \frac{x+3}{x+2}\right) &= (x+4)(x+2) \cdot 2 \\ (x+2)(x+3) + (x+4)(x+3) &= \left(x^2 + 6x + 8\right) \cdot 2 \\ x^2 + 5x + 6 + x^2 + 7x + 12 &= 2x^2 + 12x + 16 \\ 2x^2 + 12x + 18 &= 2x^2 + 12x + 16 \\ 18 &\neq 16 \Rightarrow \text{contradiction} \end{aligned}$$

9.
$$\begin{aligned} \frac{3}{x-1} &= \frac{1}{2} \\ 2(x-1) \cdot \frac{3}{x-1} &= 2(x-1) \cdot \frac{1}{2} \\ 6 &= x - 1 \\ 7 &= x \end{aligned}$$
conditional equation

10.
$$\begin{aligned} \frac{8x^2 + 72x}{9+x} &= 8x \\ (9+x) \cdot \frac{8x^2 + 72x}{9+x} &= (9+x) \cdot 8x \\ 8x^2 + 72x &= 72x + 8x^2 \end{aligned}$$
identity

11.
$$\begin{aligned}
\frac{3x}{x-1}-\frac{5}{x+3}&=3\\
(x-1)(x+3)\left(\frac{3x}{x-1}-\frac{5}{x+3}\right)&=(x-1)(x+3)\cdot 3\\
3x(x+3)-5(x-1)&=\left(x^2+2x-3\right)\cdot 3\\
3x^2+9x-5x+5&=3x^2+6x-9\\
4x+5&=6x-9\\
-2x&=-14\\
x&=7\Rightarrow \text{conditional equation}
\end{aligned}$$

12.
$$\begin{aligned}
x+\frac{1}{2x-3}&=\frac{2x^2}{2x-3}\\
(2x-3)\left(x+\frac{1}{2x-3}\right)&=(2x-3)\cdot\frac{2x^2}{2x-3}\\
(2x-3)x+1&=2x^2\\
2x^2-3x+1&=2x^2\\
-3x&=-1\\
x&=\tfrac{1}{3}\Rightarrow \text{conditional equation}
\end{aligned}$$

13.
$$\begin{aligned}
\frac{4}{x^2-13x-48}-\frac{1}{x^2+x-6}&=\frac{2}{x^2-18x+32}\\
\frac{4}{(x-16)(x+3)}-\frac{1}{(x+3)(x-2)}&=\frac{2}{(x-16)(x-2)}\\
4(x-2)-(x-16)&=2(x+3) \qquad \{\text{multiply by common denominator}\}\\
4x-8-x+16&=2x+6\\
3x+8&=2x+6\\
x&=-2\Rightarrow \text{conditional equation}
\end{aligned}$$

14.
$$\begin{aligned}
\frac{a-1}{a+3}+\frac{2a-1}{3-a}&=\frac{2-a}{a-3}\\
\frac{a-1}{a+3}+\frac{1-2a}{a-3}&=\frac{2-a}{a-3}\\
(a-1)(a-3)+(1-2a)(a+3)&=(2-a)(a+3) \qquad \{\text{multiply by common denominator}\}\\
a^2-3a-a+3+a+3-2a^2-6a&=2a+6-a^2-3a\\
-a^2-9a+6&=-a^2-a+6\\
-9a+6&=-a+6\\
0&=8a\\
0&=a\Rightarrow \text{conditional equation}
\end{aligned}$$

15.

$$C = \frac{5}{9}(F - 32)$$
$$\frac{9}{5}C = \frac{9}{5} \cdot \frac{5}{9}(F - 32)$$
$$\frac{9}{5}C = F - 32$$
$$\frac{9}{5}C + 32 = F$$

16.

$$P_n = l + \frac{si}{f}$$
$$P_n - l = \frac{si}{f}$$
$$f(P_n - l) = f \cdot \frac{si}{f}$$
$$f(P_n - l) = si$$
$$\frac{f(P_n - l)}{P_n - l} = \frac{si}{P_n - l}$$
$$f = \frac{si}{P_n - l}$$

17.

$$\frac{1}{f} = \frac{1}{f_1} + \frac{1}{f_2}$$
$$ff_1f_2 \cdot \frac{1}{f} = ff_1f_2\left(\frac{1}{f_1} + \frac{1}{f_2}\right)$$
$$f_1f_2 = ff_2 + ff_1$$
$$f_1f_2 - ff_1 = ff_2$$
$$f_1(f_2 - f) = ff_2$$
$$\frac{f_1(f_2 - f)}{f_2 - f} = \frac{ff_2}{f_2 - f}$$
$$f_1 = \frac{ff_2}{f_2 - f}$$

18.

$$S = \frac{a - lr}{1 - r}$$
$$S(1 - r) = \frac{a - lr}{1 - r}(1 - r)$$
$$S(1 - r) = a - lr$$
$$S - Sr = a - lr$$
$$lr = a - S + Sr$$
$$\frac{lr}{r} = \frac{a - S + Sr}{r}$$
$$l = \frac{a - S + Sr}{r}$$

19. Let x = the score on the first exam. Then his scores on the following tests were $x + 4$, $x + 8$ and $x + 12$.

$$\frac{\boxed{\text{Sum of scores}}}{4} = 66$$
$$\frac{x + x + 4 + x + 8 + x + 12}{4} = 66$$
$$\frac{4x + 24}{4} = 66$$
$$4x + 24 = 264$$
$$4x = 240$$
$$x = 60$$

His score on the first test was 60%.

20. Let w = the width. Then $w + 5$ = the length.

$$\boxed{\text{Perimeter}} = 100$$
$$2w + 2(w + 5) = 100$$
$$2w + 2w + 10 = 100$$
$$4w + 10 = 100$$
$$4w = 90$$
$$w = 22.5$$

The dimensions are 22.5 ft by 27.5 ft.

21. Let t = the time the cars travel.

$$\boxed{\text{Distance 1st car travels}} + \boxed{\text{Distance 2nd car travels}} = \boxed{\text{Total distance}}$$
$$45t + 50t = 285$$
$$95t = 285$$

$t = 3 \Rightarrow$ They will be 285 miles apart after 3 hours.

22. Let $t =$ the time the cars travel.

$\boxed{\text{Distance 1st car travels}} - \boxed{\text{Distance 2nd car travels}} = \boxed{\text{Distance between them}}$

$$46t - 40t = 3$$
$$6t = 3$$
$$t = 0.5 \Rightarrow \text{They will be 3 miles apart after 0.5 hours.}$$

23. Let $x =$ the liters of water added.

$\boxed{\text{Liters of alcohol at start}} + \boxed{\text{Liters of alcohol added}} = \boxed{\text{Liters of alcohol at end}}$

$$0.50(1) + 0 = 0.20(1 + x)$$
$$0.50 = 0.20 + 0.20x$$
$$0.30 = 0.20x$$
$$1.5 = x \Rightarrow \text{1.5 liters of water should be added.}$$

24. Let $x =$ hours for both working together.

$\boxed{\text{Number Scott washes in 1 hour}} \cdot \boxed{\text{Number of hours}} + \boxed{\text{Number Bill washes in 1 hour}} \cdot \boxed{\text{Number of hours}} = \boxed{\text{100 windows}}$

$$\frac{37}{3}x + \frac{27}{2}x = 100$$
$$6\left(\frac{37}{3}x + \frac{27}{2}x\right) = 6(100)$$
$$74x + 81x = 600$$
$$155x = 600$$
$$x = \frac{600}{155} \approx 3.9$$

They can wash 100 windows together in about 3.9 hours.

25. Let $x =$ hours for both pipes to fill the tank.

$\boxed{\text{1st pipe in 1 hour}} + \boxed{\text{2nd pipe in 1 hour}} = \boxed{\text{Total in 1 hour}}$

$$\frac{1}{9} + \frac{1}{12} = \frac{1}{x}$$
$$36x\left(\frac{1}{9} + \frac{1}{12}\right) = 36x\left(\frac{1}{x}\right)$$
$$4x + 3x = 36$$
$$7x = 36$$
$$x = \frac{36}{7} = 5\frac{1}{7}$$

The tank can be filled in $5\frac{1}{7}$ hours.

26. Let $x =$ the ounces of pure zinc added.

$\boxed{\text{Ounces of zinc at start}} + \boxed{\text{Ounces of zinc added}} = \boxed{\text{Ounces of zinc at end}}$

$$0.30(20) + x = 0.40(20 + x)$$
$$6 + x = 8 + 0.40x$$
$$0.60x = 2$$
$$6x = 20$$
$$x = \frac{20}{6} = 3\frac{1}{3}$$

$3\frac{1}{3}$ ounces of zinc should be added.

27. Let x = the amount invested at 11%. Then $10{,}000 - x$ = the amount invested at 14%.

$$\boxed{\text{Interest at 11\%}} + \boxed{\text{Interest at 14\%}} = \boxed{\text{Total interest}}$$

$$\begin{aligned} 0.11x + 0.14(10{,}000 - x) &= 1{,}265 \\ 0.11x + 1{,}400 - 0.14x &= 1{,}265 \\ -0.03x &= -135 \\ x &= 4{,}500 \end{aligned}$$

\$4,500 was invested at 11% and \$5,500 was invested at 14%.

28. Let x = # of rugs for equal costs.

$$\boxed{\text{Cost of 1st loom}} = \boxed{\text{Cost of 2nd loom}}$$

$$\begin{aligned} 750 + 115x &= 950 + 95x \\ 20x &= 200 \\ x &= 10 \end{aligned}$$

The costs are the same on either loom for 10 rugs.

29.
$$\begin{aligned} 2x^2 - x - 6 &= 0 \\ (2x + 3)(x - 2) &= 0 \end{aligned}$$
$$\begin{array}{lcl} 2x + 3 = 0 & \textbf{or} & x - 2 = 0 \\ 2x = -3 & & x = 2 \\ x = -\frac{3}{2} & & x = 2 \end{array}$$

30.
$$\begin{aligned} 12x^2 + 13x &= 4 \\ 12x^2 + 13x - 4 &= 0 \\ (4x - 1)(3x + 4) &= 0 \end{aligned}$$
$$\begin{array}{lcl} 4x - 1 = 0 & \textbf{or} & 3x + 4 = 0 \\ 4x = 1 & & 3x = -4 \\ x = \frac{1}{4} & & x = -\frac{4}{3} \end{array}$$

31.
$$\begin{aligned} 5x^2 - 8x &= 0 \\ x(5x - 8) &= 0 \end{aligned}$$
$$\begin{array}{lcl} x = 0 & \textbf{or} & 5x - 8 = 0 \\ x = 0 & & 5x = 8 \\ x = 0 & & x = \frac{8}{5} \end{array}$$

32.
$$\begin{aligned} 27x^2 &= 30x - 8 \\ 27x^2 - 30x + 8 &= 0 \\ (9x - 4)(3x - 2) &= 0 \end{aligned}$$
$$\begin{array}{lcl} 9x - 4 = 0 & \textbf{or} & 3x - 2 = 0 \\ 9x = 4 & & 3x = 2 \\ x = \frac{4}{9} & & x = \frac{2}{3} \end{array}$$

33.
$$\begin{aligned} 2x^2 &= 16 \\ x^2 &= 8 \\ \sqrt{x^2} &= \pm\sqrt{8} \\ x &= \pm 2\sqrt{2} \end{aligned}$$

34.
$$\begin{aligned} 12x^2 &= 60 \\ x^2 &= 5 \\ \sqrt{x^2} &= \pm\sqrt{5} \\ x &= \pm\sqrt{5} \end{aligned}$$

35.
$$\begin{aligned} (4z - 5)^2 &= 32 \\ \sqrt{(4z - 5)^2} &= \pm\sqrt{32} \\ 4z - 5 &= \pm 4\sqrt{2} \\ 4z &= 5 \pm 4\sqrt{2} \\ z &= \frac{5 \pm 4\sqrt{2}}{4} \end{aligned}$$

36.
$$\begin{aligned} (5x - 7)^2 &= 45 \\ \sqrt{(5x - 7)^2} &= \pm\sqrt{45} \\ 5x - 7 &= \pm 3\sqrt{5} \\ 5x &= 7 \pm 3\sqrt{5} \\ x &= \frac{7 \pm 3\sqrt{5}}{5} \end{aligned}$$

37.

$$\begin{aligned} x^2 - 8x + 15 &= 0 \\ x^2 - 8x &= -15 \\ x^2 - 8x + 16 &= -15 + 16 \\ (x-4)^2 &= 1 \end{aligned}$$

$$\begin{array}{lll} x - 4 = \sqrt{1} & \textbf{or} & x - 4 = -\sqrt{1} \\ x - 4 = 1 & & x - 4 = -1 \\ x = 5 & & x = 3 \end{array}$$

38.

$$\begin{aligned} 3x^2 + 18x &= -24 \\ \frac{3x^2 + 18x}{3} &= \frac{-24}{3} \\ x^2 + 6x &= -8 \\ x^2 + 6x + 9 &= -8 + 9 \\ (x+3)^2 &= 1 \end{aligned}$$

$$\begin{array}{lll} x + 3 = \sqrt{1} & \textbf{or} & x + 3 = -\sqrt{1} \\ x + 3 = 1 & & x + 3 = -1 \\ x = -2 & & x = -4 \end{array}$$

39.

$$\begin{aligned} 5x^2 - x - 1 &= 0 \\ 5x^2 - x &= 1 \\ x^2 - \frac{1}{5}x &= \frac{1}{5} \\ x^2 - \frac{1}{5}x + \frac{1}{100} &= \frac{1}{5} + \frac{1}{100} \\ \left(x - \frac{1}{10}\right)^2 &= \frac{21}{100} \end{aligned}$$

$$\begin{array}{lll} x - \frac{1}{10} = \sqrt{\frac{21}{100}} & \textbf{or} & x - \frac{1}{10} = -\sqrt{\frac{21}{100}} \\ x - \frac{1}{10} = \frac{\sqrt{21}}{10} & & x - \frac{1}{10} = -\frac{\sqrt{21}}{10} \\ x = \frac{1 + \sqrt{21}}{10} & & x = \frac{1 - \sqrt{21}}{10} \end{array}$$

40.

$$\begin{aligned} 5x^2 - x &= 0 \\ x^2 - \frac{1}{5}x &= 0 \\ x^2 - \frac{1}{5}x + \frac{1}{100} &= 0 + \frac{1}{100} \\ \left(x - \frac{1}{10}\right)^2 &= \frac{1}{100} \end{aligned}$$

$$\begin{array}{lll} x - \frac{1}{10} = \sqrt{\frac{1}{100}} & \textbf{or} & x - \frac{1}{10} = -\sqrt{\frac{1}{100}} \\ x - \frac{1}{10} = \frac{1}{10} & & x - \frac{1}{10} = -\frac{1}{10} \\ x = \frac{2}{10} = \frac{1}{5} & & x = \frac{0}{10} = 0 \end{array}$$

41. $x^2 + 5x - 14 = 0 \Rightarrow a = 1, b = 5, c = -14$

$$x = \frac{-b \pm \sqrt{b^2 - 4ac}}{2a} = \frac{-(5) \pm \sqrt{(5)^2 - 4(1)(-14)}}{2(1)} = \frac{-5 \pm \sqrt{25 + 56}}{2} = \frac{-5 \pm \sqrt{81}}{2}$$
$$= \frac{-5 \pm 9}{2}$$

$$x = \frac{-5 + 9}{2} = \frac{4}{2} = 2 \text{ or } x = \frac{-5 - 9}{2} = \frac{-14}{2} = -7$$

42. $3x^2 - 25x = 18 \Rightarrow 3x^2 - 25x - 18 = 0 \Rightarrow a = 3, b = -25, c = -18$

$$x = \frac{-b \pm \sqrt{b^2 - 4ac}}{2a} = \frac{-(-25) \pm \sqrt{(-25)^2 - 4(3)(-18)}}{2(3)} = \frac{25 \pm \sqrt{625 + 216}}{6}$$
$$= \frac{25 \pm \sqrt{841}}{6} = \frac{25 \pm 29}{6}$$

$$x = \frac{25 + 29}{6} = \frac{54}{6} = 9 \text{ or } x = \frac{25 - 29}{6} = \frac{-4}{6} = -\frac{2}{3}$$

43. $5x^2 = 1 - x \Rightarrow 5x^2 + x - 1 = 0 \Rightarrow a = 5, b = 1, c = -1$

$$x = \frac{-b \pm \sqrt{b^2 - 4ac}}{2a} = \frac{-(1) \pm \sqrt{(1)^2 - 4(5)(-1)}}{2(5)} = \frac{-1 \pm \sqrt{1 + 20}}{10} = \frac{-1 \pm \sqrt{21}}{10}$$

44. $-5 = a^2 + 2a \Rightarrow a^2 + 2a + 5 = 0 \Rightarrow a = 1, b = 2, c = 5$

$$a = \frac{-b \pm \sqrt{b^2 - 4ac}}{2a} = \frac{-(2) \pm \sqrt{(2)^2 - 4(1)(5)}}{2(1)} = \frac{-2 \pm \sqrt{4 - 20}}{2} = \frac{-2 \pm \sqrt{-16}}{2}$$
$$= \frac{-2 \pm 4i}{2} = -1 \pm 2i$$

45. $6x^2 + 5x + 1 = 0$
$a = 6, b = 5, c = 1$
$b^2 - 4ac = (5)^2 - 4(6)(1) = 25 - 24 = 1$

46. The roots are unequal rational numbers.

47. $kx^2 + 4x + 12 = 0$
$a = k, b = 4, c = 12$
Set the discriminant equal to 0:

$$b^2 - 4ac = 0$$
$$4^2 - 4(k)(12) = 0$$
$$16 - 48k = 0$$
$$-48k = -16$$
$$k = \frac{1}{3}$$

48. $4y^2 + (k + 2)y = 1 - k$
$4y^2 + (k + 2)y - 1 + k = 0$
$a = 4, b = k + 2, c = -1 + k$
Set the discriminant equal to 0:

$$b^2 - 4ac = 0$$
$$(k + 2)^2 - 4(4)(-1 + k) = 0$$
$$k^2 + 4k + 4 + 16 - 16k = 0$$
$$k^2 - 12k + 20 = 0$$
$$(k - 10)(k - 2) = 0$$

$k - 10 = 0$ **or** $k - 2 = 0$
$k = 10$ $\quad$ $k = 2$

49.
$$\frac{1}{a} - \frac{1}{5} = \frac{3}{2a}$$
$$10a\left(\tfrac{1}{a} - \tfrac{1}{5}\right) = 10a\left(\tfrac{3}{2a}\right)$$
$$10 - 2a = 15$$
$$-2a = 5$$
$$a = -\tfrac{5}{2}$$

50.
$$\frac{4}{a-4} + \frac{4}{a-1} = 5$$
$$(a-4)(a-1)\left(\tfrac{4}{a-4} + \tfrac{4}{a-1}\right) = (a-4)(a-1)5$$
$$4(a-1) + 4(a-4) = 5(a^2 - 5a + 4)$$
$$4a - 4 + 4a - 16 = 5a^2 - 25a + 20$$
$$0 = 5a^2 - 33a + 40$$
$$0 = (5a-8)(a-5)$$
$5a - 8 = 0$ **or** $a - 5 = 0$

$5a = 8$ $\qquad a = 5$

$a = \frac{8}{5}$ $\qquad a = 5$

51. Let $x =$ one side of the garden.

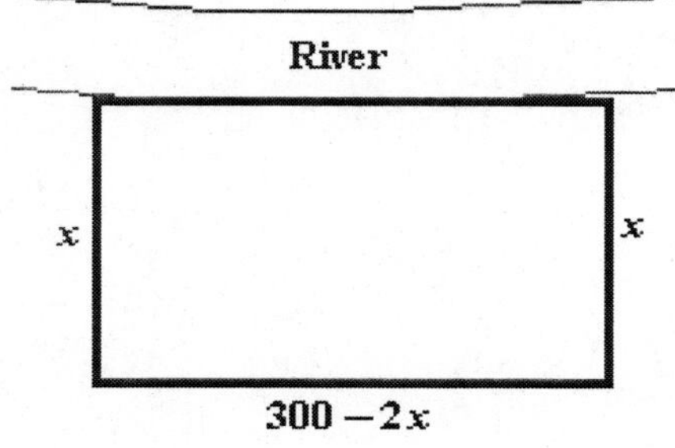

$$\text{Area} = 10450$$
$$x(300 - 2x) = 10450$$
$$-2x^2 + 300x = 10450$$
$$0 = 2x^2 - 300x + 10450$$
$$0 = 2(x^2 - 150x + 5225)$$
$$0 = 2(x - 95)(x - 55)$$
$x - 95 = 0$ **or** $x - 55 = 0$

$x = 95$ $\qquad x = 55$

The dimensions are 95 yards by 110 yards or 55 yards by 190 yards.

52. Let $r =$ the rate of the propeller-driven plane. Then the rate of the jet plane is $r + 120$.

$$\boxed{\text{Jet time}} = \boxed{\text{Propeller time}} - 3$$

	Rate	Time	Dist.
Propeller	r	$\frac{3520}{r}$	3520
Jet	$r + 120$	$\frac{3520}{r+120}$	3520

$$\frac{3520}{r+120} = \frac{3520}{r} - 3$$
$$r(r+120)\frac{3520}{r+120} = r(r+120)\left(\frac{3520}{r} - 3\right)$$
$$3520r = 3520(r+120) - 3r(r+120)$$
$$3520r = 3520r + 422400 - 3r^2 - 360r$$
$$3r^2 + 360r + 422{,}400 = 0$$
$$3(r - 320)(r + 440) = 0$$
$r - 320 = 0$ **or** $r + 440 = 0$

$r = 320$ $\qquad r = -440$

Since $r = -440$ does not make sense, the solution is $r = 320$. The prop. plane's rate is 320 mph, while the jet plane's rate is 440 mph.

53. Set $h = 48$:

$$h = -16t^2 + 64t$$
$$48 = -16t^2 + 64t$$
$$16t^2 - 64t + 48 = 0$$
$$16(t-1)(t-3) = 0$$
$$t - 1 = 0 \quad \textbf{or} \quad t - 3 = 0$$
$$t = 1 \qquad\qquad t = 3$$

The shortest time required for the ball to reach a height of 48 feet is 1 second.

54. Let $x =$ the width of the walk. Then the total dimensions are $16 + 2x$ by $20 + 2x$.

$$\boxed{\text{Total area}} - \boxed{\text{Area of pool}} = \boxed{\text{Area of walk}}$$
$$(16+2x)(20+2x) - (16)(20) = 117$$
$$320 + 72x + 4x^2 - 320 = 117$$
$$4x^2 + 72x - 117 = 0$$
$$(2x+39)(2x-3) = 0$$
$$2x + 39 = 0 \quad \textbf{or} \quad 2x - 3 = 0$$
$$x = -\tfrac{39}{2} \qquad\qquad x = \tfrac{3}{2}$$

Since $x = -\frac{39}{2}$ does not make sense, the only solution is $x = \frac{3}{2}$. The walk is $1\frac{1}{2}$ feet wide.

55. $(2-3i) + (-4+2i) = 2 - 3i - 4 + 2i$
$= -2 - i$

56. $(2-3i) - (4+2i) = 2 - 3i - 4 - 2i$
$= -2 - 5i$

57. $\left(3 - \sqrt{-36}\right) + \left(\sqrt{-16} + 2\right) = (3 - 6i) + (4i + 2) = 3 - 6i + 4i + 2 = 5 - 2i$

58. $\left(3 + \sqrt{-9}\right)\left(2 - \sqrt{-25}\right) = (3 + 3i)(2 - 5i) = 6 - 9i - 15i^2 = 6 - 9i + 15 = 21 - 9i$

59. $\dfrac{3}{i} = \dfrac{3i}{ii} = \dfrac{3i}{i^2} = \dfrac{3i}{-1} = 0 - 3i$

60. $-\dfrac{2}{i^3} = -\dfrac{2i}{i^3 i} = -\dfrac{2i}{i^4} = -\dfrac{2i}{1} = 0 - 2i$

61. $\dfrac{3}{1+i} = \dfrac{3(1-i)}{(1+i)(1-i)} = \dfrac{3(1-i)}{1^2 - i^2} = \dfrac{3-3i}{2} = \dfrac{3}{2} - \dfrac{3}{2}i$

62. $\dfrac{2i}{2-i} = \dfrac{2i(2+i)}{(2-i)(2+i)} = \dfrac{4i + 2i^2}{2^2 - i^2} = \dfrac{-2+4i}{5} = -\dfrac{2}{5} + \dfrac{4}{5}i$

63. $\dfrac{3+i}{3-i} = \dfrac{(3+i)(3+i)}{(3-i)(3+i)} = \dfrac{9 + 6i + i^2}{3^2 - i^2} = \dfrac{8+6i}{10} = \dfrac{8}{10} + \dfrac{6}{10}i = \dfrac{4}{5} + \dfrac{3}{5}i$

64. $\dfrac{3-2i}{1+i} = \dfrac{(3-2i)(1-i)}{(1+i)(1-i)} = \dfrac{3 - 5i + 2i^2}{1^2 - i^2} = \dfrac{1-5i}{2} = \dfrac{1}{2} - \dfrac{5}{2}i$

65. $i^{53} = i^{52}i = \left(i^4\right)^{13} i = 1^{13} i = 0 + i$

66. $i^{103} = i^{100} i^3 = \left(i^4\right)^{25} i^3 = 1^{25} i^3 = 0 - i$

67. $|3 - i| = \sqrt{3^2 + (-1)^2} = \sqrt{9+1} = \sqrt{10}$

68. $\left|\dfrac{1+i}{1-i}\right| = \left|\dfrac{(1+i)(1+i)}{(1-i)(1+i)}\right| = \left|\dfrac{1 + 2i + i^2}{1^2 - i^2}\right| = \left|\dfrac{2i}{2}\right| = |0 + i| = \sqrt{0^2 + 1^2} = 1$

69. $3x^2 - 2x + 1 = 0 \Rightarrow a = 3, b = -2, c = 1$

$$x = \frac{-b \pm \sqrt{b^2 - 4ac}}{2a} = \frac{-(-2) \pm \sqrt{(-2)^2 - 4(3)(1)}}{2(3)} = \frac{2 \pm \sqrt{4 - 12}}{6} = \frac{2 \pm \sqrt{-8}}{6}$$

$$= \frac{2}{6} \pm \frac{2\sqrt{2}}{6}i$$

$$= \frac{1}{3} \pm \frac{\sqrt{2}}{3}i$$

70. $3x^2 + 4 = 2x \Rightarrow 3x^2 - 2x + 4 = 0 \Rightarrow a = 3, b = -2, c = 4$

$$x = \frac{-b \pm \sqrt{b^2 - 4ac}}{2a} = \frac{-(-2) \pm \sqrt{(-2)^2 - 4(3)(4)}}{2(3)} = \frac{2 \pm \sqrt{4 - 48}}{6} = \frac{2 \pm \sqrt{-44}}{6}$$

$$= \frac{2}{6} \pm \frac{2\sqrt{11}}{6}i$$

$$= \frac{1}{3} \pm \frac{\sqrt{11}}{3}i$$

71.

$$\frac{3x}{2} - \frac{2x}{x-1} = x - 3$$

$$2(x-1)\left(\frac{3x}{2} - \frac{2x}{x-1}\right) = 2(x-1)(x-3)$$

$$3x(x-1) - 2(2x) = 2\left(x^2 - 4x + 3\right)$$

$$3x^2 - 3x - 4x = 2x^2 - 8x + 6$$

$$x^2 + x - 6 = 0$$

$$(x+3)(x-2) = 0$$

$x + 3 = 0$ **or** $x - 2 = 0$

$x = -3$ $\quad$ $x = 2$

72.

$$\frac{12}{x} - \frac{x}{2} = x - 3$$

$$2x\left(\frac{12}{x} - \frac{x}{2}\right) = 2x(x-3)$$

$$2(12) - x(x) = 2x^2 - 6x$$

$$24 - x^2 = 2x^2 - 6x$$

$$0 = 3x^2 - 6x - 24$$

$$0 = 3(x+2)(x-4)$$

$x + 2 = 0$ **or** $x - 4 = 0$

$x = -2$ $\quad$ $x = 4$

73.

$$x^4 - 2x^2 + 1 = 0$$

$$\left(x^2 - 1\right)\left(x^2 - 1\right) = 0$$

$x^2 - 1 = 0$ **or** $x^2 - 1 = 0$

$x^2 = 1$ $\quad$ $x^2 = 1$

$x = \pm 1$ $\quad$ $x = \pm 1$

74.

$$x^4 + 36 = 37x^2$$

$$x^4 - 37x^2 + 36 = 0$$

$$\left(x^2 - 36\right)\left(x^2 - 1\right) = 0$$

$x^2 - 36 = 0$ **or** $x^2 - 1 = 0$

$x^2 = 36$ $\quad$ $x^2 = 1$

$x = \pm 6$ $\quad$ $x = \pm 1$

75.

$$a - a^{1/2} - 6 = 0$$

$$\left(a^{1/2} + 2\right)\left(a^{1/2} - 3\right) = 0$$

$a^{1/2} + 2 = 0$ **or** $a^{1/2} - 3 = 0$

$a^{1/2} = -2$ $\quad$ $a^{1/2} = 3$

$\left(a^{1/2}\right)^2 = (-2)^2$ $\quad$ $\left(a^{1/2}\right)^2 = (3)^2$

$a = 4$ $\quad$ $a = 9$

$a = 4$ does not check and is extraneous.

76.
$$x^{2/3} + x^{1/3} - 6 = 0$$
$$(x^{1/3} - 2)(x^{1/3} + 3) = 0$$
$$x^{1/3} - 2 = 0 \quad \textbf{or} \quad x^{1/3} + 3 = 0$$
$$x^{1/3} = 2 \qquad x^{1/3} = -3$$
$$(x^{1/3})^3 = (2)^3 \qquad (x^{1/3})^3 = (-3)^3$$
$$x = 8 \qquad x = -27$$
Both answers check.

77.
$$\sqrt{x-1} + x = 7$$
$$\sqrt{x-1} = 7 - x$$
$$\left(\sqrt{x-1}\right)^2 = (7-x)^2$$
$$x - 1 = 49 - 14x + x^2$$
$$0 = x^2 - 15x + 50$$
$$0 = (x-5)(x-10)$$
$$x - 5 = 0 \quad \textbf{or} \quad x - 10 = 0$$
$$x = 5 \qquad x = 10$$
$x = 10$ does not check and is extraneous.

78.
$$\sqrt{a+9} - \sqrt{a} = 3$$
$$\sqrt{a+9} = 3 + \sqrt{a}$$
$$\left(\sqrt{a+9}\right)^2 = \left(3 + \sqrt{a}\right)^2$$
$$a + 9 = 9 + 6\sqrt{a} + a$$
$$0 = 6\sqrt{a}$$
$$0^2 = \left(6\sqrt{a}\right)^2$$
$$0 = 36a \Rightarrow a = 0$$
The solution checks.

79.
$$\sqrt{5-x} + \sqrt{5+x} = 4$$
$$\sqrt{5+x} = 4 - \sqrt{5-x}$$
$$\left(\sqrt{5+x}\right)^2 = \left(4 - \sqrt{5-x}\right)^2$$
$$5 + x = 16 - 8\sqrt{5-x} + 5 - x$$
$$8\sqrt{5-x} = 16 - 2x$$
$$\left(8\sqrt{5-x}\right)^2 = (16-2x)^2$$
$$64(5-x) = 256 - 64x + 4x^2$$
$$320 - 64x = 4x^2 - 64x + 256$$
$$0 = 4x^2 - 64$$
$$0 = 4(x+4)(x-4)$$
$$x + 4 = 0 \quad \textbf{or} \quad x - 4 = 0$$
$$x = -4 \qquad x = 4$$
Both solutions check.

80.
$$\sqrt{y+5} + \sqrt{y} = 1$$
$$\sqrt{y+5} = 1 - \sqrt{y}$$
$$\left(\sqrt{y+5}\right)^2 = \left(1 - \sqrt{y}\right)^2$$
$$y + 5 = 1 - 2\sqrt{y} + y$$
$$2\sqrt{y} = -4$$
$$\left(2\sqrt{y}\right)^2 = (-4)^2$$
$$4y = 16$$
$$y = 4$$
The solution does not check. $\Rightarrow$ No solution.

81.
$$2x - 9 < 5$$
$$2x < 14$$
$$x < 7 \Rightarrow (-\infty, 7)$$
7

82.
$$5x + 3 \geq 2$$
$$5x \geq -1$$
$$x \geq -\tfrac{1}{5} \Rightarrow \left[-\tfrac{1}{5}, \infty\right)$$
$-\frac{1}{5}$

83. $\dfrac{5(x-1)}{2} < x$

$5(x-1) < 2x$

$5x - 5 < 2x$

$3x < 5$

$x < \frac{5}{3} \Rightarrow \left(-\infty, \frac{5}{3}\right)$

$\frac{5}{3}$

84. $\dfrac{1}{4}x + \dfrac{2}{3}x - x > \dfrac{1}{2} + \dfrac{1}{2}(x+1)$

$12\left(\dfrac{1}{4}x + \dfrac{2}{3}x - x\right) > 12\left(\dfrac{1}{2} + \dfrac{1}{2}(x+1)\right)$

$3x + 8x - 12x > 6 + 6(x+1)$

$-x > 6 + 6x + 6$

$-12 > 7x$

$-\dfrac{12}{7} > x \Rightarrow \left(-\infty, -\dfrac{12}{7}\right)$

$-\frac{12}{7}$

85. $0 \le \dfrac{3+x}{2} < 4$

$0 \le 3 + x < 8$

$-3 \le x < 5 \Rightarrow [-3, 5)$

-3 5

86. $2 + a < 3a - 2 \le 5a + 2$

$2 + a < 3a - 2$ **and** $3a - 2 \le 5a + 2$

$4 < 2a$ $\qquad -4 \le 2a$

$a > 2$ $\qquad a \ge -2$

$a > 2$ — 2

$a > -2$ — -2

$a > 2$ **and** $a \ge -2$ — 2

Solution set: $(2, \infty)$

87. $(x+2)(x-4) > 0$

factors $= 0$: $x = -2$, $x = 4$

intervals: $(-\infty, -2)$, $(-2, 4)$, $(4, \infty)$

interval	test number	value of $(x+2)(x-4)$
$(-\infty, -2)$	-3	$+7$
$(-2, 4)$	0	-8
$(4, \infty)$	5	$+7$

Solution: $(-\infty, -2) \cup (4, \infty)$

-2 4

88. $(x-1)(x+4) < 0$

factors $= 0$: $x = 1$, $x = -4$

intervals: $(-\infty, -4)$, $(-4, 1)$, $(1, \infty)$

interval	test number	value of $(x-1)(x+4)$
$(-\infty, -4)$	-5	$+6$
$(-4, 1)$	0	-4
$(1, \infty)$	2	$+8$

Solution: $(-4, 1)$

-4 1

89. $x^2 - 2x - 3 < 0$

$(x-3)(x+1) < 0$

factors $= 0$: $x = 3$, $x = -1$

intervals: $(-\infty, -1)$, $(-1, 3)$, $(3, \infty)$

interval	test number	value of x^2-2x-3
$(-\infty, -1)$	-2	$+5$
$(-1, 3)$	0	-3
$(3, \infty)$	4	$+5$

Solution: $(-1, 3)$

-1 3

90. $2x^2 + x - 3 > 0$

$(2x+3)(x-1) > 0$

factors $= 0$: $x = -\frac{3}{2}$, $x = 1$

intervals: $\left(-\infty, -\frac{3}{2}\right)$, $\left(-\frac{3}{2}, 1\right)$, $(1, \infty)$

interval	test number	value of $2x^2+x-3$
$\left(-\infty, -\frac{3}{2}\right)$	-2	$+3$
$\left(-\frac{3}{2}, 1\right)$	0	-3
$(1, \infty)$	2	$+7$

Solution: $\left(-\infty, -\frac{3}{2}\right) \cup (1, \infty)$

$-\frac{3}{2}$ 1

91. $\dfrac{x+2}{x-3} \geq 0$

factors $= 0$: $x = -2$, $x = 3$

intervals: $(-\infty, -2)$, $(-2, 3)$, $(3, \infty)$

interval	test number	sign of $\frac{x+2}{x-3}$
$(-\infty, -2)$	-3	$+$
$(-2, 3)$	0	$-$
$(3, \infty)$	4	$+$

Include endpoints which make the numerator equal to 0. Do not include endpoints which make the denominator equal to 0.

Solution: $(-\infty, -2] \cup (3, \infty)$

-2 3

92. $\dfrac{x-1}{x+4} \leq 0$

factors $= 0$: $x = 1$, $x = -4$

intervals: $(-\infty, -4)$, $(-4, 1)$, $(1, \infty)$

interval	test number	sign of $\frac{x-1}{x+4}$
$(-\infty, -4)$	-5	$+$
$(-4, 1)$	0	$-$
$(1, \infty)$	2	$+$

Include endpoints which make the numerator equal to 0. Do not include endpoints which make the denominator equal to 0.

Solution: $(-4, 1]$

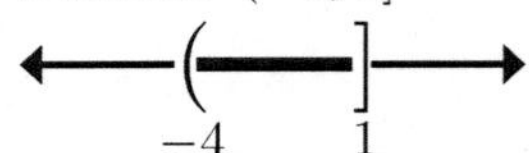

93. $\dfrac{x^2 + x - 2}{x-3} \geq 0$

$\dfrac{(x+2)(x-1)}{x-3} \geq 0$

factors $= 0$: $x = -2$, $x = 1$, $x = 3$

int.: $(-\infty, -2)$, $(-2, 1)$, $(1, 3)$, $(3, \infty)$

interval	test number	sign of $\frac{x^2+x-2}{x-3}$
$(-\infty, -2)$	-3	$-$
$(-2, 1)$	0	$+$
$(1, 3)$	2	$-$
$(3, \infty)$	4	$+$

Include endpoints which make the numerator equal to 0. Do not include endpoints which make the denominator equal to 0.

Solution: $[-2, 1] \cup (3, \infty)$

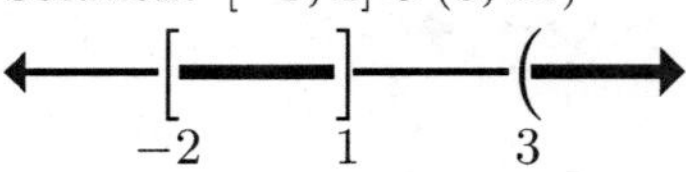

94.

$$\frac{5}{x} < 2$$
$$\frac{5}{x} - 2 < 0$$
$$\frac{5-2x}{x} < 0$$

factors = 0: $x = \frac{5}{2}, x = 0$

intervals: $(-\infty, 0), (0, \frac{5}{2}), (\frac{5}{2}, \infty)$

interval	test number	value of $\frac{5-2x}{x}$
$(-\infty, 0)$	-1	-7
$(0, \frac{5}{2})$	1	$+3$
$(\frac{5}{2}, \infty)$	3	$-\frac{1}{3}$

Solution: $(-\infty, 0) \cup (\frac{5}{2}, \infty)$

0 $\quad \frac{5}{2}$

95.

$$|x+1| = 6$$
$x + 1 = 6$ **or** $x + 1 = -6$

$x = 5 \qquad x = -7$

96.

$$|2x-1| = |2x+1|$$
$2x - 1 = 2x + 1$ **or** $2x - 1 = -(2x+1)$

$0 = 2 \qquad 2x - 1 = -2x - 1$

never true $\qquad 4x = 0$

$x = 0$

97.

$$\left|\frac{3x+11}{7}\right| - 1 = 0$$
$$\left|\frac{3x+11}{7}\right| = 1$$
$\frac{3x+11}{7} = 1$ **or** $\frac{3x+11}{7} = -1$

$3x + 11 = 7 \qquad 3x + 11 = -7$

$3x = -4 \qquad 3x = -18$

$x = -\frac{4}{3} \qquad x = -6$

98.

$$\left|\frac{2a-6}{3a}\right| - 6 = 0$$
$$\left|\frac{2a-6}{3a}\right| = 6$$
$\frac{2a-6}{3a} = 6$ **or** $\frac{2a-6}{3a} = -6$

$2a - 6 = 18a \qquad 2a - 6 = -18a$

$-16a = 6 \qquad 20a = 6$

$a = -\frac{6}{16} \qquad a = \frac{6}{20}$

$a = -\frac{3}{8} \qquad a = \frac{3}{10}$

99.

$$|x+3| < 3$$
$$-3 < x + 3 < 3$$
$$-6 < x < 0$$
$$(-6, 0)$$

$-6 \quad 0$

100.

$$|3x-7| \geq 1$$
$3x - 7 \geq 1$ **or** $3x - 7 \leq -1$

$3x \geq 8 \qquad 3x \leq 6$

$x \geq \frac{8}{3} \qquad x \leq 2$

$$(-\infty, 2] \cup [\tfrac{8}{3}, \infty)$$

$2 \quad \frac{8}{3}$

101.

$$\left|\frac{x+2}{3}\right| < 1$$
$$-1 < \frac{x+2}{3} < 1$$
$$-3 < x+2 < 3$$
$$-5 < x < 1$$
$$(-5, 1)$$

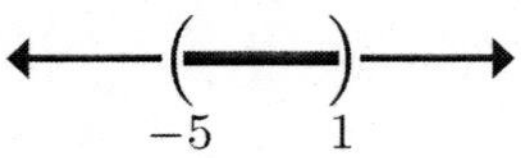

102.

$$\left|\frac{x-3}{4}\right| > 8$$
$$\frac{x-3}{4} > 8 \quad \textbf{or} \quad \frac{x-3}{4} < -8$$
$$x-3 > 32 \qquad x-3 < -32$$
$$x > 35 \qquad x < -29$$
$$(-\infty, -29) \cup (35, \infty)$$

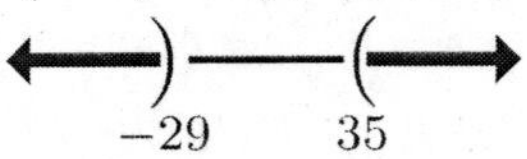

103.

$$1 < |2x+3| < 4$$
$$1 < |2x+3| \quad \textbf{and} \quad |2x+3| < 4$$

(1) $|2x+3| > 1$

$$2x+3 > 1 \quad \textbf{or} \quad 2x+3 < -1$$
$$2x > -2 \qquad 2x < -4$$
$$x > -1 \qquad x < -2$$

(2) $|2x+3| < 4$

$$-4 < 2x+3 < 4$$
$$-7 < 2x < 1$$
$$-\tfrac{7}{2} < x < \tfrac{1}{2}$$

(1) 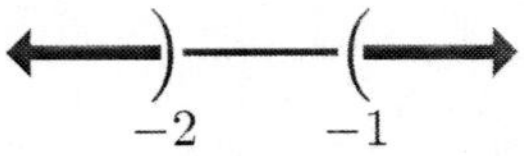

(2) 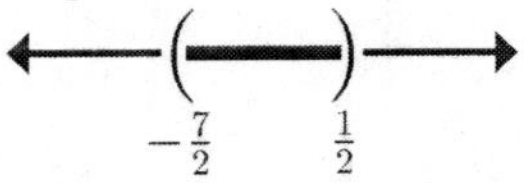

(1) 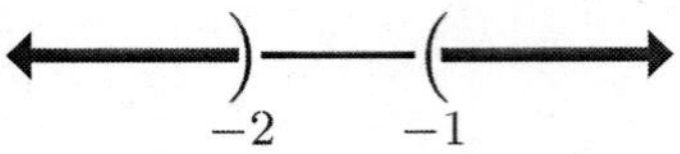

(2) 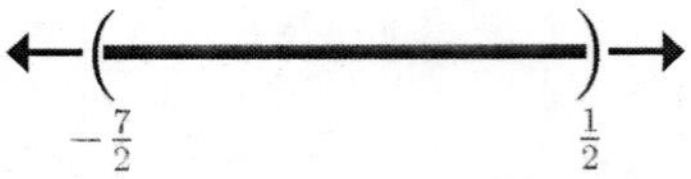

(1) and (2) 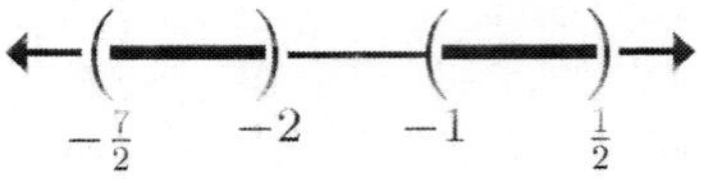

$\Rightarrow \left(-\tfrac{7}{2}, -2\right) \cup \left(-1, \tfrac{1}{2}\right)$

104.

$$0 < |3x-4| < 7$$
$$0 < |3x-4| \quad \textbf{and} \quad |3x-4| < 7$$

(1) $|3x-4| > 0$

$$3x-4 > 0 \quad \textbf{or} \quad 3x-4 < -0$$
$$3x > 4 \qquad 3x < 4$$
$$x > \tfrac{4}{3} \qquad x < \tfrac{4}{3}$$

(2) $|3x-4| < 7$

$$-7 < 3x-4 < 7$$
$$-3 < 3x < 11$$
$$-1 < x < \tfrac{11}{3}$$

(1) 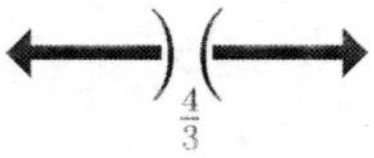

(2) 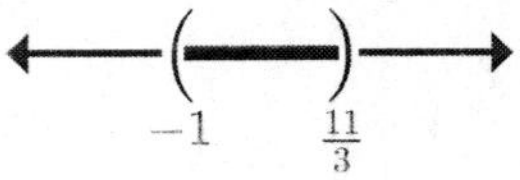

(1) 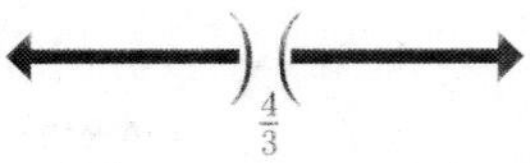

(2) 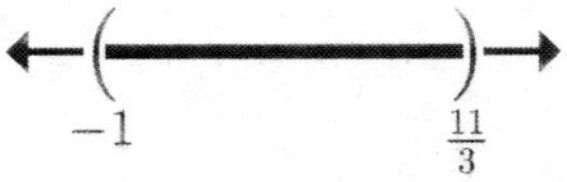

(1) and (2) 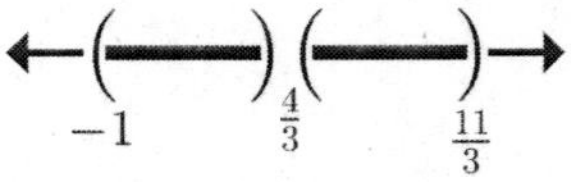

$\Rightarrow \left(-1, \tfrac{4}{3}\right) \cup \left(\tfrac{4}{3}, \tfrac{11}{3}\right)$

Chapter 1 Test (page 185)

1. $\dfrac{x}{x(x-1)} = 2$

restrictions: $x \neq 0$, $x \neq 1$

2. $\dfrac{4}{3x-2} + 3 = 7$

restrictions: $x \neq \frac{2}{3}$

3.
$$\begin{aligned} 7(2a+5) - 7 &= 6(a+8) \\ 14a + 35 - 7 &= 6a + 48 \\ 8a &= 20 \\ a &= \frac{20}{8} = \frac{5}{2} \end{aligned}$$

4.
$$\begin{aligned} \frac{3}{x^2 - 5x - 14} &= \frac{4}{x^2 + 5x + 6} \\ \frac{3}{(x-7)(x+2)} &= \frac{4}{(x+2)(x+3)} \\ (x-7)(x+2)(x+3)\frac{3}{(x-7)(x+2)} &= (x-7)(x+2)(x+3)\frac{4}{(x+2)(x+3)} \\ 3(x+3) &= 4(x-7) \\ 3x + 9 &= 4x - 28 \\ 37 &= x \end{aligned}$$

5.
$$\begin{aligned} z &= \frac{x - \mu}{\sigma} \\ \sigma z &= \sigma \cdot \frac{x - \mu}{\sigma} \\ z\sigma &= x - \mu \\ z\sigma + \mu &= x \end{aligned}$$

6.
$$\begin{aligned} \frac{1}{a} &= \frac{1}{b} + \frac{1}{c} \\ abc \cdot \frac{1}{a} &= abc\left(\frac{1}{b} + \frac{1}{c}\right) \\ bc &= ac + ab \\ bc &= a(c+b) \\ \frac{bc}{c+b} &= \frac{a(c+b)}{c+b} \\ \frac{bc}{c+b} &= a \end{aligned}$$

7. Let $x =$ the score on the final.

Note: This score is counted twice.

$$\begin{aligned} \frac{\boxed{\text{Sum of scores}}}{5} &= 80 \\ \frac{75 + 75 + 75 + x + x}{5} &= 80 \\ \frac{2x + 225}{5} &= 80 \\ 2x + 225 &= 400 \\ 2x &= 175 \\ x &= 87.5 \end{aligned}$$

The student needs to score 87.5.

8. Let $x =$ the amount invested at 6%. Then $20{,}000 - x =$ the amount invested at 7%.

$$\boxed{\text{Interest at 6\%}} + \boxed{\text{Interest at 7\%}} = \boxed{\text{Total interest}}$$

$$\begin{aligned} 0.06x + 0.07(20{,}000 - x) &= 1{,}260 \\ 0.06x + 1{,}400 - 0.07x &= 1{,}260 \\ -0.01x &= -140 \\ x &= 14{,}000 \end{aligned}$$

\$14,000 was invested at 6%.

9.
$$\begin{aligned} 4x^2 - 8x + 3 &= 0 \\ (2x-3)(2x-1) &= 0 \end{aligned}$$
$$2x - 3 = 0 \quad \textbf{or} \quad 2x - 1 = 0$$
$$2x = 3 \qquad\qquad 2x = 1$$
$$x = \tfrac{3}{2} \qquad\qquad x = \tfrac{1}{2}$$

10.
$$\begin{aligned} 2b^2 - 12 &= -5b \\ 2b^2 + 5b - 12 &= 0 \\ (2b-3)(b+4) &= 0 \end{aligned}$$
$$2b - 3 = 0 \quad \textbf{or} \quad b + 4 = 0$$
$$2b = 3 \qquad\qquad b = -4$$
$$b = \tfrac{3}{2} \qquad\qquad b = -4$$

11. $x = \dfrac{-b \pm \sqrt{b^2 - 4ac}}{2a}$

12. $3x^2 - 5x - 9 = 0 \Rightarrow a = 3, b = -5, c = -9$

$$x = \frac{-b \pm \sqrt{b^2 - 4ac}}{2a} = \frac{-(-5) \pm \sqrt{(-5)^2 - 4(3)(-9)}}{2(3)} = \frac{5 \pm \sqrt{25 + 108}}{6} = \frac{5 \pm \sqrt{133}}{6}$$

13. $x^2 + (k+1)x + k + 4 = 0$

$a = 1, b = k + 1, c = k + 4$

Set the discriminant equal to 0:
$$\begin{aligned} b^2 - 4ac &= 0 \\ (k+1)^2 - 4(1)(k+4) &= 0 \\ k^2 + 2k + 1 - 4k - 16 &= 0 \\ k^2 - 2k - 15 &= 0 \\ (k-5)(k+3) &= 0 \end{aligned}$$
$$k - 5 = 0 \quad \textbf{or} \quad k + 3 = 0$$
$$k = 5 \qquad\qquad k = -3$$

14. Set $h = 0$:
$$\begin{aligned} h &= -16t^2 + 128t \\ 0 &= -16t^2 + 128t \\ 0 &= -16t(t-8) \end{aligned}$$
$$-16t = 0 \quad \textbf{or} \quad t - 8 = 0$$
$$t = 0 \qquad\qquad t = 8$$
The ball will return after 8 seconds.

15. $(4 - 5i) - (-3 + 7i) = 4 - 5i + 3 - 7i$
$= 7 - 12i$

16. $(4 - 5i)(3 - 7i) = 12 - 43i + 35i^2$
$= 12 - 43i - 35$
$= -23 - 43i$

17. $\dfrac{2}{2-i} = \dfrac{2(2+i)}{(2-i)(2+i)} = \dfrac{4+2i}{2^2 - i^2} = \dfrac{4+2i}{5} = \dfrac{4}{5} + \dfrac{2}{5}i$

18. $\dfrac{1+i}{1-i} = \dfrac{(1+i)(1+i)}{(1-i)(1+i)} = \dfrac{1 + 2i + i^2}{1^2 - i^2} = \dfrac{2i}{2} = 0 + i$

19. $i^{13} = i^{12}i = (i^4)^3 i = 1^3 i = i$

20. $i^0 = 1$

21. $|5 - 12i| = \sqrt{5^2 + (-12)^2} = \sqrt{25 + 144} = \sqrt{169} = 13$

22. $\left|\dfrac{1}{3+i}\right| = \left|\dfrac{1(3-i)}{(3+i)(3-i)}\right| = \left|\dfrac{3-i}{3^2-i^2}\right| = \left|\dfrac{3-i}{10}\right| = \left|\dfrac{3}{10} - \dfrac{1}{10}i\right| = \sqrt{\left(\dfrac{3}{10}\right)^2 + \left(-\dfrac{1}{10}\right)^2}$

$= \sqrt{\dfrac{9}{100} + \dfrac{1}{100}}$

$= \sqrt{\dfrac{10}{100}} = \dfrac{\sqrt{10}}{10}$

23. $z^4 - 13z^2 + 36 = 0$

$(z^2-4)(z^2-9) = 0$

$z^2 - 4 = 0$ **or** $z^2 - 9 = 0$

$z^2 = 4$ $\qquad z^2 = 9$

$z = \pm 2$ $\qquad z = \pm 3$

24. $2p^{2/5} - p^{1/5} - 1 = 0$

$(2p^{1/5}+1)(p^{1/5}-1) = 0$

$2p^{1/5} + 1 = 0$ **or** $p^{1/5} - 1 = 0$

$p^{1/5} = -\frac{1}{2}$ $\qquad p^{1/5} = 1$

$(p^{1/5})^5 = (-\frac{1}{2})^5$ $\qquad (p^{1/5})^5 = (1)^5$

$p = -\frac{1}{32}$ $\qquad p = 1$

Both answers check.

25. $\sqrt{x+5} = 12$

$\left(\sqrt{x+5}\right)^2 = 12^2$

$x + 5 = 144$

$x = 139$

The answer checks.

26. $\sqrt{2z+3} = 1 - \sqrt{z+1}$

$\left(\sqrt{2z+3}\right)^2 = \left(1 - \sqrt{z+1}\right)^2$

$2z + 3 = 1 - 2\sqrt{z+1} + z + 1$

$2\sqrt{z+1} = -z - 1$

$\left(2\sqrt{z+1}\right)^2 = (-z-1)^2$

$4(z+1) = z^2 + 2z + 1$

$4z + 4 = z^2 + 2z + 1$

$0 = z^2 - 2z - 3$

$0 = (z+1)(z-3)$

$z + 1 = 0$ **or** $z - 3 = 0$

$z = -1$ $\qquad z = 3$

The answer $z = 3$ is extraneous.

27. $5x - 3 \leq 7$

$5x \leq 10$

$x \leq 2 \Rightarrow (-\infty, 2]$

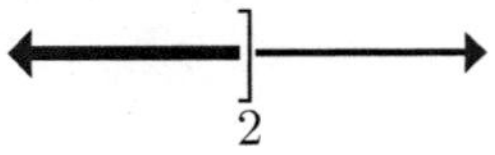

28. $\dfrac{x+3}{4} > \dfrac{2x-4}{3}$

$12 \cdot \frac{x+3}{4} > 12 \cdot \frac{2x-4}{3}$

$3(x+3) > 4(2x-4)$

$3x + 9 > 8x - 16$

$-5x > -25$

$x < 5 \Rightarrow (-\infty, 5)$

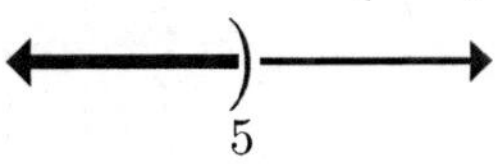

29. $5 \le 2x - 1 < 7$
$6 \le 2x < 8$
$3 \le x < 4 \Rightarrow [3, 4)$

3 4

30. $1 + x < 3x - 3 < 4x - 2$
$1 + x < 3x - 3$ **and** $3x - 3 < 4x - 2$
$-2x < -4$ $\quad -x < 1$
$x > 2$ $\quad x > -1$

$x > 2$ 2

$x > -1$ −1

$x > 2$
and
$x > -1$ 2

Solution set: $(2, \infty)$

31. $x^2 - 7x - 8 \ge 0$
$(x + 1)(x - 8) \ge 0$
factors $= 0$: $x = -1, x = 8$
intervals: $(-\infty, -1), (-1, 8), (8, \infty)$

interval	test number	value of x^2-7x-8
$(-\infty, -1)$	-2	$+10$
$(-1, 8)$	0	-8
$(8, \infty)$	9	$+10$

Solution: $(-\infty, -1] \cup [8, \infty)$

−1 8

32. $\dfrac{x + 2}{x - 1} \le 0$
factors $= 0$: $x = -2, x = 1$
intervals: $(-\infty, -2), (-2, 1), (1, \infty)$

interval	test number	sign of $\frac{x+2}{x-1}$
$(-\infty, -2)$	-3	$+$
$(-2, 1)$	0	$-$
$(1, \infty)$	2	$+$

Include endpoints which make the numerator equal to 0. Do not include endpoints which make the denominator equal to 0.
Solution: $[-2, 1)$

−2 1

33. $\left|\dfrac{3x + 2}{2}\right| = 4$

$\frac{3x+2}{2} = 4$ **or** $\frac{3x+2}{2} = -4$
$3x + 2 = 8$ $\quad 3x + 2 = -8$
$3x = 6$ $\quad 3x = -10$
$x = 2$ $\quad x = -\frac{10}{3}$

34. $|x + 3| = |x - 3|$
$x + 3 = x - 3$ **or** $x + 3 = -(x - 3)$
$0 = -6$ $\quad x + 3 = -x + 3$
not true $\quad 2x = 0$
$x = 0$

35. $|2x-5|>2$

$2x-5>2$ **or** $2x-5<-2$

$2x>7 \qquad 2x<3$

$x>\frac{7}{2} \qquad x<\frac{3}{2}$

$\left(-\infty,\frac{3}{2}\right)\cup\left(\frac{7}{2},\infty\right)$

$\frac{3}{2} \quad \frac{7}{2}$

36. $\left|\frac{2x+3}{3}\right|\le 5$

$-5\le\frac{2x+3}{3}\le 5$

$-15\le 2x+3\le 15$

$-18\le 2x\le 12$

$-9\le x\le 6$

$[-9, 6]$

$-9 \quad 6$

Cumulative Review Exercises (page 186)

1. even integers: $-2, 0, 2, 6$

2. prime numbers: $2, 5, 11$

3. $-4\le x<7\Rightarrow[-4,7)$

$-4 \quad 7$

4. $x\ge 2$ or $x<0\Rightarrow(-\infty,0)\cup[2,\infty)$

$0 \quad 2$

5. commutative property of addition

6. transitive property

7. $(81a^4)^{1/2}=\left[(9a^2)^2\right]^{1/2}=9a^2$

8. $81(a^4)^{1/2}=81\left[(a^2)^2\right]^{1/2}=81a^2$

9. $(a^{-3}b^{-2})^{-2}=(a^{-3})^{-2}(b^{-2})^{-2}=a^6b^4$

10. $\left(\frac{4x^4}{12x^2y}\right)^{-2}=\left(\frac{12x^2y}{4x^4}\right)^2=\left(\frac{3y}{x^2}\right)^2=\frac{9y^2}{x^4}$

11. $\left(\frac{4x^0y^2}{x^2y}\right)^{-2}=\left(\frac{x^2y}{4x^0y^2}\right)^2=\left(\frac{x^2}{4y}\right)^2=\frac{x^4}{16y^2}$

12. $\left(\frac{4x^{-5}y^2}{6x^{-2}y^{-3}}\right)^2=\left(\frac{2y^5}{3x^3}\right)^2=\frac{4y^{10}}{9x^6}$

13. $(a^{1/2}b)^2(ab^{1/2})^2=(ab^2)(a^2b)=a^3b^3$

14. $(a^{1/2}b^{1/2}c)^2=abc^2$

15. $\frac{3}{\sqrt{3}}=\frac{3\sqrt{3}}{\sqrt{3}\sqrt{3}}=\frac{3\sqrt{3}}{3}=\sqrt{3}$

16. $\frac{2}{\sqrt[3]{4x}}=\frac{2\sqrt[3]{2x^2}}{\sqrt[3]{4x}\sqrt[3]{2x^2}}=\frac{2\sqrt[3]{2x^2}}{\sqrt[3]{8x^3}}=\frac{2\sqrt[3]{2x^2}}{2x}=\frac{\sqrt[3]{2x^2}}{x}$

17. $\frac{3}{y-\sqrt{3}}=\frac{3\left(y+\sqrt{3}\right)}{\left(y-\sqrt{3}\right)\left(y+\sqrt{3}\right)}=\frac{3\left(y+\sqrt{3}\right)}{y^2-\left(\sqrt{3}\right)^2}=\frac{3\left(y+\sqrt{3}\right)}{y^2-3}$

CUMULATIVE REVIEW EXERCISES

18. $\dfrac{3x}{\sqrt{x}-1} = \dfrac{3x(\sqrt{x}+1)}{(\sqrt{x}-1)(\sqrt{x}+1)} = \dfrac{3x(\sqrt{x}+1)}{(\sqrt{x})^2-1^2} = \dfrac{3x(\sqrt{x}+1)}{x-1}$

19. $\sqrt{75}-3\sqrt{5} = \sqrt{25}\sqrt{3}-3\sqrt{5} = 5\sqrt{3}-3\sqrt{5}$

20. $\sqrt{18}+\sqrt{8}-2\sqrt{2} = \sqrt{9}\sqrt{2}+\sqrt{4}\sqrt{2}-2\sqrt{2} = 3\sqrt{2}+2\sqrt{2}-2\sqrt{2} = 3\sqrt{2}$

21. $\left(\sqrt{2}-\sqrt{3}\right)^2 = \left(\sqrt{2}-\sqrt{3}\right)\left(\sqrt{2}-\sqrt{3}\right) = \sqrt{4}-2\sqrt{6}+\sqrt{9} = 5-2\sqrt{6}$

22. $\left(3-\sqrt{5}\right)\left(3+\sqrt{5}\right) = 9-\sqrt{25} = 9-5 = 4$

23. $(3x^2-2x+5)-3(x^2+2x-1) = 3x^2-2x+5-3x^2-6x+3 = -8x+8$

24. $5x^2(2x^2-x)+x(x^2-x^3) = 10x^4-5x^3+x^3-x^4 = 9x^4-4x^3$

25. $(3x-5)(2x+7) = 6x^2+21x-10x-35 = 6x^2+11x-35$

26. $(z+2)(z^2-z+2) = z^3-z^2+2z+2z^2-2z+4 = z^3+z^2+4$

27.
$$\begin{array}{r|l} & 2x^2 - x + 1 \\ \hline 3x+2 & 6x^3 + x^2 + x + 2 \\ & \underline{6x^3 + 4x^2} \\ & -3x^2 + x \\ & \underline{-3x^2 - 2x} \\ & 3x + 2 \\ & \underline{3x + 2} \\ & 0 \end{array}$$

28.
$$\begin{array}{r|l} & 3x^2 + 1 + \frac{-x}{x^2+2} \\ \hline x^2+2 & 3x^4 + 0x^3 + 7x^2 - x + 2 \\ & \underline{3x^4 \qquad + 6x^2} \\ & x^2 - x + 2 \\ & \underline{x^2 \qquad + 2} \\ & -x \end{array}$$

29. $3t^2-6t = 3t(t-2)$

30. $3x^2-10x-8 = (3x+2)(x-4)$

31. $x^8-2x^4+1 = \left(x^4-1\right)\left(x^4-1\right) = \left(x^2+1\right)\left(x^2-1\right)\left(x^2+1\right)\left(x^2-1\right)$
$= \left(x^2+1\right)^2(x+1)(x-1)(x+1)(x-1)$
$= \left(x^2+1\right)^2(x+1)^2(x-1)^2$

32. $x^6-1 = (x^3)^2-1^2 = (x^3+1)(x^3-1) = (x+1)(x^2-x+1)(x-1)(x^2+x+1)$

33. $\dfrac{x^2-4}{x^2+5x+6}\cdot\dfrac{x^2-2x-15}{x^2+3x-10} = \dfrac{(x+2)(x-2)}{(x+2)(x+3)}\cdot\dfrac{(x-5)(x+3)}{(x+5)(x-2)} = \dfrac{x-5}{x+5}$

34. $\dfrac{6x^3+x^2-x}{x+2} \div \dfrac{3x^2-x}{x^2+4x+4} = \dfrac{x(6x^2+x-1)}{x+2}\cdot\dfrac{x^2+4x+4}{3x^2-x}$
$= \dfrac{x(2x+1)(3x-1)}{x+2}\cdot\dfrac{(x+2)(x+2)}{x(3x-1)} = (2x+1)(x+2)$

35. $$\frac{2}{x+3}+\frac{5x}{x-3}=\frac{2(x-3)}{(x+3)(x-3)}+\frac{5x(x+3)}{(x-3)(x+3)}=\frac{2x-6}{(x+3)(x-3)}+\frac{5x^2+15x}{(x+3)(x-3)}=\frac{5x^2+17x-6}{(x+3)(x-3)}$$

36. $$\frac{x-2}{x+3}\left(\frac{x+3}{x^2-4}-1\right)=\frac{x-2}{x+3}\left(\frac{x+3}{x^2-4}-\frac{x^2-4}{x^2-4}\right)=\frac{x-2}{x+3}\left(\frac{-x^2+x+7}{(x+2)(x-2)}\right)=\frac{-x^2+x+7}{(x+3)(x+2)}$$

37. $$\frac{\frac{1}{a}+\frac{1}{b}}{\frac{1}{ab}}=\frac{ab\left(\frac{1}{a}+\frac{1}{b}\right)}{ab\left(\frac{1}{ab}\right)}=\frac{b+a}{1}=b+a$$

38. $$\frac{x^{-1}-y^{-1}}{x-y}=\frac{\frac{1}{x}-\frac{1}{y}}{x-y}=\frac{xy\left(\frac{1}{x}-\frac{1}{y}\right)}{xy(x-y)}=\frac{y-x}{xy(x-y)}=-\frac{1}{xy}$$

39.
$$\frac{3x}{x+5}=\frac{x}{x-5}$$
$$3x(x-5)=x(x+5)$$
$$3x^2-15x=x^2+5x$$
$$2x^2-20x=0$$
$$2x(x-10)=0$$
$2x=0$ **or** $x-10=0$

$x=0$ $\quad x=10$

40.
$$8(2x-3)-3(5x+2)=4$$
$$16x-24-15x-6=4$$
$$x=34$$

41.
$$\frac{1}{R}=\frac{1}{R_1}+\frac{1}{R_2}$$
$$RR_1R_2\cdot\frac{1}{R}=RR_1R_2\left(\frac{1}{R_1}+\frac{1}{R_2}\right)$$
$$R_1R_2=RR_2+RR_1$$
$$R_1R_2=R(R_2+R_1)$$
$$\frac{R_1R_2}{R_2+R_1}=\frac{R(R_2+R_1)}{R_2+R_1}$$
$$\frac{R_1R_2}{R_2+R_1}=R$$

42.
$$S=\frac{a-lr}{1-r}$$
$$S(1-r)=\frac{a-lr}{1-r}(1-r)$$
$$S(1-r)=a-lr$$
$$S-Sr=a-lr$$
$$S-a=Sr-lr$$
$$S-a=r(S-l)$$
$$\frac{S-a}{S-l}=r$$

43.

Garage

x x

40 − 2x

Area $=192$
$$x(40-2x)=192$$
$$40x-2x^2=192$$
$$0=2x^2-40x+192$$
$$0=2(x-8)(x-12)$$
$x-8=0$ **or** $x-12=0$

$x=8$ $\quad x=12$

If $x=8$, then the dimensions are 8 feet by 24 feet.

If $x=12$, then the dimensions are 12 feet by 16 feet.

CUMULATIVE REVIEW EXERCISES

44. Let x = the amount invested at 6%. Then $25{,}000 - x$ = the amount invested at 7%.

$$\boxed{\text{Interest at 6\%}} + \boxed{\text{Interest at 7\%}} = \boxed{\text{Total interest}}$$

$$\begin{aligned} 0.06x + 0.07(25{,}000 - x) &= 1{,}670 \\ 0.06x + 1{,}750 - 0.07x &= 1{,}670 \\ -0.01x &= -80 \\ x &= 8{,}000 \Rightarrow \$8{,}000 \text{ was invested at 6\%.} \end{aligned}$$

45. $\dfrac{2+i}{2-i} = \dfrac{(2+i)(2+i)}{(2-i)(2+i)} = \dfrac{4+4i+i^2}{4-i^2} = \dfrac{3+4i}{5} = \dfrac{3}{5} + \dfrac{4}{5}i$

46. $\dfrac{i(3-i)}{(1+i)(1+i)} = \dfrac{i(3-i)(1-i)(1-i)}{(1+i)(1-i)(1+i)(1-i)} = \dfrac{(3i-i^2)(1-2i+i^2)}{(1-i^2)(1-i^2)}$

$= \dfrac{(1+3i)(-2i)}{1-2i^2+i^4} = \dfrac{-2i-6i^2}{4} = \dfrac{6-2i}{4} = \dfrac{3}{2} - \dfrac{1}{2}i$

47. $|3+4i| = \sqrt{3^2+4^2} = \sqrt{9+16} = \sqrt{25} = 5$

48. $\dfrac{5}{i^7} + 5i = \dfrac{5i}{i^7 i} + 5i = \dfrac{5i}{i^8} + 5i = \dfrac{5i}{(i^4)^2} + 5i = \dfrac{5i}{1^2} + 5i = 5i + 5i = 10i = 0 + 10i$

49.
$$\begin{aligned} \frac{x+3}{x-1} - \frac{6}{x} &= 1 \\ x(x-1)\left(\frac{x+3}{x-1} - \frac{6}{x}\right) &= x(x-1)(1) \\ x(x+3) - 6(x-1) &= x^2 - x \\ x^2 + 3x - 6x + 6 &= x^2 - x \\ -2x &= -6 \\ x &= 3 \end{aligned}$$

50.
$$\begin{aligned} x^4 + 36 &= 13x^2 \\ x^4 - 13x^2 + 36 &= 0 \\ (x^2-4)(x^2-9) &= 0 \end{aligned}$$
$$\begin{aligned} x^2 - 4 &= 0 \quad \textbf{or} \quad & x^2 - 9 &= 0 \\ x^2 &= 4 & x^2 &= 9 \\ x &= \pm 2 & x &= \pm 3 \end{aligned}$$

51.
$$\begin{aligned} \sqrt{y+2} + \sqrt{11-y} &= 5 \\ \sqrt{y+2} - 5 &= -\sqrt{11-y} \\ \left(\sqrt{y+2} - 5\right)^2 &= \left(-\sqrt{11-y}\right)^2 \\ y + 2 - 10\sqrt{y+2} + 25 &= 11 - y \\ -10\sqrt{y+2} &= -2y - 16 \\ \left(-10\sqrt{y+2}\right)^2 &= (-2y-16)^2 \\ 100(y+2) &= 4y^2 + 64y + 256 \\ 100y + 200 &= 4y^2 + 64y + 256 \\ 0 &= 4y^2 - 36y + 56 \\ 0 &= 4(y-2)(y-7) \end{aligned}$$
$$\begin{aligned} y - 2 &= 0 \quad \textbf{or} \quad & y - 7 &= 0 \\ y &= 2 & y &= 7 \end{aligned}$$
Both solutions check.

52.
$$\begin{aligned} z^{2/3} - 13z^{1/3} + 36 &= 0 \\ \left(z^{1/3} - 4\right)\left(z^{1/3} - 9\right) &= 0 \end{aligned}$$
$$\begin{aligned} z^{1/3} - 4 &= 0 \quad \textbf{or} \quad & z^{1/3} - 9 &= 0 \\ z^{1/3} &= 4 & z^{1/3} &= 9 \\ \left(z^{1/3}\right)^3 &= 4^3 & \left(z^{1/3}\right)^3 &= 9^3 \\ z &= 64 & z &= 729 \end{aligned}$$
Both solutions check.

CUMULATIVE REVIEW EXERCISES

53. $5x - 7 \le 4$

$5x \le 11$

$x \le \frac{11}{5} \Rightarrow \left(-\infty, \frac{11}{5}\right]$

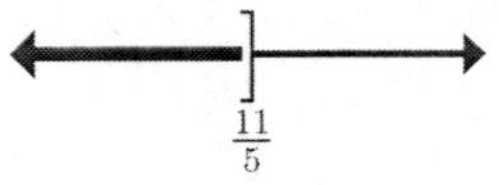

54. $x^2 - 8x + 15 > 0$

$(x-3)(x-5) > 0$

factors $= 0$: $x = 3, x = 5$

intervals: $(-\infty, 3), (3, 5), (5, \infty)$

interval	test number	value of $x^2-8x+15$
$(-\infty, 3)$	0	+15
$(3, 5)$	4	−1
$(5, \infty)$	6	+3

Solution: $(-\infty, 3) \cup (5, \infty)$

55. $\dfrac{x^2+4x+3}{x-2} \ge 0$

$\dfrac{(x+3)(x+1)}{x-2} \ge 0$

factors $= 0$: $x = -3, x = -1, x = 2$

int.: $(-\infty, -3), (-3, -1), (-1, 2), (2, \infty)$

interval	test number	sign of $\frac{x^2+4x+3}{x-2}$
$(-\infty, -3)$	−4	−
$(-3, -1)$	−2	+
$(-1, 2)$	0	−
$(2, \infty)$	3	+

Include endpoints which make the numerator equal to 0. Do not include endpoints which make the denominator equal to 0.

Solution: $[-3, -1] \cup (2, \infty)$

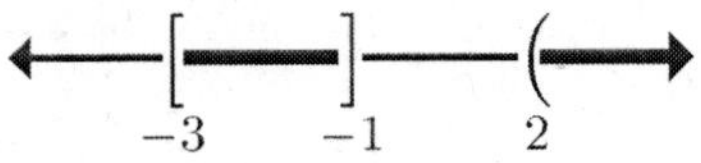

56. $\dfrac{9}{x} > x$

$\dfrac{9}{x} - x > 0$

$\dfrac{9-x^2}{x} > 0$

$\dfrac{(3+x)(3-x)}{x} > 0$

factors $= 0$: $x = -3, x = 3, x = 0$

int.: $(-\infty, -3), (-3, 0), (0, 3), (3, \infty)$

interval	test number	sign of $\frac{9-x^2}{x}$
$(-\infty, -3)$	−4	+
$(-3, 0)$	−1	−
$(0, 3)$	1	+
$(3, \infty)$	4	−

Solution: $(-\infty, -3) \cup (0, 3)$

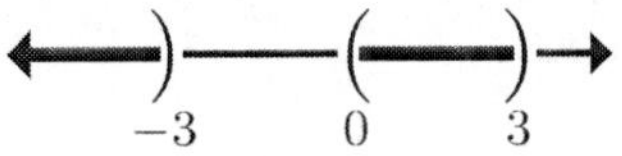

57. $|2x - 3| \ge 5$

$2x - 3 \ge 5$ **or** $2x - 3 \le -5$

$2x \ge 8$ $\quad$ $2x \le -2$

$x \ge 4$ $\quad$ $x \le -1$

$(-\infty, -1] \cup [4, \infty)$

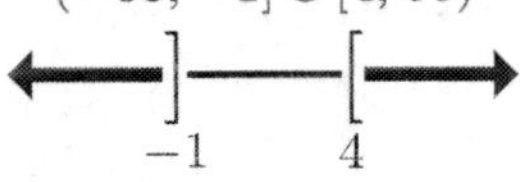

58. $\left|\dfrac{3x-5}{2}\right| < 2$

$-2 < \dfrac{3x-5}{2} < 2$

$-4 < 3x - 5 < 4$

$1 < 3x < 9$

$\frac{1}{3} < x < 3$

$\left(\frac{1}{3}, 3\right)$

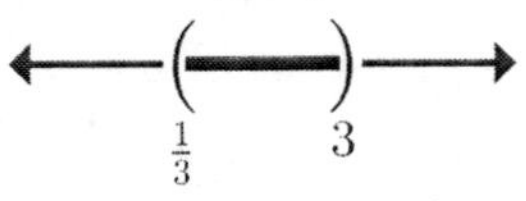

Exercises 2.1 (page 202)

1. quadrants **2.** origin **3.** to the right **4.** upward

5. first **6.** second **7.** linear **8.** y-axis

9. x-intercept **10.** vertical **11.** horizontal

12. $\sqrt{(x_2 - x_1)^2 + (y_2 - y_1)^2}$ **13.** midpoint **14.** $M\left(\frac{x_1 + x_2}{2}, \frac{y_1 + y_2}{2}\right)$

15. $A(2, 3)$ **16.** $B(-3, 5)$ **17.** $C(-2, -3)$ **18.** $D(4, -5)$

19. $E(0, 0)$ **20.** $F(-4, 0)$ **21.** $G(-5, -5)$ **22.** $H(2, -2)$

23, 25, 27, 29.

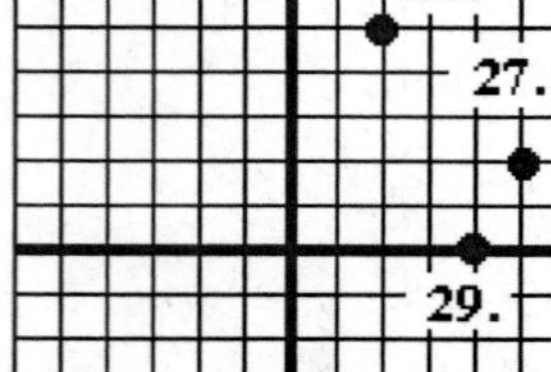

23. QI

25. QIII

27. QI

29. $+\,x$-axis

24, 26, 28, 30.

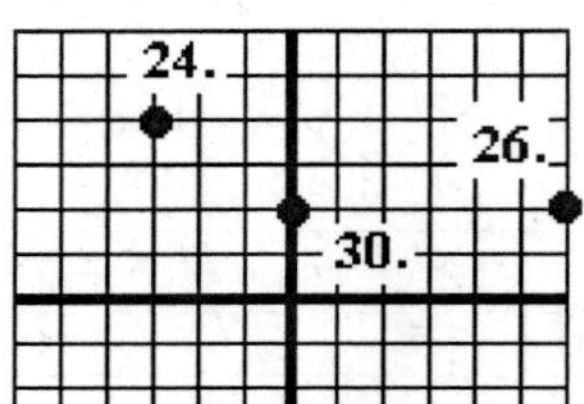

24. QII

26. QI

28. QIV

30. $+\,y$-axis

31. $y - 2x = 7$

$y = 2x + 7$

x	y
0	7
-2	3

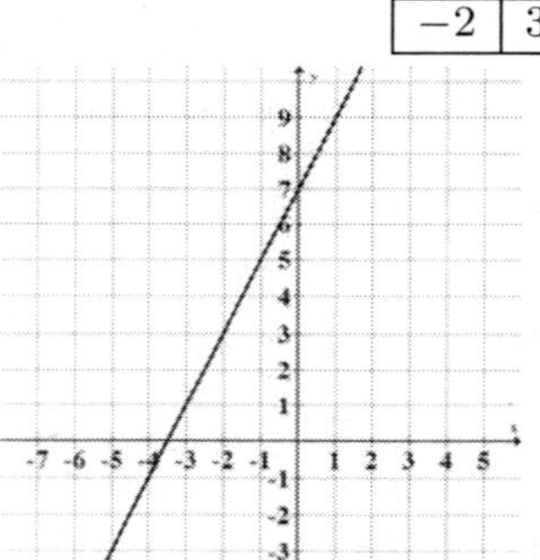

32. $y + 3 = -4x$

$y = -4x - 3$

x	y
0	-3
-1	1

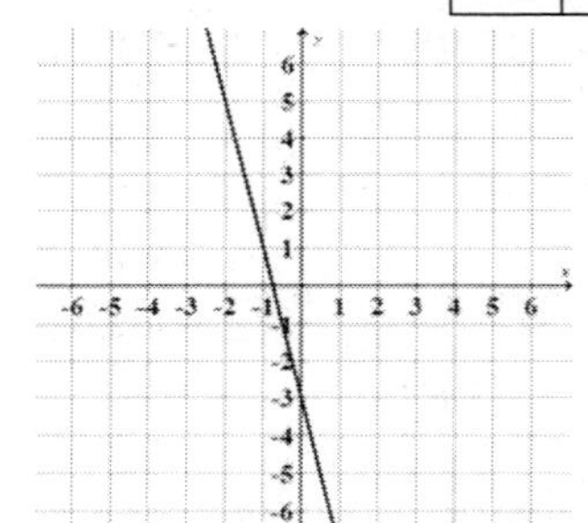

33. $y + 5x = 5$

$y = -5x + 5$

x	y
0	5
1	0

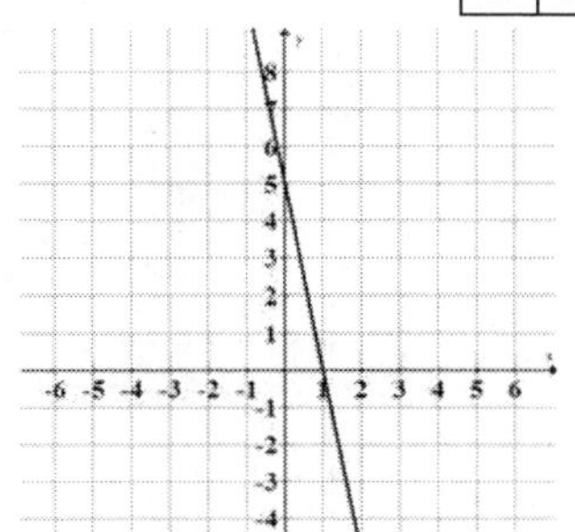

34. $y - 3x = 6$

$y = 3x + 6$

x	y
0	6
-2	0

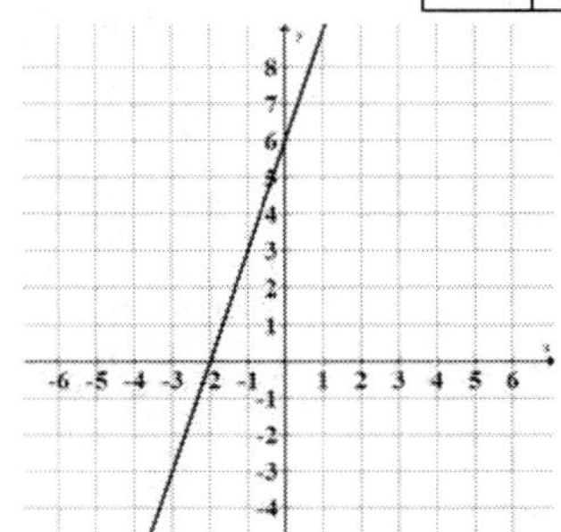

35. $6x - 3y = 10$

$-3y = -6x + 10$

$y = 2x - \frac{10}{3}$

x	y
0	$-\frac{10}{3}$
2	$\frac{2}{3}$

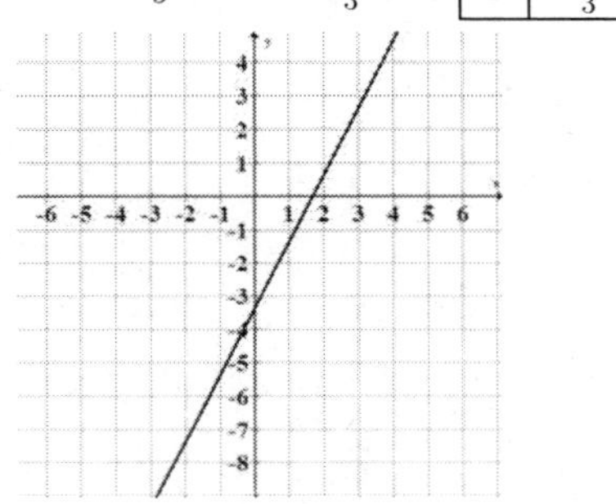

36.

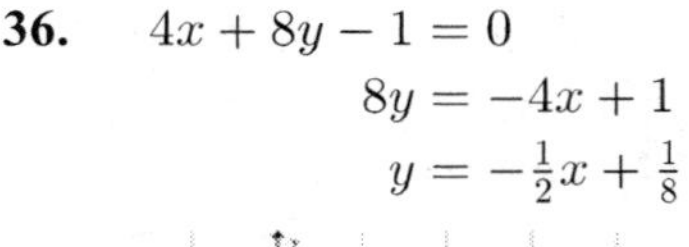

$4x + 8y - 1 = 0$

$8y = -4x + 1$

$y = -\frac{1}{2}x + \frac{1}{8}$

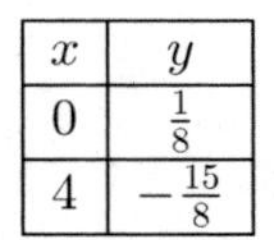

x	y
0	$\frac{1}{8}$
4	$-\frac{15}{8}$

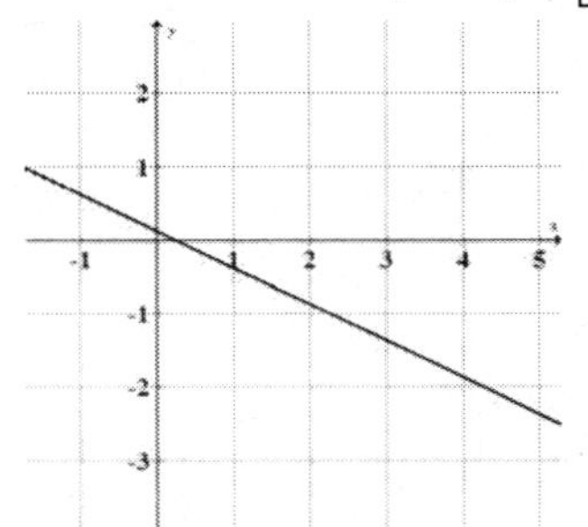

37. $3x = 6y - 1$

$-6y = -3x - 1$

$y = \frac{1}{2}x + \frac{1}{6}$

x	y
0	$\frac{1}{6}$
-2	$-\frac{5}{6}$

38. $2x + 1 = 4y$

$-4y = -2x - 1$

$y = \frac{1}{2}x + \frac{1}{4}$

x	y
0	$\frac{1}{4}$
-2	$-\frac{3}{4}$

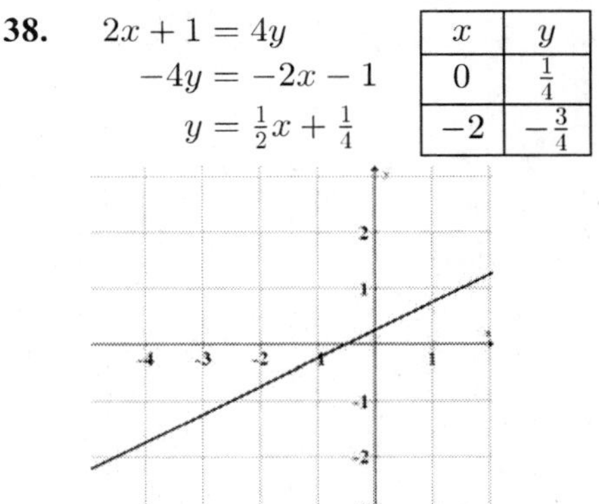

39. $2(x+y+1) = x+2$
$2x+2y+2 = x+2$
$2y = -x$
$y = -\frac{1}{2}x$

x	y
0	0
-2	1

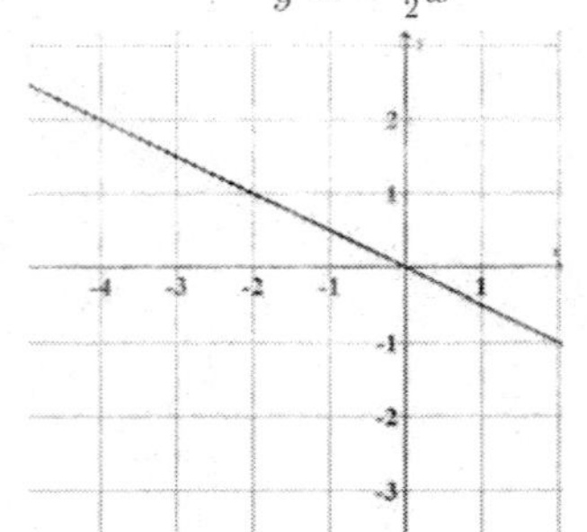

40. $5(x+2) = 3y - x$
$5x + 10 = 3y - x$
$-3y = -6x - 10$
$y = 2x + \frac{10}{3}$

x	y
0	$\frac{10}{3}$
-2	$-\frac{2}{3}$

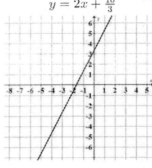

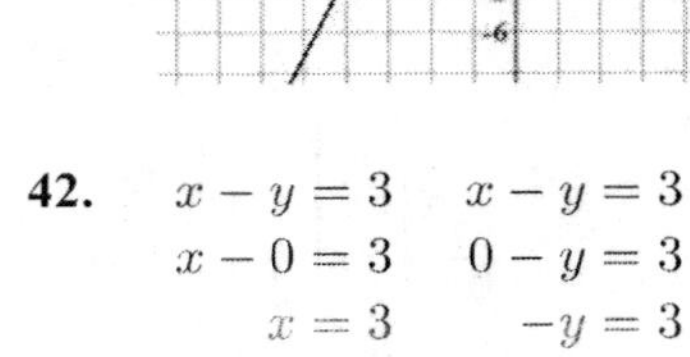

41. $x + y = 5$ $\quad$ $x + y = 5$
$x + 0 = 5$ $\quad$ $0 + y = 5$
$x = 5$ $\quad$ $y = 5$
$(5, 0)$ $\quad$ $(0, 5)$

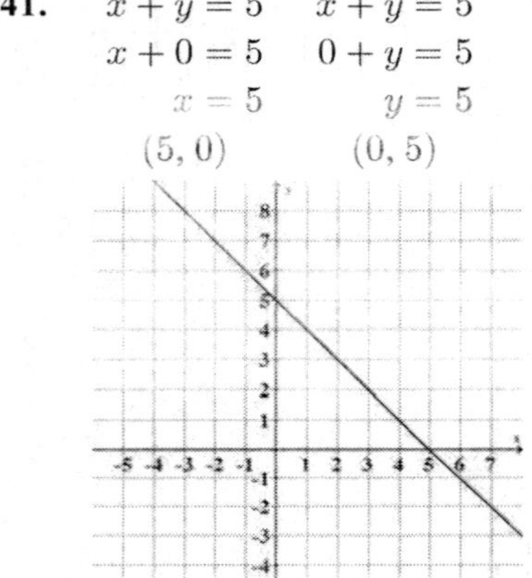

42. $x - y = 3$ $\quad$ $x - y = 3$
$x - 0 = 3$ $\quad$ $0 - y = 3$
$x = 3$ $\quad$ $-y = 3$
$(3, 0)$ $\quad$ $y = -3$
$(0, -3)$

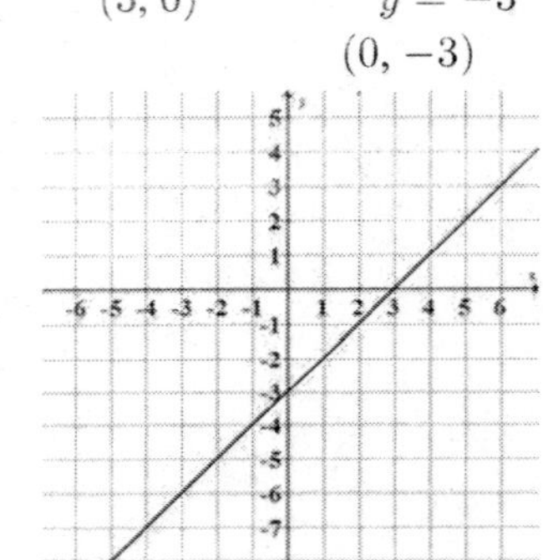

43. $2x - y = 4$ $\quad$ $2x - y = 4$
$2x - 0 = 4$ $\quad$ $2(0) - y = 4$
$2x = 4$ $\quad$ $-y = 4$
$x = 2$ $\quad$ $y = -4$
$(2, 0)$ $\quad$ $(0, -4)$

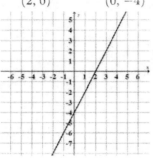

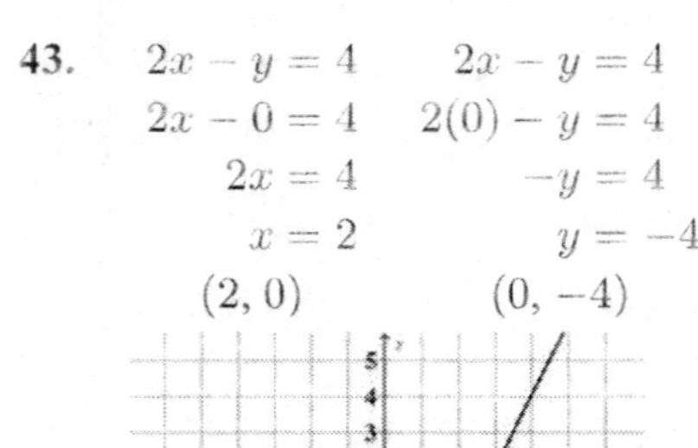

44. $3x + y = 9$ $\quad$ $3x + y = 9$
$3x + 0 = 9$ $\quad$ $3(0) + y = 9$
$3x = 9$ $\quad$ $y = 9$
$x = 3$ $\quad$ $(0, 9)$
$(3, 0)$

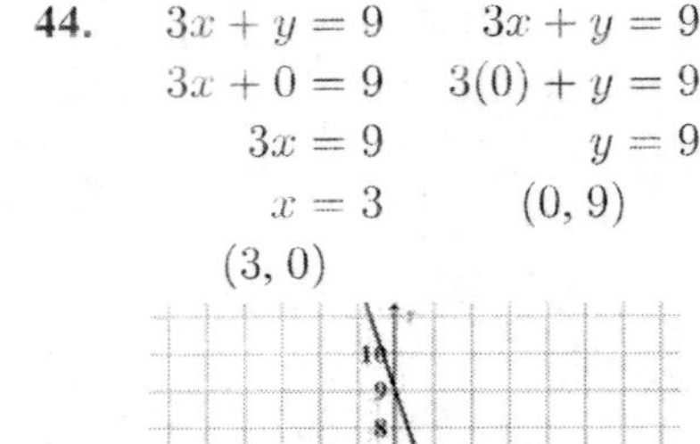

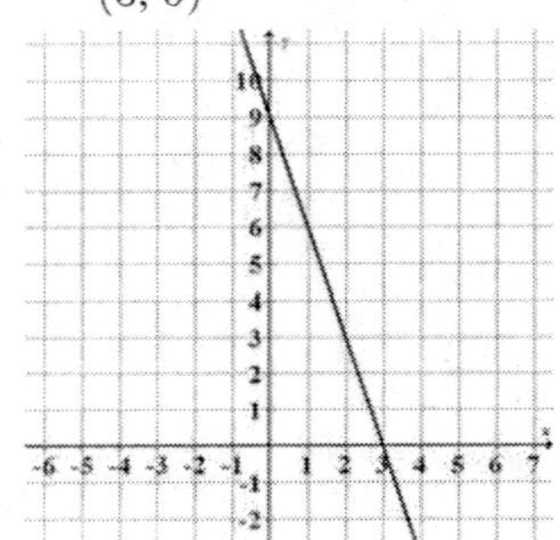

45.

$$\begin{aligned} 3x + 2y &= 6 \\ 3x + 2(0) &= 6 \\ 3x &= 6 \\ x &= 2 \\ &(2, 0) \end{aligned} \qquad \begin{aligned} 3x + 2y &= 6 \\ 3(0) + 2y &= 6 \\ 2y &= 6 \\ y &= 3 \\ &(0, 3) \end{aligned}$$

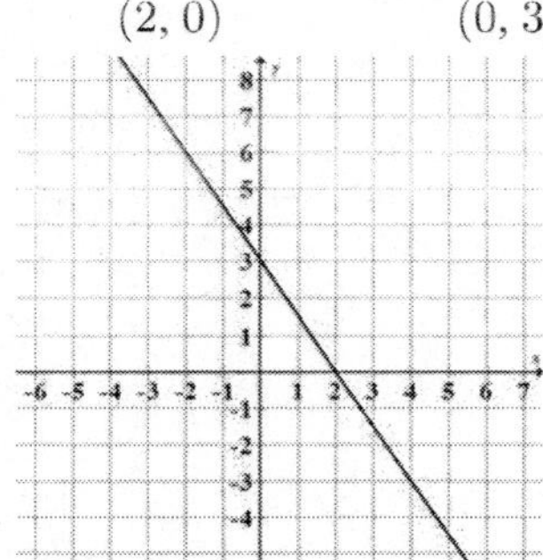

46.

$$\begin{aligned} 2x - 3y &= 6 \\ 2x - 3(0) &= 6 \\ 2x &= 6 \\ x &= 3 \\ &(3, 0) \end{aligned} \qquad \begin{aligned} 2x - 3y &= 6 \\ 2(0) - 3y &= 6 \\ -3y &= 6 \\ y &= -2 \\ &(0, -2) \end{aligned}$$

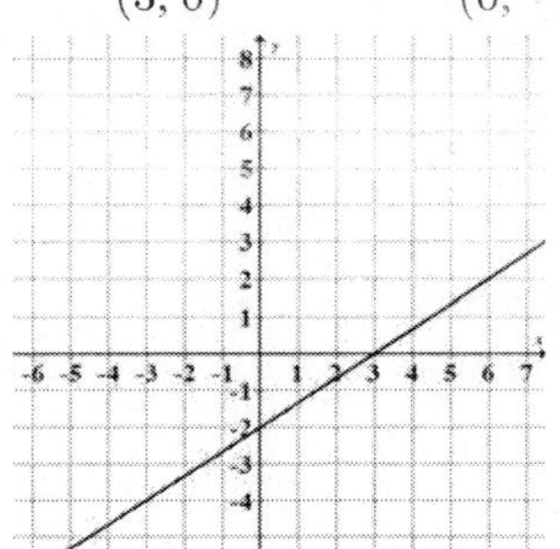

47.

$$\begin{aligned} 4x - 5y &= 20 \\ 4x - 5(0) &= 20 \\ 4x &= 20 \\ x &= 5 \\ &(5, 0) \end{aligned} \qquad \begin{aligned} 4x - 5y &= 20 \\ 4(0) - 5y &= 20 \\ -5y &= 20 \\ y &= -4 \\ &(0, -4) \end{aligned}$$

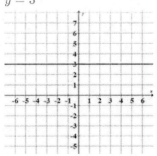

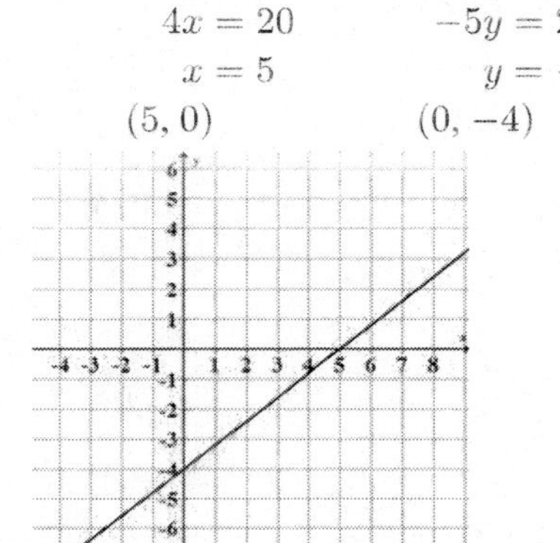

48.

$$\begin{aligned} 3x - 5y &= 15 \\ 3x - 5(0) &= 15 \\ 3x &= 15 \\ x &= 5 \\ &(5, 0) \end{aligned} \qquad \begin{aligned} 3x - 5y &= 15 \\ 3(0) - 5y &= 15 \\ -5y &= 15 \\ y &= -3 \\ &(0, -3) \end{aligned}$$

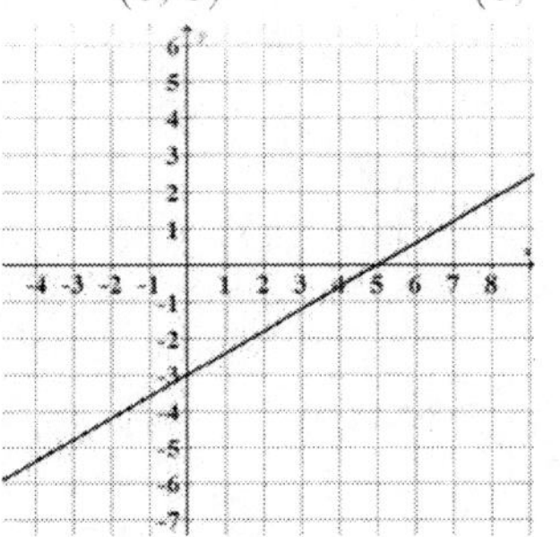

49. $y = 3$

50. $x = -4$

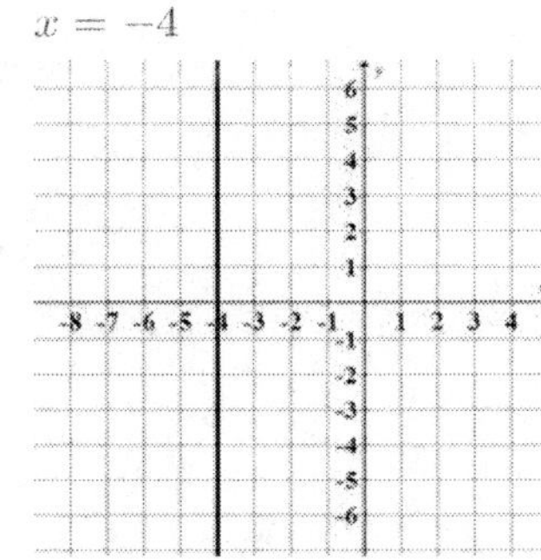

51. $3x + 5 = -1$

$3x = -6 \Rightarrow x = -2$

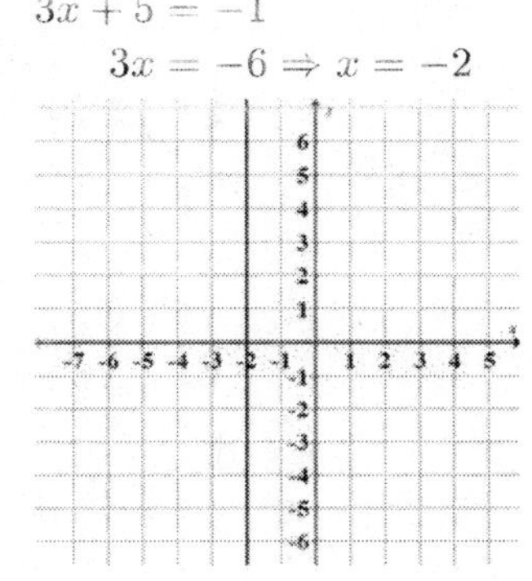

52. $7y - 1 = 6$

$7y = 7 \Rightarrow y = 1$

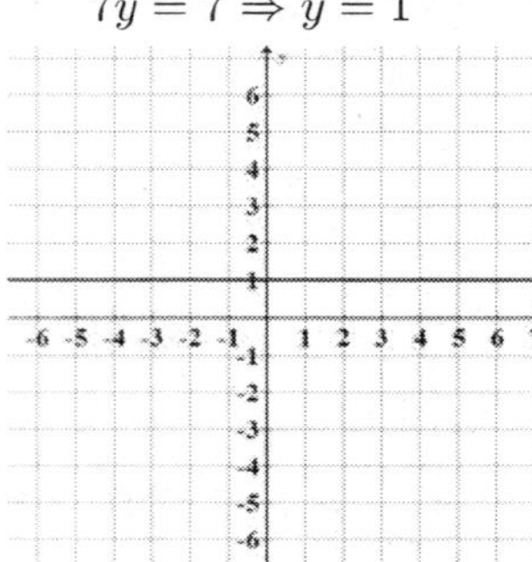

53. $3(y + 2) = y$

$3y + 6 = y$

$2y = -6 \Rightarrow y = -3$

54. $4 + 3y = 3(x + y)$

$4 + 3y = 3x + 3y$

$4 = 3x \Rightarrow x = \frac{4}{3}$

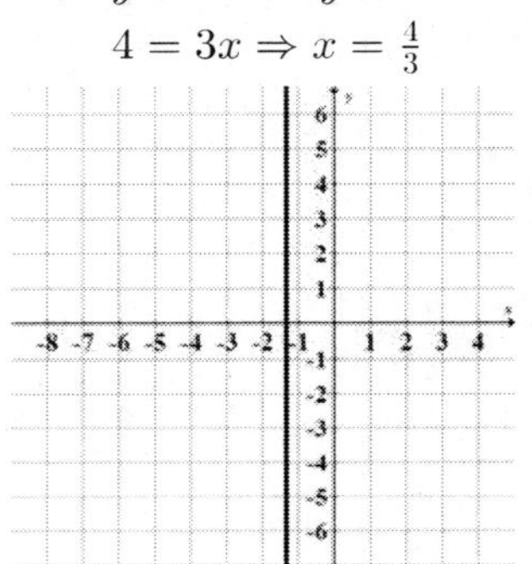

55. $3(y + 2x) = 6x + y$

$3y + 6x = 6x + y$

$2y = 0 \Rightarrow y = 0$

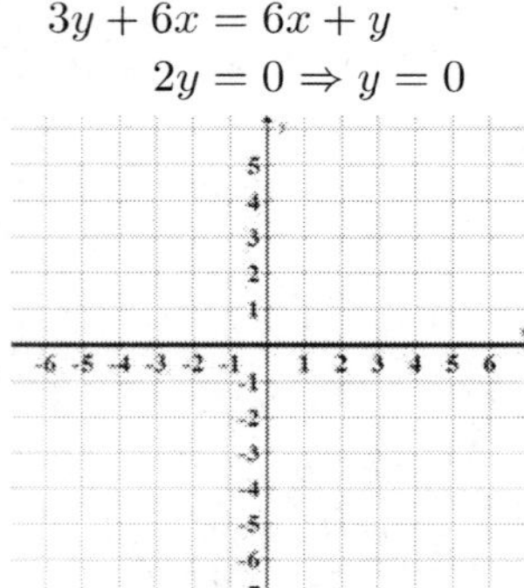

56. $5(y - x) = x + 5y$

$5y - 5x = x + 5y$

$0 = 6x \Rightarrow x = 0$

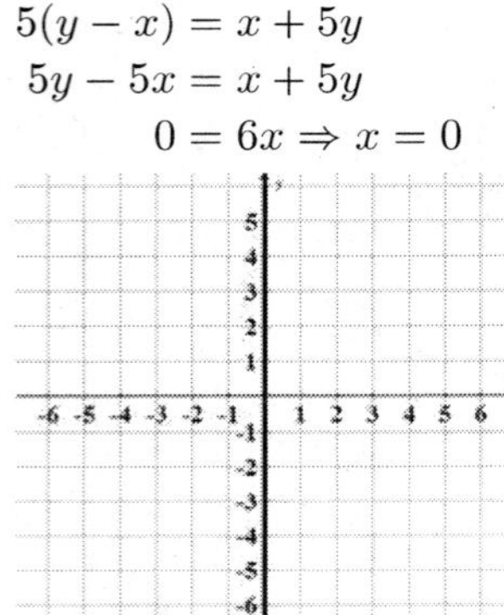

57. $y = 3.7x - 4.5$

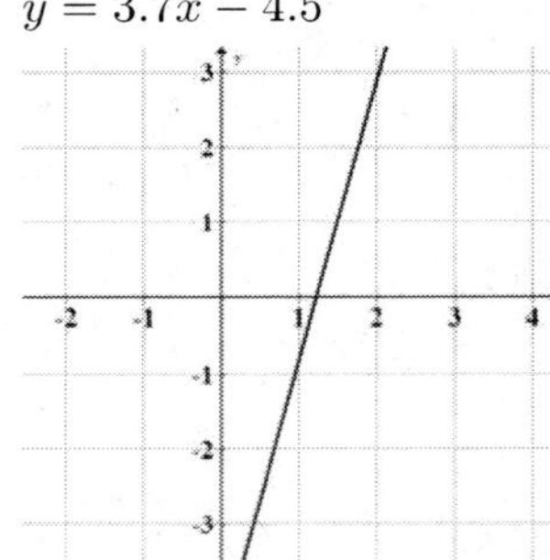

x-int: $x = 1.22$

58. $y = \dfrac{3}{5}x + \dfrac{5}{4}$

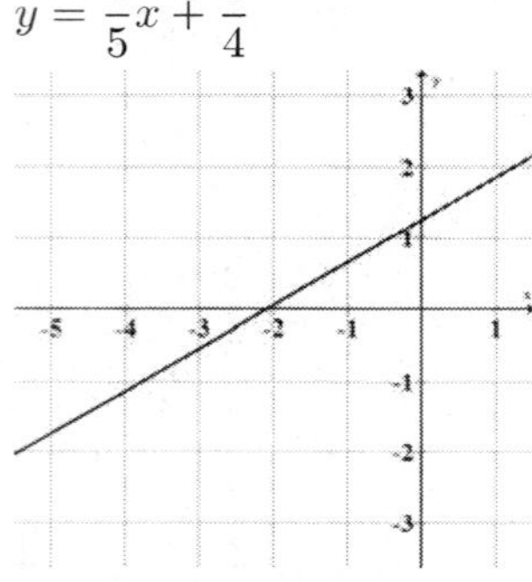

x-int: $x = -2.08$

59. $1.5x - 3y = 7$

$-3y = -1.5x + 7$

$y = 0.5x - \frac{7}{3}$

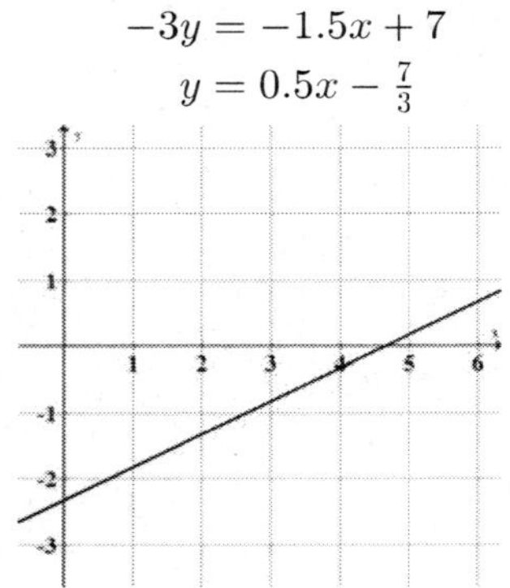

x-int: $x = 4.67$

60. $0.3x + y = 7.5$

$y = -0.3x + 7.5$

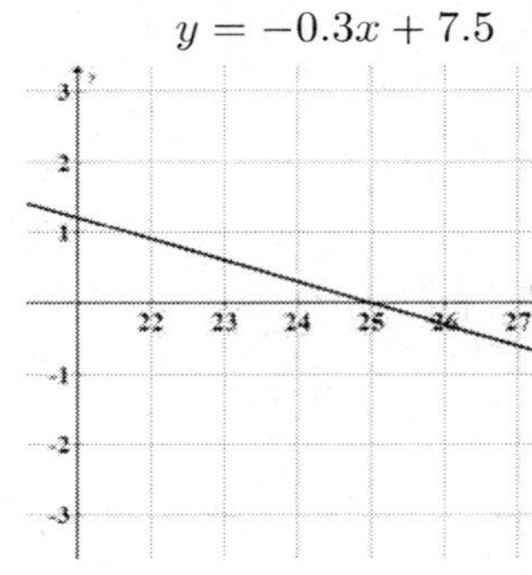

x-int: $x = 25.00$

61. $$\begin{aligned} d &= \sqrt{(x_2 - x_1)^2 + (y_2 - y_1)^2} \\ &= \sqrt{(4-0)^2 + (-3-0)^2} \\ &= \sqrt{4^2 + (-3)^2} \\ &= \sqrt{16+9} = \sqrt{25} = 5 \end{aligned}$$

62. $$\begin{aligned} d &= \sqrt{(x_2 - x_1)^2 + (y_2 - y_1)^2} \\ &= \sqrt{(-5-0)^2 + (12-0)^2} \\ &= \sqrt{(-5)^2 + (12)^2} \\ &= \sqrt{25+144} = \sqrt{169} = 13 \end{aligned}$$

63. $$\begin{aligned} d &= \sqrt{(x_2 - x_1)^2 + (y_2 - y_1)^2} \\ &= \sqrt{(-3-0)^2 + (2-0)^2} \\ &= \sqrt{(-3)^2 + (2)^2} \\ &= \sqrt{9+4} = \sqrt{13} \end{aligned}$$

64. $$\begin{aligned} d &= \sqrt{(x_2 - x_1)^2 + (y_2 - y_1)^2} \\ &= \sqrt{(5-0)^2 + (0-0)^2} \\ &= \sqrt{(5)^2 + (0)^2} \\ &= \sqrt{25+0} = \sqrt{25} = 5 \end{aligned}$$

65. $$\begin{aligned} d &= \sqrt{(x_2 - x_1)^2 + (y_2 - y_1)^2} \\ &= \sqrt{(1-0)^2 + (1-0)^2} \\ &= \sqrt{(1)^2 + (1)^2} \\ &= \sqrt{1+1} = \sqrt{2} \end{aligned}$$

66. $$\begin{aligned} d &= \sqrt{(x_2 - x_1)^2 + (y_2 - y_1)^2} \\ &= \sqrt{(6-0)^2 + (-8-0)^2} \\ &= \sqrt{(6)^2 + (-8)^2} \\ &= \sqrt{36+64} = \sqrt{100} = 10 \end{aligned}$$

67. $$\begin{aligned} d &= \sqrt{(x_2 - x_1)^2 + (y_2 - y_1)^2} \\ &= \sqrt{\left(\sqrt{3}-0\right)^2 + (1-0)^2} \\ &= \sqrt{\left(\sqrt{3}\right)^2 + (1)^2} \\ &= \sqrt{3+1} = \sqrt{4} = 2 \end{aligned}$$

68. $$\begin{aligned} d &= \sqrt{(x_2 - x_1)^2 + (y_2 - y_1)^2} \\ &= \sqrt{\left(\sqrt{7}-0\right)^2 + \left(\sqrt{2}-0\right)^2} \\ &= \sqrt{\left(\sqrt{7}\right)^2 + \left(\sqrt{2}\right)^2} \\ &= \sqrt{7+2} = \sqrt{9} = 3 \end{aligned}$$

69. $$\begin{aligned} d &= \sqrt{(x_2 - x_1)^2 + (y_2 - y_1)^2} \\ &= \sqrt{(3-6)^2 + (7-3)^2} \\ &= \sqrt{(-3)^2 + (4)^2} \\ &= \sqrt{9+16} = \sqrt{25} = 5 \end{aligned}$$

70. $$\begin{aligned} d &= \sqrt{(x_2 - x_1)^2 + (y_2 - y_1)^2} \\ &= \sqrt{(4-9)^2 + (9-21)^2} \\ &= \sqrt{(-5)^2 + (-12)^2} \\ &= \sqrt{25+144} = \sqrt{169} = 13 \end{aligned}$$

71. $$\begin{aligned} d &= \sqrt{(x_2 - x_1)^2 + (y_2 - y_1)^2} \\ &= \sqrt{[4-(-1)]^2 + [-6-6]^2} \\ &= \sqrt{(5)^2 + (-12)^2} \\ &= \sqrt{25+144} = \sqrt{169} = 13 \end{aligned}$$

72. $$\begin{aligned} d &= \sqrt{(x_2 - x_1)^2 + (y_2 - y_1)^2} \\ &= \sqrt{[0-6]^2 + [5-(-3)]^2} \\ &= \sqrt{(-6)^2 + (8)^2} \\ &= \sqrt{36+64} = \sqrt{100} = 10 \end{aligned}$$

73. $d = \sqrt{(x_2 - x_1)^2 + (y_2 - y_1)^2}$
$= \sqrt{[-2 - (-6)]^2 + [-15 - (-21)]^2}$
$= \sqrt{(4)^2 + (6)^2}$
$= \sqrt{16 + 36} = \sqrt{52} = 2\sqrt{13}$

74. $d = \sqrt{(x_2 - x_1)^2 + (y_2 - y_1)^2}$
$= \sqrt{[-7 - (-11)]^2 + [11 - 7]^2}$
$= \sqrt{(4)^2 + (4)^2}$
$= \sqrt{16 + 16} = \sqrt{32} = 4\sqrt{2}$

75. $d = \sqrt{(x_2 - x_1)^2 + (y_2 - y_1)^2}$
$= \sqrt{[3 - (-5)]^2 + [-3 - 5]^2}$
$= \sqrt{(8)^2 + (-8)^2}$
$= \sqrt{64 + 64} = \sqrt{128} = 8\sqrt{2}$

76. $d = \sqrt{(x_2 - x_1)^2 + (y_2 - y_1)^2}$
$= \sqrt{[6 - (-3)]^2 + [-3 - 2]^2}$
$= \sqrt{(9)^2 + (-5)^2}$
$= \sqrt{81 + 25} = \sqrt{106}$

77. $d = \sqrt{(x_2 - x_1)^2 + (y_2 - y_1)^2}$
$= \sqrt{[\pi - \pi]^2 + [-2 - 5]^2}$
$= \sqrt{(0)^2 + (-7)^2}$
$= \sqrt{0 + 49} = \sqrt{49} = 7$

78. $d = \sqrt{(x_2 - x_1)^2 + (y_2 - y_1)^2}$
$= \sqrt{\left[\sqrt{5} - 0\right]^2 + [0 - 2]^2}$
$= \sqrt{\left(\sqrt{5}\right)^2 + (-2)^2}$
$= \sqrt{5 + 4} = \sqrt{9} = 3$

79. $M\left(\frac{x_1 + x_2}{2}, \frac{y_1 + y_2}{2}\right) = M\left(\frac{2 + 6}{2}, \frac{4 + 8}{2}\right) = M\left(\frac{8}{2}, \frac{12}{2}\right) = M(4, 6)$

80. $M\left(\frac{x_1 + x_2}{2}, \frac{y_1 + y_2}{2}\right) = M\left(\frac{3 + (-1)}{2}, \frac{-6 + (-6)}{2}\right) = M\left(\frac{2}{2}, \frac{-12}{2}\right) = M(1, -6)$

81. $M\left(\frac{x_1 + x_2}{2}, \frac{y_1 + y_2}{2}\right) = M\left(\frac{2 + (-2)}{2}, \frac{-5 + 7}{2}\right) = M\left(\frac{0}{2}, \frac{2}{2}\right) = M(0, 1)$

82. $M\left(\frac{x_1 + x_2}{2}, \frac{y_1 + y_2}{2}\right) = M\left(\frac{0 + (-10)}{2}, \frac{3 + (-13)}{2}\right) = M\left(\frac{-10}{2}, \frac{-10}{2}\right) = M(-5, -5)$

83. $M\left(\frac{x_1 + x_2}{2}, \frac{y_1 + y_2}{2}\right) = M\left(\frac{-8 + 6}{2}, \frac{5 + (-4)}{2}\right) = M\left(\frac{-2}{2}, \frac{1}{2}\right) = M\left(-1, \frac{1}{2}\right)$

84. $M\left(\frac{x_1 + x_2}{2}, \frac{y_1 + y_2}{2}\right) = M\left(\frac{3 + 2}{2}, \frac{-2 + (-3)}{2}\right) = M\left(\frac{5}{2}, \frac{-5}{2}\right) = M\left(\frac{5}{2}, -\frac{5}{2}\right)$

85. $M\left(\frac{x_1 + x_2}{2}, \frac{y_1 + y_2}{2}\right) = M\left(\frac{0 + \sqrt{5}}{2}, \frac{0 + \sqrt{5}}{2}\right) = M\left(\frac{\sqrt{5}}{2}, \frac{\sqrt{5}}{2}\right)$

86. $M\left(\frac{x_1+x_2}{2}, \frac{y_1+y_2}{2}\right) = M\left(\frac{\sqrt{3}+0}{2}, \frac{0+\left(-\sqrt{5}\right)}{2}\right) = M\left(\frac{\sqrt{3}}{2}, \frac{-\sqrt{5}}{2}\right) = M\left(\frac{\sqrt{3}}{2}, -\frac{\sqrt{5}}{2}\right)$

87. Let Q have coordinates (x, y):
$M\left(\frac{x_1+x_2}{2}, \frac{y_1+y_2}{2}\right) = (3, 5)$
$\frac{x_1+x_2}{2} = 3 \quad \frac{y_1+y_2}{2} = 5$
$\frac{1+x}{2} = 3 \quad \frac{4+y}{2} = 5$
$1+x = 6 \quad 4+y = 10$
$x = 5 \quad y = 6$
$Q(5, 6)$

88. Let Q have coordinates (x, y):
$M\left(\frac{x_1+x_2}{2}, \frac{y_1+y_2}{2}\right) = (-5, 6)$
$\frac{x_1+x_2}{2} = -5 \quad \frac{y_1+y_2}{2} = 6$
$\frac{2+x}{2} = -5 \quad \frac{-7+y}{2} = 6$
$2+x = -10 \quad -7+y = 12$
$x = -12 \quad y = 19$
$Q(-12, 19)$

89. Let Q have coordinates (x, y):
$M\left(\frac{x_1+x_2}{2}, \frac{y_1+y_2}{2}\right) = (5, 5)$
$\frac{x_1+x_2}{2} = 5 \quad \frac{y_1+y_2}{2} = 5$
$\frac{5+x}{2} = 5 \quad \frac{-5+y}{2} = 5$
$5+x = 10 \quad -5+y = 10$
$x = 5 \quad y = 15$
$Q(5, 15)$

90. Let Q have coordinates (x, y):
$M\left(\frac{x_1+x_2}{2}, \frac{y_1+y_2}{2}\right) = (0, 0)$
$\frac{x_1+x_2}{2} = 0 \quad \frac{y_1+y_2}{2} = 0$
$\frac{-7+x}{2} = 0 \quad \frac{3+y}{2} = 0$
$-7+x = 0 \quad 3+y = 0$
$x = 7 \quad y = -3$
$Q(7, -3)$

91. Let the points be identified as $A(13, -2)$, $B(9, -8)$ and $C(5, -2)$.
$AB = \sqrt{(x_2-x_1)^2+(y_2-y_1)^2} = \sqrt{(13-9)^2+(-2-(-8))^2} = \sqrt{16+36} = \sqrt{52} = 2\sqrt{13}$
$BC = \sqrt{(x_2-x_1)^2+(y_2-y_1)^2} = \sqrt{(9-5)^2+(-8-(-2))^2} = \sqrt{16+36} = \sqrt{52} = 2\sqrt{13}$
Since AB and BC have the same length, the triangle is isosceles.

92. Let the points be identified as $A(-1, 2)$, $B(3, 1)$ and $C(4, 5)$.
$AB = \sqrt{(x_2-x_1)^2+(y_2-y_1)^2} = \sqrt{(-1-3)^2+(2-1)^2} = \sqrt{16+1} = \sqrt{17}$
$BC = \sqrt{(x_2-x_1)^2+(y_2-y_1)^2} = \sqrt{(3-4)^2+(1-5)^2} = \sqrt{1+16} = \sqrt{17}$
Since AB and BC have the same length, the triangle is isosceles.

93. $M = \left(\frac{2+6}{2}, \frac{4+10}{2}\right) = \left(\frac{8}{2}, \frac{14}{2}\right) = (4, 7)$; $N = \left(\frac{4+6}{2}, \frac{6+10}{2}\right) = \left(\frac{10}{2}, \frac{16}{2}\right) = (5, 8)$
$MN = \sqrt{(x_2-x_1)^2+(y_2-y_1)^2} = \sqrt{(4-5)^2+(7-8)^2} = \sqrt{1+1} = \sqrt{2}$

94. $M = \left(\frac{0+b}{2}, \frac{0+c}{2}\right) = \left(\frac{b}{2}, \frac{c}{2}\right)$; $N = \left(\frac{a+b}{2}, \frac{0+c}{2}\right) = \left(\frac{a+b}{2}, \frac{c}{2}\right)$

$AB = \sqrt{(x_2 - x_1)^2 + (y_2 - y_1)^2} = \sqrt{(0-a)^2 + (0-0)^2} = \sqrt{a^2} = a$

$MN = \sqrt{(x_2 - x_1)^2 + (y_2 - y_1)^2} = \sqrt{\left(\frac{b}{2} - \frac{a+b}{2}\right)^2 + \left(\frac{c}{2} - \frac{c}{2}\right)^2} = \sqrt{\frac{a^2}{4} + 0} = \frac{a}{2} = \frac{1}{2}AB$

95. $M = \left(\frac{0+a}{2}, \frac{b+0}{2}\right) = \left(\frac{a}{2}, \frac{b}{2}\right)$; $L = \left(\frac{a}{2}, 0\right)$; $N = \left(0, \frac{b}{2}\right)$

Area of $AOB = \frac{1}{2} \cdot \text{base} \cdot \text{height} = \frac{1}{2}(OA)(OB) = \frac{1}{2}(a)(b) = \frac{1}{2}ab$

Area of $OLMN = \text{length} \cdot \text{width} = (OL)(ON) = \frac{a}{2} \cdot \frac{b}{2} = \frac{1}{4}ab = \frac{1}{2}(\text{Area of } AOB)$

96. Let $x =$ the width (from A to D). Then the length (from A to B) $= 2x$.

$$\text{Perimeter} = 42$$
$$x + 2x + x + 2x = 42$$
$$6x = 42$$
$$x = 7$$

Thus, the distance from A to D is 7 and the distance from A to B is $2(7) = 14$. Thus, the x-coordinate of C is $-3 + 14$, or 11. The y-coordinate of C is $-2 + 7$, or 5. Point C then has coordinates $(11, 5)$.

97. $y = 17500x + 225000$
$y = 17500(5) + 225000$
$y = 87500 + 225000$
$y = 312500$
The value will be $312,500.

98. Set $y = 0$:
$y = -1360x + 17{,}000$
$0 = -1360x + 17{,}000$
$1360x = 17{,}000$
$x = 12.5$
The car will be worthless after 12.5 years.

99. $p = -\frac{1}{10}q + 170$
$150 = -\frac{1}{10}q + 170$
$\frac{1}{10}q = 20$
$q = 200$
200 scanners will be sold.

100. $p = \frac{1}{10}q + 130$
$150 = \frac{1}{10}q + 130$
$20 = \frac{1}{10}q$
$200 = q$
200 TVs will be produced.

101. $V = \frac{nv}{N}$
$60 = \frac{12v}{20}$
$1200 = 12v$
$100 = v$
The smaller gear is spinning at 100 rpm.

102. $n = 430 - 0.005d$
$350 = 430 - 0.005d$
$0.005d = 80$
$d = 16{,}000$
$16,000 would reduce the number to 350.

103.

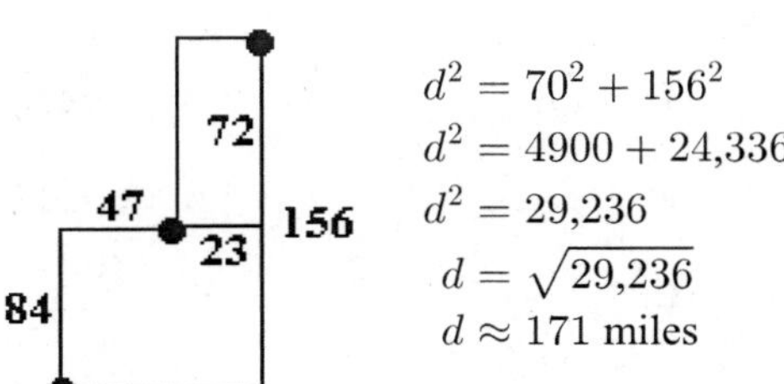

$$d^2 = 70^2 + 156^2$$
$$d^2 = 4900 + 24{,}336$$
$$d^2 = 29{,}236$$
$$d = \sqrt{29{,}236}$$
$$d \approx 171 \text{ miles}$$

104.

19.3
5.0
5.0
11.7
4.3
3.0
10.0
3.7

$$d^2 = 10^2 + 3^2$$
$$d^2 = 100 + 9$$
$$d^2 = 109$$
$$d = \sqrt{109}$$
$$d \approx 10.4 \text{ mm}$$

105-108. Answers may vary.

109. $[-3, 2)$ -3 2

$(-2, 3]$ -2 3

$[-3, 2) \cup (-2, 3]$ -3 3

110. $(-1, 4)$ -1 4

$[-2, 2]$ -2 2

$(-1, 4) \cap [-2, 2]$ -1 2

111. $[-3, -2)$ -3 -2

$(2, 3]$ 2 3

$[-3, 2) \cap (-2, 3]$ no intersection

112. $[-4, -3) \cup (2, 3]$

-4 -3 2 3

113.

$$\frac{3}{y+6} = \frac{4}{y+4}$$
$$(y+6)(y+4) \cdot \frac{3}{y+6} = (y+6)(y+4) \cdot \frac{4}{y+4}$$
$$3(y+4) = 4(y+6)$$
$$3y + 12 = 4y + 24$$
$$-12 = y$$

114.

$$\frac{z+4}{z^2+z} - \frac{z+1}{z^2+2z} = \frac{8}{z^2+3z+2}$$
$$\frac{z+4}{z(z+1)} - \frac{z+1}{z(z+2)} = \frac{8}{(z+2)(z+1)}$$
$$(z+2)(z+4) - (z+1)(z+1) = z(8) \quad \{\text{multiply by common denominator}\}$$
$$\left(z^2+6z+8\right) - \left(z^2+2z+1\right) = 8z$$
$$z^2 + 6z + 8 - z^2 - 2z - 1 = 8z$$
$$-4z = -7 \Rightarrow z = \tfrac{7}{4}$$

Exercises 2.2 (page 214)

1. divided **2.** y **3.** run **4.** same order

5. the change in **6.** horizontal **7.** vertical **8.** parallel

9. perpendicular **10.** -1

11. $m = \frac{y_2 - y_1}{x_2 - x_1} = \frac{2-(-1)}{2-(-1)} = \frac{3}{3} = 1$

12. $m = \frac{y_2 - y_1}{x_2 - x_1} = \frac{3-(-1)}{5-3} = \frac{4}{2} = 2$

13. $m = \frac{y_2 - y_1}{x_2 - x_1} = \frac{-2-3}{6-(-6)} = \frac{-5}{12} = -\frac{5}{12}$

14. $m = \frac{y_2 - y_1}{x_2 - x_1} = \frac{10-5}{3-2} = \frac{5}{1} = 5$

15. $m = \frac{y_2 - y_1}{x_2 - x_1} = \frac{5-(-2)}{-1-3} = \frac{7}{-4} = -\frac{7}{4}$

16. $m = \frac{y_2 - y_1}{x_2 - x_1} = \frac{16-7}{6-3} = \frac{9}{3} = 3$

17. $m = \frac{y_2 - y_1}{x_2 - x_1} = \frac{1-(-7)}{4-8} = \frac{8}{-4} = -2$

18. $m = \frac{y_2 - y_1}{x_2 - x_1} = \frac{17-17}{17-5} = \frac{0}{12} = 0$

19. $m = \frac{y_2 - y_1}{x_2 - x_1} = \frac{-3-3}{-4-(-4)} = \frac{-6}{0} \Rightarrow$ und.

20. $m = \frac{y_2 - y_1}{x_2 - x_1} = \frac{2-\sqrt{7}}{\sqrt{7}-2} = -1$

21. $m = \frac{y_2 - y_1}{x_2 - x_1} = \frac{\frac{7}{3}-\frac{2}{3}}{\frac{5}{2}-\frac{3}{2}} = \frac{\frac{5}{3}}{\frac{2}{2}} = \frac{\frac{5}{3}}{1} = \frac{5}{3}$

22. $m = \frac{y_2 - y_1}{x_2 - x_1} = \frac{-\frac{5}{3}-\frac{1}{3}}{\frac{3}{5}-(-\frac{2}{5})} = \frac{-\frac{6}{3}}{\frac{5}{5}} = -2$

23. $m = \frac{y_2 - y_1}{x_2 - x_1} = \frac{a-c}{(b+c)-(a+b)}$
$= \frac{a-c}{c-a} = -1$

24. $m = \frac{y_2 - y_1}{x_2 - x_1} = \frac{a-0}{(a+b)-b} = \frac{a}{a} = 1$

25. $y = 3x + 2$

x	y
0	2
1	5

$m = \frac{y_2 - y_1}{x_2 - x_1} = \frac{5-2}{1-0}$
$= \frac{3}{1} = 3$

26. $y = 5x - 8$

x	y
0	-8
1	-3

$m = \frac{y_2 - y_1}{x_2 - x_1} = \frac{-3-(-8)}{1-0}$
$= \frac{5}{1} = 5$

27. $5x - 10y = 3$

x	y
0	$-\frac{3}{10}$
1	$\frac{1}{5}$

$m = \frac{y_2 - y_1}{x_2 - x_1}$
$= \frac{\frac{1}{5}-(-\frac{3}{10})}{1-0}$
$= \frac{\frac{5}{10}}{1} = \frac{1}{2}$

28. $8y + 2x = 5$

x	y
0	$\frac{5}{8}$
1	$\frac{3}{8}$

$m = \frac{y_2 - y_1}{x_2 - x_1}$
$= \frac{\frac{3}{8}-\frac{5}{8}}{1-0}$
$= \frac{-\frac{2}{8}}{1} = -\frac{1}{4}$

29. $3(y+2) = 2x - 3$
$3y - 2x = -9$

x	y
0	-3
3	-1

$$m = \frac{y_2 - y_1}{x_2 - x_1} = \frac{-1-(-3)}{3-0} = \frac{2}{3}$$

30. $4(x-2) = 3y + 2$
$4x - 3y = 10$

x	y
0	$-\frac{10}{3}$
1	-2

$$m = \frac{y_2 - y_1}{x_2 - x_1} = \frac{-2-(-\frac{10}{3})}{1-0} = \frac{\frac{4}{3}}{1} = \frac{4}{3}$$

31. $3(y+x) = 3(x-1)$
$3y = -3$
$y = -1$

x	y
0	-1
1	-1

$$m = \frac{y_2 - y_1}{x_2 - x_1} = \frac{-1-(-1)}{1-0} = \frac{0}{1} = 0$$

32. $2x + 5 = 2(y+x)$
$5 = 2y$
$\frac{5}{2} = y$

x	y
0	$\frac{5}{2}$
1	$\frac{5}{2}$

$$m = \frac{y_2 - y_1}{x_2 - x_1} = \frac{\frac{5}{2} - \frac{5}{2}}{1-0} = \frac{0}{1} = 0$$

33. horizontal $\Rightarrow m = 0$

34. $2y = 5$
$y = \frac{5}{2}$
horizontal $\Rightarrow m = 0$

35. vertical $\Rightarrow m$ is undefined.

36. $x - 7 = 0$
$x = 7$
vertical $\Rightarrow m$ is undefined.

37. The slope is negative.

38. The slope is zero.

39. The slope is positive.

40. The slope is positive.

41. The slope is undefined.

42. The slope is negative.

43. $m_1 m_2 = 3(-\frac{1}{3}) = -1$
perpendicular

44. $m_1 \neq m_2$; $m_1 m_2 = \frac{2}{3} \cdot \frac{3}{2} = 1 \neq -1$
neither

45. $m_1 = \sqrt{8} = 2\sqrt{2} = m_2$
parallel

46. $m_1 m_2 = 1(-1) = -1$
perpendicular

47. $m_1 m_2 = -\sqrt{2}\left(\frac{\sqrt{2}}{2}\right) = -1$
perpendicular

48. $m_2 = \sqrt{28} = 2\sqrt{7} = m_1$
parallel

49. $m_1 m_2 = -0.125(8) = -1$
perpendicular

50. $m_1 = 0.125 = \frac{1}{8} = m_2$
parallel

51. $m_1 m_2 = ab^{-1}(-a^{-1}b) = -a^0 b^0 = -1$
perpendicular

52. $m_1 = \left(\frac{a}{b}\right)^{-1} = \frac{b}{a} \neq -\frac{b}{a} = m_2$
$m_1 m_2 = \frac{b}{a}\left(-\frac{b}{a}\right) \neq -1 \Rightarrow$ neither

For Exercises 53-58 use the slope of line through R and S calculated below:

$$m_{RS} = \frac{y_2 - y_1}{x_2 - x_1} = \frac{7-5}{2-(-3)} = \frac{2}{5}$$

53. $m_{PQ} = \frac{y_2 - y_1}{x_2 - x_1} = \frac{6-4}{7-2} = \frac{2}{5} = m_{RS} \Rightarrow \text{parallel}$

54. $m_{PQ} = \frac{y_2 - y_1}{x_2 - x_1} = \frac{4-8}{-13-(-3)} = \frac{-4}{-10} = \frac{2}{5} = m_{RS} \Rightarrow \text{parallel}$

55. $m_{PQ} = \frac{y_2 - y_1}{x_2 - x_1} = \frac{1-6}{-2-(-4)} = \frac{-5}{2} = -\frac{5}{2} \Rightarrow \text{perpendicular}$

56. $m_{PQ} = \frac{y_2 - y_1}{x_2 - x_1} = \frac{1-(-9)}{4-0} = \frac{10}{4} = \frac{5}{2} \Rightarrow \text{neither}$

57. $m_{PQ} = \frac{y_2 - y_1}{x_2 - x_1} = \frac{6a-a}{3a-a} = \frac{5a}{2a} = \frac{5}{2} \Rightarrow \text{neither}$

58. $m_{PQ} = \frac{y_2 - y_1}{x_2 - x_1} = \frac{6b-b}{-b-b} = \frac{5b}{-2b} = -\frac{5}{2} \Rightarrow \text{perpendicular}$

59. $m_{PQ} = \frac{y_2 - y_1}{x_2 - x_1} = \frac{9-7}{2-(-3)} = \frac{2}{5}; m_{RS} = \frac{y_2 - y_1}{x_2 - x_1} = \frac{-6-(-4)}{x-10} = \frac{-2}{x-10}$

$\frac{2}{5} \cdot \frac{-1}{-1} = \frac{-2}{-5}; x - 10 = -5 \Rightarrow \boxed{x = 5}$

60. $m_{PQ} = \frac{y_2 - y_1}{x_2 - x_1} = \frac{7-(-3)}{5-2} = \frac{10}{3}; m_{RS} = \frac{y_2 - y_1}{x_2 - x_1} = \frac{y-(-1)}{6-3} = \frac{y+1}{3}$

$10 = y + 1 \Rightarrow \boxed{y = 9}$

61. $m_{PQ} = \frac{y_2 - y_1}{x_2 - x_1} = \frac{0-(-7)}{1-2} = \frac{7}{-1} = -7; m_{RS} = \frac{y_2 - y_1}{x_2 - x_1} = \frac{y-5}{-2-(-9)} = \frac{y-5}{7}$

$-7 = \frac{-7}{1}$; Perp. slope $= \frac{1}{7}; y - 5 = 1 \Rightarrow \boxed{y = 6}$

62. $m_{PQ} = \frac{y_2 - y_1}{x_2 - x_1} = \frac{4-(-2)}{3-1} = \frac{6}{2} = 3; m_{RS} = \frac{y_2 - y_1}{x_2 - x_1} = \frac{5-6}{6-x} = \frac{-1}{6-x}$

$3 = \frac{3}{1}$; Perp. slope $= -\frac{1}{3} = \frac{-1}{3}$; $6 - x = 3 \Rightarrow \boxed{x = 3}$

63. $m_{PQ} = \frac{y_2 - y_1}{x_2 - x_1} = \frac{9-8}{-6-(-2)} = \frac{1}{-4} = -\frac{1}{4}$

$m_{PR} = \frac{y_2 - y_1}{x_2 - x_1} = \frac{5-8}{2-(-2)} = \frac{-3}{4} = -\frac{3}{4} \Rightarrow \text{not on same line}$

64. $m_{PQ} = \dfrac{y_2 - y_1}{x_2 - x_1} = \dfrac{-2-(-1)}{3-1} = \dfrac{-1}{2} = -\dfrac{1}{2}$

$m_{PR} = \dfrac{y_2 - y_1}{x_2 - x_1} = \dfrac{0-(-1)}{-3-1} = \dfrac{1}{-4} = -\dfrac{1}{4} \Rightarrow$ not on same line

65. $m_{PQ} = \dfrac{y_2 - y_1}{x_2 - x_1} = \dfrac{0-a}{0-(-a)} = \dfrac{-a}{a} = -1$

$m_{PR} = \dfrac{y_2 - y_1}{x_2 - x_1} = \dfrac{-a-a}{a-(-a)} = \dfrac{-2a}{2a} = -1 \Rightarrow$ on same line

66. $m_{PQ} = \dfrac{y_2 - y_1}{x_2 - x_1} = \dfrac{b-(a+b)}{(a+b)-a} = \dfrac{-a}{b} = -\dfrac{a}{b}$

$m_{PR} = \dfrac{y_2 - y_1}{x_2 - x_1} = \dfrac{a-(a+b)}{(a-b)-a} = \dfrac{-b}{-b} = 1 \Rightarrow$ not on same line

67. $m_{PQ} = \dfrac{y_2 - y_1}{x_2 - x_1} = \dfrac{-5-4}{2-5} = \dfrac{-9}{-3} = 3$

$m_{PR} = \dfrac{y_2 - y_1}{x_2 - x_1} = \dfrac{-3-4}{8-5} = \dfrac{-7}{3} = -\dfrac{7}{3}$

$m_{QR} = \dfrac{y_2 - y_1}{x_2 - x_1} = \dfrac{-3-(-5)}{8-2} = \dfrac{2}{6} = \dfrac{1}{3} \Rightarrow$ None are perpendicular.

68. $m_{PQ} = \dfrac{y_2 - y_1}{x_2 - x_1} = \dfrac{6-(-2)}{4-8} = \dfrac{8}{-4} = -2$

$m_{PR} = \dfrac{y_2 - y_1}{x_2 - x_1} = \dfrac{7-(-2)}{6-8} = \dfrac{9}{-2} = -\dfrac{9}{2}$

$m_{QR} = \dfrac{y_2 - y_1}{x_2 - x_1} = \dfrac{7-6}{6-4} = \dfrac{1}{2} \Rightarrow PQ$ and QR are perpendicular.

69. $m_{PQ} = \dfrac{y_2 - y_1}{x_2 - x_1} = \dfrac{9-3}{1-1} = \dfrac{6}{0} \Rightarrow$ undefined $\Rightarrow$ vertical

$m_{PR} = \dfrac{y_2 - y_1}{x_2 - x_1} = \dfrac{3-3}{7-1} = \dfrac{0}{6} = 0 \Rightarrow$ horizontal

$m_{QR} = \dfrac{y_2 - y_1}{x_2 - x_1} = \dfrac{3-9}{7-1} = \dfrac{-6}{6} = -1 \Rightarrow PQ$ and PR are perpendicular.

70. $m_{PQ} = \dfrac{y_2 - y_1}{x_2 - x_1} = \dfrac{2-(-3)}{-3-2} = \dfrac{5}{-5} = -1$

$m_{PR} = \dfrac{y_2 - y_1}{x_2 - x_1} = \dfrac{8-(-3)}{3-2} = \dfrac{11}{1} = 11$

$m_{QR} = \dfrac{y_2 - y_1}{x_2 - x_1} = \dfrac{8-2}{3-(-3)} = \dfrac{6}{6} = 1 \Rightarrow PQ$ and QR are perpendicular.

71. $m_{PQ} = \frac{y_2 - y_1}{x_2 - x_1} = \frac{b - 0}{a - 0} = \frac{b}{a}$

$m_{PR} = \frac{y_2 - y_1}{x_2 - x_1} = \frac{a - 0}{-b - 0} = \frac{a}{-b} = -\frac{a}{b}$

$m_{QR} = \frac{y_2 - y_1}{x_2 - x_1} = \frac{a - b}{-b - a} = \frac{a - b}{-b - a} \Rightarrow PQ$ and PR are perpendicular.

72. $m_{PQ} = \frac{y_2 - y_1}{x_2 - x_1} = \frac{a - b}{-b - a} = \frac{a - b}{-(a + b)} = -\frac{a - b}{a + b}$

$m_{PR} = \frac{y_2 - y_1}{x_2 - x_1} = \frac{(a + b) - b}{(a - b) - a} = \frac{a}{-b} = -\frac{a}{b}$

$m_{QR} = \frac{y_2 - y_1}{x_2 - x_1} = \frac{(a + b) - a}{(a - b) - (-b)} = \frac{b}{a} \Rightarrow PR$ and QR are perpendicular.

73. $m_{AB} = \frac{y_2 - y_1}{x_2 - x_1} = \frac{4 - (-1)}{-3 - (-1)} = \frac{5}{-2} = -\frac{5}{2}$

$m_{AC} = \frac{y_2 - y_1}{x_2 - x_1} = \frac{1 - (-1)}{4 - (-1)} = \frac{2}{5} \Rightarrow AB$ and AC are perpendicular. $\Rightarrow$ right triangle

74. $m_{DE} = \frac{y_2 - y_1}{x_2 - x_1} = \frac{3 - 1}{-1 - 0} = \frac{2}{-1} = -2$

$m_{EF} = \frac{y_2 - y_1}{x_2 - x_1} = \frac{5 - 3}{3 - (-1)} = \frac{2}{4} = \frac{1}{2} \Rightarrow DE$ and EF are perpendicular. $\Rightarrow$ right triangle

75. $m_{AB} = \frac{y_2 - y_1}{x_2 - x_1} = \frac{0 - (-1)}{3 - 1} = \frac{1}{2}$; $d(A, B) = \sqrt{(1 - 3)^2 + (-1 - 0)^2} = \sqrt{5}$

$m_{BC} = \frac{y_2 - y_1}{x_2 - x_1} = \frac{2 - 0}{2 - 3} = \frac{2}{-1} = -2$; $d(B, C) = \sqrt{(3 - 2)^2 + (0 - 2)^2} = \sqrt{5}$

$m_{CD} = \frac{y_2 - y_1}{x_2 - x_1} = \frac{1 - 2}{0 - 2} = \frac{-1}{-2} = \frac{1}{2}$; $d(C, D) = \sqrt{(2 - 0)^2 + (2 - 1)^2} = \sqrt{5}$

$m_{DA} = \frac{y_2 - y_1}{x_2 - x_1} = \frac{1 - (-1)}{0 - 1} = \frac{2}{-1} = -2$; $d(D, A) = \sqrt{(1 - 0)^2 + (-1 - 1)^2} = \sqrt{5}$

Adjacent sides are perpendicular and congruent, so the figure is a square.

76. $m_{EF} = \frac{y_2 - y_1}{x_2 - x_1} = \frac{0 - (-1)}{3 - (-1)} = \frac{1}{4}$; $d(E, F) = \sqrt{(-1 - 3)^2 + (-1 - 0)^2} = \sqrt{17}$

$m_{FG} = \frac{y_2 - y_1}{x_2 - x_1} = \frac{4 - 0}{2 - 3} = \frac{4}{-1} = -4$; $d(F, G) = \sqrt{(3 - 2)^2 + (0 - 4)^2} = \sqrt{17}$

$m_{GH} = \frac{y_2 - y_1}{x_2 - x_1} = \frac{3 - 4}{-2 - 2} = \frac{-1}{-4} = \frac{1}{4}$; $d(G, H) = \sqrt{(2 - (-2))^2 + (4 - 3)^2} = \sqrt{17}$

$m_{HE} = \frac{y_2 - y_1}{x_2 - x_1} = \frac{3 - (-1)}{-2 - (-1)} = \frac{4}{-1} = -4$; $d(H, E) = \sqrt{(-1 - (-2))^2 + (-1 - 3)^2} = \sqrt{17}$

Adjacent sides are perpendicular and congruent, so the figure is a square.

77. $m_{AB} = \frac{y_2 - y_1}{x_2 - x_1} = \frac{3-(-2)}{3-(-2)} = \frac{5}{5} = 1$

$m_{BC} = \frac{y_2 - y_1}{x_2 - x_1} = \frac{6-3}{2-3} = \frac{3}{-1} = -3$

$m_{CD} = \frac{y_2 - y_1}{x_2 - x_1} = \frac{1-6}{-3-2} = \frac{-5}{-5} = 1$

$m_{DA} = \frac{y_2 - y_1}{x_2 - x_1} = \frac{1-(-2)}{-3-(-2)} = \frac{3}{-1} = -3$

Opposite sides are parallel, so the figure is a parallelogram.

78. $m_{EF} = \frac{y_2 - y_1}{x_2 - x_1} = \frac{1-(-2)}{5-1} = \frac{3}{4}$

$m_{FG} = \frac{y_2 - y_1}{x_2 - x_1} = \frac{4-1}{3-5} = \frac{3}{-2} = -\frac{3}{2}$

$m_{GH} = \frac{y_2 - y_1}{x_2 - x_1} = \frac{4-4}{-3-3} = \frac{0}{-6} = 0$

$m_{HE} = \frac{y_2 - y_1}{x_2 - x_1} = \frac{4-(-2)}{-3-1} = \frac{6}{-4} = -\frac{3}{2}$

Exactly one pair of sides is parallel, so the figure is a trapezoid.

79. $M\left(\frac{5+7}{2}, \frac{9+5}{2}\right) = M\left(\frac{12}{2}, \frac{14}{2}\right) = M(6,7);\ N\left(\frac{1+7}{2}, \frac{3+5}{2}\right) = N\left(\frac{8}{2}, \frac{8}{2}\right) = N(4,4)$

$m_{MN} = \frac{y_2 - y_1}{x_2 - x_1} = \frac{4-7}{4-6} = \frac{-3}{-2} = \frac{3}{2};\ m_{AC} = \frac{y_2 - y_1}{x_2 - x_1} = \frac{9-3}{5-1} = \frac{6}{4} = \frac{3}{2} \Rightarrow MN \parallel AC$

80. $d(AB) = \sqrt{(0-a)^2 + (0-0)^2} = \sqrt{a^2 + 0^2} = \sqrt{a^2} = a$

$d(AC) = \sqrt{(0-b)^2 + (0-c)^2} = \sqrt{b^2 + c^2}$. From the given information, $a = \sqrt{b^2+c^2}$.

$m_{AD} = \frac{y_2 - y_1}{x_2 - x_1} = \frac{c-0}{(a+b)-0} = \frac{c}{a+b};\ m_{BC} = \frac{y_2 - y_1}{x_2 - x_1} = \frac{0-c}{a-b} = \frac{-c}{a-b}$

$m_{AD}m_{BC} = \frac{c}{a+b} \cdot \frac{-c}{a-b} = \frac{-c^2}{a^2-b^2} = \frac{-c^2}{\left(\sqrt{b^2+c^2}\right)^2 - b^2} = \frac{-c^2}{b^2+c^2-b^2} = \frac{-c^2}{c^2} = -1$

Thus, AD is perpendicular to BC.

81. $m = \frac{y_2 - y_1}{x_2 - x_1} = \frac{26-12}{5-1} = \frac{14}{4} = 3.5$

The rate of growth was 3.5 students per year.

82. $m = \frac{y_2 - y_1}{x_2 - x_1} = \frac{110{,}000 - 50{,}000}{3-1}$

$= \frac{60{,}000}{2} = 30{,}000$

The sales increased \$30,000 per year.

83. $m = \frac{y_2 - y_1}{x_2 - x_1} = \frac{6700 - 2200}{10-3}$

$= \frac{4500}{7} \approx 642.86$

The cost decreased about \$642.86 per year.

84. The cost absorbed by the hospital was \$245 in 1995, \$375 in 2000 and \$505 in 2005.

$m = \frac{y_2 - y_1}{x_2 - x_1} = \frac{505-245}{2005-1995} = \frac{260}{10} = 26$

The cost absorbed by the hospital increased by \$26 per year.

85. $\dfrac{\Delta T}{\Delta t}$ = the hourly rate of change of temperature.
(Let $t = x$ and $T = y$.)

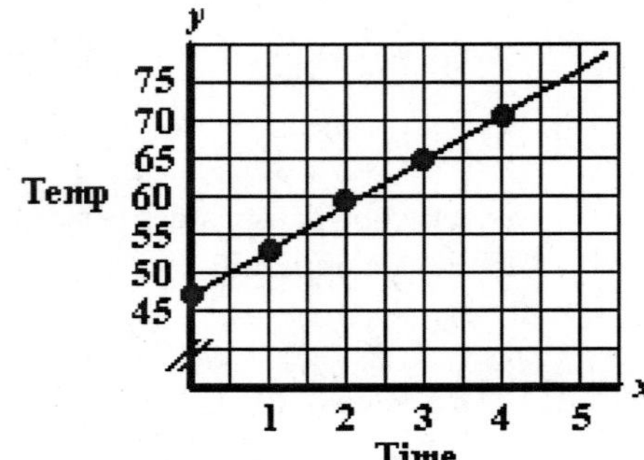

86. $\dfrac{\Delta D}{\Delta d}$ = the daily rate of change of the Dow Jones average.

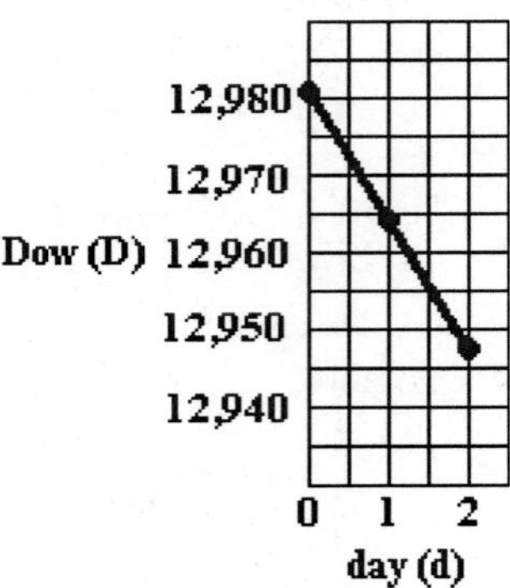

87. $D = 590t$; The slope is the speed of the plane.

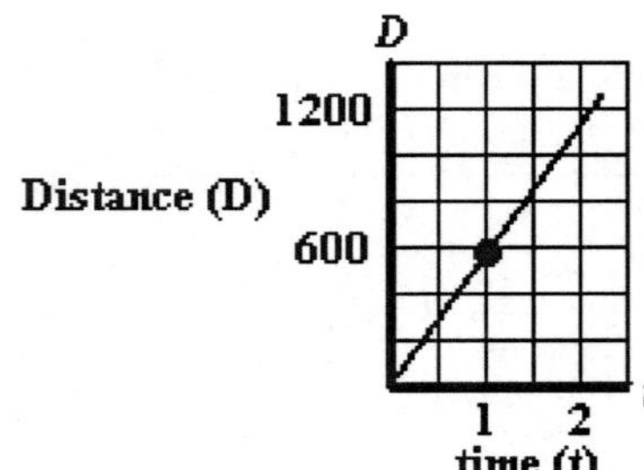

88. $A = 25n$; The slope is the monthly increase of the value of the account.

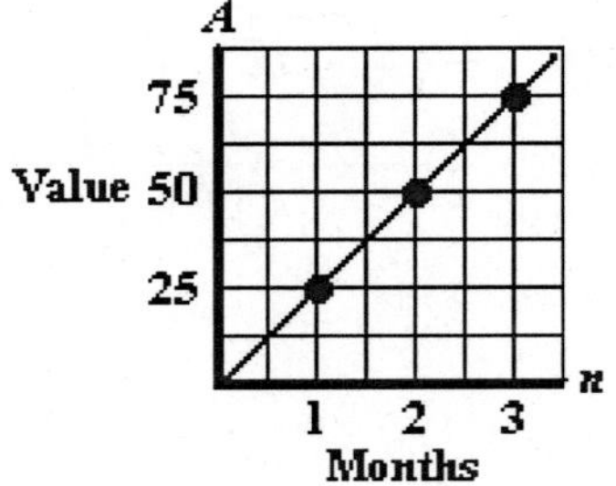

89. **Answers may vary.**

90. **Answers may vary.**

91.
$$\begin{aligned} 3x + 7y &= 21 \\ 7y &= -3x + 21 \\ \frac{7y}{7} &= \frac{-3x}{7} + \frac{21}{7} \\ y &= -\frac{3}{7}x + 3 \end{aligned}$$

92.
$$\begin{aligned} y - 3 &= 5(x + 2) \\ y - 3 &= 5x + 10 \\ y &= 5x + 13 \end{aligned}$$

93.
$$\begin{aligned} \frac{x}{5} + \frac{y}{2} &= 1 \\ 2\left(\frac{x}{5} + \frac{y}{2}\right) &= 2(1) \\ \frac{2}{5}x + y &= 2 \\ y &= -\frac{2}{5}x + 2 \end{aligned}$$

94.
$$\begin{aligned} x - 5y &= 15 \\ -5y &= -x + 15 \\ \frac{-5y}{-5} &= \frac{-x}{-5} + \frac{15}{-5} \\ y &= \frac{1}{5}x - 3 \end{aligned}$$

95. $6p^2 + p - 12 = (2p+3)(3p-4)$

96. $b^3 - 27 = b^3 - 3^3 = (b-3)(b^2 + b(3) + 3^2)$
$= (b-3)(b^2 + 3b + 9)$

97. $mp + mq + np + nq = m(p+q) + n(p+q) = (p+q)(m+n)$

98. $x^4 + x^2 - 2 = (x^2+2)(x^2-1) = (x^2+2)(x+1)(x-1)$

Exercises 2.3 (page 229)

1. $y - y_1 = m(x - x_1)$

2. m, y-intercept

3. slope-intercept

4. $Ax + By = C$

5. $-\dfrac{A}{B}$

6. $\left(0, \dfrac{C}{B}\right)$

7.
$$\begin{aligned} y - y_1 &= m(x - x_1) \\ y - 4 &= 2(x-2) \\ y - 4 &= 2x - 4 \\ -2x + y &= 0 \\ 2x - y &= 0 \end{aligned}$$

8.
$$\begin{aligned} y - y_1 &= m(x - x_1) \\ y - 5 &= -3(x-3) \\ y - 5 &= -3x + 9 \\ 3x + y &= 14 \end{aligned}$$

9.
$$\begin{aligned} y - y_1 &= m(x - x_1) \\ y - \frac{1}{2} &= 2\left(x + \frac{3}{2}\right) \\ y - \frac{1}{2} &= 2x + 3 \\ 2y - 1 &= 4x + 6 \\ -4x + 2y &= 7 \\ 4x - 2y &= -7 \end{aligned}$$

10.
$$\begin{aligned} y - y_1 &= m(x - x_1) \\ y + 2 &= -6\left(x - \frac{1}{4}\right) \\ y + 2 &= -6x + \frac{3}{2} \\ 2y + 4 &= -12x + 3 \\ 12x + 2y &= -1 \end{aligned}$$

11.
$$\begin{aligned} y - y_1 &= m(x - x_1) \\ y - 1 &= \frac{2}{5}(x+1) \\ 5(y-1) &= 2(x+1) \\ 5y - 5 &= 2x + 2 \\ -2x + 5y &= 7 \\ 2x - 5y &= -7 \end{aligned}$$

12.
$$\begin{aligned} y - y_1 &= m(x - x_1) \\ y + 3 &= -\frac{1}{5}(x+2) \\ 5(y+3) &= -(x+2) \\ 5y + 15 &= -x - 2 \\ x + 5y &= -17 \end{aligned}$$

13.
$$\begin{aligned} y - y_1 &= m(x - x_1) \\ y + 3 &= 0(x+6) \\ y + 3 &= 0 \\ y &= -3 \end{aligned}$$

14.
$$\begin{aligned} y - y_1 &= m(x - x_1) \\ y - 5 &= 0(x-7) \\ y - 5 &= 0 \\ y &= 5 \end{aligned}$$

15. m is und $\Rightarrow$ vertical
$x =$ constant
$x = -6$

16. m is und $\Rightarrow$ vertical
$x =$ constant
$x = 6$

17.
$$\begin{aligned} y - y_1 &= m(x - x_1) \\ y - 0 &= \pi(x - \pi) \\ y &= \pi x - \pi^2 \\ -\pi x + y &= -\pi^2 \\ \pi x - y &= \pi^2 \end{aligned}$$

18.
$$\begin{aligned} y - y_1 &= m(x - x_1) \\ y - \pi &= \pi(x - 0) \\ y - \pi &= \pi x \\ -\pi x + y &= \pi \\ \pi x - y &= -\pi \end{aligned}$$

19. From the graph, $m = \frac{2}{3}$ and the line passes through (2, 5).

$$\begin{aligned} y - y_1 &= m(x - x_1) \\ y - 5 &= \frac{2}{3}(x - 2) \\ 3(y - 5) &= 3 \cdot \frac{2}{3}(x - 2) \\ 3y - 15 &= 2(x - 2) \\ 3y - 15 &= 2x - 4 \\ -2x + 3y &= 11 \\ 2x - 3y &= -11 \end{aligned}$$

20. From the graph, $m = -\frac{2}{3}$ and the line passes through (−3, 2).

$$\begin{aligned} y - y_1 &= m(x - x_1) \\ y - 2 &= -\frac{2}{3}(x + 3) \\ 3(y - 2) &= 3 \cdot \left(-\frac{2}{3}\right)(x + 3) \\ 3y - 6 &= -2(x + 3) \\ 3y - 6 &= -2x - 6 \\ 2x + 3y &= 0 \end{aligned}$$

21. $m = \dfrac{y_2 - y_1}{x_2 - x_1} = \dfrac{4 - 0}{4 - 0} = \dfrac{4}{4} = 1$

$$\begin{aligned} y - y_1 &= m(x - x_1) \\ y - 0 &= 1(x - 0) \\ y &= x \end{aligned}$$

22. $m = \dfrac{y_2 - y_1}{x_2 - x_1} = \dfrac{0 - (-5)}{0 - (-5)} = \dfrac{5}{5} = 1$

$$\begin{aligned} y - y_1 &= m(x - x_1) \\ y - 0 &= 1(x - 0) \\ y &= x \end{aligned}$$

23. $m = \dfrac{y_2 - y_1}{x_2 - x_1} = \dfrac{-3 - 4}{0 - 3} = \dfrac{-7}{-3} = \dfrac{7}{3}$

$$\begin{aligned} y - y_1 &= m(x - x_1) \\ y + 3 &= \frac{7}{3}(x - 0) \\ y &= \frac{7}{3}x - 3 \end{aligned}$$

24. $m = \dfrac{y_2 - y_1}{x_2 - x_1} = \dfrac{-8 - 0}{6 - 4} = \dfrac{-8}{2} = -4$

$$\begin{aligned} y - y_1 &= m(x - x_1) \\ y - 0 &= -4(x - 4) \\ y &= -4x + 16 \end{aligned}$$

25. From the graph, $m = -\frac{9}{5}$ and the line passes through (−2, 4)

$$\begin{aligned} y - y_1 &= m(x - x_1) \\ y - 4 &= -\frac{9}{5}(x + 2) \\ y - 4 &= -\frac{9}{5}x - \frac{18}{5} \\ y &= -\frac{9}{5}x - \frac{18}{5} + 4 \\ y &= -\frac{9}{5}x + \frac{2}{5} \end{aligned}$$

26. From the graph, $m = \frac{8}{5}$ and the line passes through (2, 3).

$$\begin{aligned} y - y_1 &= m(x - x_1) \\ y - 3 &= \frac{8}{5}(x - 2) \\ y - 3 &= \frac{8}{5}x - \frac{16}{5} \\ y &= \frac{8}{5}x - \frac{16}{5} + 3 \\ y &= \frac{8}{5}x - \frac{1}{5} \end{aligned}$$

27. $y = mx + b$
$y = 3x - 2$

28. $y = mx + b$
$y = -\dfrac{1}{3}x + \dfrac{2}{3}$

29. $y = mx + b$
$y = 5x - \dfrac{1}{5}$

30. $y = mx + b$
$y = \sqrt{2}x + \sqrt{2}$

31. $y = mx + b$
$y = ax + \dfrac{1}{a}$

32. $y = mx + b$
$y = ax + 2a$

33. $y = mx + b$
$y = ax + a$

34. $y = mx + b$
$y = \dfrac{1}{a}x + a$

35.
$$\begin{aligned} y &= mx + b \\ 0 &= \frac{3}{2}(0) + b \\ 0 &= b \end{aligned}$$
$$\begin{aligned} y &= mx + b \\ y &= \frac{3}{2}x + 0 \\ 2y &= 3x \\ -3x + 2y &= 0 \\ 3x - 2y &= 0 \end{aligned}$$

36.
$$\begin{aligned} y &= mx + b \\ -7 &= -\frac{2}{3}(-3) + b \\ -7 &= 2 + b \\ -9 &= b \end{aligned}$$
$$\begin{aligned} y &= mx + b \\ y &= -\frac{2}{3}x - 9 \\ 3y &= -2x - 27 \\ 2x + 3y &= -27 \end{aligned}$$

37.
$$\begin{aligned} y &= mx + b \\ 5 &= -3(-3) + b \\ 5 &= 9 + b \\ -4 &= b \end{aligned}$$
$$\begin{aligned} y &= mx + b \\ y &= -3x - 4 \\ 3x + y &= -4 \end{aligned}$$

38.
$$\begin{aligned} y &= mx + b \\ 1 &= 1(-5) + b \\ 1 &= -5 + b \\ 6 &= b \end{aligned}$$
$$\begin{aligned} y &= mx + b \\ y &= 1x + 6 \\ -x + y &= 6 \\ x - y &= -6 \end{aligned}$$

39.
$$\begin{aligned} y &= mx + b \\ \sqrt{2} &= \sqrt{2}(0) + b \\ \sqrt{2} &= b \end{aligned}$$
$$\begin{aligned} y &= mx + b \\ y &= \sqrt{2}x + \sqrt{2} \\ -\sqrt{2}x + y &= \sqrt{2} \\ \sqrt{2}x - y &= -\sqrt{2} \end{aligned}$$

40.
$$\begin{aligned} y &= mx + b \\ 0 &= 2\sqrt{3}\left(-\sqrt{3}\right) + b \\ 0 &= -6 + b \\ 6 &= b \end{aligned}$$
$$\begin{aligned} y &= mx + b \\ y &= 2\sqrt{3}x + 6 \\ -2\sqrt{3}x + y &= 6 \\ 2\sqrt{3}x - y &= -6 \end{aligned}$$

41. $x - y = 1$

$y = x - 1 \Rightarrow m = 1, (0, -1)$

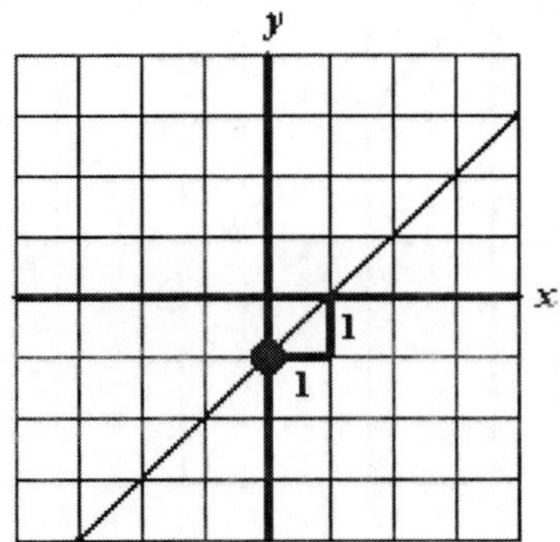

42. 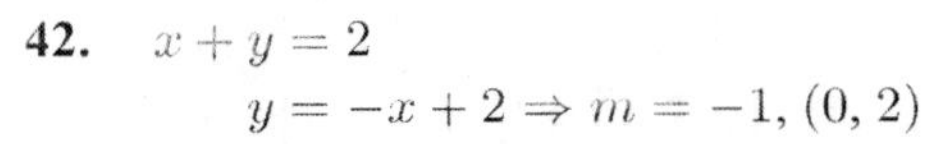
$x + y = 2$

$y = -x + 2 \Rightarrow m = -1, (0, 2)$

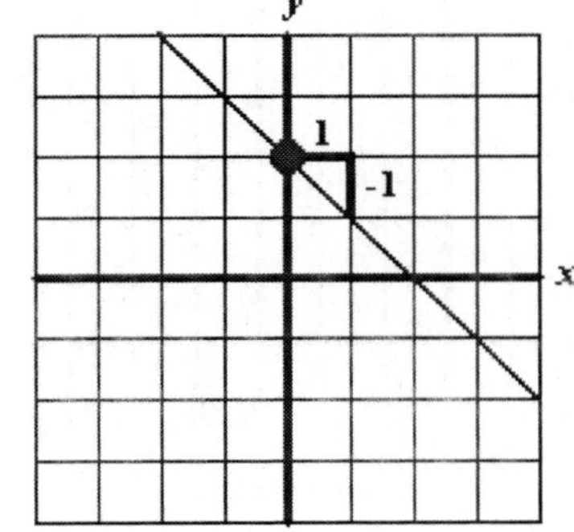

43.
$$x = \frac{3}{2}y - 3$$
$$2x = 3y - 6$$
$$-3y = -2x - 6$$
$$y = \frac{2}{3}x + 2 \Rightarrow m = \frac{2}{3}, (0, 2)$$

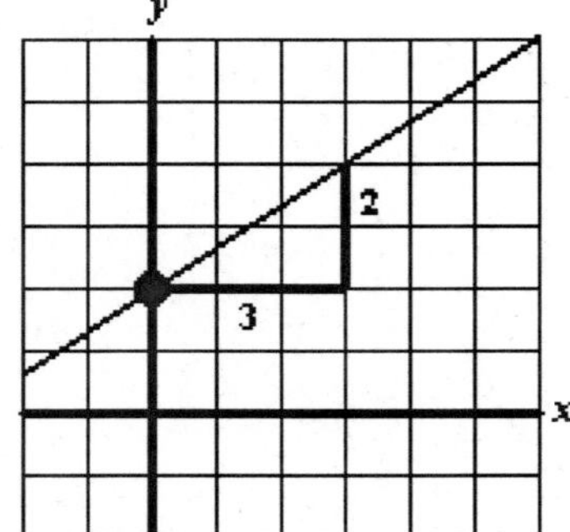

44.
$$x = -\frac{4}{5}y + 2$$
$$5x = -4y + 10$$
$$4y = -5x + 10$$
$$y = -\frac{5}{4}x + \frac{5}{2} \Rightarrow m = -\frac{5}{4}, \left(0, \frac{5}{2}\right)$$

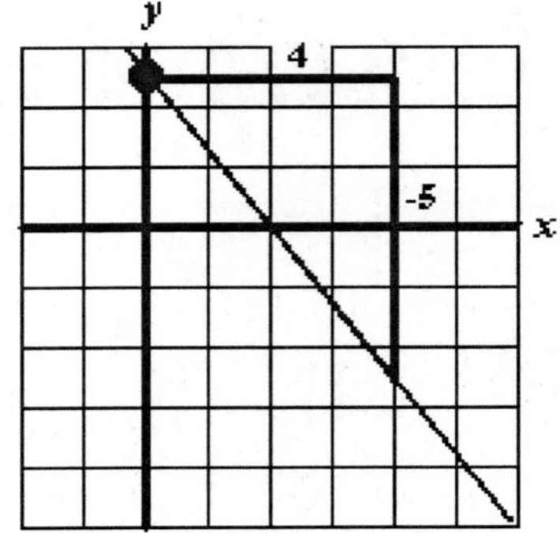

45.
$$3(y - 4) = -2(x - 3)$$
$$3y - 12 = -2x + 6$$
$$3y = -2x + 18$$
$$y = -\frac{2}{3}x + 6 \Rightarrow m = -\frac{2}{3}, (0, 6)$$

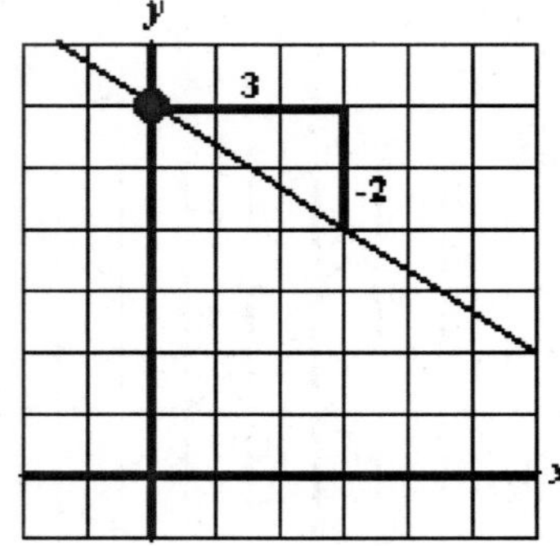

46.
$$-4(2x + 3) = 3(3y + 8)$$
$$-8x - 12 = 9y + 24$$
$$-9y = 8x + 36$$
$$y = -\frac{8}{9}x - 4\text{:}\ m = -\frac{8}{9}, (0, -4)$$

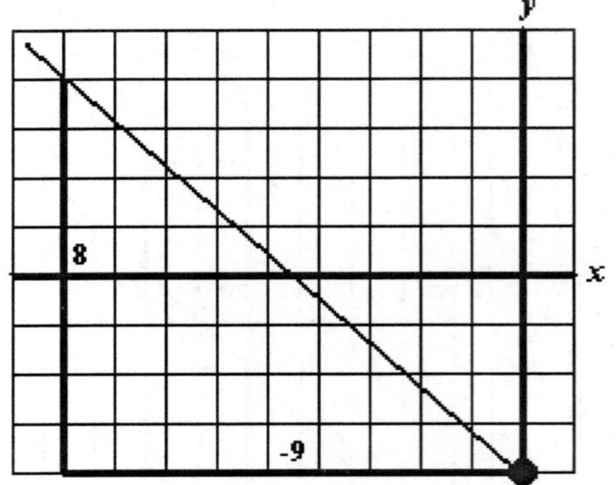

47.
$$3x - 2y = 8$$
$$-2y = -3x + 8$$
$$y = \frac{3}{2}x - 4$$
$$m = \frac{3}{2}, (0, -4)$$

48.
$$-2x + 4y = 12$$
$$4y = 2x + 12$$
$$y = \frac{1}{2}x + 3$$
$$m = \frac{1}{2}, (0, 3)$$

49.
$$-2(x + 3y) = 5$$
$$-2x - 6y = 5$$
$$-6y = 2x + 5$$
$$y = -\frac{1}{3}x - \frac{5}{6}$$
$$m = -\frac{1}{3}, \left(0, -\frac{5}{6}\right)$$

50. $5(2x-3y)=4$
$10x-15y=4$
$-15y=-10x+4$
$y=\frac{2}{3}x-\frac{4}{15}$
$m=\frac{2}{3},\ \left(0,-\frac{4}{15}\right)$

51. $x=\frac{2y-4}{7}$
$7x=2y-4$
$-2y=-7x-4$
$y=\frac{7}{2}x+2$
$m=\frac{7}{2},\ (0,2)$

52. $3x+4=-\frac{2(y-3)}{5}$
$15x+20=-2(y-3)$
$15x+20=-2y+6$
$2y=-15x-14$
$y=-\frac{15}{2}x-7$
$m=-\frac{15}{2},\ (0,-7)$

53. $y=3x+4$ $\quad y=3x-7$
$m=3$ $\quad m=3$
The lines are parallel.

54. $y=4x-13$ $\quad y=\frac{1}{4}x+13$
$m=4$ $\quad m=\frac{1}{4}$
The lines are neither.

55. $x+y=2$ $\quad y=x+5$
$y=-x+2$ $\quad m=1$
$m=-1$
The lines are perpendicular.

56. $x=y+2$ $\quad y=x+3$
$-y=-x+2$ $\quad m=1$
$y=x-2$
$m=1$
The lines are parallel.

57. $y=3x+7$ $\quad 2y=6x-9$
$m=3$ $\quad y=3x-\frac{9}{2}$
$m=3$
The lines are parallel.

58. $2x+3y=9$ $\quad 3x-2y=5$
$3y=-2x+9$ $\quad -2y=-3x+5$
$y=-\frac{2}{3}x+3$ $\quad y=\frac{3}{2}x-\frac{5}{2}$
$m=-\frac{2}{3}$ $\quad m=\frac{3}{2}$
The lines are perpendicular.

59. $x=3y+4$ $\quad y=-3x+7$
$-3y=-x+4$ $\quad m=-3$
$y=\frac{1}{3}x-\frac{4}{3}$
$m=\frac{1}{3}$
The lines are perpendicular.

60. $3x+6y=1$ $\quad y=\frac{1}{2}x$
$6y=-3x+1$ $\quad m=\frac{1}{2}$
$y=-\frac{1}{2}x+\frac{1}{6}$
$m=-\frac{1}{2}$
The lines are neither.

61. $y=3$ $\quad x=4$
horizontal vertical
The lines are perpendicular.

62. $y=-3$ $\quad y=-7$
horizontal horizontal
The lines are parallel.

63. $x = \frac{y-2}{3}$ $\quad 3(y-3)+x=0$

$3x = y - 2$ $\quad 3y - 9 + x = 0$

$-y = -3x - 2$ $\quad 3y = -x + 9$

$y = 3x + 2$ $\quad y = -\frac{1}{3}x + 3$

$m = 3$ $\quad m = -\frac{1}{3}$

The lines are perpendicular.

64. $2y = 8$ $\quad 3(2+x) = 3(y+2)$

$y = 4$ $\quad 6 + 3x = 3y + 6$

horizontal $\quad -3y = -3x$

$y = x$

$m = 1$

neither

65. $y = 4x - 7$ $\quad y - y_1 = m(x - x_1)$

$m = 4$ $\quad y - 0 = 4(x - 0)$

Use $m = 4$. $\quad \boxed{y = 4x}$

66. $x = -3y - 12$ $\quad y - y_1 = m(x - x_1)$

$3y = -x - 12$ $\quad y - 0 = -\frac{1}{3}(x - 0)$

$y = -\frac{1}{3}x - 4$ $\quad \boxed{y = -\frac{1}{3}x}$

$m = -\frac{1}{3}$

Use $m = -\frac{1}{3}$.

67. $4x - y = 7$ $\quad y - y_1 = m(x - x_1)$

$-y = -4x + 7$ $\quad y - 5 = 4(x - 2)$

$y = 4x - 7$ $\quad y - 5 = 4x - 8$

$m = 4$ $\quad \boxed{y = 4x - 3}$

Use $m = 4$.

68. $y + 3x = -12$ $\quad y - y_1 = m(x - x_1)$

$y = -3x - 12$ $\quad y - 3 = -3(x + 6)$

$m = -3$ $\quad y - 3 = -3x - 18$

Use $m = -3$. $\quad \boxed{y = -3x - 15}$

69. $x = \frac{5}{4}y - 2$ $\quad y - y_1 = m(x - x_1)$

$4x = 5y - 8$ $\quad y + 2 = \frac{4}{5}(x - 4)$

$-5y = -4x - 8$ $\quad y + 2 = \frac{4}{5}x - \frac{16}{5}$

$y = \frac{4}{5}x + \frac{8}{5}$ $\quad \boxed{y = \frac{4}{5}x - \frac{26}{5}}$

$m = \frac{4}{5}$

Use $m = \frac{4}{5}$.

70. $x = -\frac{3}{4}y + 5$ $\quad y - y_1 = m(x - x_1)$

$4x = -3y + 20$ $\quad y + 5 = -\frac{4}{3}(x - 1)$

$3y = -4x + 20$ $\quad y + 5 = -\frac{4}{3}x + \frac{4}{3}$

$y = -\frac{4}{3}x + \frac{20}{3}$ $\quad \boxed{y = -\frac{4}{3}x - \frac{11}{3}}$

$m = -\frac{4}{3}$

Use $m = -\frac{4}{3}$.

71. $y = 4x - 7$ $\quad y - y_1 = m(x - x_1)$

$m = 4$ $\quad y - 0 = -\frac{1}{4}(x - 0)$

Use $m = -\frac{1}{4}$. $\quad \boxed{y = -\frac{1}{4}x}$

72. $x = -3y - 12$ $\quad y - y_1 = m(x - x_1)$

$3y = -x - 12$ $\quad y - 0 = 3(x - 0)$

$y = -\frac{1}{3}x - 4$ $\quad \boxed{y = 3x}$

$m = -\frac{1}{3}$

Use $m = 3$.

73. $4x - y = 7$

$-y = -4x + 7$

$y = 4x - 7$

$m = 4$

Use $m = -\frac{1}{4}$.

$y - y_1 = m(x - x_1)$

$y - 5 = -\frac{1}{4}(x - 2)$

$y - 5 = -\frac{1}{4}x + \frac{1}{2}$

$\boxed{y = -\frac{1}{4}x + \frac{11}{2}}$

74. $y + 3x = -12$

$y = -3x - 12$

$m = -3$

Use $m = \frac{1}{3}$.

$y - y_1 = m(x - x_1)$

$y - 3 = \frac{1}{3}(x + 6)$

$y - 3 = \frac{1}{3}x + 2$

$\boxed{y = \frac{1}{3}x + 5}$

75. $x = \frac{5}{4}y - 2$

$4x = 5y - 8$

$-5y = -4x - 8$

$y = \frac{4}{5}x + \frac{8}{5}$

$m = \frac{4}{5}$

Use $m = -\frac{5}{4}$.

$y - y_1 = m(x - x_1)$

$y + 2 = -\frac{5}{4}(x - 4)$

$y + 2 = -\frac{5}{4}x + 5$

$\boxed{y = -\frac{5}{4}x + 3}$

76. $x = -\frac{3}{4}y + 5$

$4x = -3y + 20$

$3y = -4x + 20$

$y = -\frac{4}{3}x + \frac{20}{3}$

$m = -\frac{4}{3}$

Use $m = \frac{3}{4}$.

$y - y_1 = m(x - x_1)$

$y + 5 = \frac{3}{4}(x - 1)$

$y + 5 = \frac{3}{4}x - \frac{3}{4}$

$\boxed{y = \frac{3}{4}x - \frac{23}{4}}$

77. $4x + 5y = 20 \Rightarrow A = 4, B = 5, C = 20$

$m = -\frac{A}{B} = -\frac{4}{5}$

$b = \frac{C}{B} = \frac{20}{5} = 4 \Rightarrow (0, 4)$

78. $9x - 12y = 17 \Rightarrow A = 9, B = -12, C = 17$

$m = -\frac{A}{B} = -\frac{9}{-12} = \frac{3}{4}$

$b = \frac{C}{B} = \frac{17}{-12} = -\frac{17}{12} \Rightarrow \left(0, -\frac{17}{12}\right)$

79. $2x + 3y = 12 \Rightarrow A = 2, B = 3, C = 12$

$m = -\frac{A}{B} = -\frac{2}{3}$

$b = \frac{C}{B} = \frac{12}{3} = 4 \Rightarrow (0, 4)$

80. $5x + 6y = 30 \Rightarrow A = 5, B = 6, C = 30$

$m = -\frac{A}{B} = -\frac{5}{6}$

$b = \frac{C}{B} = \frac{30}{6} = 5 \Rightarrow (0, 5)$

81. Since $y = 3$ is the equation of a horizontal line, any perpendicular line will be vertical. Find the midpoint:

$x = \frac{2 + (-6)}{2} = -2;\ y = \frac{4 + 10}{2} = 7$

The vertical line through $(-2, 7)$ is $x = -2$.

82. Since $y = -8$ is the equation of a horizontal line, any parallel line will be horizontal. Find the midpoint:

$x = \frac{-4 + (-2)}{2} = -3;\ y = \frac{2 + 8}{2} = 5$

The horizontal line through $(-3, 5)$ is $y = 5$.

83. Since $x = 3$ is the equation of a vertical line, any parallel line will be vertical. Find the midpoint:

$x = \frac{2 + 8}{2} = 5;\ y = \frac{-4 + 12}{2} = 4$

The vertical line through $(5, 4)$ is $x = 5$.

84. Since $x = 3$ is the equation of a vertical line, any perpendicular line will be horizontal. Find the midpoint:

$x = \frac{-2 + 4}{2} = 1;\ y = \frac{2 + (-8)}{2} = -3$

The horizontal line through $(1, -3)$: $y = -3$.

85. Let $x =$ the number of years the truck has been owned and let $y =$ the value of the truck. Then two points on the line are given: $(0, 24300)$ and $(7, 1900)$.

$$m = \frac{24300 - 1900}{0 - 7} = \frac{22400}{-7} = -3200$$
$$y - y_1 = m(x - x_1)$$
$$y - 24300 = -3200(x - 0)$$
$$y - 24300 = -3200x$$
$$y = -3200x + 24300$$

86. Let $x =$ the number of years the laptop has been owned and let $y =$ the value of the laptop. Then two points on the line are given: $(0, 2700)$ and $(4, 300)$.

$$m = \frac{2700 - 300}{0 - 4} = \frac{2400}{-4} = -600$$
$$y - y_1 = m(x - x_1)$$
$$y - 2700 = -600(x - 0)$$
$$y - 2700 = -600x$$
$$y = -600x + 2700$$

87. Let $x =$ the number of years the building has been owned and let $y =$ the value of the building. Then two points on the line are given: $(0, 475000)$ and $(10, 950000)$.

$$m = \frac{950000 - 475000}{10 - 0} = \frac{475000}{10} = 47500$$
$$y - y_1 = m(x - x_1)$$
$$y - 475000 = 47500(x - 0)$$
$$y - 475000 = 47500x$$
$$y = 47500x + 475000$$

88. Let $x =$ the number of years the house has been owned and let $y =$ the value of the house. Then two points on the line are given: $(0, 112000)$ and $(12, 224000)$.

$$m = \frac{224000 - 112000}{12 - 0} = \frac{112000}{12} = \frac{28000}{3}$$
$$y - y_1 = m(x - x_1)$$
$$y - 112000 = \frac{28000}{3}(x - 0)$$
$$y - 112000 = \frac{28000}{3}x$$
$$y = \frac{28000}{3}x + 112000$$

89. Let $x =$ the number of years the TV has been owned and let $y =$ the value of the TV. Then two points on the line are given: $(0, 1900)$ and $(3, 1190)$.

$$m = \frac{1900 - 1190}{0 - 3} = \frac{710}{-3} = -\frac{710}{3}$$
$$y - y_1 = m(x - x_1)$$
$$y - 1900 = -\frac{710}{3}(x - 0)$$
$$y - 1900 = -\frac{710}{3}x$$
$$y = -\frac{710}{3}x + 1900$$

90. Let $x =$ the number of years the radio has been owned and let $y =$ the value of the radio. Then two points on the line are given: $(0, 555)$ and $(5, 80)$.

$$m = \frac{555 - 80}{0 - 5} = \frac{475}{-5} = -95$$
$$y - y_1 = m(x - x_1)$$
$$y - 555 = -95(x - 0)$$
$$y - 555 = -95x$$
$$y = -95x + 555$$

Let $x = 3$ and find the value of y:

$$y = -95x + 555$$
$$= -95(3) + 555 = 270$$

It will be worth \$270.

91. Let $x =$ the number of years the copier has been owned and let $y =$ the value of the copier. Then one point on the line is given: $(0, 1050)$. Since the copier depreciates by \$120 per year, $m = -120$.

$$y - y_1 = m(x - x_1)$$
$$y - 1050 = -120(x - 0)$$
$$y - 1050 = -120x$$
$$y = -120x + 1050$$

Let $x = 8$ and find the value of y:

$$y = -120x + 1050$$
$$= -120(8) + 1050 = 90$$

The salvage value will be \$90.

92. Let $x =$ the number of years the boat has been owned and let $y =$ the value of the boat. Then two points on the line are given: $(0, 27600)$ and $(12, 0)$.

$$m = \frac{27600 - 0}{0 - 12} = \frac{27600}{-12} = -2300$$

The boat depreciates at a rate of \$2300 per year.

93. Let $x =$ the number of years the table has been owned and let $y =$ the value of the table. Then one point on the line is given: $(2, 450)$. Since the table appreciates by \$40 per year, $m = 40$.

$$y - y_1 = m(x - x_1)$$
$$y - 450 = 40(x - 2)$$
$$y - 450 = 40x - 80$$
$$y = 40x + 370$$

Let $x = 13$ and find the value of y:

$$y = 40x + 370$$
$$= 40(13) + 370 = 890$$

The value will be \$890.

94. Let $x =$ the number of years the clock has been owned and let $y =$ the value of the clock. Then two points on the line are given: $(2, 350)$ and $(5, 530)$.

$$m = \frac{530 - 350}{5 - 2} = \frac{180}{3} = 60$$
$$y - y_1 = m(x - x_1)$$
$$y - 350 = 60(x - 2)$$
$$y - 350 = 60x - 120$$
$$y = 60x + 230$$

Let $x = 7$ and find the value of y:

$$y = 60x + 230$$
$$= 60(7) + 230 = 650$$

It will be worth \$650.

95. Let $x =$ the number of years the cottage has been owned and let $y =$ the value of the cottage. Then one point on the line is given: $(3, 47700)$. Since the cottage appreciates by \$3500 per year, $m = 3500$.

$$y - y_1 = m(x - x_1)$$
$$y - 47700 = 3500(x - 3)$$
$$y - 47700 = 3500x - 10500$$
$$y = 3500x + 37200$$

Let $x = 0$ and find the value of y:

$$y = 3500x + 37200$$
$$= 3500(0) + 37200 = 37200$$

The purchase price was \$37,200.

96. Let $x =$ the number of hours of service needed and let $y =$ the total charge. Then two points on the line are given: $(2, 70)$ and $(4, 105)$

$$m = \frac{105 - 70}{4 - 2} = \frac{35}{2} = 17.50$$
$$y - y_1 = m(x - x_1)$$
$$y - 70 = 17.50(x - 2)$$
$$y - 70 = 17.50x - 35$$
$$y = 17.50x + 35$$

The hourly charge is \$17.50.

97. Let $x =$ the hours of labor and let $y =$ the labor charge. Then $m =$ the hourly charge.

$$y = mx \qquad y = 46x$$
$$69 = m(1.5) \qquad y = 46(5) = 230$$
$$46 = m$$

The charge will be \$230.

98. Let $x =$ the number of hundreds of copies and let $y =$ the total charge. Then $m =$ the charge per copy and $b =$ the fixed charge.

$$y = mx + b \qquad y = x + 45$$
$$y = 1x + b \qquad y = 10 + 45 = 55$$
$$52 = 1(7) + b$$
$$45 = b$$

The charge will be \$55.

99. Let $x =$ the number of fires and let $y =$ the population. Then two points on the line are given: $(300, 57000)$ and $(325, 59000)$.

$$m = \frac{59000 - 57000}{325 - 300} = \frac{2000}{25} = 80$$
$$y - y_1 = m(x - x_1)$$
$$y - 57000 = 80(x - 300)$$
$$y - 57000 = 80x - 24000$$
$$y = 80x + 33000$$

Let $y = 100000$ and find the value of x:

$$y = 80x + 33000$$
$$100000 = 80x + 33000$$
$$67000 = 80x$$
$$837.5 = x \Rightarrow$$ There will be about 838 fires when the population is 100,000.

100. Let $x =$ the number of feet of gutter and let $y =$ the total charge. Then $m =$ the charge per foot. One point on the line is given: $(250, 435)$

$$y = mx + b$$
$$435 = m(250) + 60$$
$$375 = 250m$$
$$1.5 = m$$

Let $x = 300$ and find the value of y:

$$y = 1.5x + 60$$
$$= 1.5(300) + 60 = 510$$

It will cost \$510.

101. Let F replace x and C replace y. Then two points on the line are given: $(32, 0)$ and $(212, 100)$.

$$m = \frac{100 - 0}{212 - 32} = \frac{100}{180} = \frac{5}{9}$$
$$C - C_1 = m(F - F_1)$$
$$C - 0 = \frac{5}{9}(F - 32)$$
$$C = \frac{5}{9}(F - 32)$$

102. Two points on the line are given: $(1, 88)$ and $(0, 0)$.

$$m = \frac{88 - 0}{1 - 0} = \frac{88}{1} = 88$$
$$y - y_1 = m(x - x_1)$$
$$y - 0 = 88(x - 0)$$
$$y = 88x$$

103. Let $y =$ the percent who smoke and let $x =$ the # of years since 1974. Two points are given: (0, 47) and (20, 29).

$$m = \frac{29-47}{20-0} = \frac{-18}{20} = -\frac{9}{10}$$

$$y - y_1 = m(x - x_1)$$

$$y - 47 = -\frac{9}{10}(x - 0)$$

$$\boxed{y = -\frac{9}{10}x + 47}$$

Let $x = 40$:

$$y = -\frac{9}{10}(40) + 47 = -36 + 47 = 11$$

11% will smoke in 2014.

104. Let f replace x and h replace y. Then two points on the line are given: (62.5, 200) and (40.2, 150).

$$m = \frac{150-200}{40.2-62.5} = \frac{-50}{-22.3} \approx 2.242$$

$$h - h_1 = m(f - f_1)$$

$$h - 200 = 2.242(f - 62.5)$$

$$h - 200 = 2.242f - 140.125$$

$$\boxed{h = 2.242f + 59.875}$$

Let $f = 50$:

$$h = 2.242(50) + 59.875 \approx 172$$

He would be about 172 cm tall.

105. Two points on the line are given: (0, 37.5) and (2, 45).

$$m = \frac{45-37.5}{2-0} = \frac{7.5}{2} = 3.75$$

$$y - y_1 = m(x - x_1)$$

$$y - 37.5 = 3.75(x - 0)$$

$$y = 3.75x + 37.5$$

Let $x = 4$ and find the value of y:

$$y = 3.75x + 37.5$$
$$= 3.75(4) + 37.5$$
$$= 15 + 37.5 = 52.5$$

The price will be \$52.50 in the year 2014.

106. Let January be represented by $x = 0$, and later months by $x = 1, 2, 3, \ldots$ Let y represent the inventory. Then two points on the line are given: (0, 375) and (3, 264).

$$m = \frac{375-264}{0-3} = \frac{111}{-3} = -37$$

$$y - y_1 = m(x - x_1)$$

$$y - 375 = -37(x - 0)$$

$$y = -37x + 375$$

Let $x = 2$ and find the value of y:

$$y = -37x + 375$$
$$= -37(2) + 375 = 301$$

The March inventory will be about 301.

107. The equation describing the production is $y = -70x + 1900$, where x represents the number of years and y is the level of production. Let $x = 3\frac{1}{2} = \frac{7}{2}$.

$$y = -70x + 1900$$
$$= -70\left(\frac{7}{2}\right) + 1900 = 1655$$

The production will be 1655 barrels per day.

108. Let $x =$ the number of years the piping has been owned and let $y =$ the value of the piping. Then two points on the line are given: (0, 137000) and (12, −33000).

$$m = \frac{-33000-137000}{12-0} = -\frac{42500}{3}$$

$$y - y_1 = m(x - x_1)$$

$$y - 137000 = -\frac{42500}{3}(x - 0)$$

$$y = -\frac{42500}{3}x + 137000$$

109. **a.**

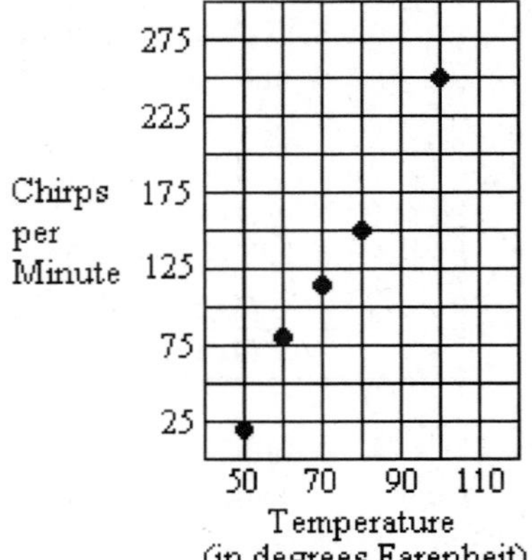

b. Use (50, 20) and (100, 250) for the regression line.

$$m = \frac{250-20}{100-50} = \frac{230}{50} = \frac{23}{5}$$
$$y - y_1 = m(x - x_1)$$
$$y - 20 = \frac{23}{5}(x - 50)$$
$$y - 20 = \frac{23}{5}x - 230$$
$$y = \frac{23}{5}x - 210$$

c. $y = \frac{23}{5}(90) - 210 = 204$

The rate will be about 204 chirps per minute.

110. **a.**

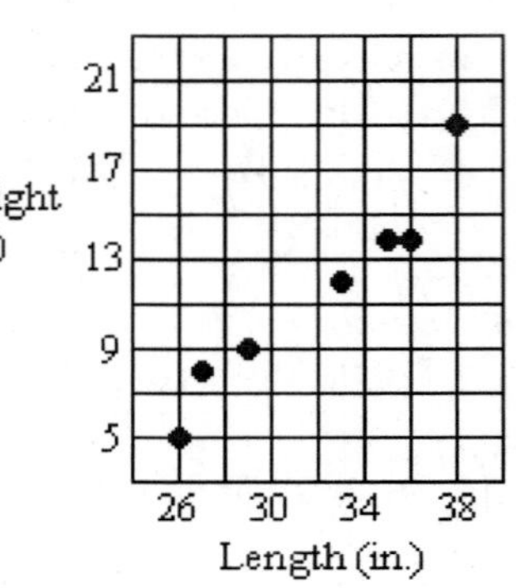

b. Use (26, 5) and (38, 19) for the regression line.

$$m = \frac{19-5}{38-26} = \frac{14}{12} = \frac{7}{6}$$
$$y - y_1 = m(x - x_1)$$
$$y - 5 = \frac{7}{6}(x - 26)$$
$$y - 5 = \frac{7}{6}x - \frac{91}{3}$$
$$y = \frac{7}{6}x - \frac{76}{3}$$

c. $y = \frac{7}{6}(32) - \frac{76}{3} = 12$

The weight will be about 12 pounds.

111. $y = 4.44x - 196.62$

112. $y = 0.96x - 19.22$

113. Answers may vary.

114. Answers may vary.

115.
$$m = \frac{b-0}{0-a} = -\frac{b}{a}$$
$$y - y_1 = m(x - x_1)$$
$$y - b = -\frac{b}{a}(x - 0)$$
$$y - b = -\frac{b}{a}x$$
$$ay - ab = -bx$$
$$bx + ay = ab$$
$$\frac{bx + ay}{ab} = \frac{ab}{ab}$$
$$\frac{x}{a} + \frac{y}{b} = 1$$

116.

x-intercept	y-intercept
$bx + ay = ab$	$bx + ay = ab$
$bx + a(0) = ab$	$b(0) + ay = ab$
$bx = ab$	$ay = ab$
$x = a$	$y = b$
$(a, 0)$	$(0, b)$

117-122. Answers may vary.

123. $x^7x^3x^{-5} = x^{7+3-5} = x^5$

124. $\dfrac{y^3y^{-4}}{y^{-5}} = \dfrac{y^{-1}}{y^{-5}} = y^{-1-(-5)} = y^4$

125. $\left(\dfrac{81}{25}\right)^{-3/2} = \left(\dfrac{25}{81}\right)^{3/2} = \left[\dfrac{5}{9}\right]^3 = \dfrac{125}{729}$

126. $\sqrt[3]{27x^7} = \sqrt[3]{27x^6}\sqrt[3]{x} = 3x^2\sqrt[3]{x}$

127. $\sqrt{27} - 2\sqrt{12} = \sqrt{9}\sqrt{3} - 2\sqrt{4}\sqrt{3} = 3\sqrt{3} - 2(2)\sqrt{3} = 3\sqrt{3} - 4\sqrt{3} = -\sqrt{3}$

128. $\dfrac{5}{\sqrt{5}} = \dfrac{5\sqrt{5}}{\sqrt{5}\sqrt{5}} = \dfrac{5\sqrt{5}}{5} = \sqrt{5}$

129. $\dfrac{5}{\sqrt{x}+2} = \dfrac{5}{\sqrt{x}+2} \cdot \dfrac{\sqrt{x}-2}{\sqrt{x}-2} = \dfrac{5(\sqrt{x}-2)}{(\sqrt{x})^2 - 2^2} = \dfrac{5(\sqrt{x}-2)}{x-4}$

130. $(\sqrt{x}-2)^2 = (\sqrt{x}-2)(\sqrt{x}-2) = x - 2\sqrt{x} - 2\sqrt{x} + 4 = x - 4\sqrt{x} + 4$

Exercises 2.4 (page 250)

1. x-intercept

2. y-axis

3. axis of symmetry

4. y-axis

5. x-axis

6. origin

7. circle, center

8. radius

9. $x^2 + y^2 = r^2$

10. $(x-h)^2 + (y-k)^2 = r^2$

11.
$y = x^2 - 4$
$0 = (x+2)(x-2)$
$x = -2,\ x = 2$
x-int: $(-2, 0), (2, 0)$

$y = x^2 - 4$
$y = 0^2 - 4$
$y = -4$
y-int: $(0, -4)$

12.
$y = x^2 - 9$
$0 = x^2 - 9$
$0 = (x+3)(x-3)$
$x = -3,\ x = 3$
x-int: $(-3, 0), (3, 0)$

$y = x^2 - 9$
$y = 0^2 - 9$
$y = -9$
y-int: $(0, -9)$

13.
$y = 4x^2 - 2x$
$0 = 2x(2x-1)$
$x = 0,\ x = \frac{1}{2}$
x-int: $(0, 0), \left(\frac{1}{2}, 0\right)$

$y = 4x^2 - 2x$
$y = 4(0)^2 - 2(0)$
$y = 0$
y-int: $(0, 0)$

14.
$y = 2x - 4x^2$
$0 = 2x(1-2x)$
$x = 0,\ x = \frac{1}{2}$
x-int: $(0, 0), \left(\frac{1}{2}, 0\right)$

$y = 2x - 4x^2$
$y = 2(0) - 4(0)^2$
$y = 0$
y-int: $(0, 0)$

15.
$y = x^2 - 4x - 5$
$0 = (x+1)(x-5)$
$x = -1,\ x = 5$
x-int: $(-1, 0), (5, 0)$

$y = x^2 - 4x - 5$
$y = 0^2 - 4(0) - 5$
$y = -5$
y-int: $(0, -5)$

16.
$y = x^2 - 10x + 21$
$0 = (x-3)(x-7)$
$x = 3,\ x = 7$
x-int: $(3, 0), (7, 0)$

$y = x^2 - 10x + 21$
$y = 0^2 - 10(0) + 21$
$y = 21$
y-int: $(0, 21)$

17. $y = x^2 + x - 2$
$0 = (x+2)(x-1)$
$x = -2, x = 1$
x-int: $(-2, 0), (1, 0)$

$y = x^2 + x - 2$
$y = 0^2 + 0 - 2$
$y = -2$
y-int: $(0, -2)$

18. $y = x^2 + 2x - 3$
$0 = (x+3)(x-1)$
$x = -3, x = 1$
x-int: $(-3, 0), (1, 0)$

$y = x^2 + 2x - 3$
$y = 0^2 + 2(0) - 3$
$y = -3$
y-int: $(0, -3)$

19. $y = x^3 - 9x$
$0 = x(x^2 - 9)$
$0 = x(x+3)(x-3)$
$x = 0, x = -3, x = 3$
x-int: $(0, 0), (-3, 0), (3, 0)$

$y = x^3 - 9x$
$y = 0^3 - 9(0)$
$y = 0$
y-int: $(0, 0)$

20. $y = x^3 + x$
$0 = x(x^2 + 1)$
$x = 0, \{x^2 + 1 \neq 0\}$
x-int: $(0, 0)$

$y = x^3 + x$
$y = 0^3 + 0$
$y = 0$
y-int: $(0, 0)$

21. $y = x^4 - 1$
$0 = (x^2+1)(x^2-1)$
$0 = (x^2+1)(x+1)(x-1)$
$x = -1, x = 1$
x-int: $(-1, 0), (1, 0)$

$y = x^4 - 1$
$y = 0^4 - 1$
$y = -1$
y-int: $(0, -1)$

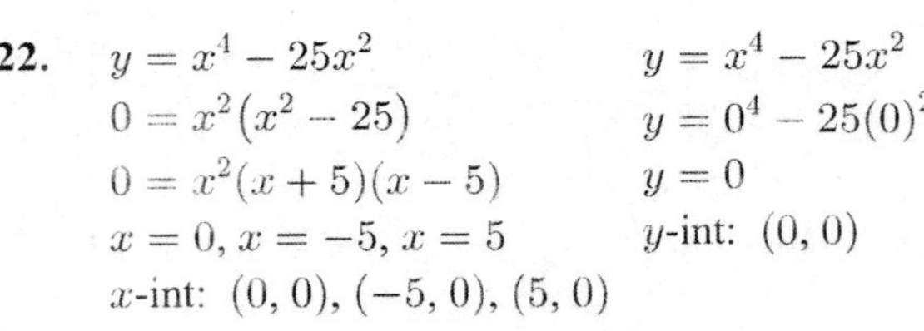

22. $y = x^4 - 25x^2$
$0 = x^2(x^2 - 25)$
$0 = x^2(x+5)(x-5)$
$x = 0, x = -5, x = 5$
x-int: $(0, 0), (-5, 0), (5, 0)$

$y = x^4 - 25x^2$
$y = 0^4 - 25(0)^2$
$y = 0$
y-int: $(0, 0)$

23. $y = x^2$
x-int: $(0, 0)$
y-int: $(0, 0)$

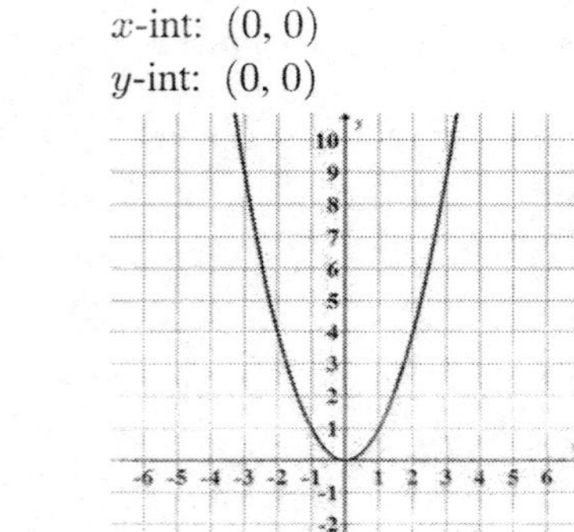

24. $y = -x^2$
x-int: $(0, 0)$
y-int: $(0, 0)$

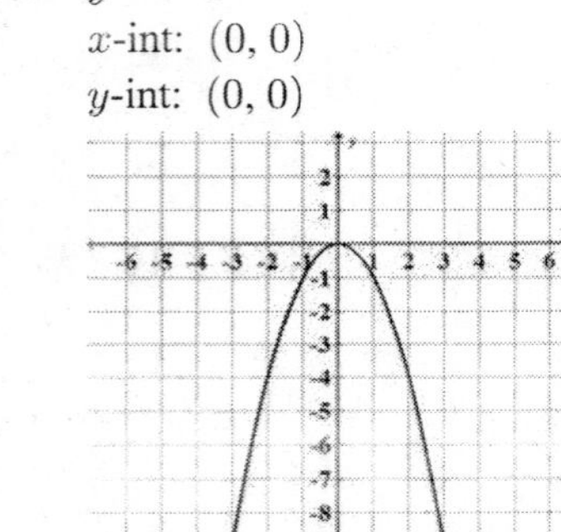

25. $y = -x^2 + 2$
x-int: $\left(\sqrt{2}, 0\right), \left(-\sqrt{2}, 0\right)$
y-int: $(0, 2)$

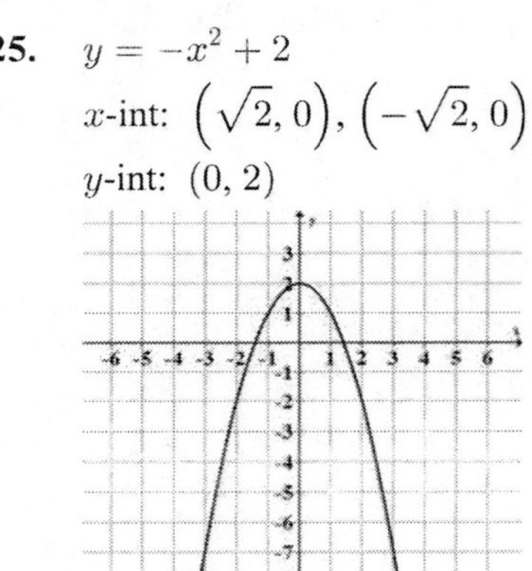

26. $y = x^2 - 1$
x-int: $(1, 0), (-1, 0)$
y-int: $(0, -1)$

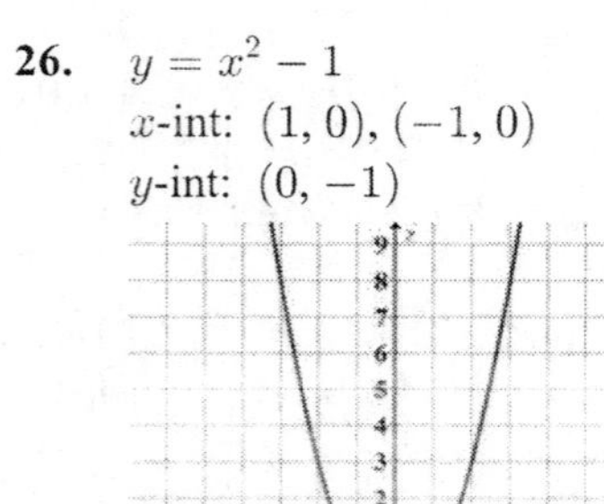

27. $y = x^2 - 4x$
x-int: $(0, 0), (4, 0)$
y-int: $(0, 0)$

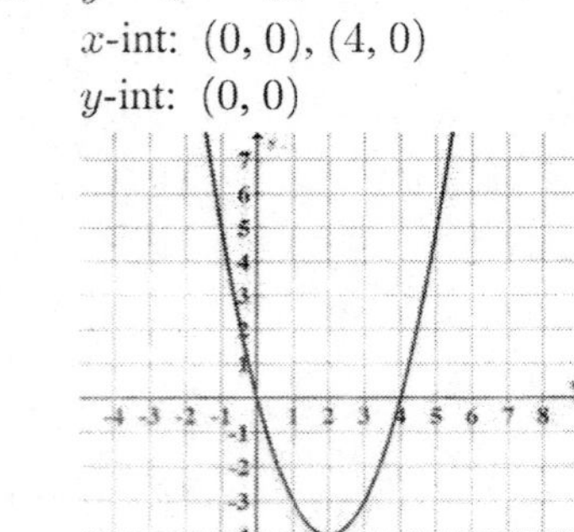

28. $y = x^2 + 2x$
x-int: $(0, 0), (-2, 0)$
y-int: $(0, 0)$

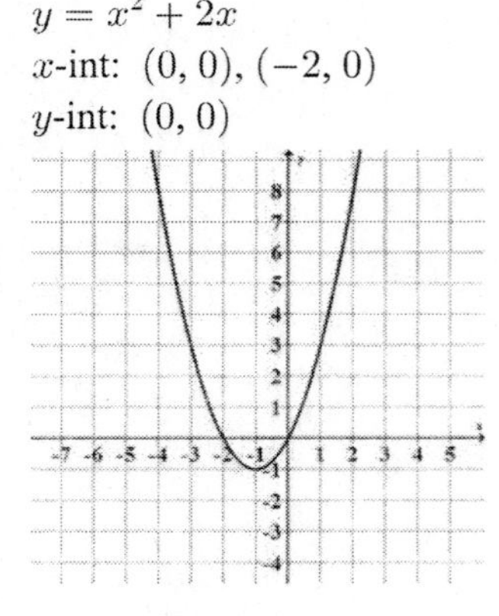

29. $y = \frac{1}{2}x^2 - 2x$

x-int: $(0, 0), (4, 0)$

y-int: $(0, 0)$

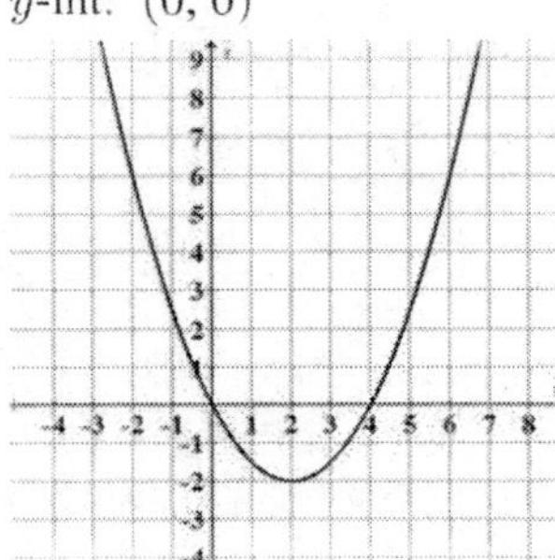

30. $y = \frac{1}{2}x^2 + 3$

x-int: none

y-int: $(0, 3)$

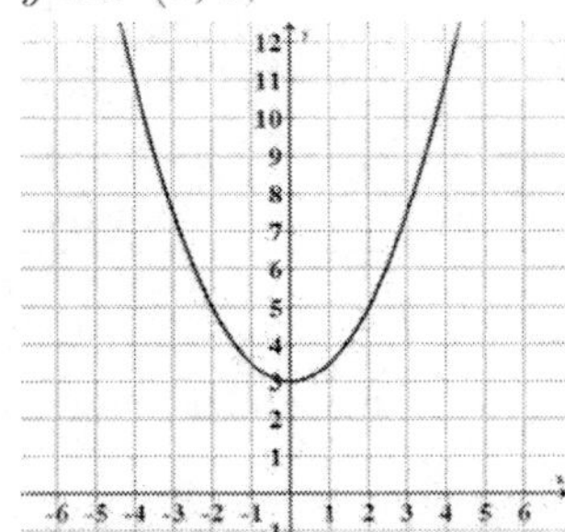

31. $y = x^2 + 2$

x-axis	y-axis	origin
$-y = x^2 + 2$	$y = (-x)^2 + 2$	$-y = (-x)^2 + 2$
not equivalent: no symmetry	$y = x^2 + 2$	$-y = x^2 + 2$
	equivalent: symmetry	not equivalent: no symmetry

32. $y = 3x + 2$

x-axis	y-axis	origin
$-y = 3x + 2$	$y = 3(-x) + 2$	$-y = 3(-x) + 2$
not equivalent: no symmetry	$y = -3x + 2$	$-y = -3x + 2$
	not equivalent: no symmetry	$y = 3x - 2$
		not equivalent: no symmetry

33. $y^2 + 1 = x$

x-axis	y-axis	origin
$(-y)^2 + 1 = x$	$y^2 + 1 = -x$	$(-y)^2 + 1 = -x$
$y^2 + 1 = x$	not equivalent: no symmetry	$y^2 + 1 = -x$
equivalent: symmetry		not equivalent: no symmetry

34. $y^2 + y = x$

x-axis	y-axis	origin
$(-y)^2 + (-y) = x$	$y^2 + y = -x$	$(-y)^2 + (-y) = -x$
$y^2 - y = x$	not equivalent: no symmetry	$y^2 - y = -x$
not equivalent: no symmetry		$-y^2 + y = x$
		not equivalent: no symmetry

35. $y^2 = x^2$

x-axis	y-axis	origin
$(-y)^2 = x^2$	$y^2 = (-x)^2$	$(-y)^2 = (-x)^2$
$y^2 = x^2$	$y^2 = x^2$	$y^2 = x^2$
equivalent: **symmetry**	equivalent: **symmetry**	equivalent: **symmetry**

36. $y = 3x + 7$

x-axis	y-axis	origin
$-y = 3x + 7$	$y = 3(-x) + 7$	$-y = 3(-x) + 7$
not equivalent: no symmetry	$y = -3x + 7$	$-y = -3x + 7$
	not equivalent: no symmetry	$y = 3x - 7$
		not equivalent: no symmetry

37. $y = 3x^2 + 7$

x-axis	y-axis	origin
$-y = 3x^2 + 7$	$y = 3(-x)^2 + 7$	$-y = 3(-x)^2 + 7$
not equivalent: no symmetry	$y = 3x^2 + 7$	$-y = 3x^2 + 7$
	equivalent: **symmetry**	not equivalent: no symmetry

38. $x^2 + y^2 = 1$

x-axis	y-axis	origin
$x^2 + (-y)^2 = 1$	$(-x)^2 + y^2 = 1$	$(-x)^2 + (-y)^2 = 1$
$x^2 + y^2 = 1$	$x^2 + y^2 = 1$	$x^2 + y^2 = 1$
equivalent: **symmetry**	equivalent: **symmetry**	equivalent: **symmetry**

39. $y = 3x^3 + 7$

x-axis	y-axis	origin
$-y = 3x^3 + 7$	$y = 3(-x)^3 + 7$	$-y = 3(-x)^3 + 7$
not equivalent: no symmetry	$y = -3x^3 + 7$	$-y = -3x^3 + 7$
	not equivalent: no symmetry	$y = 3x^3 - 7$
		not equivalent: no symmetry

40. $y = 3x^3 + 7x$

x-axis	y-axis	origin
$-y = 3x^3 + 7x$	$y = 3(-x)^3 + 7x$	$-y = 3(-x)^3 + 7(-x)$
not equivalent: no symmetry	$y = -3x^3 + 7x$	$-y = -3x - 7x$
	not equivalent: no symmetry	$y = 3x^3 + 7x$
		equivalent: **symmetry**

41. $y^2 = 3x$

x-axis	y-axis	origin
$(-y)^2 = 3x$	$y^2 = 3(-x)$	$(-y)^2 = 3(-x)$
$y^2 = 3x$	$y^2 = -3x$	$y^2 = -3x$
equivalent: **symmetry**	not equivalent: no symmetry	not equivalent: no symmetry

42. $y = 3x^4 + 7$

x-axis	y-axis	origin
$-y = 3x^4 + 7$	$y = 3(-x)^4 + 7$	$-y = 3(-x)^4 + 7$
not equivalent: no symmetry	$y = 3x^4 + 7$	$-y = 3x^4 + 7$
	equivalent: **symmetry**	not equivalent: no symmetry

43. $y = |x|$

x-axis	y-axis	origin
$-y = |x|$	$y = |-x|$	$-y = |-x|$
not equivalent: no symmetry	$y = |-1||x|$	$-y = |-1||x|$
	$y = |x|$	$-y = |x|$
	equivalent: **symmetry**	not equivalent: no symmetry

44. $y = |x + 1|$

x-axis	y-axis	origin
$-y = |x + 1|$	$y = |-x + 1|$	$-y = |-x + 1|$
not equivalent: no symmetry	not equivalent: no symmetry	not equivalent: no symmetry

45. $|y| = x$

x-axis	y-axis	origin
$|-y| = x$	$|y| = -x$	$|-y| = -x$
$|-1||y| = x$	not equivalent: no symmetry	$|-1||y| = -x$
$|y| = x$		$|y| = -x$
equivalent: **symmetry**		not equivalent: no symmetry

46. $|y| = |x|$

x-axis	y-axis	origin
$|-y| = |x|$	$|y| = |-x|$	$|-y| = |-x|$
$|-1||y| = |x|$	$|y| = |-1||x|$	$|-1||y| = |-1||x|$
$|y| = |x|$	$|y| = |x|$	$|y| = |x|$
equivalent: **symmetry**	equivalent: **symmetry**	equivalent: **symmetry**

47. $y = x^2 + 4x$
x-int: $(0, 0), (-4, 0)$
y-int: $(0, 0)$
symmetry: none

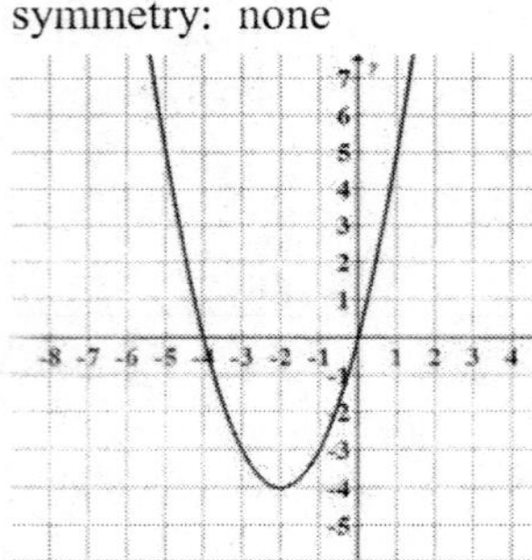

48. $y = x^2 - 6x$
x-int: $(0, 0), (6, 0)$
y-int: $(0, 0)$
symmetry: none

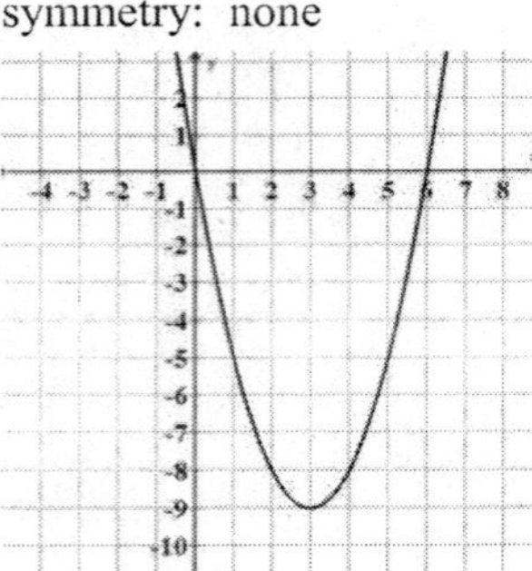

49. $y = x^3$
x-int: $(0, 0)$
y-int: $(0, 0)$
symmetry: origin

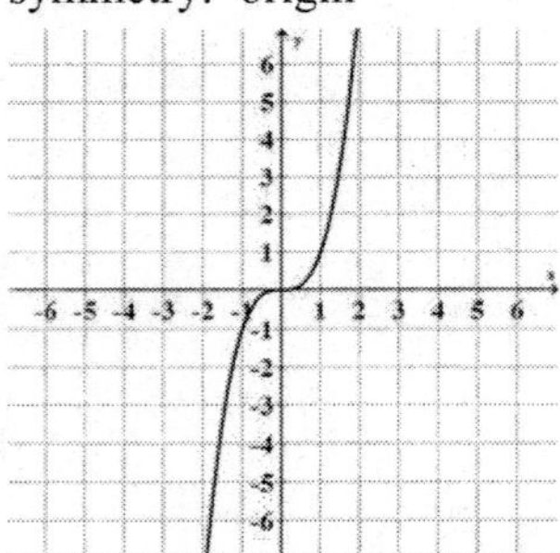

50. $y = x^3 + x$
x-int: $(0, 0)$
y-int: $(0, 0)$
symmetry: origin

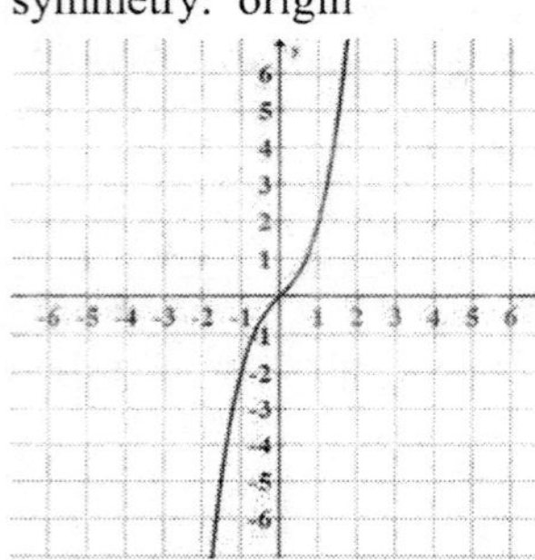

51. $y = |x - 2|$
x-int: $(2, 0)$
y-int: $(0, 2)$
symmetry: none

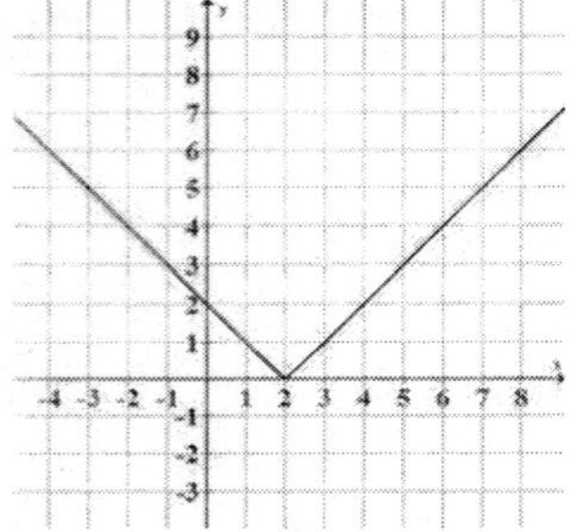

52. $y = |x| - 2$
x-int: $(-2, 0), (2, 0)$
y-int: $(0, -2)$
symmetry: y-axis

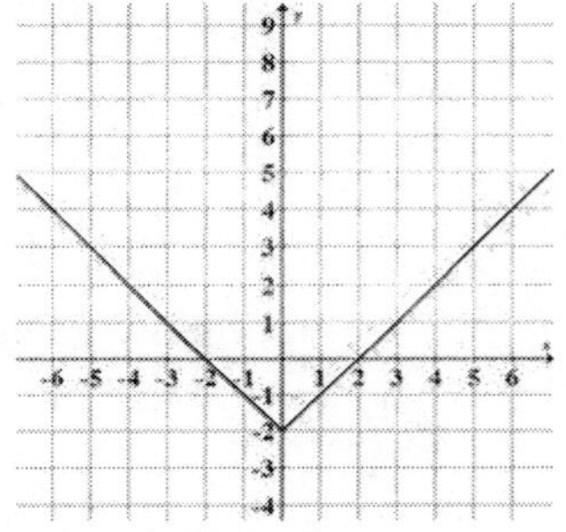

53. $y = 3 - |x|$
x-int: $(-3, 0), (3, 0)$
y-int: $(0, 3)$
symmetry: y-axis

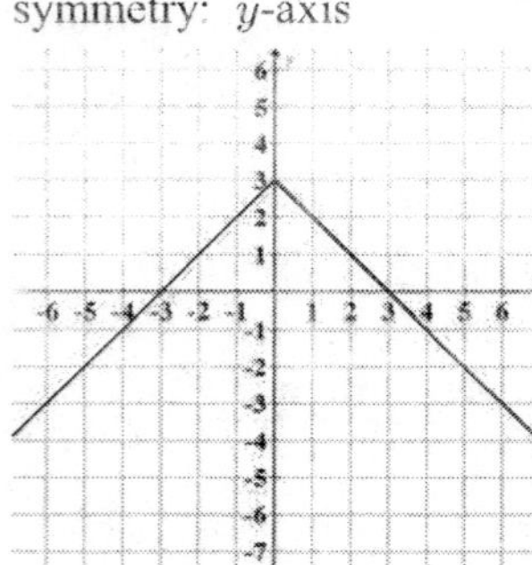

54. $y = 3|x|$
x-int: $(0, 0)$
y-int: $(0, 0)$
symmetry: y-axis

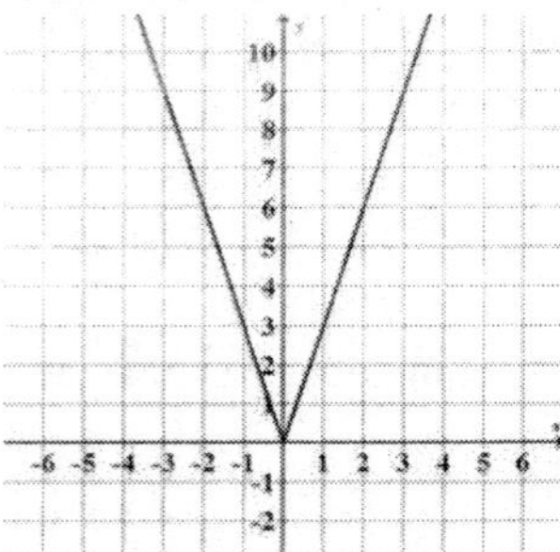

55. $y^2 = -x$
x-int: $(0, 0)$
y-int: $(0, 0)$
symmetry: x-axis

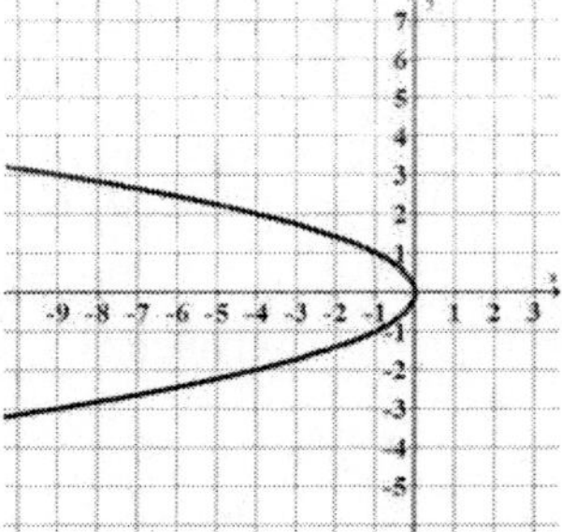

56. $y^2 = 4x$
x-int: $(0, 0)$
y-int: $(0, 0)$
symmetry: x-axis

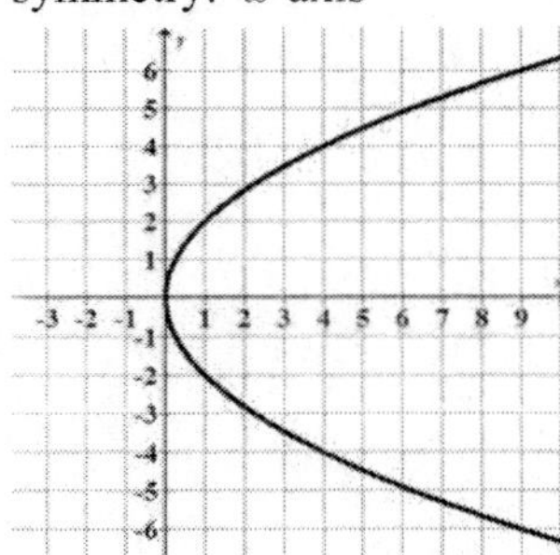

57. $y^2 = 9x$
x-int: $(0, 0)$
y-int: $(0, 0)$
symmetry: x-axis

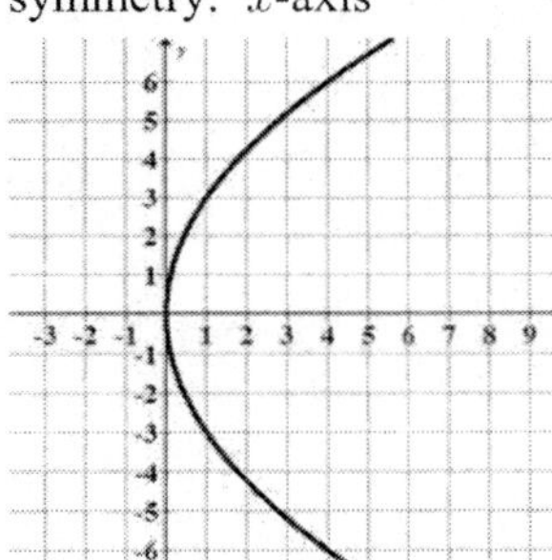

58. $y^2 = -4x$
x-int: $(0, 0)$
y-int: $(0, 0)$
symmetry: x-axis

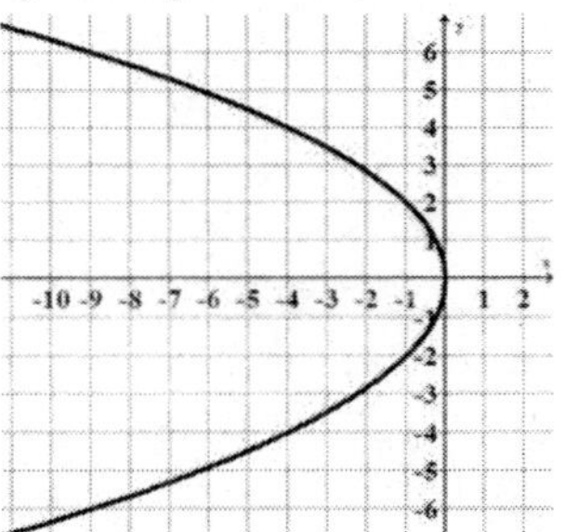

59. $y = \sqrt{x} - 1$
x-int: $(1, 0)$
y-int: $(0, -1)$
symmetry: none

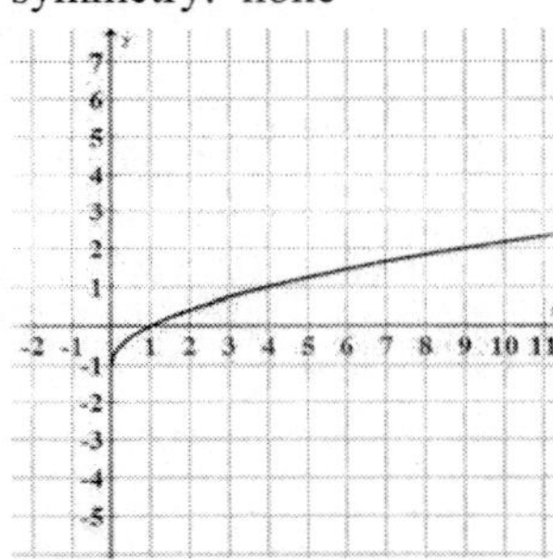

60. $y = 1 - \sqrt{x}$
x-int: $(1, 0)$
y-int: $(0, 1)$
symmetry: none

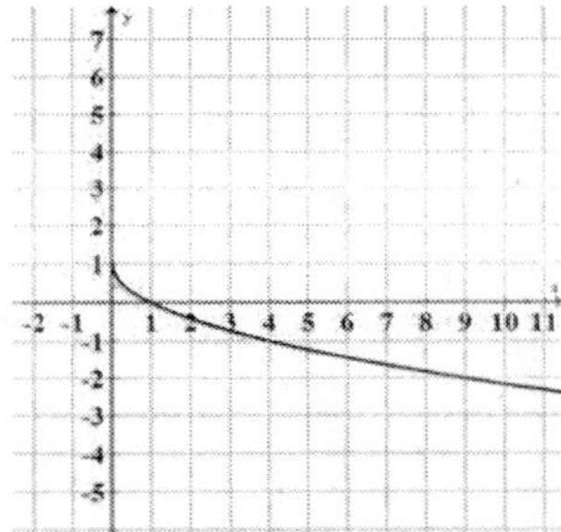

61. $xy = 4$
x-int: none
y-int: none
symmetry: origin

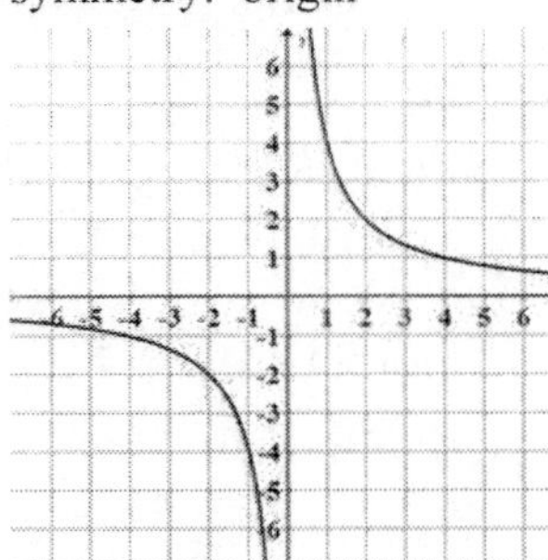

62. $xy = -9$
x-int: none
y-int: none
symmetry: origin

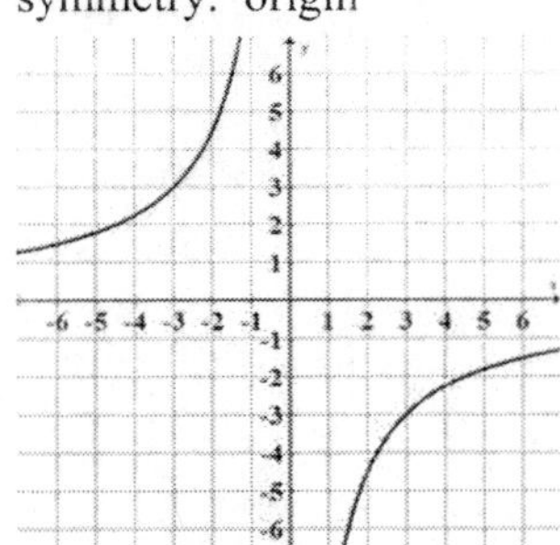

63.
$$x^2 + y^2 = 100$$
$$(x-0)^2 + (y-0)^2 = 10^2$$
$$\text{C: } (0, 0);\ r = 10$$

64.
$$x^2 + y^2 = 81$$
$$(x-0)^2 + (y-0)^2 = 9^2$$
$$\text{C: } (0, 0);\ r = 9$$

65.
$$x^2 + (y-5)^2 = 49$$
$$(x-0)^2 + (y-5)^2 = 7^2$$
$$\text{C: } (0, 5);\ r = 7$$

66.
$$x^2 + (y+3)^2 = 8$$
$$(x-0)^2 + (y-(-3))^2 = \left(\sqrt{8}\right)^2$$
$$(x-0)^2 + (y-(-3))^2 = \left(2\sqrt{2}\right)^2$$
$$\text{C: } (0, -3);\ r = 2\sqrt{2}$$

67.
$$(x+6)^2 + y^2 = \tfrac{1}{4}$$
$$(x-(-6))^2 + (y-0)^2 = \left(\tfrac{1}{2}\right)^2$$
$$\text{C: } (-6, 0);\ r = \tfrac{1}{2}$$

68.
$$(x-5)^2 + y^2 = \tfrac{16}{25}$$
$$(x-5)^2 + (y-0)^2 = \left(\tfrac{4}{5}\right)^2$$
$$\text{C: } (5, 0);\ r = \tfrac{4}{5}$$

69.
$$(x-4)^2 + (y-1)^2 = 9$$
$$(x-4)^2 + (y-1)^2 = 3^2$$
$$\text{C: } (4, 1);\ r = 3$$

70.
$$(x+11)^2 + (y+7)^2 = 121$$
$$(x-(-11))^2 + (y-(-7))^2 = 11^2$$
$$\text{C: } (-11, -7);\ r = 11$$

71.
$$\left(x-\tfrac{1}{4}\right)^2 + (y+2)^2 = 45$$
$$\left(x-\tfrac{1}{4}\right)^2 + (y-(-2))^2 = \left(\sqrt{45}\right)^2$$
$$\left(x-\tfrac{1}{4}\right)^2 + (y-(-2))^2 = \left(3\sqrt{5}\right)^2$$
$$\text{C: } \left(\tfrac{1}{4}, -2\right);\ r = 3\sqrt{5}$$

72.
$$\left(x+\sqrt{5}\right)^2 + (y-3)^2 = 1$$
$$\left(x-\left(-\sqrt{5}\right)\right)^2 + (y-3)^2 = (1)^2$$
$$\text{C: } \left(-\sqrt{5}, 3\right);\ r = 1$$

73.
$$(x-0)^2 + (y-0)^2 = 5^2$$
$$x^2 + y^2 = 25$$

74.
$$(x-0)^2 + (y-0)^2 = \left(\sqrt{3}\right)^2$$
$$x^2 + y^2 = 3$$

75.
$$(x-0)^2 + (y-(-6))^2 = 6^2$$
$$x^2 + (y+6)^2 = 36$$

76.
$$(x-0)^2 + (y-7)^2 = 9^2$$
$$x^2 + (y-7)^2 = 81$$

77.
$$(x-8)^2 + (y-0)^2 = \left(\tfrac{1}{5}\right)^2$$
$$(x-8)^2 + y^2 = \tfrac{1}{25}$$

78.
$$(x-(-10))^2 + (y-0)^2 = \left(\sqrt{11}\right)^2$$
$$(x+10)^2 + y^2 = 11$$

79.
$$(x-(-2))^2 + (y-12)^2 = 13^2$$
$$(x+2)^2 + (y-12)^2 = 169$$

80.
$$\left(x-\tfrac{2}{7}\right)^2 + (y-(-5))^2 = 7^2$$
$$\left(x-\tfrac{2}{7}\right)^2 + (y+5)^2 = 49$$

81. $x^2 + y^2 = 1^2 \Rightarrow x^2 + y^2 - 1 = 0$

82. $x^2 + y^2 = 4^2 \Rightarrow x^2 + y^2 - 16 = 0$

83.
$$\begin{aligned}(x-6)^2+(y-8)^2&=4^2\\ x^2-12x+36+y^2-16y+64&=16\\ x^2+y^2-12x-16y+84&=0\end{aligned}$$

84.
$$\begin{aligned}(x-5)^2+(y-3)^2&=2^2\\ x^2-10x+25+y^2-6y+9&=4\\ x^2+y^2-10x-6y+30&=0\end{aligned}$$

85.
$$\begin{aligned}(x-3)^2+(y+4)^2&=\left(\sqrt{2}\right)^2\\ x^2-6x+9+y^2+8y+16&=2\\ x^2+y^2-6x+8y+23&=0\end{aligned}$$

86.
$$\begin{aligned}(x+9)^2+(y-8)^2&=\left(2\sqrt{3}\right)^2\\ x^2+18x+81+y^2-16y+64&=12\\ x^2+y^2+18x-16y+133&=0\end{aligned}$$

87. Center: $x=\dfrac{3+3}{2}=3,\ y=\dfrac{-2+8}{2}=3$

$r=$ distance from center to endpoint

$$\begin{aligned}&=\sqrt{(3-3)^2+(3-8)^2}=5\\ (x-3)^2+(y-3)^2&=5^2\\ x^2-6x+9+y^2-6y+9&=25\\ x^2+y^2-6x-6y-7&=0\end{aligned}$$

88. Center: $x=\dfrac{-5+5}{2}=0,\ y=\dfrac{-9+9}{2}=0$

$r=$ distance from center to endpoint

$$\begin{aligned}&=\sqrt{(0-5)^2+(0-9)^2}=\sqrt{106}\\ (x-0)^2+(y-0)^2&=\left(\sqrt{106}\right)^2\\ x^2+y^2&=106\\ x^2+y^2-106&=0\end{aligned}$$

89. $r=$ distance from center to origin

$$\begin{aligned}&=\sqrt{(0-(-3))^2+(0-4)^2}=5\\ (x+3)^2+(y-4)^2&=5^2\\ x^2+6x+9+y^2-8y+16&=25\\ x^2+y^2+6x-8y&=0\end{aligned}$$

90. $r=$ distance from center to origin

$$\begin{aligned}&=\sqrt{(0-(-2))^2+(0-6)^2}=\sqrt{40}\\ (x+2)^2+(y-6)^2&=\left(\sqrt{40}\right)^2\\ x^2+4x+4+y^2-12y+36&=40\\ x^2+y^2+4x-12y&=0\end{aligned}$$

91.
$$\begin{aligned}x^2+y^2-6x+4y+4&=0\\ x^2-6x+y^2+4y&=-4\\ x^2-6x+9+y^2+4y+4&=-4+9+4\\ (x-3)^2+(y+2)^2&=9\end{aligned}$$

92.
$$\begin{aligned}x^2+y^2+4x-8y-5&=0\\ x^2+4x+y^2-8y&=5\\ x^2+4x+4+y^2-8y+16&=5+4+16\\ (x+2)^2+(y-4)^2&=25\end{aligned}$$

93.
$$\begin{aligned}x^2+y^2-10x-12y+57&=0\\ x^2-10x+y^2-12y&=-57\\ x^2-10x+25+y^2-12y+36&=-57+25+36\\ (x-5)^2+(y-6)^2&=4\end{aligned}$$

94.
$$\begin{aligned}x^2+y^2+2x+18y+57&=0\\ x^2+2x+y^2+18y&=-57\\ x^2+2x+1+y^2+18y+81&=-57+1+81\\ (x+1)^2+(y+9)^2&=25\end{aligned}$$

SECTION 2.4

95.
$$\begin{aligned} 2x^2 + 2y^2 - 8x - 16y + 22 &= 0 \\ x^2 + y^2 - 4x - 8y + 11 &= 0 \\ x^2 - 4x + y^2 - 8y &= -11 \\ x^2 - 4x + 4 + y^2 - 8y + 16 &= -11 + 4 + 16 \\ (x-2)^2 + (y-4)^2 &= 9 \end{aligned}$$

96.
$$\begin{aligned} 3x^2 + 3y^2 + 6x - 30y + 3 &= 0 \\ x^2 + y^2 + 2x - 10y + 1 &= 0 \\ x^2 + 2x + y^2 - 10y &= -1 \\ x^2 + 2x + 1 + y^2 - 10y + 25 &= -1 + 1 + 25 \\ (x+1)^2 + (y-5)^2 &= 25 \end{aligned}$$

97.
$$\begin{aligned} x^2 + y^2 - 25 &= 0 \\ x^2 + y^2 &= 25 \end{aligned}$$
$C(0,0)$, $r = 5$

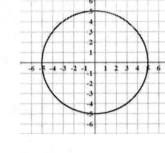

98.
$$\begin{aligned} x^2 + y^2 - 8 &= 0 \\ x^2 + y^2 &= 8 \end{aligned}$$
$C(0,0)$, $r = \sqrt{8} = 2\sqrt{2}$

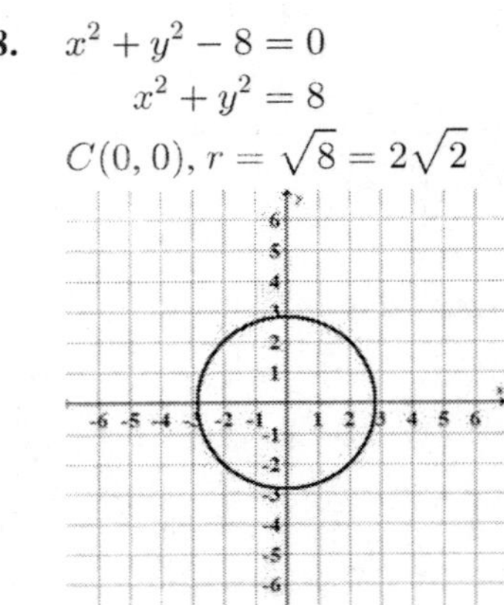

99. $(x-1)^2 + (y+2)^2 = 4$
$C(1,-2)$, $r = 2$

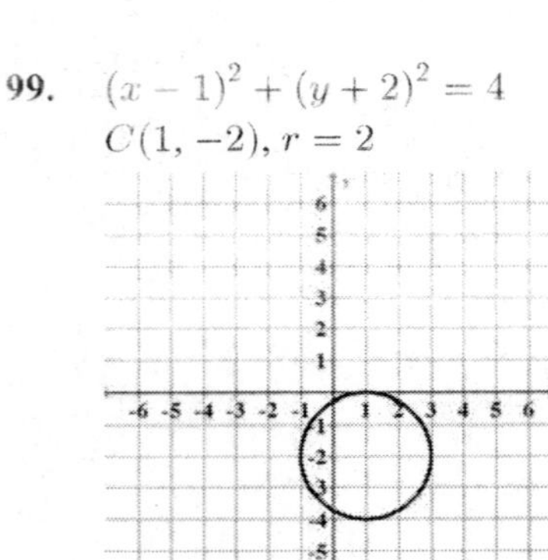

100. $(x+1)^2 + (y-2)^2 = 9$
$C(-1,2)$, $r = 3$

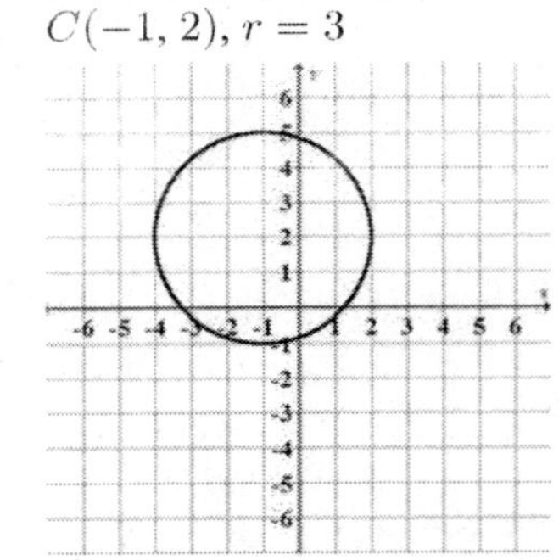

101. $x^2 + y^2 + 2x - 24 = 0$

$x^2 + 2x + y^2 = 24$

$x^2 + 2x + 1 + y^2 = 24 + 1$

$(x + 1)^2 + y^2 = 25$

$C(-1, 0), r = 5$

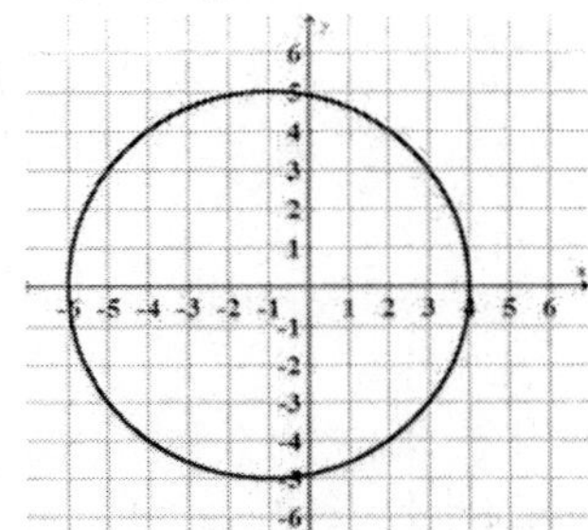

102. $x^2 + y^2 - 4y = 12$

$x^2 + y^2 - 4y + 4 = 12 + 4$

$x^2 + (y - 2)^2 = 16$

$C(0, 2), r = 4$

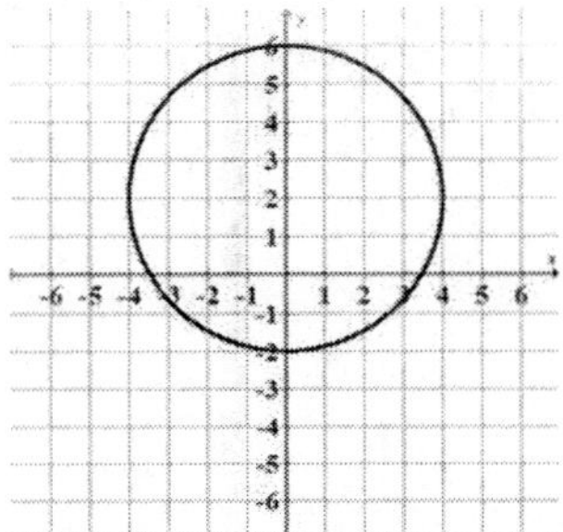

103. $x^2 + y^2 + 4x + 2y - 11 = 0$

$x^2 + 4x + y^2 + 2y = 11$

$x^2 + 4x + 4 + y^2 + 2y + 1 = 11 + 4 + 1$

$(x + 2)^2 + (y + 1)^2 = 16$

$C(-2, -1), r = 4$

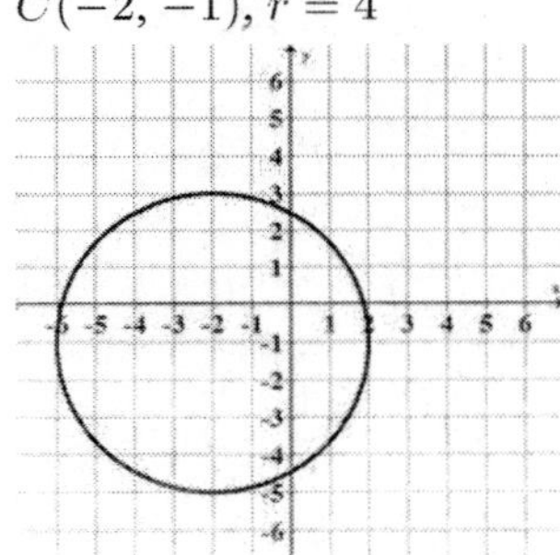

104. $x^2 + y^2 - 6x + 2y + 1 = 0$

$x^2 - 6x + y^2 + 2y = -1$

$x^2 - 6x + 9 + y^2 + 2y + 1 = -1 + 9 + 1$

$(x - 3)^2 + (y + 1)^2 = 9$

$C(3, -1), r = 3$

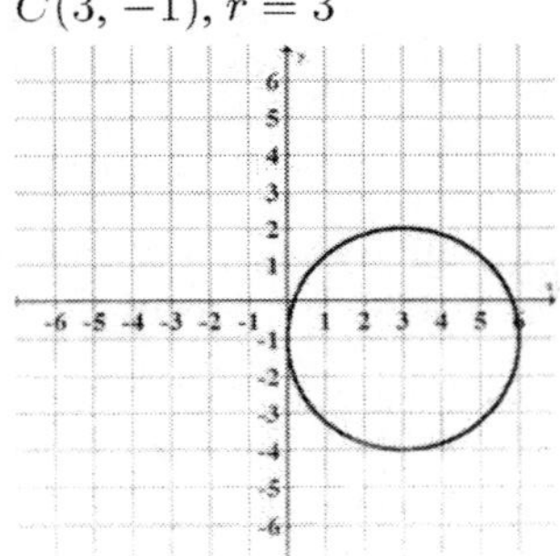

105. $$9x^2 + 9y^2 - 12y = 5$$
$$x^2 + y^2 - \frac{4}{3}y = \frac{5}{9}$$
$$x^2 + y^2 - \frac{4}{3}y + \frac{4}{9} = \frac{5}{9} + \frac{4}{9}$$
$$x^2 + \left(y - \frac{2}{3}\right)^2 = 1$$
$$C\left(0, \frac{2}{3}\right), r = 1$$

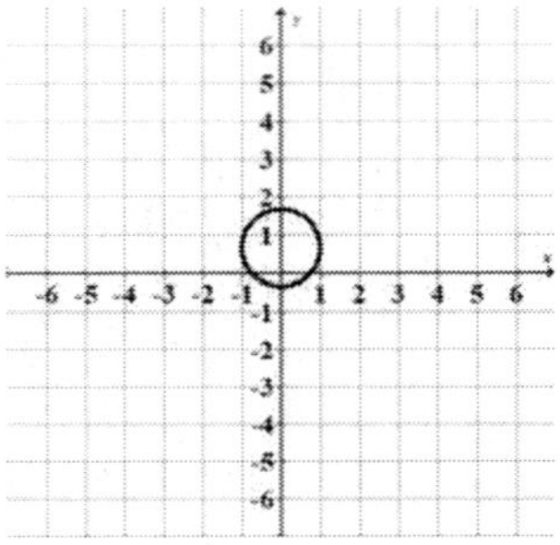

106. $$4x^2 + 4y^2 + 4y = 15$$
$$x^2 + y^2 + y = \frac{15}{4}$$
$$x^2 + y^2 + y + \frac{1}{4} = \frac{15}{4} + \frac{1}{4}$$
$$x^2 + \left(y + \frac{1}{2}\right)^2 = 4$$
$$C\left(0, -\frac{1}{2}\right), r = 2$$

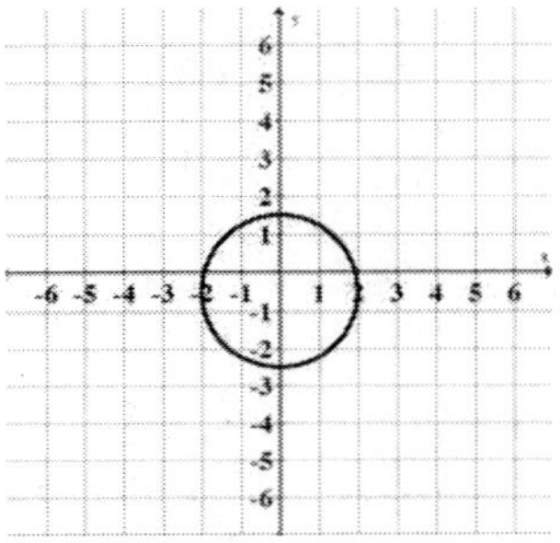

107. $$4x^2 + 4y^2 - 4x + 8y + 1 = 0$$
$$x^2 + y^2 - x + 2y = -\frac{1}{4}$$
$$x^2 - x + \frac{1}{4} + y^2 + 2y + 1 = -\frac{1}{4} + \frac{1}{4} + 1$$
$$\left(x - \frac{1}{2}\right)^2 + (y + 1)^2 = 1$$
$$C\left(\frac{1}{2}, -1\right), r = 1$$

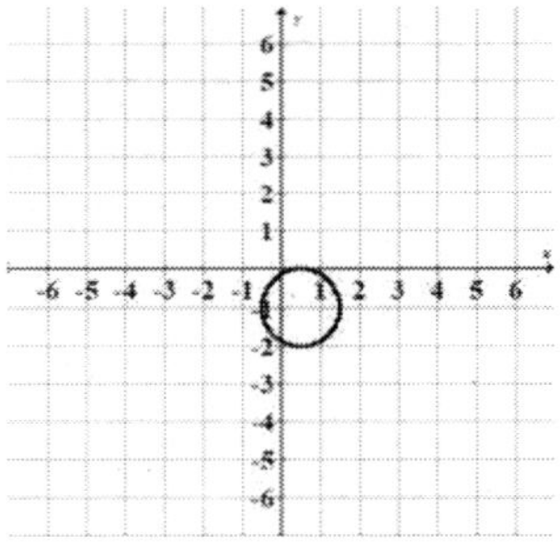

108. $$9x^2 + 9y^2 - 6x + 18y + 1 = 0$$
$$x^2 + y^2 - \frac{2}{3}x + 2y = -\frac{1}{9}$$
$$x^2 - \frac{2}{3}x + \frac{1}{9} + y^2 + 2y + 1 = -\frac{1}{9} + \frac{1}{9} + 1$$
$$\left(x - \frac{1}{3}\right)^2 + (y + 1)^2 = 1$$
$$C\left(\frac{1}{3}, -1\right), r = 1$$

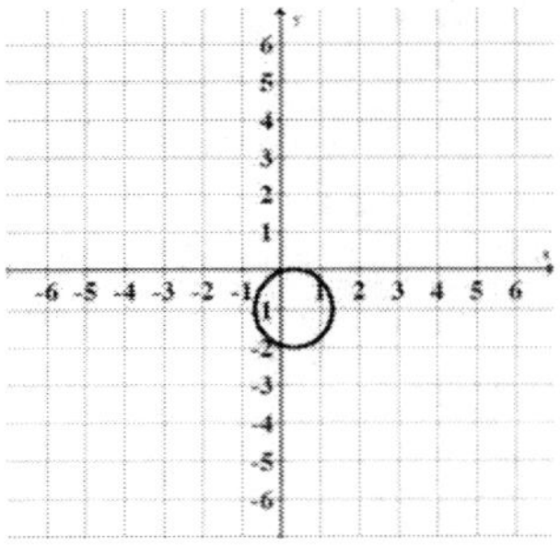

SECTION 2.4

109. $y = 2x^2 - x + 1$
Vertex: $(0.25, 0.88)$

110. $y = x^2 + 5x - 6$
Vertex: $(-2.50, -12.25)$

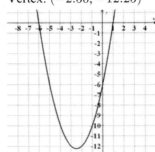

111. $y = 7 + x - x^2$
Vertex: $(0.50, 7.25)$

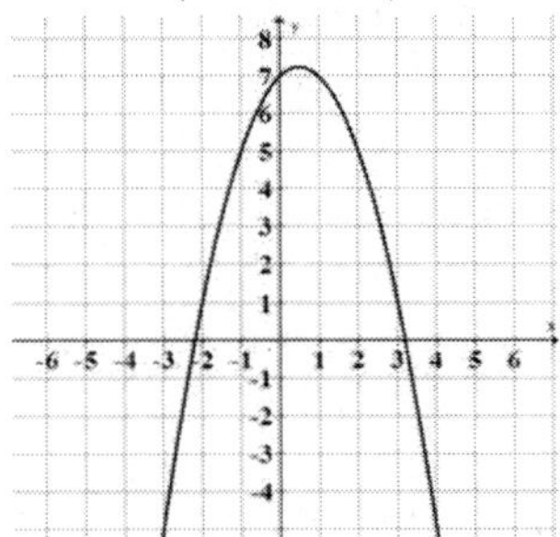

112. $y = 2x^2 - 3x + 2$
Vertex: $(0.75, 0.88)$

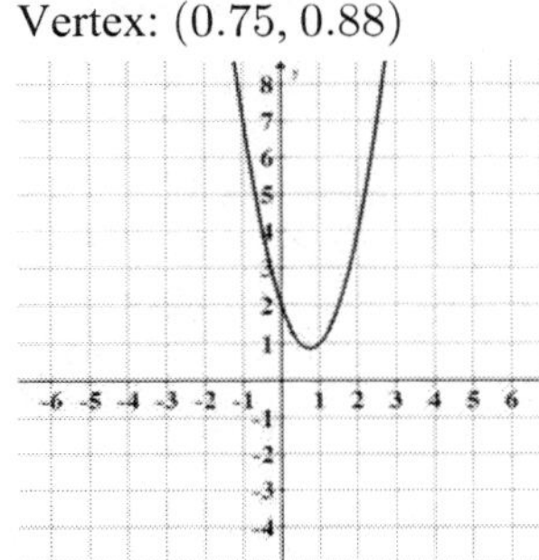

113. Graph $y = x^2 - 7$.
Find the x-intercepts.
$x = -2.65,\ x = 2.65$

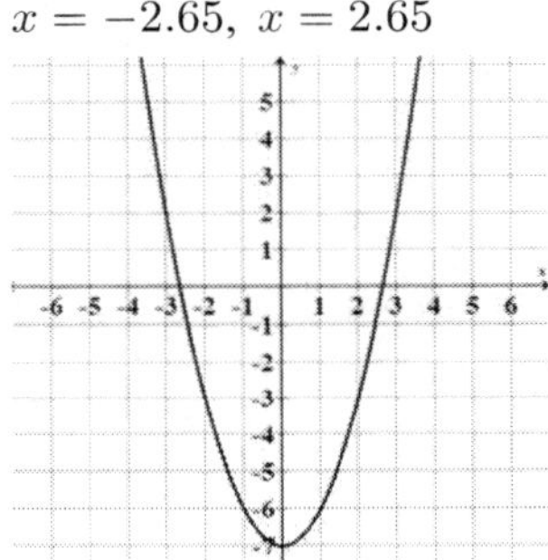

114. Graph $y = x^2 - 3x + 2$.
Find the x-intercepts.
$x = 1.00,\ x = 2.00$

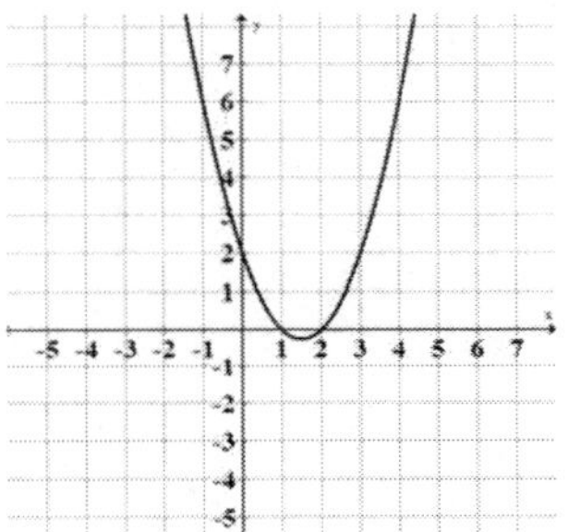

115. Graph $y = x^3 - 3$.
Find the x-intercepts.
$x = 1.44$

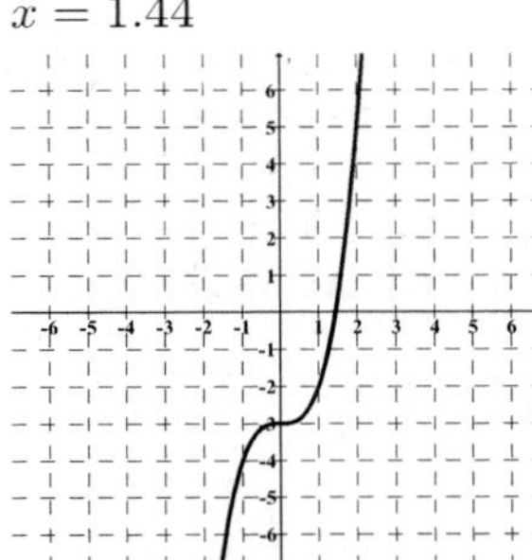

116. Graph $y = 3x^3 - x^2 - x$.
Find the x-intercepts.
$x = -0.44,\ x = 0,$
$x = 0.77$

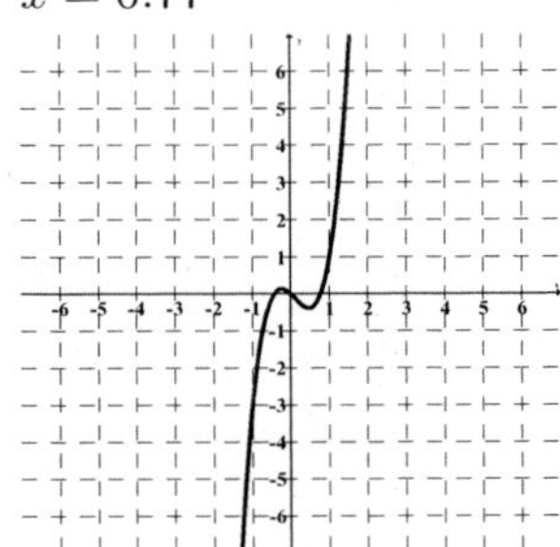

117. Let $y = 0$:
$y = 64t - 16t^2$
$0 = 16t(4 - t)$
$t = 0$ or $t = 4$
It strikes the ground after 4 seconds.

118. From **#117**, the flight lasts 4 seconds. Thus, half the flight is 2 seconds. Let $t = 2$:
$y = 64t - 16t^2$
$y = 64(2) - 16(2)^2 = 128 - 64 = 64$; The highest point is 64 feet above ground.

119. $D = 0.08V^2 + 0.9V$;

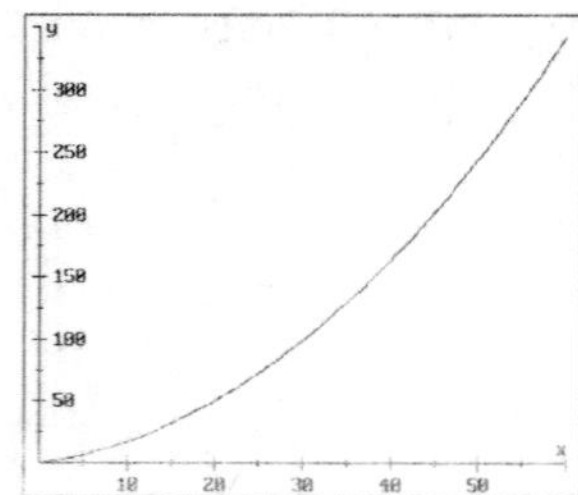

120. Refer to the graph for **#119**.
The y-coordinate for $x = 30$ is $y = 99$.
The y-coordinate for $x = 60$ is $y = 342$.
$342 - 99 = 243$
At 60 mph, 243 more feet is required to stop than at 30 mph.

121. $r = \frac{12}{2} = 6$
$$(x - 0)^2 + (y - 0)^2 = 6^2$$
$$x^2 + y^2 = 36$$

122. $r = 10(2 \text{ in.}) = 20$ in.
$$(x - 0)^2 + (y - 0)^2 = 20^2$$
$$x^2 + y^2 = 400$$

123. $r = \frac{60}{2} = 30$
$$(x - 0)^2 + (y - 35)^2 = 30^2$$
$$x^2 + (y - 35)^2 = 900$$

124. $r = \frac{30}{2} = 15$
$$(x - 5)^2 + (y - 10)^2 = 15^2$$
$$(x - 5)^2 + (y - 10)^2 = 225$$

125. $r = \sqrt{(10 - 7)^2 + (0 - 4)^2} = 5$
$$(x - 7)^2 + (y - 4)^2 = 5^2$$
$$x^2 - 14x + 49 + y^2 - 8y + 16 = 25$$
$$x^2 + y^2 - 14x - 8y + 40 = 0$$

126.

First tire
$$C(12, 12),\ r = 12$$
$$(x - 12)^2 + (y - 12)^2 = 12^2$$
$$x^2 - 24x + 144 + y^2 - 24y + 144 = 144$$
$$x^2 + y^2 - 24x - 24y + 144 = 0$$

Second tire

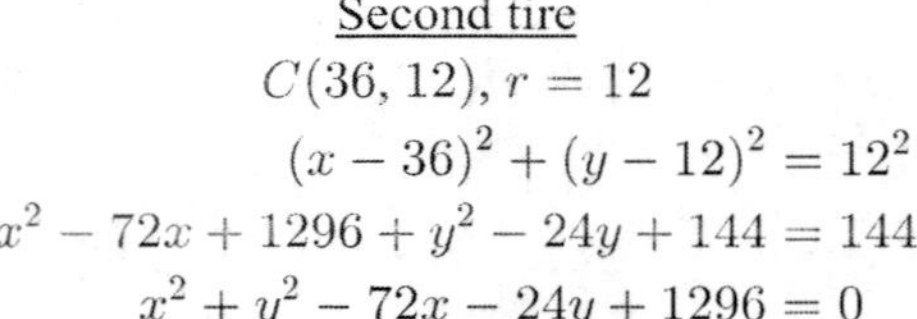
$$C(36, 12),\ r = 12$$
$$(x - 36)^2 + (y - 12)^2 = 12^2$$
$$x^2 - 72x + 1296 + y^2 - 24y + 144 = 144$$
$$x^2 + y^2 - 72x - 24y + 1296 = 0$$

127. Graph $y = x^2 + x - 6$. Find the x-coordinates where the graph is below the x-axis.
Solution: $(-3, 2)$

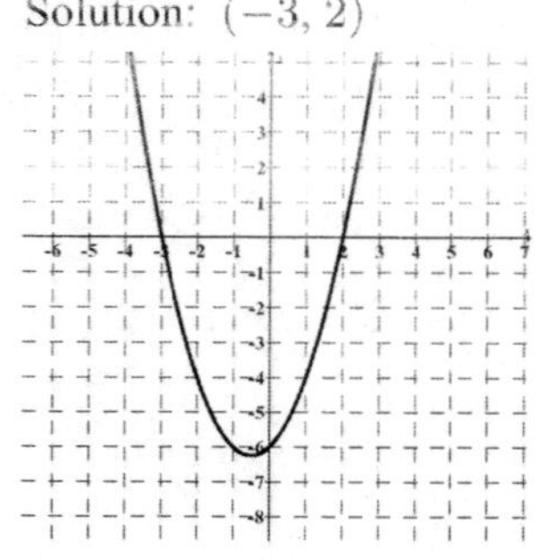

128. Graph $y = x^2 - 3x - 10$. Find the x-coordinates where the graph is above the x-axis.
Solution: $(-\infty, -2) \cup (5, \infty)$

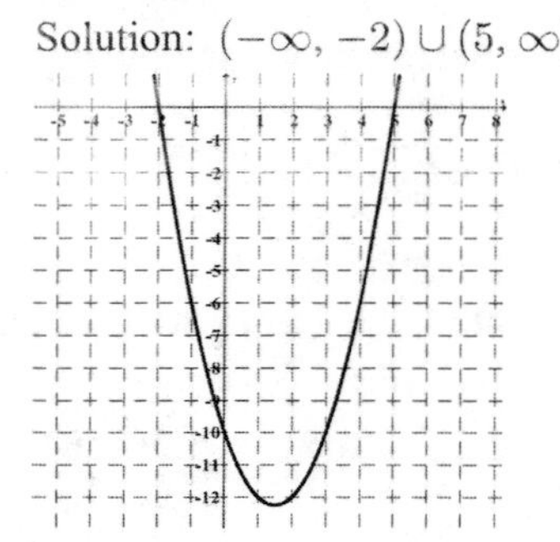

129.
$$\begin{aligned} x^2 - 4x + y^2 - 6y + 13 &= 0 \\ x^2 - 4x + 4 + y^2 - 6y + 9 &= -13 + 4 + 9 \\ (x+2)^2 + (y-3)^2 &= 0 \Rightarrow \text{a single point} \end{aligned}$$

130.
$$\begin{aligned} x^2 - 12x + y^2 + 4y + 43 &= 0 \\ x^2 - 12x + 36 + y^2 + 4y + 4 &= -43 + 36 + 4 \\ (x-6)^2 + (y+2)^2 &= -3 \Rightarrow \text{nonexistent} \end{aligned}$$

131.
$$\begin{aligned} 3(x+2) + x &= 5x \\ 3x + 6 + x &= 5x \\ 4x + 6 &= 5x \\ 6 &= x \end{aligned}$$

132.
$$\begin{aligned} 12b + 6(3-b) &= b + 3 \\ 12b + 18 - 6b &= b + 3 \\ 6b + 18 &= b + 3 \\ 5b &= -15 \\ b &= -3 \end{aligned}$$

133.
$$\begin{aligned} \frac{5(2-x)}{3} - 1 &= x + 5 \\ 3\left[\frac{10-5x}{3} - 1\right] &= 3(x+5) \\ 10 - 5x - 3 &= 3x + 15 \\ -5x + 7 &= 3x + 15 \\ -8x &= 8 \\ x &= -1 \end{aligned}$$

134.
$$\begin{aligned} \frac{r-1}{3} &= \frac{r+2}{6} + 2 \\ 6 \cdot \frac{r-1}{3} &= 6\left(\frac{r+2}{6} + 2\right) \\ 2(r-1) &= r + 2 + 12 \\ 2r - 2 &= r + 14 \\ r &= 16 \end{aligned}$$

135. Let x = the ounces of copper added.
Since 1 ounce out of 4 ounces are to be gold, the final result should be 25% gold.

Ounces of gold at start	+	Ounces of gold added	=	Ounces of gold at end

$$\begin{aligned} 20 + 0 &= 0.25(60 + x) \\ 20 &= 15 + 0.25x \\ 5 &= 0.25x \\ 20 &= x \end{aligned}$$

20 ounces of copper should be added.

136. Let x = pounds of cheaper coffee.
Then $80 - x$ = pounds of other coffee

Value of cheaper	+	Value of other	=	Total value

$$\begin{aligned} 3.25x + 3.85(80 - x) &= 272 \\ 3.25x + 308 - 3.85x &= 272 \\ -0.60x &= -36 \\ x &= 60 \end{aligned}$$

60 pounds of the cheaper coffee should be used.

Exercises 2.5 (page 261)

1. quotient
2. ratios
3. means
4. extremes
5. extremes, means
6. $y = kx$
7. inverse
8. constant

SECTION 2.5

9. joint

10. x^2, z

11.
$$\frac{4}{x} = \frac{2}{7}$$
$$4 \cdot 7 = 2 \cdot x$$
$$28 = 2x$$
$$14 = x$$

12.
$$\frac{5}{2} = \frac{x}{6}$$
$$5 \cdot 6 = x \cdot 2$$
$$30 = 2x$$
$$15 = x$$

13.
$$\frac{x}{2} = \frac{3}{x+1}$$
$$x(x+1) = 3 \cdot 2$$
$$x^2 + x = 6$$
$$x^2 + x - 6 = 0$$
$$(x+3)(x-2) = 0$$
$$x = -3 \text{ or } x = 2$$

14.
$$\frac{x+5}{6} = \frac{7}{8-x}$$
$$(x+5)(8-x) = 7 \cdot 6$$
$$-x^2 + 3x + 40 = 42$$
$$0 = x^2 - 3x + 2$$
$$0 = (x-2)(x-1)$$
$$x = 1 \text{ or } x = 2$$

15. Let $x =$ the number of women.
$$\tfrac{3}{5} = \tfrac{x}{30}$$
$$3 \cdot 30 = 5 \cdot x$$
$$90 = 5x$$
$18 = x \Rightarrow$ There are 18 women.

16. Let $x =$ the number of bags of lime.
$$\tfrac{3}{7} = \tfrac{x}{21}$$
$$3 \cdot 21 = x \cdot 7$$
$$63 = 7x$$
$9 = x \Rightarrow$ 9 bags of lime should be used.

17.
$$y = kx$$
$$15 = k(30)$$
$$\tfrac{1}{2} = k$$

18.
$$z = kt$$
$$21 = k(7)$$
$$3 = k$$

19.
$$I = \frac{k}{R}$$
$$50 = \frac{k}{20}$$
$$1000 = k$$

20.
$$R = \frac{k}{I^2}$$
$$100 = \frac{k}{25^2}$$
$$100 = \frac{k}{625}$$
$$62500 = k$$

21.
$$E = kIR$$
$$125 = k(5)(25)$$
$$125 = 125k$$
$$1 = k$$

22.
$$z = k(x+y)$$
$$28 = k(2+5)$$
$$28 = 7k$$
$$4 = k$$

23.
$$y = kx \qquad y = \tfrac{15}{4}x$$
$$15 = k(4) \qquad y = \tfrac{15}{4} \cdot \tfrac{7}{5}$$
$$\tfrac{15}{4} = k \qquad y = \tfrac{21}{4}$$

24.
$$w = kz \qquad w = -3z$$
$$-6 = k(2) \qquad w = -3(-3)$$
$$-3 = k \qquad w = 9$$

25.
$$w = \frac{k}{z} \qquad w = \frac{30}{z}$$
$$10 = \frac{k}{3} \qquad w = \frac{30}{5}$$
$$30 = k \qquad w = 6$$

26.
$$y = \frac{k}{x} \qquad y = \frac{200}{x}$$
$$100 = \frac{k}{2} \qquad y = \frac{200}{50}$$
$$200 = k \qquad y = 4$$

27.
$$P = krs \qquad P = -\tfrac{2}{5}rs$$
$$16 = k(5)(-8) \qquad P = -\tfrac{2}{5}(2)(10)$$
$$16 = -40k \qquad P = -8$$
$$-\tfrac{16}{40} = k$$
$$-\tfrac{2}{5} = k$$

28.
$$m = kn^2\sqrt{q} \qquad m = 3n^2\sqrt{q}$$
$$24 = k(2)^2\sqrt{4} \qquad m = 3(5)^2\sqrt{9}$$
$$24 = k(4)(2) \qquad m = 3(25)(3)$$
$$24 = 8k \qquad m = 225$$
$$3 = k$$

29. direct

30. neither

31. neither

32. inverse

33. Let $x =$ the amount of caffeine.
$$\tfrac{55}{12} = \tfrac{x}{44} \qquad \tfrac{47}{12} = \tfrac{x}{44} \qquad \tfrac{37}{12} = \tfrac{x}{44}$$
$$55 \cdot 44 = 12 \cdot x \qquad 47 \cdot 44 = 12 \cdot x \qquad 37 \cdot 44 = 12 \cdot x$$
$$2420 = 12x \qquad 2068 = 12x \qquad 1628 = 12x$$
$$202 \text{ mg} \approx x \qquad 172 \text{ mg} \approx x \qquad 136 \text{ mg} \approx x$$

34. Let $x =$ the number of phones.
$$\tfrac{221}{250} = \tfrac{x}{280000}$$
$$221 \cdot 280000 = 250 \cdot x$$
$$61880000 = 250x$$
$$247{,}520 = x$$
247,520 have cellular phones.

35. Let $x =$ the amount of adhesive needed.
$$\frac{\frac{1}{2}}{140} = \frac{x}{500}$$
$$\frac{1}{2} \cdot 500 = 140 \cdot x$$
$$250 = 140x$$
$$1.79 \approx x$$
About 2 gallons of adhesive will be needed.

36. Let $x =$ the dosage.
$$\tfrac{0.006}{1} = \tfrac{x}{30}$$
$$0.006 \cdot 30 = 1 \cdot x$$
$$0.18 = x$$
The dosage should be 0.18 g, or 180 mg.

37.
$$V = \frac{kT}{P} \qquad V = \frac{\frac{80}{33}T}{P}$$
$$20 = \frac{k(330)}{40} \qquad V = \frac{\frac{80}{33}(300)}{50}$$
$$800 = 330k \qquad V = \frac{\frac{8000}{11}}{50}$$
$$\frac{800}{330} = k \qquad V = \frac{160}{11} = 14\frac{6}{11} \text{ ft}^3$$
$$\frac{80}{33} = k$$

38.
$$f = kd \qquad f = 25d$$
$$5 = k(0.2) \qquad f = 25(0.35)$$
$$25 = k \qquad f = 8.75 \text{ Newtons}$$

39.
$$d = kt^2 \qquad d = 16t^2$$
$$16 = k(1)^2 \qquad 144 = 16t^2$$
$$16 = k \qquad 9 = t^2$$
$$3 = t \Rightarrow 3 \text{ seconds}$$

40.
$$P = \frac{kV^2}{R} \qquad P = \frac{V^2}{R}$$
$$20 = \frac{k(20)^2}{20} \qquad 40 = \frac{V^2}{10}$$
$$400 = 400k \qquad 400 = V^2$$
$$1 = k \qquad 20 = V \Rightarrow 20 \text{ volts}$$

41.
$$t = kl^2 \qquad t = l^2$$
$$1 = k(1)^2 \qquad 2 = l^2$$
$$1 = k \qquad \sqrt{2} = l \Rightarrow \sqrt{2} \text{ meters}$$

42.
$$f = k\sqrt{T} \qquad f = \frac{144}{\sqrt{2}}\sqrt{T}$$
$$144 = k\sqrt{2} \qquad f = \frac{144}{\sqrt{2}}\sqrt{18}$$
$$\frac{144}{\sqrt{2}} = k \qquad f = 144\sqrt{9}$$
$$f = 144(3) = 432 \text{ hertz}$$

43.
$$I = \frac{k}{d^2} \qquad I = \frac{6000}{d^2}$$
$$60 = \frac{k}{10^2} \qquad I = \frac{6000}{20^2}$$
$$60 = \frac{k}{100} \qquad I = \frac{6000}{400}$$
$$6000 = k \qquad I = 15 \Rightarrow 15 \text{ lumens}$$

44.
$$I = \frac{k}{d^2} \qquad I = \frac{22500}{d^2}$$
$$100 = \frac{k}{15^2} \qquad I = \frac{22500}{25^2}$$
$$100 = \frac{k}{225} \qquad I = \frac{22500}{625}$$
$$22500 = k \qquad I = 36 \Rightarrow 36 \text{ lumens}$$

45.
$$E = kmv^2 = k(2m)(3v)^2$$
$$= k(2m)(9v^2)$$
$$= 18 \cdot kmv^2$$
The energy is multiplied by 18.

46.
$$P = kRC^2 \qquad P = RC^2$$
$$10 = k(10)(1)^2 \qquad P = 5(3)^2$$
$$10 = 10k \qquad P = 5(9)$$
$$1 = k \qquad P = 45 \text{ watts}$$

47.
$$G = \frac{km_1m_2}{d^2} = \frac{k(3m_1)(3m_2)}{(2d)^2}$$
$$= \frac{k \cdot 9m_1m_2}{4d^2}$$
$$= \frac{9}{4} \cdot \frac{km_1m_2}{d^2}$$
The force is multiplied by $\frac{9}{4}$.

48.
$$G = \frac{km_1m_2}{d^2} = \frac{k(2m_1)(3m_2)}{\left(\frac{d}{2}\right)^2}$$
$$= \frac{k \cdot 6m_1m_2}{\frac{d^2}{4}}$$
$$= 24 \cdot \frac{km_1m_2}{d^2}$$
The force is multiplied by 24.

49. Consider this figure:

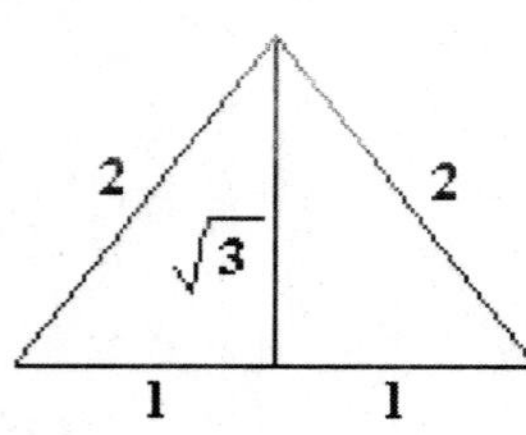

$h = \sqrt{3}$ can be computed using the Pythagorean Theorem.
$$A = \frac{1}{2}bh = \frac{1}{2}(2)\sqrt{3} = \sqrt{3}$$
$$A = ks^2$$
$$\sqrt{3} = k(2)^2$$
$$\sqrt{3} = 4k$$
$$\frac{\sqrt{3}}{4} = k$$

50. Consider this figure:

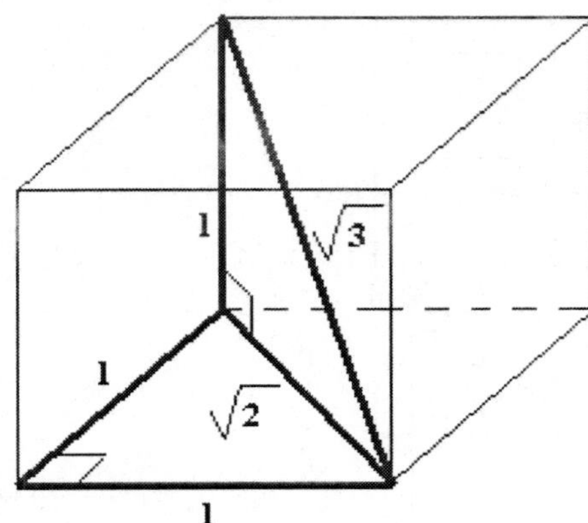

The diagonal is obtained by repeatedly using the Pythagorean Theorem.

$$d = ks$$
$$\sqrt{3} = k(1)$$
$$\sqrt{3} = k$$

51-56. Answers may vary.

57. $\frac{1}{x+2} + \frac{2}{x+1} = \frac{1(x+1)}{(x+2)(x+1)} + \frac{2(x+2)}{(x+1)(x+2)} = \frac{x+1+2x+4}{(x+1)(x+2)} = \frac{3x+5}{(x+1)(x+2)}$

58. $\frac{x^2-1}{x+1} \cdot \frac{x-1}{x^2-2x+1} = \frac{(x+1)(x-1)}{x+1} \cdot \frac{x-1}{(x-1)(x-1)} = 1$

59. $\frac{x^2+3x-4}{x^2-5x+4} \div \frac{x-1}{x^2-3x-4} = \frac{x^2+3x-4}{x^2-5x+4} \cdot \frac{x^2-3x-4}{x-1} = \frac{(x+4)(x-1)}{(x-4)(x-1)} \cdot \frac{(x-4)(x+1)}{x-1}$
$= \frac{(x+4)(x+1)}{x-1}$

60. $\frac{x+2}{3x-3} \div (2x+4) = \frac{x+2}{3x-3} \cdot \frac{1}{2x+4} = \frac{x+2}{3(x-1)} \cdot \frac{1}{2(x+2)} = \frac{1}{6(x-1)}$

61. $\frac{x^2+4-(x+2)^2}{4x^2} = \frac{x^2+4-(x^2+4x+4)}{4x^2} = \frac{x^2+4-x^2-4x-4}{4x^2} = \frac{-4x}{4x^2} = -\frac{1}{x}$

62. $\frac{\frac{1}{x}-\frac{1}{3}}{\frac{1}{x}-1} = \frac{3x\left(\frac{1}{x}-\frac{1}{3}\right)}{3x\left(\frac{1}{x}-1\right)} = \frac{3-x}{3-3x}$

Chapter 2 Review (page 265)

1. $A(2, 0)$ **2.** $B(-2, 1)$ **3.** $C(0, -1)$ **4.** $D(3, -1)$

5. $A(-3, 5)$: QII

6. $B(5, -3)$: QIV

7. $C(0, -7)$: negative y-axis

8. $D\left(-\frac{1}{2}, 0\right)$: negative x-axis

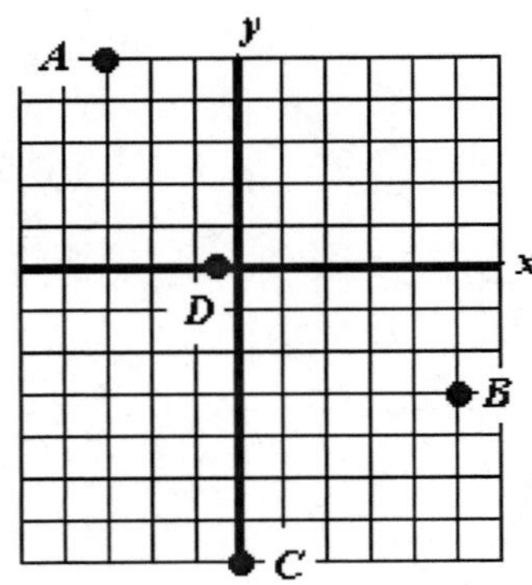

9.

$$
\begin{aligned}
2x - y &= 6 \\
-y &= -2x + 6 \\
y &= 2x - 6
\end{aligned}
$$

x	y
0	-6
2	-2

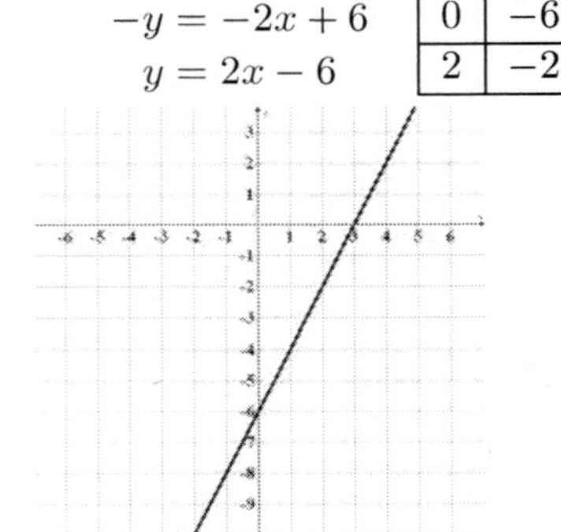

10.

$$
\begin{aligned}
2x + 5y &= -10 \\
5y &= -2x - 10 \\
y &= -\frac{2}{5}x - 2
\end{aligned}
$$

x	y
0	-2
-5	0

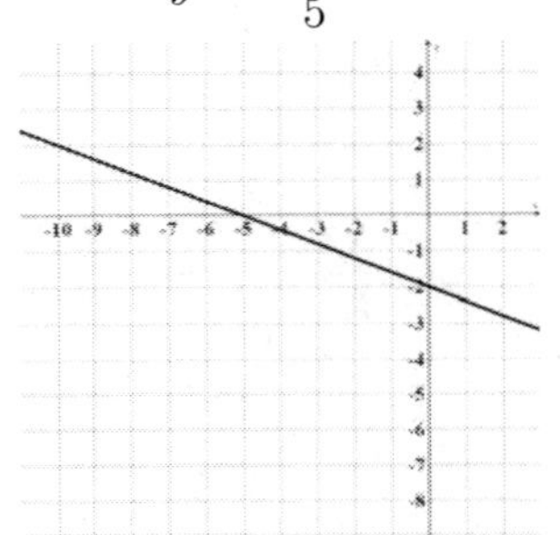

11.

$$
\begin{aligned}
3x - 5y &= 15 \\
3x - 5(0) &= 15 \\
3x &= 15 \\
x &= 5
\end{aligned}
\qquad
\begin{aligned}
3x - 5y &= 15 \\
3(0) - 5y &= 15 \\
-5y &= 15 \\
y &= -3
\end{aligned}
$$

$(5, 0)$ $(0, -3)$

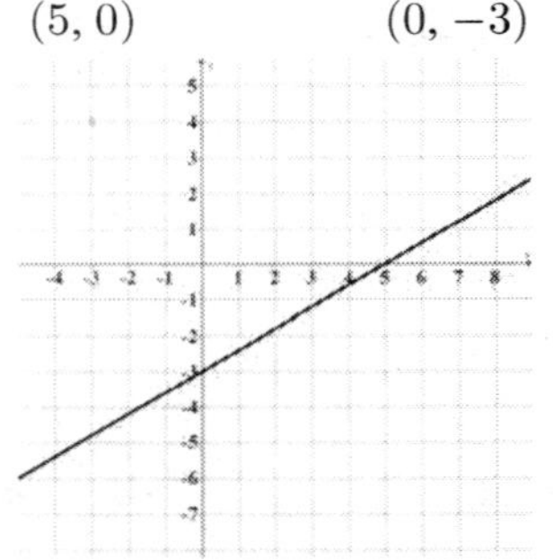

12.

$$
\begin{aligned}
x + y &= 7 \\
x + 0 &= 7 \\
x &= 7
\end{aligned}
\qquad
\begin{aligned}
x + y &= 7 \\
0 + y &= 7 \\
y &= 7
\end{aligned}
$$

$(7, 0)$ $(0, 7)$

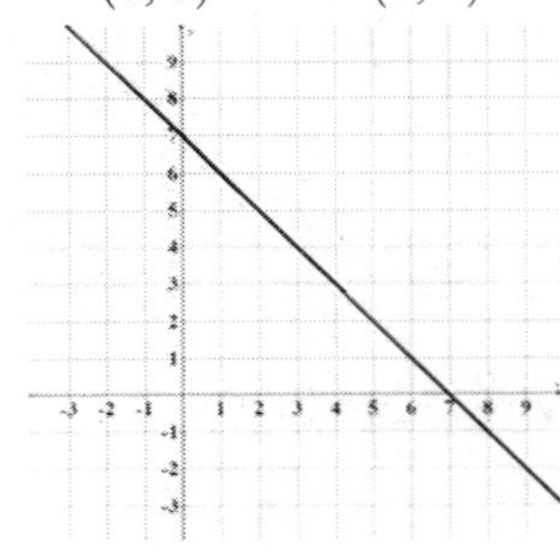

13. $x + y = -7$ $\quad x + y = -7$
$x + 0 = -7$ $\quad 0 + y = -7$
$x = -7$ $\quad y = -7$
$(-7, 0)$ $\quad (0, -7)$

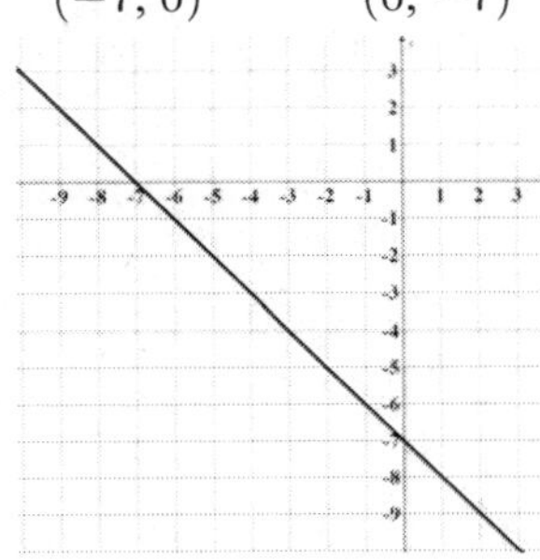

14. $x - 5y = 5$ $\quad x - 5y = 5$
$x - 5(0) = 5$ $\quad 0 - 5y = 5$
$x = 5$ $\quad -5y = 5$
$(5, 0)$ $\quad y = -1$
$(0, -1)$

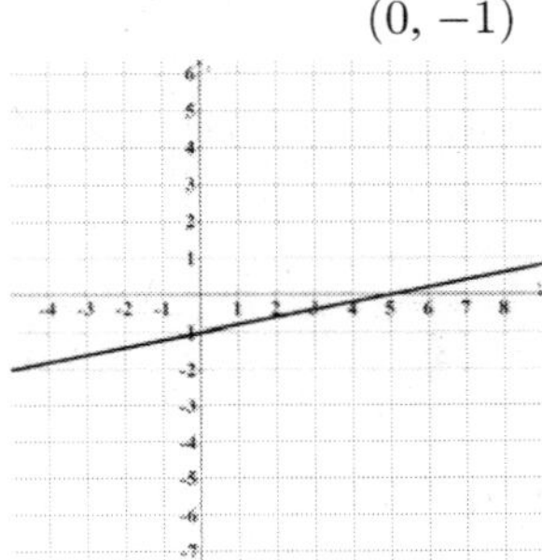

15. $y = 4 \Rightarrow$ horizontal

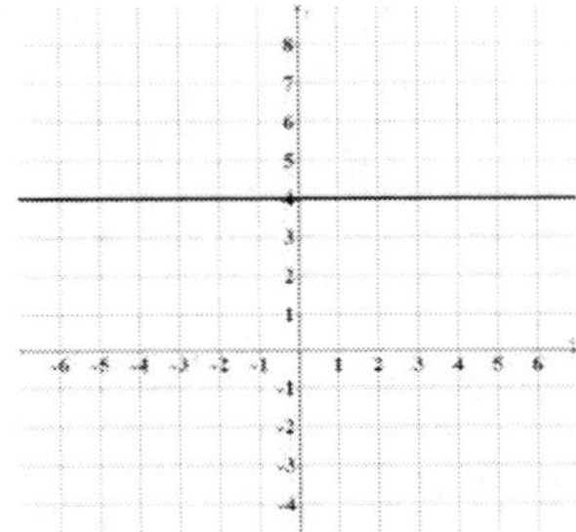

16. $x = -2 \Rightarrow$ vertical

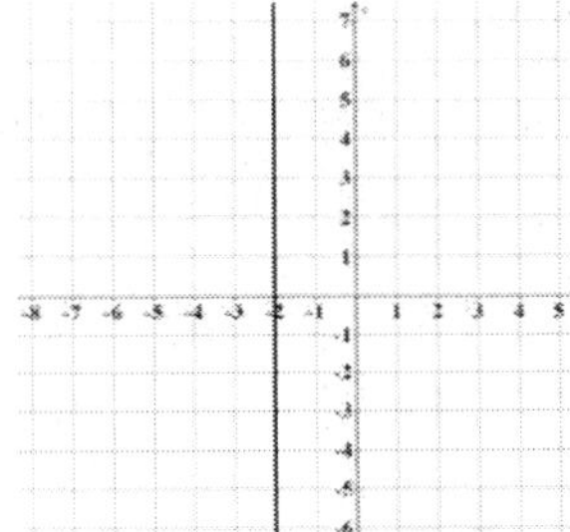

17. Let $x = 3$: $y = -2200x + 18{,}750 = -2200(3) + 18{,}750 = -6600 + 18{,}750 = \$12{,}150$

18. Let $x = 5$: $y = 16{,}500x + 250{,}000 = 16{,}500(5) + 250{,}000 = 82{,}500 + 250{,}000 = \$332{,}500$

19.
$$\begin{aligned} d &= \sqrt{(x_2 - x_1)^2 + (y_2 - y_1)^2} \\ &= \sqrt{(-3 - 3)^2 + (7 - (-1))^2} \\ &= \sqrt{(-6)^2 + (8)^2} \\ &= \sqrt{36 + 64} = \sqrt{100} = 10 \end{aligned}$$

20.
$$\begin{aligned} d &= \sqrt{(x_2 - x_1)^2 + (y_2 - y_1)^2} \\ &= \sqrt{(-12 - (-8))^2 + (10 - 6)^2} \\ &= \sqrt{(-4)^2 + 4^2} \\ &= \sqrt{16 + 16} = \sqrt{32} = 4\sqrt{2} \end{aligned}$$

21.
$$\begin{aligned} d &= \sqrt{(x_2 - x_1)^2 + (y_2 - y_1)^2} \\ &= \sqrt{\left(\sqrt{3} - \sqrt{3}\right)^2 + (9 - 7)^2} \\ &= \sqrt{0^2 + (2)^2} \\ &= \sqrt{0 + 4} = \sqrt{4} = 2 \end{aligned}$$

22.
$$\begin{aligned} d &= \sqrt{(x_2 - x_1)^2 + (y_2 - y_1)^2} \\ &= \sqrt{(a - (-a))^2 + (-a - a)^2} \\ &= \sqrt{(2a)^2 + (-2a)^2} \\ &= \sqrt{4a^2 + 4a^2} = \sqrt{8a^2} = 2\sqrt{2}|a| \end{aligned}$$

23. $M\left(\frac{x_1+x_2}{2}, \frac{y_1+y_2}{2}\right) = M\left(\frac{-3+3}{2}, \frac{7+(-1)}{2}\right) = M\left(\frac{0}{2}, \frac{6}{2}\right) = M(0,3)$

24. $M\left(\frac{x_1+x_2}{2}, \frac{y_1+y_2}{2}\right) = M\left(\frac{0+(-12)}{2}, \frac{5+10}{2}\right) = M\left(\frac{-12}{2}, \frac{15}{2}\right) = M\left(-6, \frac{15}{2}\right)$

25. $M\left(\frac{x_1+x_2}{2}, \frac{y_1+y_2}{2}\right) = M\left(\frac{\sqrt{3}+\sqrt{3}}{2}, \frac{9+7}{2}\right) = M\left(\frac{2\sqrt{3}}{2}, \frac{16}{2}\right) = M\left(\sqrt{3}, 8\right)$

26. $M\left(\frac{x_1+x_2}{2}, \frac{y_1+y_2}{2}\right) = M\left(\frac{a+(-a)}{2}, \frac{-a+a}{2}\right) = M\left(\frac{0}{2}, \frac{0}{2}\right) = M(0,0)$

27. $m = \frac{y_2-y_1}{x_2-x_1} = \frac{7-(-5)}{1-3} = \frac{12}{-2} = -6$

28. $m = \frac{y_2-y_1}{x_2-x_1} = \frac{-7-7}{-5-2} = \frac{-14}{-7} = 2$

29. $m = \frac{y_2-y_1}{x_2-x_1} = \frac{b-a}{a-b} = -1$

30. $m = \frac{y_2-y_1}{x_2-x_1} = \frac{(b-a)-b}{b-(a+b)} = \frac{-a}{-a} = 1$

31. $y = 3x + 6$ $\quad m = \frac{y_2-y_1}{x_2-x_1} = \frac{9-6}{1-0} = \frac{3}{1} = 3$

x	y
0	6
1	9

32. $y = 5x - 6$ $\quad m = \frac{y_2-y_1}{x_2-x_1} = \frac{-1-(-6)}{1-0} = \frac{5}{1} = 5$

x	y
0	−6
1	−1

33. The slope is zero.

34. The slope is undefined.

35. The slope is negative.

36. The slope is positive.

37. $m_1m_2 = 5\left(-\frac{1}{5}\right) = -1$
perpendicular

38. $m_1 \neq m_2;\ m_1m_2 = \frac{2}{7}\cdot\frac{7}{2} = 1 \neq -1$
neither

39. $m = \frac{y_2-y_1}{x_2-x_1} = \frac{10-5}{6-(-2)} = \frac{5}{8}$

$$m = \frac{y_2-y_1}{x_2-x_1} = \frac{y-2}{10-2} = \frac{5}{8}$$
$$8(y-2) = 5(8)$$
$$8y - 16 = 40$$
$$8y = 56$$
$$y = 7$$

40. $m = \frac{y_2-y_1}{x_2-x_1} = \frac{10-5}{6-(-2)} = \frac{5}{8}$

$$m = \frac{y_2-y_1}{x_2-x_1} = \frac{-3-5}{x-(-2)} = \frac{-8}{5}$$
$$5(-8) = -8(x+2)$$
$$-40 = -8x - 16$$
$$8x = 24$$
$$x = 3$$

41. $m = \frac{\Delta y}{\Delta x} = \frac{3000}{15} = 200$ ft. per minute

42. $m = \frac{\Delta y}{\Delta x} = \frac{147{,}500 - 50{,}000}{3-1} = \frac{97{,}500}{2} = \$48{,}750$ per year

43. $m = \dfrac{y_2 - y_1}{x_2 - x_1} = \dfrac{7-0}{-5-0} = -\dfrac{7}{5}$

$$\begin{aligned} y - y_1 &= m(x - x_1) \\ y - 0 &= -\frac{7}{5}(x - 0) \\ y &= -\frac{7}{5}x \\ 5y &= 5\left(-\frac{7}{5}x\right) \\ 5y &= -7x \\ 7x + 5y &= 0 \end{aligned}$$

44.
$$\begin{aligned} y - y_1 &= m(x - x_1) \\ y - 1 &= -4(x + 2) \\ y - 1 &= -4x - 8 \\ 4x + y &= -7 \end{aligned}$$

45.
$$\begin{aligned} y - y_1 &= m(x - x_1) \\ y + 1 &= -\frac{1}{5}(x - 2) \\ 5(y + 1) &= 5 \cdot \left[-\frac{1}{5}(x - 2)\right] \\ 5y + 5 &= -(x - 2) \\ 5y + 5 &= -x + 2 \\ x + 5y &= -3 \end{aligned}$$

46. $m = \dfrac{y_2 - y_1}{x_2 - x_1} = \dfrac{1 - (-5)}{4 - 7} = \dfrac{6}{-3} = -2$

$$\begin{aligned} y - y_1 &= m(x - x_1) \\ y + 5 &= -2(x - 7) \\ y + 5 &= -2x + 14 \\ 2x + y &= 9 \end{aligned}$$

47. $y = mx + b$

$y = \dfrac{2}{3}x + 3$

48. $y = mx + b$

$y = -\dfrac{3}{2}x - 5$

49. $y = \dfrac{3}{5}x - 2$

$m = \dfrac{3}{5}, b = -2$

50. $y = -\dfrac{4}{3}x + 3$

$m = -\dfrac{4}{3}, b = 3$

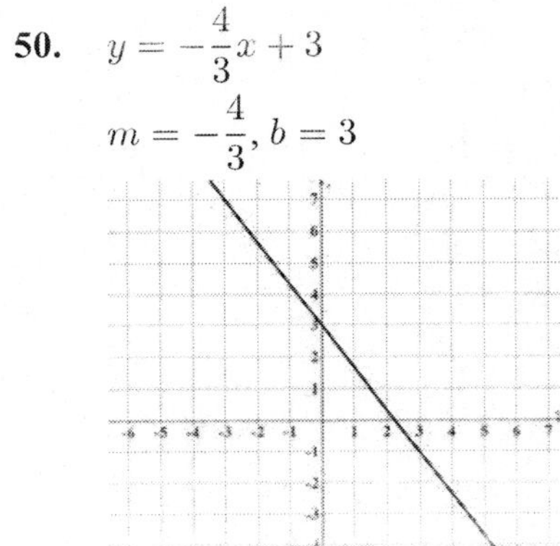

51.
$$\begin{aligned} 3x - 2y &= 10 \\ -2y &= -3x + 10 \\ y &= \tfrac{3}{2}x - 5 \end{aligned}$$
$m = \frac{3}{2}$, (0, –5)

52.
$$\begin{aligned} 2x + 4y &= -8 \\ 4y &= -2x - 8 \\ y &= -\tfrac{1}{2}x - 2 \end{aligned}$$
$m = -\frac{1}{2}$, (0, –2)

53.
$$\begin{aligned} -2y &= -3x + 10 \\ y &= \tfrac{3}{2}x - 5 \end{aligned}$$
$m = \frac{3}{2}$, (0, –5)

54. $2x = -4y - 8$
$4y = -2x - 8$
$y = -\frac{1}{2}x - 2$
$m = -\frac{1}{2}, (0, -2)$

55. $5x + 2y = 7$
$2y = -5x + 7$
$y = -\frac{5}{2}x + \frac{7}{2}$
$m = -\frac{5}{2}, (0, \frac{7}{2})$

56. $3x - 4y = 14$
$-4y = -3x + 14$
$y = \frac{3}{4}x - \frac{7}{2}$
$m = \frac{3}{4}, (0, -\frac{7}{2})$

57. $m = 0 \Rightarrow$ horizontal
$y = 17$

58. m is undefined $\Rightarrow$ vertical
$x = -5$

59. $3x - 4y = 7$
$-4y = -3x + 7$
$y = \dfrac{3}{4}x - \dfrac{7}{4}$
$m = \dfrac{3}{4}$
Use $m = \dfrac{3}{4}$.
$y - y_1 = m(x - x_1)$
$y - 0 = \dfrac{3}{4}(x - 2)$
$y = \frac{3}{4}x - \frac{3}{2}$

60. $m = \dfrac{y_2 - y_1}{x_2 - x_1} = \dfrac{-10 - 4}{4 - 2} = -7$
$y - y_1 = m(x - x_1)$
$y + 2 = -7(x - 7)$
$y + 2 = -7x + 49$
$y = -7x + 47$

61. $x + 3y = 4$
$3y = -x + 4$
$y = -\dfrac{1}{3}x + \dfrac{4}{3}$
$m = -\dfrac{1}{3}$
Use $m = 3$.
$y - y_1 = m(x - x_1)$
$y - 5 = 3(x - 0)$
$y - 5 = 3x$
$y = 3x + 5$

62. $m = \dfrac{y_2 - y_1}{x_2 - x_1} = \dfrac{-10 - 4}{4 - 2} = -7$
$y - y_1 = m(x - x_1)$
$y + 2 = \frac{1}{7}(x - 7)$
$y + 2 = \frac{1}{7}x - 1$
$y = \frac{1}{7}x - 3$

63. $y = 3x + 8$ $2y = 6x - 19$
$m = 3$ $y = 3x - \frac{19}{2}$
$m = 3$
The lines are parallel.

64. $2x + 3y = 6$ $3x - 2y = 15$
$3y = -2x + 6$ $-2y = -3x + 15$
$y = -\frac{2}{3}x + 2$ $y = \frac{3}{2}x - \frac{15}{2}$
$m = -\frac{2}{3}$ $m = \frac{3}{2}$
The lines are perpendicular.

65. $y = 4x - 8x^2$ $y = 4x - 8x^2$
$0 = 4x(1 - 2x)$ $y = 4(0) - 8(0)^2$
$x = 0, x = \frac{1}{2}$ $y = 0$
x-int: $(0, 0), (\frac{1}{2}, 0)$ y-int: $(0, 0)$

66. $y = x^2 - 10x - 24$ $y = x^2 - 10x - 24$
$0 = (x - 12)(x + 2)$ $y = 0^2 - 10(0) - 24$
$x = 12, x = -2$ $y = -24$
x-int: $(12, 0), (-2, 0)$ y-int: $(0, -24)$

67. $y^2 = 8x$

x-axis	y-axis	origin
$(-y)^2 = 8x$	$y^2 = 8(-x)$	$(-y)^2 = 8(-x)$
$y^2 = 8x$	$y^2 = -8x$	$y^2 = -8x$
equivalent: **symmetry**	not equivalent: no symmetry	not equivalent: no symmetry

68. $y = 3x^4 + 6$

x-axis	y-axis	origin
$-y = 3x^4 + 6$	$y = 3(-x)^4 + 6$	$-y = 3(-x)^4 + 6$
not equivalent: no symmetry	$y = 3x^4 + 6$	$-y = 3x^4 + 6$
	equivalent: **symmetry**	not equivalent: no symmetry

69. $y = -2\lvert x\rvert$

x-axis	y-axis	origin
$-y = -2\lvert x\rvert$	$y = -2\lvert -x\rvert$	$-y = -2\lvert -x\rvert$
$y = 2\lvert x\rvert$	$y = -2\lvert -1\rvert\lvert x\rvert$	$y = 2\lvert -x\rvert$
not equivalent: no symmetry	$y = -2\lvert x\rvert$	$y = 2\lvert -1\rvert\lvert x\rvert$
	equivalent: **symmetry**	$y = 2\lvert x\rvert$
		not equivalent: no symmetry

70. $y = \lvert x + 2\rvert$

x-axis	y-axis	origin
$-y = \lvert x + 2\rvert$	$y = \lvert -x + 2\rvert$	$-y = \lvert -x + 2\rvert$
not equivalent: no symmetry	not equivalent: no symmetry	not equivalent: no symmetry

71. $y = x^2 + 2$
x-int: none, y-int: $(0, 2)$
symmetry: y-axis

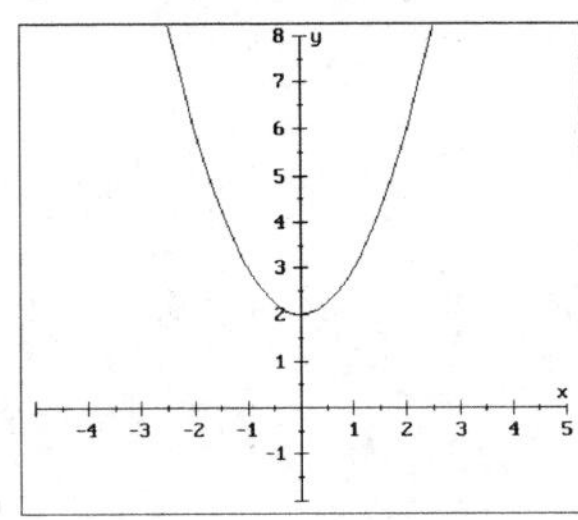

72. $y = x^3 - 2$
x-int: $\left(\sqrt[3]{2}, 0\right)$,
y-int: $(0, -2)$
symmetry: none

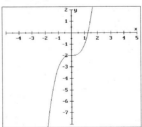

73. $y = \frac{1}{2}\lvert x\rvert$
x-int: $(0, 0)$, y-int: $(0, 0)$
symmetry: y-axis

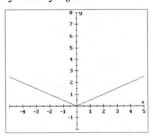

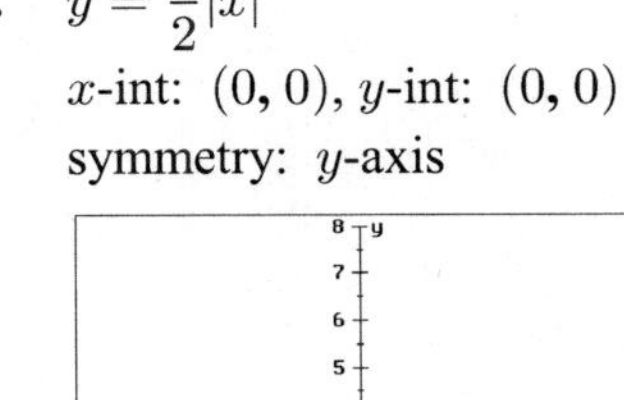

74. $y = -\sqrt{x-4}$
x-int: $(4, 0)$, y-int: none
symmetry: none

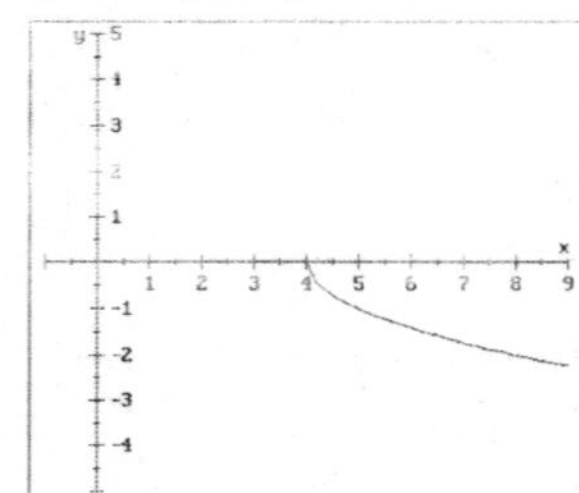

75. $y = \sqrt{x} + 2$
x-int: none, y-int: $(0, 2)$
symmetry: none

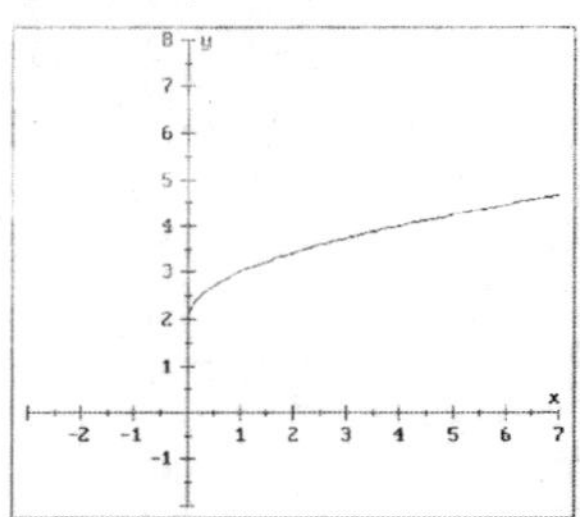

76. $y = |x+1| + 2$
x-int: none, y-int: $(0, 3)$
symmetry: none

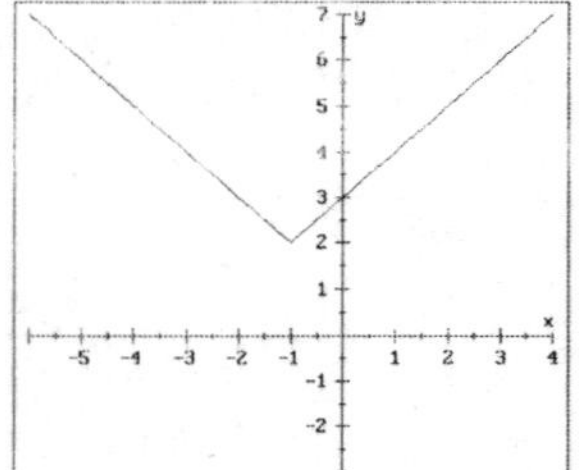

77. $y = |x-4| + 2$

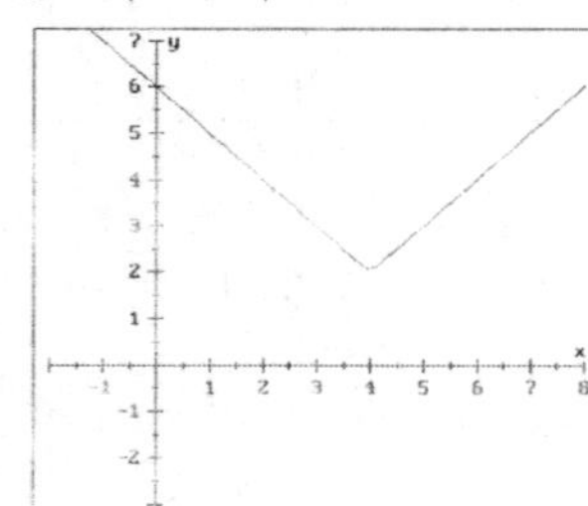

78. $y = -\sqrt{x+2} + 3$

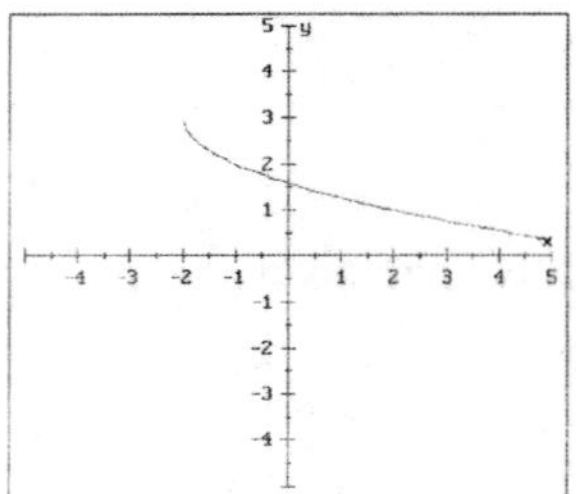

79. $y = x + 2|x|$

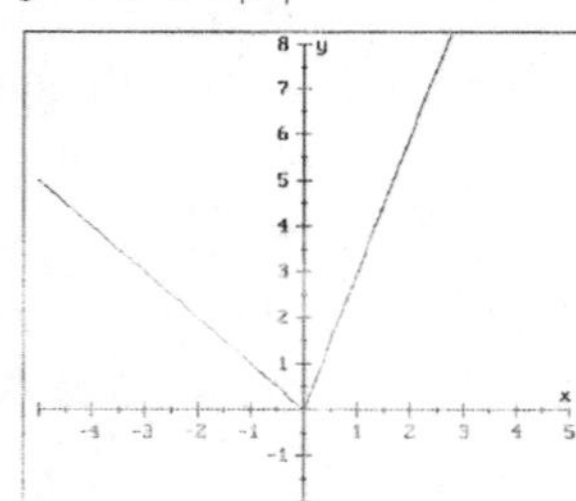

80. $y^2 = x - 3$
Graph $y = \pm\sqrt{x-3}$.

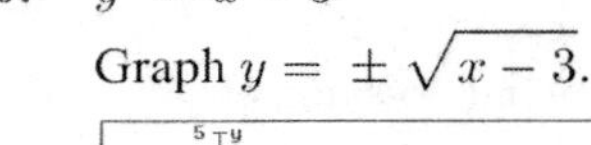

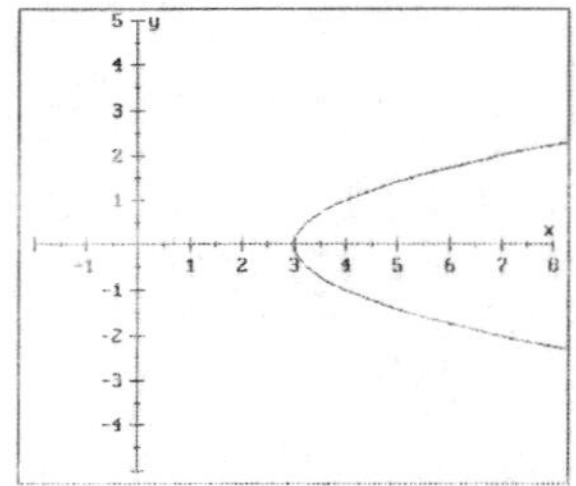

81.
$$x^2 + y^2 = 64$$
$$(x-0)^2 + (y-0)^2 = 8^2$$
C: $(0, 0)$; $r = 8$

82.
$$x^2 + (y-6)^2 = 100$$
$$(x-0)^2 + (y-6)^2 = 10^2$$
C: $(0, 6)$; $r = 10$

83.
$$(x+7)^2 + y^2 = \tfrac{1}{4}$$
$$(x-(-7))^2 + (y-0)^2 = \left(\tfrac{1}{2}\right)^2$$
C: $(-7, 0)$; $r = \frac{1}{2}$

84.
$$(x-5)^2 + (y+1)^2 = 9$$
$$(x-5)^2 + (y-(-1))^2 = 3^2$$
C: $(5, -1)$; $r = 3$

85. $(x-0)^2+(y-0)^2=7^2$
$x^2+y^2=49$

86. $(x-3)^2+(y-0)^2=\left(\frac{1}{5}\right)^2$
$(x-3)^2+y^2=\frac{1}{25}$

87. $(x-(-2))^2+(y-12)^2=5^2$
$(x+2)^2+(y-12)^2=25$

88. $\left(x-\frac{2}{7}\right)^2+(y-5)^2=9^2$
$\left(x-\frac{2}{7}\right)^2+(y-5)^2=81$

89. $C(-3,4);\ r=12$
$(x-h)^2+(y-k)^2=r^2$
$(x+3)^2+(y-4)^2=144$
or $x^2+y^2+6x-8y-119=0$

90. Center: $x=\dfrac{-6+5}{2}=-\dfrac{1}{2}$
$y=\dfrac{-3+8}{2}=\dfrac{5}{2}$
$r=$ distance from center to endpoint
$=\sqrt{\left(-\frac{1}{2}-5\right)^2+\left(\frac{5}{2}-8\right)^2}=\sqrt{\frac{121}{2}}$
$\left(x+\frac{1}{2}\right)^2+\left(y-\frac{5}{2}\right)^2=\frac{121}{2}$, or
$x^2+y^2+x-5y-54=0$

91. $x^2+y^2+6x-4y+4=0$
$x^2+6x+y^2-4y=-4$
$x^2+6x+9+y^2-4y+4=-4+9+4$
$(x+3)^2+(y-2)^2=9$

92. $2x^2+2y^2-8x-16y-10=0$
$x^2+y^2-4x-8y-5=0$
$x^2-4x+y^2-8y=5$
$x^2-4x+4+y^2-8y+16=5+4+16$
$(x-2)^2+(y-4)^2=25$

93. $x^2+y^2-16=0$
$(x-0)^2+(y-0)^2=16$
$C(0,0),\ r=4$

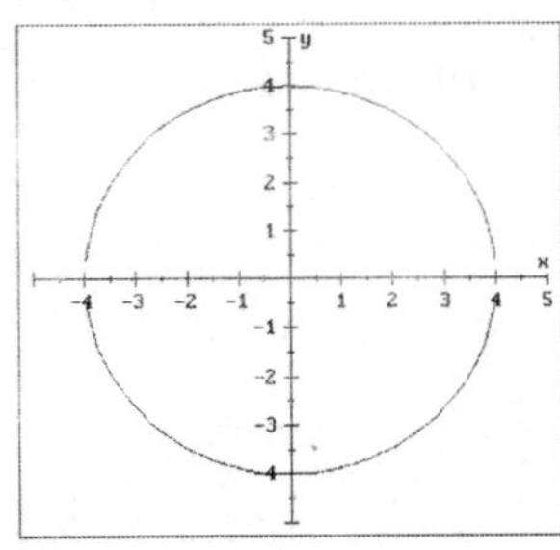

94. $x^2+y^2-4x=5$
$x^2-4x+y^2=5$
$x^2-4x+4+y^2=5+4$
$(x-2)^2+y^2=9$
$C(2,0),\ r=3$

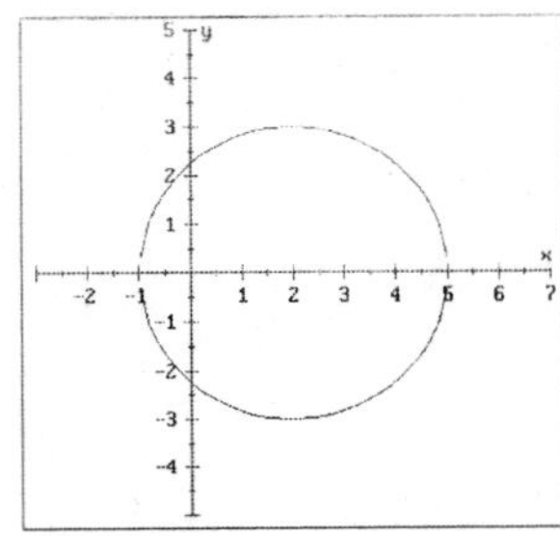

95.

$$x^2 + y^2 - 2y = 15$$
$$x^2 + y^2 - 2y + 1 = 15 + 1$$
$$x^2 + (y - 1)^2 = 16$$

$C(0, 1)$, $r = 4$

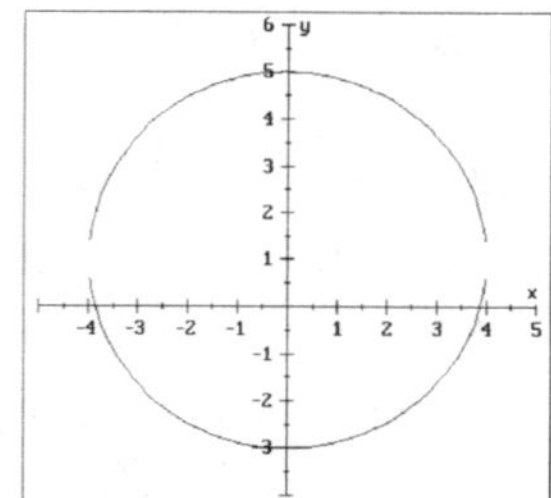

96.

$$x^2 + y^2 - 4x + 2y = 4$$
$$x^2 - 4x + 4 + y^2 + 2y + 1 = 4 + 4 + 1$$
$$(x - 2)^2 + (y + 1)^2 = 9$$

$C(2, -1)$, $r = 3$

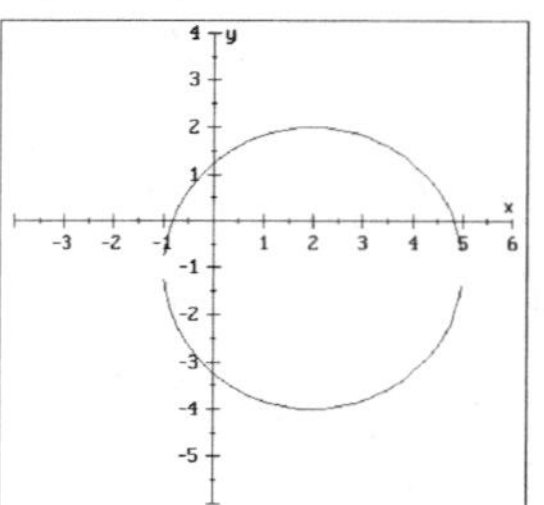

97. Graph $y = x^2 - 11$.
Find the x-intercepts.
$x = -3.32,\ x = 3.32$

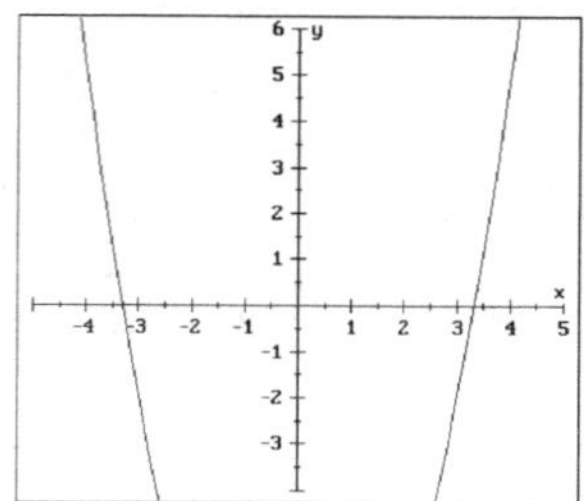

98. Graph $y = x^3 - x$.
Find the x-intercepts.
$x = -1,\ x = 0, x = 1$

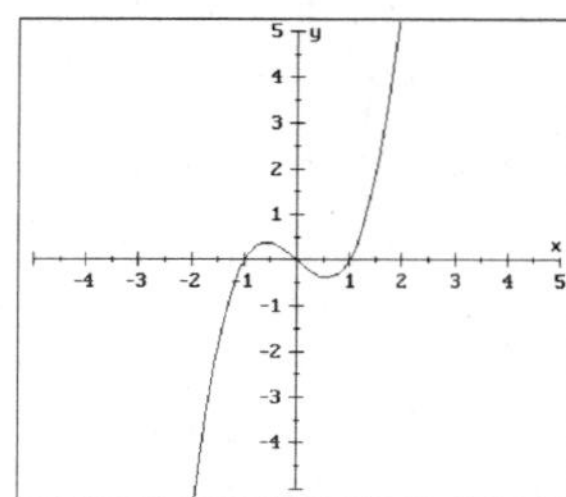

99. Graph $y = |x^2 - 2| - 1$.
Find the x-intercepts.
$x = -1.73,\ x = -1, x = 1, x = 1.73$

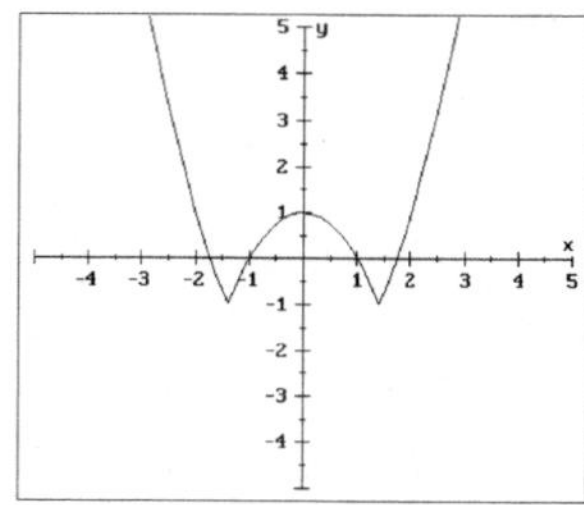

100. Graph $y = x^2 - 3x - 5$.
Find the x-intercepts.
$x = -1.19,\ x = 4.19$

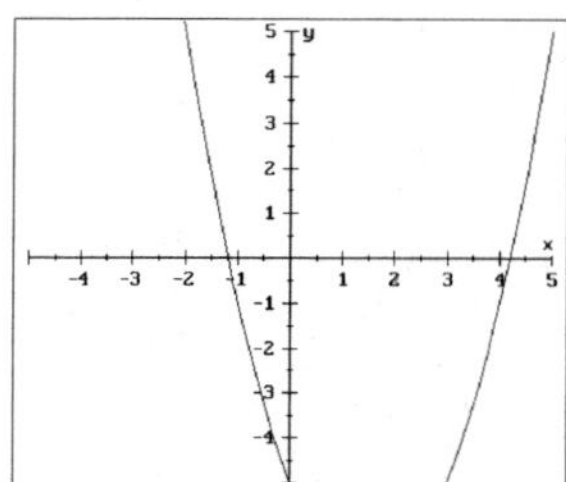

101.
$$\frac{x+3}{10} = \frac{x-1}{x}$$
$$x(x+3) = 10(x-1)$$
$$x^2 + 3x = 10x - 10$$
$$x^2 - 7x + 10 = 0$$
$$(x-5)(x-2) = 0$$
$$x = 5 \text{ or } x = 2$$

102.
$$\frac{x-1}{2} = \frac{12}{x+1}$$
$$(x+1)(x-1) = 2(12)$$
$$x^2 - 1 = 24$$
$$x^2 = 25$$
$$x = \pm 5$$

103.
$$f = ks \qquad f = \frac{3}{5}s$$
$$3 = k(5) \qquad f = \frac{3}{5}(3)$$
$$\frac{3}{5} = k \qquad f = \frac{9}{5}\text{pounds}$$

104.
$$E = kv^2$$
30 mph   50 mph
$$E = k(30)^2 \qquad E = k(50)^2$$
$$E = 900k \qquad E = 2500k$$
$$\text{Factor of increase} = \frac{2500k}{900k} = \frac{25}{9}$$

105.
$$V = \frac{kT}{P} \qquad V = \frac{\frac{100}{3}T}{P}$$
$$400 = \frac{k(300)}{25} \qquad V = \frac{\frac{100}{3}(200)}{20}$$
$$10000 = 300k \qquad V = \frac{1000}{3}$$
$$\frac{100}{3} = k \qquad V = 333\tfrac{1}{3}\text{ cm}^3$$

106. $A = klw$
$A = 1lw \Rightarrow k = 1$

107.
$$R = \frac{kL}{D^2} \qquad R = \frac{0.0005L}{D^2}$$
$$200 = \frac{k(1000)}{(.05)^2} \qquad V = \frac{0.0005(1500)}{(0.08)^2}$$
$$200 = \frac{1000k}{.0025} \qquad V \approx 117 \text{ ohms}$$
$$0.0005 = k$$

108. Let $x =$ # rolls and $y =$ total charge. Then the equation is $y = mx + b$, where m is the charge per roll and b is the fixed amount.
Given points: $(11, 177)$ and $(20, 294)$
$$m = \frac{y_2 - y_1}{x_2 - x_1} = \frac{294 - 177}{20 - 11} = \frac{117}{9} = 13$$
$$y - y_1 = m(x - x_1) \qquad \text{Let } x = 27:$$
$$y - 177 = 13(x - 11) \qquad y = 13x + 34$$
$$y = 13x + 34 \qquad y = 13(27) + 34$$
$$y = \$385$$

109. $14x + 18y = 5040$
Let $x = 180$:
$$14(180) + 18y = 5040$$
$$2520 + 18y = 5040$$
$$18y = 2520$$
$$y = 140 \text{ hours of tutoring Spanish.}$$

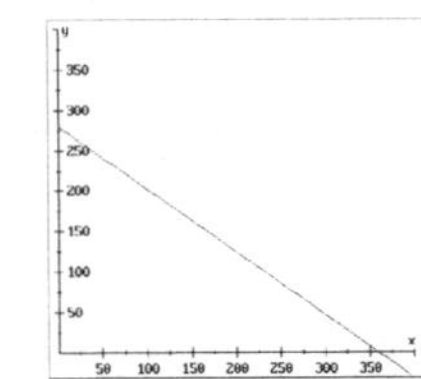

Chapter 2 Test (page 275)

1. $(-3, \pi) \Rightarrow$ QII

2. $(0, -8) \Rightarrow$ negative y-axis

3.
$$\begin{aligned} x + 3y &= 6 \\ x + 3(0) &= 6 \\ x &= 6 \\ (6, 0)& \end{aligned} \qquad \begin{aligned} x + 3y &= 6 \\ 0 + 3y &= 6 \\ y &= 2 \\ (0, 2)& \end{aligned}$$

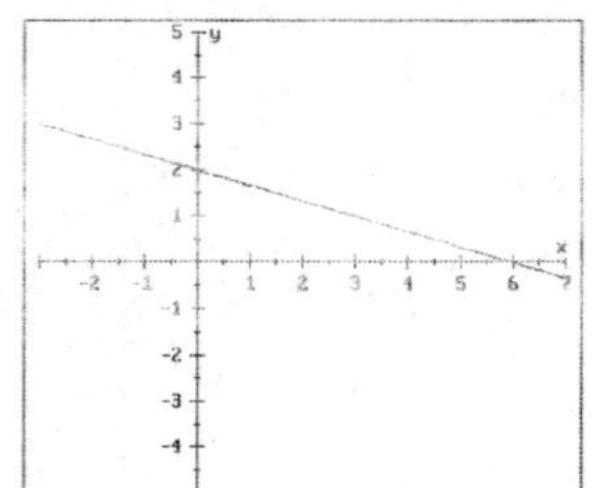

4.
$$\begin{aligned} 2x - 5y &= 10 \\ 2x - 5(0) &= 10 \\ x &= 5 \\ (5, 0)& \end{aligned} \qquad \begin{aligned} 2x - 5y &= 10 \\ 2(0) - 5y &= 10 \\ y &= -2 \\ (0, -2)& \end{aligned}$$

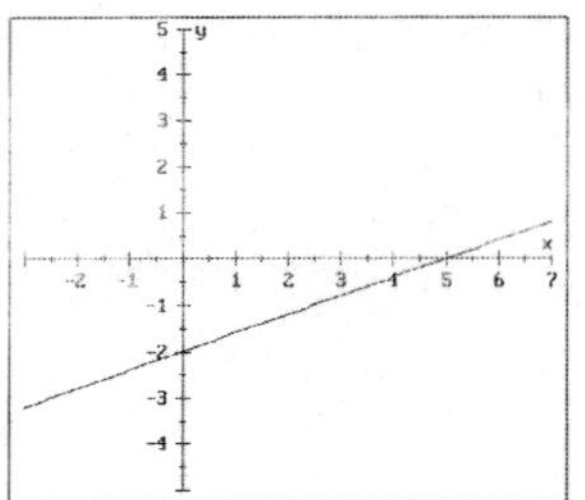

5.
$$\begin{aligned} 2(x + y) &= 3x + 5 \\ 2x + 2y &= 3x + 5 \\ 2y &= x + 5 \\ y &= \tfrac{1}{2}x + \tfrac{5}{2} \end{aligned}$$

x	y
0	$\frac{5}{2}$
1	3

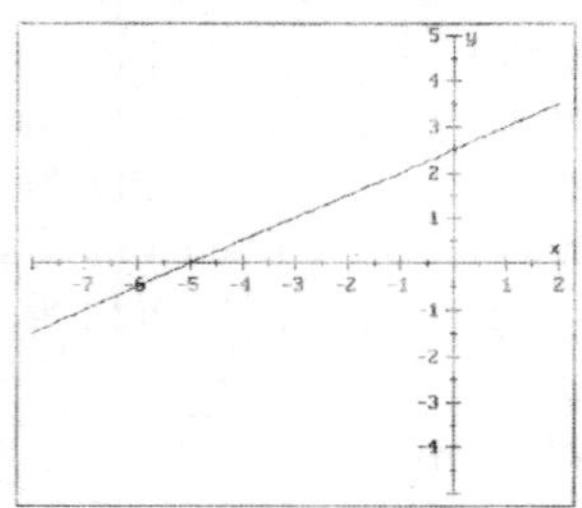

6.
$$\begin{aligned} 3x - 5y &= 3(x - 5) \\ 3x - 5y &= 3x - 15 \\ -5y &= -15 \\ y &= 3 \end{aligned}$$

x	y
0	3
-2	3

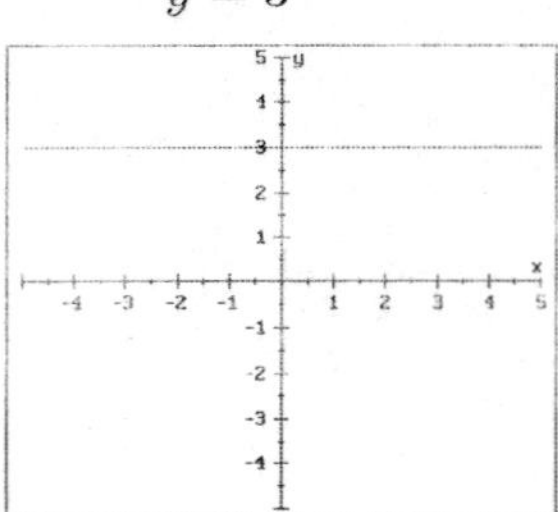

7. $\frac{1}{2}(x-2y)=y-1$

$\frac{1}{2}x-y=y-1$

$x-2y=2y-2$

$-4y=-x-2$

$y=\frac{1}{4}x+\frac{1}{2}$

x	y
0	$\frac{1}{2}$
2	1

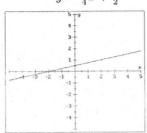

8. $\dfrac{x+y-5}{7}=3x$

$x+y-5=21x$

$y=20x+5$

x	y
0	5
$-\frac{1}{4}$	0

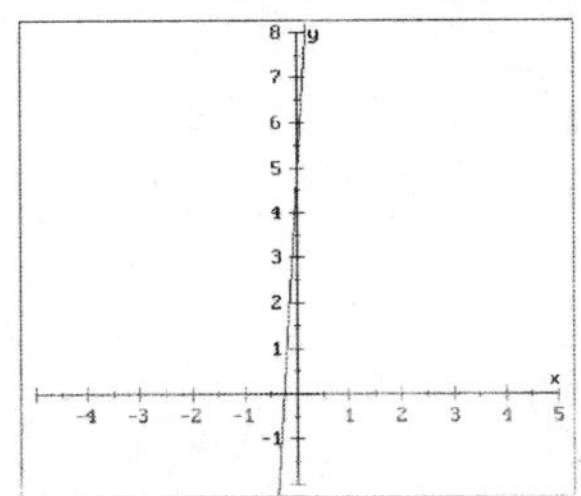

9. $d=\sqrt{(x_2-x_1)^2+(y_2-y_1)^2}$

$=\sqrt{(1-(-3))^2+(-1-4)^2}$

$=\sqrt{(4)^2+(-5)^2}$

$=\sqrt{16+25}=\sqrt{41}$

10. $d=\sqrt{(x_2-x_1)^2+(y_2-y_1)^2}$

$=\sqrt{(0-(-\pi))^2+(\pi-0)^2}$

$=\sqrt{\pi^2+\pi^2}$

$=\sqrt{2\pi^2}=\pi\sqrt{2}\approx 4.44$

11. $M\left(\dfrac{x_1+x_2}{2},\dfrac{y_1+y_2}{2}\right)=M\left(\dfrac{3+(-3)}{2},\dfrac{-7+7}{2}\right)=M\left(\dfrac{0}{2},\dfrac{0}{2}\right)=M(0,0)$

12. $M\left(\dfrac{x_1+x_2}{2},\dfrac{y_1+y_2}{2}\right)=M\left(\dfrac{0+\sqrt{8}}{2},\dfrac{\sqrt{2}+\sqrt{18}}{2}\right)=M\left(\dfrac{2\sqrt{2}}{2},\dfrac{4\sqrt{2}}{2}\right)=M\left(\sqrt{2},2\sqrt{2}\right)$

13. $m=\dfrac{y_2-y_1}{x_2-x_1}=\dfrac{1-(-9)}{-5-3}=\dfrac{10}{-8}=-\dfrac{5}{4}$

14. $m=\dfrac{y_2-y_1}{x_2-x_1}=\dfrac{0-3}{-\sqrt{12}-\sqrt{3}}=\dfrac{-3}{-3\sqrt{3}}=\dfrac{1}{\sqrt{3}}=\dfrac{\sqrt{3}}{3}$

15. $y=3x-2$ $\quad$ $y=2x-3$

$m=3$ $\quad$ $m=2$

neither

16. $2x-3y=5$

$-3y=-2x+5$

$y=\frac{2}{3}x-\frac{5}{3}$

$m=\frac{2}{3}$

$3x+2y=7$

$2y=-3x+7$

$y=-\frac{3}{2}x+\frac{7}{2}$

$m=-\frac{3}{2}$

perpendicular

17. $y - y_1 = m(x - x_1)$
$y + 5 = 2(x - 3)$
$y + 5 = 2x - 6$
$y = 2x - 11$

18. $y = mx + b$
$y = 3x + \frac{1}{2}$

19. $2x - y = 3$
$-y = -2x + 3$
$y = 2x - 3$
$m = 2$ $\quad y = 2x + 5$

20. $2x - y = 3$
$-y = -2x + 3$
$y = 2x - 3$
$m = 2$ $\quad y = -\frac{1}{2}x + 5$

21. $m = \dfrac{y_2 - y_1}{x_2 - x_1} = \dfrac{\frac{1}{2} - (-\frac{3}{2})}{3 - 2} = \dfrac{\frac{4}{2}}{1} = 2$
$y - y_1 = m(x - x_1)$
$y - \frac{1}{2} = 2(x - 3)$
$y - \frac{1}{2} = 2x - 6$
$y = 2x - \frac{11}{2}$

22. If the line is parallel to the y-axis, then it is a vertical line: $x = 3$

23. $y = x^3 - 16x$
$0 = x(x^2 - 16)$
$0 = x(x + 4)(x - 4)$
$x = 0, x = -4, x = 4$
x-int: $(0, 0), (-4, 0), (4, 0)$

$y = x^3 - 16x$
$y = 0^3 - 16(0)$
$y = 0$
y-int: $(0, 0)$

24. $y = |x - 4|$
$0 = |x - 4|$
$0 = x - 4$
$4 = x$
x-int: $(4, 0)$

$y = |x - 4|$
$y = |0 - 4|$
$y = |-4|$
$y = 4$
y-int: $(0, 4)$

25. $y^2 = x - 1$

x-axis	y-axis	origin
$(-y)^2 = x - 1$	$y^2 = -x - 1$	$(-y)^2 = -x - 1$
$y^2 = x - 1$	not equivalent: no symmetry	$y^2 = -x - 1$
equivalent: **symmetry**		not equivalent: no symmetry

26. $y = x^4 + 1$

x-axis	y-axis	origin
$-y = x^4 + 1$	$y = (-x)^4 + 1$	$-y = (-x)^4 + 1$
not equivalent: no symmetry	$y = x^4 + 1$	$-y = x^4 + 1$
	equivalent: **symmetry**	not equivalent: no symmetry

CHAPTER 2 TEST

27. $y = x^2 - 9$
x-int: $(3, 0)$, $(-3, 0)$
y-int: $(0, -9)$
symmetry: y-axis

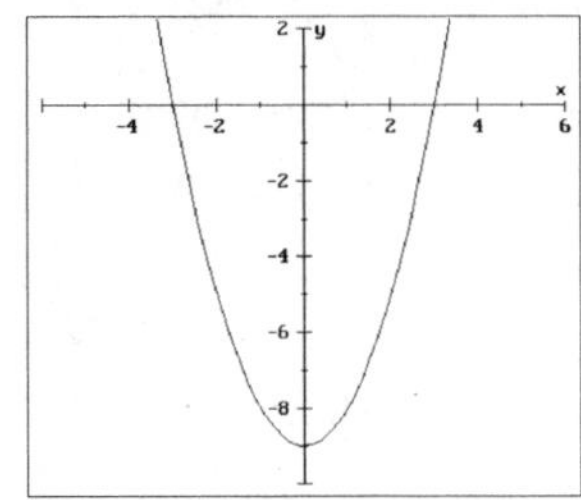

28. $x = |y|$
x-int: $(0, 0)$
y-int: $(0, 0)$
symmetry: x-axis

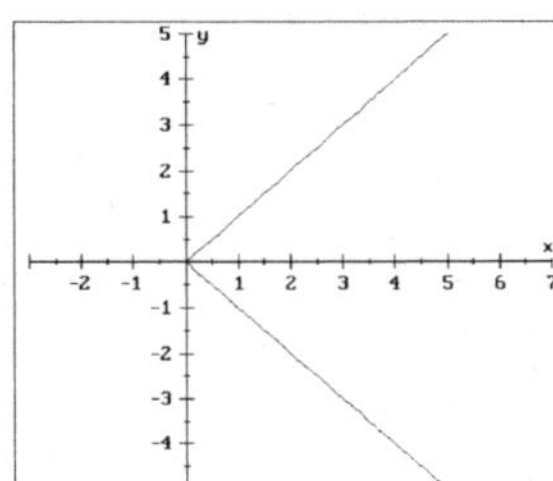

29. $y = 2\sqrt{x}$
x-int: $(0, 0)$
y-int: $(0, 0)$
symmetry: none

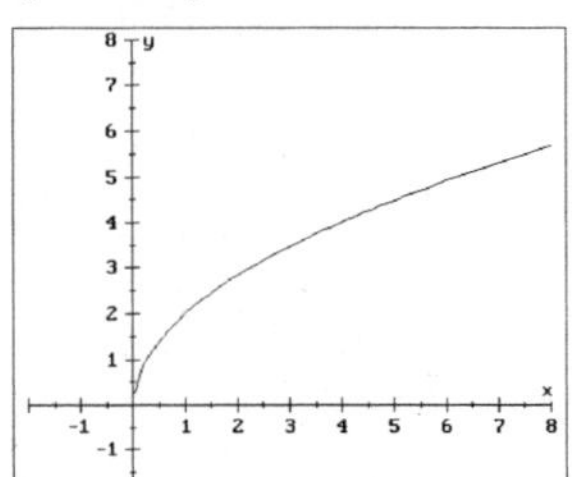

30. $x = y^3$
x-int: $(0, 0)$
y-int: $(0, 0)$
symmetry: origin

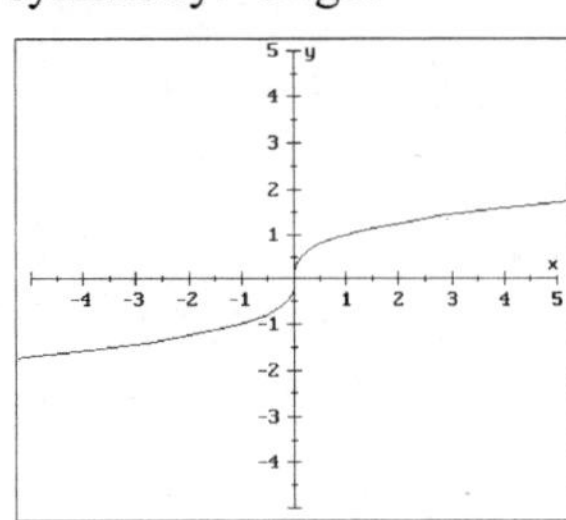

31. $C(5, 7); r = 8$

$$(x - h)^2 + (y - k)^2 = r^2$$
$$(x - 5)^2 + (y - 7)^2 = 64$$

32. $r = \sqrt{(2 - 6)^2 + (4 - 8)^2}$

$$= \sqrt{32}$$
$$(x - h)^2 + (y - k)^2 = r^2$$
$$(x - 2)^2 + (y - 4)^2 = 32$$

33. $x^2 + y^2 = 9$
$C(0, 0)$, $r = 3$

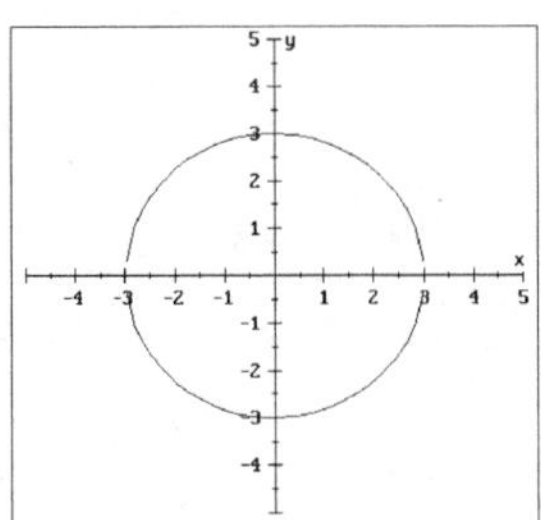

34. $x^2 - 4x + y^2 + 3 = 0$

$$x^2 - 4x + y^2 = -3$$
$$x^2 - 4x + 4 + y^2 = -3 + 4$$
$$(x - 2)^2 + y^2 = 1$$
$$C(2, 0),\ r = 1$$

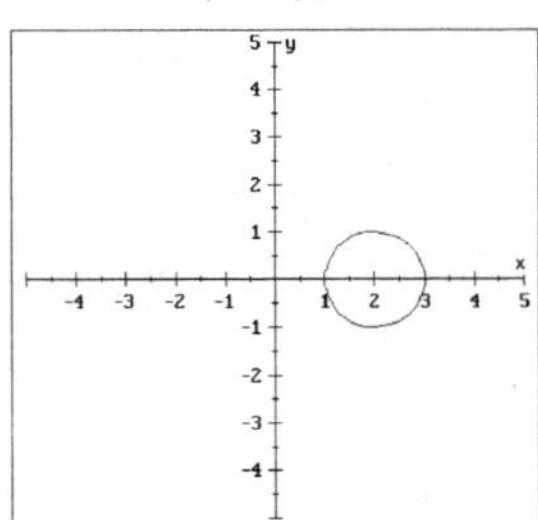

35. $y = kz^2$

36. $w = krs^2$

37. $P = kQ$ $\quad P = \frac{7}{2}Q$
$7 = k(2)$ $\quad P = \frac{7}{2}(5)$
$\frac{7}{2} = k$ $\quad P = \frac{35}{2}$

38. $y = \frac{kx}{z^2}$ $\quad y = \frac{\frac{64}{3}x}{z^2}$
$16 = \frac{k(3)}{2^2}$ $\quad 2 = \frac{\frac{64}{3}x}{3^2}$
$16 = \frac{3k}{4}$ $\quad 2 = \frac{\frac{64}{3}x}{9}$
$64 = 3k$ $\quad 18 = \frac{64}{3}x$
$\frac{64}{3} = k$ $\quad 54 = 64x$
$\frac{54}{64} = x$
$\frac{27}{32} = x$

39. Graph $y = x^2 - 7$.
Find any positive x-intercepts.
$x = 2.65$

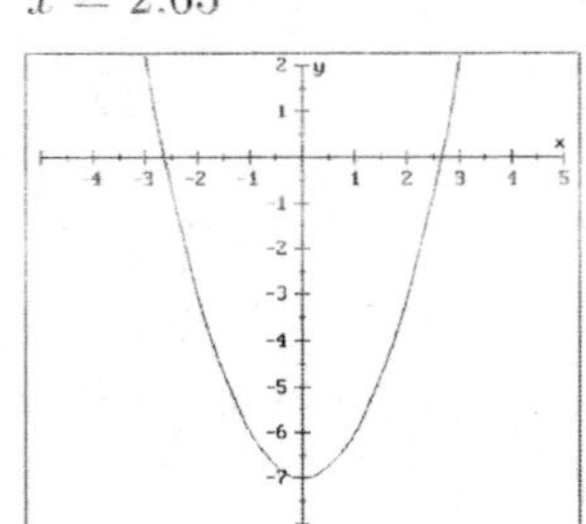

40. Graph $y = x^2 - 5x - 5$.
Find any positive x-intercepts.
$x = 5.85$

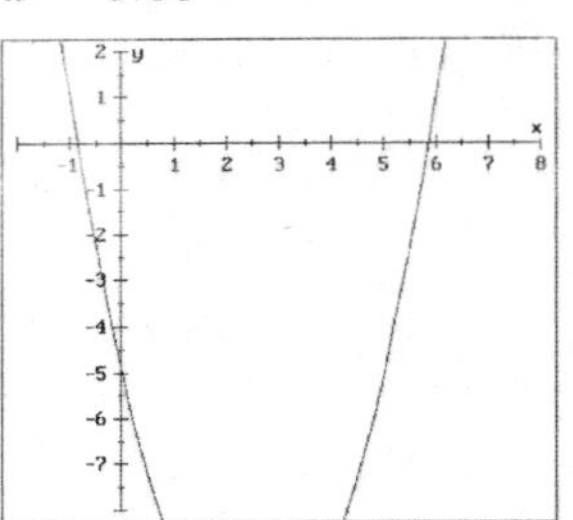

Exercises 3.1 (page 290)

1. function
2. relation
3. domain
4. range
5. $y = f(x)$
6. (x, y), domain, range
7. x
8. dependent
9. vertical, once
10. linear

11. $y = x$
Each value of x is paired with only one value of y.
function

12. $y - 2x = 0$
$y = 2x$
Each value of x is paired with only one value of y.
function

13. $y^2 = x$
$y = \pm\sqrt{x}$
At least one value of x is paired with more than one value of y. **not a function**

14. $|y| = x$
$y = \pm x$
At least one value of x is paired with more than one value of y. **not a function**

15. $y = x^2$
Each value of x is paired with only one value of y.
function

16. $y - 7 = 7$
$y = 14$
Each value of x is paired with only one value of y.
function

17. $y^2 - 4x = 1$
$y^2 = 4x + 1$
$y = \pm\sqrt{4x+1}$
At least one value of x is paired with more than one value of y. **not a function**

18. $|x - 2| = y$
$y = |x - 2|$
Each value of x is paired with only one value of y.
function

19. $|x| = |y|$
$|y| = |x|$
$y = \pm|x|$
At least one value of x is paired with more than one value of y. **not a function**

20. $x = 7$
At least one value of x is paired with more than one value of y. **not a function**

21. $y = 7$
Each value of x is paired with only one value of y.
function

22. $|x + y| = 7$
$x + y = \pm 7$
$y = -x \pm 7$
At least one value of x is paired with more than one value of y. **not a function**

23. $f(x) = 3x + 5 \Rightarrow$ domain $= (-\infty, \infty)$

24. $f(x) = -5x + 2 \Rightarrow$ domain $= (-\infty, \infty)$

25. $f(x) = x^2 - x + 1 \Rightarrow$ domain $= (-\infty, \infty)$

26. $f(x) = x^3 - 3x + 2 \Rightarrow$ domain $= (-\infty, \infty)$

27. $f(x) = \sqrt{x-2} \Rightarrow x - 2 \geq 0$
domain $= [2, \infty)$

28. $f(x) = \sqrt{2x+3} \Rightarrow 2x + 3 \geq 0$
domain $= \left[-\dfrac{3}{2}, \infty\right)$

29. $f(x) = \sqrt{4-x} \Rightarrow 4 - x \geq 0$
domain $= (-\infty, 4]$

30. $f(x) = 3\sqrt{2-x} \Rightarrow 2 - x \geq 0$
domain $= (-\infty, 2]$

31. $f(x) = \sqrt{x^2-1} \Rightarrow x^2 - 1 \geq 0$
domain $= (-\infty, -1] \cup [1, \infty)$

32. $f(x) = \sqrt{x^2-2x-3} \Rightarrow x^2 - 2x - 3 \geq 0$
domain $= (-\infty, -1] \cup [3, \infty)$

33. $f(x) = \sqrt[3]{x+1} \Rightarrow$ domain $= (-\infty, \infty)$

34. $f(x) = \sqrt[3]{5-x} \Rightarrow$ domain $= (-\infty, \infty)$

35. $f(x) = \dfrac{3}{x+1} \Rightarrow x \neq -1$
domain $= (-\infty, -1) \cup (-1, \infty)$

36. $f(x) = \dfrac{-7}{x+3} \Rightarrow x \neq -3$
domain $= (-\infty, -3) \cup (-3, \infty)$

37. $f(x) = \dfrac{x}{x-3} \Rightarrow x \neq 3$
domain $= (-\infty, 3) \cup (3, \infty)$

38. $f(x) = \dfrac{x+2}{x-1} \Rightarrow x \neq 1$
domain $= (-\infty, 1) \cup (1, \infty)$

39. $f(x) = \dfrac{x}{x^2 - 4} = \dfrac{x}{(x+2)(x-2)}$

$x \neq -2, x \neq 2$

domain $= (-\infty, -2) \cup (-2, 2) \cup (2, \infty)$

40. $f(x) = \dfrac{2x}{x^2 - 9} = \dfrac{2x}{(x+3)(x-3)}$

$x \neq -3, x \neq 3$

domain $= (-\infty, -3) \cup (-3, 3) \cup (3, \infty)$

41. $f(x) = \dfrac{1}{x^2 - 4x - 5} = \dfrac{1}{(x+1)(x-5)}$

$x \neq -1, x \neq 5$

domain $= (-\infty, -1) \cup (-1, 5) \cup (5, \infty)$

42. $f(x) = \dfrac{x}{2x^2 - 16x + 30} = \dfrac{x}{2(x-3)(x-5)}$

$x \neq 3, x \neq 5$

domain $= (-\infty, 3) \cup (3, 5) \cup (5, \infty)$

43. $f(x) = 3x - 2$

$f(2) = 3(2) - 2$	$f(-3) = 3(-3) - 2$	$f(k) = 3k - 2$	$f(k^2 - 1) = 3(k^2 - 1) - 2$
$= 6 - 2$	$= -9 - 2$		$= 3k^2 - 3 - 2$
$= 4$	$= -11$		$= 3k^2 - 5$

44. $f(x) = 5x + 7$

$f(2) = 5(2) + 7$	$f(-3) = 5(-3) + 7$	$f(k) = 5k + 7$	$f(k^2 - 1) = 5(k^2 - 1) + 7$
$= 10 + 7$	$= -15 + 7$		$= 5k^2 - 5 + 7$
$= 17$	$= -8$		$= 5k^2 + 2$

45. $f(x) = \frac{1}{2}x + 3$

$f(2) = \frac{1}{2}(2) + 3$	$f(-3) = \frac{1}{2}(-3) + 3$	$f(k) = \frac{1}{2}k + 3$	$f(k^2 - 1) = \frac{1}{2}(k^2 - 1) + 3$
$= 1 + 3$	$= -\frac{3}{2} + 3$		$= \frac{1}{2}k^2 - \frac{1}{2} + 3$
$= 4$	$= \frac{3}{2}$		$= \frac{1}{2}k^2 + \frac{5}{2}$

46. $f(x) = \frac{2}{3}x + 5$

$f(2) = \frac{2}{3}(2) + 5$	$f(-3) = \frac{2}{3}(-3) + 5$	$f(k) = \frac{2}{3}k + 5$	$f(k^2 - 1) = \frac{2}{3}(k^2 - 1) + 5$
$= \frac{4}{3} + 5$	$= -2 + 5$		$= \frac{2}{3}k^2 - \frac{2}{3} + 5$
$= \frac{19}{3}$	$= 3$		$= \frac{2}{3}k^2 + \frac{13}{3}$

47. $f(x) = x^2$

$f(2) = 2^2$	$f(-3) = (-3)^2$	$f(k) = k^2$	$f(k^2 - 1) = (k^2 - 1)^2$
$= 4$	$= 9$		$= (k^2 - 1)(k^2 - 1)$
			$= k^4 - 2k^2 + 1$

48. $f(x) = 3 - x^2$

$f(2) = 3 - 2^2 = 3 - 4 = -1$	$f(-3) = 3 - (-3)^2 = 3 - 9 = -6$	$f(k) = 3 - k^2$	$f(k^2-1) = 3 - (k^2-1)^2 = 3 - (k^2-1)(k^2-1) = 3 - (k^4 - 2k^2 + 1) = -k^4 + 2k^2 + 2$

49. $f(x) = x^2 + 3x - 1$

$f(2) = 2^2 + 3(2) - 1 = 4 + 6 - 1 = 9$	$f(-3) = (-3)^2 + 3(-3) - 1 = 9 - 9 - 1 = -1$	$f(k) = k^2 + 3k - 1$

$$\begin{aligned} f(k^2-1) &= (k^2-1)^2 + 3(k^2-1) - 1 \\ &= k^4 - 2k^2 + 1 + 3k^2 - 3 - 1 \\ &= k^4 + k^2 - 3 \end{aligned}$$

50. $f(x) = -x^2 - 2x + 1$

$f(2) = -(2)^2 - 2(2) + 1 = -4 - 4 + 1 = -7$	$f(-3) = -(-3)^2 - 2(-3) + 1 = -9 + 6 + 1 = -2$	$f(k) = -k^2 - 2k + 1$

$$\begin{aligned} f(k^2-1) &= -(k^2-1)^2 - 2(k^2-1) + 1 \\ &= -(k^4 - 2k^2 + 1) - 2k^2 + 2 + 1 \\ &= -k^4 + 2k^2 - 1 - 2k^2 + 3 \\ &= -k^4 + 2 \end{aligned}$$

51. $f(x) = |x^2 + 1|$

$f(2) = \lvert 2^2 + 1\rvert = \lvert 5\rvert = 5$	$f(-3) = \lvert(-3)^2 + 1\rvert = \lvert 10\rvert = 10$	$f(k) = \lvert k^2 + 1\rvert = k^2 + 1$ $[k^2 + 1 \geq 0]$	$f(k^2-1) = \lvert(k^2-1)^2 + 1\rvert = (k^2-1)^2 + 1 = k^4 - 2k^2 + 1 + 1 = k^4 - 2k^2 + 2$ $[(k^2-1)^2 + 1 \geq 0]$

52. $f(x) = |x^2 + x + 4|$

$f(2) = \lvert 2^2 + 2 + 4\rvert = \lvert 4 + 2 + 4\rvert = \lvert 10\rvert = 10$	$f(-3) = \lvert(-3)^2 + (-3) + 4\rvert = \lvert 9 - 3 + 4\rvert = \lvert 10\rvert = 10$	$f(k) = \lvert k^2 + k + 4\rvert = k^2 + k + 4$ $[k^2 + k + 4 \geq 0]$

continued on next page

52. continued

$$\begin{aligned} f(k^2-1) &= \left|(k^2-1)^2+(k^2-1)+4\right| \\ &= \left|(k^2-1)^2+k^2+3\right| \\ &= (k^2-1)^2+k^2+3 \\ &= k^4-2k^2+1+k^2+3 \\ &= k^4-k^2+4 \\ &\left[(k^2-1)^2+k^2+3\geq 0\right] \end{aligned}$$

53. $f(x)=\dfrac{2}{x+4}$

$f(2)=\dfrac{2}{2+4}=\dfrac{2}{6}=\dfrac{1}{3}$	$f(-3)=\dfrac{2}{-3+4}=\dfrac{2}{1}=2$	$f(k)=\dfrac{2}{k+4}$	$f(k^2-1)=\dfrac{2}{k^2-1+4}=\dfrac{2}{k^2+3}$

54. $f(x)=\dfrac{3}{x-5}$

$f(2)=\dfrac{3}{2-5}=\dfrac{3}{-3}=-1$	$f(-3)=\dfrac{3}{-3-5}=\dfrac{3}{-8}=-\dfrac{3}{8}$	$f(k)=\dfrac{3}{k-5}$	$f(k^2-1)=\dfrac{3}{k^2-1-5}=\dfrac{3}{k^2-6}$

55. $f(x)=\dfrac{1}{x^2-1}$

$f(2)=\dfrac{1}{2^2-1}=\dfrac{1}{4-1}=\dfrac{1}{3}$	$f(-3)=\dfrac{1}{(-3)^2-1}=\dfrac{1}{9-1}=\dfrac{1}{8}$	$f(k)=\dfrac{1}{k^2-1}$	$f(k^2-1)=\dfrac{1}{(k^2-1)^2-1}=\dfrac{1}{k^4-2k^2+1-1}=\dfrac{1}{k^4-2k^2}$

56. $f(x)=\dfrac{3}{x^2+3}$

$f(2)=\dfrac{3}{2^2+3}=\dfrac{3}{4+3}=\dfrac{3}{7}$	$f(-3)=\dfrac{3}{(-3)^2+3}=\dfrac{3}{9+3}=\dfrac{3}{12}=\dfrac{1}{4}$	$f(k)=\dfrac{3}{k^2+3}$	$f(k^2-1)=\dfrac{3}{(k^2-1)^2+3}=\dfrac{3}{k^4-2k^2+1+3}=\dfrac{3}{k^4-2k^2+4}$

57. $f(x) = \sqrt{x^2+1}$

$f(2) = \sqrt{2^2+1}$ $= \sqrt{4+1}$ $= \sqrt{5}$	$f(-3) = \sqrt{(-3)^2+1}$ $= \sqrt{9+1}$ $= \sqrt{10}$	$f(k) = \sqrt{k^2+1}$	$f(k^2-1) = \sqrt{(k^2-1)^2+1}$ $= \sqrt{k^4-2k^2+1+1}$ $= \sqrt{k^4-2k^2+2}$

58. $f(x) = \sqrt{x^2-1}$

$f(2) = \sqrt{2^2-1}$ $= \sqrt{4-1}$ $= \sqrt{3}$	$f(-3) = \sqrt{(-3)^2-1}$ $= \sqrt{9-1}$ $= \sqrt{8} = 2\sqrt{2}$	$f(k) = \sqrt{k^2-1}$	$f(k^2-1) = \sqrt{(k^2-1)^2-1}$ $= \sqrt{k^4-2k^2+1-1}$ $= \sqrt{k^4-2k^2}$ $= \sqrt{k^2(k^2-2)}$ $= \lvert k\rvert\sqrt{k^2-2}$

59. $$\frac{f(x+h)-f(x)}{h} = \frac{[3(x+h)+1]-[3x+1]}{h} = \frac{[3x+3h+1]-[3x+1]}{h} = \frac{3x+3h+1-3x-1}{h} = \frac{3h}{h} = 3$$

60. $$\frac{f(x+h)-f(x)}{h} = \frac{[5(x+h)-1]-[5x-1]}{h} = \frac{[5x+5h-1]-[5x-1]}{h} = \frac{5x+5h-1-5x+1}{h} = \frac{5h}{h} = 5$$

61. $$\frac{f(x+h)-f(x)}{h} = \frac{\left[(x+h)^2+1\right]-[x^2+1]}{h} = \frac{[x^2+2xh+h^2+1]-[x^2+1]}{h} = \frac{x^2+2xh+h^2+1-x^2-1}{h} = \frac{2xh+h^2}{h} = \frac{h(2x+h)}{h} = 2x+h$$

62. $$\frac{f(x+h)-f(x)}{h} = \frac{\left[(x+h)^2-3\right]-[x^2-3]}{h} = \frac{[x^2+2xh+h^2-3]-[x^2-3]}{h} = \frac{x^2+2xh+h^2-3-x^2+3}{h} = \frac{2xh+h^2}{h} = \frac{h(2x+h)}{h} = 2x+h$$

63. $$\frac{f(x+h)-f(x)}{h} = \frac{\left[4(x+h)^2-6\right]-[4x^2-6]}{h} = \frac{[4x^2+8xh+4h^2-6]-[4x^2-6]}{h} = \frac{4x^2+8xh+4h^2-6-4x^2+6}{h} = \frac{8xh+4h^2}{h} = \frac{h(8x+4h)}{h} = 8x+4h$$

64. $$\frac{f(x+h)-f(x)}{h} = \frac{\left[5(x+h)^2+3\right]-\left[5x^2+3\right]}{h} = \frac{\left[5x^2+10xh+5h^2+3\right]-\left[5x^2+3\right]}{h}$$
$$= \frac{5x^2+10xh+5h^2+3-5x^2-3}{h}$$
$$= \frac{10xh+5h^2}{h} = \frac{h(10x+5h)}{h} = 10x+5h$$

65. $$\frac{f(x+h)-f(x)}{h} = \frac{\left[(x+h)^2+3(x+h)-7\right]-\left[x^2+3x-7\right]}{h}$$
$$= \frac{\left[x^2+2xh+h^2+3x+3h-7\right]-\left[x^2+3x-7\right]}{h}$$
$$= \frac{x^2+2xh+h^2+3x+3h-7-x^2-3x+7}{h}$$
$$= \frac{2xh+h^2+3h}{h} = \frac{h(2x+h+3)}{h} = 2x+h+3$$

66. $$\frac{f(x+h)-f(x)}{h} = \frac{\left[(x+h)^2-5(x+h)+1\right]-\left[x^2-5x+1\right]}{h}$$
$$= \frac{\left[x^2+2xh+h^2-5x-5h+1\right]-\left[x^2-5x+1\right]}{h}$$
$$= \frac{x^2+2xh+h^2-5x-5h+1-x^2+5x-1}{h}$$
$$= \frac{2xh+h^2-5h}{h} = \frac{h(2x+h-5)}{h} = 2x+h-5$$

67. $$\frac{f(x+h)-f(x)}{h} = \frac{\left[2(x+h)^2-4(x+h)+2\right]-\left[2x^2-4x+2\right]}{h}$$
$$= \frac{\left[2x^2+4xh+2h^2-4x-4h+2\right]-\left[2x^2-4x+2\right]}{h}$$
$$= \frac{2x^2+4xh+2h^2-4x-4h+2-2x^2+4x-2}{h}$$
$$= \frac{4xh+2h^2-4h}{h} = \frac{h(4x+2h-4)}{h} = 4x+2h-4$$

68. $$\frac{f(x+h)-f(x)}{h} = \frac{\left[3(x+h)^2+2(x+h)-3\right]-\left[3x^2+2x-3\right]}{h}$$
$$= \frac{\left[3x^2+6xh+3h^2+2x+2h-3\right]-\left[3x^2+2x-3\right]}{h}$$
$$= \frac{3x^2+6xh+3h^2+2x+2h-3-3x^2-2x+3}{h}$$
$$= \frac{6xh+3h^2+2h}{h} = \frac{h(6x+3h+2)}{h} = 6x+3h+2$$

69. $\dfrac{f(x+h)-f(x)}{h}=\dfrac{(x+h)^3-x^3}{h}=\dfrac{[x^3+3x^2h+3xh^2+h^3]-[x^3]}{h}$

$=\dfrac{3x^2h+3xh^2+h^3}{h}$

$=\dfrac{h(3x^2+3xh+h^2)}{h}=3x^2+3xh+h^2$

70. $\dfrac{f(x+h)-f(x)}{h}=\dfrac{\frac{1}{x+h}-\frac{1}{x}}{h}=\dfrac{\left(\frac{1}{x+h}-\frac{1}{x}\right)\cdot x(x+h)}{h\cdot x(x+h)}$

$=\dfrac{x-(x+h)}{xh(x+h)}=\dfrac{-h}{xh(x+h)}=-\dfrac{1}{x(x+h)}$

71. $f(x)=2x+3$

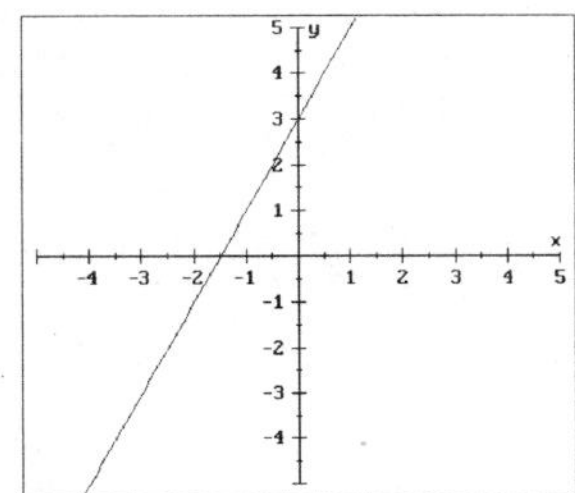

domain $=(-\infty,\infty)$
range $=(-\infty,\infty)$

72. $f(x)=3x+2$

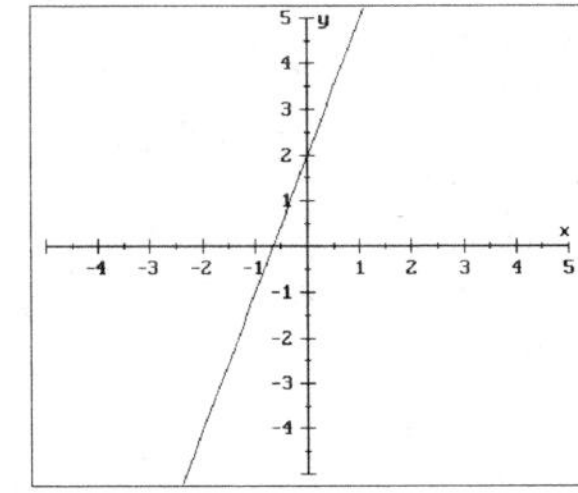

domain $=(-\infty,\infty)$
range $=(-\infty,\infty)$

73. $f(x)=-\dfrac{3}{4}x+4$

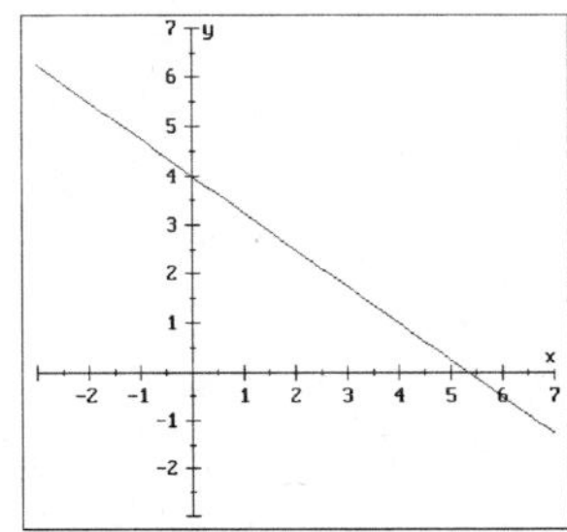

domain $=(-\infty,\infty)$
range $=(-\infty,\infty)$

74. $f(x)=\dfrac{1}{2}x-3$

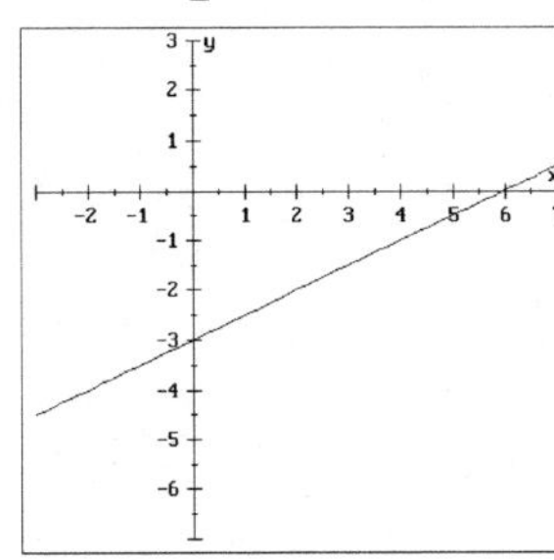

domain $=(-\infty,\infty)$
range $=(-\infty,\infty)$

75. $2x=3y-3$
$-3y=-2x-3$
$y=\dfrac{2}{3}x+1$

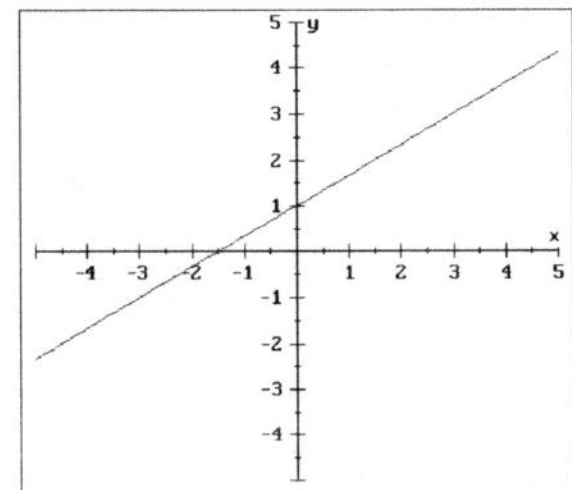

domain $=(-\infty,\infty)$
range $=(-\infty,\infty)$

76. $3x=2(y+1)$
$3x=2y+2$
$y=\dfrac{3}{2}x-1$

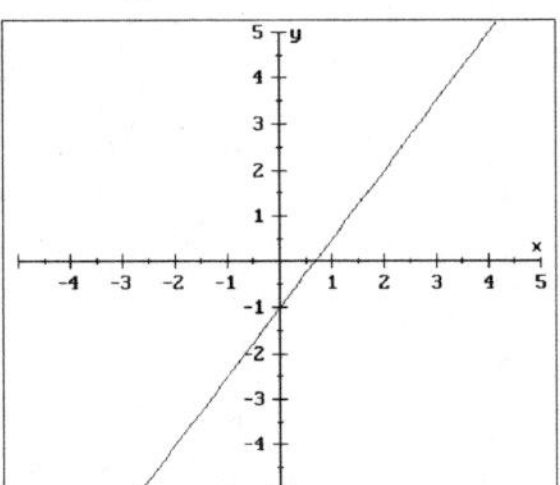

domain $=(-\infty,\infty)$
range $=(-\infty,\infty)$

77. $f(x) = x^2 - 4$

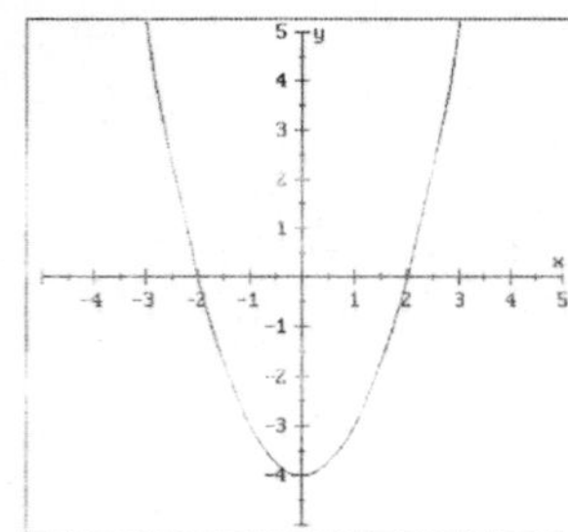

domain $= (-\infty, \infty)$
range $= [-4, \infty)$

78. $f(x) = -x^2 + 3$

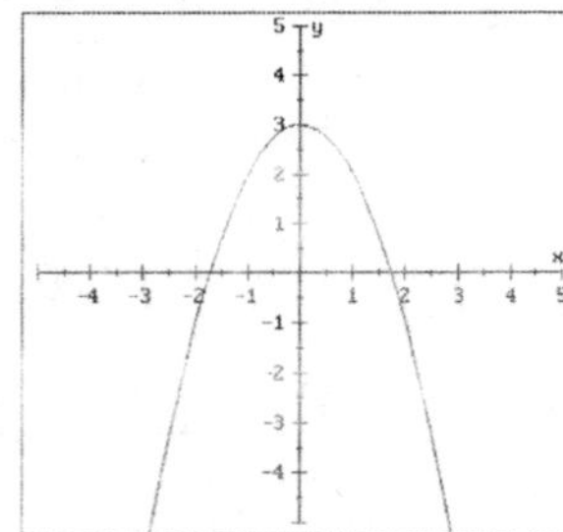

domain $= (-\infty, \infty)$
range $= (-\infty, 3]$

79. $f(x) = -x^3 + 2$

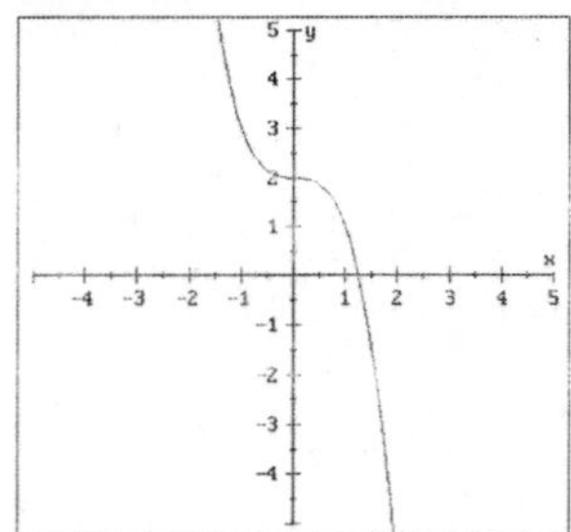

domain $= (-\infty, \infty)$
range $= (-\infty, \infty)$

80. $f(x) = -x^3 + 1$

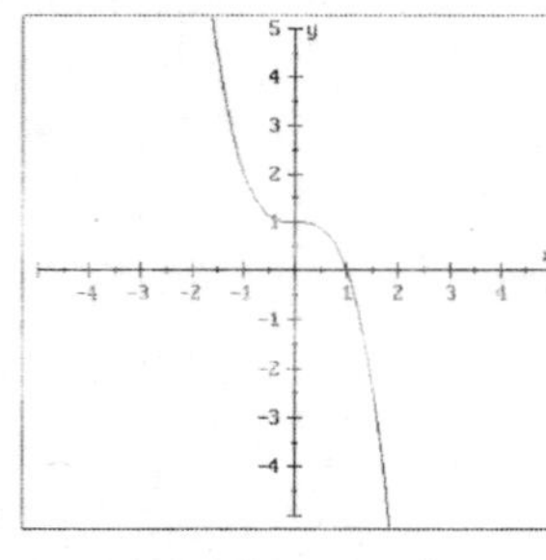

domain $= (-\infty, \infty)$
range $= (-\infty, \infty)$

81. $f(x) = -|x|$

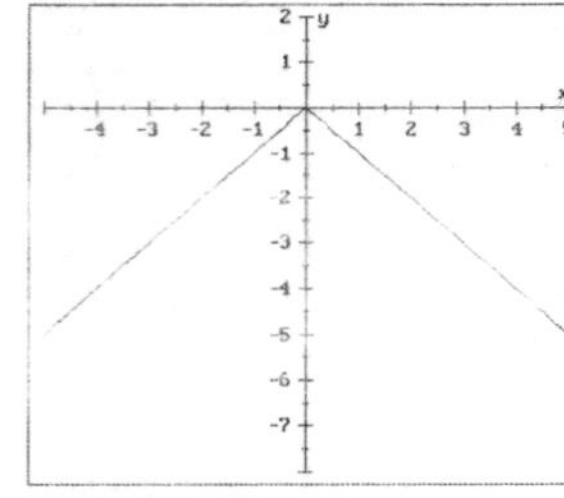

domain $= (-\infty, \infty)$
range $= (-\infty, 0]$

82. $f(x) = -|x| - 3$

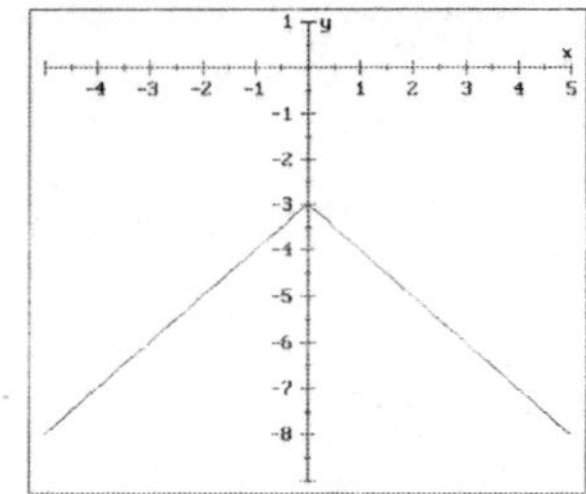

domain $= (-\infty, \infty)$
range $= (-\infty, -3]$

83. $f(x) = |x - 2|$

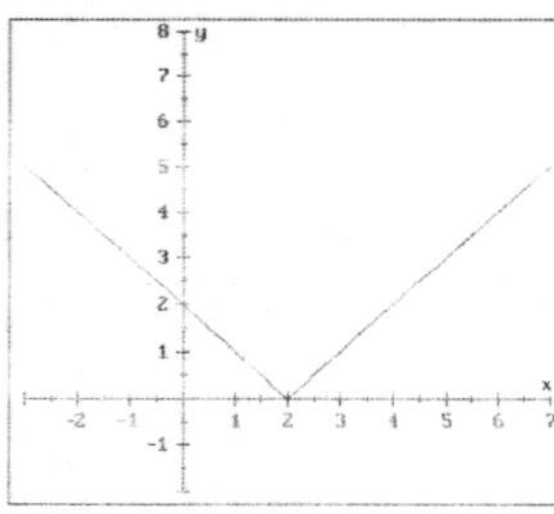

domain $= (-\infty, \infty)$
range $= [0, \infty)$

84. $f(x) = -|x - 2|$

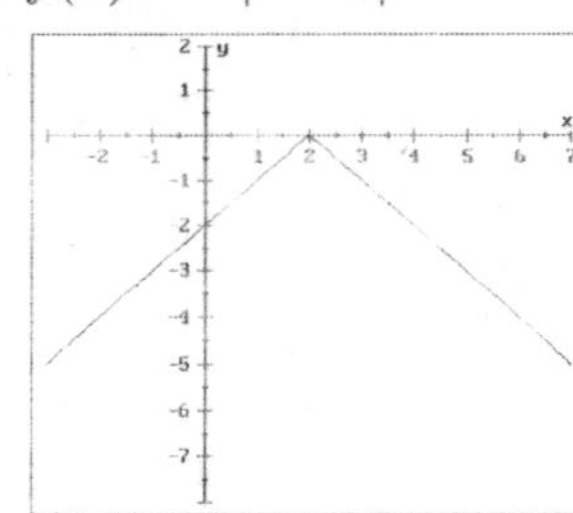

domain $= (-\infty, \infty)$
range $= (-\infty, 0]$

85. $f(x) = \left|\frac{1}{2}x + 3\right|$

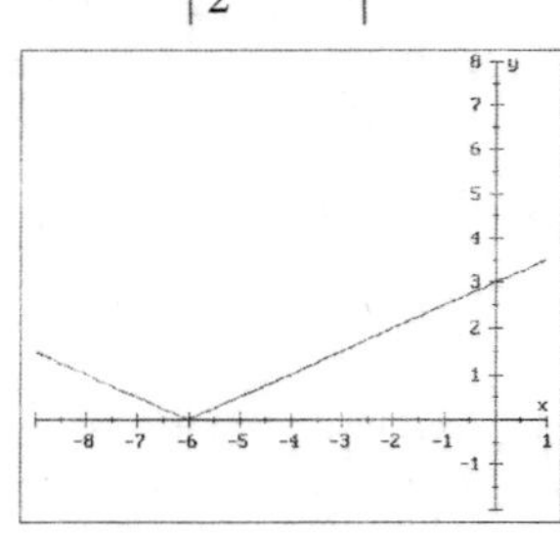

domain $= (-\infty, \infty)$
range $= [0, \infty)$

86. $f(x) = -\left|\frac{1}{2}x + 3\right|$

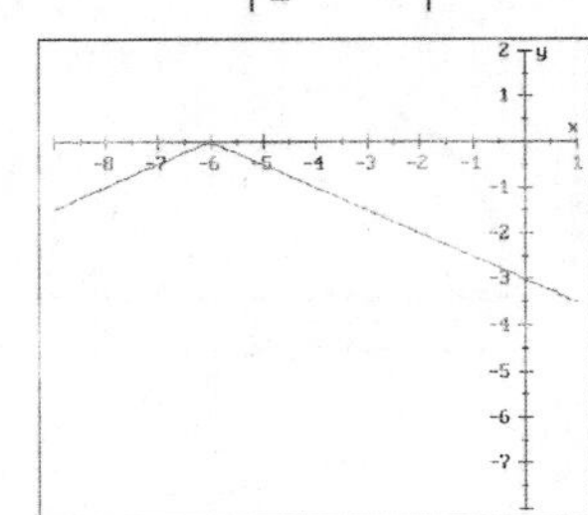

domain $= (-\infty, \infty)$;
range $= (-\infty, 0]$

87. $f(x) = -\sqrt{x+1}$

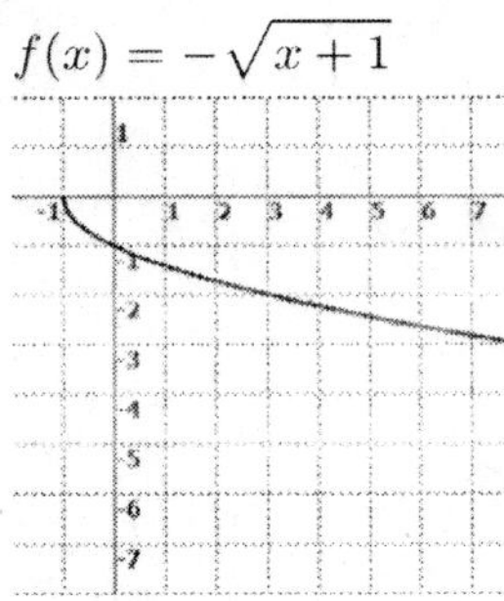

domain $= [-1, \infty)$
range $= [0, \infty)$

88. $f(x) = \sqrt{x} + 2$

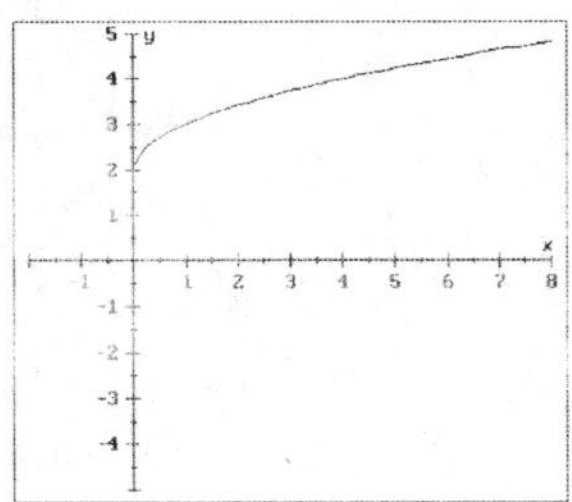

domain $= [0, \infty)$
range $= [2, \infty)$

89. $f(x) = \sqrt{2x - 4}$

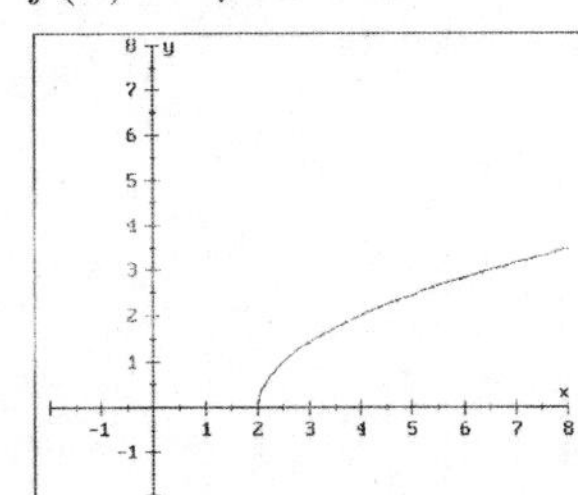

domain $= [2, \infty)$; range $= [0, \infty)$

90. 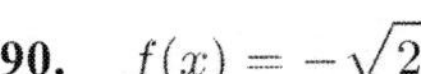 $f(x) = -\sqrt{2x - 4}$

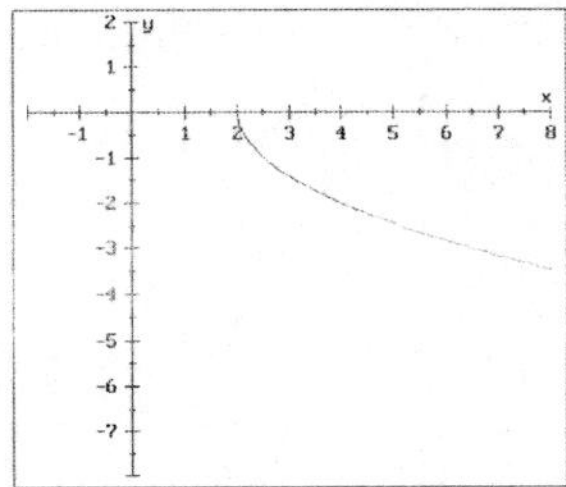

domain $= [2, \infty)$; range $= (-\infty, 0]$

91. $f(x) = \sqrt[3]{x} + 2$

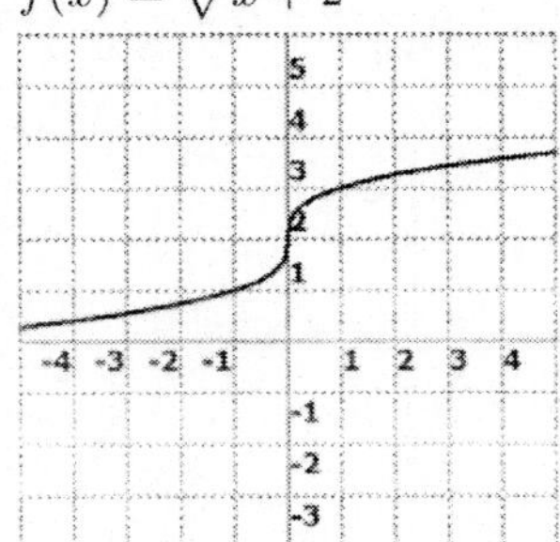

domain $= (-\infty, \infty)$; range $= (-\infty, \infty)$

92. $f(x) = -\sqrt[3]{x} + 1$

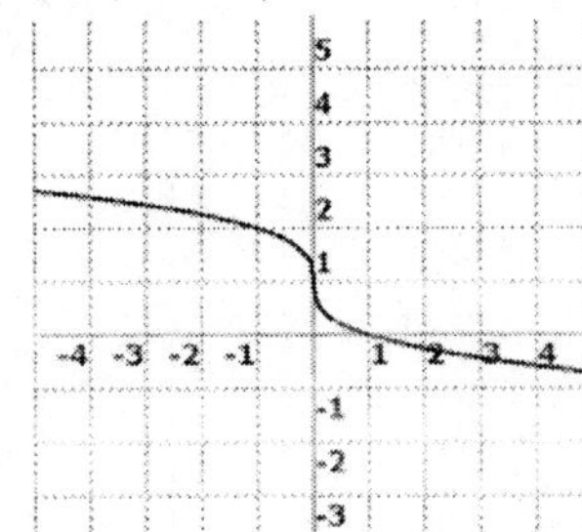

domain $= (-\infty, \infty)$; range $= (-\infty, \infty)$

93.

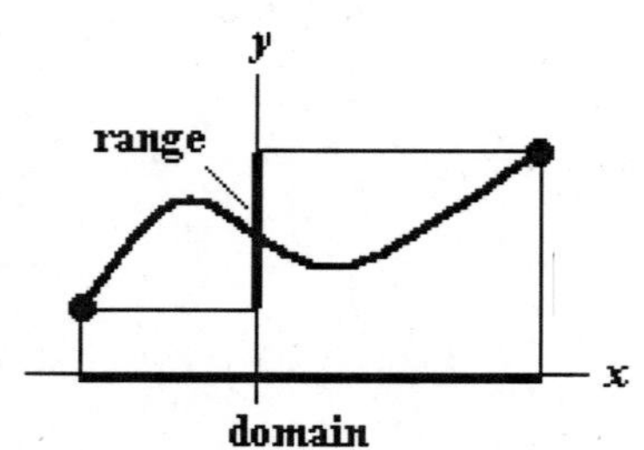

94.

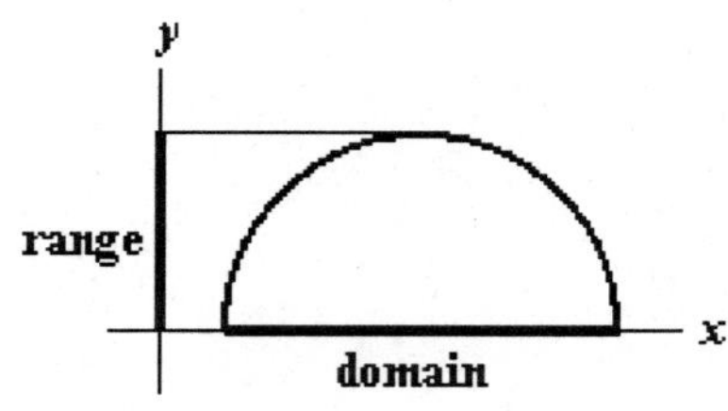

95. function

96. not a function

97. function

98. not a function

99. function

100. function

101. $f(x) = |3x + 2|$

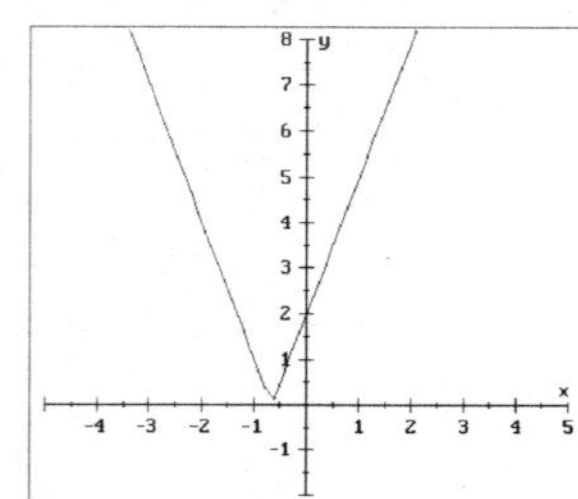

domain: $(-\infty, \infty)$; range: $[0, \infty)$

102. $f(x) = \sqrt{2x - 5}$

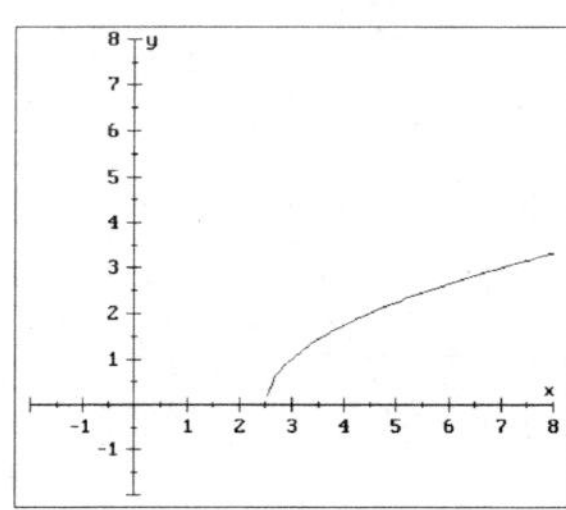

domain: $\left[\frac{5}{2}, \infty\right)$; range: $[0, \infty)$

103. $f(x) = \sqrt[3]{5x - 1}$

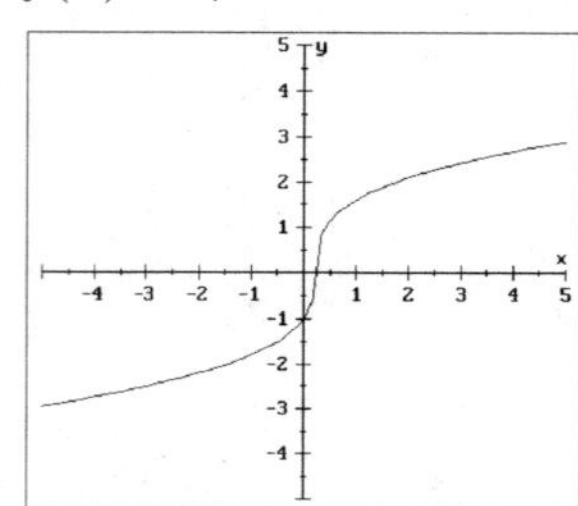

domain: $(-\infty, \infty)$; range: $(-\infty, \infty)$

104. $f(x) = -\sqrt[3]{3x + 2}$

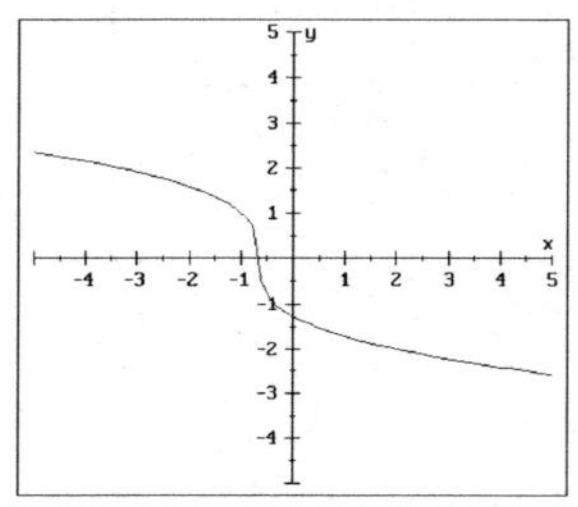

domain: $(-\infty, \infty)$; range: $(-\infty, \infty)$

105. **a.** $C(x) = 8x + 75$
b. $C(85) = 8(85) + 75 = \$755$

106. $b(h) = 45h + 60$

107. **a.** $C(t) = 0.07t + 9.99$
b. $C(20) = 0.07(20) + 9.99 = \$11.39$

108. **a.** $I(h) = 2.5h - 40$
b. $I(175) = 2.5(175) - 40 = \$397.50$

109. **a.** $C(f) = 95f + 14000$
b. $C(2600) = 95(2600) + 14{,}000 = \$261{,}000$

110. $F = mC + b$ $\quad$ $F = mC + 32$ $\quad$ $F(C) = \frac{9}{5}C + 32$

$32 = m(0) + b$ $\quad$ $-40 = m(-40) + 32$

$32 = b$ $\quad$ $-72 = -40m$

$\frac{9}{5} = m$

111. Let (x, c) be a point on the line. Then the points $(100, 17)$ and $(500, 57)$ are on the line.

$$m = \frac{\Delta c}{\Delta x} = \frac{57 - 17}{500 - 100} = \frac{40}{400} = 0.10$$

$$C = mx + b$$
$$17 = 0.10(100) + b$$
$$17 = 10 + b$$
$$7 = b \Rightarrow \boxed{C(x) = 0.10x + 7}$$

112. Let (n, c) be a point on the line. Then the points $(1000, 4.7)$ and $(9000, 14.3)$ are on the line.

$$m = \frac{\Delta c}{\Delta n} = \frac{14.30 - 4.70}{9000 - 1000} = \frac{9.60}{8000} = 0.0012$$

$$C = mx + b$$
$$4.7 = 0.0012(1000) + b$$
$$4.7 = 1.2 + b$$
$$3.5 = b \Rightarrow \boxed{C(n) = 0.0012n + 3.5}$$

113. Let (t, n) be a point on the line. Then the points $(0, 6400)$ and $(4, 13168)$ are on the line.

$$m = \frac{\Delta n}{\Delta t} = \frac{13168 - 6400}{4 - 0} = \frac{6768}{4} = 1692$$

$$n = mt + b$$
$$6400 = 1692(0) + b$$
$$6400 = b \Rightarrow \boxed{n(t) = 1692t + 6400}$$

114. Let (t, v) be a point on the line. Then the points $(0, 2)$ and $(2, -66)$ are on the line.

$$m = \frac{\Delta v}{\Delta t} = \frac{-66 - 2}{2 - 0} = \frac{-68}{2} = -34$$

$$v = mt + b$$
$$2 = -34(0) + b$$
$$2 = b \Rightarrow \boxed{v(t) = -34t + 2}$$

115. Let (D, E) be a point on the line. Then the points $(50, 69.555)$ and $(125, 173.8875)$ are on the line.

$$m = \frac{\Delta E}{\Delta D} = \frac{173.8875 - 69.555}{125 - 50} = \frac{104.3325}{75} = 1.3911$$

$$E = mD + b$$
$$69.555 = 1.3911(50) + b$$
$$69.555 = 69.555 + b \Rightarrow b = 0 \Rightarrow \boxed{E(D) = 1.3911D}$$

116. Let (D, P) be a point on the line. Then the points $(50, 600.11)$ and $(125, 1500.275)$ are on the line.

$$m = \frac{\Delta P}{\Delta D} = \frac{1500.275 - 600.11}{125 - 50} = \frac{900.165}{75} = 12.0022$$

$$P = mD + b$$

$$600.11 = 12.0022(50) + b$$

$$600.11 = 600.11 + b \Rightarrow b = 0 \Rightarrow \boxed{P(D) = 12.0022D}$$

117. $f(x) = 3x + 2$

$0 = 3x + 2$

$-2 = 3x$

$-\frac{2}{3} = x$

118. $f(x) = -2x - 5$

$0 = -2x - 5$

$2x = -5$

$x = -\frac{5}{2}$

119-122. Answers may vary.

123. natural: $1, 7, 8$

124. rational: $-3, -1, 0, 0.5, \frac{3}{4}, 1, 7, 8$

125. prime: 7

126. even: $0, 8$

127. $(-4, 7]$

128. $(-\infty, -3) \cup [5, \infty)$

129. $(-3, 5) \cup [6, \infty)$: 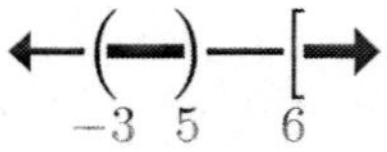

130. $(-\infty, 0) \cup (0, \infty)$: 

Exercises 3.2 (page 305)

1. $f(x) = ax^2 + bx + c$

2. $f(x) = a(x - h)^2 + k$

3. $(3, 5)$

4. axis of symmetry

5. upward

6. downward

7. $-\frac{b}{2a}$

8. $c - \frac{b^2}{4a}$

9. $f(x) = \frac{1}{2}x^2 + 3$
$a = \frac{1}{2} \Rightarrow a > 0$
up, minimum

10. $f(x) = 2x^2 - 3x$
$a = 2 \Rightarrow a > 0$
up, minimum

11. $f(x) = -3(x + 1)^2 + 2$
$a = -3 \Rightarrow a < 0$
down, maximum

12. $f(x) = -5(x - 1)^2 - 1$
$a = -5 \Rightarrow a < 0$
down, maximum

13. $f(x) = -2x^2 + 5x - 1$
$a = -2 \Rightarrow a < 0$
down, maximum

14. $f(x) = 2x^2 - 3x + 1$
$a = 2 \Rightarrow a > 0$
up, minimum

15. $y = x^2 - 1 = (x - 0)^2 - 1$
Vertex: $(0, -1)$

16. $y = -x^2 + 2 = -(x - 0)^2 + 2$
Vertex: $(0, 2)$

17. $f(x) = (x - 3)^2 + 5$
Vertex: $(3, 5)$

18. $f(x) = -2(x - 3)^2 + 4$
Vertex: $(3, 4)$

19. $f(x) = -2(x + 6)^2 - 4$
Vertex: $(-6, -4)$

20. $f(x) = \frac{1}{3}(x + 1)^2 - 5$
Vertex: $(-1, -5)$

21. $f(x) = \frac{2}{3}(x - 3)^2$
Vertex: $(3, 0)$

22. $f(x) = 7(x + 2)^2 + 8$
Vertex: $(-2, 8)$

23. $f(x) = x^2 - 4x + 4$; $a = 1, b = -4, c = 4$

$$x = -\frac{b}{2a} = -\frac{-4}{2(1)} = 2$$

$$y = x^2 - 4x + 4 = 2^2 - 4(2) + 4 = 0$$

Vertex: $(2, 0)$

24. $y = x^2 - 10x + 25$; $a = 1, b = -10, c = 25$

$$x = -\frac{b}{2a} = -\frac{-10}{2(1)} = 5$$

$$y = x^2 - 10x + 25 = 5^2 - 10(5) + 25 = 0$$

Vertex: $(5, 0)$

25. $y = x^2 + 6x - 3$; $a = 1, b = 6, c = -3$

$$x = -\frac{b}{2a} = -\frac{6}{2(1)} = -3$$

$$y = x^2 + 6x - 3 = (-3)^2 + 6(-3) - 3 = -12$$

Vertex: $(-3, -12)$

26. $y = -x^2 + 9x - 2$; $a = -1, b = 9, c = -2$

$$x = -\frac{b}{2a} = -\frac{9}{2(-1)} = \frac{9}{2}$$

$$y = -x^2 + 9x - 2 = -\left(\frac{9}{2}\right)^2 + 9\left(\frac{9}{2}\right) - 2 = \frac{73}{4}$$

Vertex: $\left(\frac{9}{2}, \frac{73}{4}\right)$

27. $y = -2x^2 + 12x - 17$;
$a = -2, b = 12, c = -17$

$$x = -\frac{b}{2a} = -\frac{12}{2(-2)} = 3$$

$$y = -2x^2 + 12x - 17 = -2(3)^2 + 12(3) - 17 = 1$$

Vertex: $(3, 1)$

28. $y = 2x^2 + 16x + 33$;
$a = 2, b = 16, c = 33$

$$x = -\frac{b}{2a} = -\frac{16}{2(2)} = -4$$

$$y = 2x^2 + 16x + 33 = 2(-4)^2 + 16(-4) + 33 = 1$$

Vertex: $(-4, 1)$

29. $y = 3x^2 - 4x + 5$;
$a = 3, b = -4, c = 5$

$$x = -\frac{b}{2a} = -\frac{-4}{2(3)} = \frac{4}{6} = \frac{2}{3}$$

$$y = 3x^2 - 4x + 5 = 3\left(\frac{2}{3}\right)^2 - 4\left(\frac{2}{3}\right) + 5 = \frac{11}{3}$$

Vertex: $\left(\frac{2}{3}, \frac{11}{3}\right)$

30. $y = -4x^2 + 3x + 4$;
$a = -4, b = 3, c = 4$

$$x = -\frac{b}{2a} = -\frac{3}{2(-4)} = \frac{3}{8}$$

$$y = -4x^2 + 3x + 4 = -4\left(\frac{3}{8}\right)^2 + 3\left(\frac{3}{8}\right) + 4 = \frac{73}{16}$$

Vertex: $\left(\frac{3}{8}, \frac{73}{16}\right)$

31. $y = \frac{1}{2}x^2 + 4x - 3;$

$a = \frac{1}{2}, b = 4, c = -3$

$x = -\frac{b}{2a} = -\frac{4}{2\left(\frac{1}{2}\right)} = -4$

$y = \frac{1}{2}x^2 + 4x - 3$

$= \frac{1}{2}(-4)^2 + 4(-4) - 3 = -11$

Vertex: $(-4, -11)$

32. $y = -\frac{2}{3}x^2 + 3x - 5;$

$a = -\frac{2}{3}, b = 3, c = -5$

$x = -\frac{b}{2a} = -\frac{3}{2\left(-\frac{2}{3}\right)} = \frac{3}{\frac{4}{3}} = \frac{9}{4}$

$y = -\frac{2}{3}x^2 + 3x - 5$

$= -\frac{2}{3}\left(\frac{9}{4}\right)^2 + 3\left(\frac{9}{4}\right) - 5 = -\frac{13}{8}$

Vertex: $\left(\frac{9}{4}, -\frac{13}{8}\right)$

33. $f(x) = x^2 - 4 = (x - 0)^2 - 4$

$a = 1 \Rightarrow$ up, vertex: $(0, -4)$

$0 = x^2 - 4$

$0 = (x + 2)(x - 2)$

$x = -2, x = 2 \Rightarrow (-2, 0), (2, 0)$

$f(0) = -4 \Rightarrow (0, -4)$

$f(1) = -3 \Rightarrow (1, -3)$

$(-1, -3)$ on graph by symmetry

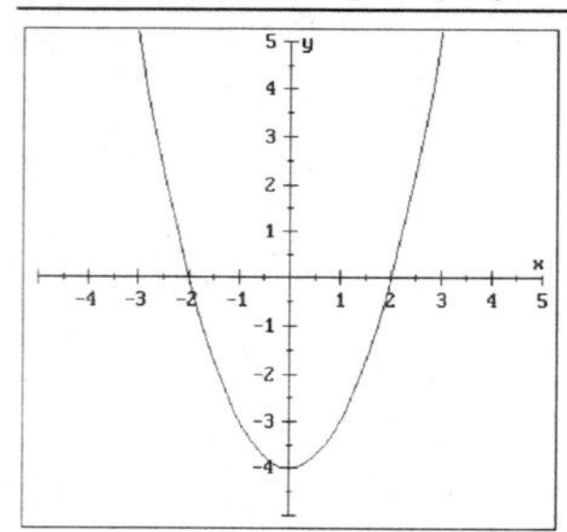

34. $f(x) = x^2 + 1 = (x - 0)^2 + 1$

$a = 1 \Rightarrow$ up, vertex: $(0, 1)$

$0 = x^2 + 1 \Rightarrow$ impossible

no x-intercepts

$f(0) = 1 \Rightarrow (0, 1)$

$f(1) = 2 \Rightarrow (1, 2)$

$(-1, 2)$ on graph by symmetry

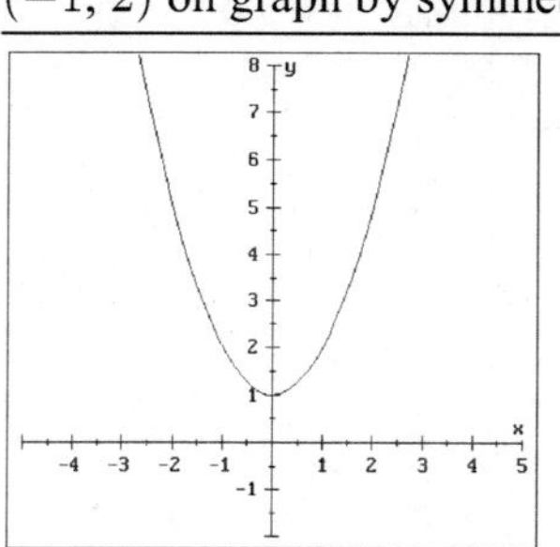

35. $f(x) = -3x^2 + 6 = -3(x - 0)^2 + 6$

$a = -3 \Rightarrow$ down, vertex: $(0, 6)$

$0 = -3x^2 + 6$

$x^2 = 2$

$x = \pm\sqrt{2} \Rightarrow \left(-\sqrt{2}, 0\right), \left(\sqrt{2}, 0\right)$

$f(0) = 6 \Rightarrow (0, 6)$

$f(1) = 3 \Rightarrow (1, 3)$

$(-1, 3)$ on graph by symmetry

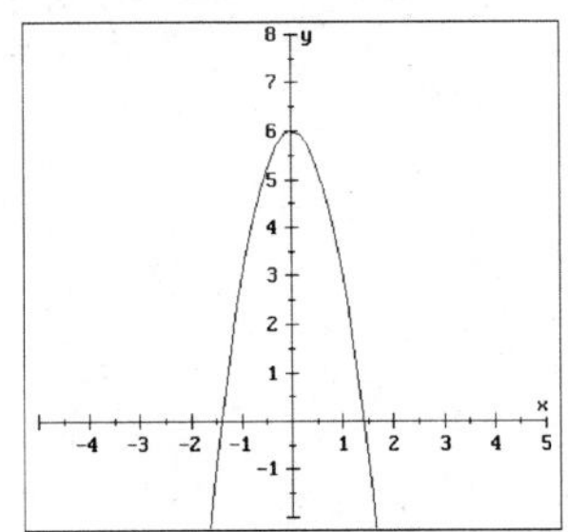

36. $f(x) = -4x^2 + 4 = -4(x - 0)^2 + 4$

$a = -4 \Rightarrow$ down, vertex: $(0, 4)$

$0 = -4x^2 + 4$

$x^2 = 1$

$x = \pm 1 \Rightarrow (-1, 0), (1, 0)$

$f(0) = 4 \Rightarrow (0, 4)$

$f(2) = -12 \Rightarrow (2, -12)$

$(-2, -12)$ on graph by symmetry

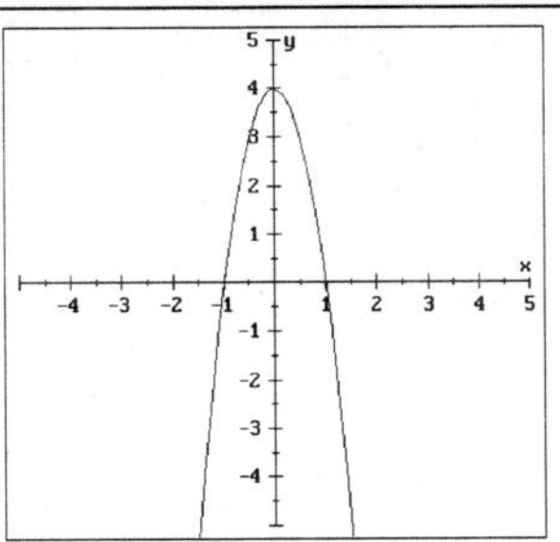

37. $f(x) = -\frac{1}{2}x^2 + 8 = -\frac{1}{2}(x - 0)^2 + 8$

$a = -\frac{1}{2} \Rightarrow$ down, vertex: $(0, 8)$

$0 = -\frac{1}{2}x^2 + 8$

$x^2 = 16$

$x = \pm 4 \Rightarrow (-4, 0), (4, 0)$

$f(0) = 8 \Rightarrow (0, 8)$

$f(2) = 6 \Rightarrow (2, 6)$

$(-2, 6)$ on graph by symmetry

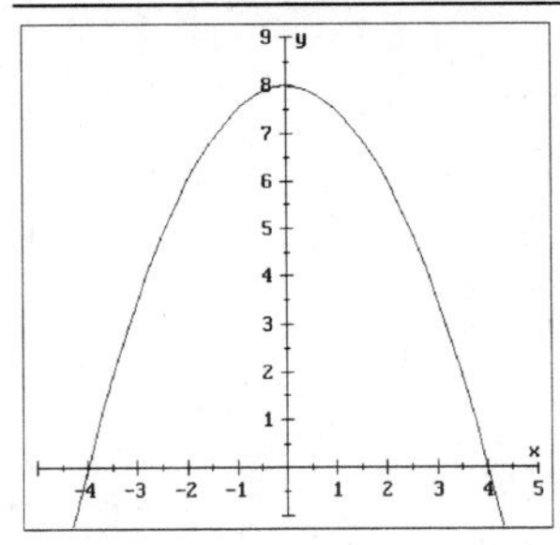

38. $f(x) = \frac{1}{2}x^2 - 2 = \frac{1}{2}(x - 0)^2 - 2$

$a = \frac{1}{2} \Rightarrow$ up, vertex: $(0, -2)$

$0 = \frac{1}{2}x^2 - 2$

$4 = x^2$

$x = \pm 2 \Rightarrow (-2, 0), (2, 0)$

$f(0) = -2 \Rightarrow (0, -2)$

$f(4) = 6 \Rightarrow (4, 6)$

$(-4, 6)$ on graph by symmetry

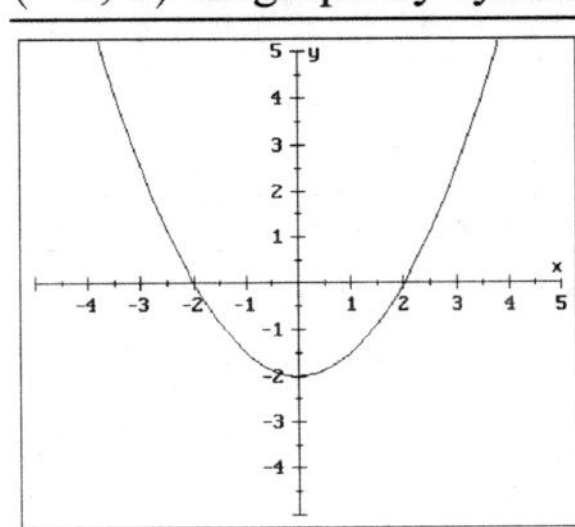

39. $f(x) = (x-3)^2 - 1$

$a = 1 \Rightarrow$ up, vertex: $(3, -1)$

$$0 = (x-3)^2 - 1$$
$$1 = (x-3)^2$$
$$\pm 1 = x - 3$$
$$3 \pm 1 = x$$

$x = 2, x = 4 \Rightarrow (2, 0), (4, 0)$

$f(0) = 8 \Rightarrow (0, 8)$

$(6, 8)$ on graph by symmetry

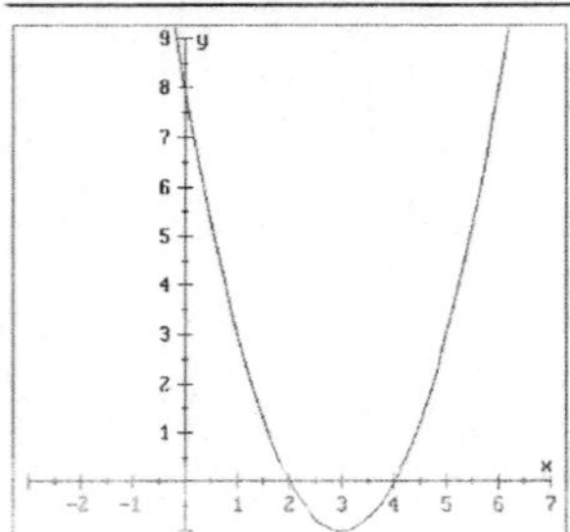

40. $f(x) = (x+3)^2 - 1$

$a = 1 \Rightarrow$ up, vertex: $(-3, -1)$

$$0 = (x+3)^2 - 1$$
$$1 = (x+3)^2$$
$$\pm 1 = x + 3$$
$$-3 \pm 1 = x$$

$x = -4, x = -2 \Rightarrow (-4, 0), (-2, 0)$

$f(0) = 8 \Rightarrow (0, 8)$

$(-6, 8)$ on graph by symmetry

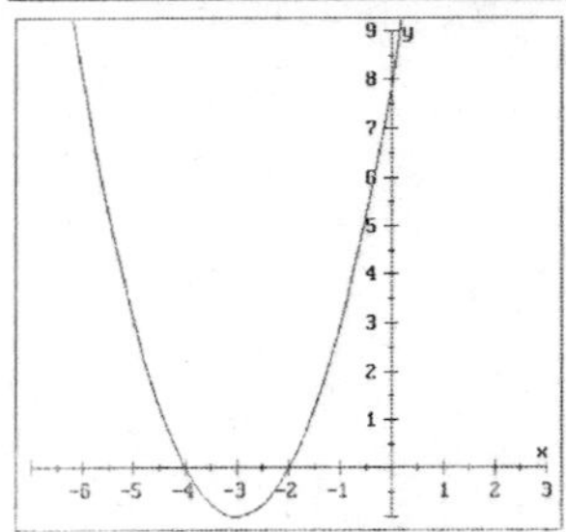

41. $f(x) = 2(x+1)^2 - 2$

$a = 2 \Rightarrow$ up, vertex: $(-1, -2)$

$$0 = 2(x+1)^2 - 2$$
$$2 = 2(x+1)^2$$
$$1 = (x+1)^2$$
$$\pm 1 = x + 1$$
$$-1 \pm 1 = x$$

$x = -2, x = 0 \Rightarrow (-2, 0), (0, 0)$

$f(0) = 0 \Rightarrow (0, 0)$

$f(1) = 6 \Rightarrow (1, 6)$

$(-3, 6)$ on graph by symmetry

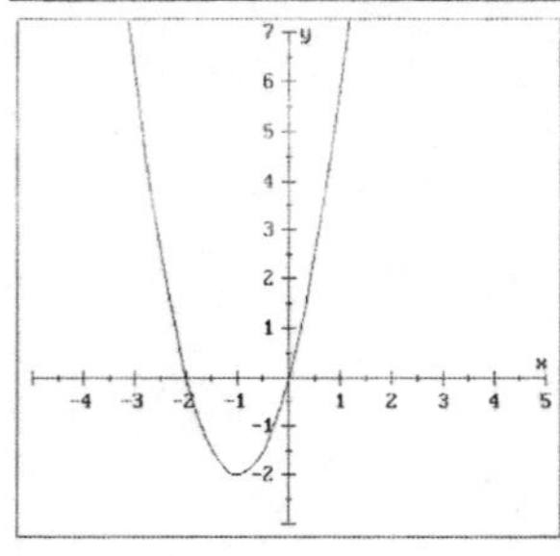

42. $f(x) = -\frac{3}{4}(x-2)^2$

$a = -\frac{3}{4} \Rightarrow$ down, vertex: $(2, 0)$

$$0 = -\tfrac{3}{4}(x-2)^2$$
$$0 = (x-2)^2$$
$$\pm 0 = x - 2$$

$x = 2 \Rightarrow (2, 0)$

$f(0) = -3 \Rightarrow (0, -3)$

$(4, -3)$ on graph by symmetry

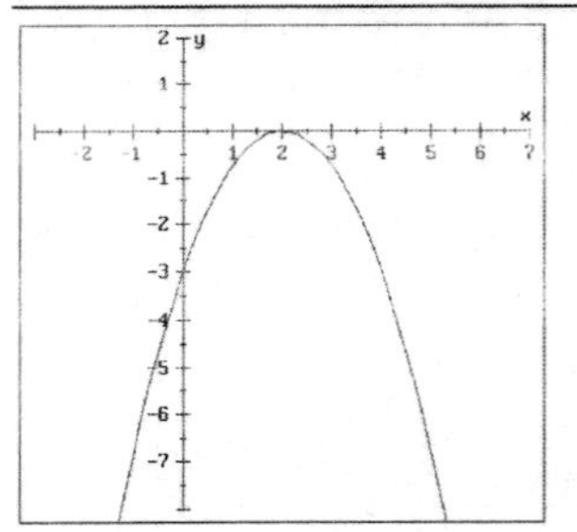

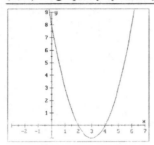

43. $f(x) = -(x+4)^2 + 1$

$a = -1 \Rightarrow$ down, vertex: $(-4, 1)$

$$0 = -(x+4)^2 + 1$$
$$(x+4)^2 = 1$$
$$x + 4 = \pm 1$$
$$x = -4 \pm 1$$

$x = -5, x = -3 \Rightarrow (-5, 0), (-3, 0)$

$f(0) = -15 \Rightarrow (0, -15)$

$(-8, -15)$ on graph by symmetry

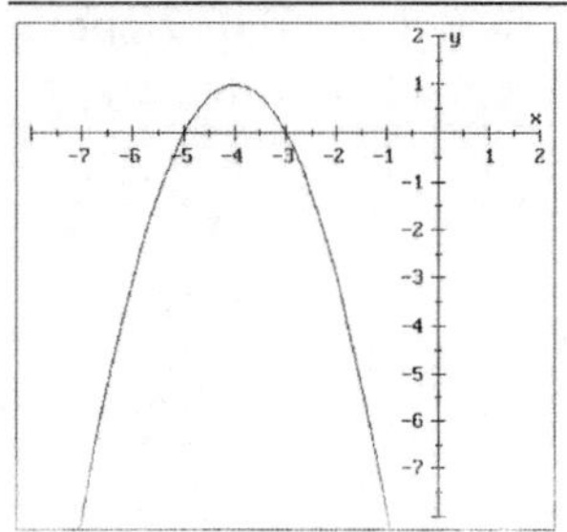

44. $f(x) = -3(x-4)^2 + 3$

$a = -3 \Rightarrow$ down, vertex: $(4, 3)$

$$0 = -3(x-4)^2 + 3$$
$$3(x-4)^2 = 3$$
$$(x-4)^2 = 1$$
$$x - 4 = \pm 1$$
$$x = 4 \pm 1$$

$x = 3, x = 5 \Rightarrow (3, 0), (5, 0)$

$f(0) = -45 \Rightarrow (0, -45)$

$(8, -45)$ on graph by symmetry

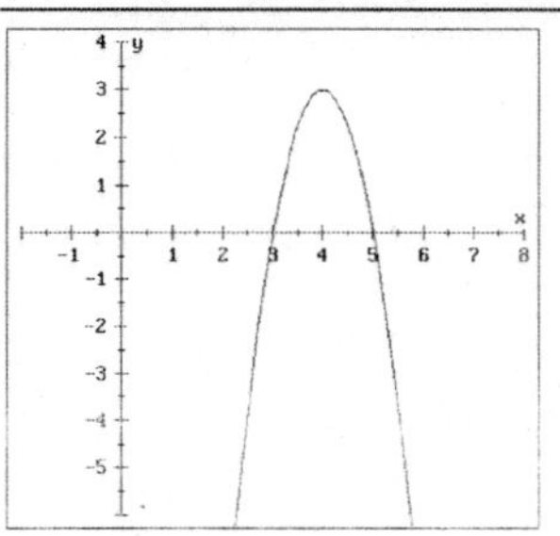

45. $f(x) = -3(x-2)^2 + 6$

$a = -3 \Rightarrow$ down, vertex: $(2, 6)$

$$0 = -3(x-2)^2 + 6$$
$$3(x-2)^2 = 6$$
$$(x-2)^2 = 2$$
$$x - 2 = \pm\sqrt{2}$$
$$x = 2 \pm \sqrt{2}$$

$\left(2-\sqrt{2}, 0\right), \left(2+\sqrt{2}, 0\right)$

$f(0) = -6 \Rightarrow (0, -6)$

$(4, -6)$ on graph by symmetry

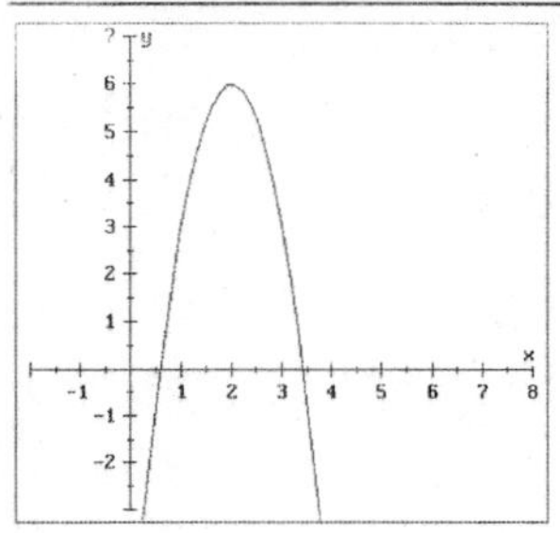

46. $f(x) = 2(x-3)^2 - 4$

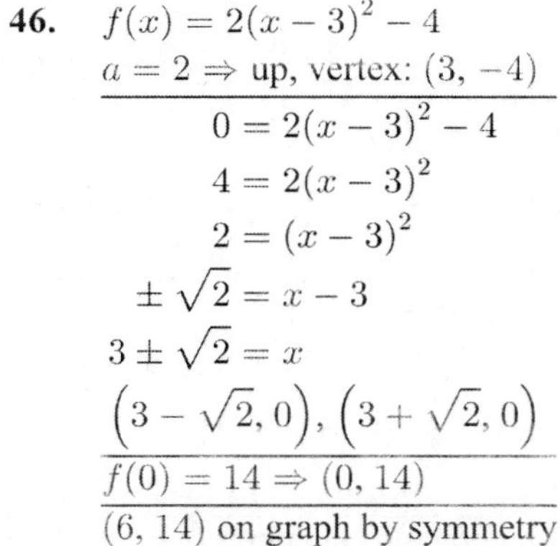

$a = 2 \Rightarrow$ up, vertex: $(3, -4)$

$$0 = 2(x-3)^2 - 4$$
$$4 = 2(x-3)^2$$
$$2 = (x-3)^2$$
$$\pm\sqrt{2} = x - 3$$
$$3 \pm \sqrt{2} = x$$

$\left(3-\sqrt{2}, 0\right), \left(3+\sqrt{2}, 0\right)$

$f(0) = 14 \Rightarrow (0, 14)$

$(6, 14)$ on graph by symmetry

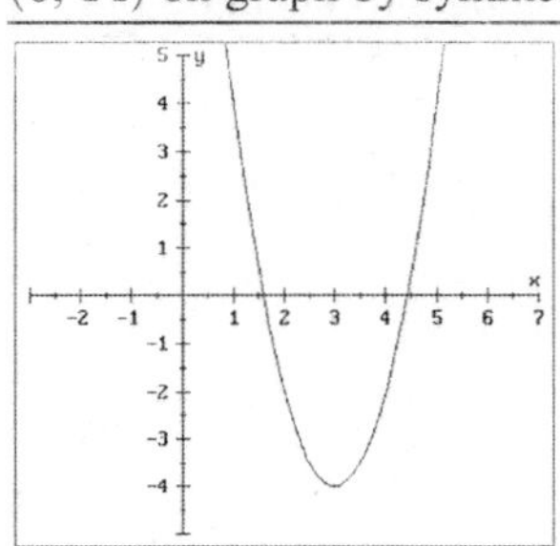

47. $f(x) = x^2 + 2x;\ a = 1, b = 2, c = 0$

$x = -\frac{b}{2a} = -\frac{2}{2(1)} = -1$

$y = x^2 + 2x = (-1)^2 + 2(-1) = -1$

vertex: $(-1, -1)$, $a = 1 \Rightarrow$ up

$0 = x^2 + 2x$

$0 = x(x + 2)$

$x = 0$ or $x = -2 \Rightarrow (0, 0), (-2, 0)$

$f(0) = 0 \Rightarrow (0, 0)$

$f(1) = 3 \Rightarrow (1, 3)$ on graph

$(-3, 3)$ on graph by symmetry

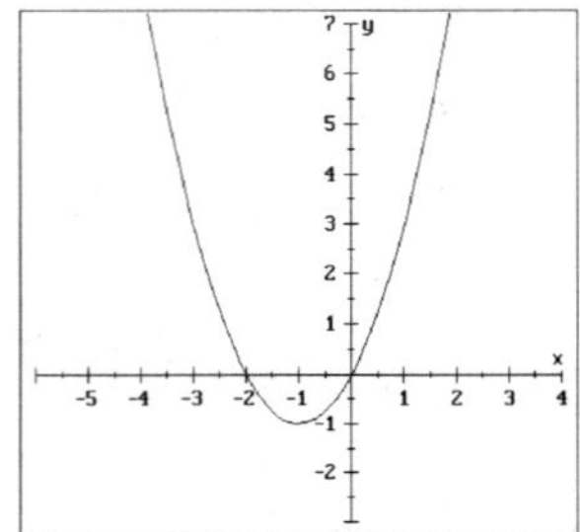

48. $f(x) = x^2 - 6x;\ a = 1, b = -6, c = 0$

$x = -\frac{b}{2a} = -\frac{-6}{2(1)} = 3$

$y = x^2 - 6x = (3)^2 - 6(3) = -9$

vertex: $(3, -9)$, $a = 1 \Rightarrow$ up

$0 = x^2 - 6x$

$0 = x(x - 6)$

$x = 0$ or $x = 6 \Rightarrow (0, 0), (6, 0)$

$f(0) = 0 \Rightarrow (0, 0)$

$f(1) = -5 \Rightarrow (1, -5)$ on graph

$(5, -5)$ on graph by symmetry

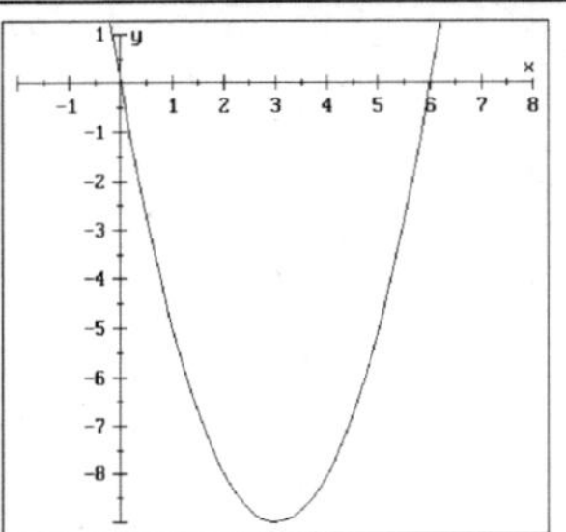

49. $f(x) = x^2 - 4x + 1;\ a = 1, b = -4, c = 1$

$x = -\frac{b}{2a} = -\frac{-4}{2(1)} = 2$

$y = x^2 - 4x + 1 = 2^2 - 4(2) + 1 = -3$

vertex: $(2, -3)$, $a = 1 \Rightarrow$ up

$0 = x^2 - 4x + 1$

$x = 2 \pm \sqrt{3}$ by quadratic formula

$\left(2 - \sqrt{3}, 0\right), \left(2 + \sqrt{3}, 0\right)$

$f(0) = 0 \Rightarrow (0, 1)$

$(4, 1)$ on graph by symmetry

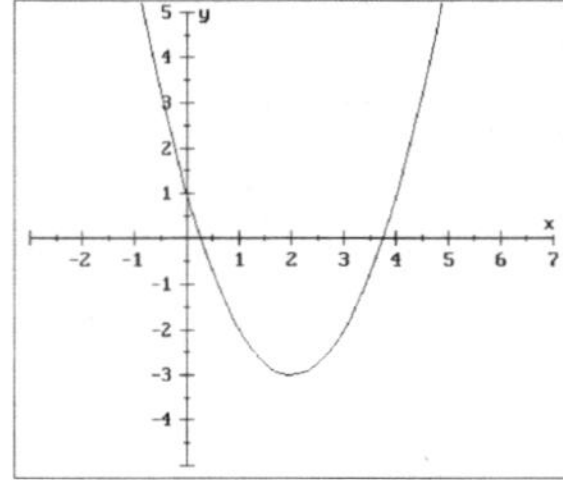

50. $f(x) = x^2 - 6x - 7;\ a = 1, b = -6, c = -7$

$x = -\frac{b}{2a} = -\frac{-6}{2(1)} = 3$

$y = x^2 - 6x - 7 = 3^2 - 6(3) - 7 = -16$

vertex: $(3, -16)$, $a = 1 \Rightarrow$ up

$0 = x^2 - 6x - 7$

$0 = (x + 1)(x - 7)$

$x = -1$ or $x = 7 \Rightarrow (-1, 0), (7, 0)$

$f(0) = -7 \Rightarrow (0, -7)$

$(6, -7)$ on graph by symmetry

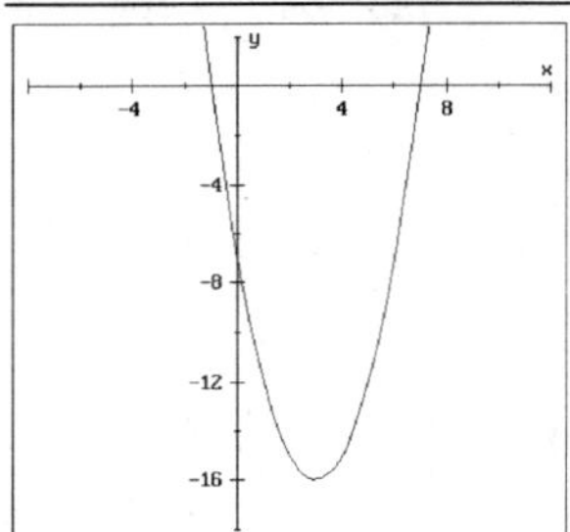

51. $f(x) = 2x^2 - 12x + 10$

$a = 2,\ b = -12,\ c = 10$

$x = -\frac{b}{2a} = -\frac{-12}{2(2)} = 3$

$y = 2(3)^2 - 12(3) + 10 = -8$

vertex: $(3, -8)$, $a = 2 \Rightarrow$ up

$0 = 2x^2 - 12x + 10$

$0 = 2(x^2 - 6x + 5)$

$0 = 2(x - 1)(x - 5)$

$x = 1$ or $x = 5 \Rightarrow (1, 0), (5, 0)$

$f(0) = 10 \Rightarrow (0, 10)$

$(6, 10)$ on graph by symmetry

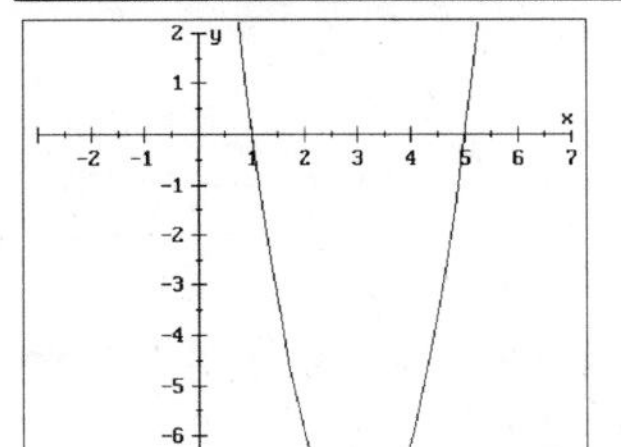

52. $f(x) = -x^2 - 4x + 1$

$a = -1,\ b = -4,\ c = 1$

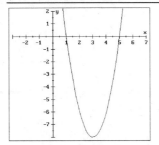

$x = -\frac{b}{2a} = -\frac{-4}{2(-1)} = -2$

$y = -(-2)^2 - 4(-2) + 1 = 5$

vertex: $(-2, 5)$, $a = -1 \Rightarrow$ down

$0 = -x^2 - 4x + 1$

$x = -2 \pm \sqrt{5}$ by quadratic formula

$\left(-2 - \sqrt{5}, 0\right), \left(-2 + \sqrt{5}, 0\right)$

$f(0) = 0 \Rightarrow (0, 1)$

$(-4, 1)$ on graph by symmetry

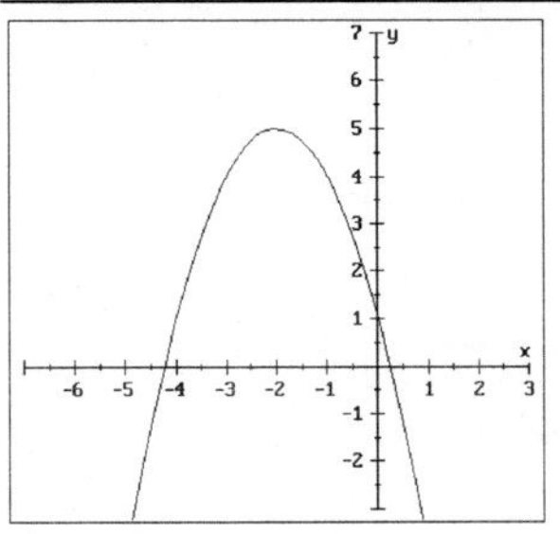

53. $f(x) = -3x^2 - 6x - 9$

$a = -3,\ b = -6,\ c = -9$

$x = -\frac{b}{2a} = -\frac{-6}{2(-3)} = -1$

$y = -3(-1)^2 - 6(-1) - 9 = -6$

vertex: $(-1, -6)$, $a = -3 \Rightarrow$ down

$0 = -3x^2 - 6x - 9$

$0 = -3(x^2 + 2x + 3)$

impossible $\Rightarrow$ no x-intercepts

$f(0) = -9 \Rightarrow (0, -9)$

$(-2, -9)$ on graph by symmetry

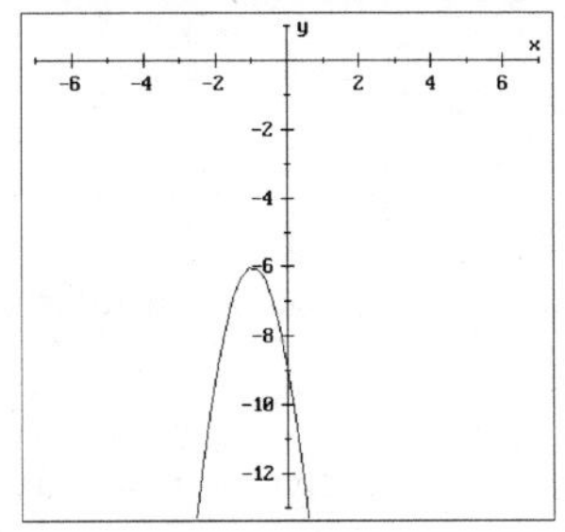

54. $f(x) = -3x^2 - 3x + 18$

$a = -3,\ b = -3,\ c = 18$

$x = -\frac{b}{2a} = -\frac{-3}{2(-3)} = -\frac{1}{2}$

$y = -3\left(-\frac{1}{2}\right)^2 - 3\left(-\frac{1}{2}\right) + 18 = 18\frac{3}{4}$

vertex: $\left(-\frac{1}{2}, 18\frac{3}{4}\right)$, $a = -3 \Rightarrow$ down

$0 = -3x^2 - 3x + 18$

$0 = -3(x^2 + x - 6)$

$0 = -3(x + 3)(x - 2)$

$x = -3$ or $x = 2 \Rightarrow (-3, 0)$ or $(2, 0)$

$f(0) = 18 \Rightarrow (0, 18)$

$(-1, 18)$ on graph by symmetry

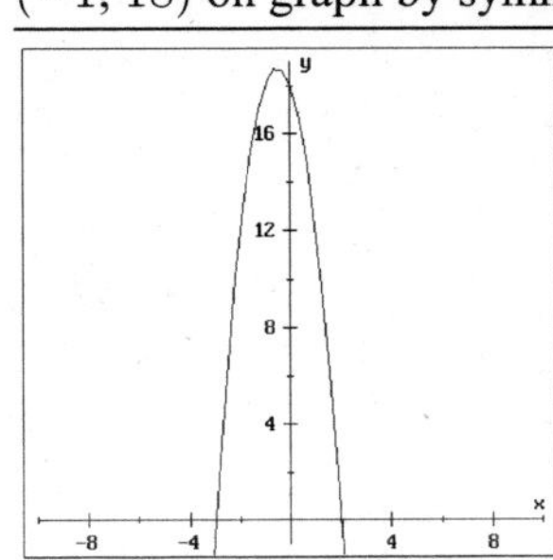

55. Let x = the width of the region.

Then $\dfrac{300-2x}{2} = 150 - x$ = the length.

Area = width · length

$$y = x(150 - x)$$
$$y = -x^2 + 150x$$

$a = -1, b = 150, c = 0$

$$x = -\frac{b}{2a} = -\frac{150}{2(-1)} = 75$$

$150 - x = 150 - 75 = 75$

$y = 75(150 - 75) = 5625$

The dimensions are 75 ft by 75 ft, with an area of 5625 ft^2.

56. Let x = the width of the region.

Then $\dfrac{100-2x}{2} = 50 - x$ = the length.

Area = width · length

$$y = x(50 - x)$$
$$y = -x^2 + 50x$$

$a = -1, b = 50, c = 0$

$$x = -\frac{b}{2a} = -\frac{50}{2(-1)} = 25$$

57. Let x = the width.
Then $50 - x$ = the length.

Area = lw

$$y = (50 - x)x$$
$$y = -x^2 + 50x$$

$a = -1, b = 50, c = 0$

$$x = -\frac{b}{2a} = -\frac{50}{2(-1)} = 25$$

$y = (50 - 25)25 = 625$

The maximum area occurs when the dimensions are 25 ft by 25 ft.

58. Set up the variables:

x x x

$\dfrac{1800-3x}{2}$

Area = lw

$$y = x\left(\frac{1800-3x}{2}\right)$$
$$y = -\tfrac{3}{2}x^2 + 900x$$

$a = -\tfrac{3}{2}, b = 900, c = 0$

$$x = -\frac{b}{2a} = -\frac{900}{2\left(-\frac{3}{2}\right)} = 300$$

$y = -\tfrac{3}{2}(300)^2 + 900(300) = 135{,}000$

The maximum area occurs with dimensions of 300 ft by 450 ft, for an area of 135,000 ft^2.

59. Set up the variables :

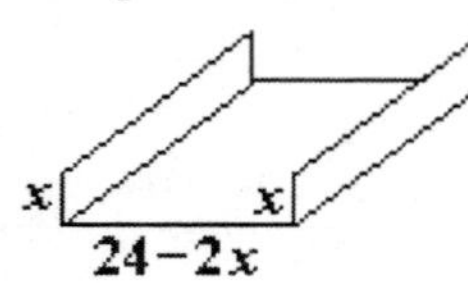

Area = lw

$$y = x(24 - 2x)$$
$$y = 24x - 2x^2$$
$$y = -2x^2 + 24x$$

$a = -2, b = 24, c = 0$

$$x = -\frac{b}{2a} = -\frac{24}{2(-2)} = 6$$

$y = -2x^2 + 24x = -2(6^2) + 24(6) = 72$

The maximum area occurs when the depth is 6 inches and the width is 12 inches.

60. Set up the variables as indicated in the figure:

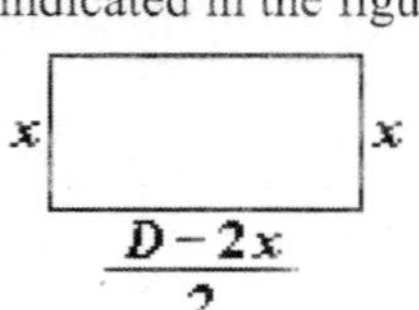

Area = lw

$$y = x\left(\frac{D-2x}{2}\right)$$
$$y = \frac{D}{2}x - x^2$$
$$y = -x^2 + \frac{D}{2}x$$

$a = -1, b = \dfrac{D}{2}, c = 0$

Find the vertex:

$$x = -\frac{b}{2a} = -\frac{\frac{D}{2}}{2(-1)} = \frac{D}{4}$$

The maximum area occurs when the width is $\dfrac{D}{4}$ inches. Thus, the maximum area results when the rectangle is a square.

61. $x^2 + 20y - 400 = 0$

$$20y = -x^2 + 400$$
$$y = -\frac{1}{20}x^2 + 20$$

$a = -\frac{1}{20}$, $b = 0$, $c = 20$

$$x = -\frac{b}{2a} = -\frac{0}{2\left(-\frac{1}{20}\right)} = 0$$

$$y = -\frac{1}{20}x^2 + 20 = -\frac{1}{20}(0)^2 + 20 = 20$$

The maximum height is 20 feet.

62. $y = 400x - 16x^2$

$$y = -16x^2 + 400x$$

$a = -16$, $b = 400$, $c = 0$

$$x = -\frac{b}{2a} = -\frac{400}{2(-16)} = \frac{25}{2}$$

$$y = 400x - 16x^2 = 400\left(\frac{25}{2}\right) - 16\left(\frac{25}{2}\right)^2$$
$$= 2500$$

The maximum height is 2500 units.

63. $f(x) = -0.06x^2 + 1.5x + 6 \Rightarrow a = -0.06$, $b = 1.5$, $c = 6$

$$x = -\frac{b}{2a} = -\frac{1.5}{2(-0.06)} = 12.5$$

$$f(12.5) = -0.06(12.5)^2 + 1.5(12.5) + 6 = 15.375$$

The maximum height is about 15.4 ft.

64. Since the triangle is a 45°-45°-90° triangle, we get the figure below:

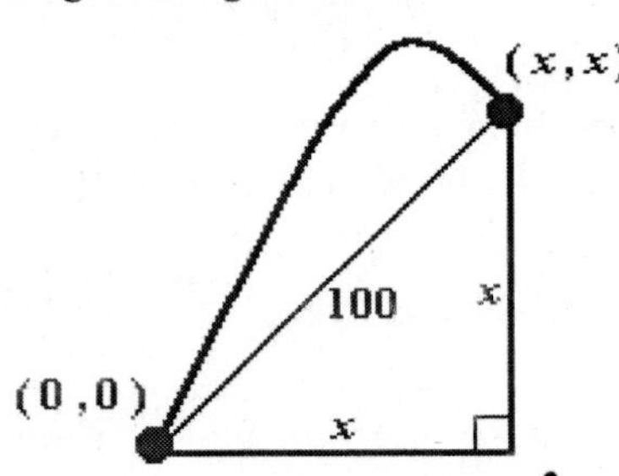

Use the Pythagorean Theorem to find x:

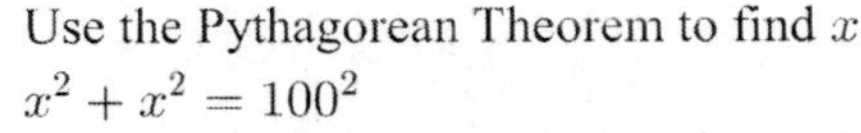

$$x^2 + x^2 = 100^2$$
$$2x^2 = 100^2$$
$$x^2 = \frac{100^2}{2}$$
$$x = \pm\sqrt{\frac{100^2}{2}} = \pm\frac{100}{\sqrt{2}}$$

Use the positive value for x.

The point $\left(\frac{100}{\sqrt{2}}, \frac{100}{\sqrt{2}}\right)$ must be on the graph: $y = -x^2 + ax$

$$\frac{100}{\sqrt{2}} = -\left(\frac{100}{\sqrt{2}}\right)^2 + a\left(\frac{100}{\sqrt{2}}\right)$$
$$\frac{100\sqrt{2}}{2} = -\frac{100^2}{2} + a\left(\frac{100\sqrt{2}}{2}\right)$$
$$100\sqrt{2} = -100^2 + \left(100\sqrt{2}\right)a$$
$$100\sqrt{2} + 100^2 = \left(100\sqrt{2}\right)a$$
$$\frac{100\sqrt{2} + 100^2}{100\sqrt{2}} = a \Rightarrow a = 1 + \frac{100}{\sqrt{2}} \Rightarrow a = 1 + 50\sqrt{2}$$

65. $s(t) = 144 + 64t - 16t^2 = -16t^2 + 64t + 144 \Rightarrow a = -16, b = 64, c = 144$

$t = -\frac{b}{2a} = -\frac{64}{2(-16)} = 2$

$s(2) = -16(2)^2 + 64(2) + 144 = 208$

The maximum height is 208 ft.

66. Revenue = Price · # Sold

$y = p(2400 - p)$

$y = 2400p - p^2$

$y = -p^2 + 2400p$

$a = -1, b = 2400, c = 0$

Find the vertex:

$p = -\frac{b}{2a} = -\frac{2400}{2(-1)} = 1200$

The maximum revenue occurs when the price is \$1200.

67. $C(x) = 1.5x^2 - 144x + 5856 \Rightarrow a = 1.5, b = -144, c = 5856$

$x = -\frac{b}{2a} = -\frac{-144}{2(1.5)} = 48$

$C(48) = 1.5(48)^2 - 144(48) + 5856 = 2400$

48 cameras should be made, for a minimum cost of \$2400.

68. Let x = # of penny decreases.

Then Fare = $180 - x$ (cents)

Riders = $150{,}000 + 1000x$

Revenue = Fare · # Riders

$y = (180 - x)(150{,}000 + 1000x)$

$y = 27{,}000{,}000 + 30{,}000x - 1000x^2$

$a = -1000, b = 30{,}000, c = 27{,}000{,}000$

Find the vertex:

$x = -\frac{b}{2a} = -\frac{30{,}000}{2(-1000)} = 15$

The maximum revenue occurs when the fare is decreased by 15 pennies, or when the fare is decreased to \$1.65.

69. Let x = # of \$5 increases.

Then Rate = $90 + 5x$

Rooms = $200 - 10x$

Revenue = Rate · # Rooms

$y = (90 + 5x)(200 - 10x)$

$y = 18{,}000 + 100x - 50x^2$

$a = -50, b = 100, c = 18{,}000$

Find the vertex:

$x = -\frac{b}{2a} = -\frac{100}{2(-50)} = 1$

The maximum revenue occurs when the room rate increases by 1 five-dollar increment, or when the rate is \$95.

70. Let x = # of blocks of tickets sold (over one).

Then Charge = $10 - 0.50x$ (cents)

Tickets = $100 + 100x$

Revenue = Charge · # Tickets

$y = (10 - 0.50x)(100 + 100x)$

$y = 1000 + 950x - 50x^2$

$a = -50, b = 950, c = 1000$

Find the vertex:

$x = -\frac{b}{2a} = -\frac{950}{2(-50)} = 9.5$

The maximum revenue occurs when 9 or 10 additional blocks are sold, or when there are a total of 10 or 11 blocks sold.

71. $s = 80t - 16t^2$
$a = -16, b = 80, c = 0$
Find the x-coord. of the vertex:
$x = t = -\frac{b}{2a} = -\frac{80}{2(-16)} = \frac{5}{2} = 2.5$
The max. height occurs after 2.5 seconds.

72. Let $s = 0$:
$s = 80t - 16t^2$
$0 = 80t - 16t^2$
$0 = 16t(5 - t)$
$t = 0$ or $t = 5$: The object returns after 5 sec.

73. $s = 80t - 16t^2$
$a = -16, b = 80, c = 0$
Find the y-coord. of the vertex.
Note: The x-coord. was found in **#71**.
$y = s = 80t - 16t^2 = 80(2.5) - 16(2.5)^2$
$= 100$
The max. height is 100 ft.

74. Refer to **#71** and **#72** to answer the question.

75. $y = 2x^2 + 9x - 56$
Vertex: $(-2.25, -66.13)$

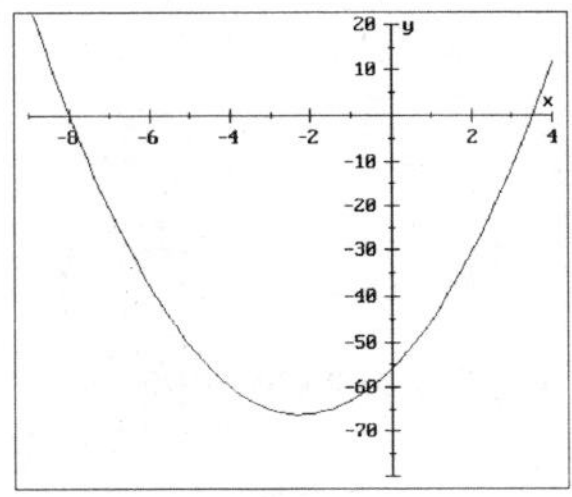

76. $y = 14x - \frac{x^2}{5}$
Vertex: $(35, 245)$

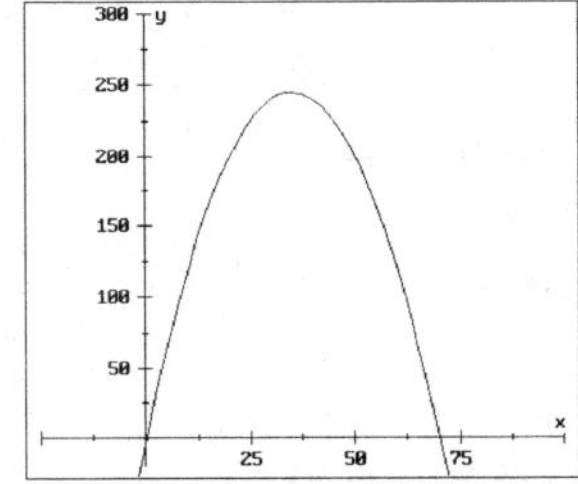

77. $y = (x - 7)(5x + 2)$
Vertex: $(3.3, -68.5)$

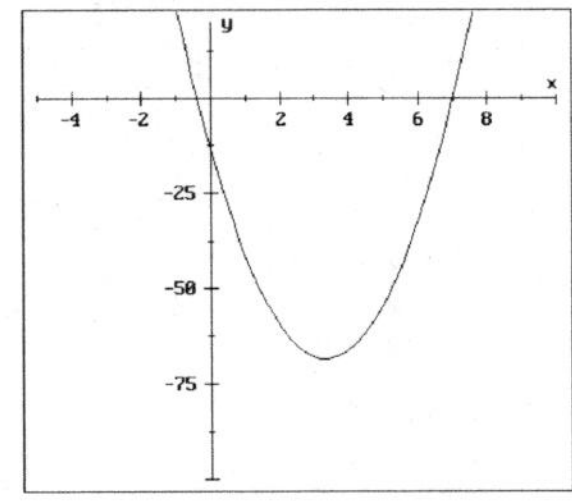

78. $y = -x(0.2 + 0.1x)$
Vertex: $(-1, 0.1)$

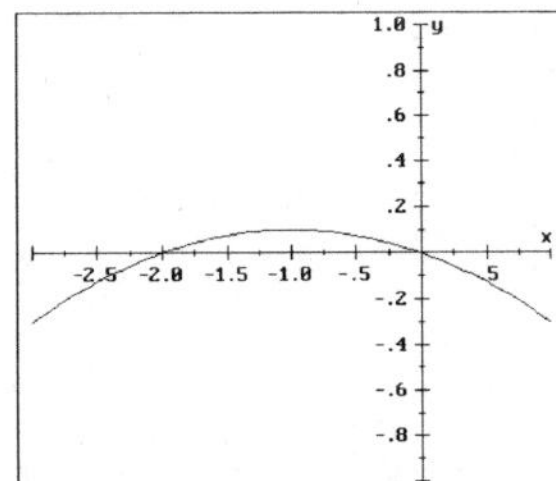

79. $f(x) = x^2 - 5x + 6$
$0 = x^2 - 5x + 6$
$0 = (x - 2)(x - 3)$
$x = 2$ or $x = 3$

80. $f(x) = 6x^2 + x - 2$
$0 = 6x^2 + x - 2$
$0 = (2x - 1)(3x + 2)$
$x = \frac{1}{2}$ or $x = -\frac{2}{3}$

81. The equation of the line is $y = -\frac{3}{4}x + 9$.
Thus the point $(x, y) = \left(x, -\frac{3}{4}x + 9\right)$.
Area $= x\left(-\frac{3}{4}x + 9\right)$
$y = -\frac{3}{4}x^2 + 9x$

$a = -\frac{3}{4}, b = 9, c = 0$
Find the x-coord. of the vertex:
$$x = -\frac{b}{2a} = -\frac{9}{2\left(-\frac{3}{4}\right)} = 6$$
Thus, the dimensions are 6 by $4\frac{1}{2}$ units.

82. The point $(x, y) = (x, 1 - x)$.
Area $= \frac{1}{2}bh$
$y = \frac{1}{2}x(1 - x)$
$y = \frac{1}{2}x - \frac{1}{2}x^2$

$a = -\frac{1}{2}, b = \frac{1}{2}, c = 0$
Find the x-coord. of the vertex:
$$x = -\frac{b}{2a} = -\frac{\frac{1}{2}}{2\left(-\frac{1}{2}\right)} = \frac{1}{2}$$
Thus, point P has coordinates $\left(\frac{1}{2}, \frac{1}{2}\right)$.

83. Let $x =$ one number.
Then $6 - x =$ the other number.
Sum of squares $= x^2 + (6 - x)^2$
$y = x^2 + 36 - 12x + x^2$
$y = 2x^2 - 12x + 36$

$a = 2, b = -12, c = 36$
Find the x-coord. of the vertex:
$$x = -\frac{b}{2a} = -\frac{-12}{2(2)} = 3$$
Thus, the numbers are both 3.

84. Let $x =$ the number.
Then $x^2 =$ its square.
Amt. by which it exceeds square $= x - x^2$
$y = x - x^2$

$a = -1, b = 1, c = 0$
Find the x-coord. of the vertex:
$$x = -\frac{b}{2a} = -\frac{1}{2(-1)} = \frac{1}{2}$$
The number $\frac{1}{2}$ is the number which most exceeds its square.

85-86. Answers will vary.

87. $f(a) = a^2 - 3a$
$f(-a) = (-a)^2 - 3(-a)$
$= a^2 + 3a$

88. $f(a) = a^3 - 3a$
$f(-a) = (-a)^3 - 3(-a)$
$= -a^3 + 3a$

89. $f(a) = (5 - a)^2$
$f(-a) = [5 - (-a)]^2$
$= (5 + a)^2$

90. $f(a) = \frac{1}{a^2-4}$
$f(-a) = \frac{1}{(-a)^2-4}$
$= \frac{1}{a^2-4}$

91. $f(a) = 7$
$f(-a) = 7$

92. $f(a) = -|a|$
$f(-a) = -|-a|$
$= -|-1||a| = -|a|$

Exercises 3.3 (page 321)

1. 4 **2.** turning **3.** $n - 1$ **4.** y-axis

5. odd **6.** increasing **7.** Piecewise-defined **8.** decreasing

9. 3 **10.** constant

11. $f(x) = x^3 - 9x$

$$\begin{aligned} f(-x) &= (-x)^3 - 9(-x) \\ &= -x^3 + 9x \\ &= -f(x) \Rightarrow \text{odd} \end{aligned}$$

x-int.	y-int.
$x^3 - 9x = 0$	$f(0) = 0^3 - 9(0)$
$x(x^2 - 9) = 0$	$y = 0$
$x(x + 3)(x - 3) = 0$	$(0, 0)$
$x = 0, x = -3, x = 3$	
$(0, 0), (-3, 0), (3, 0)$	

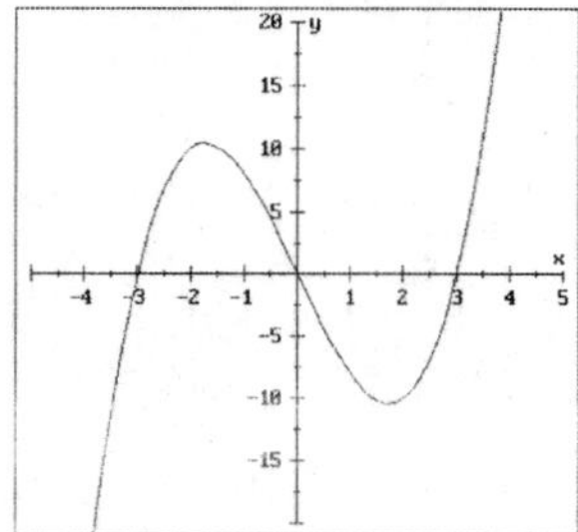

12. $f(x) = x^3 - 16x$

$$\begin{aligned} f(-x) &= (-x)^3 - 16(-x) \\ &= -x^3 + 16x \\ &= -f(x) \Rightarrow \text{odd} \end{aligned}$$

x-int.	y-int.
$x^3 - 16x = 0$	$f(0) = 0^3 - 16(0)$
$x(x^2 - 16) = 0$	$y = 0$
$x(x + 4)(x - 4) = 0$	$(0, 0)$
$x = 0, x = -4, x = 4$	
$(0, 0), (-4, 0), (4, 0)$	

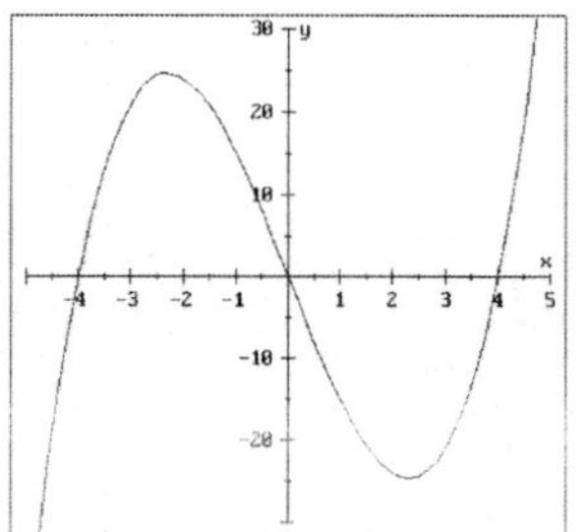

13. $f(x) = -x^3 - 4x^2$

$$\begin{aligned} f(-x) &= -(-x)^3 - 4(-x)^2 \\ &= x^3 - 4x^2 \end{aligned}$$

neither even nor odd

x-int.	y-int.
$-x^3 - 4x^2 = 0$	$f(0) = -(0^3) - 4(0)^2$
$-x^2(x + 4) = 0$	$y = 0$
$x = 0, x = -4$	$(0, 0)$
$(0, 0), (-4, 0)$	

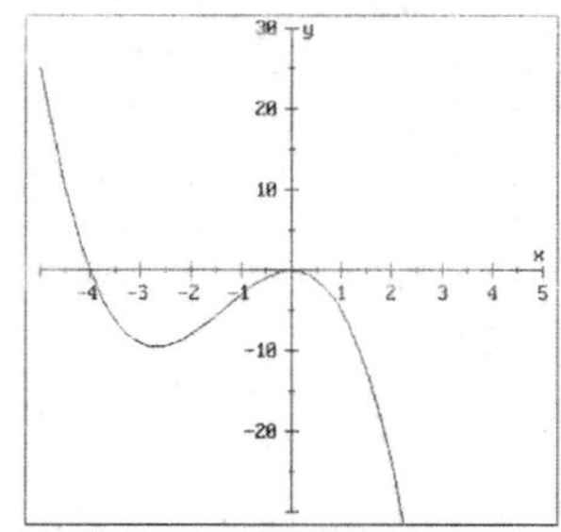

14. $f(x) = x^3 - x$

$$\begin{aligned} f(-x) &= (-x)^3 - (-x) \\ &= -x^3 + x \\ &= -f(x) \Rightarrow \text{odd} \end{aligned}$$

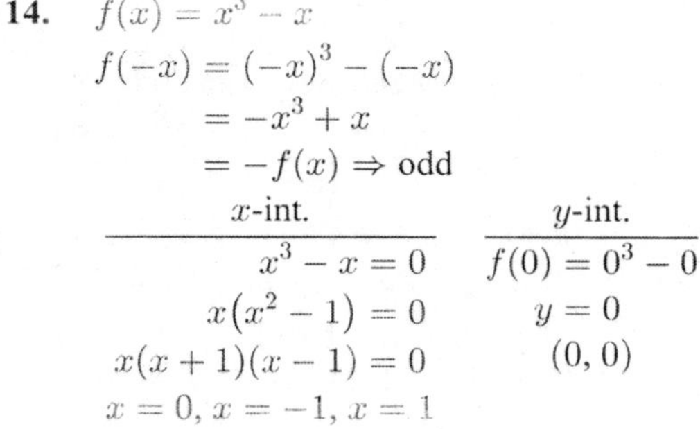

x-int.	y-int.
$x^3 - x = 0$	$f(0) = 0^3 - 0$
$x(x^2 - 1) = 0$	$y = 0$
$x(x + 1)(x - 1) = 0$	$(0, 0)$
$x = 0, x = -1, x = 1$	
$(0, 0), (-1, 0), (1, 0)$	

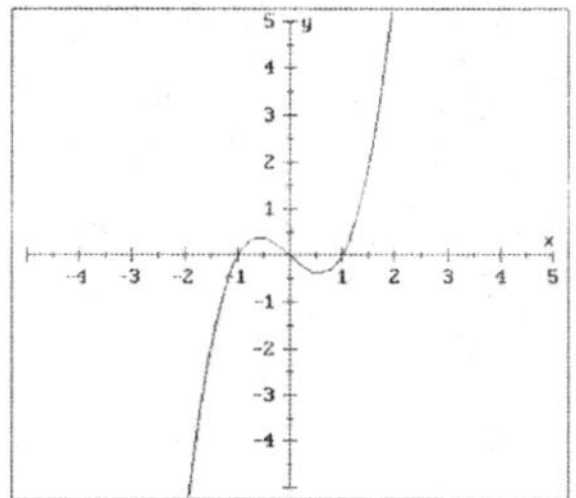

15. $f(x) = x^3 + x^2$

$f(-x) = (-x)^3 + (-x)^2$

$= -x^3 + x^2 \Rightarrow$ neither even nor odd

x-int.	y-int.
$x^3 + x^2 = 0$	$f(0) = 0^3 + 0^2$
$x^2(x+1) = 0$	$y = 0$
$x = 0, x = -1$	$(0, 0)$
$(0, 0), (-1, 0)$	

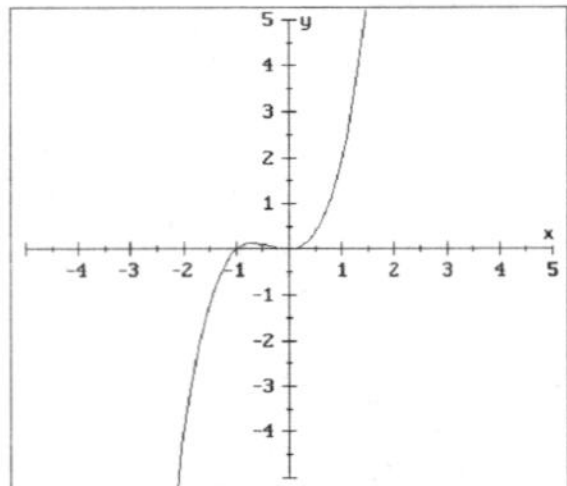

16. $f(x) = -x^3 + 1$

$f(-x) = -(-x)^3 + 1$

$= -(-x^3) + 1$

$= x^3 + 1 \Rightarrow$ neither even nor odd

x-int.	y-int.
$-x^3 + 1 = 0$	$f(0) = -0^3 + 1$
$1 = x^3$	$y = 1$
$1 = x$	$(0, 1)$
$(1, 0)$	

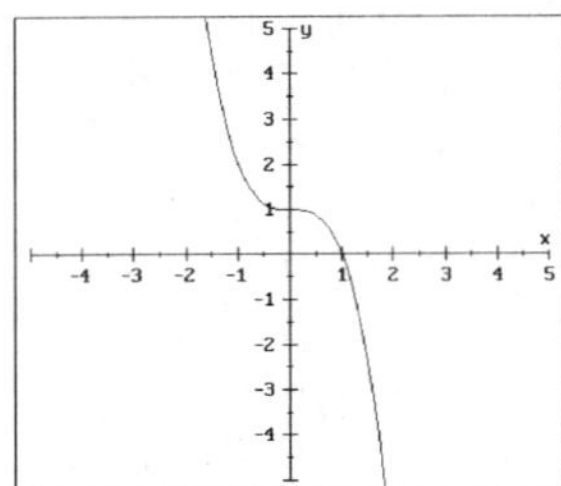

17. $f(x) = x^3 - x^2 - 4x + 4$

$f(-x) = (-x)^3 - (-x)^2 - 4(-x) + 4$

$= -x^3 - x^2 + 4x + 4$

$\Rightarrow$ neither even nor odd

x-int.	y-int.
$x^3 - x^2 - 4x + 4 = 0$	$f(0) = 4$
$x^2(x-1) - 4(x-1) = 0$	$y = 4$
$(x-1)(x^2-4) = 0$	$(0, 4)$
$x = 1$ or $x^2 = 4$	
$x = 1, x = 2, x = -2$	
$(1, 0), (2, 0), (-2, 0)$	

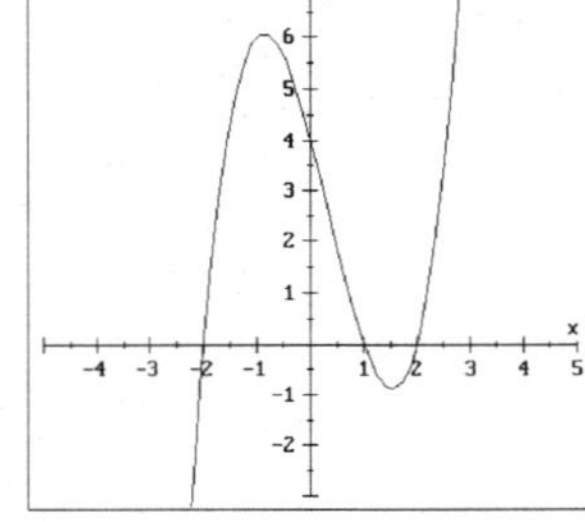

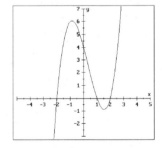

18. $f(x) = 4x^3 - 4x^2 - x + 1$

$f(-x) = 4(-x)^3 - 4(-x)^2 - (-x) + 1$

$= -4x^3 - 4x^2 + x + 1$

$\Rightarrow$ neither even nor odd

x-int.	y-int.
$4x^3 - 4x^2 - x + 1 = 0$	$f(0) = 1$
$4x^2(x-1) - (x-1) = 0$	$y = 1$
$(x-1)(4x^2-1) = 0$	$(0, 1)$
$x = 1$ or $x^2 = \frac{1}{4}$	
$x = 1, x = \frac{1}{2}, x = -\frac{1}{2}$	
$(1, 0), \left(\frac{1}{2}, 0\right), \left(-\frac{1}{2}, 0\right)$	

19. $f(x) = x^4 - 2x^2 + 1$
$f(-x) = (-x)^4 - 2(-x)^2 + 1$
$= x^4 - 2x^2 + 1 \Rightarrow$ even

x-int.	y-int.
$x^4 - 2x^2 + 1 = 0$	$f(0) = 1$
$(x^2 - 1)(x^2 - 1) = 0$	$y = 1$
$x^2 = 1$	$(0, 1)$
$x = 1, x = -1$	
$(1, 0), (-1, 0)$	

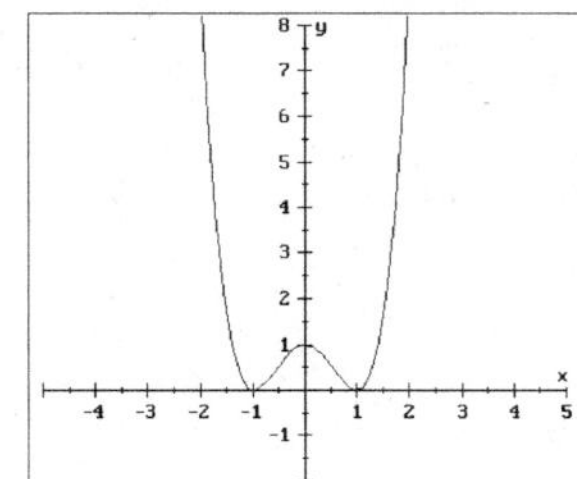

20. $f(x) = x^4 - 5x^2 + 4$
$f(-x) = (-x)^4 - 5(-x)^2 + 4$
$= x^4 - 5x^2 + 4 \Rightarrow$ even

x-int.	y-int.
$x^4 - 5x^2 + 4 = 0$	$f(0) = 4$
$(x^2 - 1)(x^2 - 4) = 0$	$y = 4$
$x^2 = 1$ or $x^2 = 4$	$(0, 4)$
$x = 1, x = -1, x = 2, x = -2$	
$(1, 0), (-1, 0), (2, 0), (-2, 0)$	

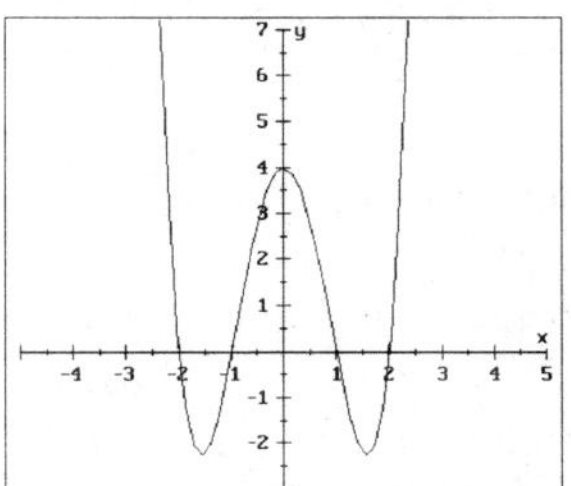

21. $f(x) = -x^4 + 5x^2 - 4$
$f(-x) = -(-x)^4 + 5(-x)^2 - 4$
$= -x^4 + 5x^2 - 4 \Rightarrow$ even

x-int.	y-int.
$-x^4 + 5x^2 - 4 = 0$	$f(0) = -4$
$-(x^4 - 5x^2 + 4) = 0$	$y = -4$
$(x^2 - 1)(x^2 - 4) = 0$	$(0, -4)$
$x^2 = 1$ or $x^2 = 4$	
$x = \pm 1, x = \pm 2$	
$(\pm 1, 0), (\pm 2, 0)$	

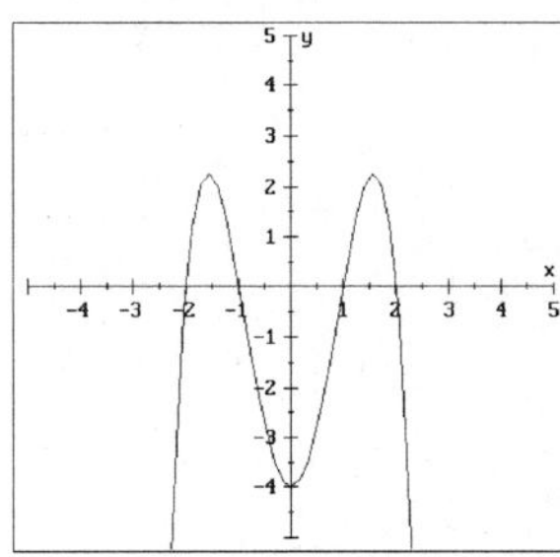

22. $f(x) = x(x - 3)(x - 2)(x + 1)$
$f(-x) = -x(-x - 3)(-x - 2)(-x + 1)$
$\Rightarrow$ neither even nor odd

x-int.	y-int.
$x(x - 3)(x - 2)(x + 1) = 0$	$f(0) = 0$
$x = 0, x = 3, x = 2, x = -1$	$y = 0$
$(0, 0), (3, 0), (2, 0), (-1, 0)$	$(0, 0)$

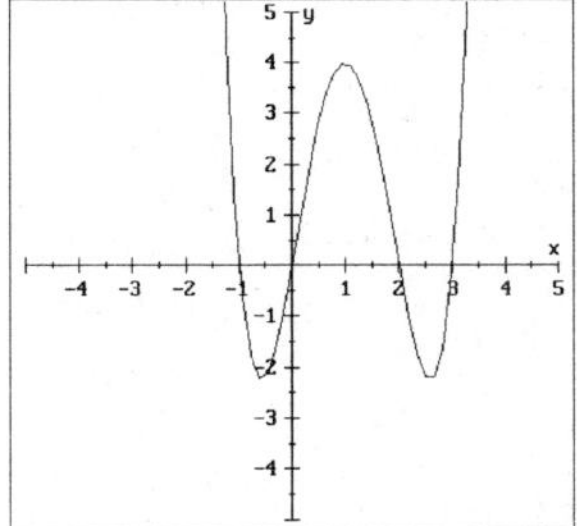

23. $f(x) = x^4 + x^2$
$f(-x) = (-x)^4 + (-x)^2$
$= x^4 + x^2 = f(x) \Rightarrow$ even

24. $f(x) = x^3 - 2x$
$f(-x) = (-x)^3 - 2(-x)$
$= -x^3 + 2x = -f(x) \Rightarrow$ odd

25. $f(x) = x^3 + x^2$
$f(-x) = (-x)^3 + (-x)^2$
$= -x^3 + x^2 \Rightarrow$ neither

26. $f(x) = x^6 - x^2$
$f(-x) = (-x)^6 - (-x)^2$
$= x^6 - x^2 = f(x) \Rightarrow$ even

27. $f(x) = x^5 + x^3$
$f(-x) = (-x)^5 + (-x)^3$
$= -x^5 - x^3 = -f(x) \Rightarrow$ odd

28. $f(x) = x^3 - x^2$
$f(-x) = (-x)^3 - (-x)^2$
$= -x^3 - x^2 \Rightarrow$ neither

29. $f(x) = 2x^3 - 3x$
$f(-x) = 2(-x)^3 - 3(-x)$
$= -2x^3 + 3x = -f(x) \Rightarrow$ odd

30. $f(x) = 4x^2 - 5$
$f(-x) = 4(-x)^2 - 5$
$= 4x^2 - 5 = f(x) \Rightarrow$ even

31. symmetric about x-axis $\Rightarrow$ even

32. symmetric about x-axis $\Rightarrow$ even

33. symmetric about origin $\Rightarrow$ odd

34. symmetric about origin $\Rightarrow$ odd

35. no symmetry $\Rightarrow$ neither

36. no symmetry $\Rightarrow$ neither

37. decreasing: $(-\infty, 0)$; increasing: $(0, \infty)$

38. constant: $(-\infty, 0)$; decreasing: $(0, \infty)$

39. increasing: $(-\infty, 0)$; decreasing: $(0, \infty)$

40. decreasing: $(-\infty, 0)$; constant: $(0, \infty)$

41. decreasing: $(-\infty, -2)$; constant: $(-2, 2)$; increasing: $(2, \infty)$

42. increasing: $(-\infty, 0)$; decreasing: $(0, 3)$; constant: $(3, \infty)$

43. $f(x) = x^2 - 4x + 4$

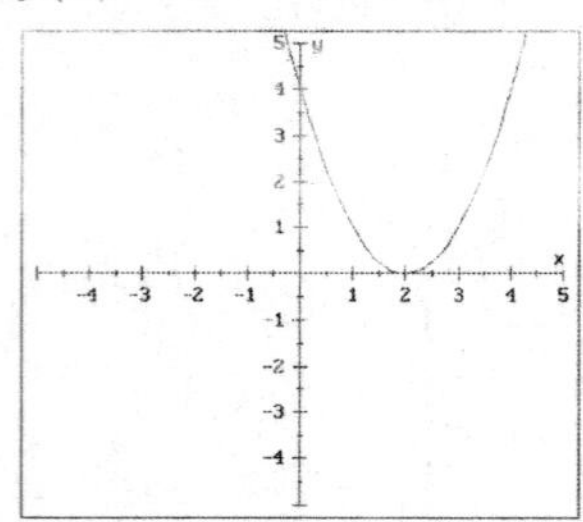

decreasing: $(-\infty, 2)$; increasing: $(2, \infty)$

44. $f(x) = 4 - x^2$

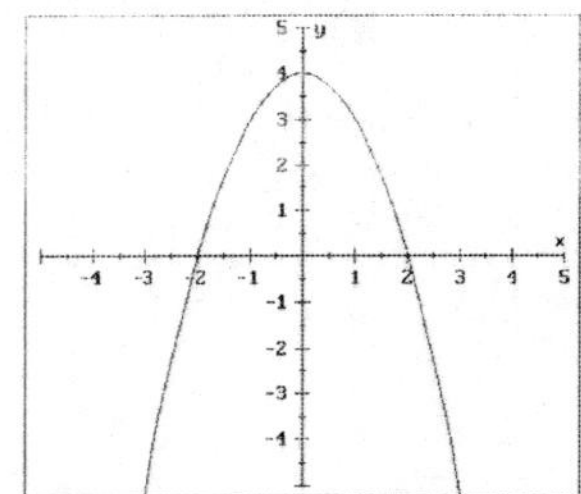

increasing: $(-\infty, 0)$; decreasing: $(0, \infty)$

45. **a.** $f(-2) = 2(-2) + 2 = -2$
b. $f(0) = 3$

46. **a.** $f(1) = 1^2 = 1$
b. $f(5) = 5^2 = 25$

47. **a.** $f(-1) = 2$
b. $f(1) = 2 - 1 = 1$
c. $f(2) = 2 + 1 = 3$

48. **a.** $f(-0.5) = 2(-0.5) = -1$
b. $f(0) = 3 - 0 = 3$
c. $f(2) = |2| = 2$

49. $f(x) = \begin{cases} x+2 & \text{if } x < 0 \\ 2 & \text{if } x \ge 0 \end{cases}$

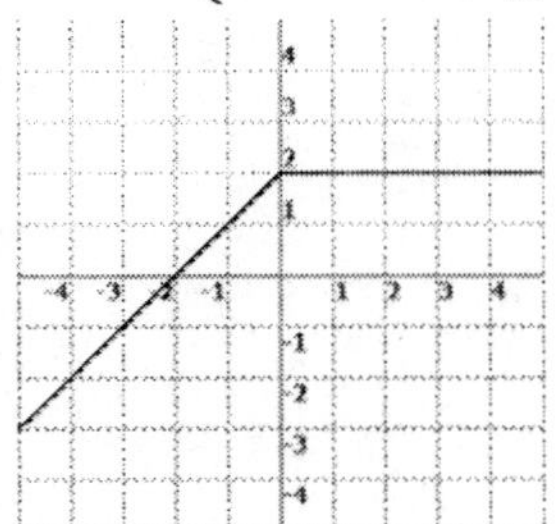

50. $f(x) = \begin{cases} 2x & \text{if } x < 0 \\ -2x & \text{if } x \ge 0 \end{cases}$

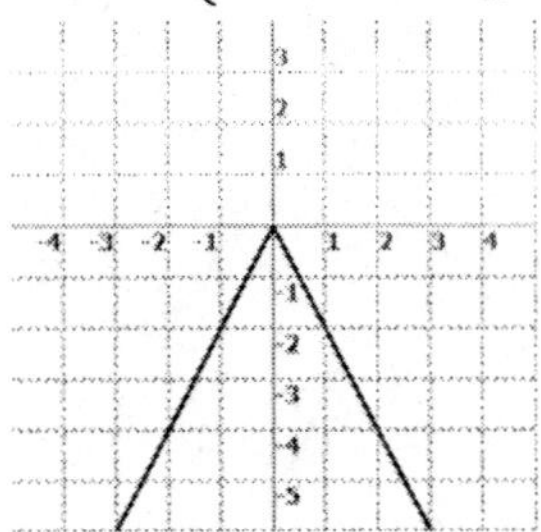

51. $f(x) = \begin{cases} x & \text{if } x \le 0 \\ 2 & \text{if } x > 0 \end{cases}$

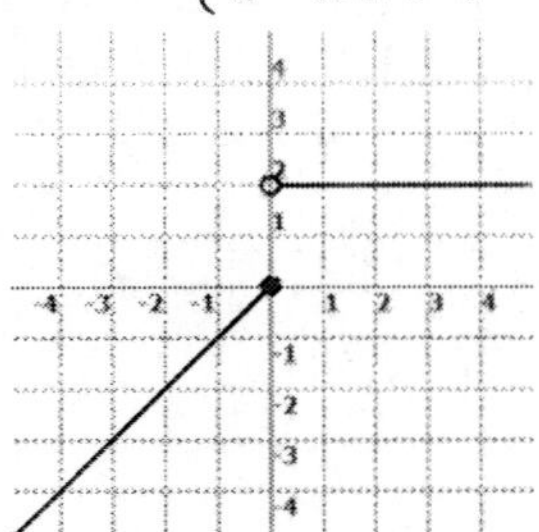

52. $f(x) = \begin{cases} -x & \text{if } x < 0 \\ \frac{1}{2}x & \text{if } x > 0 \end{cases}$

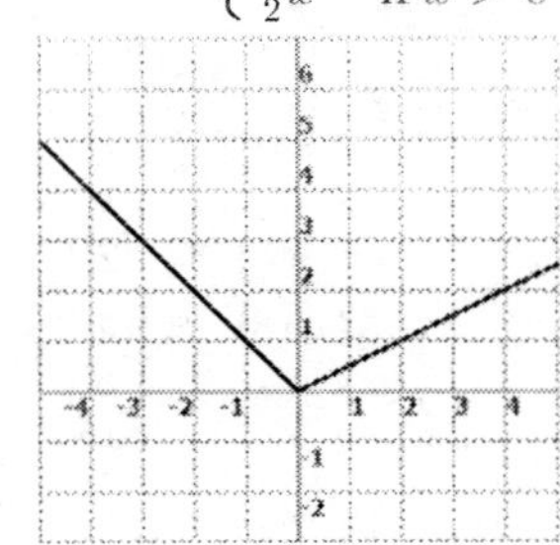

53. $f(x) = \begin{cases} -4-x & \text{if } x < 1 \\ 3 & \text{if } x \ge 1 \end{cases}$

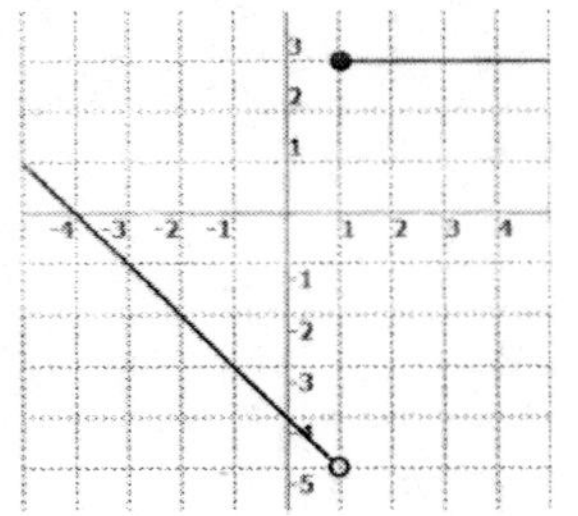

54. $f(x) = \begin{cases} -5-x & \text{if } x < 1 \\ -3 & \text{if } x \ge 1 \end{cases}$

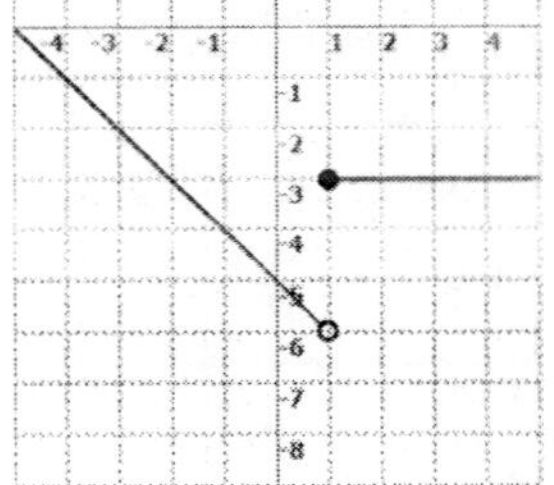

55. $f(x) = \begin{cases} -x & \text{if } x < 0 \\ x^2 & \text{if } x \ge 0 \end{cases}$

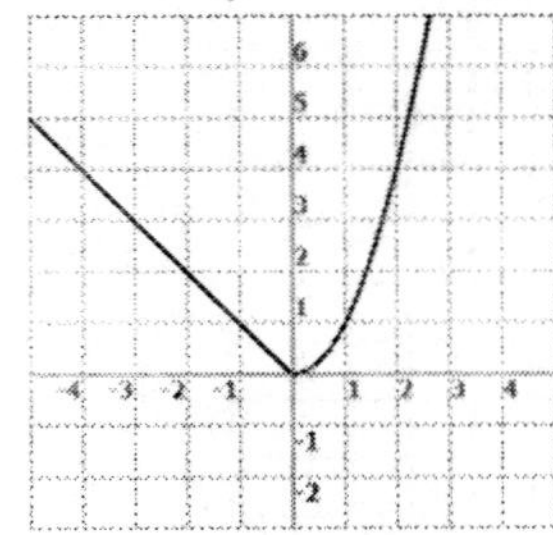

56. $f(x) = \begin{cases} |x| & \text{if } x < 0 \\ \sqrt{x} & \text{if } x \ge 0 \end{cases}$

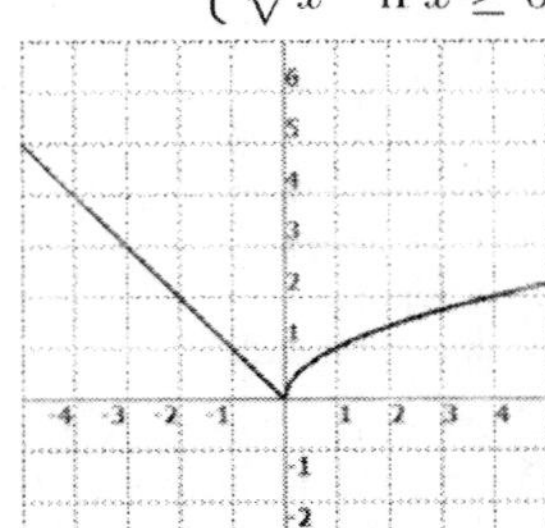

57. $f(x)=\begin{cases}0 & \text{if } x<0\\ x^2 & \text{if } 0\le x\le 2\\ 4-2x & \text{if } x>2\end{cases}$

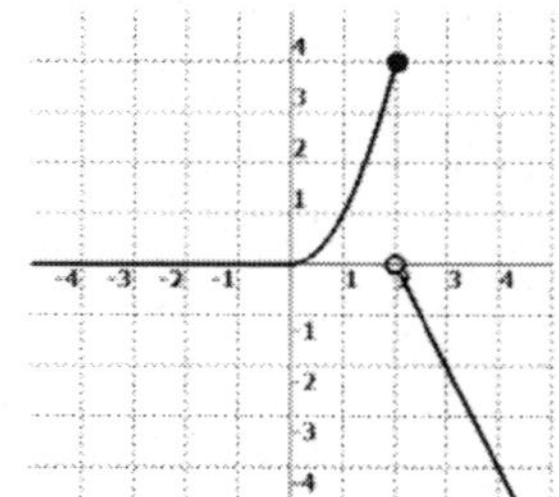

58. $f(x)=\begin{cases}2 & \text{if } x<0\\ 2-x & \text{if } 0\le x<2\\ x & \text{if } x\ge 2\end{cases}$

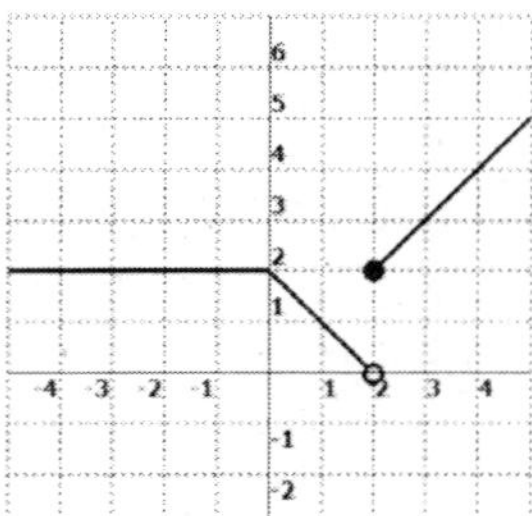

59. **a.** $f(3)=[[3]]=3$
b. $f(-4)=[[-4]]=-4$
c. $f(-2.3)=[[-2.3]]=-3$

60. **a.** $f(4)=[[3(4)]]=[[12]]=12$
b. $f(-2)=[[3(-2)]]=[[-6]]=-6$
c. $f(-1.2)=[[3(-1.2)]]=[[-3.6]]=-4$

61. **a.** $f(-1)=[[-1+3]]=[[2]]=2$ **b.** $f(\frac{2}{3})=\left[\left[\frac{2}{3}+3\right]\right]=\left[\left[3\frac{2}{3}\right]\right]=3$
c. $f(1.3)=[[1.3+3]]=[[4.3]]=4$

62. **a.** $f(-3)=[[4(-3)]]-1=[[-12]]-1=-12-1=-13$
b. $f(0)=[[4(0)]]-1=[[0]]-1=0-1=-1$
c. $f(\pi)=[[4(\pi)]]-1=12-1=11$

63. $y=[[2x]]$

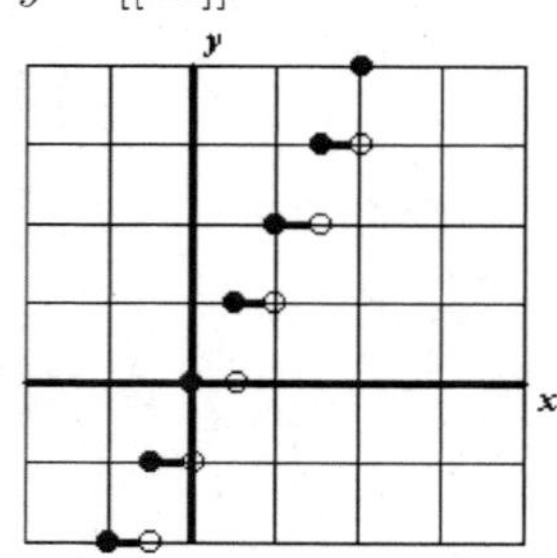

64. $y=\left[\left[\dfrac{1}{3}x+3\right]\right]$

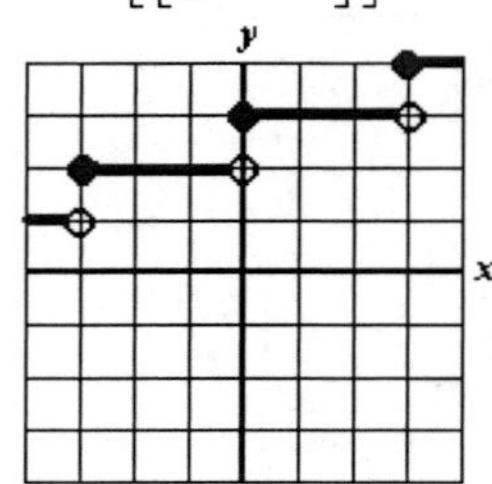

65. $y=[[x]]-1$

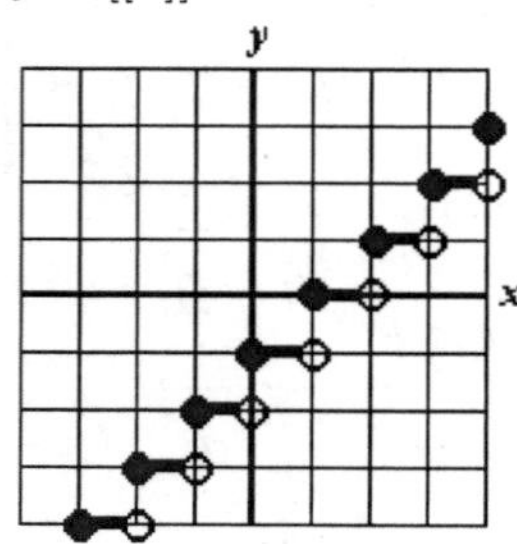

66. $y=[[x+2]]$

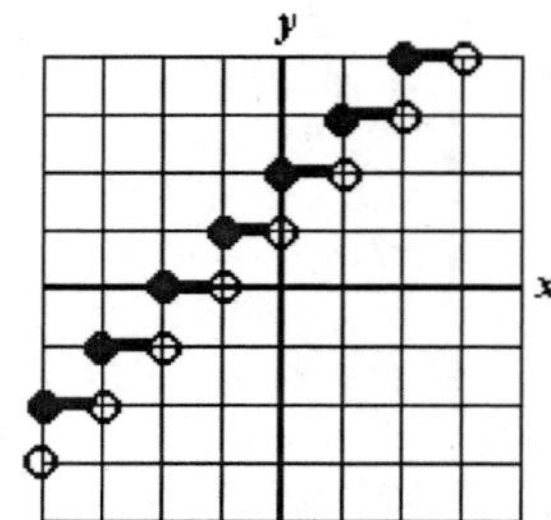

67.

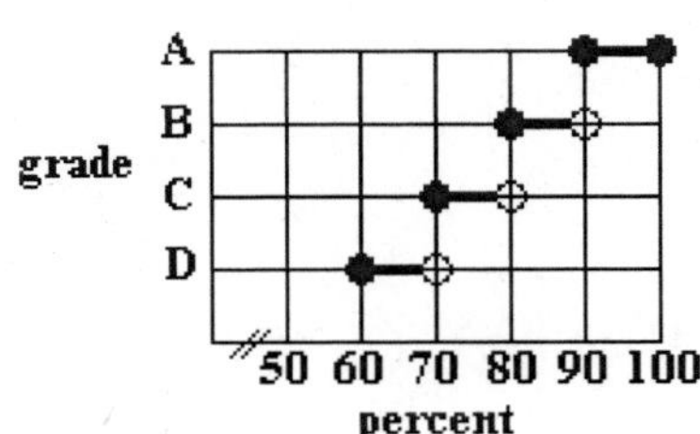

$$\frac{67+73+84+87+93}{5}=\frac{404}{5}=80.8$$

The student's grade is B.

68. Refer to **#67**.

$$\frac{53+65+64+73+89+82}{6}=\frac{426}{6}=71$$

The student's grade is C.

69. \$32 for 275 miles

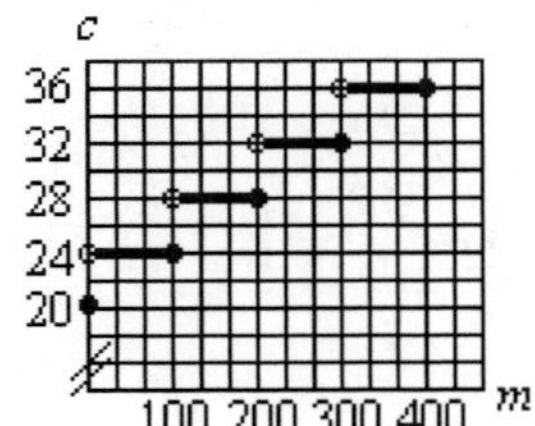

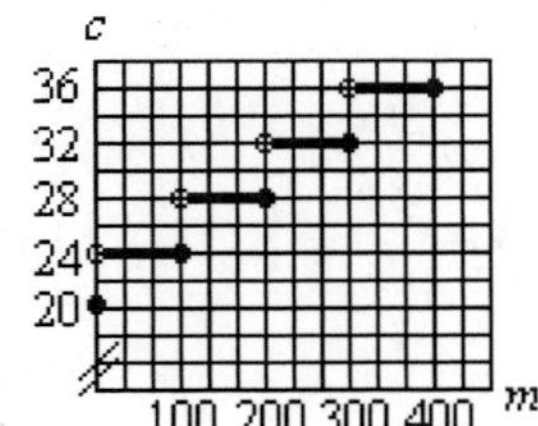

70. \$23 for $10\frac{1}{4}$ miles

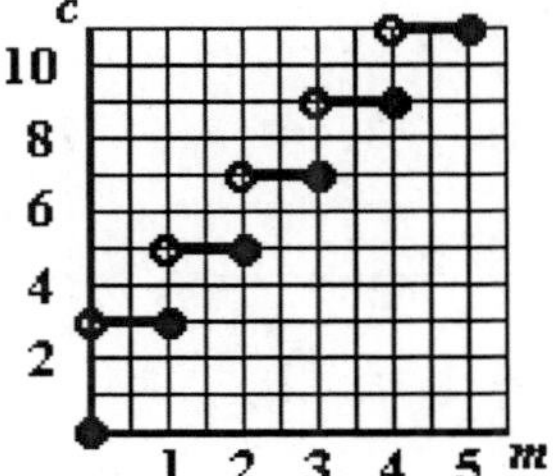

71. \$12 per hour ⇒
\$0.20 per minute
\$1.60 for $7\frac{1}{2}$ minutes

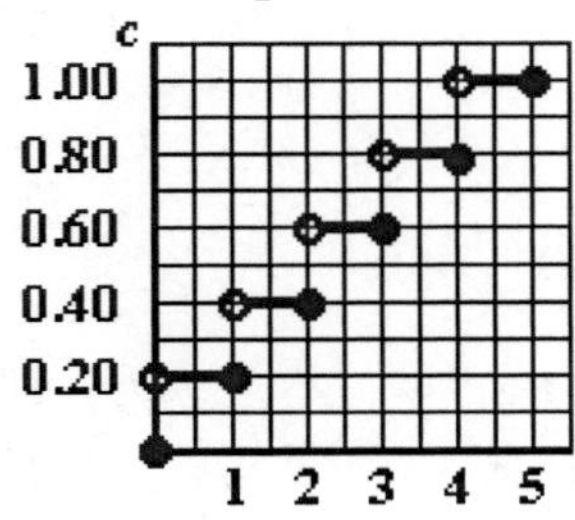

72. \$190 for 4 hours

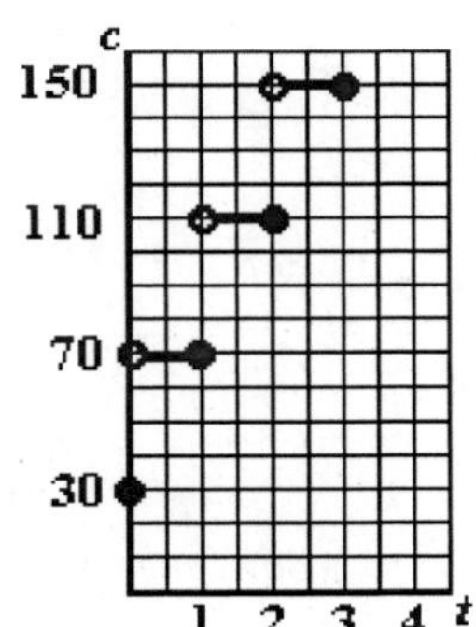

73.

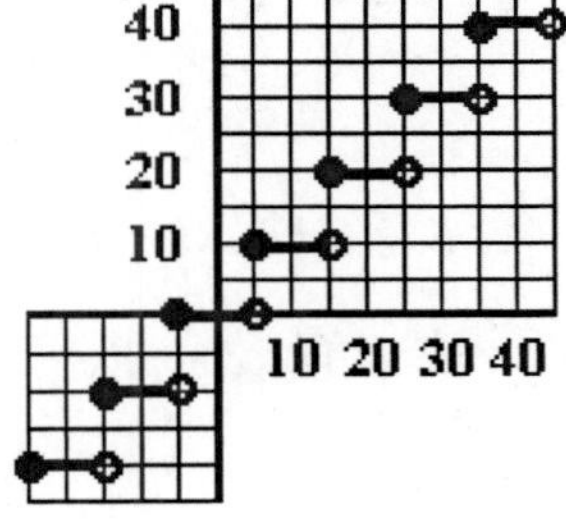

74. $y = \text{sgn } x$

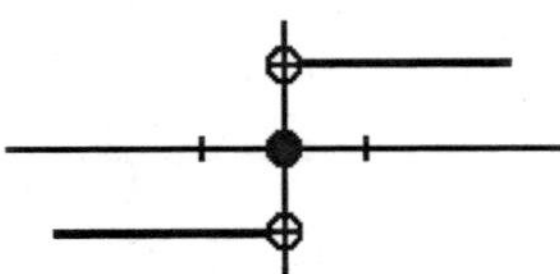

domain $= (-\infty, \infty)$
range $= \{-1, 0, 1\}$

75. $y = \frac{|x|}{x}$, Not defined at $x = 0$, so not the same

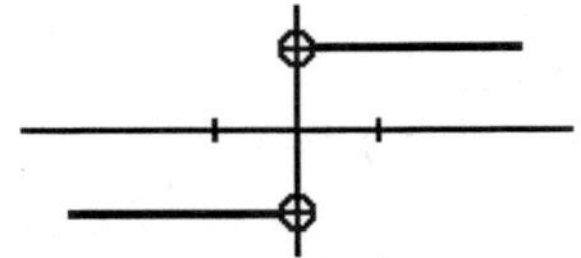

76. $y = x + |x|$

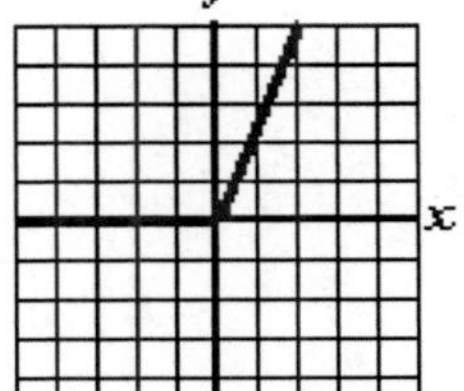

77-80. Answers may vary.

81. $f(x+1) = 3(x+1) + 2 = 3x + 5$
$f(x) + 1 = (3x + 2) + 1 = 3x + 3$

82. $f(x-2) = (x-2)^2 = x^2 - 4x + 4$
$f(x) - 2 = (x^2) - 2 = x^2 - 2$

83. $f(x-3) = \dfrac{3(x-3)+1}{5} = \dfrac{3x-8}{5}$
$f(x) - 3 = \dfrac{3x+1}{5} - 3 = \dfrac{3x-14}{5}$

84. $f(x+8) = 8$
$f(x) + 8 = 8 + 8 = 16$

85.
$$\begin{aligned} 2x^2 - 3 &= x \\ 2x^2 - x - 3 &= 0 \\ (2x-3)(x+1) &= 0 \\ 2x = 3 \text{ or } x &= -1 \\ x = \tfrac{3}{2}, x &= -1 \end{aligned}$$

86. $4x^2 = 24x - 37 \Rightarrow 4x^2 - 24x + 37 = 0 \Rightarrow a = 4, b = -24, c = 37$

$$x = \frac{-b \pm \sqrt{b^2 - 4ac}}{2a} = \frac{-(-24) \pm \sqrt{(-24)^2 - 4(4)(37)}}{2(4)} = \frac{24 \pm \sqrt{576 - 592}}{8} = \frac{24 \pm \sqrt{-16}}{8} = \frac{24 \pm 4i}{8} = 3 \pm \tfrac{1}{2}i$$

Exercises 3.4 (page 339)

1. upward
2. $f(x) - 7$
3. to the right
4. to the left
5. 2, downward
6. right, upward
7. y-axis
8. $y = -f(x)$
9. horizontally
10. vertically

11. $g(x) = x^2 - 2$
Shift $f(x) = x^2$ D 2

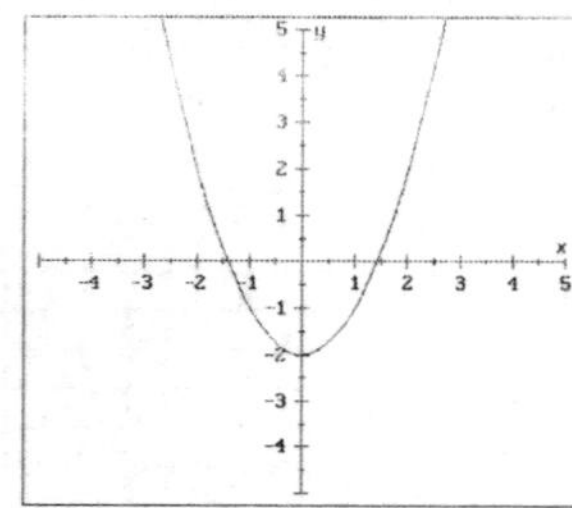

12. $g(x) = (x-2)^2$
Shift $f(x) = x^2$ R 2

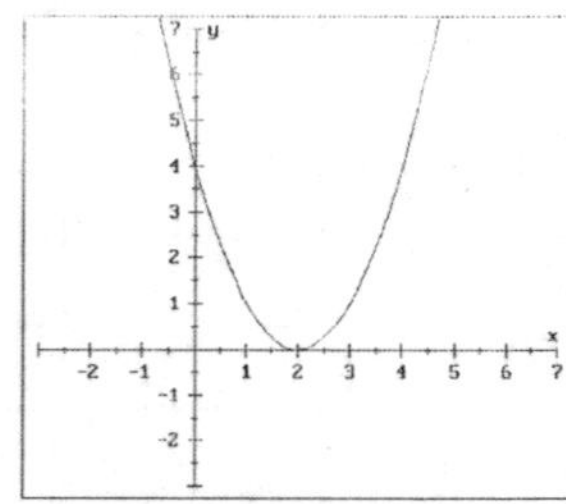

13. $g(x) = (x+3)^2$
Shift $f(x) = x^2$ L 3

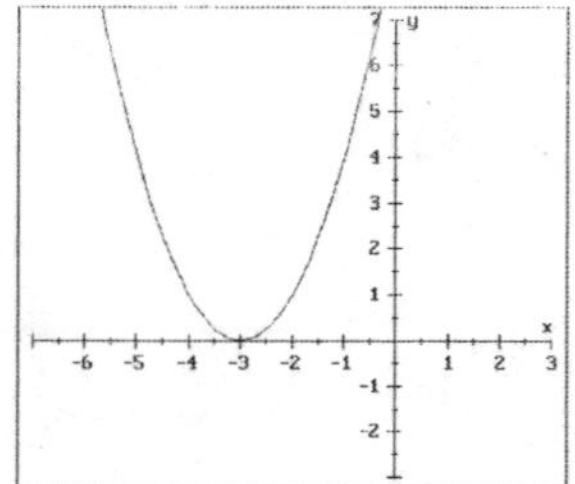

14. $g(x) = x^2 + 3$
Shift $f(x) = x^2$ U 3

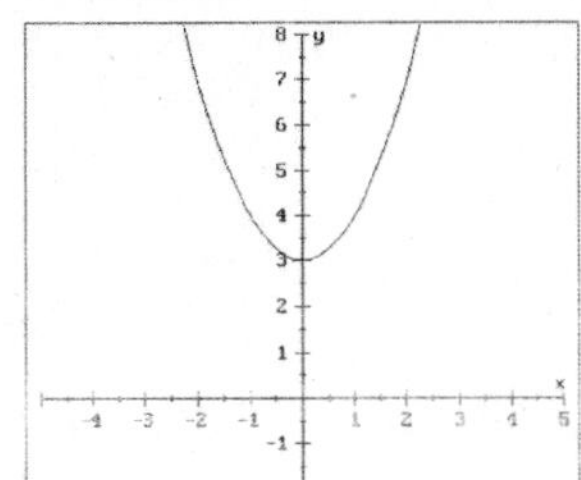

15. $h(x) = (x+1)^2 + 2$
Shift $f(x) = x^2$ U 2, L 1

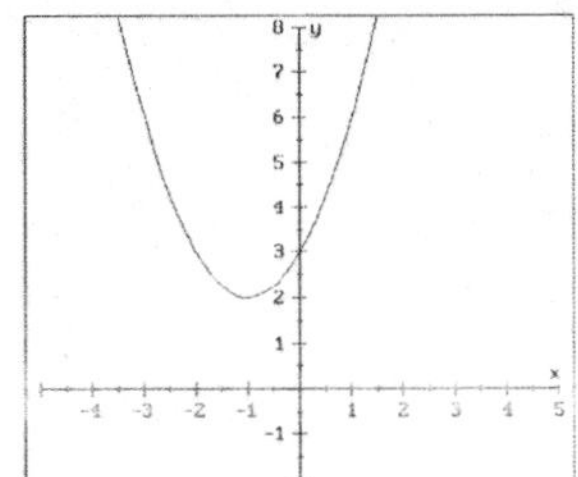

16. $h(x) = (x-3)^2 - 1$
Shift $f(x) = x^2$ D 1, R 3

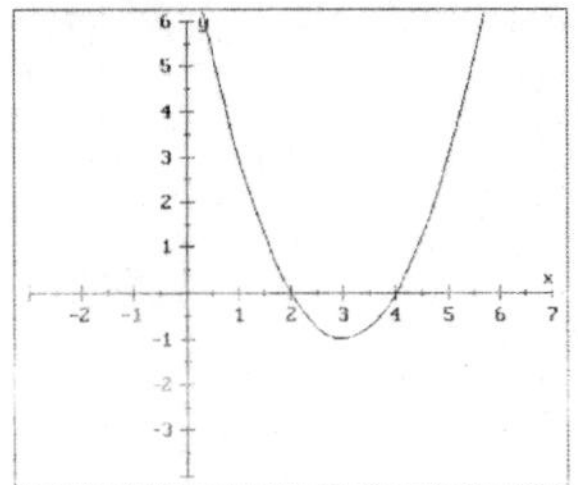

17. $h(x) = \left(x + \frac{1}{2}\right)^2 - \frac{1}{2}$
Shift $f(x) = x^2$ D $\frac{1}{2}$, L $\frac{1}{2}$

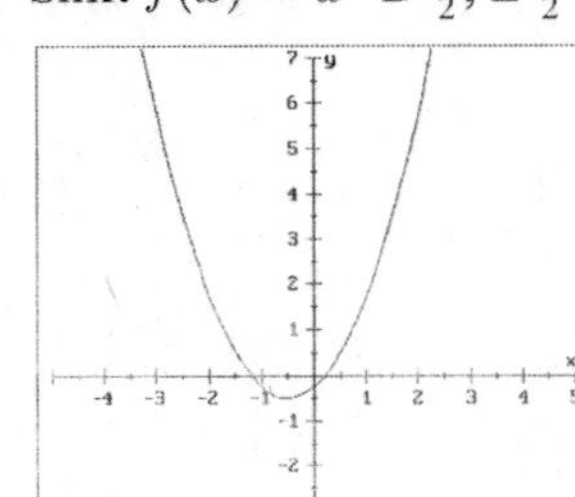

18. $h(x) = \left(x - \frac{3}{2}\right)^2 + \frac{5}{2}$
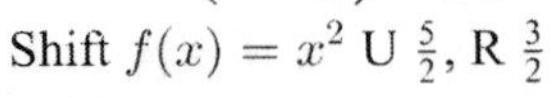
Shift $f(x) = x^2$ U $\frac{5}{2}$, R $\frac{3}{2}$

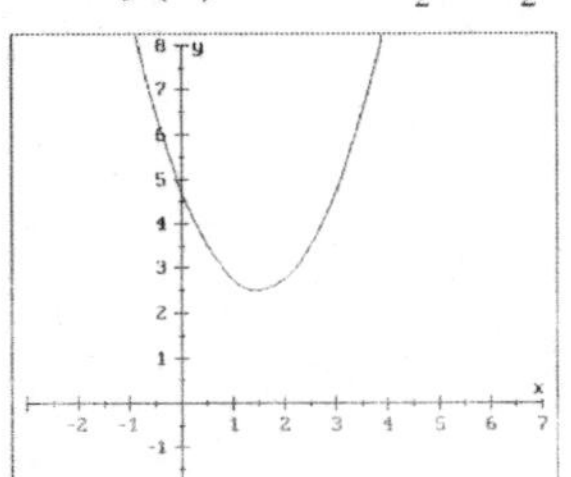

19. $g(x) = x^3 + 1$
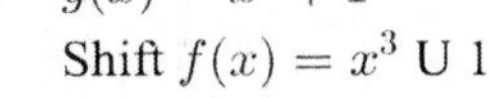
Shift $f(x) = x^3$ U 1

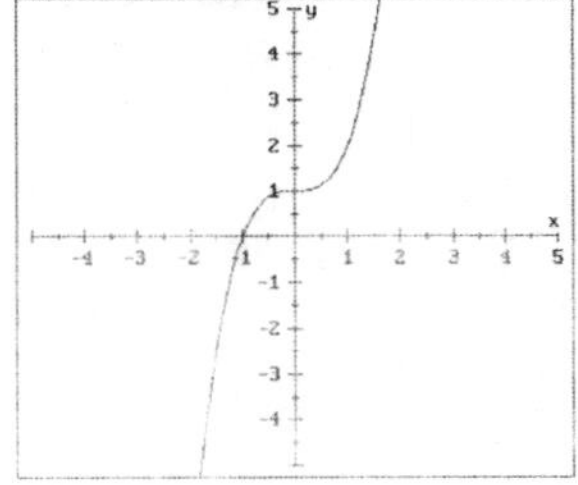

20. $g(x) = x^3 - 3$
Shift $f(x) = x^3$ D 3

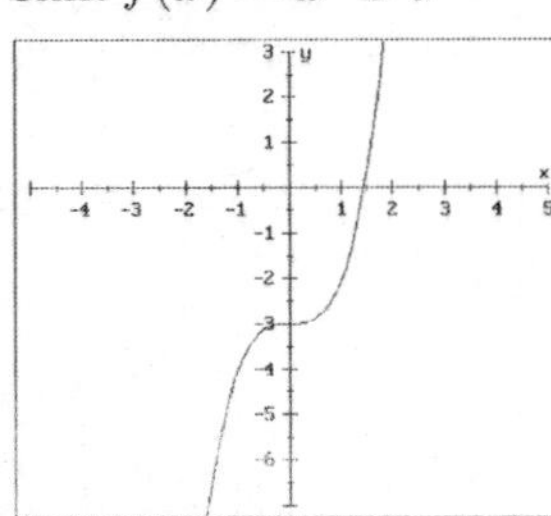

21. $g(x) = (x-2)^3$
Shift $f(x) = x^3$ R 2

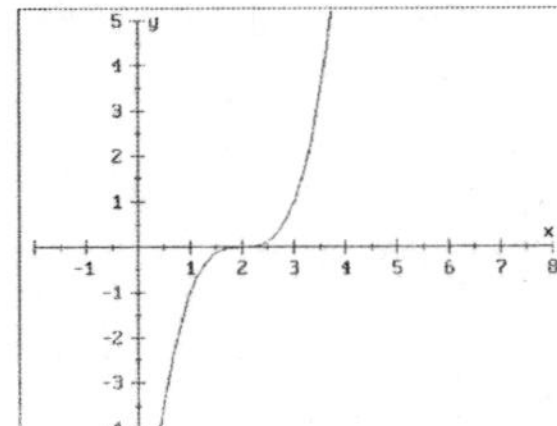

22. $g(x) = (x+3)^3$
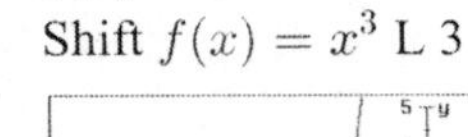
Shift $f(x) = x^3$ L 3

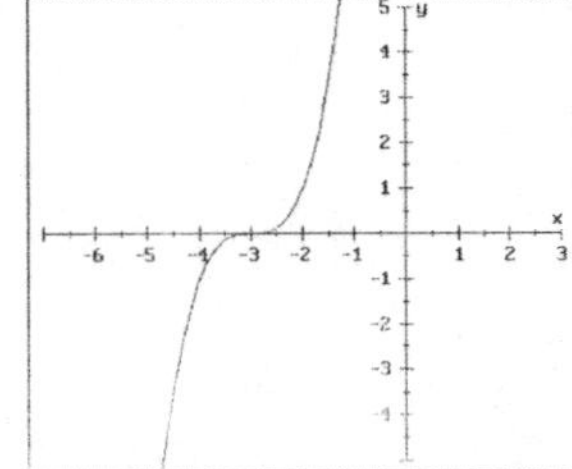

SECTION 3.4

23. $h(x) = (x - 2)^3 - 3$
Shift $f(x) = x^3$ D 3, R 2

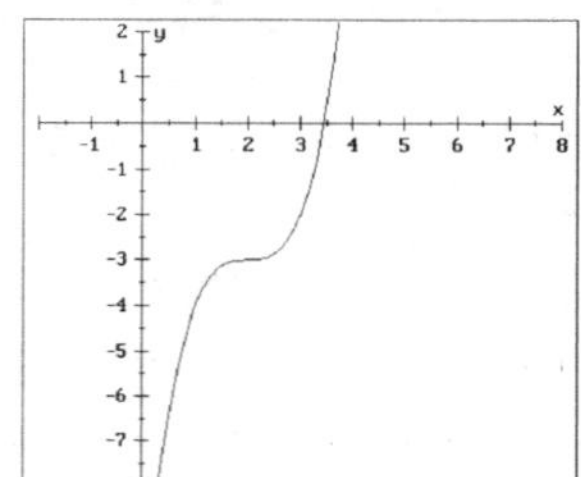

24. $h(x) = (x + 1)^3 + 4$
Shift $f(x) = x^3$ U 4, L 1

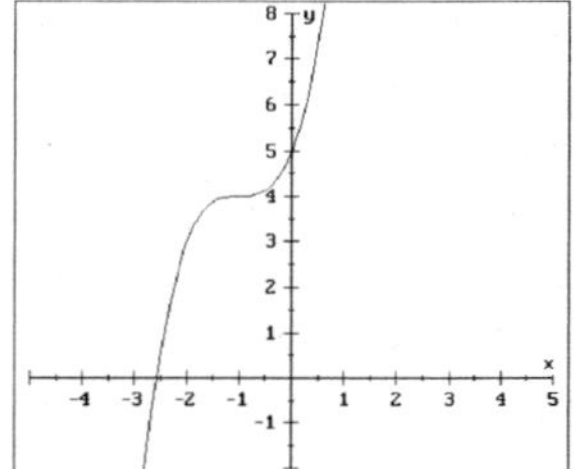

25. $y + 2 = x^3$
$y = x^3 - 2$
Shift $y = x^3$ D 2

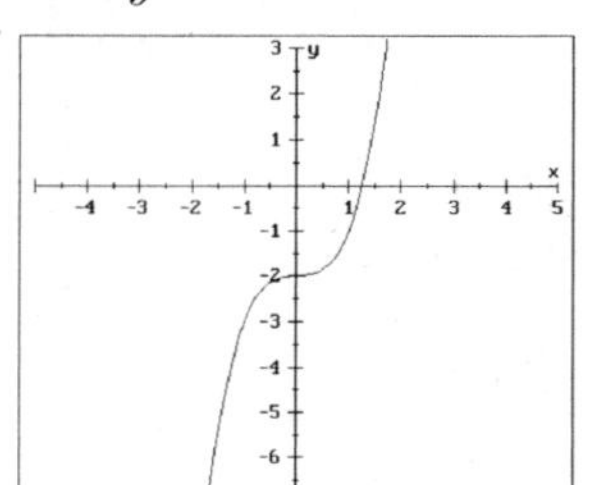

26. $y - 7 = (x - 5)^3$
$y = (x - 5)^3 + 7$
Shift $y = x^3$ U 7, R 5

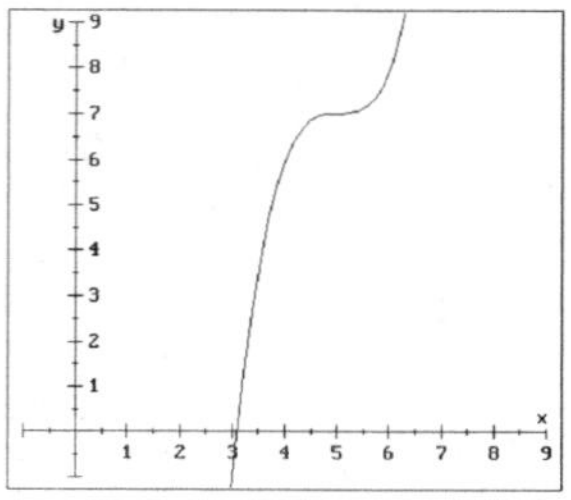

27. $g(x) = |x| + 2$
Shift $f(x) = |x|$ U 2

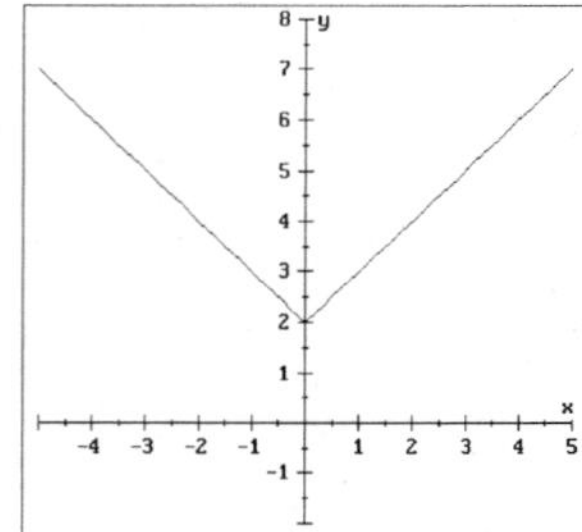

28. $g(x) = |x| - 2$

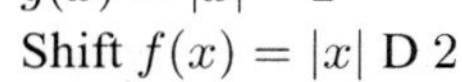

Shift $f(x) = |x|$ D 2

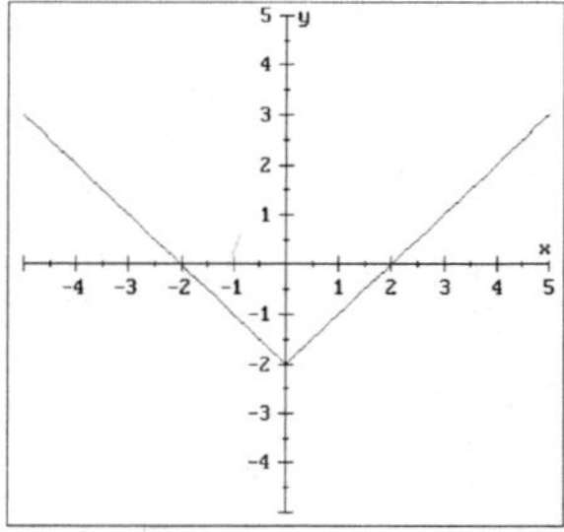

29. $g(x) = |x - 5|$
Shift $f(x) = |x|$ R 5

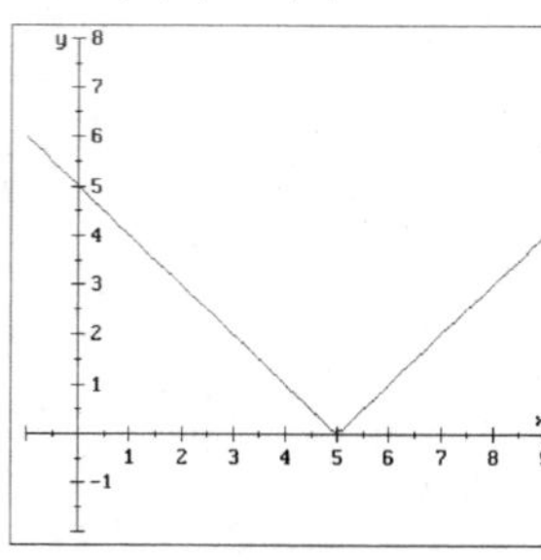

30. $g(x) = |x + 4|$
Shift $f(x) = |x|$ L 4

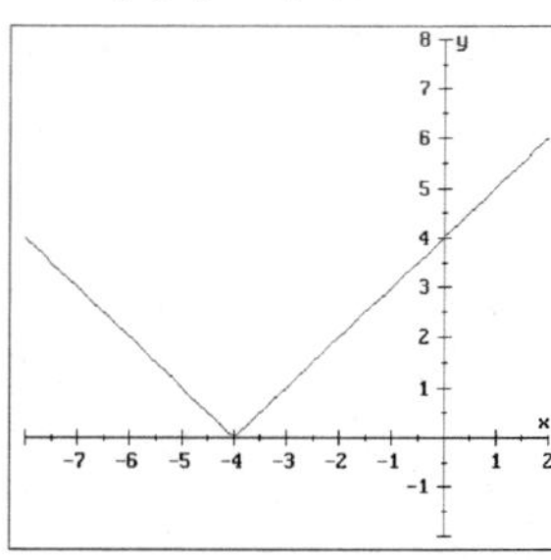

31. $f(x) = |x + 2| - 1$
Shift $f(x) = |x|$ D 1, L 2

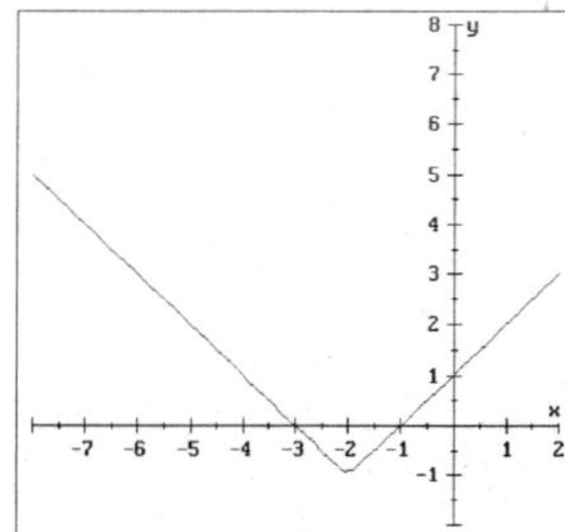

32. $h(x) = |x - 3| + 3$
Shift $f(x) = |x|$ U 3, R 3

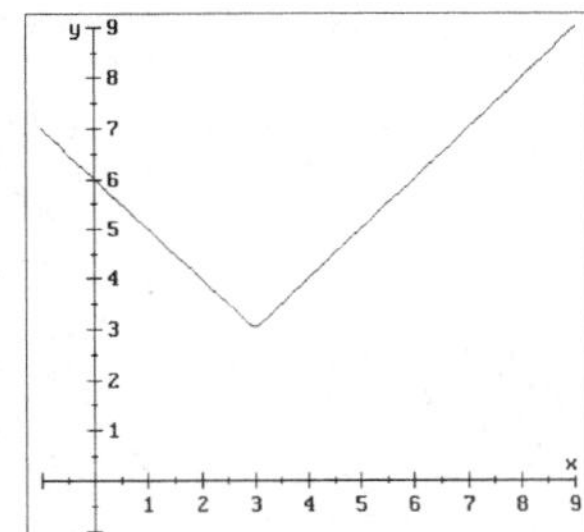

33. $g(x) = \sqrt{x} + 1$
Shift $f(x) = \sqrt{x}$ U 1

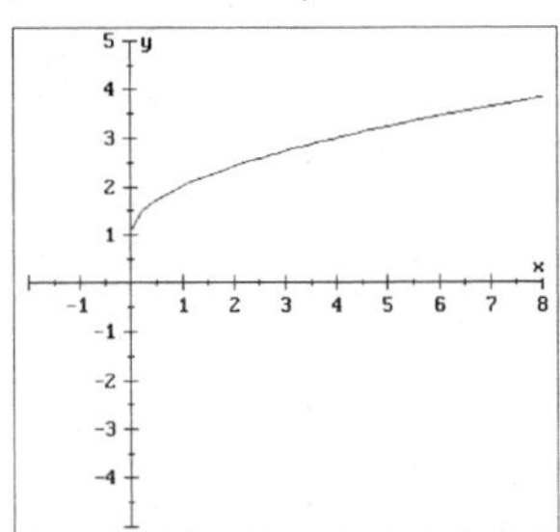

34. $g(x) = \sqrt{x} - 3$
Shift $f(x) = \sqrt{x}$ D 3

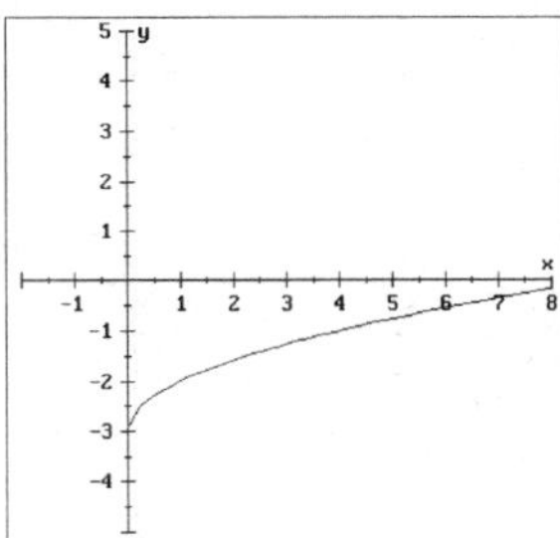

35. $g(x) = \sqrt{x + 2}$
Shift $f(x) = \sqrt{x}$ L 2

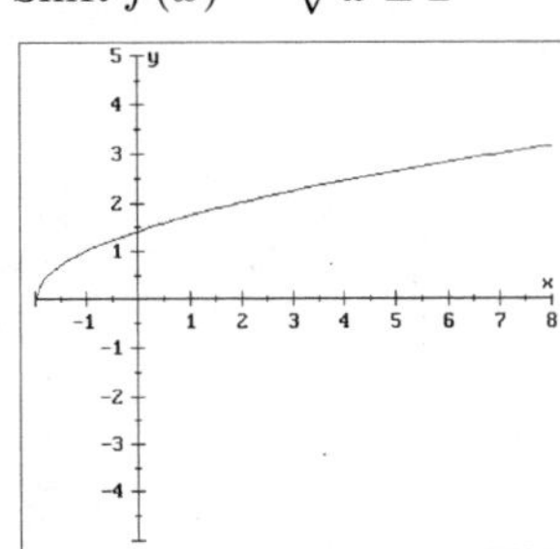

36. $g(x) = \sqrt{x - 4}$
Shift $f(x) = \sqrt{x}$ R 4

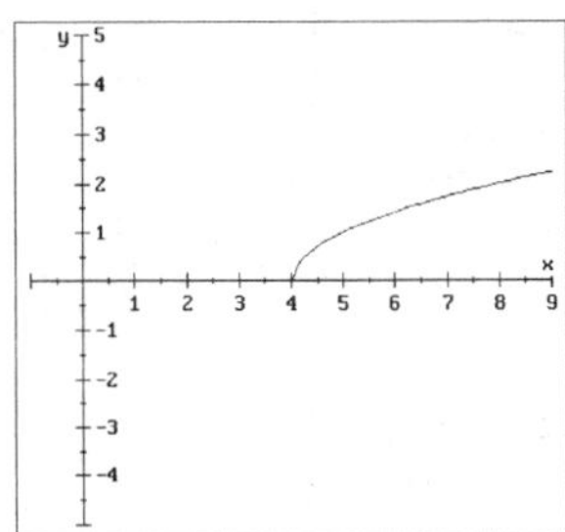

37. $h(x) = \sqrt{x - 2} - 1$
Shift $f(x) = \sqrt{x}$ D 1, R 2

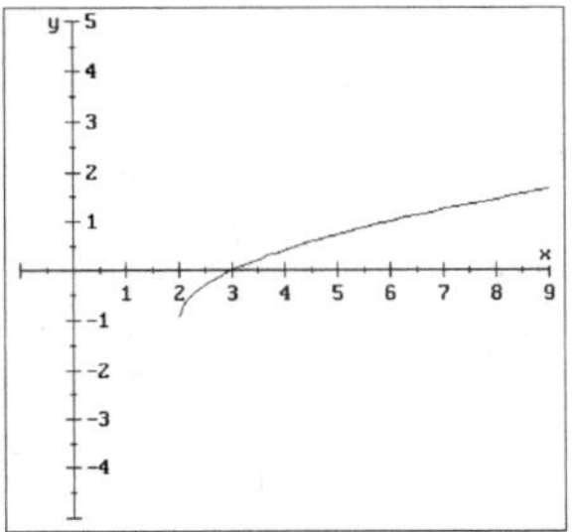

38. $h(x) = \sqrt{x + 2} + 3$
Shift $f(x) = \sqrt{x}$ U 3, L 2

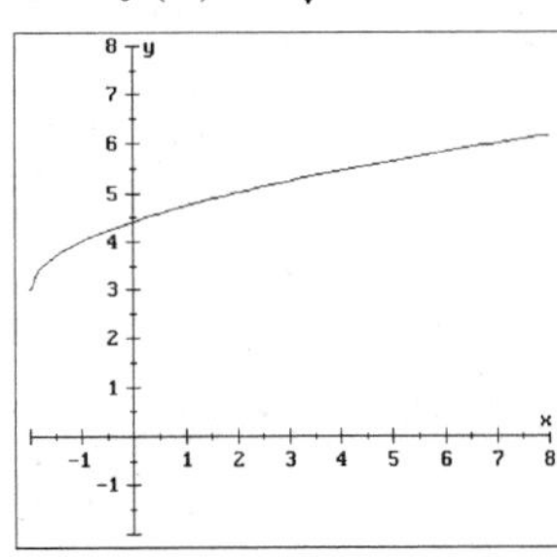

39. $g(x) = \sqrt[3]{x} - 4$
Shift $f(x) = \sqrt[3]{x}$ D 4

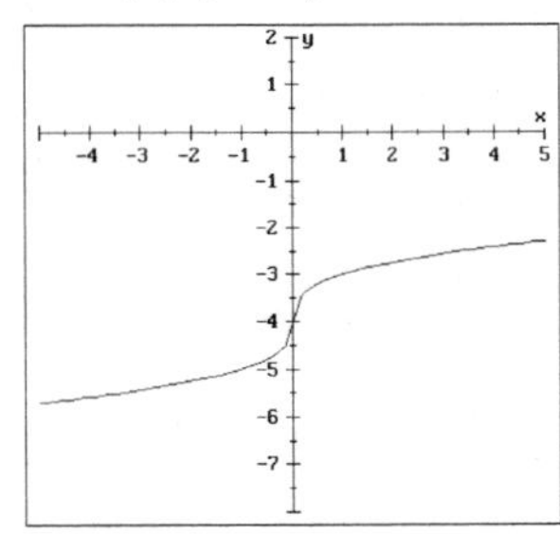

40. $g(x) = \sqrt[3]{x} + 3$
Shift $f(x) = \sqrt[3]{x}$ U 3

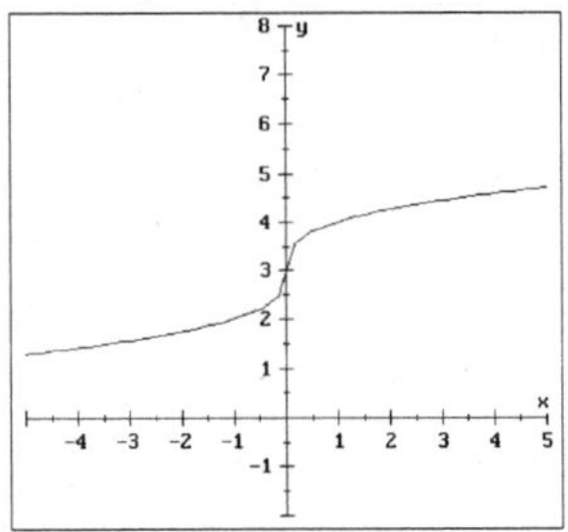

41. $g(x) = \sqrt[3]{x-2}$
Shift $f(x) = \sqrt[3]{x}$ R 2

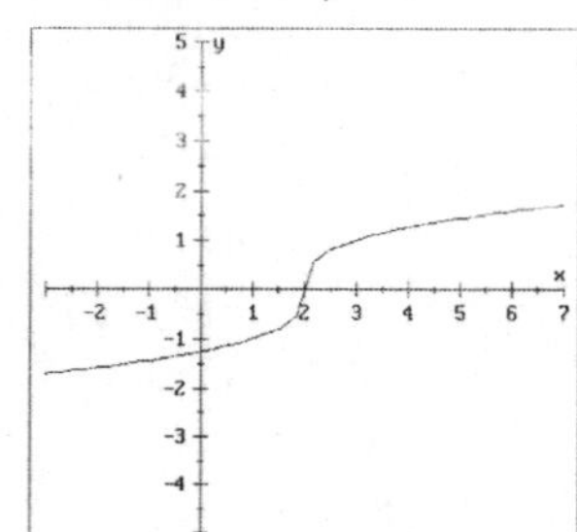

42. $g(x) = \sqrt[3]{x+5}$
Shift $f(x) = \sqrt[3]{x}$ L 5

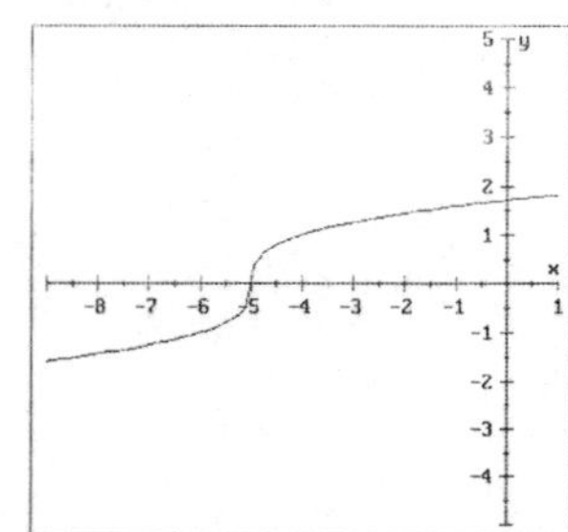

43. $h(x) = \sqrt[3]{x+1} - 1$
Shift $f(x) = \sqrt[3]{x}$ D 1, L 1

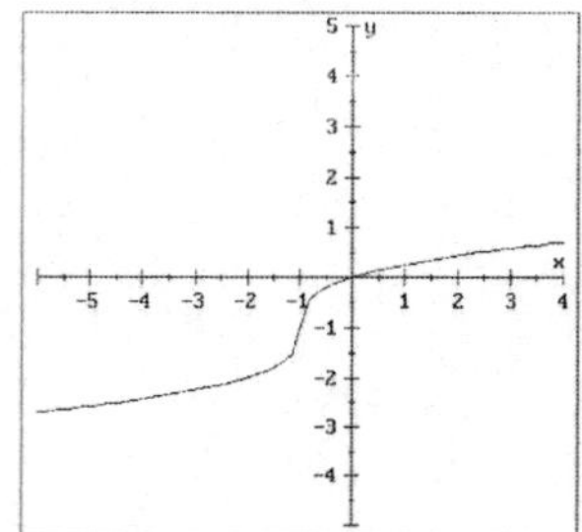

44. $h(x) = \sqrt[3]{x-1} - 1$
Shift $f(x) = \sqrt[3]{x}$ D 1, R 1

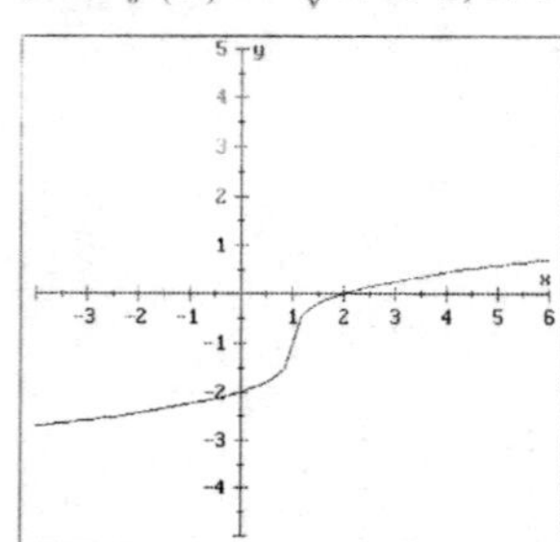

45. $f(x) = -x^2$
Reflect $y = x^2$ about x

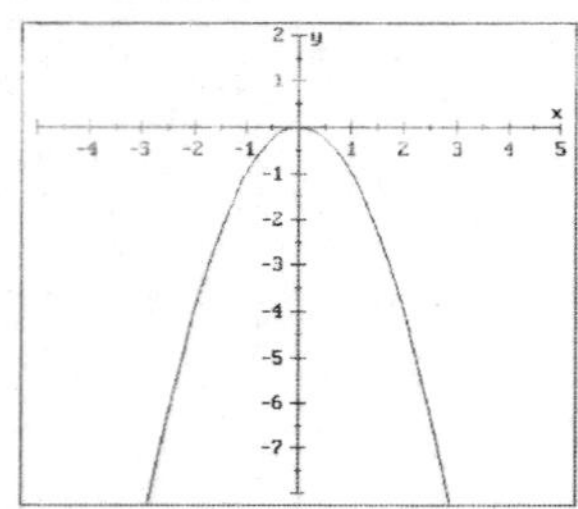

46. $g(x) = (-x)^3$
Reflect $y = x^3$ about y

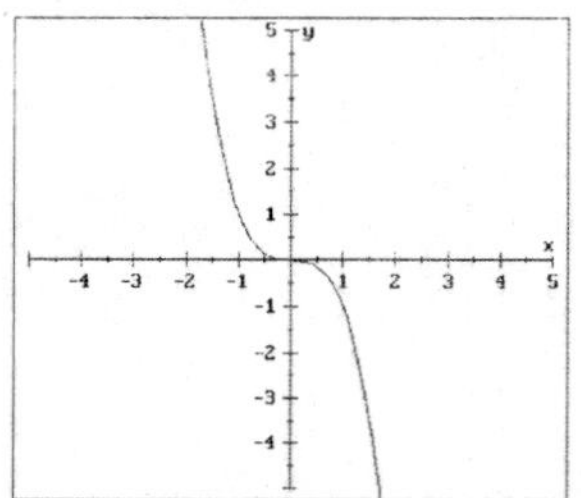

47. $h(x) = -x^3$
Reflect $y = x^3$ about x

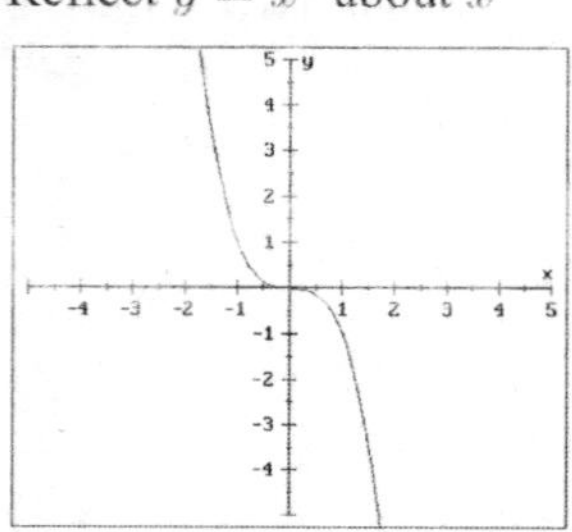

48. $f(x) = -|x|$
Reflect $y = |x|$ about x

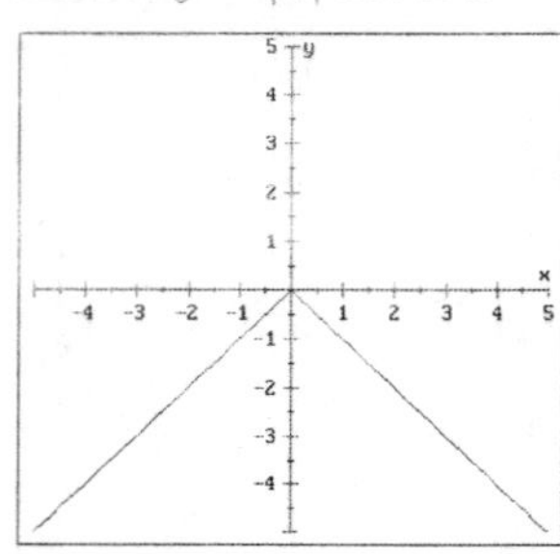

49. $f(x) = -\sqrt{x}$
Reflect $y = \sqrt{x}$ about x

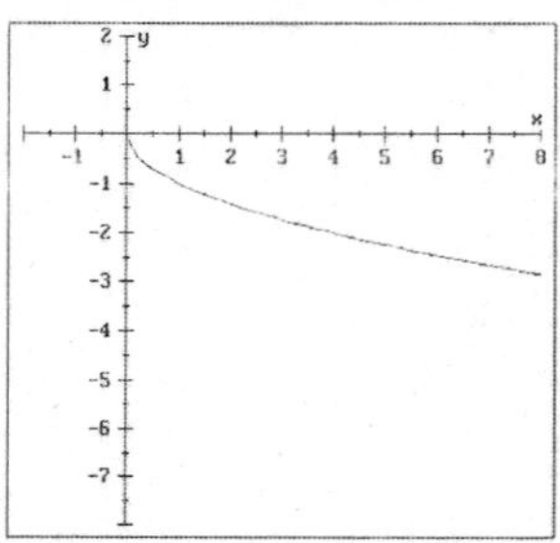

50. $g(x) = \sqrt[3]{-x}$
Reflect $y = \sqrt[3]{x}$ about y

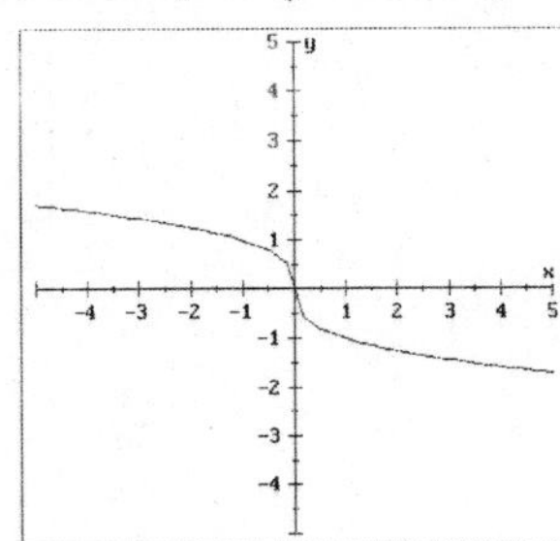

51. $f(x) = |-x|$
Reflect $y = |x|$ about y

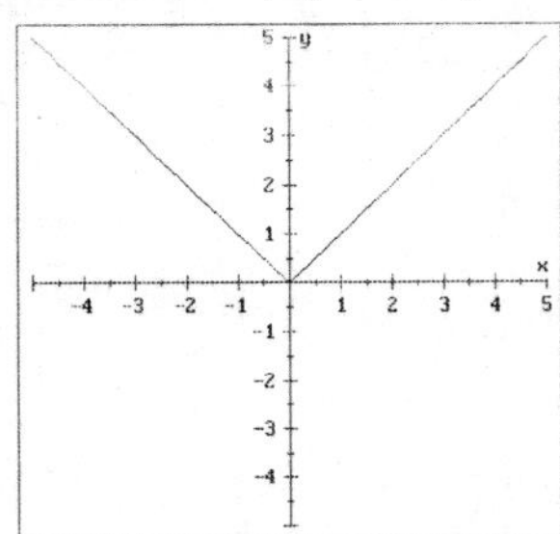

52. $g(x) = (-x)^2$
Reflect $y = x^2$ about y

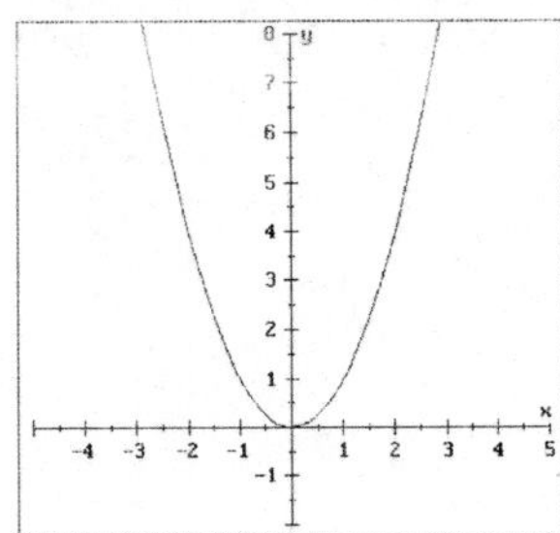

53. $f(x) = 2x^2$: Stretch
$y = x^2$ vert. by a factor of 2

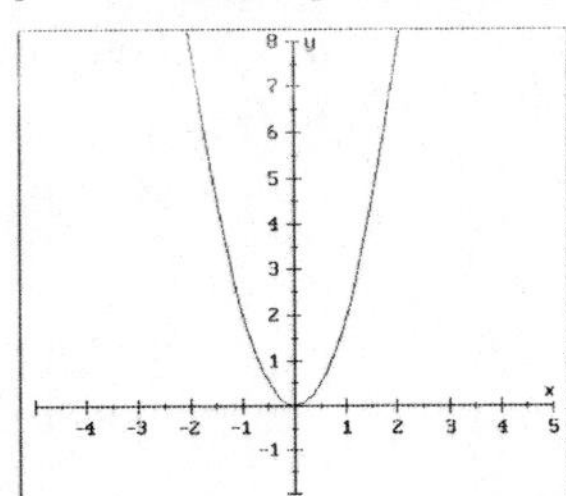

54. $g(x) = \frac{1}{2}x^2$: Shrink
$y = x^2$ vert. by a factor of $\frac{1}{2}$

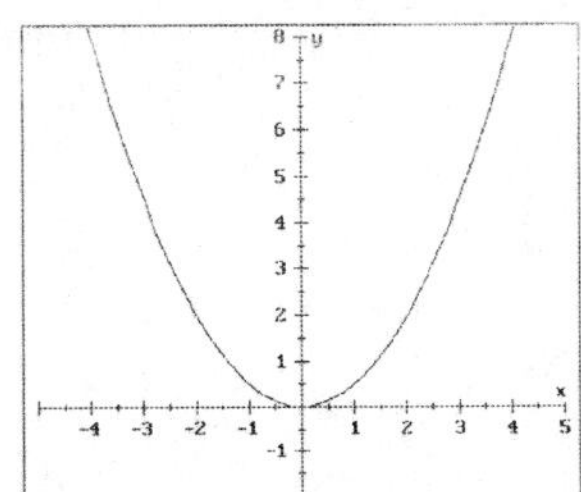

55. $h(x) = -3x^2$: Stretch
$y = x^2$ vert. by a factor of 3
Reflect about x

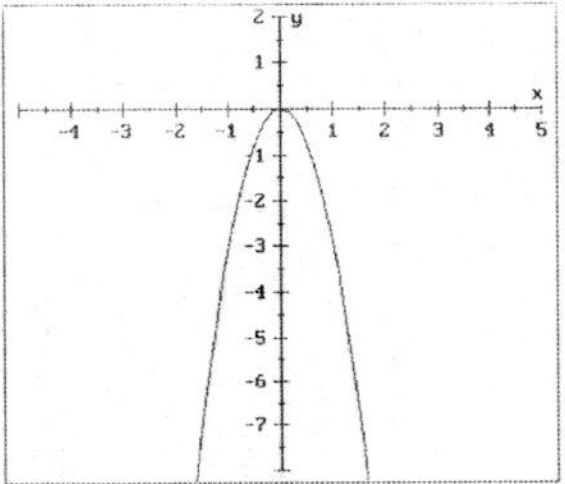

56. $f(x) = -\frac{1}{3}x^2$: Shrink
$y = x^2$ vert. by a factor of $\frac{1}{3}$
Reflect about x

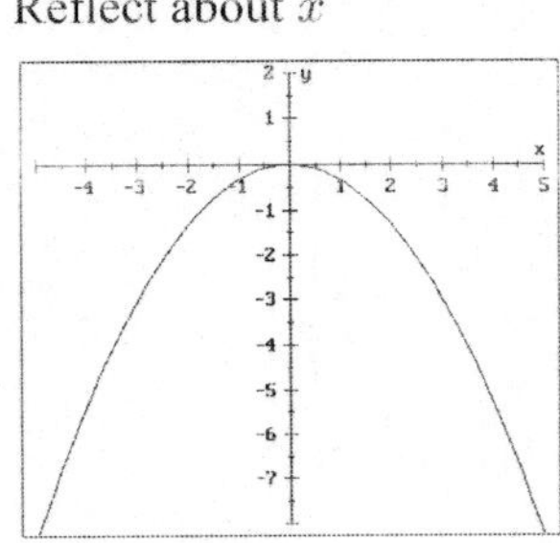

57. $f(x) = \frac{1}{2}x^3$: Shrink
$y = x^3$ vert. by a factor of $\frac{1}{2}$

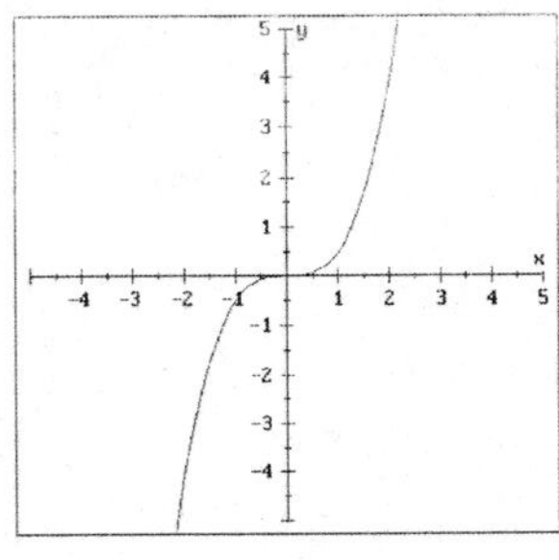

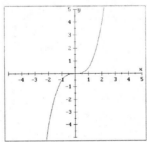

58. $g(x) = 2x^3$: Stretch
$y = x^3$ vert. by a factor of 2

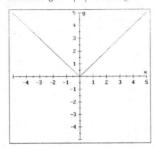

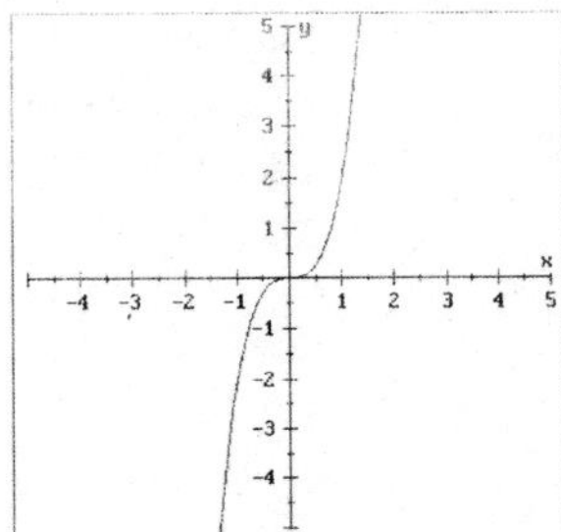

59. $h(x) = -3|x|$: Stretch $y = |x|$ vert. by a factor of 3 Reflect about x

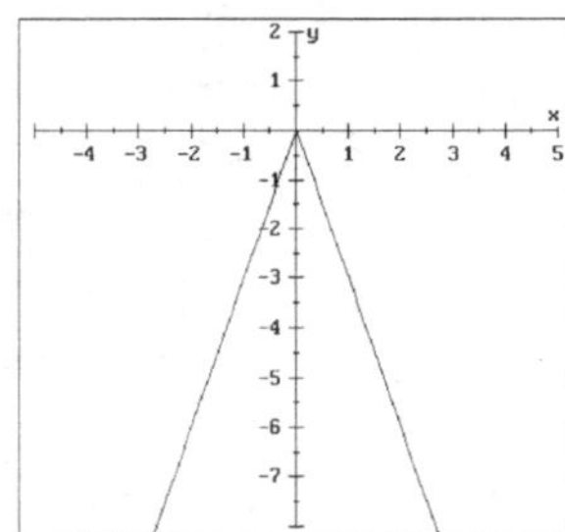

60. $f(x) = \frac{1}{3}|x|$: Shrink $y = |x|$ vert. by a factor of $\frac{1}{3}$

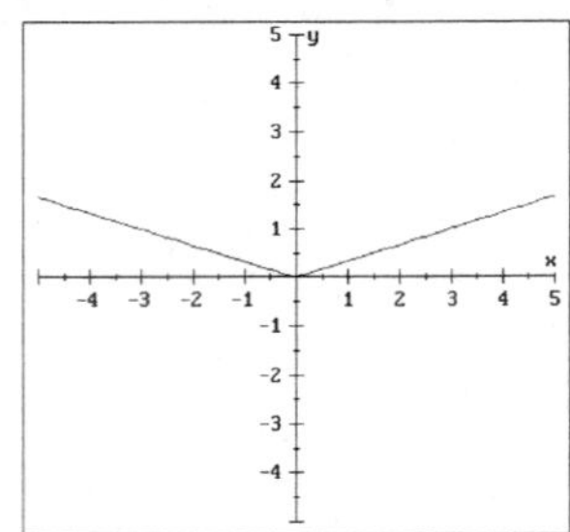

61. $f(x) = \left(\frac{1}{2}x\right)^3$: Stretch $y = x^3$ hor. by a factor of 2

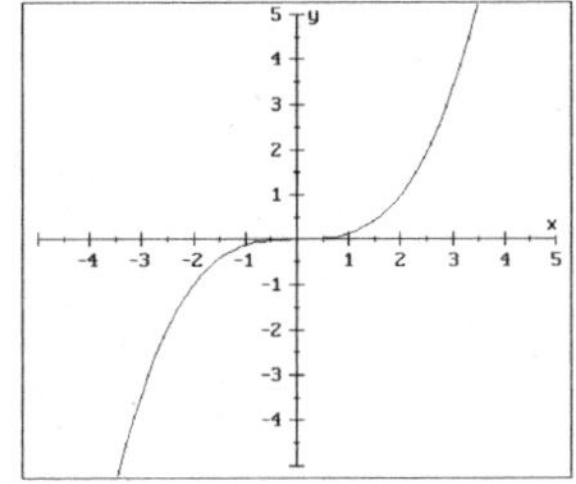

62. $f(x) = (2x)^3$: Shrink $y = x^3$ hor. by a factor of 2

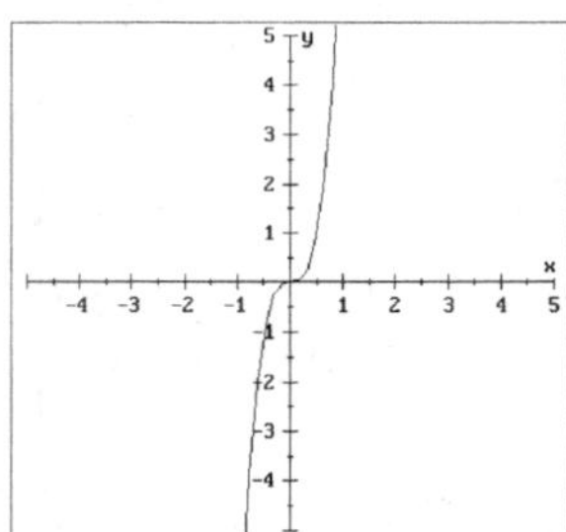

63. $f(x) = (2x)^2$: Shrink $y = x^2$ hor. by a factor of 2

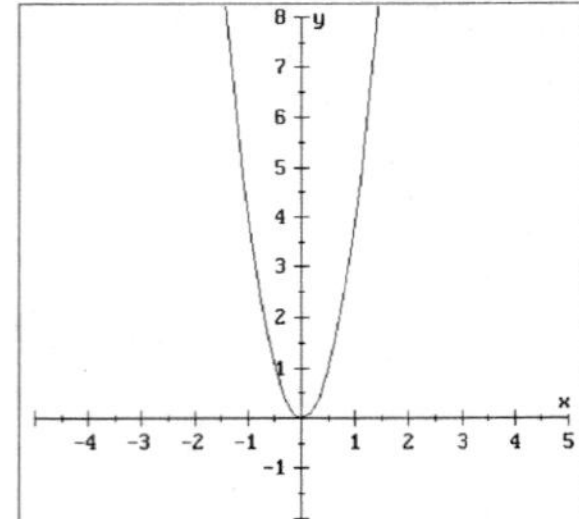

64. $f(x) = (-2x)^3$: Shrink $y = x^3$ hor. by a factor of $\frac{1}{2}$ Reflect about y

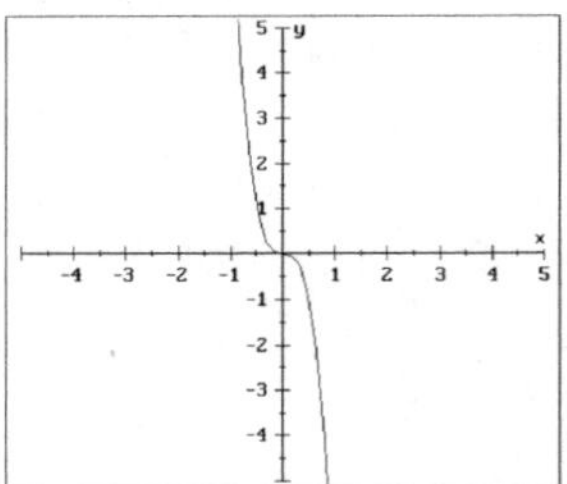

65. $g(x) = 3(x+2)^2 - 1$ Start with $y = x^2$ Shift L 2, Stretch vert. by a factor of 3, Shift D 1

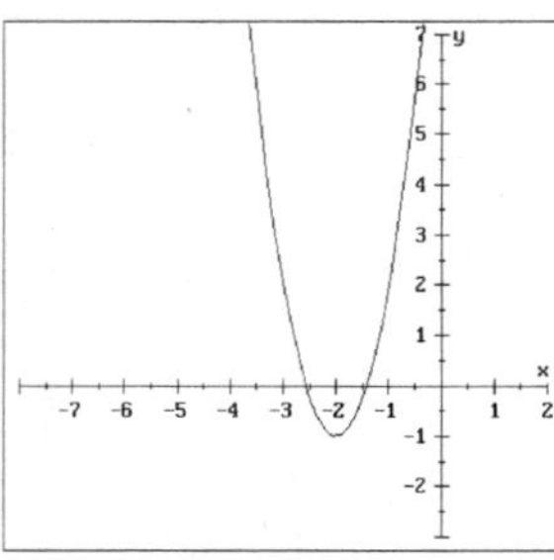

66. $g(x) = -\frac{1}{3}(x+1)^2 + 1$ Start with $y = x^2$, Shift L1 Shrink vert. by a factor of $\frac{1}{3}$, Reflect x, Shift U1

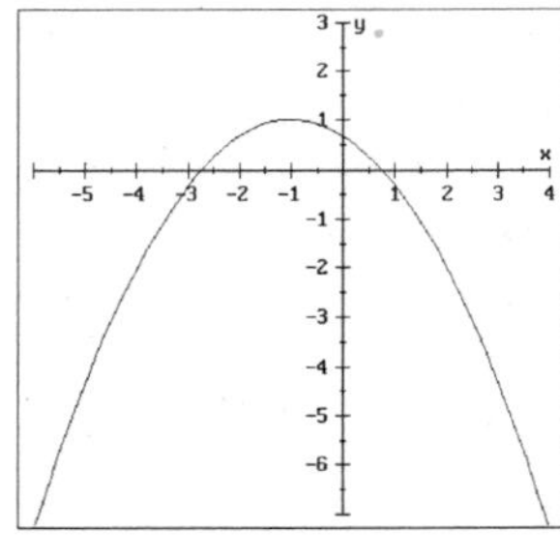

67. $h(x) = -2|x| + 3$ Start with $y = |x|$ Stretch vert. by a factor of 2; Reflect x; Shift U 3

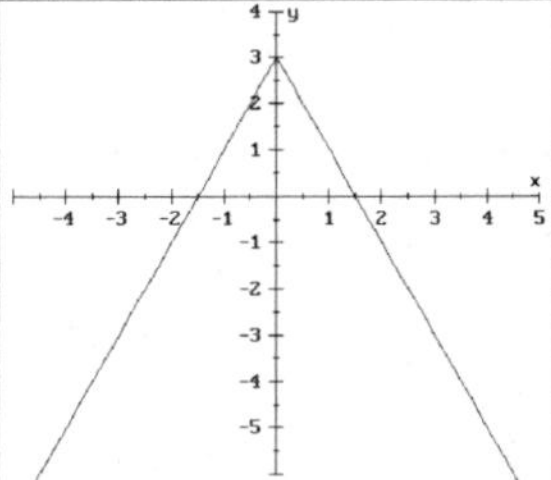

68. $f(x) = -2|x+3|$
Start with $y = |x|$
Shift L 3, Stretch vert. by a factor of 2, Reflect x

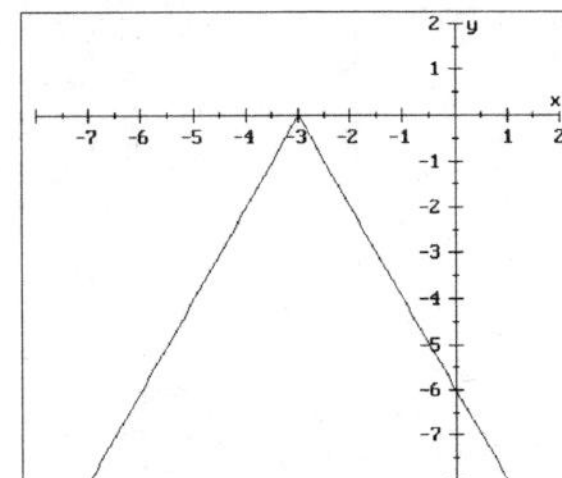

69. $f(x) = 2|x-2|+1$
Start with $y = |x|$
Shift R 2, Stretch vert. by a factor of 2, Shift U 1

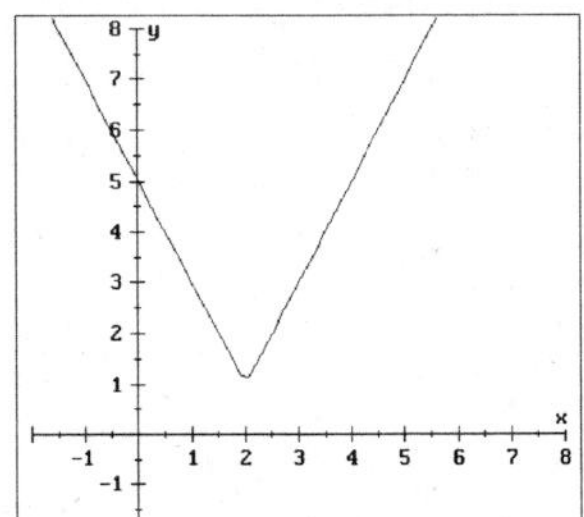

70. $f(x) = -3|x+5|-2$
Start with $y = |x|$
Shift L 5, Stretch vert. by a factor of 3, Reflect x, Shift D 2

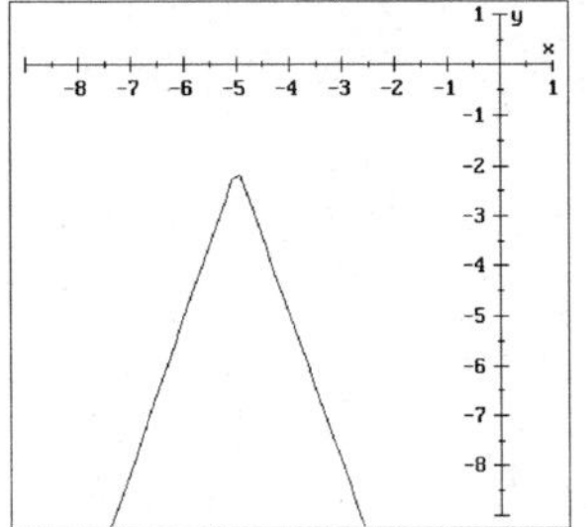

71. $f(x) = 2\sqrt{x}+3$
Start with $y = \sqrt{x}$
Stretch vert. by a factor of 2, Shift U 3

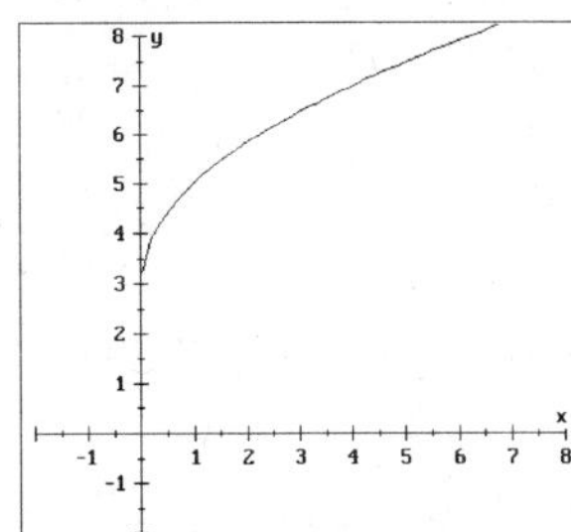

72. $g(x) = 2\sqrt{x+3}$
Start with $y = \sqrt{x}$
Shift L 3, Stretch vert. by a factor of 2

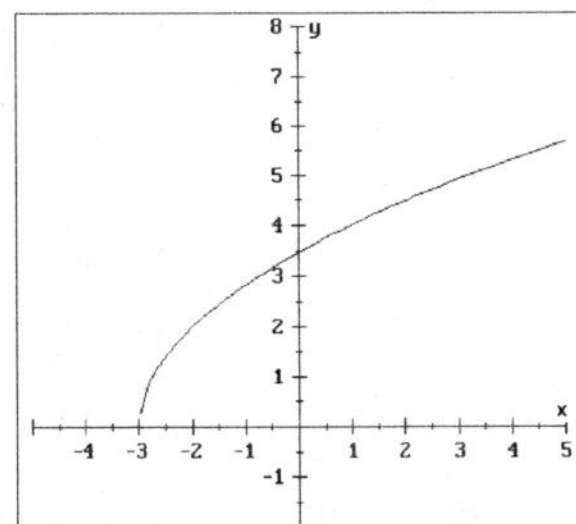

73. $h(x) = 2\sqrt{x-2}+1$
Start with $y = \sqrt{x}$
Shift R 2, Stretch vert. by a factor of 2, Shift U 1

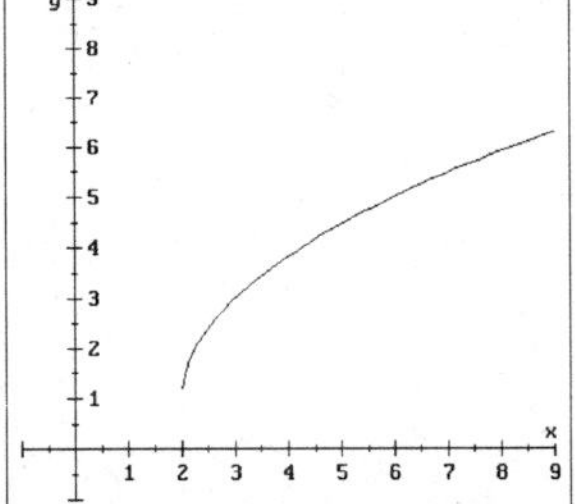

74. $h(x) = \frac{1}{2}\sqrt{x+5}-2$
Start with $y = \sqrt{x}$
Shift L 5, Shrink vert. by a factor of $\frac{1}{2}$, Shift D 2

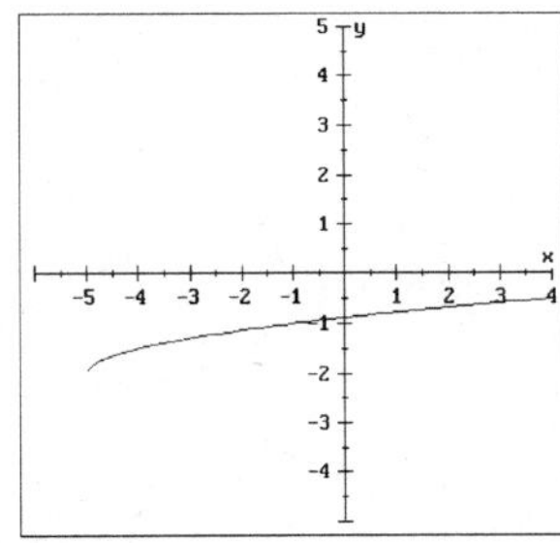

75. $g(x) = -2(x+2)^3-1$
Start with $y = x^3$
Shift L 2, Stretch vert. by a factor of 2, Reflect x, Shift D 1

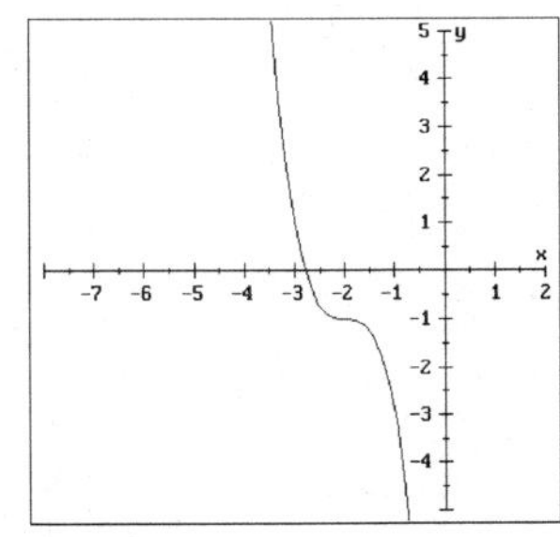

76. $g(x) = \frac{1}{3}(x+1)^3-1$
Start with $y = x^3$
Shift L 1, Shrink vert. by a factor of $\frac{1}{3}$, Shift D 1

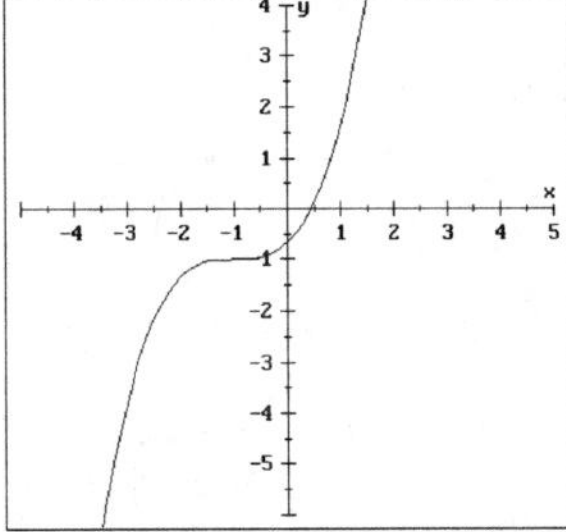

77. $f(x) = 2\sqrt[3]{x} + 4$
Start with $y = \sqrt[3]{x}$
Stretch vert. by a factor of 2, Shift U 4

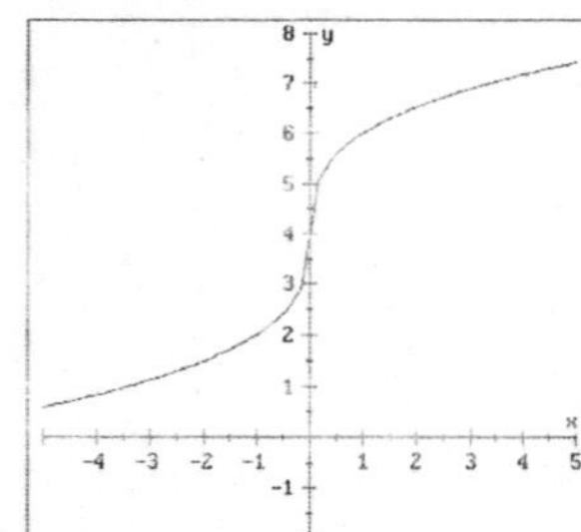

78. $f(x) = -2\sqrt[3]{x+1}$
Start with $y = \sqrt[3]{x}$
Shift L 1, Stretch vert. by a factor of 2, Reflect x

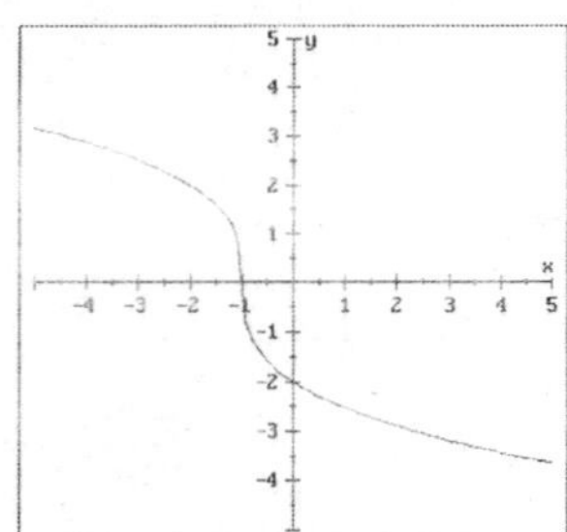

79. Shift $y = f(x)$ U 1

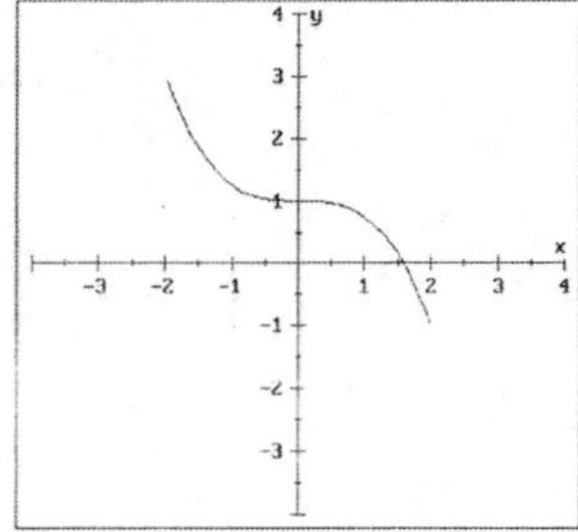

80. Shift $y = f(x)$ L 1

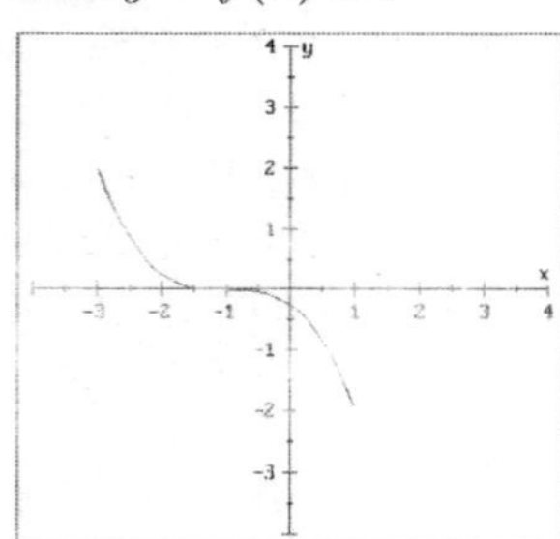

81. Stretch $y = f(x)$ vert. by a factor of 2

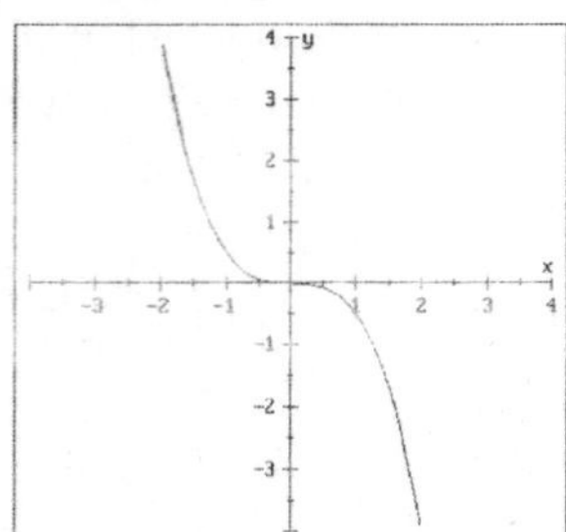

82. Stretch $y = f(x)$ hor. by a factor of 2

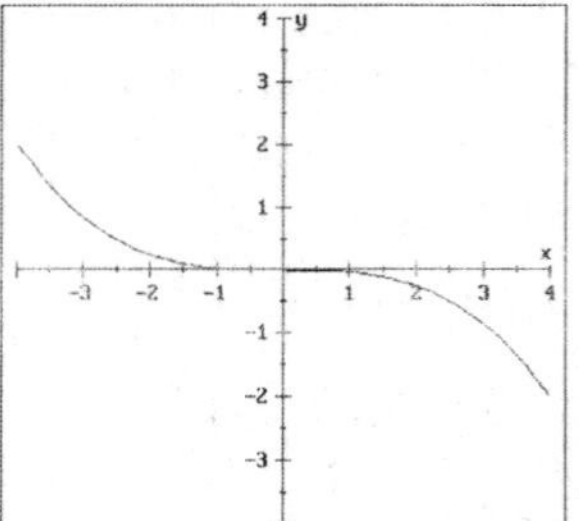

83. Shift $y = f(x)$ U 1, R 2

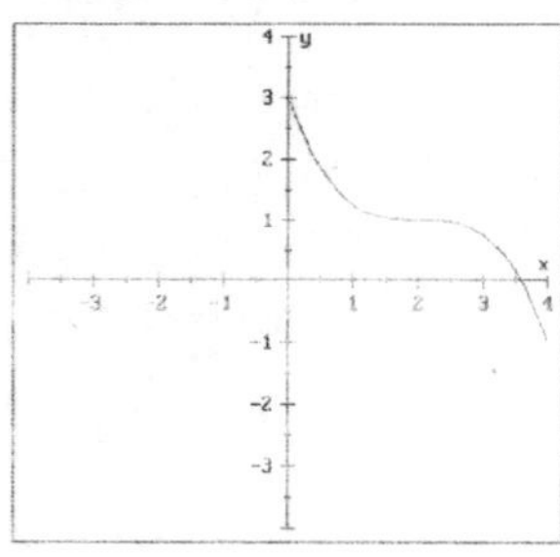

84. Reflect $y = f(x)$ about x

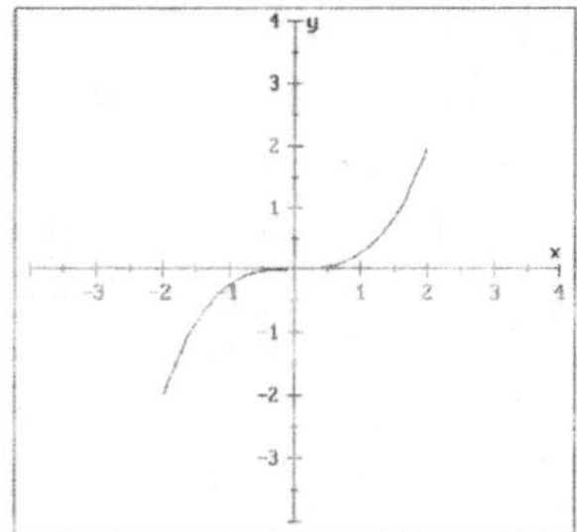

85. Stretch $y = f(x)$ vert. by a factor of 2, reflect about y

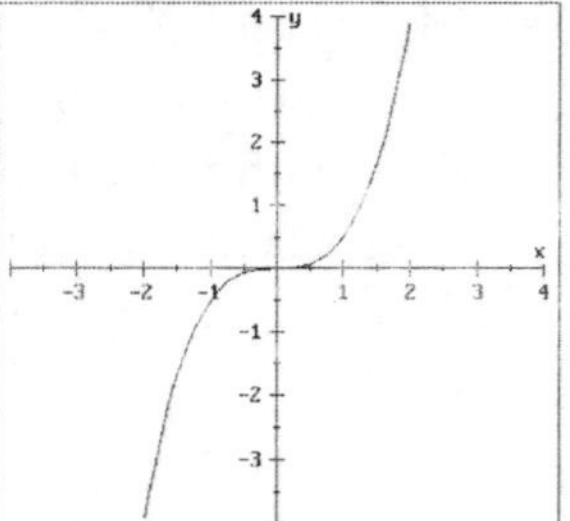

86. Shift $y = f(x)$ D 2, L 1

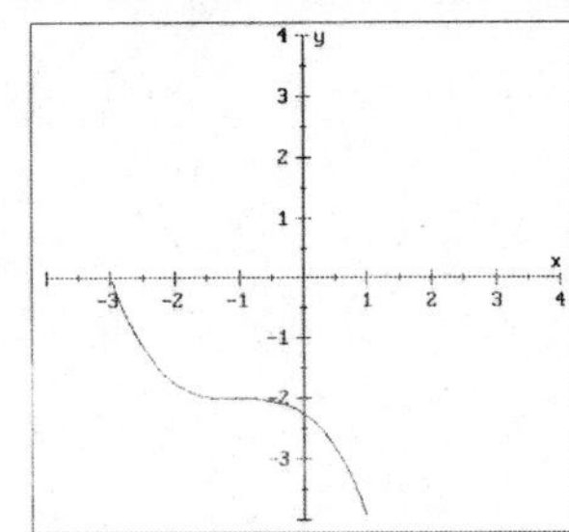

87. **Answers may vary.**

88. **Answers may vary.**

89. **Answers may vary.**

90. **Answers may vary.**

91. **Answers may vary.**

92. **Answers may vary.**

93. $\dfrac{x^2+x-6}{x^2+5x+6} = \dfrac{(x+3)(x-2)}{(x+2)(x+3)} = \dfrac{x-2}{x+2}$

94. $\dfrac{2x^2+3x}{2x^2+x-3} = \dfrac{x(2x+3)}{(2x+3)(x-1)} = \dfrac{x}{x-1}$

95. $f(x) = \dfrac{x+7}{x-3}$; domain $= (-\infty, 3) \cup (3, \infty)$

96. $f(x) = \dfrac{x^2+1}{x^2+3x+2} = \dfrac{x^2+1}{(x+2)(x+1)}$
domain $= (-\infty, -2) \cup (-2, -1) \cup (-1, \infty)$

97.

$$\begin{array}{r|l} & x + 2 + \frac{-2}{x+1} \\ x+1 & x^2 + 3x + 0 \\ & x^2 + x \\ \hline & 2x + 0 \\ & 2x + 2 \\ \hline & -2 \end{array}$$

98.

$$\begin{array}{r|l} & x - 1 + \frac{4}{x+1} \\ x+1 & x^2 + 0x + 3 \\ & x^2 + x \\ \hline & -x + 3 \\ & -x - 1 \\ \hline & 4 \end{array}$$

Exercises 3.5 (page 361)

1. asymptote

2. nonzero

3. vertical

4. y-intercept

5. x-intercept

6. $y = 0$

7. same

8. slant asymptote

9. horizontal or slant; vertical

10. missing

11. vertical: $x = 2$, horizontal: $y = 1$
domain: $(-\infty, 2) \cup (2, \infty)$
range: $(-\infty, 1) \cup (1, \infty)$

12. vertical: $x = -2$, $x = 2$, horizontal: $y = 0$
domain: $(-\infty, -2) \cup (-2, 2) \cup (2, \infty)$
range: $(-\infty, \infty)$

13. $t = f(30) = \frac{600}{30} = 20$ hr

14. $t = f(40) = \frac{600}{40} = 15$ hr

15. $t = f(50) = \frac{600}{50} = 12$ hr

16. $t = f(60) = \frac{600}{60} = 10$ hr

17. $c = f(10) = \dfrac{50{,}000(10)}{100-10} \approx \$5555.56$

18. $c = f(30) = \dfrac{50{,}000(30)}{100-30} \approx \$21{,}428.57$

19. $c = f(50) = \dfrac{50{,}000(50)}{100-50} = \$50{,}000.00$

20. $c = f(80) = \dfrac{50{,}000(80)}{100-80} = \$200{,}000.00$

21. $f(x) = \dfrac{x^2}{x-2}$; den $= 0 \Rightarrow x = 2$
domain $= (-\infty, 2) \cup (2, \infty)$

22. $f(x) = \dfrac{x^3 - 3x^2 + 1}{x+3}$; den $= 0 \Rightarrow x = -3$
domain $= (-\infty, -3) \cup (-3, \infty)$

23. $f(x) = \dfrac{2x^2 + 7x - 2}{x^2 - 25} = \dfrac{2x^2 + 7x - 2}{(x+5)(x-5)}$
den $= 0 \Rightarrow x = -5, x = 5$
domain $= (-\infty, -5) \cup (-5, 5) \cup (5, \infty)$

24. $f(x) = \dfrac{5x^2 + 1}{x^2 + 5}$
den $= 0 \Rightarrow$ never true
domain $= (-\infty, \infty)$

25. $f(x) = \dfrac{x-1}{x^3 - x} = \dfrac{x-1}{x(x+1)(x-1)}$; den $= 0 \Rightarrow x = 0, x = -1, x = 1$
domain $= (-\infty, -1) \cup (-1, 0) \cup (0, 1) \cup (1, \infty)$

26. $f(x) = \dfrac{x+2}{2x^2 - 9x + 9} = \dfrac{x+2}{(2x-3)(x-3)}$; den $= 0 \Rightarrow x = \dfrac{3}{2}, x = 3$
domain $= \left(-\infty, \frac{3}{2}\right) \cup \left(\frac{3}{2}, 3\right) \cup (3, \infty)$

27. $f(x) = \dfrac{3x^2 + 5}{x^2 + 1}$; den $= 0 \Rightarrow$ never true
domain $= (-\infty, \infty)$

28. $f(x) = \dfrac{7x^2 - x + 2}{x^4 + 4}$; den $= 0 \Rightarrow$ never true
domain $= (-\infty, \infty)$

29. $f(x) = \dfrac{x}{x-3}$; den $= 0 \Rightarrow x = 3$
vertical: $x = 3$

30. $f(x) = \dfrac{2x}{2x+5}$; den $= 0 \Rightarrow x = -\frac{5}{2}$
vertical: $x = -\frac{5}{2}$

31. $f(x) = \dfrac{x+2}{x^2 - 1} = \dfrac{x+2}{(x+1)(x-1)}$
den $= 0 \Rightarrow x = -1, x = 1$
vertical: $x = -1, x = 1$

32. $f(x) = \dfrac{x-4}{x^2 - 16} = \dfrac{x-4}{(x+4)(x-4)} = \dfrac{1}{x+4}$
den $= 0 \Rightarrow x = -4$
vertical: $x = -4$

33. $f(x) = \dfrac{1}{x^2 - x - 6} = \dfrac{1}{(x+2)(x-3)}$
den $= 0 \Rightarrow x = -2, x = 3$
vertical: $x = -2, x = 3$

34. $f(x) = \dfrac{x+2}{2x^2 - 6x - 8} = \dfrac{x+2}{2(x^2 - 3x - 4)}$
$= \dfrac{x+2}{2(x+1)(x-4)}$
den $= 0 \Rightarrow x = -1, x = 4$
vertical: $x = -1, x = 4$

35. $f(x) = \dfrac{x^2}{x^2 + 5}$; den $= 0 \Rightarrow$ never true
vertical: none

36. $f(x) = \dfrac{x^3 - 3x^2 + 1}{2x^2 + 3}$; den $= 0 \Rightarrow$ never true
vertical: none

37. $f(x) = \dfrac{2x - 1}{x}$; deg(num) = deg(den)
horizontal: $y = \dfrac{2}{1}$, or $y = 2$

38. $f(x) = \dfrac{x^2 + 1}{3x^2 - 5}$; deg(num) = deg(den)
horizontal: $y = \dfrac{1}{3}$

39. $f(x) = \dfrac{x^2 + x - 2}{2x^2 - 4}$; deg(num) = deg(den)
horizontal: $y = \dfrac{1}{2}$

40. $f(x) = \dfrac{5x^2 + 1}{5 - x^2}$; deg(num) = deg(den)
horizontal: $y = \dfrac{5}{-1}$, or $y = -5$

41. $f(x) = \dfrac{x + 1}{x^3 - 4x}$; deg(num) < deg(den)
horizontal: $y = 0$

42. $f(x) = \dfrac{x}{2x^2 - x + 11}$; deg(num) < deg(den)
horizontal: $y = 0$

43. $f(x) = \dfrac{x^2}{x - 2}$; deg(num) > deg(den)
horizontal: none

44. $f(x) = \dfrac{x^4 + 1}{x - 3}$; deg(num) > deg(den)
horizontal: none

45. $f(x) = \dfrac{x^2 - 5x - 6}{x - 2} = x - 3 + \dfrac{-12}{x - 2}$
slant: $y = x - 3$

46. $f(x) = \dfrac{x^2 - 2x + 11}{x + 3} = x - 5 + \dfrac{26}{x + 3}$
slant: $y = x - 5$

47. $f(x) = \dfrac{2x^2 - 5x + 1}{x - 4} = 2x + 3 + \dfrac{13}{x - 4}$
slant: $y = 2x + 3$

48. $f(x) = \dfrac{5x^3 + 1}{x + 5}$; deg(num) = 3 and deg(den) = 1; slant: none

49. $f(x) = \dfrac{x^3 + 2x^2 - x - 1}{x^2 - 1}$
$= x + 2 + \dfrac{1}{x^2 - 1}$
slant: $y = x + 2$

50. $f(x) = \dfrac{-x^3 + 3x^2 - x + 1}{x^2 + 1}$
$= -x + 3 + \dfrac{-2}{x^2 + 1}$
slant: $y = -x + 3$

51. $y = \dfrac{1}{x - 2}$
Vert: $x = 2$; Horiz: $y = 0$
Slant: none; x-intercepts: none
y-intercepts: $\left(0, -\frac{1}{2}\right)$; Symmetry: none

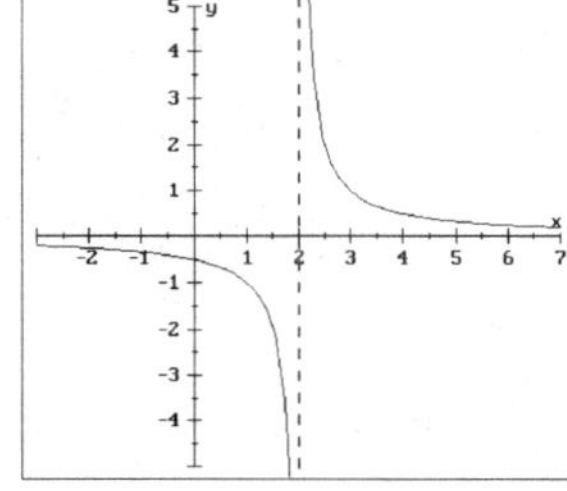

52. $y = \dfrac{3}{x + 3}$
Vert: $x = -3$; Horiz: $y = 0$
Slant: none; x-intercepts: none
y-intercepts: $(0, 1)$; Symmetry: none

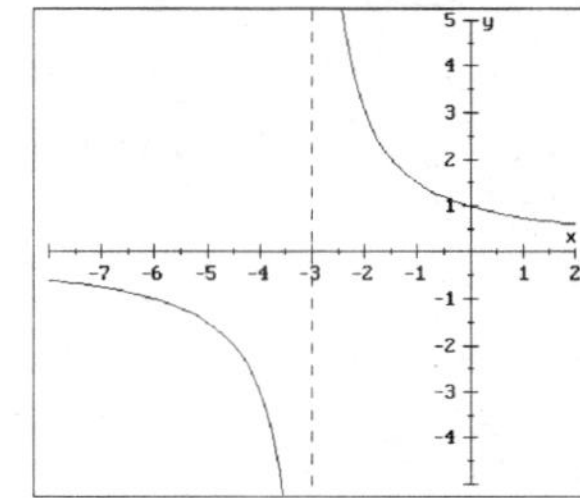

53. $y = \dfrac{x}{x-1}$

Vert: $x = 1$; Horiz: $y = \frac{1}{1} = 1$

Slant: none; x-intercepts: $(0, 0)$

y-intercepts: $(0, 0)$; Symmetry: none

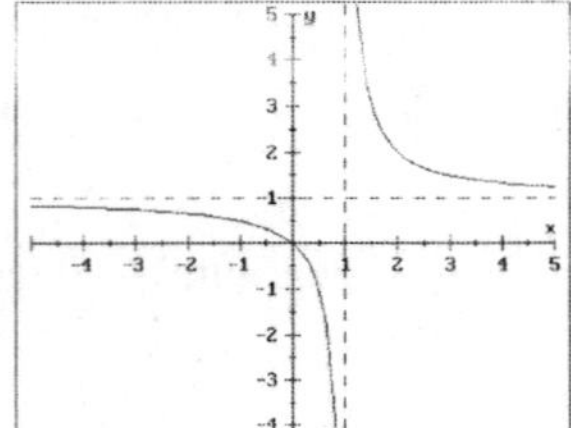

54. $y = \dfrac{x}{x+2}$

Vert: $x = -2$; Horiz: $y = \frac{1}{1} = 1$

Slant: none; x-intercepts: $(0, 0)$

y-intercepts: $(0, 0)$; Symmetry: none

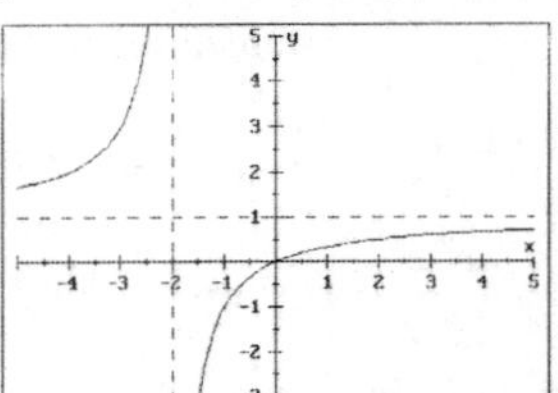

55. $f(x) = \dfrac{x+1}{x+2}$

Vert: $x = -2$; Horiz: $y = \frac{1}{1} = 1$

Slant: none; x-intercepts: $(-1, 0)$

y-intercepts: $\left(0, \frac{1}{2}\right)$; Symmetry: none

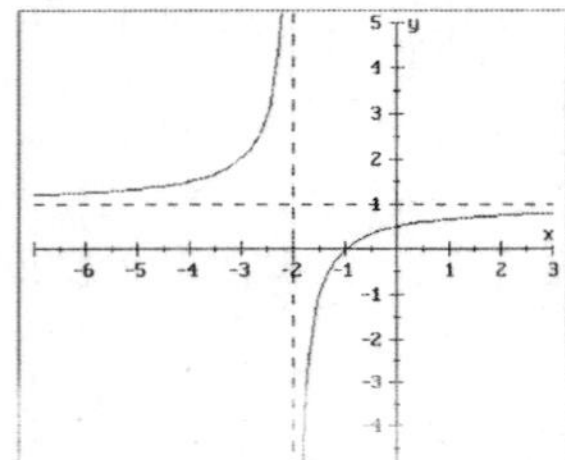

56. $f(x) = \dfrac{x-1}{x-2}$

Vert: $x = 2$; Horiz: $y = \frac{1}{1} = 1$

Slant: none; x-intercepts: $(1, 0)$

y-intercepts: $\left(0, \frac{1}{2}\right)$; Symmetry: none

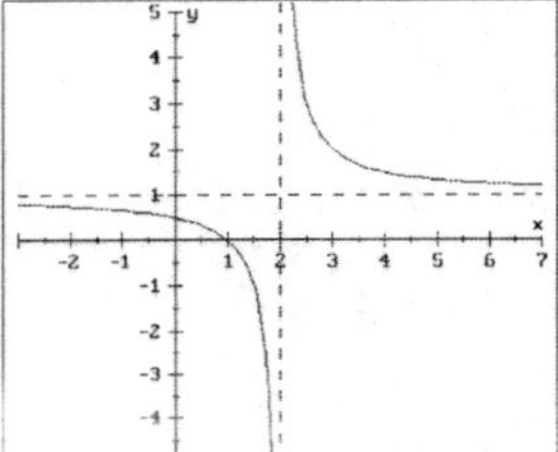

57. $f(x) = \dfrac{2x-1}{x-1}$

Vert: $x = 1$; Horiz: $y = \frac{2}{1} = 2$

Slant: none; x-intercepts: $\left(\frac{1}{2}, 0\right)$

y-intercepts: $(0, 1)$; Symmetry: none

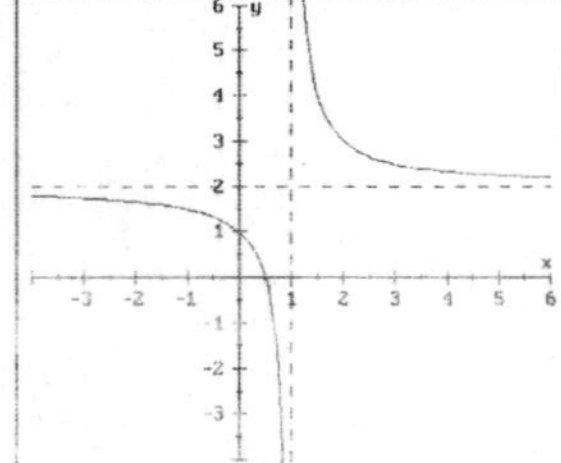

58. $f(x) = \dfrac{3x+2}{x^2-4} = \dfrac{3x+2}{(x+2)(x-2)}$

Vert: $x = -2$, $x = 2$; Horiz: $y = 0$

Slant: none; x-intercepts: $\left(-\frac{2}{3}, 0\right)$

y-intercepts: $\left(0, -\frac{1}{2}\right)$; Symmetry: none

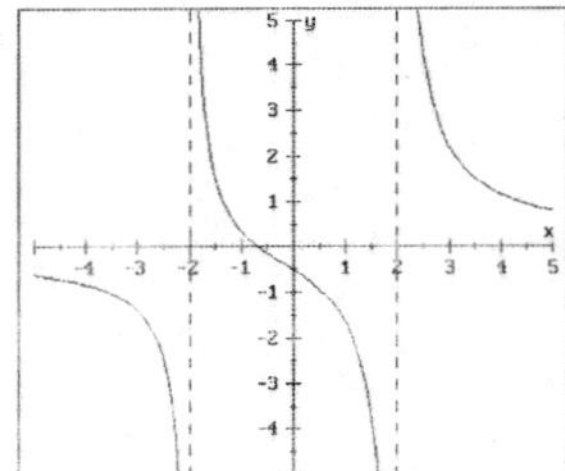

59. $g(x)=\frac{x^2-9}{x^2-4}=\frac{(x+3)(x-3)}{(x+2)(x-2)}$

Vert: $x=-2$, $x=2$; Horiz: $y=\frac{1}{1}=1$

Slant: none; x-intercepts: $(-3,0)$, $(3,0)$

y-intercepts: $\left(0,\frac{9}{4}\right)$; Symmetry: y-axis

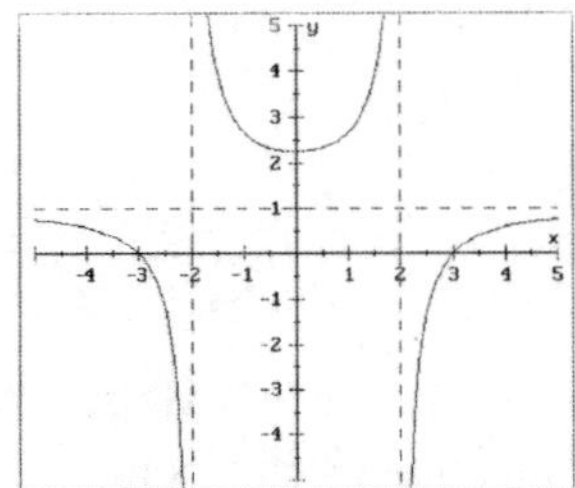

60. $g(x)=\frac{x^2-4}{x^2-9}=\frac{(x+2)(x-2)}{(x+3)(x-3)}$

Vert: $x=-3$, $x=3$; Horiz: $y=\frac{1}{1}=1$

Slant: none; x-intercepts: $(-2,0)$, $(2,0)$

y-intercepts: $\left(0,\frac{4}{9}\right)$; Symmetry: y-axis

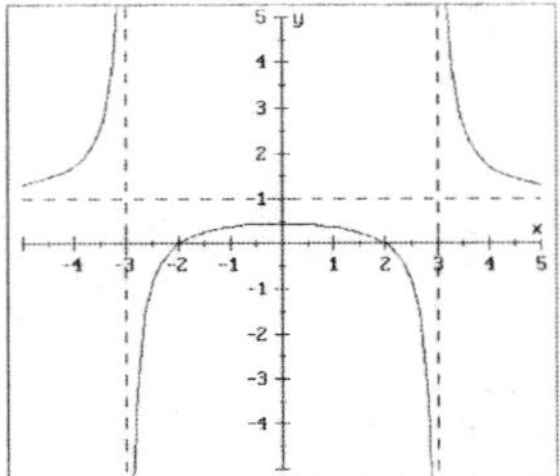

61. $g(x)=\frac{x^2-x-2}{x^2-4x+3}=\frac{(x+1)(x-2)}{(x-3)(x-1)}$

Vert: $x=3$, $x=1$; Horiz: $y=\frac{1}{1}=1$

Slant: none; x-intercepts: $(-1,0)$, $(2,0)$

y-intercepts: $\left(0,-\frac{2}{3}\right)$; Symmetry: none

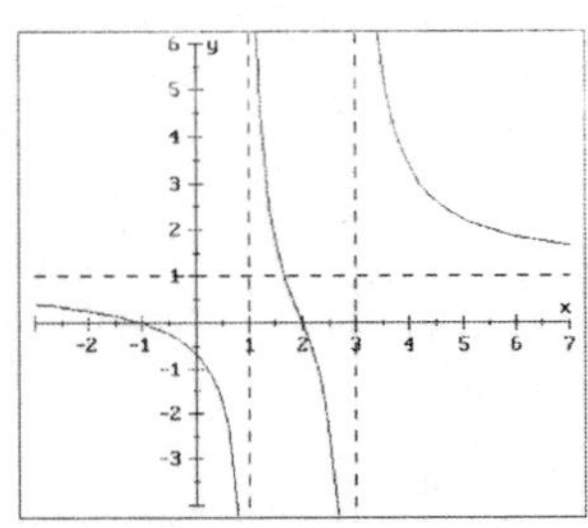

62. $g(x)=\frac{x^2+7x+12}{x^2-7x+12}=\frac{(x+3)(x+4)}{(x-3)(x-4)}$

Vert: $x=3$, $x=4$; Horiz: $y=\frac{1}{1}=1$

Slant: none; x-intercepts: $(-3,0)$, $(-4,0)$

y-intercepts: $(0,1)$; Symmetry: none

Because of the differences in scale, 3 different views of the graph are needed to see all of the characteristic parts of the graph:

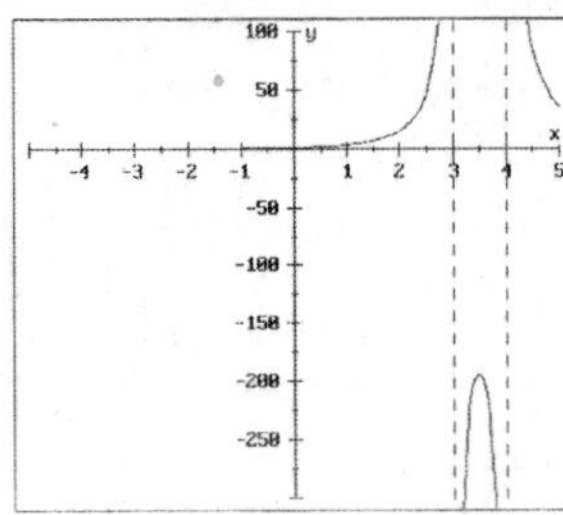

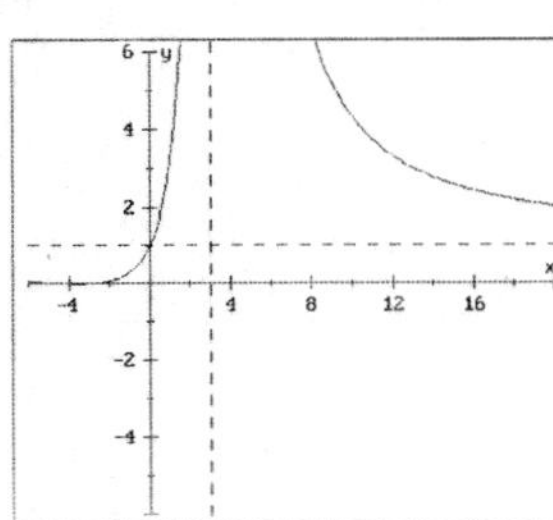

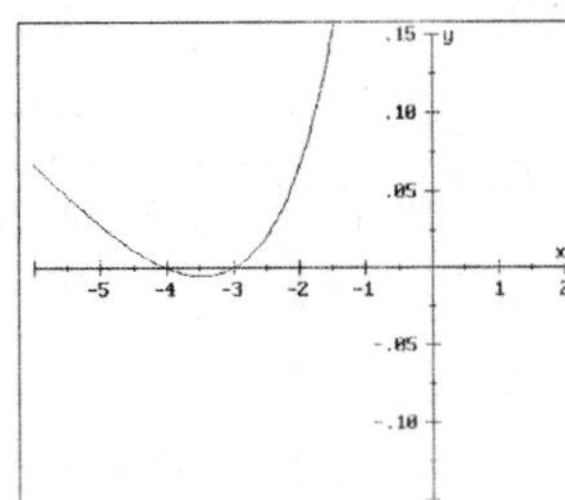

63. $y = \dfrac{x^2 + 2x - 3}{x^3 - 4x} = \dfrac{(x-1)(x+3)}{x(x+2)(x-2)}$

Vert: $x = 0$, $x = -2$, $x = 2$; Horiz: $y = 0$
Slant: none; x-intercepts: $(1, 0)$, $(-3, 0)$
y-intercepts: none; Symmetry: none

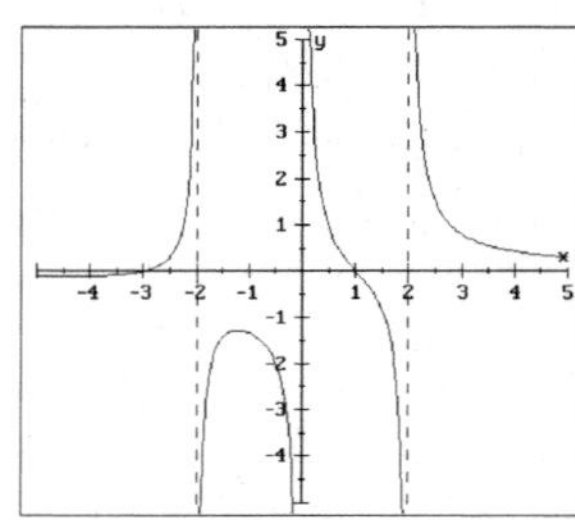

64. $y = \dfrac{3x^2 - 4x + 1}{2x^3 + 3x^2 + x} = \dfrac{(3x-1)(x-1)}{x(2x+1)(x+1)}$

Vert: $x = 0$, $x = -\frac{1}{2}$, $x = -1$; Horiz: $y = 0$
Slant: none; x-intercepts: $\left(\frac{1}{3}, 0\right)$, $(1, 0)$
y-intercepts: none; Symmetry: none

Because of the differences in scale, 2 different views of the graph are needed to see all of the characteristic parts of the graph:

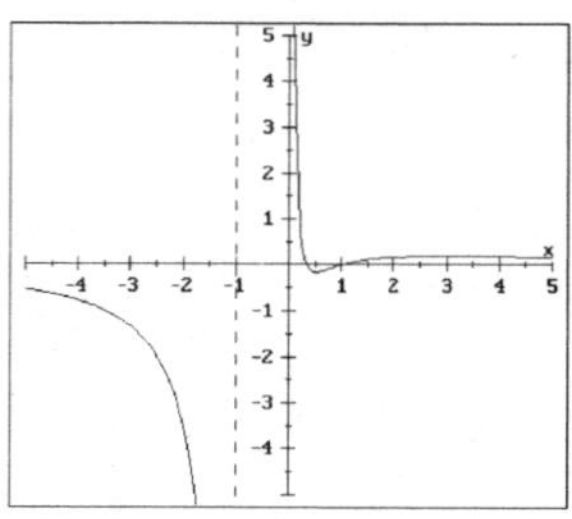

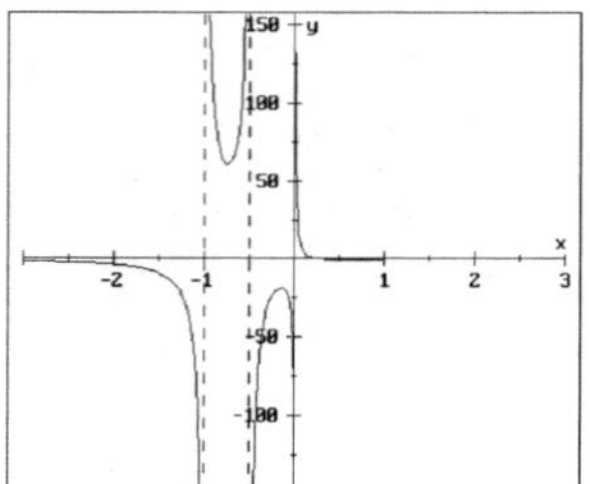

65. $y = \dfrac{x^2 - 9}{x^2} = \dfrac{(x+3)(x-3)}{x^2}$

Vert: $x = 0$; Horiz: $y = \frac{1}{1} = 1$
Slant: none; x-intercepts: $(3, 0)$, $(-3, 0)$
y-intercepts: none; Symmetry: y-axis

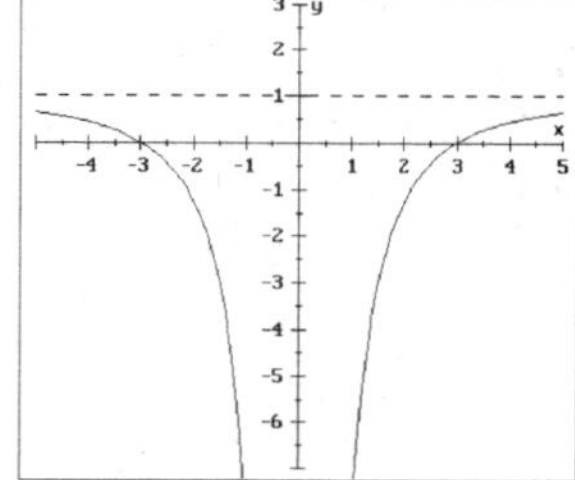

66. $y = \dfrac{3x^2 - 12}{x^2} = \dfrac{3(x+2)(x-2)}{x^2}$

Vert: $x = 0$; Horiz: $y = \frac{3}{1} = 3$
Slant: none; x-intercepts: $(2, 0)$, $(-2, 0)$
y-intercepts: none; Symmetry: y-axis

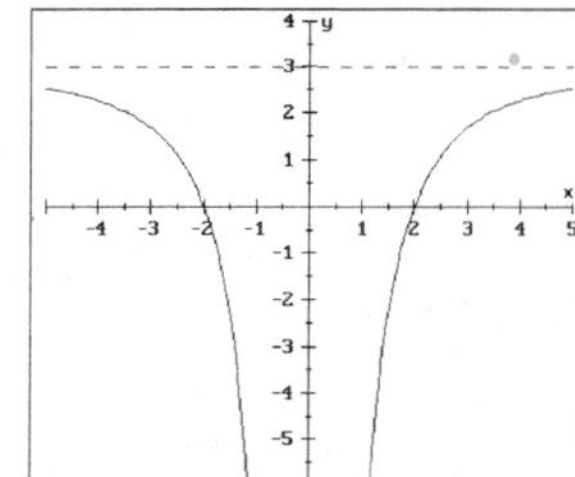

67. $f(x) = \dfrac{x}{(x+3)^2}$

Vert: $x = -3$; Horiz: $y = 0$
Slant: none; x-intercepts: $(0, 0)$
y-intercepts: $(0, 0)$; Symmetry: none

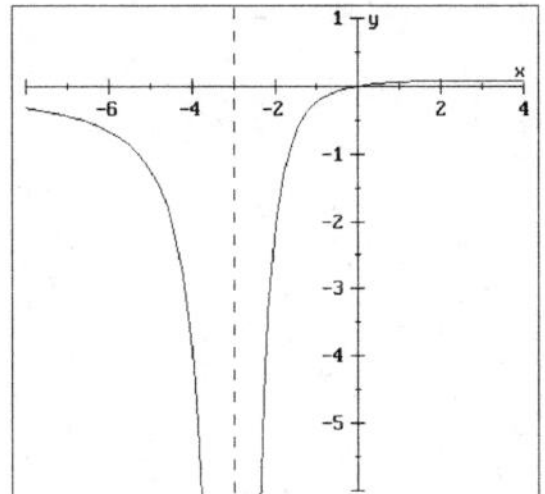

68. $f(x) = \dfrac{x}{(x-1)^2}$

Vert: $x = 1$; Horiz: $y = 0$
Slant: none; x-intercepts: $(0, 0)$
y-intercepts: $(0, 0)$; Symmetry: none

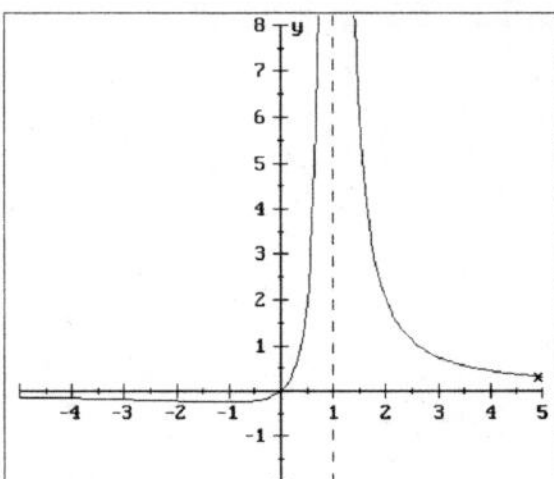

69. $f(x) = \dfrac{x+1}{x^2(x-2)}$

Vert: $x = 0$, $x = 2$; Horiz: $y = 0$
Slant: none; x-intercepts: $(-1, 0)$
y-intercepts: none; Symmetry: none

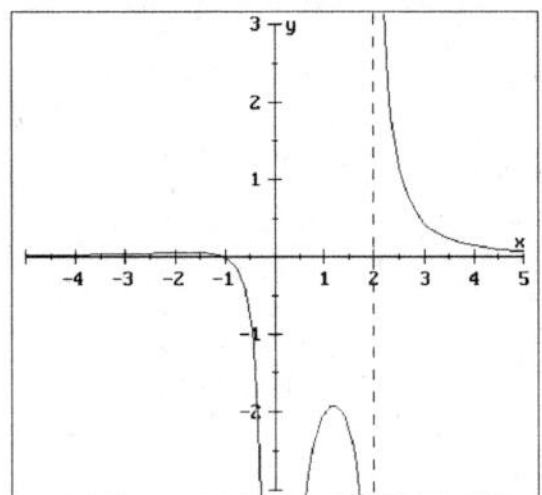

70. $f(x) = \dfrac{x-1}{x^2(x+2)^2}$

Vert: $x = 0$, $x = -2$; Horiz: $y = 0$
Slant: none; x-intercepts: $(1, 0)$
y-intercepts: none; Symmetry: none

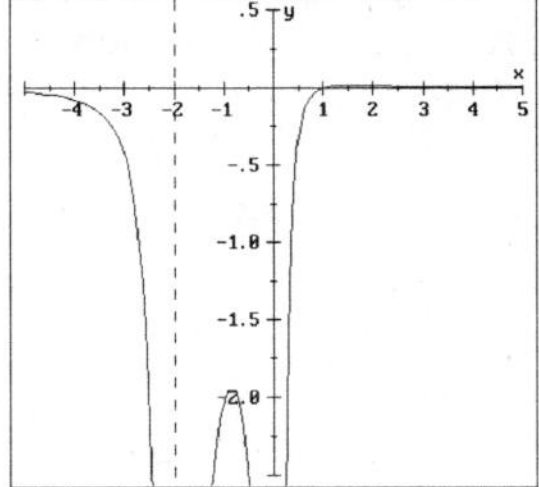

71. $y = \dfrac{x}{x^2+1}$

Vert: none; Horiz: $y = 0$
Slant: none; x-intercepts: $(0, 0)$
y-intercepts: $(0, 0)$; Symmetry: origin

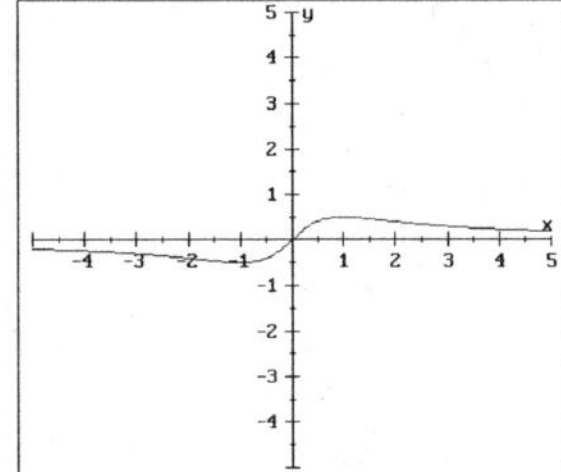

72. $y = \dfrac{x-1}{x^2+2}$

Vert: none; Horiz: $y = 0$
Slant: none; x-intercepts: $(1, 0)$
y-intercepts: $\left(0, -\frac{1}{2}\right)$; Symmetry: none

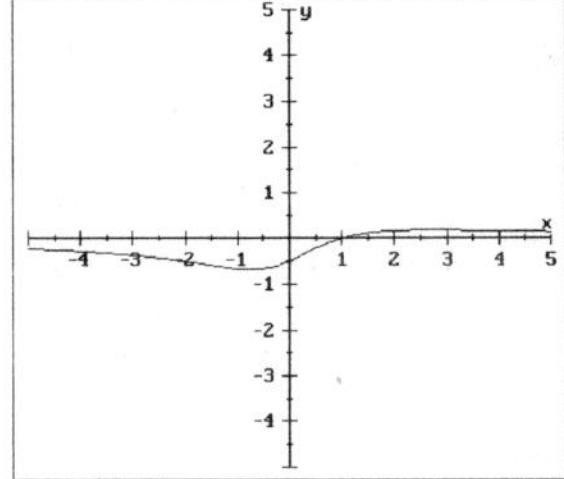

73. $y = \dfrac{3x^2}{x^2+1}$

Vert: none; Horiz: $y = \frac{3}{1} = 3$

Slant: none; x-intercepts: $(0, 0)$

y-intercepts: $(0, 0)$; Symmetry: y-axis

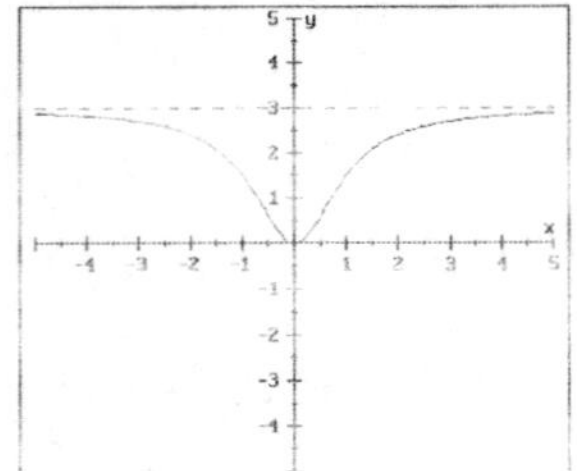

74. $y = \dfrac{x^2-9}{2x^2+1} = \dfrac{(x+3)(x-3)}{2x^2+1}$

Vert: none; Horiz: $y = \frac{1}{2}$

Slant: none; x-intercepts: $(3, 0)$, $(-3, 0)$

y-intercepts: $(0, -9)$; Symmetry: y-axis

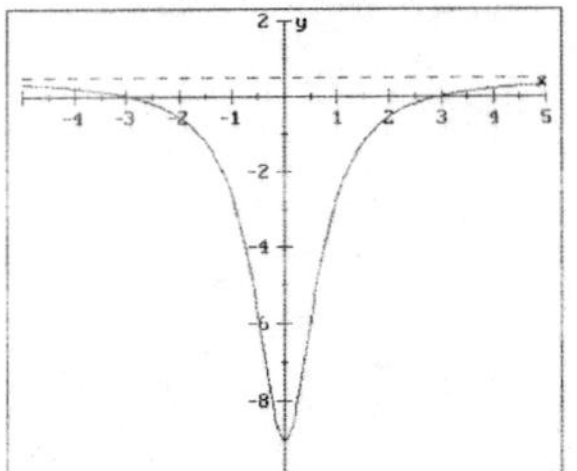

75. $h(x) = \dfrac{x^2-2x-8}{x-1} = \dfrac{(x+2)(x-4)}{x-1}$

$= x - 1 + \dfrac{-9}{x-1}$

Vert: $x = 1$; Horiz: none; Slant: $y = x - 1$

x-intercepts: $(4, 0)$, $(-2, 0)$

y-intercepts: $(0, 8)$; Symmetry: none

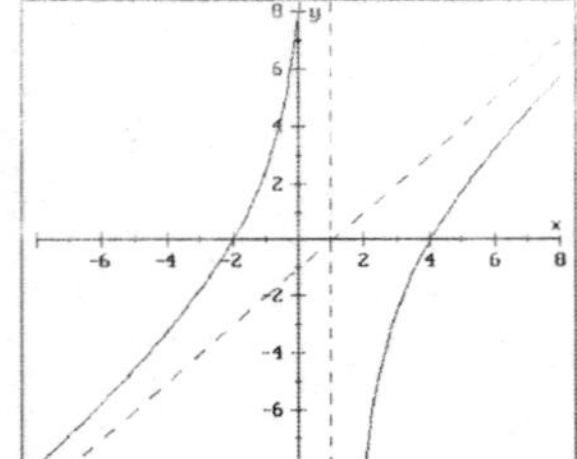

76. $h(x) = \dfrac{x^2+x-6}{x+2} = \dfrac{(x+3)(x-2)}{x+2}$

$= x - 1 + \dfrac{-4}{x+2}$

Vert: $x = -2$; Horiz: none; Slant: $y = x - 1$

x-intercepts: $(2, 0)$, $(-3, 0)$

y-intercepts: $(0, -3)$; Symmetry: none

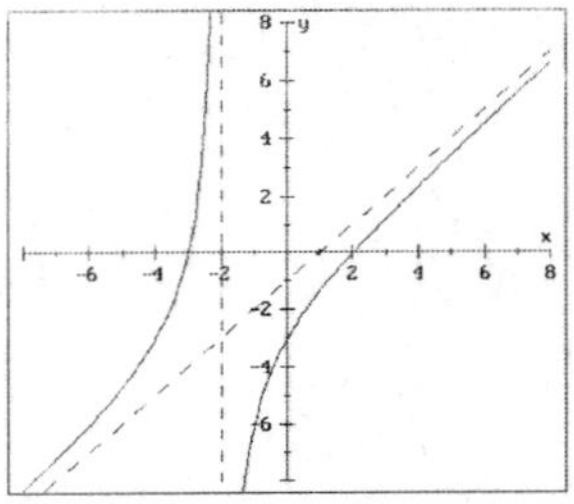

77. $f(x) = \dfrac{x^3 + x^2 + 6x}{x^2 - 1} = \dfrac{x(x^2 + x + 6)}{(x+1)(x-1)}$
$= x + 1 + \dfrac{7x + 1}{x^2 - 1}$

Vert: $x = -1$, $x = 1$; Horiz: none
Slant: $y = x + 1$; x-intercepts: $(0, 0)$
y-intercepts: $(0, 0)$; Symmetry: none

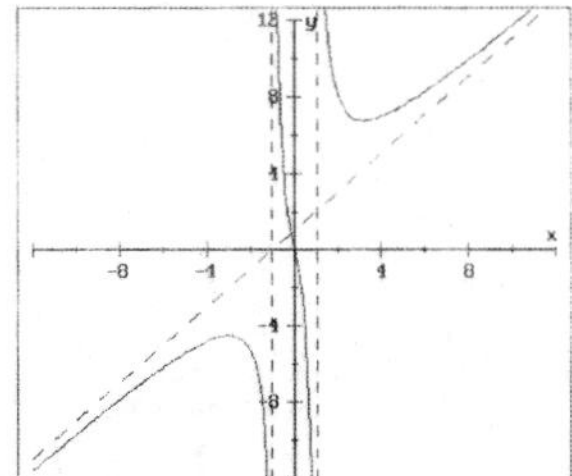

78. $f(x) = \dfrac{x^3 - 2x^2 + x}{x^2 - 4} = \dfrac{x(x-1)^2}{(x+2)(x-2)}$
$= x - 2 + \dfrac{5x - 8}{x^2 - 4}$

Vert: $x = -2$, $x = 2$; Horiz: none
Slant: $y = x - 2$; x-intercepts: $(0, 0)$, $(1, 0)$
y-intercepts: $(0, 0)$; Symmetry: none

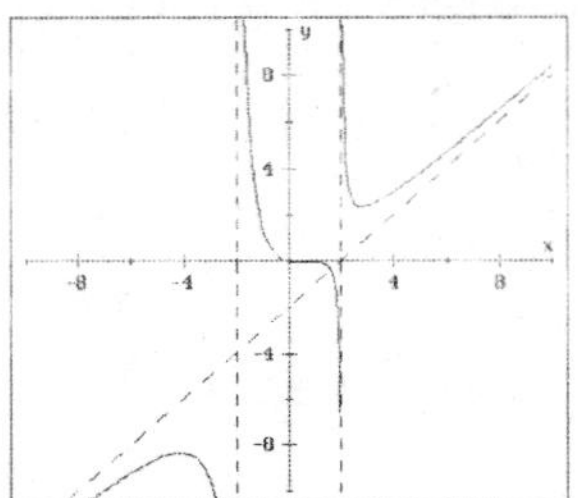

79. $f(x) = \dfrac{x^2}{x} = x$ (if $x \neq 0$)

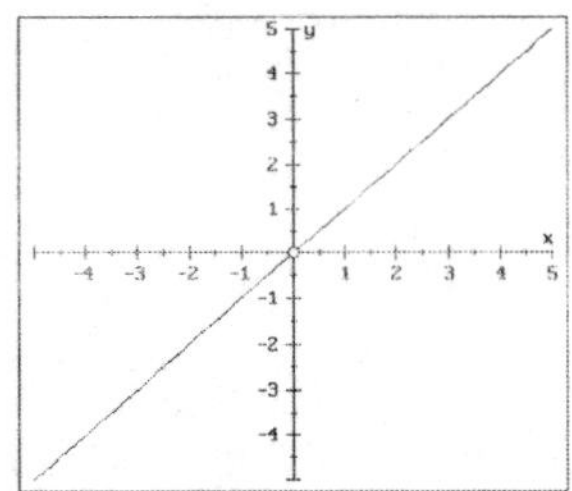

80. $f(x) = \dfrac{x^2 - 1}{x - 1} = \dfrac{(x+1)(x-1)}{x - 1} = x + 1$
(if $x \neq 1$)

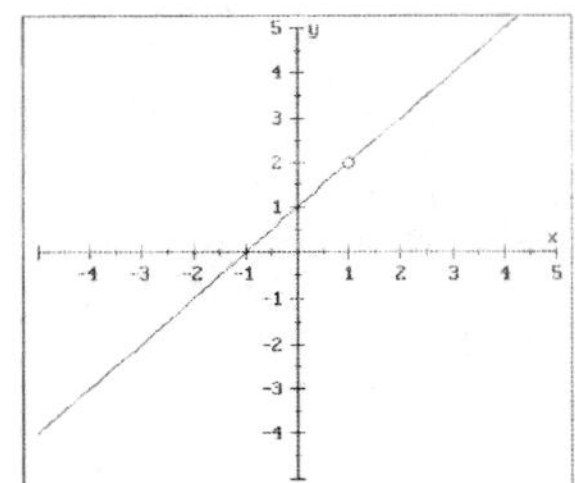

81. $f(x) = \dfrac{x^3 + x}{x} = \dfrac{x(x^2 + 1)}{x} = x^2 + 1$
(if $x \neq 0$)

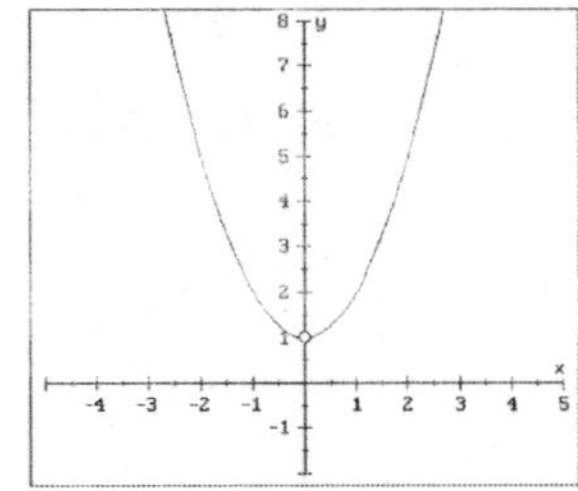

82. $f(x) = \dfrac{x^3 - x^2}{x - 1} = \dfrac{x^2(x - 1)}{x - 1} = x^2$
(if $x \neq 1$)

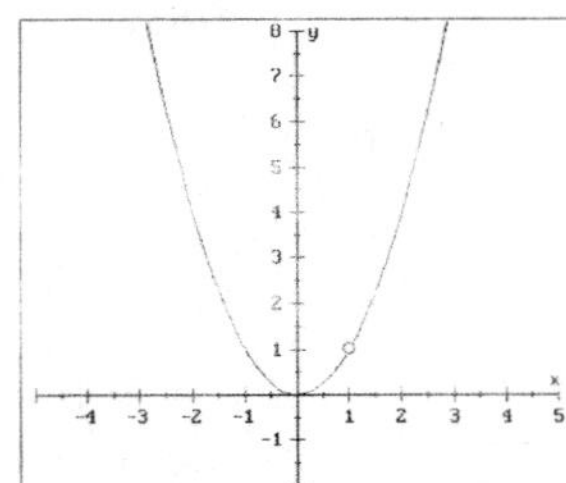

SECTION 3.5

83. $f(x) = \dfrac{x^2 - 2x + 1}{x - 1} = \dfrac{(x-1)(x-1)}{x-1}$
$= x - 1 \text{ (if } x \neq 1)$

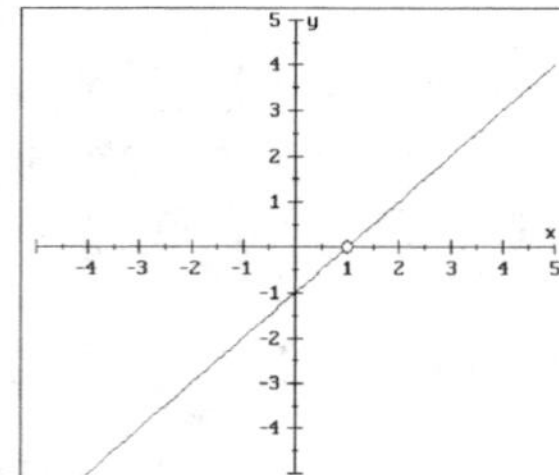

84. $f(x) = \dfrac{2x^2 + 3x - 2}{x + 2} = \dfrac{(2x-1)(x+2)}{x+2}$
$= 2x - 1 \text{ (if } x \neq -2)$

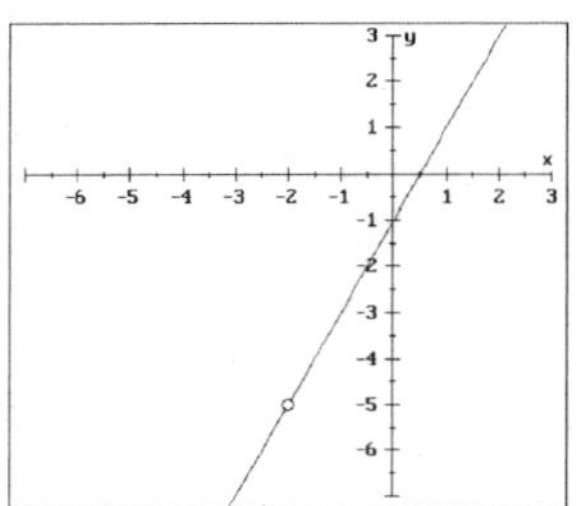

85. $f(x) = \dfrac{x^3 - 1}{x - 1} = \dfrac{(x-1)(x^2+x+1)}{x-1}$
$= x^2 + x + 1 \text{ (if } x \neq 1)$

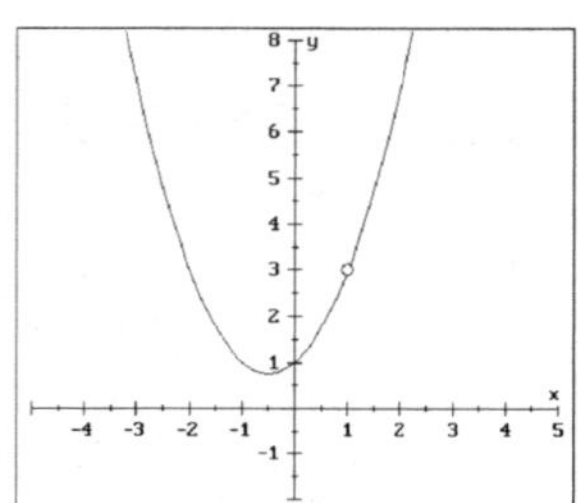

86. $f(x) = \dfrac{x^2 - x}{x^2} = \dfrac{x(x-1)}{x^2}$
$= \dfrac{x-1}{x} \text{ (if } x \neq 0)$

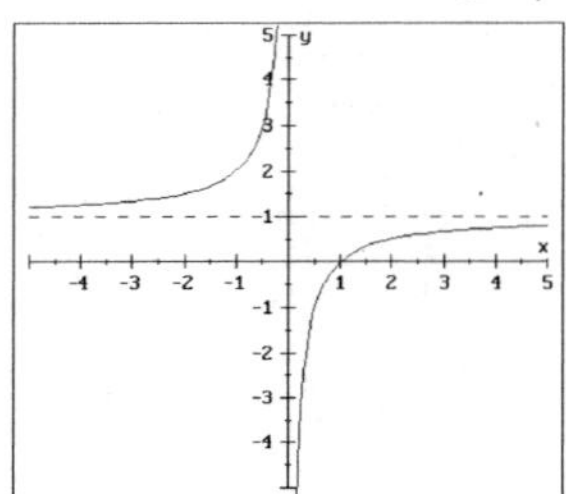

87. **a.** $c(x) = 3.25x + 700$

b. $c(500) = 3.25(500) + 700 = \$2325$

c. $\overline{c}(x) = \dfrac{3.25x + 700}{x}$

d. $\overline{c}(500) = \dfrac{3.25(500) + 700}{500} = \$4.65$

e. $\overline{c}(1000) = \dfrac{3.25(1000) + 700}{1000} = \$3.95$

f. $\overline{c}(2000) = \dfrac{3.25(2000) + 700}{2000} = \$3.60$

88. **a.** $c(n) = 0.20n + 10$

b. $c(775) = 0.20(775) + 10 = 165$

c. $\overline{c}(n) = \dfrac{0.20n + 10}{0.20}$

d. $\overline{c}(775) = \dfrac{0.20(775) + 10}{775} \approx \$0.21$

e. $\overline{c}(3200) = \dfrac{0.20(3200) + 10}{3200} \approx \$0.20$

89. **a.** $c(n) = 0.095n + 8.50$

b. $\overline{c}(n) = \dfrac{0.095n + 8.50}{n}$

c. $\overline{c}(850) = \dfrac{0.095(850) + 8.50}{850}$
$= \$0.105 = 10.5¢$

90. **a.** Let $t = 21$:
$f(21) = \dfrac{21^2 + 3(21)}{2(21) + 3} = 11.2$ days

b. Let $t + 3 = 25$, so $t = 22$:
$f(22) = \dfrac{22^2 + 3(22)}{2(22) + 3} \approx 11.7$ days

91. **Answers may vary.**

92. **Answers may vary.**

93. $y = \dfrac{ax + b}{cx^2 + d} = \dfrac{\frac{ax+b}{x^2}}{\frac{cx^2+d}{x^2}} = \dfrac{\frac{ax}{x^2} + \frac{b}{x^2}}{\frac{cx^2}{x^2} + \frac{d}{x^2}} = \dfrac{\frac{a}{x} + \frac{b}{x^2}}{c + \frac{d}{x^2}}$

As x approaches $\pm\infty$, $y \approx \dfrac{0 + 0}{c + 0} = 0$. Thus the horizontal asymptote is $y = 0$.

94. $y = \dfrac{ax^3 + b}{cx^2 + d} = \dfrac{\frac{ax^3+b}{x^2}}{\frac{cx^2+d}{x^2}} = \dfrac{\frac{ax^3}{x^2} + \frac{b}{x^2}}{\frac{cx^2}{x^2} + \frac{d}{x^2}} = \dfrac{ax + \frac{b}{x^2}}{c + \frac{d}{x^2}}$

As x approaches $\pm\infty$, $y \approx \dfrac{ax + 0}{c + 0} = \dfrac{a}{c}x$. Thus the slant asymptote is $y = \dfrac{a}{c}x$.

95. $y = \dfrac{ax^2 + b}{cx^2 + d} = \dfrac{\frac{ax^2+b}{x^2}}{\frac{cx^2+d}{x^2}} = \dfrac{\frac{ax^2}{x^2} + \frac{b}{x^2}}{\frac{cx^2}{x^2} + \frac{d}{x^2}} = \dfrac{a + \frac{b}{x^2}}{c + \frac{d}{x^2}}$

As x approaches $\pm\infty$, $y \approx \dfrac{a + 0}{c + 0} = \dfrac{a}{c}$. Thus the horizontal asymptote is $y = \dfrac{a}{c}$.

96. $y = \dfrac{x^3 + 1}{x} = \dfrac{\frac{x^3}{x} + \frac{1}{x}}{\frac{x}{x}} = \dfrac{x^2 + \frac{1}{x}}{1}$. As x approaches $\pm\infty$, $y \approx \dfrac{x^2 + 0}{1} = x^2$.

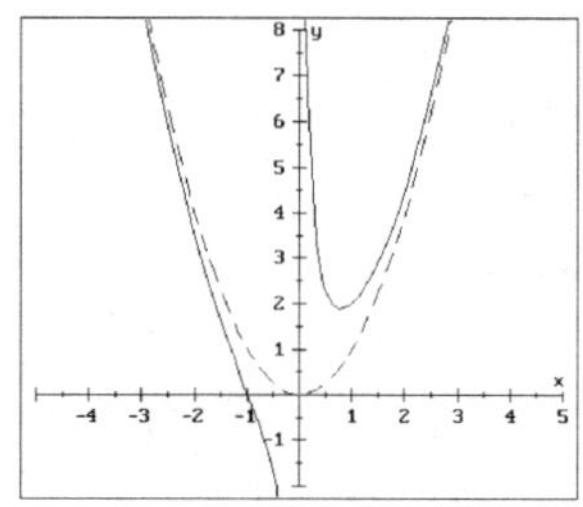

The dotted graph to the left is the graph of the equation $y = x^2$.

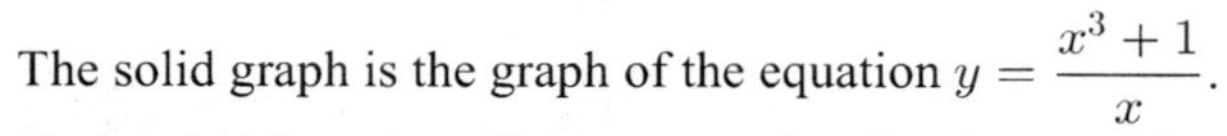

The solid graph is the graph of the equation $y = \dfrac{x^3 + 1}{x}$.

Notice that for x-coordinates more than 2 units away from $x = 0$, the two graphs are very similar. Thus $y = x^2$ is called a parabolic **asymptote** of the function $f(x) = \dfrac{x^3 + 1}{x}$.

97-100. **Answers may vary.**

101. $(2x^2 + 3x) + (x^2 - 2x) = 2x^2 + 3x + x^2 - 2x = 3x^2 + x$

102. $(3x+2)-(x^2+2)=3x+2-x^2-2=-x^2+3x$

103. $(5x+2)(2x+5)=10x^2+25x+4x+10=10x^2+29x+10$

104. $\dfrac{2x^2+3x+1}{x+1}=\dfrac{(2x+1)(x+1)}{x+1}=2x+1$

105. $f(x+1)=3(x+1)+2=3x+3+2=3x+5$

106. $f(2x+1)=(2x+1)^2+(2x+1)=4x^2+4x+1+2x+1=4x^2+6x+2$

Exercises 3.6 (page 378)

1. $f(x)+g(x)$ **2.** $f(x)-g(x)$ **3.** $f(x)g(x)$ **4.** $\dfrac{f(x)}{g(x)}$

5. intersection **6.** $f(g(x))$ **7.** $g(f(x))$ **8.** $g(-5)$

9. commutative **10.** domain; domain

11. $(f+g)(x)=f(x)+g(x)=(2x+1)+(3x-2)=5x-1$; domain $=(-\infty,\infty)$

12. $(f-g)(x)=f(x)-g(x)=(2x+1)-(3x-2)=-x+3$; domain $=(-\infty,\infty)$

13. $(f\cdot g)(x)=f(x)g(x)=(2x+1)(3x-2)=6x^2-x-2$; domain $=(-\infty,\infty)$

14. $(f/g)(x)=\dfrac{f(x)}{g(x)}=\dfrac{2x+1}{3x-2}$; domain $=\left(-\infty,\frac{2}{3}\right)\cup\left(\frac{2}{3},\infty\right)$

15. $(f-g)(x)=f(x)-g(x)=(x^2+x)-(x^2-1)=x+1$; domain $=(-\infty,\infty)$

16. $(f+g)(x)=f(x)+g(x)=(x^2+x)+(x^2-1)=2x^2+x-1$; domain $=(-\infty,\infty)$

17. $(f/g)(x)=\dfrac{f(x)}{g(x)}=\dfrac{x^2+x}{x^2-1}=\dfrac{x(x+1)}{(x+1)(x-1)}=\dfrac{x}{x-1}$; domain $=(-\infty,-1)\cup(-1,1)\cup(1,\infty)$

18. $(f\cdot g)(x)=f(x)g(x)=(x^2+x)(x^2-1)=x^4+x^3-x^2-x$; domain $=(-\infty,\infty)$

19. $(f+g)(x)=f(x)+g(x)=(x^2-7)+\left(\sqrt{x}\right)=x^2+\sqrt{x}-7$; domain $=[0,\infty)$

20. $(f-g)(x)=f(x)-g(x)=(x^2-7)-\left(\sqrt{x}\right)=x^2-\sqrt{x}-7$; domain $=[0,\infty)$

21. $(f/g)(x)=\dfrac{f(x)}{g(x)}=\dfrac{x^2-7}{\sqrt{x}}$; domain $=(0,\infty)$

22. $(f\cdot g)(x)=f(x)g(x)=(x^2-7)\left(\sqrt{x}\right)=x^2\sqrt{x}-7\sqrt{x}$; domain $=[0,\infty)$

23. $(f+g)(2) = f(2) + g(2) = \left[(2)^2 - 1\right] + [3(2) - 2] = 3 + 4 = 7$

24. $(f+g)(-3) = f(-3) + g(-3) = \left[(-3)^2 - 1\right] + [3(-3) - 2] = 8 + (-11) = -3$

25. $(f-g)(0) = f(0) - g(0) = \left[(0)^2 - 1\right] - [3(0) - 2] = -1 - (-2) = 1$

26. $(f-g)(-5) = f(-5) - g(-5) = \left[(-5)^2 - 1\right] - [3(-5) - 2] = 24 - (-17) = 41$

27. $(f \cdot g)(2) = f(2) \cdot g(2) = \left[(2)^2 - 1\right] \cdot [3(2) - 2] = (3)(4) = 12$

28. $(f \cdot g)(-1) = f(-1) \cdot g(-1) = \left[(-1)^2 - 1\right] \cdot [3(-1) - 2] = (0)(-5) = 0$

29. $(f/g)\left(\frac{2}{3}\right) = \dfrac{f\left(\frac{2}{3}\right)}{g\left(\frac{2}{3}\right)} = \dfrac{\left[\left(\frac{2}{3}\right)^2 - 1\right]}{\left[3\left(\frac{2}{3}\right) - 2\right]} = \dfrac{-\frac{5}{9}}{0} \Rightarrow$ undefined

30. $(f/g)(t) = \dfrac{f(t)}{g(t)} = \dfrac{t^2 - 1}{3t - 2}$

31. Let $f(x) = 3x^2$ and $g(x) = 2x$.
Then $(f+g)(x) = 3x^2 + 2x = h(x)$.

32. Let $f(x) = 3$ and $g(x) = x^2$.
Then $(f \cdot g)(x) = 3x^2 = h(x)$.

33. Let $f(x) = 3x^2$ and $g(x) = x^2 - 1$.
Then $(f/g)(x) = \dfrac{3x^2}{x^2 - 1} = h(x)$.

34. Let $f(x) = 5x$ and $g(x) = -x^2$.
Then $(f-g)(x) = 5x + x^2 = h(x)$.

35. Let $f(x) = 3x^3$ and $g(x) = -x$.
Then $(f-g)(x) = 3x^3 + x$
$= x(3x^2 + 1) = h(x)$.

36. Let $f(x) = 9x^2$ and $g(x) = -4$.
Then $(f+g)(x) = 9x^2 - 4$
$= (3x - 2)(3x + 2) = h(x)$.

37. Let $f(x) = x + 9$ and $g(x) = x - 2$.
Then $(f \cdot g)(x) = (x+9)(x-2)$
$= x^2 + 7x - 18 = h(x)$.

38. Let $f(x) = 5x^6$ and $g(x) = x$.
Then $(f/g)(x) = \dfrac{5x^6}{x} = 5x^5 = h(x)$.

39. $(f \circ g)(2) = f(g(2)) = f(5(2) - 2) = f(8) = 2(8) - 5 = 11$

40. $(g \circ f)(-3) = g(f(-3)) = g(2(-3) - 5) = g(-11) = 5(-11) - 2 = -57$

41. $(f \circ f)\left(-\frac{1}{2}\right) = f\left(f\left(-\frac{1}{2}\right)\right) = f\left(2\left(-\frac{1}{2}\right) - 5\right) = f(-6) = 2(-6) - 5 = -17$

42. $(g \circ g)\left(\frac{3}{5}\right) = g\left(g\left(\frac{3}{5}\right)\right) = g\left(5\left(\frac{3}{5}\right) - 2\right) = g(1) = 5(1) - 2 = 3$

43. $(f \circ g)(-3) = f(g(-3)) = f(4(-3) + 4) = f(-8) = 3(-8)^2 - 2 = 190$

44. $(g \circ f)(3) = g(f(3)) = g\left(3(3)^2 - 2\right) = g(25) = 4(25) + 4 = 104$

45. $(f \circ f)\left(\sqrt{3}\right) = f\left(f\left(\sqrt{3}\right)\right) = f\left(3\left(\sqrt{3}\right)^2 - 2\right) = f(7) = 3(7)^2 - 2 = 145$

46. $(g \circ g)(-4) = g(g(-4)) = g(4(-4) + 4) = g(-12) = 4(-12) + 4 = -44$

47. The domain of $f \circ g$ is the set of all real numbers in the domain of $g(x)$ such that $g(x)$ is in the domain of $f(x)$. Domain of $g(x)$: $(-\infty, \infty)$. Domain of $f(x) = (-\infty, \infty)$. Thus, all values of $g(x)$ are in the domain of $f(x)$. $\boxed{\text{Domain of } f \circ g\text{: } (-\infty, \infty)}$
$(f \circ g)(x) = f(g(x)) = f(x + 1) = 3(x + 1) = 3x + 3$

48. The domain of $g \circ f$ is the set of all real numbers in the domain of $f(x)$ such that $f(x)$ is in the domain of $g(x)$. Domain of $f(x)$: $(-\infty, \infty)$. Domain of $g(x) = (-\infty, \infty)$. Thus, all values of $f(x)$ are in the domain of $g(x)$. $\boxed{\text{Domain of } g \circ f\text{: } (-\infty, \infty)}$
$(g \circ f)(x) = g(f(x)) = g(3x) = 3x + 1$

49. The domain of $f \circ f$ is the set of all real numbers in the domain of $f(x)$ such that $f(x)$ is in the domain of $f(x)$. Domain of $f(x)$: $(-\infty, \infty)$. Thus, all values of $f(x)$ are in the domain of $f(x)$.
$\boxed{\text{Domain of } f \circ f\text{: } (-\infty, \infty)}$ $(f \circ f)(x) = f(f(x)) = f(3x) = 3(3x) = 9x$

50. The domain of $g \circ g$ is the set of all real numbers in the domain of $g(x)$ such that $g(x)$ is in the domain of $g(x)$. Domain of $g(x)$: $(-\infty, \infty)$. Thus, all values of $g(x)$ are in the domain of $g(x)$.
$\boxed{\text{Domain of } g \circ g\text{: } (-\infty, \infty)}$ $(g \circ g)(x) = g(g(x)) = g(x + 1) = x + 1 + 1 = x + 2$

51. The domain of $g \circ f$ is the set of all real numbers in the domain of $f(x)$ such that $f(x)$ is in the domain of $g(x)$. Domain of $f(x)$: $(-\infty, \infty)$. Domain of $g(x) = (-\infty, \infty)$. Thus, all values of $f(x)$ are in the domain of $g(x)$. $\boxed{\text{Domain of } g \circ f\text{: } (-\infty, \infty)}$
$(g \circ f)(x) = g(f(x)) = g\left(x^2\right) = 2x^2$

52. The domain of $f \circ g$ is the set of all real numbers in the domain of $g(x)$ such that $g(x)$ is in the domain of $f(x)$. Domain of $g(x)$: $(-\infty, \infty)$. Domain of $f(x) = (-\infty, \infty)$. Thus, all values of $g(x)$ are in the domain of $f(x)$. $\boxed{\text{Domain of } f \circ g\text{: } (-\infty, \infty)}$
$(f \circ g)(x) = f(g(x)) = f(2x) = (2x)^2 = 4x^2$

53. The domain of $g \circ g$ is the set of all real numbers in the domain of $g(x)$ such that $g(x)$ is in the domain of $g(x)$. Domain of $g(x)$: $(-\infty, \infty)$. Thus, all values of $g(x)$ are in the domain of $g(x)$.
$\boxed{\text{Domain of } g \circ g\text{: } (-\infty, \infty)}$ $(g \circ g)(x) = g(g(x)) = g(2x) = 2(2x) = 4x$

54. The domain of $f \circ f$ is the set of all real numbers in the domain of $f(x)$ such that $f(x)$ is in the domain of $f(x)$. Domain of $f(x)$: $(-\infty, \infty)$. Thus, all values of $f(x)$ are in the domain of $f(x)$.
$\boxed{\text{Domain of } f \circ f\text{: } (-\infty, \infty)}$ $(f \circ f)(x) = f(f(x)) = f\left(x^2\right) = \left(x^2\right)^2 = x^4$

55. The domain of $f \circ g$ is the set of all real numbers in the domain of $g(x)$ such that $g(x)$ is in the domain of $f(x)$. Domain of $g(x)$: $(-\infty, \infty)$. Domain of $f(x) = [0, \infty)$. Thus, we must have $g(x) \geq 0 \Rightarrow x + 1 \geq 0 \Rightarrow x \geq -1$. $\boxed{\text{Domain of } f \circ g\text{: } [-1, \infty)}$
$(f \circ g)(x) = f(g(x)) = f(x+1) = \sqrt{x+1}$

56. The domain of $g \circ f$ is the set of all real numbers in the domain of $f(x)$ such that $f(x)$ is in the domain of $g(x)$. Domain of $f(x)$: $[0, \infty)$. Domain of $g(x) = (-\infty, \infty)$. Thus, all values of $f(x)$ are in the domain of $g(x)$. $\boxed{\text{Domain of } g \circ f\text{: } [0, \infty)}$
$(g \circ f)(x) = g(f(x)) = g\left(\sqrt{x}\right) = \sqrt{x} + 1$

57. The domain of $f \circ f$ is the set of all real numbers in the domain of $f(x)$ such that $f(x)$ is in the domain of $f(x)$. Domain of $f(x)$: $[0, \infty)$. Thus, we must have $f(x) \geq 0 \Rightarrow \sqrt{x} \geq 0$. This is true for all real values of x. $\boxed{\text{Domain of } f \circ f\text{: } [0, \infty)}$
$(f \circ f)(x) = f(f(x)) = f\left(\sqrt{x}\right) = \sqrt{\sqrt{x}} = \left((x)^{1/2}\right)^{1/2} = x^{1/4} = \sqrt[4]{x}$

58. The domain of $g \circ g$ is the set of all real numbers in the domain of $g(x)$ such that $g(x)$ is in the domain of $g(x)$. Domain of $g(x)$: $(-\infty, \infty)$. Thus, all values of $g(x)$ are in the domain of $g(x)$.
$\boxed{\text{Domain of } g \circ g\text{: } (-\infty, \infty)}$ $(g \circ g)(x) = g(g(x)) = g(x+1) = (x+1) + 1 = x + 2$

59. The domain of $g \circ f$ is the set of all real numbers in the domain of $f(x)$ such that $f(x)$ is in the domain of $g(x)$. Domain of $f(x)$: $[-1, \infty)$. Domain of $g(x) = (-\infty, \infty)$. Thus, all values of $f(x)$ are in the domain of $g(x)$. $\boxed{\text{Domain of } g \circ f\text{: } [-1, \infty)}$
$(g \circ f)(x) = g(f(x)) = g\left(\sqrt{x+1}\right) = \left(\sqrt{x+1}\right)^2 - 1 = x$

60. The domain of $f \circ g$ is the set of all real numbers in the domain of $g(x)$ such that $g(x)$ is in the domain of $f(x)$. Domain of $g(x)$: $(-\infty, \infty)$. Domain of $f(x) = [-1, \infty)$. Thus, we must have $g(x) \geq -1 \Rightarrow x^2 - 1 \geq -1 \Rightarrow x^2 \geq 0$. This is true for all real values of x.
$\boxed{\text{Domain of } f \circ g\text{: } (-\infty, \infty)}$ $(f \circ g)(x) = f(g(x)) = f\left(x^2 - 1\right) = \sqrt{x^2 - 1 + 1} = \sqrt{x^2} = |x|$

61. The domain of $g \circ g$ is the set of all real numbers in the domain of $g(x)$ such that $g(x)$ is in the domain of $g(x)$. Domain of $g(x)$: $(-\infty, \infty)$. Thus, all values of $g(x)$ are in the domain of $g(x)$.
$\boxed{\text{Domain of } g \circ g\text{: } (-\infty, \infty)}$ $(g \circ g)(x) = g(g(x)) = g\left(x^2 - 1\right) = \left(x^2 - 1\right)^2 - 1 = x^4 - 2x^2$

62. The domain of $f \circ f$ is the set of all real numbers in the domain of $f(x)$ such that $f(x)$ is in the domain of $f(x)$. Domain of $f(x)$: $[-1, \infty)$. Thus, we must have $f(x) \geq -1 \Rightarrow \sqrt{x+1} \geq -1$. This is true for all real values of x. $\boxed{\text{Domain of } f \circ f\text{: } [-1, \infty)}$
$(f \circ f)(x) = f(f(x)) = f\left(\sqrt{x+1}\right) = \sqrt{\sqrt{x+1} + 1}$

63. The domain of $f \circ g$ is the set of all real numbers in the domain of $g(x)$ such that $g(x)$ is in the domain of $f(x)$. Domain of $g(x)$: $(-\infty, 2) \cup (2, \infty)$. Domain of $f(x) = (-\infty, 1) \cup (1, \infty)$. Thus, we must have $g(x) \neq 1 \Rightarrow \dfrac{1}{x-2} \neq 1 \Rightarrow 1 \neq x-2 \Rightarrow x \neq 3$

$\boxed{\text{Domain of } f \circ g\text{: } (-\infty, 2) \cup (2, 3) \cup (3, \infty)}$

$$(f \circ g)(x) = f(g(x)) = f\left(\frac{1}{x-2}\right) = \frac{1}{\frac{1}{x-2} - 1} = \frac{1}{\frac{1}{x-2} - 1} \cdot \frac{x-2}{x-2} = \frac{x-2}{1-(x-2)} = \frac{x-2}{3-x}$$

64. The domain of $g \circ f$ is the set of all real numbers in the domain of $f(x)$ such that $f(x)$ is in the domain of $g(x)$. Domain of $f(x)$: $(-\infty, 1) \cup (1, \infty)$. Domain of $g(x) = (-\infty, 2) \cup (2, \infty)$. Thus, we must have $f(x) \neq 2 \Rightarrow \dfrac{1}{x-1} \neq 2 \Rightarrow 1 \neq 2(x-1) \Rightarrow 1 \neq 2x-2 \Rightarrow 2x \neq 3 \Rightarrow x \neq \frac{3}{2}$

$\boxed{\text{Domain of } f \circ g\text{: } (-\infty, 1) \cup \left(1, \tfrac{3}{2}\right) \cup \left(\tfrac{3}{2}, \infty\right)}$

$$(g \circ f)(x) = g(f(x)) = g\left(\frac{1}{x-1}\right) = \frac{1}{\frac{1}{x-1} - 2} = \frac{1}{\frac{1}{x-1} - 2} \cdot \frac{x-1}{x-1} = \frac{x-1}{1-2(x-1)} = \frac{x-1}{3-2x}$$

65. The domain of $f \circ f$ is the set of all real numbers in the domain of $f(x)$ such that $f(x)$ is in the domain of $f(x)$. Domain of $f(x)$: $(-\infty, 1) \cup (1, \infty)$. Thus, we must have $f(x) \neq 1 \Rightarrow$ $\dfrac{1}{x-1} \neq 1 \Rightarrow 1 \neq x-1 \Rightarrow x \neq 2$ $\boxed{\text{Domain of } f \circ f\text{: } (-\infty, 1) \cup (1, 2) \cup (2, \infty)}$

$$(f \circ f)(x) = f(f(x)) = f\left(\frac{1}{x-1}\right) = \frac{1}{\frac{1}{x-1} - 1} = \frac{1}{\frac{1}{x-1} - 1} \cdot \frac{x-1}{x-1} = \frac{x-1}{1-(x-1)} = \frac{x-1}{2-x}$$

66. The domain of $g \circ g$ is the set of all real numbers in the domain of $g(x)$ such that $g(x)$ is in the domain of $g(x)$. Domain of $g(x)$: $(-\infty, 2) \cup (2, \infty)$. Thus, we must have $g(x) \neq 2 \Rightarrow$ $\dfrac{1}{x-2} \neq 2 \Rightarrow 1 \neq 2x-4 \Rightarrow x \neq \frac{5}{2}$ $\boxed{\text{Domain of } g \circ g\text{: } (-\infty, 2) \cup \left(2, \tfrac{5}{2}\right) \cup \left(\tfrac{5}{2}, \infty\right)}$

$$(g \circ g)(x) = g(g(x)) = g\left(\frac{1}{x-2}\right) = \frac{1}{\frac{1}{x-2} - 2} = \frac{1}{\frac{1}{x-2} - 2} \cdot \frac{x-2}{x-2} = \frac{x-2}{1-2(x-2)} = \frac{x-2}{5-2x}$$

67. Let $f(x) = x - 2$ and $g(x) = 3x$.
Then $(f \circ g)(x) = f(g(x))$
$= f(3x) = 3x - 2$.

68. Let $f(x) = x - 5$ and $g(x) = 7x$.
Then $(f \circ g)(x) = f(g(x))$
$= f(7x) = 7x - 5$.

69. Let $f(x) = x - 2$ and $g(x) = x^2$.
Then $(f \circ g)(x) = f(g(x))$
$= f(x^2) = x^2 - 2$.

70. Let $f(x) = x - 3$ and $g(x) = x^3$.
Then $(f \circ g)(x) = f(g(x))$
$= f(x^3) = x^3 - 3$.

71. Let $f(x) = x^2$ and $g(x) = x - 2$.
Then $(f \circ g)(x) = f(g(x))$
$= f(x-2) = (x-2)^2$.

72. Let $f(x) = x^3$ and $g(x) = x - 3$.
Then $(f \circ g)(x) = f(g(x))$
$= f(x-3) = (x-3)^3$.

73. Let $f(x) = \sqrt{x}$ and $g(x) = x + 2$.
Then $(f \circ g)(x) = f(g(x))$
$= f(x+2) = \sqrt{x+2}$.

74. Let $f(x) = \dfrac{1}{x}$ and $g(x) = x - 5$.
Then $(f \circ g)(x) = f(g(x))$
$= f(x-5) = \dfrac{1}{x-5}$.

75. Let $f(x) = x + 2$ and $g(x) = \sqrt{x}$.
Then $(f \circ g)(x) = f(g(x))$
$= f(\sqrt{x}) = \sqrt{x} + 2$.

76. Let $f(x) = x - 5$ and $g(x) = \dfrac{1}{x}$.
Then $(f \circ g)(x) = f(g(x))$
$= f\left(\dfrac{1}{x}\right) = \dfrac{1}{x} - 5$.

77. Let $f(x) = x$ and $g(x) = x$.
Then $(f \circ g)(x) = f(g(x))$
$= f(x) = x$.

78. Let $f(x) = 3$ and $g(x) = x$.
Then $(f \circ g)(x) = f(g(x))$
$= f(x) = 3$.

79. $(f+g)(-4) = f(-4) + g(-4)$
$= -2 + 2 = 0$

80. $(f-g)(1) = f(1) - g(1)$
$= 1 - 3 = -2$

81. $(f \cdot g)(5) = f(5) \cdot g(5) = -2(0) = 0$

82. $(f/g)(-1) = \dfrac{f(-1)}{g(-1)} = \dfrac{\frac{1}{2}}{2} = \dfrac{1}{4}$

83. $(f \circ g)(3) = f(g(3)) = f(2) = 1$

84. $(g \circ f)(2) = g(f(2)) = g(1) = 3$

85. $(f \circ f)(-2) = f(f(-2)) = f(0) = 1$

86. $(g \circ g)(-5) = g(g(-5)) = g(1) = 3$

87. $(f+g)(2) = f(2) + g(2) = 4 + 4 = 8$

88. $(f/g)(4) = \dfrac{f(4)}{g(4)} = \dfrac{9}{16}$

89. $(f \circ g)(2) = f(g(2)) = f(4) = 9$

90. $(g \circ f)(2) = g(f(2)) = g(4) = 16$

91. **a.** $(R - C)(x) = 300x - (60{,}000 + 40x)$
$= 260x - 60{,}000$

b. $(R - C)(500) = 260(500) - 60{,}000$
$= 70{,}000$

92. **a.** $A = 13w$

b. $w^2 + 13^2 = d^2$
$w^2 = d^2 - 13^2$
$w = \sqrt{d^2 - 169}$

c. $A = 13w$
$= 13\sqrt{d^2 - 169}$

93. $r(t) = \dfrac{d(t)}{2} = \dfrac{3t}{2}$; $A(t) = \pi(r(t))^2 = \pi\left(\dfrac{3t}{2}\right)^2 = \dfrac{9}{4}\pi t^2$
$A(120) = \dfrac{9}{4}\pi(120)^2 \approx 101{,}787.6$ square inches

94. If the perimeter is P, then each side is $s = \dfrac{P}{4}$. Area $= s^2 = \left(\dfrac{P}{4}\right)^2 = \dfrac{P^2}{16}$.

95. If the area is A and the length of a side is s, then $s^2 = A \Rightarrow s = \sqrt{A}$. Then $P = 4s = 4\sqrt{A}$.

96. Use the relationship $C = \frac{5}{9}(F - 32)$.

$F = mt + b$
$F = -81t + 1200$

$$\begin{aligned} C \circ F = C(F) &= \tfrac{5}{9}((-81t + 1200) - 32) \\ &= \tfrac{5}{9}(-81t + 1168) \\ &= -45t + \tfrac{5840}{9} \end{aligned}$$

97. $(f + f)(x) = f(x) + f(x) = 3x + 3x = 6x$
$f(x + x) = f(2x) = 3(2x) = 6x$

98. $(g + g)(x) = g(x) + g(x) = x^2 + x^2 = 2x^2$
$g(x + x) = g(2x) = (2x)^2 = 4x^2$

99. $$(f \circ f)(x) = f(f(x)) = f\left(\frac{x-1}{x+1}\right) = \frac{\frac{x-1}{x+1} - 1}{\frac{x-1}{x+1} + 1} = \frac{(x+1)\left(\frac{x-1}{x+1} - 1\right)}{(x+1)\left(\frac{x-1}{x+1} + 1\right)} = \frac{x - 1 - (x+1)}{x - 1 + x + 1} = \frac{-2}{2x} = -\frac{1}{x}$$

100. $$(g \circ g)(x) = g(g(x)) = g\left(\frac{x}{x-1}\right) = \frac{\frac{x}{x-1}}{\frac{x}{x-1} - 1} = \frac{(x-1)\frac{x}{x-1}}{(x-1)\left(\frac{x}{x-1} - 1\right)} = \frac{x}{x - (x-1)} = \frac{x}{1} = x$$

101-104. Answers may vary.

105.
$$\begin{aligned} x &= 3y - 7 \\ x + 7 &= 3y \\ \frac{x+7}{3} &= y \end{aligned}$$

106.
$$\begin{aligned} x &= \frac{7}{y} \\ xy &= 7 \\ y &= \frac{7}{x} \end{aligned}$$

107.
$$\begin{aligned} x &= \frac{y}{y+3} \\ x(y+3) &= y \\ xy + 3x &= y \\ xy - y &= -3x \\ y(x-1) &= -3x \\ y &= \frac{-3x}{x-1} = \frac{3x}{1-x} \end{aligned}$$

108.
$$\begin{aligned} x &= \frac{y-1}{y} \\ xy &= y - 1 \\ xy - y &= -1 \\ y(x-1) &= -1 \\ y &= \frac{-1}{x-1} = \frac{1}{1-x} \end{aligned}$$

Exercises 3.7 (page 390)

1. one-to-one

2. horizontal

3. identity

4. $y = x$

5. $y = 3x$
one-to-one

6. $y = \frac{1}{2}x$
one-to-one

7. $y = x^2 + 3$
$x = 1$ and $x = -1$ both correspond to $y = 4$.
not one-to-one

8. $y = x^4 - x^2$
$x = 1$ and $x = -1$ both correspond to $y = 0$.
not one-to-one

9. $y = x^3 - x$
$x = 1$ and $x = -1$ both correspond to $y = 0$.
not one-to-one

10. $y = x^2 - x$
$x = 0$ and $x = 1$ both correspond to $y = 0$.
not one-to-one

11. $y = |x|$
$x = 1$ and $x = -1$ both correspond to $y = 1$.
not one-to-one

12. $y = |x - 3|$
$x = 4$ and $x = 2$ both correspond to $y = 1$.
not one-to-one

13. $y = 5$
$x = 1$ and $x = 2$ both correspond to $y = 5$.
not one-to-one

14. $y = \sqrt{x-5}; x \geq 5$
one-to-one

15. $y = (x-2)^2,\ x \geq 2$
one-to-one

16. $y = \dfrac{1}{x}$
one-to-one

17. one-to-one

18. not one-to-one

19. not one-to-one (not a function)

20. one-to-one

21. $(f \circ g)(x) = f(g(x)) = f\left(\frac{1}{5}x\right) = 5\left(\frac{1}{5}x\right) = x$

$(g \circ f)(x) = g(f(x)) = g(5x) = \frac{1}{5}(5x) = x$

22. $(f \circ g)(x) = f(g(x)) = f\left(\frac{x-5}{4}\right) = 4\left(\frac{x-5}{4}\right) + 5 = x - 5 + 5 = x$

$(g \circ f)(x) = g(f(x)) = g(4x+5) = \frac{(4x+5)-5}{4} = \frac{4x}{4} = x$

23. $(f \circ g)(x) = f(g(x)) = f\left(\frac{1}{x-1}\right) = \frac{\frac{1}{x-1}+1}{\frac{1}{x-1}} = \frac{(x-1)\left(\frac{1}{x-1}+1\right)}{(x-1)\frac{1}{x-1}} = \frac{1+x-1}{1} = x$

$(g \circ f)(x) = g(f(x)) = g\left(\frac{x+1}{x}\right) = \frac{1}{\frac{x+1}{x}-1} = \frac{x(1)}{x\left(\frac{x+1}{x}-1\right)} = \frac{x}{x+1-x} = \frac{x}{1} = x$

24. $(f \circ g)(x) = f(g(x)) = f\left(\frac{x+1}{x-1}\right) = \frac{\frac{x+1}{x-1}+1}{\frac{x+1}{x-1}-1} = \frac{(x-1)\left(\frac{x+1}{x-1}+1\right)}{(x-1)\left(\frac{x+1}{x-1}-1\right)} = \frac{x+1+x-1}{x+1-(x-1)} = x$

Note that $(g \circ f)(x)$ will involve the same calculations.

25.
$$\begin{aligned} y = f(x) &= 3x \\ x &= 3y \\ \frac{x}{3} &= y \\ f^{-1}(x) &= \frac{x}{3} = \frac{1}{3}x \end{aligned}$$

$$\begin{aligned} (f \circ f^{-1})(x) &= f\left(f^{-1}(x)\right) \\ &= f\left(\frac{x}{3}\right) \\ &= 3\left(\frac{x}{3}\right) \\ &= x \end{aligned}$$

$$\begin{aligned} (f^{-1} \circ f)(x) &= f^{-1}(f(x)) \\ &= f^{-1}(3x) \\ &= \frac{3x}{3} \\ &= x \end{aligned}$$

26. $y = f(x) = \frac{1}{3}x \qquad x = \frac{1}{3}y \qquad 3x = y \qquad f^{-1}(x) = 3x$

$$(f \circ f^{-1})(x) = f(f^{-1}(x)) = f(3x) = \frac{1}{3}(3x) = x$$

$$(f^{-1} \circ f)(x) = f^{-1}(f(x)) = f^{-1}\left(\frac{1}{3}x\right) = 3\left(\frac{1}{3}x\right) = x$$

27. $y = f(x) = 3x + 2 \qquad x = 3y + 2 \qquad x - 2 = 3y \qquad \frac{x-2}{3} = y \qquad f^{-1}(x) = \frac{x-2}{3}$

$$(f \circ f^{-1})(x) = f(f^{-1}(x)) = f\left(\frac{x-2}{3}\right) = 3\left(\frac{x-2}{3}\right) + 2 = x - 2 + 2 = x$$

$$(f^{-1} \circ f)(x) = f^{-1}(f(x)) = f^{-1}(3x+2) = \frac{(3x+2)-2}{3} = \frac{3x}{3} = x$$

28. $y = f(x) = 2x - 5 \qquad x = 2y - 5 \qquad x + 5 = 2y \qquad \frac{x+5}{2} = y \qquad f^{-1}(x) = \frac{x+5}{2}$

$$(f \circ f^{-1})(x) = f(f^{-1}(x)) = f\left(\frac{x+5}{2}\right) = 2\left(\frac{x+5}{2}\right) - 5 = x + 5 - 5 = x$$

$$(f^{-1} \circ f)(x) = f^{-1}(f(x)) = f^{-1}(2x-5) = \frac{(2x-5)+5}{2} = \frac{2x}{2} = x$$

29. $y = f(x) = x^3 + 2 \qquad x = y^3 + 2 \qquad x - 2 = y^3 \qquad \sqrt[3]{x-2} = y \qquad f^{-1}(x) = \sqrt[3]{x-2}$

$$(f \circ f^{-1})(x) = f(f^{-1}(x)) = f\left(\sqrt[3]{x-2}\right) = \left(\sqrt[3]{x-2}\right)^3 + 2 = x - 2 + 2 = x$$

$$(f^{-1} \circ f)(x) = f^{-1}(f(x)) = f^{-1}(x^3+2) = \sqrt[3]{(x^3+2)-2} = \sqrt[3]{x^3} = x$$

30. $y = f(x) = (x+2)^3 \qquad x = (y+2)^3 \qquad \sqrt[3]{x} = y + 2 \qquad \sqrt[3]{x} - 2 = y \qquad f^{-1}(x) = \sqrt[3]{x} - 2$

$$(f \circ f^{-1})(x) = f(f^{-1}(x)) = f\left(\sqrt[3]{x} - 2\right) = \left(\left(\sqrt[3]{x} - 2\right) + 2\right)^3 = \left(\sqrt[3]{x}\right)^3 = x$$

$$(f^{-1} \circ f)(x) = f^{-1}(f(x)) = f^{-1}\left((x+2)^3\right) = \sqrt[3]{(x+2)^3} - 2 = x + 2 - 2 = x$$

31. $y = f(x) = \sqrt[5]{x} \qquad x = \sqrt[5]{y} \qquad x^5 = y \qquad f^{-1}(x) = x^5$

$$(f \circ f^{-1})(x) = f(f^{-1}(x)) = f(x^5) = \sqrt[5]{x^5} = x$$

$$(f^{-1} \circ f)(x) = f^{-1}(f(x)) = f^{-1}\left(\sqrt[5]{x}\right) = \left(\sqrt[5]{x}\right)^5 = x$$

32.

$$\begin{aligned} y = f(x) &= \sqrt[5]{x} + 4 \\ x &= \sqrt[5]{y} + 4 \\ x - 4 &= \sqrt[5]{y} \\ (x-4)^5 &= y \\ f^{-1}(x) &= (x-4)^5 \end{aligned}$$

$$\begin{aligned} (f \circ f^{-1})(x) &= f(f^{-1}(x)) \\ &= f((x-4)^5) \\ &= \sqrt[5]{(x-4)^5} + 4 \\ &= x - 4 + 4 = x \end{aligned}$$

$$\begin{aligned} (f^{-1} \circ f)(x) &= f^{-1}(f(x)) \\ &= f^{-1}(\sqrt[5]{x} + 4) \\ &= ((\sqrt[5]{x} + 4) - 4)^5 \\ &= (\sqrt[5]{x})^5 = x \end{aligned}$$

33.

$$\begin{aligned} y = f(x) &= \frac{1}{x+3} \\ x &= \frac{1}{y+3} \\ x(y+3) &= 1 \\ y + 3 &= \frac{1}{x} \\ f^{-1}(x) &= \frac{1}{x} - 3 \end{aligned}$$

$$\begin{aligned} (f \circ f^{-1})(x) &= f(f^{-1}(x)) \\ &= f\left(\frac{1}{x} - 3\right) \\ &= \frac{1}{\frac{1}{x} - 3 + 3} \\ &= \frac{1}{\frac{1}{x}} \\ &= x \end{aligned}$$

$$\begin{aligned} (f^{-1} \circ f)(x) &= f^{-1}(f(x)) \\ &= f^{-1}\left(\frac{1}{x+3}\right) \\ &= \frac{1}{\frac{1}{x+3}} - 3 \\ &= x + 3 - 3 \\ &= x \end{aligned}$$

34.

$$\begin{aligned} y = f(x) &= \frac{1}{x-2} \\ x &= \frac{1}{y-2} \\ x(y-2) &= 1 \\ y - 2 &= \frac{1}{x} \\ f^{-1}(x) &= \frac{1}{x} + 2 \end{aligned}$$

$$\begin{aligned} (f \circ f^{-1})(x) &= f(f^{-1}(x)) \\ &= f\left(\frac{1}{x} + 2\right) \\ &= \frac{1}{\frac{1}{x} + 2 - 2} \\ &= \frac{1}{\frac{1}{x}} \\ &= x \end{aligned}$$

$$\begin{aligned} (f^{-1} \circ f)(x) &= f^{-1}(f(x)) \\ &= f^{-1}\left(\frac{1}{x-2}\right) \\ &= \frac{1}{\frac{1}{x-2}} + 2 \\ &= x - 2 + 2 \\ &= x \end{aligned}$$

35.

$$\begin{aligned} y = f(x) &= \frac{1}{2x} \\ x &= \frac{1}{2y} \\ x(2y) &= 1 \\ 2xy &= 1 \\ y &= \frac{1}{2x} \\ f^{-1}(x) &= \frac{1}{2x} \end{aligned}$$

$$\begin{aligned} (f \circ f^{-1})(x) &= f(f^{-1}(x)) \\ &= f\left(\frac{1}{2x}\right) \\ &= \frac{1}{2\left(\frac{1}{2x}\right)} \\ &= \frac{1}{\frac{1}{x}} \\ &= x \end{aligned}$$

$$\begin{aligned} (f^{-1} \circ f)(x) &= f^{-1}(f(x)) \\ &= f^{-1}\left(\frac{1}{2x}\right) \\ &= \frac{1}{2\left(\frac{1}{2x}\right)} \\ &= \frac{1}{\frac{1}{x}} \\ &= x \end{aligned}$$

36.
$$\begin{aligned} y = f(x) &= \frac{1}{x^3} \\ x &= \frac{1}{y^3} \\ xy^3 &= 1 \\ y^3 &= \frac{1}{x} \\ y &= \sqrt[3]{\frac{1}{x}} \\ f^{-1}(x) &= \sqrt[3]{\frac{1}{x}} \end{aligned}$$

$$\begin{aligned} (f \circ f^{-1})(x) &= f\big(f^{-1}(x)\big) \\ &= f\left(\sqrt[3]{\frac{1}{x}}\right) \\ &= \frac{1}{\left(\sqrt[3]{\frac{1}{x}}\right)^3} \\ &= \frac{1}{\frac{1}{x}} \\ &= x \end{aligned}$$

$$\begin{aligned} (f^{-1} \circ f)(x) &= f^{-1}(f(x)) \\ &= f^{-1}\left(\frac{1}{x^3}\right) \\ &= \sqrt[3]{\frac{1}{\frac{1}{x^3}}} \\ &= \sqrt[3]{\frac{x^3}{1}} \\ &= x \end{aligned}$$

37.
$$\begin{aligned} y = f(x) &= 5x \\ x &= 5y \\ \frac{x}{5} &= y \\ f^{-1}(x) &= \frac{1}{5}x \end{aligned}$$

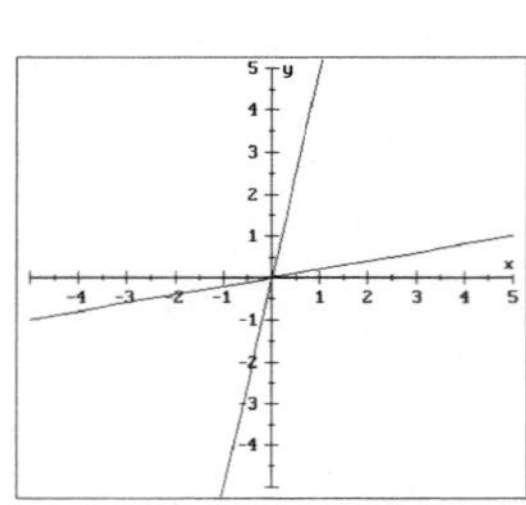

38.
$$\begin{aligned} y = f(x) &= \frac{3}{2}x \\ x &= \frac{3}{2}y \\ \frac{2}{3}x &= y \\ f^{-1}(x) &= \frac{2}{3}x \end{aligned}$$

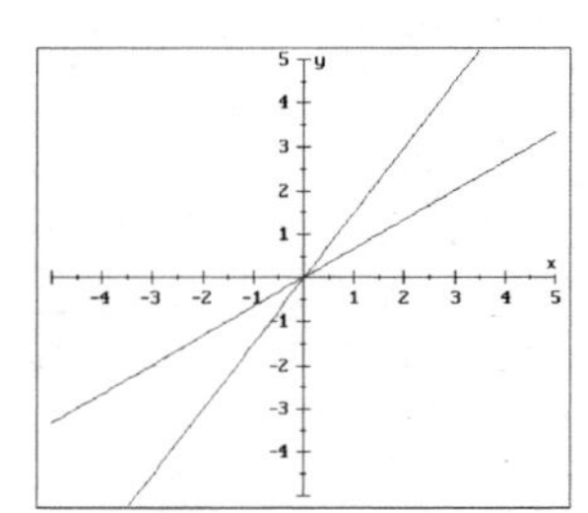

39.
$$\begin{aligned} y = f(x) &= 2x - 4 \\ x &= 2y - 4 \\ x + 4 &= 2y \\ \frac{x+4}{2} &= y \\ f^{-1}(x) &= \frac{x+4}{2} \end{aligned}$$

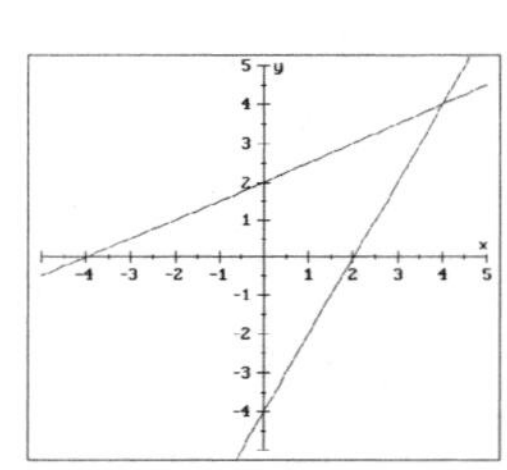

40.
$$\begin{aligned} y = f(x) &= \tfrac{3}{2}x - 2 \\ x &= \tfrac{3}{2}y - 2 \\ x + 2 &= \tfrac{3}{2}y \\ \tfrac{2}{3}(x+2) &= y \\ f^{-1}(x) &= \tfrac{2}{3}(x+2) \end{aligned}$$

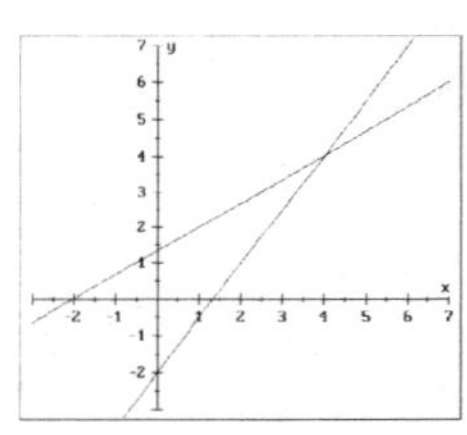

41.

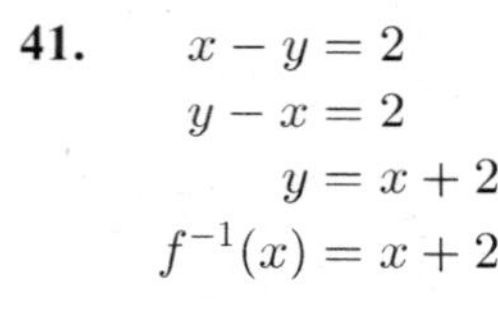

$$\begin{aligned} x - y &= 2 \\ y - x &= 2 \\ y &= x + 2 \\ f^{-1}(x) &= x + 2 \end{aligned}$$

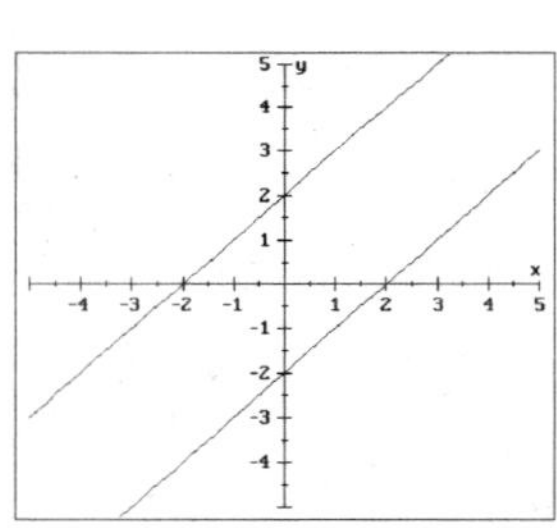

42.
$$\begin{aligned} x + y &= 0 \\ y + x &= 0 \\ y &= -x \\ f^{-1}(x) &= -x \end{aligned}$$

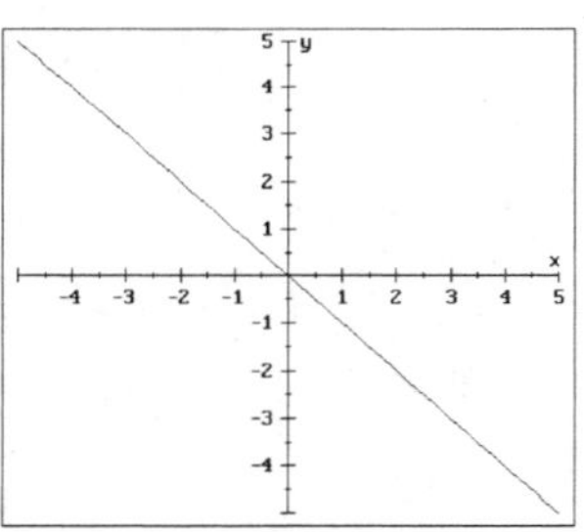

43. $2x + y = 4$

$2y + x = 4$

$2y = 4 - x$

$y = \dfrac{4 - x}{2}$

$f^{-1}(x) = \dfrac{4 - x}{2}$

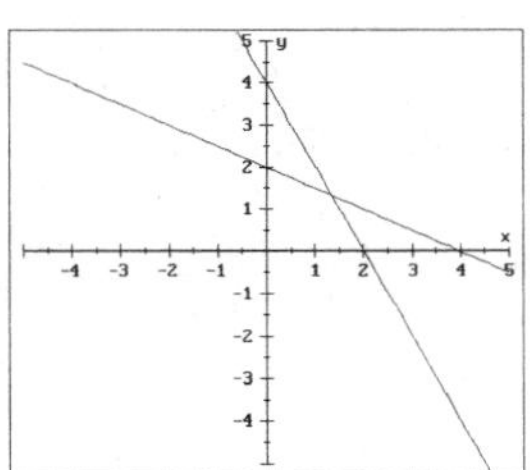

44. $3x + 2y = 6$

$3y + 2x = 6$

$3y = 6 - 2x$

$y = \dfrac{6 - 2x}{3}$

$f^{-1}(x) = \dfrac{6 - 2x}{3}$

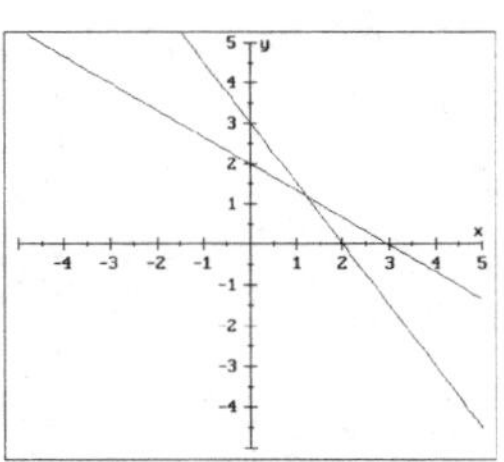

45. $y = f(x) = \sqrt[3]{x - 4}$

$x = \sqrt[3]{y - 4}$

$x^3 = y - 4$

$x^3 + 4 = y$

$f^{-1}(x) = x^3 + 4$

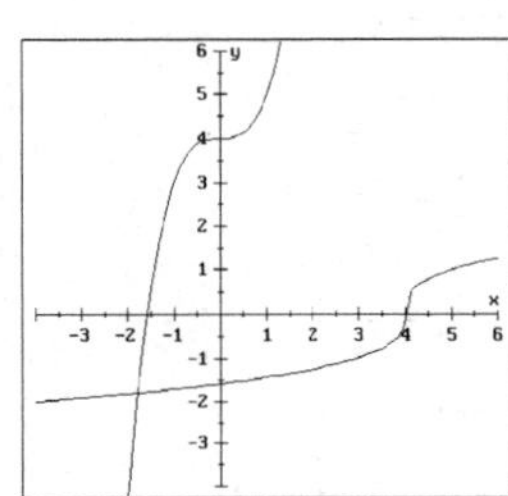

46. $y = f(x) = \sqrt[3]{x + 3}$

$x = \sqrt[3]{y + 3}$

$x^3 = y + 3$

$x^3 - 3 = y$

$f^{-1}(x) = x^3 - 3$

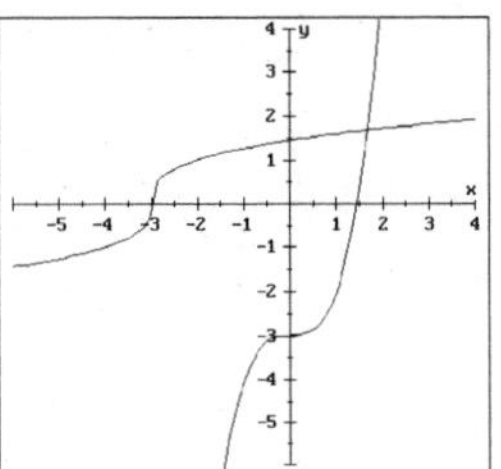

47. $y = f(x) = (x - 6)^3$

$x = (y - 6)^3$

$\sqrt[3]{x} = y - 6$

$\sqrt[3]{x} + 6 = y$

$f^{-1}(x) = \sqrt[3]{x} + 6$

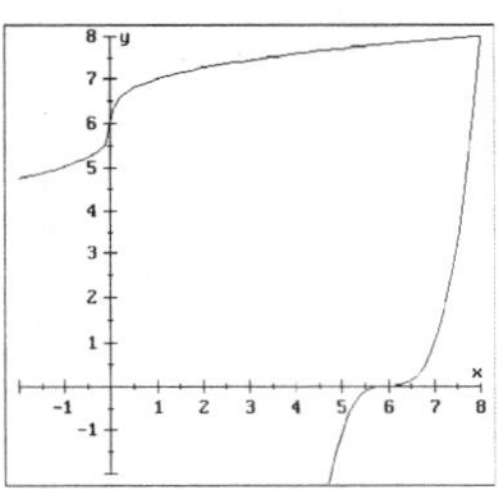

48. $y = f(x) = x^3 + 2$

$x = y^3 + 2$

$x - 2 = y^3$

$\sqrt[3]{x - 2} = y$

$f^{-1}(x) = \sqrt[3]{x - 2}$

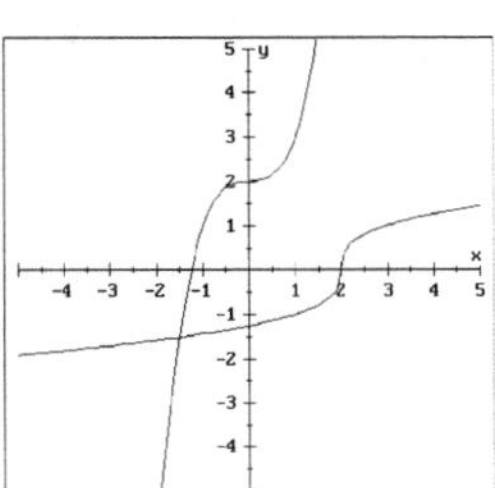

49.
$$\begin{aligned} y &= \frac{1}{2x} \\ x &= \frac{1}{2y} \\ 2xy &= 1 \\ y &= \frac{1}{2x} \\ f^{-1}(x) &= \frac{1}{2x} \end{aligned}$$

50.
$$\begin{aligned} y &= \frac{1}{x-3} \\ x &= \frac{1}{y-3} \\ x(y-3) &= 1 \\ y-3 &= \frac{1}{x} \\ f^{-1}(x) &= \frac{1}{x}+3 \end{aligned}$$

51.
$$\begin{aligned} y &= \frac{x+1}{x-1} \\ x &= \frac{y+1}{y-1} \\ x(y-1) &= y+1 \\ xy-x &= y+1 \\ xy-y &= x+1 \\ y(x-1) &= x+1 \\ f^{-1}(x) &= \frac{x+1}{x-1} \end{aligned}$$

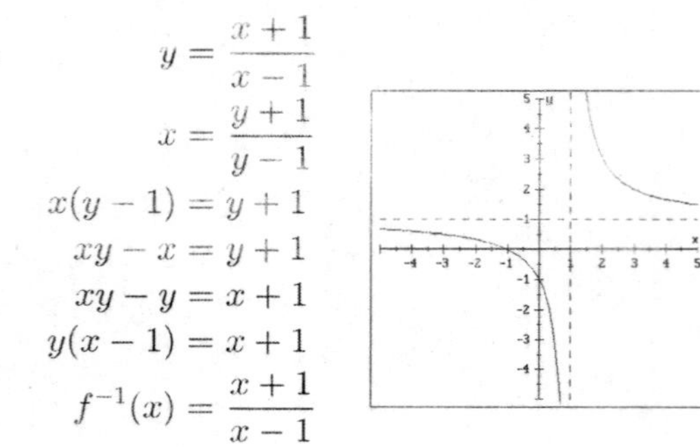

52.
$$\begin{aligned} y &= \frac{x-1}{x} \\ x &= \frac{y-1}{y} \\ xy &= y-1 \\ xy-y &= -1 \\ y(x-1) &= -1 \\ f^{-1}(x) &= \frac{-1}{x-1} \\ &= \frac{1}{1-x} \end{aligned}$$

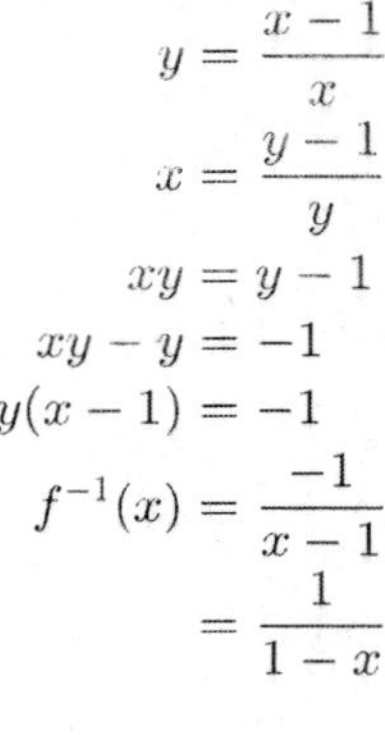

53.
$$\begin{aligned} f(x) &= x^2-3 \quad && x \le 0 \\ y &= x^2-3 && x \le 0 \\ x &= y^2-3 && y \le 0 \\ x+3 &= y^2 && y \le 0 \\ \pm\sqrt{x+3} &= y && y \le 0 \end{aligned}$$

Thus, $f^{-1}(x) = -\sqrt{x+3}\ (x \ge -3)$.

54.
$$\begin{aligned} f(x) &= \frac{1}{x^2} \quad && x > 0 \\ y &= \frac{1}{x^2} && x > 0 \\ x &= \frac{1}{y^2} && y > 0 \\ xy^2 &= 1 && y > 0 \\ y^2 &= \frac{1}{x} && y > 0 \\ y &= \pm\sqrt{\frac{1}{x}} && y > 0 \end{aligned}$$

Thus, $f^{-1}(x) = \sqrt{\frac{1}{x}}\ (x > 0)$.

55.

$$\begin{aligned} f(x) &= x^4 - 8 \quad x \geq 0 \\ y &= x^4 - 8 \quad x \geq 0 \\ x &= y^4 - 8 \quad y \geq 0 \\ x + 8 &= y^4 \quad y \geq 0 \\ \pm \sqrt[4]{x+8} &= y \quad y \geq 0 \end{aligned}$$

Thus, $f^{-1}(x) = \sqrt[4]{x+8}$ $(x \geq -8)$.

56.

$$\begin{aligned} f(x) &= \frac{-1}{x^4} \quad x < 0 \\ y &= \frac{-1}{x^4} \quad x < 0 \\ x &= \frac{-1}{y^4} \quad y < 0 \\ xy^4 &= -1 \quad y < 0 \\ y^4 &= \frac{-1}{x} \quad y < 0 \\ y &= \pm \sqrt[4]{\frac{-1}{x}} \quad y < 0 \end{aligned}$$

Thus, $f^{-1}(x) = -\sqrt[4]{\frac{-1}{x}}$ $(x < 0)$.

57.

$$\begin{aligned} f(x) &= \sqrt{4 - x^2} \quad 0 \leq x \leq 2 \\ y &= \sqrt{4 - x^2} \quad 0 \leq x \leq 2 \\ x &= \sqrt{4 - y^2} \quad 0 \leq y \leq 2 \\ x^2 &= 4 - y^2 \quad 0 \leq y \leq 2 \\ y^2 &= 4 - x^2 \quad 0 \leq y \leq 2 \\ y &= \pm \sqrt{4 - x^2} \quad 0 \leq y \leq 2 \end{aligned}$$

Thus, $f^{-1}(x) = \sqrt{4 - x^2}$ $(0 \leq x \leq 2)$.

58.

$$\begin{aligned} f(x) &= \sqrt{x^2 - 1} \quad x \leq -1 \\ y &= \sqrt{x^2 - 1} \quad x \leq -1 \\ x &= \sqrt{y^2 - 1} \quad y \leq -1 \\ x^2 &= y^2 - 1 \quad y \leq -1 \\ y^2 &= x^2 + 1 \quad y \leq -1 \\ y &= \pm \sqrt{x^2 + 1} \quad y \leq -1 \end{aligned}$$

Thus, $f^{-1}(x) = -\sqrt{x^2 + 1}$ $(x \geq 0)$.

59. $f(x) = \dfrac{x}{x-2}$

Domain of $f = \boxed{(-\infty, 2) \cup (2, \infty)}$

$f^{-1}(x) = \dfrac{2x}{x-1}$

Range of f = Domain of f^{-1}

$= \boxed{(-\infty, 1) \cup (1, \infty)}$

60. $f(x) = \dfrac{x-2}{x+3}$

Domain of $f = \boxed{(-\infty, -3) \cup (-3, \infty)}$

$f^{-1}(x) = \dfrac{3x+2}{1-x}$

Range of f = Domain of f^{-1}

$= \boxed{(-\infty, 1) \cup (1, \infty)}$

61. $f(x) = \dfrac{1}{x} - 2$

Domain of $f = \boxed{(-\infty, 0) \cup (0, \infty)}$

$f^{-1}(x) = \dfrac{1}{x+2}$

Range of f = Domain of f^{-1}

$= \boxed{(-\infty, -2) \cup (-2, \infty)}$

62. $f(x) = \dfrac{3}{x} - \dfrac{1}{2}$

Domain of $f = \boxed{(-\infty, 0) \cup (0, \infty)}$

$f^{-1}(x) = \dfrac{3}{x + \frac{1}{2}}$

Range of f = Domain of f^{-1}

$= \boxed{(-\infty, -\tfrac{1}{2}) \cup (-\tfrac{1}{2}, \infty)}$

63. **a.** $y = 0.75x + 8.50$

b. $y = 0.75(4) + 8.50$
$= \$11.50$

c.
$$\begin{aligned} y &= 0.75x + 8.50 \\ x &= 0.75y + 8.50 \\ x - 8.50 &= 0.75y \\ \frac{x - 8.50}{0.75} &= y \end{aligned}$$

d.
$$\begin{aligned} y &= \frac{x - 8.50}{0.75} \\ &= \frac{10 - 8.50}{0.75} \\ &= \frac{1.50}{0.75} = 2 \end{aligned}$$

64. **a.** $y = \dfrac{0.05x + 11}{x}$

b. $y = \dfrac{0.05(68) + 11}{68}$
$\approx \$0.212 = 21.2¢$

c.
$$\begin{aligned} y &= \frac{0.05x + 11}{x} \\ x &= \frac{0.05y + 11}{y} \\ xy &= 0.05y + 11 \\ xy - 0.05y &= 11 \\ y(x - 0.05) &= 11 \\ y &= \frac{11}{x - 0.05} \end{aligned}$$

d.
$$\begin{aligned} y &= \frac{11}{x - 0.05} \\ &= \frac{11}{0.15 - 0.05} \\ &= \frac{11}{0.10} = 110 \end{aligned}$$

65. **Answers may vary.**

66. **Answers may vary.**

67. $f(0) = 3$, so $f^{-1}(3) = 0$.

68. $f(0) = -3$, so $f^{-1}(-3) = 0$.

69. $a \geq 0$

70. $a = 0$

71. $16^{3/4} = \left(16^{1/4}\right)^3 = 8$

72. $25^{-1/2} = \dfrac{1}{25^{1/2}} = \dfrac{1}{5}$

73. $(-8)^{2/3} = \left((-8)^{1/3}\right)^2 = 4$

74. $-8^{2/3} = -1 \cdot 8^{2/3} = -1\left(\left(8^{1/3}\right)^2\right) = -4$

75. $\left(\dfrac{64}{125}\right)^{-1/3} = \left(\dfrac{125}{64}\right)^{1/3} = \dfrac{5}{4}$

76. $49^{3/2} = \left(49^{1/2}\right)^3 = 343$

77. $49^{-1/2} = \dfrac{1}{49^{1/2}} = \dfrac{1}{7}$

78.
$$\begin{aligned} \left(\frac{9}{25}\right)^{-3/2} &= \left(\frac{25}{9}\right)^{3/2} = \left(\left(\frac{25}{9}\right)^{1/2}\right)^3 \\ &= \frac{125}{27} \end{aligned}$$

Chapter 3 Review (page 394)

1. $y = 3$
Each value of x is paired with only one value of y.
function

2.
$$\begin{aligned} y + 5x^2 &= 2 \\ y &= -5x^2 + 2 \end{aligned}$$
Each value of x is paired with only one value of y.
function

3.
$$\begin{aligned} y^2 - x &= 5 \\ y^2 &= x + 5 \\ y &= \pm\sqrt{x + 5} \end{aligned}$$
Each value of x is paired with more than one value of y. **not a function**

CHAPTER 3 REVIEW

4. $y = |x| + x$
Each value of x is paired with only one value of y.
function

5. $f(x) = y = 3x^2 - 5$
domain $= (-\infty, \infty)$

6. $f(x) = y = \dfrac{3x}{x-5}$
domain $= (-\infty, 5) \cup (5, \infty)$

7. $f(x) = y = \sqrt{x-1}$
domain $= [1, \infty)$

8. $f(x) = y = \sqrt{x^2+1}$
$x^2 + 1 \geq 0 \Rightarrow$ domain $= (-\infty, \infty)$

9. $f(x) = 5x - 2$
$f(2) = 5(2) - 2 = 8$
$f(-3) = 5(-3) - 2 = -17$
$f(k) = 5k - 2$

10. $f(x) = \dfrac{6}{x-5}$
$f(2) = \frac{6}{2-5} = \frac{6}{-3} = -2$
$f(-3) = \frac{6}{-3-5} = \frac{6}{-8} = -\frac{3}{4}$
$f(k) = \frac{6}{k-5}$

11. $f(x) = |x - 2|$
$f(2) = |2 - 2| = |0| = 0$
$f(-3) = |-3 - 2| = |-5| = 5$
$f(k) = |k - 2|$

12. $f(x) = \dfrac{x^2-3}{x^2+3}$
$f(2) = \frac{2^2-3}{2^2+3} = \frac{1}{7}$
$f(-3) = \frac{(-3)^2-3}{(-3)^2+3} = \frac{6}{12} = \frac{1}{2}$
$f(k) = \frac{k^2-3}{k^2+3}$

13.
$$\frac{f(x+h)-f(x)}{h} = \frac{[5(x+h)-6]-[5x-6]}{h} = \frac{[5x+5h-6]-[5x-6]}{h} = \frac{5x+5h-6-5x+6}{h} = \frac{5h}{h} = 5$$

14.
$$\begin{aligned}\frac{f(x+h)-f(x)}{h} &= \frac{\left[2(x+h)^2-7(x+h)+3\right]-[2x^2-7x+3]}{h} \\ &= \frac{[2x^2+4xh+2h^2-7x-7h+3]-[2x^2-7x+3]}{h} \\ &= \frac{2x^2+4xh+2h^2-7x-7h+3-2x^2+7x-3}{h} \\ &= \frac{4xh+2h^2-7h}{h} = \frac{h(4x+2h-7)}{h} = 4x+2h-7\end{aligned}$$

15. $f(x) = -x^2 + 4$

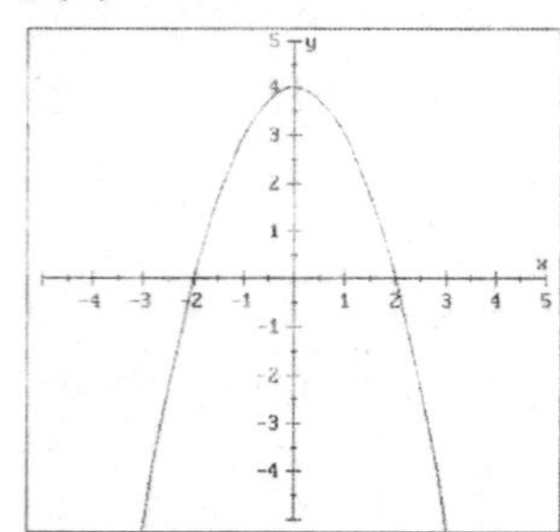

domain $= (-\infty, \infty)$
range $= (-\infty, 4]$

16. $f(x) = 3|x - 2|$

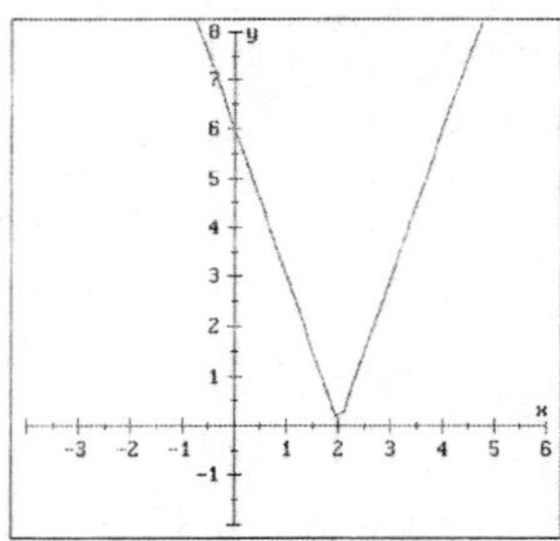

domain $= (-\infty, \infty)$
range $= [0, \infty)$

17. function

18. not a function

19. **a.** $I(h) = 3.5h - 50$
b. $I(200) = 3.5(200) - 50 = \$650$

20. Let (x, C) be a point on the line. Then the points $(100, 20)$ and $(500, 80)$ are on the line.

$$m = \frac{\Delta C}{\Delta x} = \frac{80 - 20}{500 - 100} = \frac{60}{400} = 0.15$$
$$C = mx + b$$
$$20 = 0.15(100) + b$$
$$20 = 15 + b$$
$$5 = b \Rightarrow \boxed{C(x) = 0.15x + 5}$$

21. $f(x) = \frac{1}{2}x^2 + 4$
$a = \frac{1}{2} \Rightarrow a > 0$
upward, minimum

22. $f(x) = -4(x + 1)^2 + 5$
$a = -4 \Rightarrow a < 0$
downward, maximum

23. $f(x) = 2(x - 1)^2 + 6$
Vertex: $(1, 6)$

24. $f(x) = -2(x + 4)^2 - 5$
Vertex: $(-4, -5)$

25. $y = x^2 + 6x - 4;\ a = 1, b = 6, c = -4$
$$x = -\frac{b}{2a} = -\frac{6}{2(1)} = -3$$
$$y = x^2 + 6x - 4 = (-3)^2 + 6(-3) - 4 = -13$$
Vertex: $(-3, -13)$

26. $y = -4x^2 + 4x - 9;\ a = -4, b = 4, c = -9$
$$x = -\frac{b}{2a} = -\frac{4}{2(-4)} = \frac{1}{2}$$
$$y = -4x^2 + 4x - 9 = -4\left(\tfrac{1}{2}\right)^2 + 4\left(\tfrac{1}{2}\right) - 9 = -8$$
Vertex: $\left(\frac{1}{2}, -8\right)$

27. $f(x) = (x-2)^2 - 3$
$a = 1 \Rightarrow$ up, vertex: $(2, -3)$

$0 = (x-2)^2 - 3$
$3 = (x-2)^2$
$\pm\sqrt{3} = x - 2$
$2 \pm \sqrt{3} = x$
$\left(2-\sqrt{3}, 0\right), \left(2+\sqrt{3}, 0\right)$

$f(0) = 1 \Rightarrow (0, 1)$

$f(1) = -2 \Rightarrow (1, -2)$
$(3, -2)$ on graph by symmetry

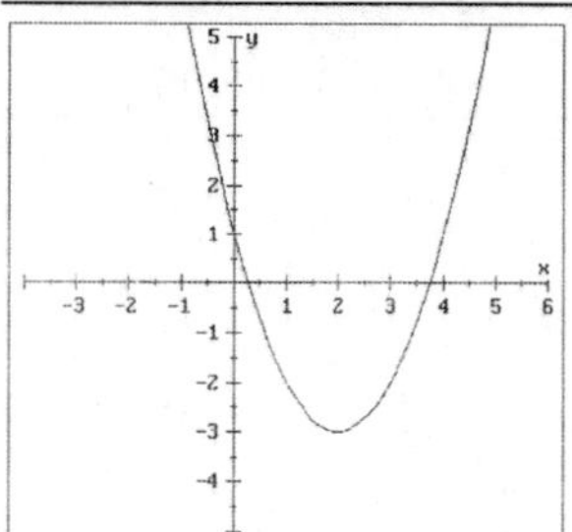

28. $f(x) = -(x-4)^2 + 4$
$a = -1 \Rightarrow$ down, vertex: $(4, 4)$

$0 = -(x-4)^2 + 4$
$(x-4)^2 = 4$
$x - 4 = \pm 2$
$x = 4 \pm 2$
$x = 2$ or $x = 6 \Rightarrow (2, 0), (6, 0)$

$f(0) = -12 \Rightarrow (0, -12)$

$f(3) = 3 \Rightarrow (3, 3)$
$(5, 3)$ on graph by symmetry

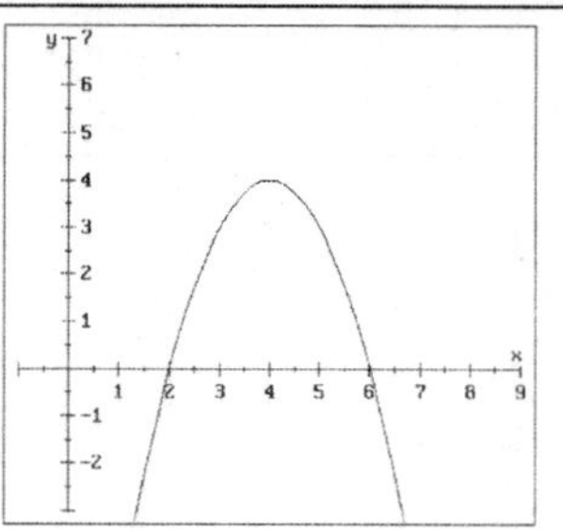

29. $f(x) = x^2 - x;\ a = 1, b = -1, c = 0$
$x = -\frac{b}{2a} = -\frac{-1}{2(1)} = \frac{1}{2}$
$y = x^2 - x = \left(\frac{1}{2}\right)^2 - \frac{1}{2} = -\frac{1}{4}$
vertex: $\left(\frac{1}{2}, -\frac{1}{4}\right)$, $a = 1 \Rightarrow$ up

$0 = x^2 - x$
$0 = x(x-1)$
$x = 0$ or $x = 1 \Rightarrow (0, 0), (1, 0)$

$f(0) = 0 \Rightarrow (0, 0)$

$f(2) = 2 \Rightarrow (2, 2)$ on graph
$(-1, 2)$ on graph by symmetry

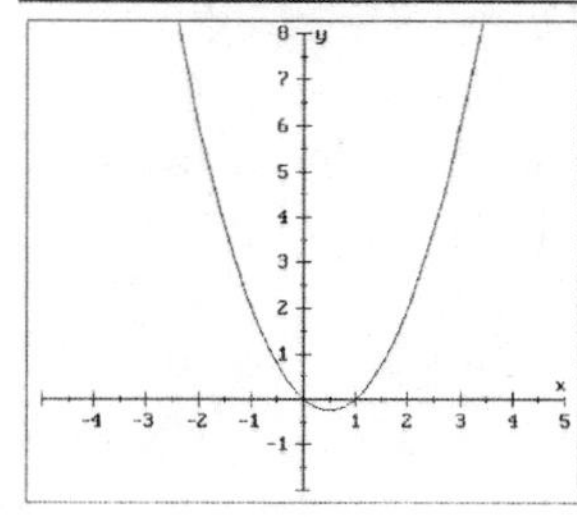

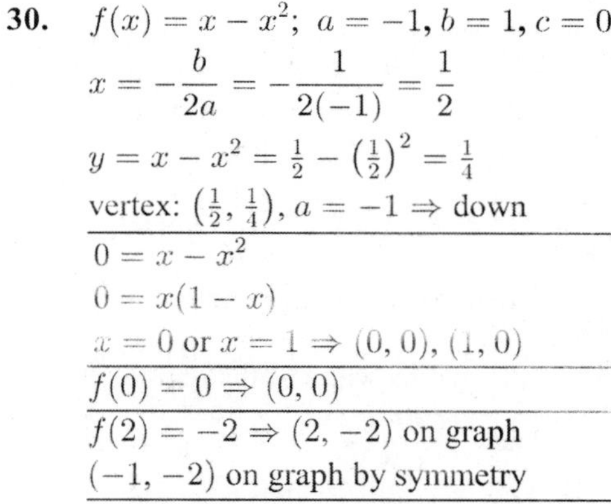

30. $f(x) = x - x^2;\ a = -1, b = 1, c = 0$
$x = -\frac{b}{2a} = -\frac{1}{2(-1)} = \frac{1}{2}$
$y = x - x^2 = \frac{1}{2} - \left(\frac{1}{2}\right)^2 = \frac{1}{4}$
vertex: $\left(\frac{1}{2}, \frac{1}{4}\right)$, $a = -1 \Rightarrow$ down

$0 = x - x^2$
$0 = x(1-x)$
$x = 0$ or $x = 1 \Rightarrow (0, 0), (1, 0)$

$f(0) = 0 \Rightarrow (0, 0)$

$f(2) = -2 \Rightarrow (2, -2)$ on graph
$(-1, -2)$ on graph by symmetry

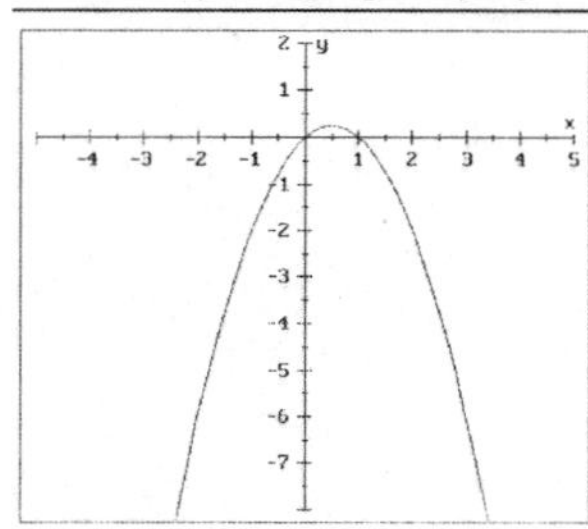

31. $y = x^2 - 3x - 4$; $a = 1, b = -3, c = -4$

$x = -\frac{b}{2a} = -\frac{-3}{2(1)} = \frac{3}{2}$

$y = x^2 - 3x - 4 = \left(\frac{3}{2}\right)^2 - 3\left(\frac{3}{2}\right) - 4$
$= -\frac{25}{4}$

vertex: $\left(\frac{3}{2}, -\frac{25}{4}\right)$, $a = 1 \Rightarrow$ up

$0 = x^2 - 3x - 4$
$0 = (x + 1)(x - 4)$
$x = -1$ or $x = 4 \Rightarrow (-1, 0), (4, 0)$

$f(0) = -4 \Rightarrow (0, -4)$

$f(2) = -6 \Rightarrow (2, -6)$ on graph
$(1, -6)$ on graph by symmetry

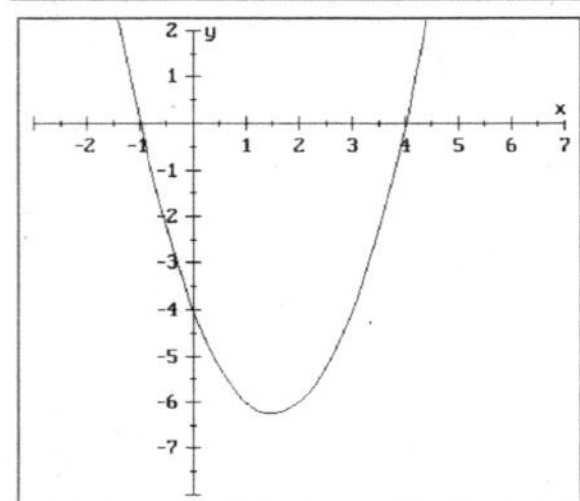

32. $y = 3x^2 - 8x - 3$; $a = 3, b = -8, c = -3$

$x = -\frac{b}{2a} = -\frac{-8}{2(3)} = \frac{4}{3}$

$y = 3x^2 - 8x - 3 = 3\left(\frac{4}{3}\right)^2 - 8\left(\frac{4}{3}\right) - 3$
$= -\frac{25}{3}$

vertex: $\left(\frac{4}{3}, -\frac{25}{3}\right)$, $a = 3 \Rightarrow$ up

$0 = 3x^2 - 8x - 3$
$0 = (3x + 1)(x - 3)$
$x = -\frac{1}{3}$ or $x = 3 \Rightarrow \left(-\frac{1}{3}, 0\right), (3, 0)$

$f(0) = -3 \Rightarrow (0, -3)$

$f(1) = -8 \Rightarrow (1, -8)$ on graph
$\left(\frac{5}{3}, -8\right)$ on graph by symmetry

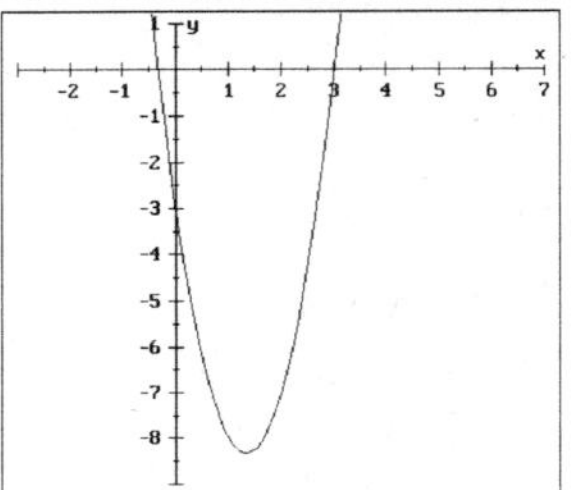

33. $3x^2 + y - 300 = 0$
$y = -3x^2 + 300$
$a = -3, b = 0, c = 300$
$x = -\frac{b}{2a} = -\frac{0}{2(-3)} = 0$
$y = -3(0)^2 + 300 = 300$
The maximum height is 300 units.

34. Let the numbers be x and $1 - x$.
Product $= x(1 - x)$
$y = x - x^2$: $a = -1, b = 1, c = 0$
vertex: $x = -\frac{b}{2a} = -\frac{1}{2(-1)} = \frac{1}{2}$
Both numbers are $\frac{1}{2}$.

35. Let $x =$ the width of the region.
Then $\frac{1400 - 2x}{2} = 700 - x =$ the length.
Area = width · length
$y = x(700 - x)$
$y = -x^2 + 700x$
$a = -1, b = 700, c = 0$
$x = -\frac{b}{2a} = -\frac{700}{2(-1)} = 350$
$700 - x = 700 - 350 = 350$
$y = 350(700 - 350) = 122{,}500$
The dimensions are 350 ft by 350 ft, with an area of 122,500 ft^2.

36. $C(x) = 1.5x^2 - 150x + 4850$
$a = 1.5, b = -150, c = 4850$
$x = -\frac{b}{2a} = -\frac{-150}{2(1.5)} = 50$
$C(50) = 1.5(50)^2 - 150(50) + 4850 = 1100$
50 cameras should be made, for a minimum cost of \$1100.

37. $y = f(x) = x^3 - x$

$f(-x) = (-x)^3 - (-x)$
$= -x^3 + x$
$= -f(x) \Rightarrow$ odd

x-int.	y-int.
$x^3 - x = 0$	$y = 0^3 - 0$
$x(x^2 - 1) = 0$	$y = 0$
$x(x+1)(x-1) = 0$	$(0, 0)$
$x = 0, x = -1, x = 1$	
$(0, 0), (-1, 0), (1, 0)$	

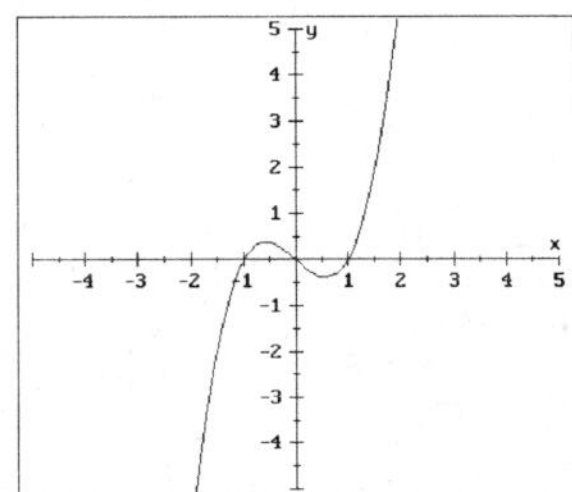

38. $f(x) = x^2 - 4x$

$f(-x) = (-x)^2 - 4(-x)$
$= x^2 + 4x$
$\Rightarrow$ neither even nor odd

x-int.	y-int.
$x^2 - 4x = 0$	$y = 0^2 - 4(0)$
$x(x-4) = 0$	$y = 0$
$x = 0, x = 4$	$(0, 0)$
$(0, 0), (4, 0)$	

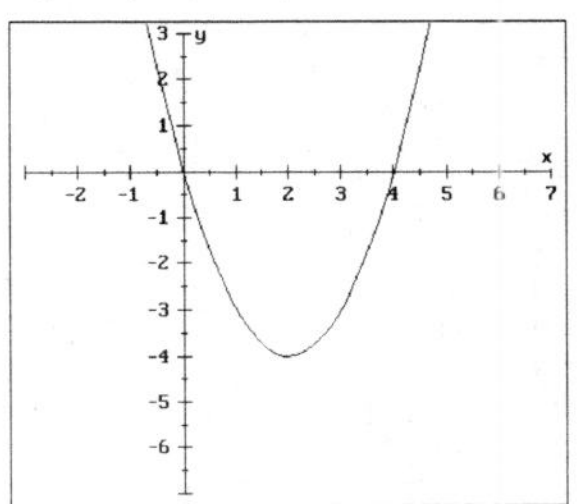

39. $f(x) = x^3 - x^2$

$f(-x) = (-x)^3 - (-x)^2$
$= -x^3 - x^2$
$\Rightarrow$ neither even nor odd

x-int.	y-int.
$x^3 - x^2 = 0$	$y = 0^3 - 0^2$
$x^2(x-1) = 0$	$y = 0$
$x = 0, x = 1$	$(0, 0)$
$(0, 0), (1, 0)$	

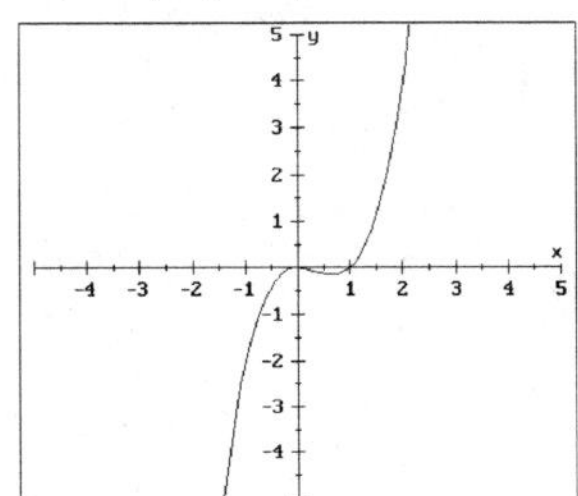

40. $y = f(x) = 1 - x^4$

$f(-x) = 1 - (-x)^4$
$= 1 - x^4 = f(x) \Rightarrow$ even

x-int.	y-int.
$1 - x^4 = 0$	$y = 1 - 0^4$
$(1 + x^2)(1 - x^2) = 0$	$y = 1$
$x^2 = -1, x^2 = 1$	$(0, 1)$
$x = -1, x = 1$	
$(-1, 0), (1, 0)$	

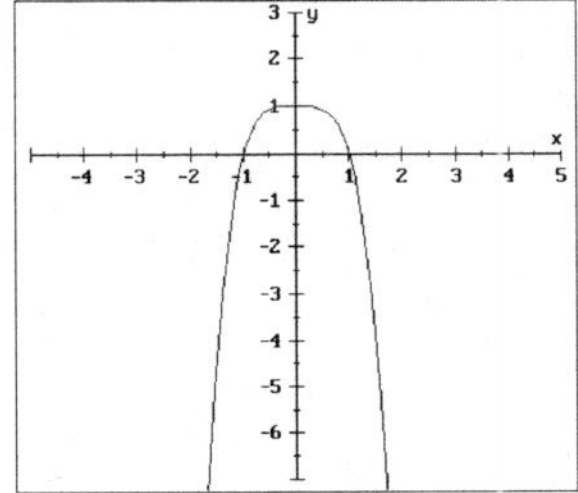

41. **a.** $f(-2) = 2$
b. $f(3) = 3^2 = 9$

42. **a.** $f\left(\frac{3}{2}\right) = 2 - \frac{3}{2} = \frac{1}{2}$
b. $f(2) = 2 + 1 = 3$

43. inc: $(-\infty, 0)$; dec: $(0, \infty)$

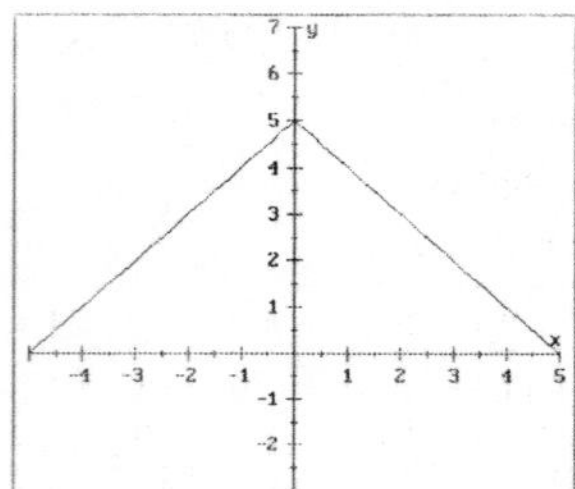

44. inc: $(-\infty, 0)$; const: $(0, \infty)$

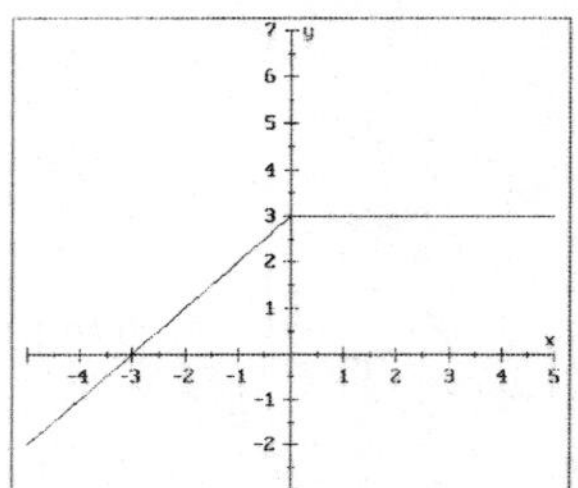

45. $f(1.7) = [[2(1.7)]] = [[3.4]] = 3$

46. $f(4.99) = [[4.99 - 5]] = [[-0.01]] = -1$

47. $f(x) = [[x]] + 2$

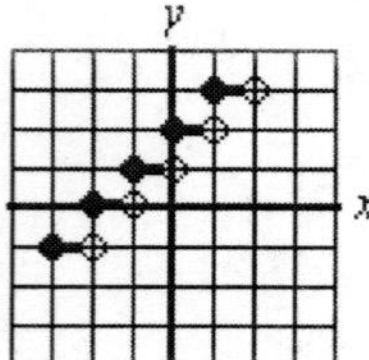

48. $f(x) = [[x - 1]]$

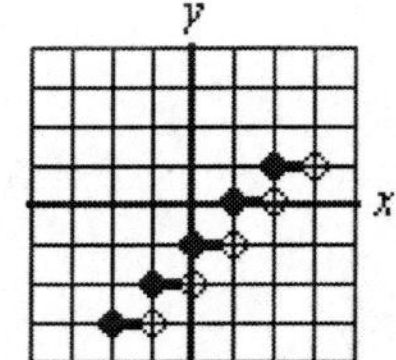

49. $20 + 3(8) = \$44$

50. $4 + 11(2) = \$26$

51. $g(x) = x^2 + 5$
Shift $y = x^2$ U 5

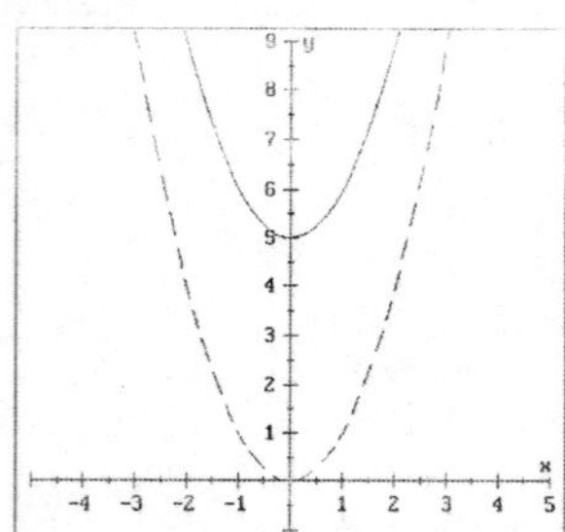

52. $g(x) = (x - 7)^3$
Shift $y = x^3$ R 7

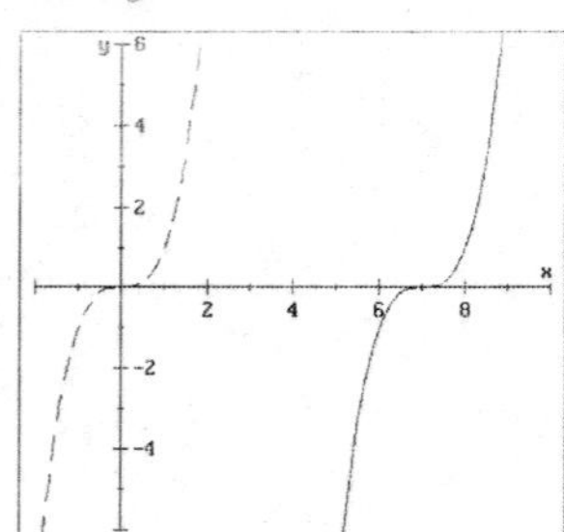

53. $g(x) = \sqrt{x+2} + 3$
Shift $y = \sqrt{x}$ U 3, L 2

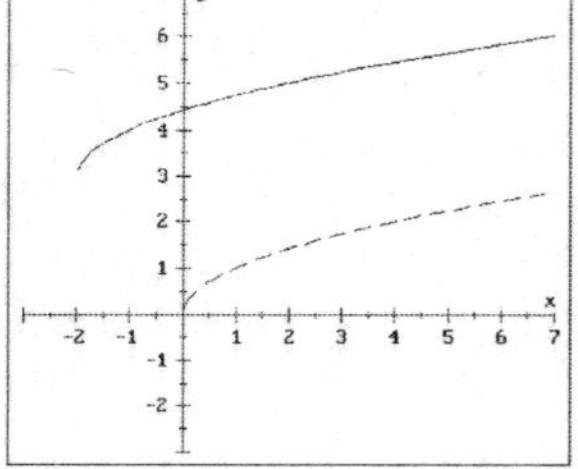

54. $g(x) = |x - 4| + 2$
Shift $y = |x|$ U 2, R 4

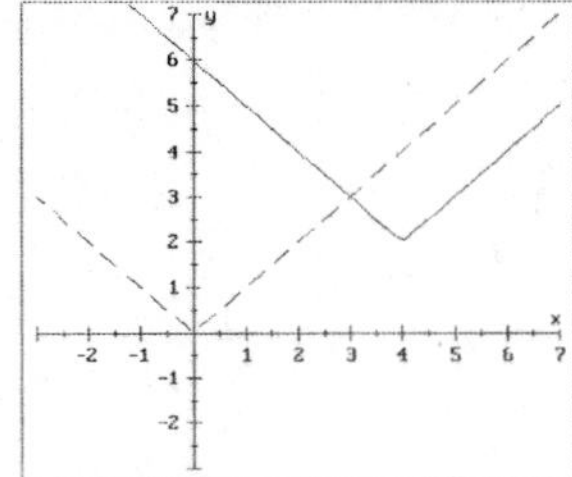

55. $g(x) = \frac{1}{3}x^3$: Shrink $y = x^3$ vert. by a factor of $\frac{1}{3}$

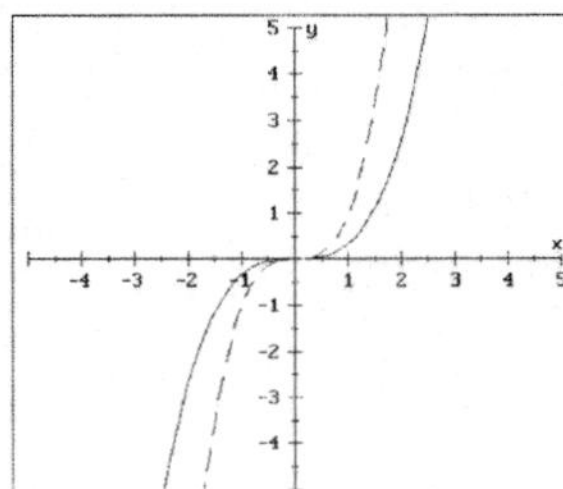

56. $g(x) = (-5x)^3$
Shrink $y = x^3$ horiz. by a factor of $\frac{1}{5}$. Reflect about y.

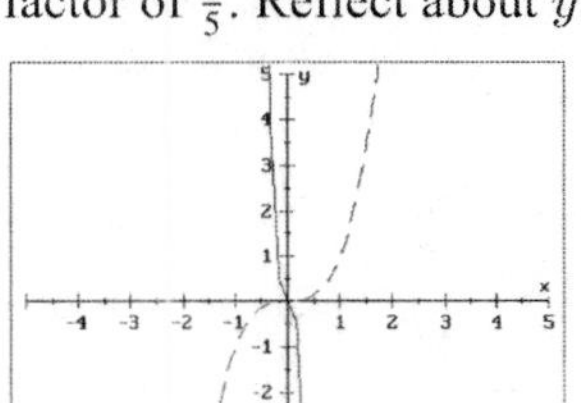

57. $g(x) = -|x - 4| + 3$
Start with $y = |x|$
Shift R 4, Reflect x,
Shift U 3

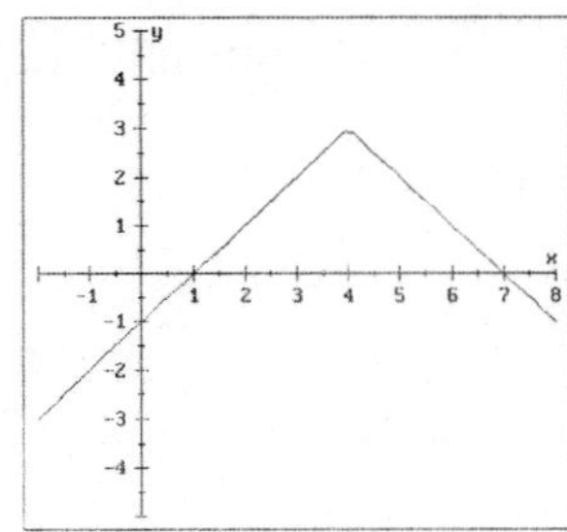

58. $g(x) = \frac{1}{4}|x - 4| + 1$
Start with $y = |x|$
Shift R 4, Shrink vert. by a factor of $\frac{1}{4}$, Shift U 1

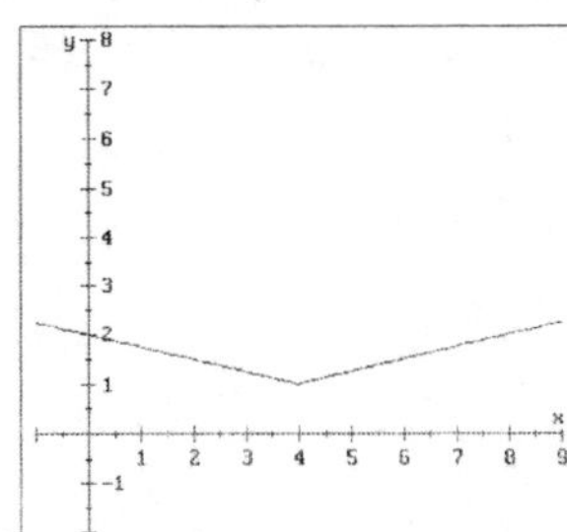

59. $g(x) = 3\sqrt{x + 3} + 2$
Start with $y = \sqrt{x}$
Shift L 3, Stretch vert. by a factor of 3, Shift U 2

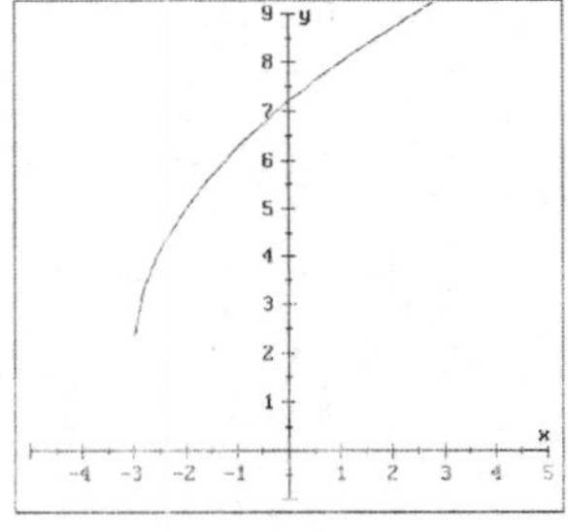

60. $g(x) = \frac{1}{3}(x + 3)^3 + 2$
Start with $y = x^3$
Shift L 3, Shrink vert. by a factor of $\frac{1}{3}$, Shift U 2

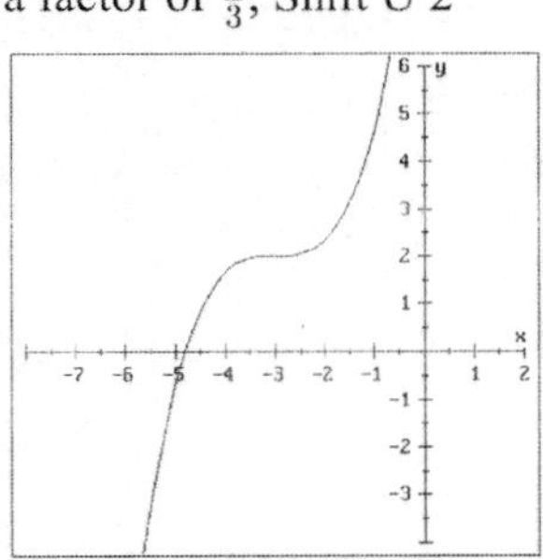

61. $f(x) = \sqrt{-x} + 3$
Start with $y = \sqrt{x}$
Reflect y, Shift U 3

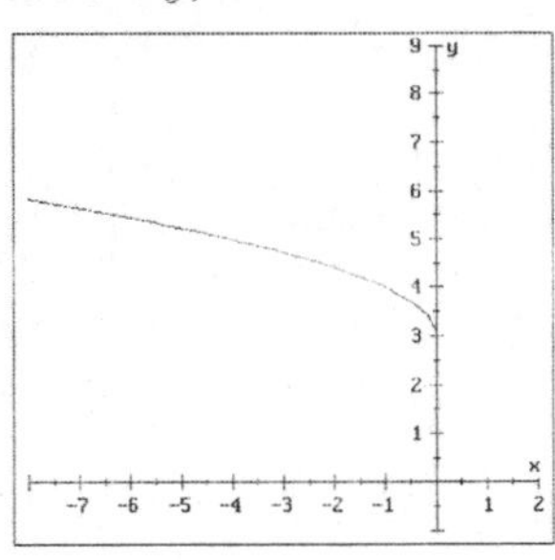

62. $g(x) = 2\sqrt[3]{x} - 5$
Start with $y = \sqrt[3]{x}$
Stretch vert. by a factor of 2, Shift D 5

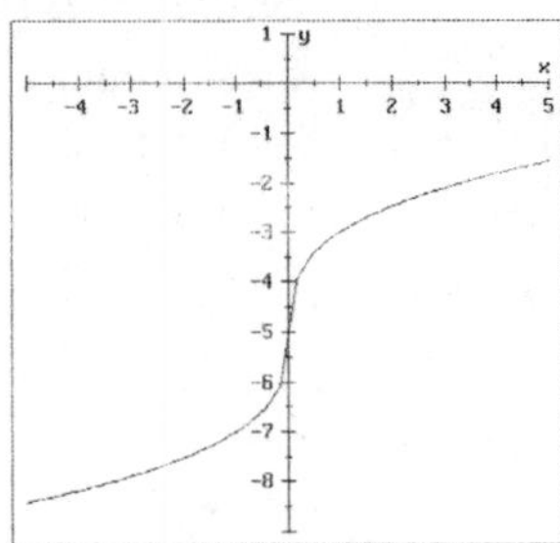

63. $f(x) = \dfrac{3x^2 + x - 2}{x^2 - 25} = \dfrac{(3x-2)(x+1)}{(x+5)(x-5)}$
den $= 0 \Rightarrow x = -5$ or $x = 5$
domain $= (-\infty, -5) \cup (-5, 5) \cup (5, \infty)$

64. $f(x) = \dfrac{2x^2 + 1}{x^2 + 7}$
den $= 0 \Rightarrow$ never true
domain $= (-\infty, \infty)$

65. $f(x) = \dfrac{x+5}{x^2 - 1} = \dfrac{x+5}{(x+1)(x-1)}$
den $= 0 \Rightarrow x = -1$ or $x = 1$
vertical: $x = -1$ or $x = 1$

66. $f(x) = \dfrac{x-7}{x^2 - 49} = \dfrac{x-7}{(x+7)(x-7)}$
$= \dfrac{1}{x+7}$
den $= 0 \Rightarrow x = -7$
vertical: $x = -7$

67. $f(x) = \dfrac{x}{x^2 + x - 6} = \dfrac{x}{(x+3)(x-2)}$
den $= 0 \Rightarrow x = -3$ or $x = 2$
vertical: $x = -3$ or $x = 2$

68. $f(x) = \dfrac{5x+2}{2x^2 - 6x - 8} = \dfrac{5x+2}{(2x+2)(x-4)}$
den $= 0 \Rightarrow x = -1$ or $x = 4$
vertical: $x = -1$ or $x = 4$

69. $f(x) = \dfrac{2x^2 + x - 2}{4x^2 - 4}$; deg(num) = deg(den)
horizontal: $y = \dfrac{2}{4}$, or $y = \dfrac{1}{2}$

70. $f(x) = \dfrac{5x^2 + 4}{4 - x^2}$; deg(num) = deg(den)
horizontal: $y = \dfrac{5}{-1}$, or $y = -5$

71. $f(x) = \dfrac{x+1}{x^3 - 4x}$; deg(num) < deg(den)
horizontal: $y = 0$

72. $f(x) = \dfrac{x^3}{2x^2 - 6x - 8}$; deg(num) > deg(den)
horizontal: none

73. $f(x) = \dfrac{2x^2 - 5x + 1}{x - 4} = 2x + 3 + \dfrac{13}{x-4}$
slant: $y = 2x + 3$

74. $f(x) = \dfrac{5x^3 + 1}{x + 5}$; deg(num) = 3,
deg(den) = 1 $\Rightarrow$ slant: none

75. $f(x) = \dfrac{2x}{x - 4}$
Vert: $x = 4$; Horiz: $y = \frac{2}{1} = 2$
Slant: none; x-intercepts: $(0, 0)$
y-intercepts: $(0, 0)$; Symmetry: none

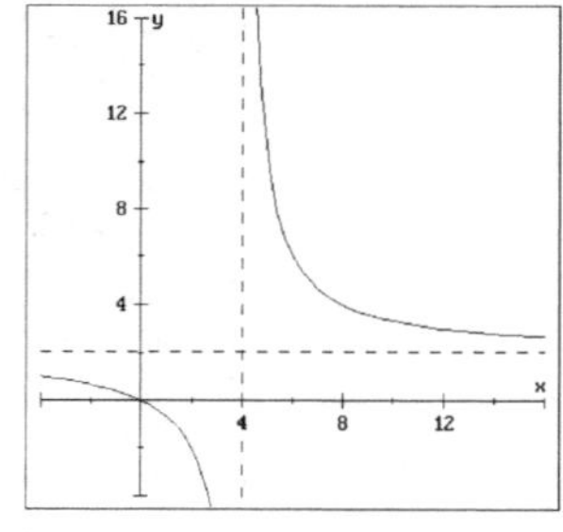

76. $f(x) = \dfrac{-4x}{x + 4}$
Vert: $x = -4$; Horiz: $y = \frac{-4}{1} = -4$
Slant: none; x-intercepts: $(0, 0)$
y-intercepts: $(0, 0)$; Symmetry: none

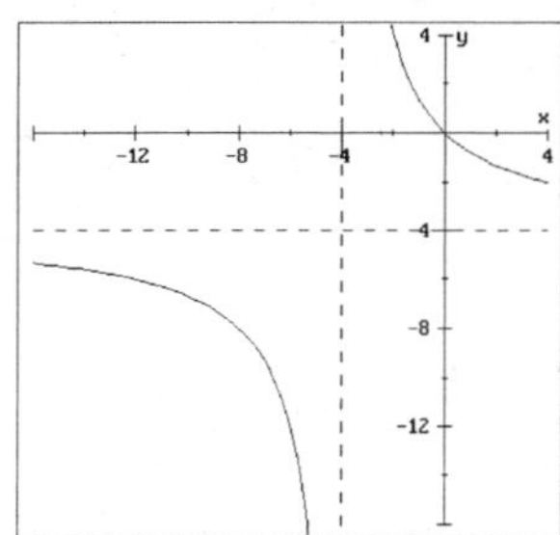

77. $f(x) = \dfrac{x}{(x-1)^2}$
Vert: $x = 1$; Horiz: $y = 0$
Slant: none; x-intercepts: $(0, 0)$
y-intercepts: $(0, 0)$; Symmetry: none

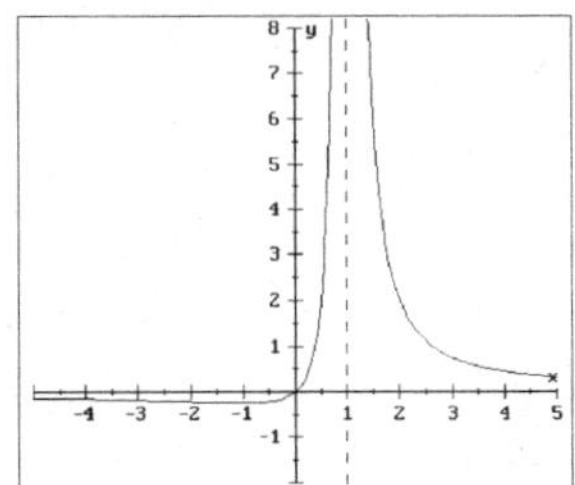

78. $f(x) = \dfrac{(x-1)^2}{x}$: Vert: $x = 0$
Horiz: none; Slant: $y = x - 2$
x-intercepts: $(1, 0)$
y-intercepts: none; Symmetry: none

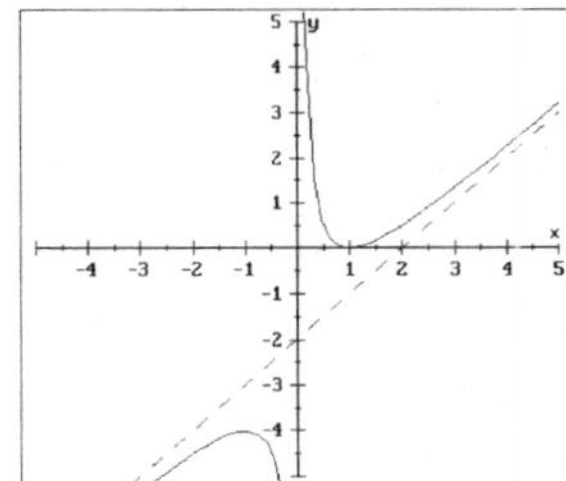

79. $y = \dfrac{x^2 - x - 2}{x^2 + x - 2} = \dfrac{(x+1)(x-2)}{(x+2)(x-1)}$
Vert: $x = -2, x = 1$; Horiz: $y = 1$
Slant: none; x-intercepts: $(-1, 0)$, $(2, 0)$
y-intercepts: $(0, 1)$; Symmetry: none

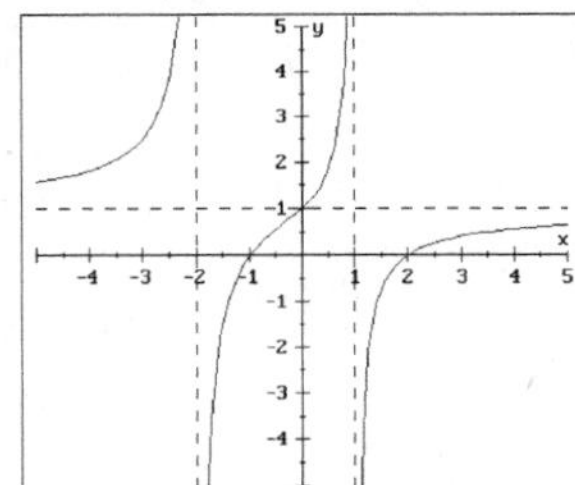

80. $y = \dfrac{x^3 + x}{x^2 - 4} = \dfrac{x(x^2+1)}{(x+2)(x-2)}$
Vert: $x = -2, x = 2$;
Slant: $y = x$;
x-int: $(0, 0)$$y$-int: $(0, 0)$;
Symmetry: none

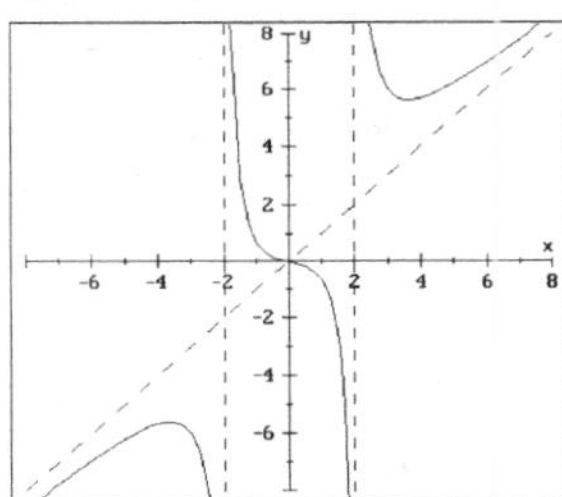

81. $(f+g)(x) = f(x) + g(x) = (x^2 - 1) + (2x + 1) = x^2 + 2x$; domain $= (-\infty, \infty)$

82. $(f \cdot g)(x) = f(x)g(x) = (x^2 - 1)(2x + 1) = 2x^3 + x^2 - 2x - 1$; domain $= (-\infty, \infty)$

83. $(f-g)(x) = f(x) - g(x) = (x^2 - 1) - (2x + 1) = x^2 - 2x - 2$; domain $= (-\infty, \infty)$

84. $(f/g)(x) = \dfrac{f(x)}{g(x)} = \dfrac{x^2 - 1}{2x + 1}$; domain $= \left(-\infty, -\frac{1}{2}\right) \cup \left(-\frac{1}{2}, \infty\right)$

85. $(f+g)(-3) = f(-3) + g(-3) = \left[2(-3)^2 - 1\right] + \left[2(-3) - 1\right] = 17 + (-7) = 10$

86. $(f-g)(-5) = f(-5) - g(-5) = \left[2(-5)^2 - 1\right] - \left[2(-5) - 1\right] = 49 - (-11) = 60$

87. $(f \cdot g)(2) = f(2) \cdot g(2) = \left[2(2)^2 - 1\right] \cdot \left[2(2) - 1\right] = 7 \cdot 3 = 21$

88. $(f/g)\left(\frac{1}{2}\right) = \dfrac{f\left(\frac{1}{2}\right)}{g\left(\frac{1}{2}\right)} = \dfrac{2\left(\frac{1}{2}\right)^2 - 1}{2\left(\frac{1}{2}\right) - 1} = \dfrac{-\frac{1}{2}}{0} \Rightarrow$ undefined

89. The domain of $f \circ g$ is the set of all real numbers in the domain of $g(x)$ such that $g(x)$ is in the domain of $f(x)$. Domain of $g(x)$: $(-\infty, \infty)$. Domain of $f(x) = (-\infty, \infty)$. Thus, all values of $g(x)$ are in the domain of $f(x)$. $\boxed{\text{Domain of } f \circ g\text{: } (-\infty, \infty)}$
$(f \circ g)(x) = f(g(x)) = f(2x + 1) = (2x + 1)^2 - 1 = 4x^2 + 4x + 1 - 1 = 4x^2 + 4x$

90. The domain of $g \circ f$ is the set of all real numbers in the domain of $f(x)$ such that $f(x)$ is in the domain of $g(x)$. Domain of $f(x)$: $(-\infty, \infty)$. Domain of $g(x) = (-\infty, \infty)$. Thus, all values of $f(x)$ are in the domain of $g(x)$. $\boxed{\text{Domain of } g \circ f\text{: } (-\infty, \infty)}$
$(g \circ f)(x) = g(f(x)) = g(x^2 - 1) = 2(x^2 - 1) + 1 = 2x^2 - 2 + 1 = 2x^2 - 1$

91. $(f \circ g)(-2) = f(g(-2)) = f(3(-2) + 1) = f(-5) = (-5)^2 - 5 = 20$

92. $(g \circ f)(-2) = g(f(-2)) = g((-2)^2 - 5) = g(-1) = 3(-1) + 1 = -2$

93. Let $f(x) = x^2$ and $g(x) = x - 5$.
Then $(f \circ g)(x) = f(g(x))$
$= f(x - 5) = (x - 5)^2$.

94. Let $f(x) = x^3$ and $g(x) = x + 6$.
Then $(f \circ g)(x) = f(g(x))$
$= f(x + 6) = (x + 6)^3$.

95. $f(x) = x^2 + 7$; $x = 1$ and $x = -1$ both correspond to $f(x) = 8$. Not one-to-one

96. one-to-one

97. one-to-one

98. not one-to-one

99. $(f \circ g)(x) = f(g(x)) = f\left(\dfrac{x + 3}{8}\right) = 8\left(\dfrac{x + 3}{8}\right) - 3 = x + 3 - 3 = x$

$(g \circ f)(x) = g(f(x)) = g(8x - 3) = \dfrac{(8x - 3) + 3}{8} = \dfrac{8x}{8} = x$

100. $(f \circ g)(x) = f(g(x)) = f\left(2 - \dfrac{1}{x}\right) = \dfrac{1}{2 - \left(2 - \frac{1}{x}\right)} = \dfrac{1}{\frac{1}{x}} = x$

$(g \circ f)(x) = g(f(x)) = g\left(\dfrac{1}{2 - x}\right) = 2 - \dfrac{1}{\frac{1}{2-x}} = 2 - (2 - x) = x$

101.
$$\begin{aligned} y = f(x) &= 7x - 1 \\ x &= 7y - 1 \\ x + 1 &= 7y \\ \frac{x+1}{7} &= y \\ f^{-1}(x) &= \frac{x+1}{7} \end{aligned}$$

102.
$$\begin{aligned} y = f(x) &= \frac{1}{2-x} \\ x &= \frac{1}{2-y} \\ x(2-y) &= 1 \\ 2 - y &= \frac{1}{x} \\ 2 - \frac{1}{x} &= y \\ f^{-1}(x) &= 2 - \frac{1}{x} \end{aligned}$$

103.
$$\begin{aligned} y = f(x) &= \frac{x}{1-x} \\ x &= \frac{y}{1-y} \\ x(1-y) &= y \\ x - xy &= y \\ x &= xy + y \\ x &= y(x+1) \\ \frac{x}{x+1} &= y \\ f^{-1}(x) &= \frac{x}{x+1} \end{aligned}$$

104.
$$\begin{aligned} y = f(x) &= \frac{3}{x^3} \\ x &= \frac{3}{y^3} \\ xy^3 &= 3 \\ y^3 &= \frac{3}{x} \\ y &= \sqrt[3]{\frac{3}{x}} \\ f^{-1}(x) &= \sqrt[3]{\frac{3}{x}} \end{aligned}$$

105.
$$\begin{aligned} y = f(x) &= 2x - 5 \\ x &= 2y - 5 \\ x + 5 &= 2y \\ \frac{x+5}{2} &= y \\ f^{-1}(x) &= \frac{x+5}{2} \end{aligned}$$

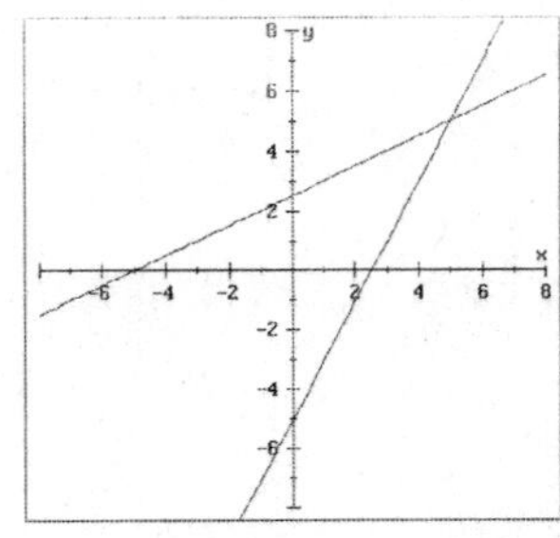

106.
$$\begin{aligned} y &= \frac{2x+3}{5x-10} \\ x &= \frac{2y+3}{5y-10} \\ x(5y-10) &= 2y + 3 \\ 5xy - 10x &= 2y + 3 \\ 5xy - 2y &= 10x + 3 \\ y(5x-2) &= 10x + 3 \\ y &= \frac{10x+3}{5x-2} \end{aligned}$$

Range of f = Domain of f^{-1}

$= \boxed{\left(-\infty, \tfrac{2}{5}\right) \cup \left(\tfrac{2}{5}, \infty\right)}$

Chapter 3 Test (page 409)

1. $f(x) = \dfrac{3}{x-5}$: domain $= (-\infty, 5) \cup (5, \infty)$

2. $f(x) = \sqrt{x+3}$: domain $= [-3, \infty)$

3. $f(-1) = \dfrac{-1}{-1-1} = \dfrac{-1}{-2} = \dfrac{1}{2}$

$f(2) = \dfrac{2}{2-1} = \dfrac{2}{1} = 2$

4. $f(-1) = \sqrt{-1+7} = \sqrt{6}$

$f(2) = \sqrt{2+7} = \sqrt{9} = 3$

5. $y = 3(x-7)^2 - 3$

Vertex: $(7, -3)$

6. $y = x^2 - 2x - 3;\ a = 1, b = -2, c = -3$

vertex: $x = -\frac{b}{2a} = -\frac{-2}{2(1)} = 1$

$y = x^2 - 2x - 3 = 1^2 - 2(1) - 3 = -4$

7. $y = 3x^2 - 24x + 38$

$a = 3, b = -24, c = 38$

vertex: $x = -\frac{b}{2a} = -\frac{-24}{2(3)} = 4$

$y = 3x^2 - 24x + 38 = 3(4)^2 - 24(4) + 38$

$= -10$

8. $y = 5 - 4x - x^2;\ a = -1, b = -4, c = 5$

vertex: $x = -\frac{b}{2a} = -\frac{-4}{2(-1)} = -2$

$y = 5 - 4x - x^2 = 5 - 4(-2) - (-2)^2$

$= 9$

9. $y = f(x) = x^4 - x^2$

$f(-x) = (-x)^4 - (-x)^2$

$= x^4 - x^2 = f(x) \Rightarrow$ even

x-int.	y-int.
$x^4 - x^2 = 0$	$y = 0^4 - 0^2$
$x^2(x^2 - 1) = 0$	$y = 0$
$x^2 = 0, x^2 = 1$	$(0, 0)$
$x = 0, x = -1, x = 1$	
$(0, 0), (-1, 0), (1, 0)$	

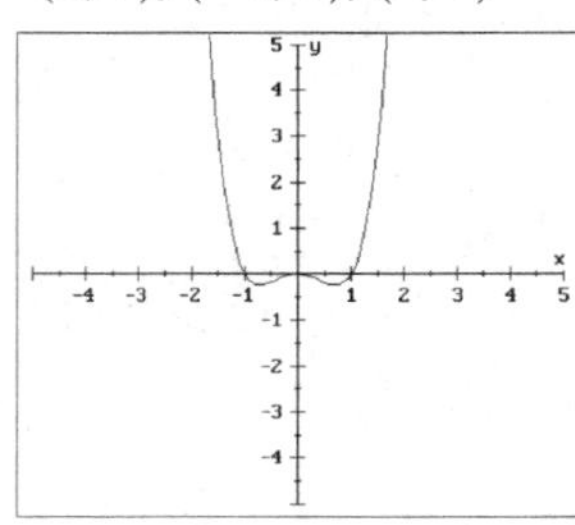

10. $y = f(x) = x^5 - x^3$

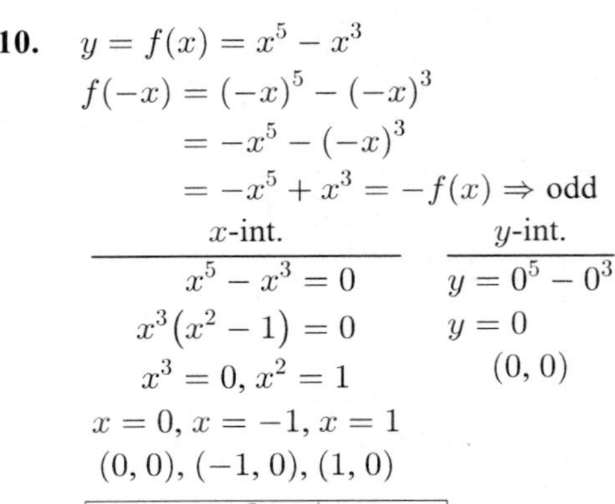

$f(-x) = (-x)^5 - (-x)^3$

$= -x^5 - (-x)^3$

$= -x^5 + x^3 = -f(x) \Rightarrow$ odd

x-int.	y-int.
$x^5 - x^3 = 0$	$y = 0^5 - 0^3$
$x^3(x^2 - 1) = 0$	$y = 0$
$x^3 = 0, x^2 = 1$	$(0, 0)$
$x = 0, x = -1, x = 1$	
$(0, 0), (-1, 0), (1, 0)$	

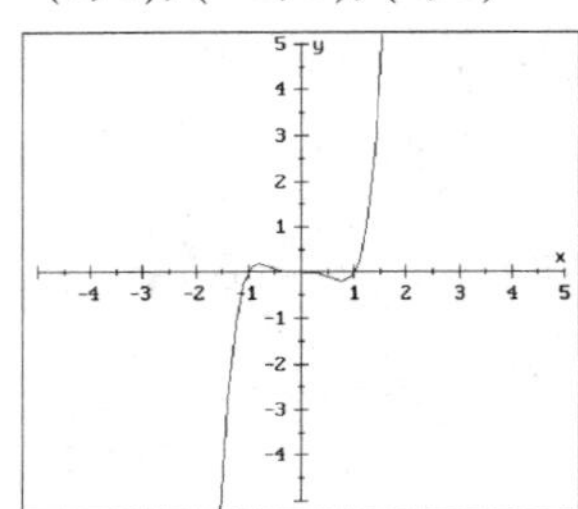

11. $h = 100t - 16t^2$: $a = -16, b = 100, c = 0$

$x = -\dfrac{b}{2a} = -\dfrac{100}{2(-16)} = \dfrac{25}{8}$ seconds

12. $h = 100t - 16t^2$: $a = -16, b = 100, c = 0$

From **#11**, $x = \frac{25}{8}$.

$y = 100\left(\frac{25}{8}\right) - 16\left(\frac{25}{8}\right)^2 = \frac{625}{4}$ feet

13. The roadway is at $y = 0$, so the distance to the lowest point will be the y-coord. of the vertex:

$$x^2 - 2500y + 25000 = 0$$
$$x^2 + 25000 = 2500y$$
$$\frac{1}{2500}x^2 + 10 = y$$
$$y = c - \frac{b^2}{4a} = 10 - \frac{0^2}{4\left(\frac{1}{2500}\right)} = 10$$

The lowest point is 10 ft above.

14. Let $x = \pm 500$:

$$x^2 - 2500y + 25000 = 0$$
$$(\pm 500)^2 - 2500y + 25000 = 0$$
$$250{,}000 - 2500y + 25{,}000 = 0$$
$$275{,}000 = 2500y$$
$$110 = y$$

The cable attaches to the vertical pillars 110 feet above the roadway.

15. $y = (x-3)^2 + 1$
Shift $y = x^2$ U 1, R 3

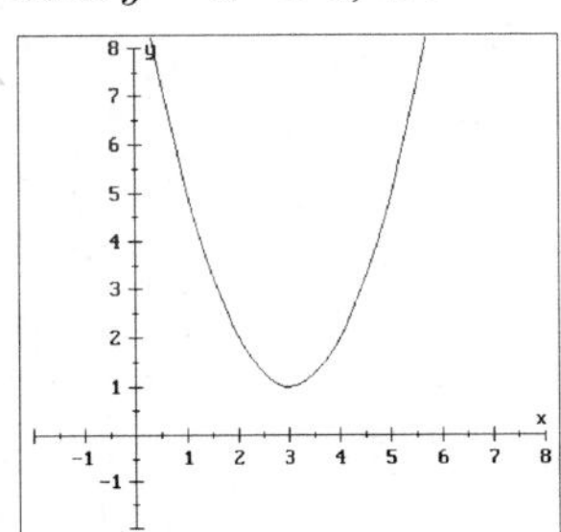

16. $y = \sqrt{x-1} + 5$
Shift $y = \sqrt{x}$ U 5, R 1

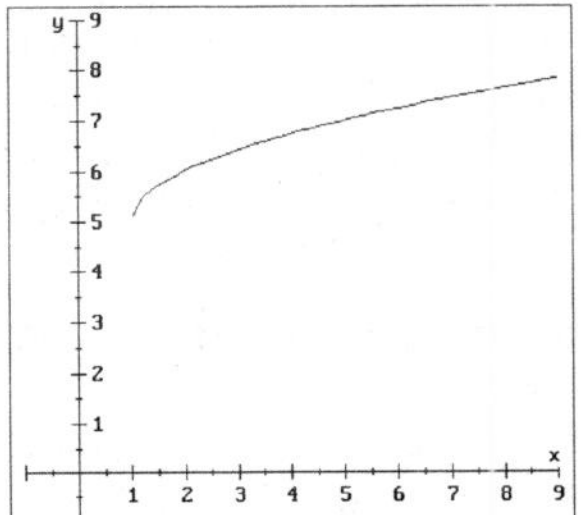

17. $y = \dfrac{x-1}{x^2-9} = \dfrac{x-1}{(x+3)(x-3)}$
Vert: $x = -3, x = 3$; Horiz: $y = 0$

18. $y = \dfrac{x^2-5x-14}{x-3} = \dfrac{(x-7)(x+2)}{(x-3)}$
$= x - 2 + \frac{-20}{x-3}$
Vert: $x = 3$; Slant: $y = x - 2$

19. $y = \dfrac{x^2}{x^2-9} = \dfrac{x^2}{(x+3)(x-3)}$
Vert: $x = -3, x = 3$; Horiz: $y = 1$
Slant: none; x-intercepts: $(0, 0)$
y-intercepts: $(0, 0)$; Symmetry: y-axis

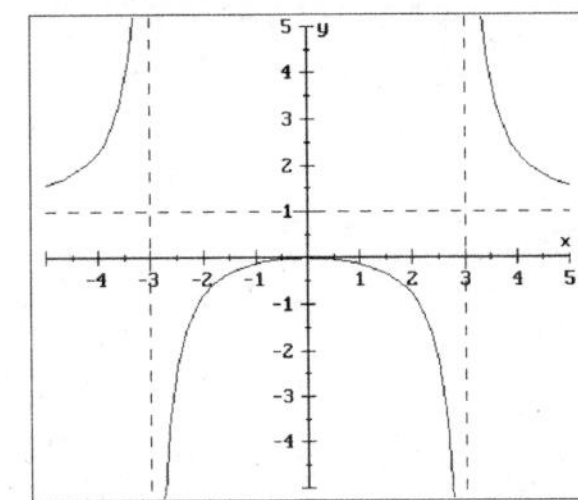

20. $y = \dfrac{x}{x^2+1}$
Vert: none; Horiz: $y = 0$
Slant: none; x-intercepts: $(0, 0)$
y-intercepts: $(0, 0)$; Symmetry: origin

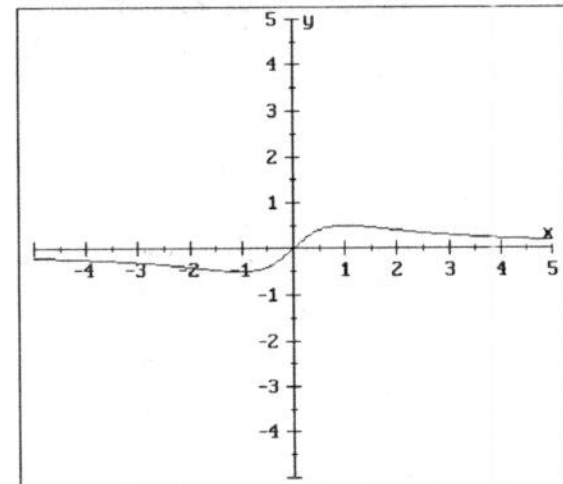

21. $y = \dfrac{2x^2 - 3x - 2}{x - 2} = \dfrac{(2x+1)(x-2)}{x-2}$
$= 2x + 1 \text{ (if } x \neq 2)$

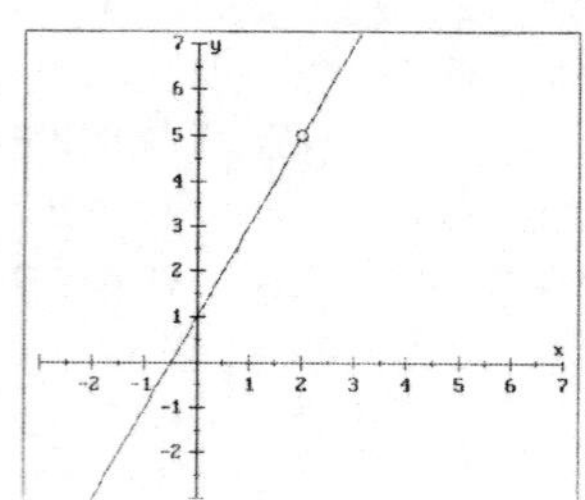

22. $y = \dfrac{x}{x^2 - x} = \dfrac{x}{x(x-1)} = \dfrac{1}{x-1} \text{ (if } x \neq 0)$

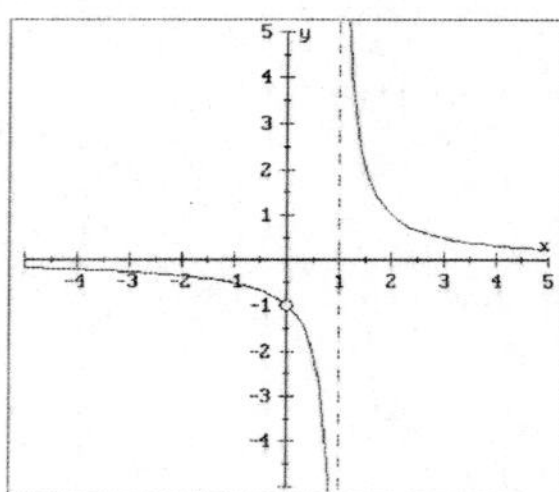

23. $(f+g)(x) = f(x) + g(x) = (3x) + (x^2 + 2) = x^2 + 3x + 2$

24. $(g \circ f)(x) = g(f(x)) = g(3x) = (3x)^2 + 2 = 9x^2 + 2$

25. $(f/g)(x) = \dfrac{f(x)}{g(x)} = \dfrac{3x}{x^2 + 2}$

26. $(f \circ g)(x) = f(g(x)) = f(x^2 + 2) = 3(x^2 + 2) = 3x^2 + 6$

27.
$$\begin{aligned} y &= \frac{x+1}{x-1} \\ x &= \frac{y+1}{y-1} \\ x(y-1) &= y+1 \\ xy - x &= y+1 \\ xy - y &= x+1 \\ y(x-1) &= x+1 \\ f^{-1}(x) &= \frac{x+1}{x-1} \end{aligned}$$

28.
$$\begin{aligned} y &= x^3 - 3 \\ x &= y^3 - 3 \\ x + 3 &= y^3 \\ \sqrt[3]{x+3} &= y \\ f^{-1}(x) &= \sqrt[3]{x+3} \end{aligned}$$

29. $f(x) = \dfrac{3}{x} - 2$; $f^{-1}(x) = \dfrac{3}{x+2}$
Range of f = Domain of f^{-1}
$= \boxed{(-\infty, -2) \cup (-2, \infty)}$

30. $f(x) = \dfrac{3x-1}{x-3}$; $f^{-1}(x) = \dfrac{3x-1}{x-3}$
Range of f = Domain of f^{-1}
$= \boxed{(-\infty, 3) \cup (3, \infty)}$

Cumulative Review Exercises (page 410)

1.
$$\begin{aligned} 5x - 3y &= 15 \\ 5x - 3(0) &= 15 \\ 5x &= 15 \\ x &= 3 \\ &(3, 0) \end{aligned} \qquad \begin{aligned} 5x - 3y &= 15 \\ 5(0) - 3y &= 15 \\ -3y &= 15 \\ y &= -5 \\ &(0, -5) \end{aligned}$$

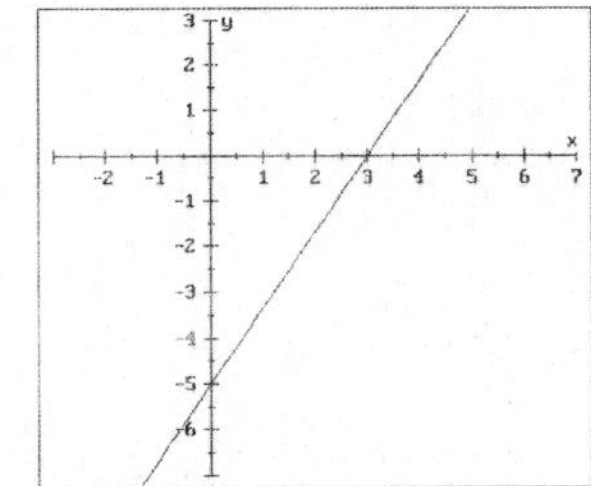

2.
$$\begin{aligned} 3x + 2y &= 12 \\ 3x + 2(0) &= 12 \\ 3x &= 12 \\ x &= 4 \\ &(4, 0) \end{aligned} \qquad \begin{aligned} 3x + 2y &= 12 \\ 3(0) + 2y &= 12 \\ 2y &= 12 \\ y &= 6 \\ &(0, 6) \end{aligned}$$

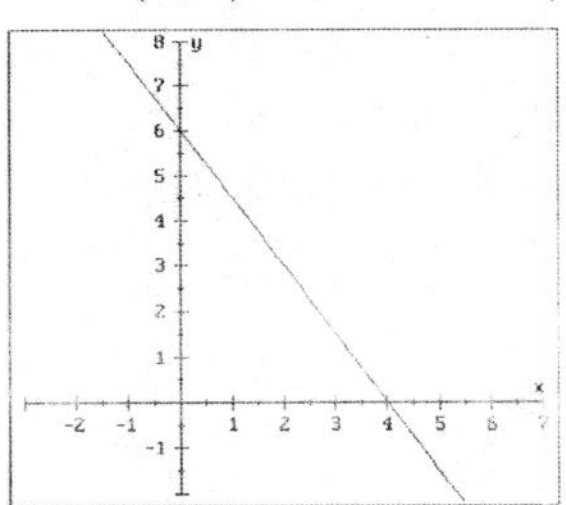

3. **a.** $d = \sqrt{(x_2 - x_1)^2 + (y_2 - y_1)^2} = \sqrt{(-2 - 3)^2 + \left(\frac{7}{2} - \left(-\frac{1}{2}\right)\right)^2} = \sqrt{25 + 16} = \sqrt{41}$

b. $x = \dfrac{x_1 + x_2}{2} = \dfrac{-2 + 3}{2} = \dfrac{1}{2};\ y = \dfrac{\frac{7}{2} + \left(-\frac{1}{2}\right)}{2} = \dfrac{\frac{6}{2}}{2} = \dfrac{3}{2}\quad \left(\dfrac{1}{2}, \dfrac{3}{2}\right)$

c. $m = \dfrac{-\frac{1}{2} - \frac{7}{2}}{3 - (-2)} = \dfrac{-\frac{8}{2}}{5} = -\dfrac{4}{5}$

4. **a.** $d = \sqrt{(x_2 - x_1)^2 + (y_2 - y_1)^2} = \sqrt{(3 - (-7))^2 + (7 - 3)^2} = \sqrt{100 + 16} = \sqrt{116} = 2\sqrt{29}$

b. $x = \dfrac{x_1 + x_2}{2} = \dfrac{3 + (-7)}{2} = \dfrac{-4}{2} = -2;\ y = \dfrac{7 + 3}{2} = \dfrac{10}{2} = 5\quad (-2, 5)$

c. $m = \dfrac{3 - 7}{-7 - 3} = \dfrac{-4}{-10} = \dfrac{2}{5}$

5.
$$\begin{aligned} m &= \frac{y_2 - y_1}{x_2 - x_1} = \frac{-7 - 5}{3 - (-3)} = \frac{-12}{6} = -2 \\ y - y_1 &= m(x - x_1) \\ y - 5 &= -2(x + 3) \\ y &= -2x - 1 \end{aligned}$$

6.
$$\begin{aligned} y - y_1 &= m(x - x_1) \\ y - \tfrac{5}{2} &= \tfrac{7}{2}\left(x - \tfrac{3}{2}\right) \\ y &= \tfrac{7}{2}x - \tfrac{21}{4} + \tfrac{5}{2} \\ y &= \tfrac{7}{2}x - \tfrac{11}{4} \end{aligned}$$

7. $3x - 5y = 7$

$-5y = -3x + 7$

$y = \frac{3}{5}x - \frac{7}{5}$

$m = \frac{3}{5}$

Use $m = \frac{3}{5}$.

$y - y_1 = m(x - x_1)$

$y - 3 = \frac{3}{5}(x + 5)$

$y - 3 = \frac{3}{5}x + 3$

$\boxed{y = \frac{3}{5}x + 6}$

8. $x - 4y = 12$

$-4y = -x + 12$

$y = \dfrac{1}{4}x - 3$

$m = \dfrac{1}{4}$

Use $m = -4$.

$y - y_1 = m(x - x_1)$

$y - 0 = -4(x - 0)$

$\boxed{y = -4x}$

9. $x^2 = y - 2$

symmetry: y-axis

x-int: none, y-int: (0, 2)

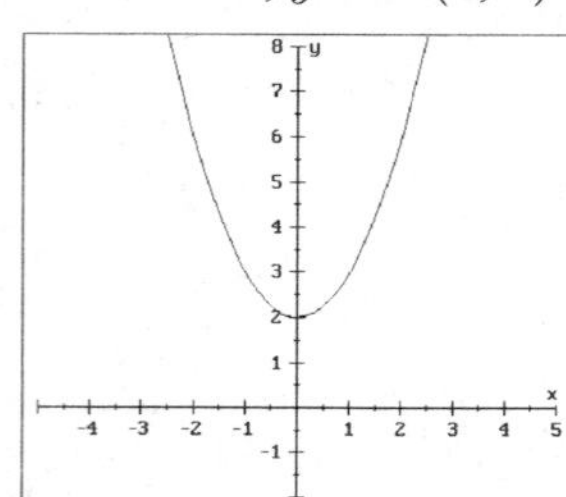

10. $y^2 = x - 2$

symmetry: x-axis

x-int: (2, 0), y-int: none

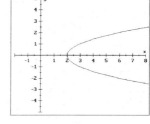

11. $x^2 + y^2 = 100$

Circle: $C(0, 0)$; $r = 10$

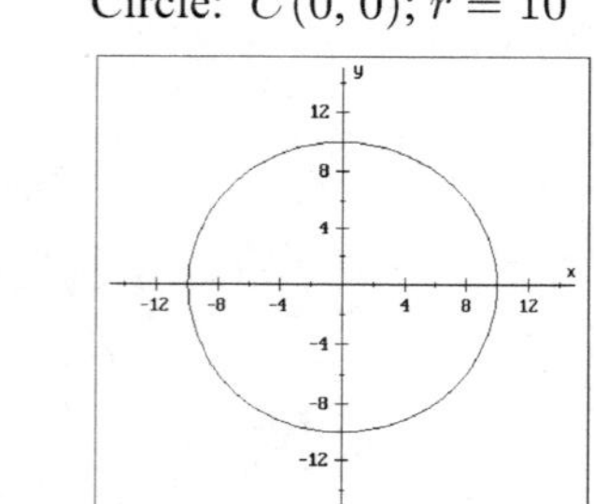

12. $x^2 - 2x + y^2 = 8$

$(x - 1)^2 + y^2 = 9$

Circle: $C(1, 0)$; $r = 3$

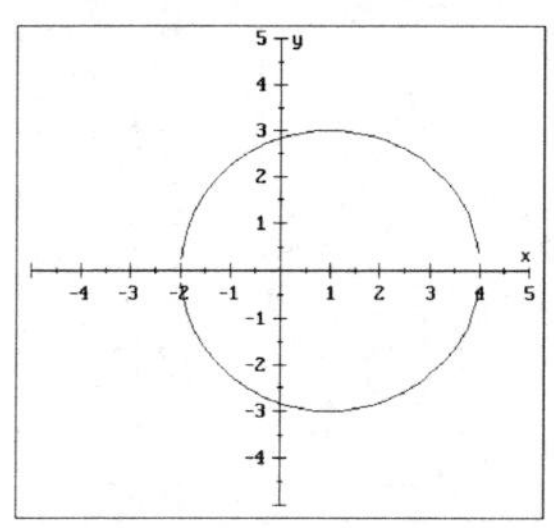

13. $\dfrac{x - 2}{x} = \dfrac{x - 6}{5}$

$5(x - 2) = x(x - 6)$

$5x - 10 = x^2 - 6x$

$0 = x^2 - 11x + 10$

$0 = (x - 10)(x - 1)$

$x = 10$ or $x = 1$

14.

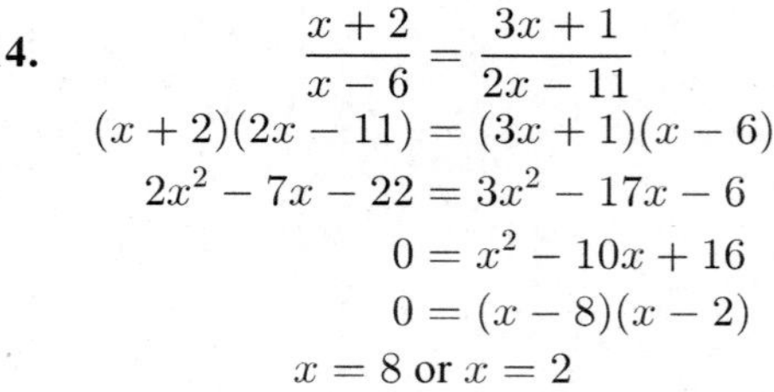

$\dfrac{x + 2}{x - 6} = \dfrac{3x + 1}{2x - 11}$

$(x + 2)(2x - 11) = (3x + 1)(x - 6)$

$2x^2 - 7x - 22 = 3x^2 - 17x - 6$

$0 = x^2 - 10x + 16$

$0 = (x - 8)(x - 2)$

$x = 8$ or $x = 2$

15. $m = \dfrac{54-37}{4-2} = \dfrac{17}{2} = 8.5$

$y = mx + b$
$y = 8.5x + b$
$37 = 8.5(2) + b$
$37 = 17 + b$
$20 = b$

$y = 8.5x + 20$
$y = 8.5(5) + 20$
$y = 62.50$
It will cost \$62.50.

16. $E = ks^2$

$E = k(50)^2 \quad E = k(20)^2$
$E = 2500k \quad E = 400k$
$\dfrac{50 \text{ mph } E}{20 \text{ mph } E} = \dfrac{2500k}{400k} = \dfrac{25}{4}$

17. $y = 3x - 1$: Each value of x is paired with only one value of y. $\Rightarrow$ **function**

18. $y = x^2 + 3$: Each value of x is paired with only one value of y. $\Rightarrow$ **function**

19. $y = \dfrac{1}{x-2}$: Each value of x is paired with only one value of y. $\Rightarrow$ **function**

20. $y^2 = 4x$
$y = \pm\sqrt{4x}$: Each value of x is paired with more than one value of y. $\Rightarrow$ **not a function**

21. $y = f(x) = x^2 + 5$: domain $= (-\infty, \infty)$

22. $y = f(x) = \dfrac{7}{x+2}$
domain $= (-\infty, -2) \cup (-2, \infty)$

23. $y = f(x) = -\sqrt{x-2} \Rightarrow$ domain $= [2, \infty)$

24. $y = f(x) = \sqrt{x+4} \Rightarrow$ domain $= [-4, \infty)$

25. $y = x^2 + 5x - 6;\ a = 1, b = 5, c = -6$
vertex: $x = -\frac{b}{2a} = -\frac{5}{2(1)} = -\frac{5}{2}$
$y = x^2 + 5x - 6 = \left(-\frac{5}{2}\right)^2 + 5\left(-\frac{5}{2}\right) - 6$
$= -\frac{49}{4}$

26. $y = -x^2 + 5x + 6;\ a = -1, b = 5, c = 6$
vertex: $x = -\frac{b}{2a} = -\frac{5}{2(-1)} = \frac{5}{2}$
$y = -x^2 + 5x + 6 = -\left(\frac{5}{2}\right)^2 + 5\left(\frac{5}{2}\right) + 6$
$= \frac{49}{4}$

27. $y = x^2 - 4$: Shift $y = x^2$ D 4.

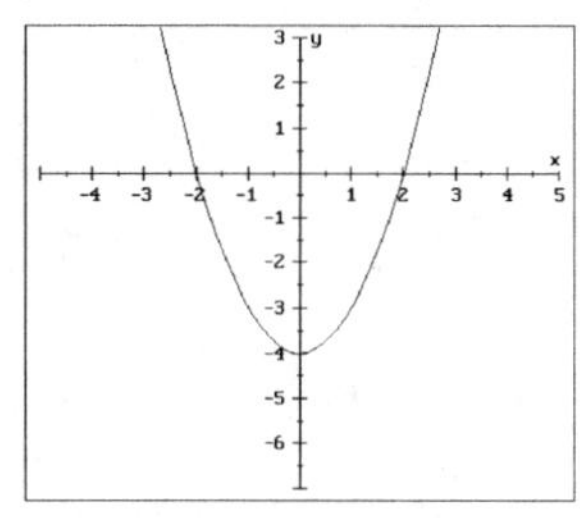

28. 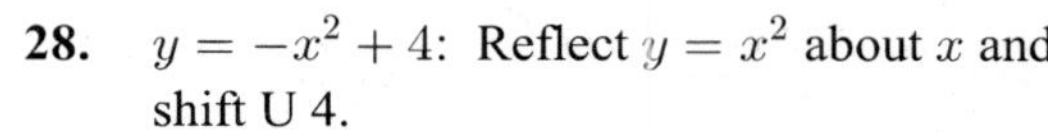
$y = -x^2 + 4$: Reflect $y = x^2$ about x and shift U 4.

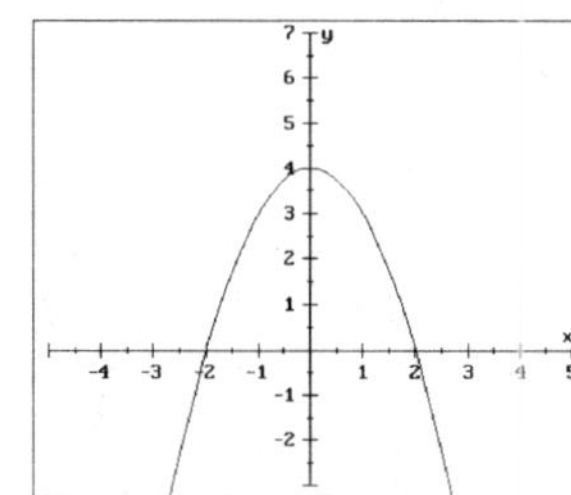

29. $y = f(x) = x^3 + x$

$$f(-x) = (-x)^3 + (-x) = -x^3 - x = -f(x) \Rightarrow \text{odd}$$

x-int.	y-int.
$x^3 + x = 0$	$y = 0^3 + 0$
$x(x^2+1) = 0$	$y = 0$
$x = 0$	$(0, 0)$
$(0, 0)$	

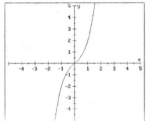

30. $f(x) = -x^4 + 2x^2 + 1$

$$f(-x) = -(-x)^4 + 2(-x)^2 + 1 = -x^4 + 2x^2 + 1 \Rightarrow \text{even}$$

x-int.	y-int.
$-x^4 + 2x^2 + 1 = 0$	$f(0) = 1$
$x^4 - 2x^2 - 1 = 0$	$y = 1$
not rational numbers	$(0, 1)$

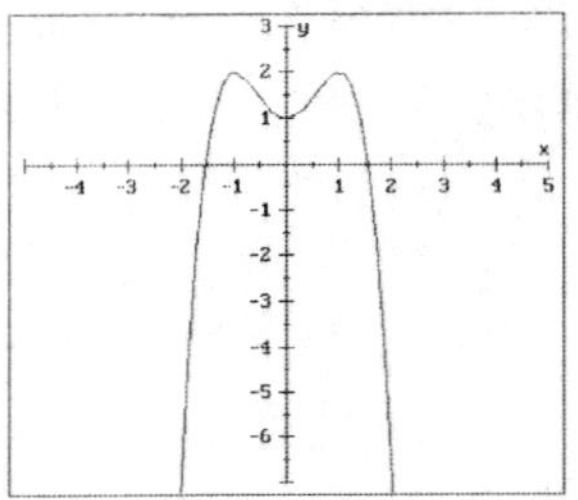

31. $y = \dfrac{x}{x-3}$

Vertical: $x = 3$; Horizontal: $y = 1$
Slant: none; x-intercepts: $(0, 0)$
y-intercepts: $(0, 0)$; Symmetry: none

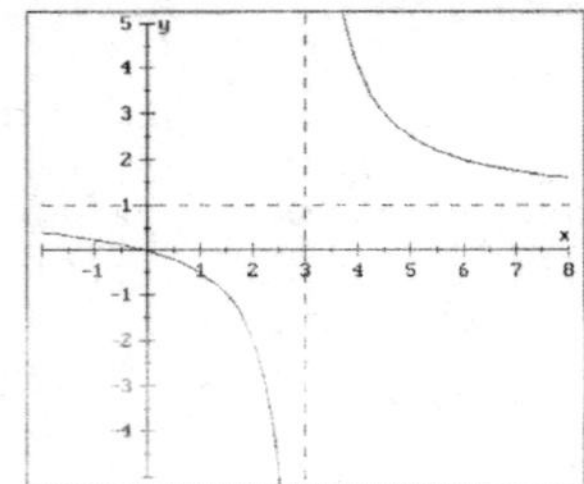

32. $y = \dfrac{x^2-1}{x^2-9} = \dfrac{(x+1)(x-1)}{(x+3)(x-3)}$

Vertical: $x = -3$, $x = 3$; Horizontal: $y = 1$
Slant: none; x-intercepts: $(-1, 0)$, $(1, 0)$
y-intercepts: $\left(0, \frac{1}{9}\right)$; Symmetry: y-axis

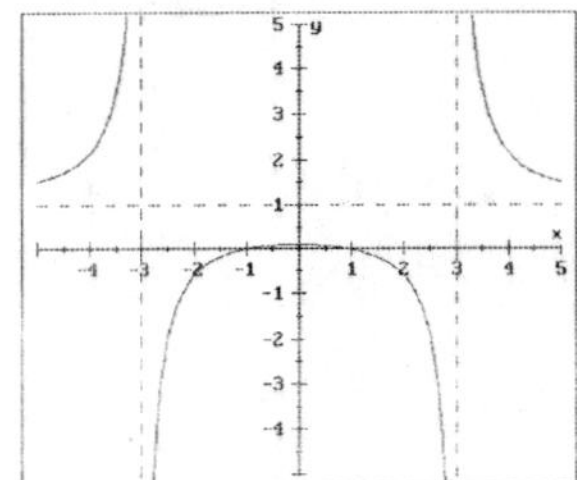

33. $(f+g)(x) = f(x) + g(x) = (3x-4) + (x^2+1) = x^2 + 3x - 3$; domain $= (-\infty, \infty)$

34. $(f-g)(x) = f(x) - g(x) = (3x-4) - (x^2+1) = -x^2 + 3x - 5$; domain $= (-\infty, \infty)$

35. $(f \cdot g)(x) = f(x)g(x) = (3x-4)(x^2+1) = 3x^3 - 4x^2 + 3x - 4$; domain $= (-\infty, \infty)$

36. $(f/g)(x) = \frac{f(x)}{g(x)} = \frac{3x-4}{x^2+1}$; domain $= (-\infty, \infty)$

37. $(f \circ g)(2) = f(g(2)) = f((2^2+1)) = f(5) = 3(5) - 4 = 11$

38. $(g \circ f)(2) = g(f(2)) = g(3(2)-4) = g(2) = 2^2 + 1 = 5$

39. $(f \circ g)(x) = f(g(x)) = f(x^2+1) = 3(x^2+1) - 4 = 3x^2 - 1$

40. $(g \circ f)(x) = g(f(x)) = g(3x-4) = (3x-4)^2 + 1 = 9x^2 - 24x + 16 + 1 = 9x^2 - 24x + 17$

41.
$$\begin{aligned} y &= 3x+2 \\ x &= 3y+2 \\ x-2 &= 3y \\ \tfrac{x-2}{3} &= y \\ f^{-1}(x) &= \tfrac{x-2}{3} \end{aligned}$$

42.
$$\begin{aligned} y &= \tfrac{1}{x-3} \\ x &= \tfrac{1}{y-3} \\ x(y-3) &= 1 \\ y-3 &= \tfrac{1}{x} \\ y &= \tfrac{1}{x}+3 \\ f^{-1}(x) &= \tfrac{1}{x}+3 \end{aligned}$$

43.
$$\begin{aligned} y &= x^2+5 \\ x &= y^2+5 \\ x-5 &= y^2 \\ \pm\sqrt{x-5} &= y \\ \sqrt{x-5} &= y \ \ (y \geq 0) \\ f^{-1}(x) &= \sqrt{x-5} \end{aligned}$$

44.
$$\begin{aligned} 3x-y &= 1 \\ 3y-x &= 1 \\ 3y &= x+1 \\ y &= \tfrac{x+1}{3} \\ f^{-1}(x) &= \tfrac{x+1}{3} \end{aligned}$$

45. $y = kwz$

46. $y = \dfrac{kx}{t^2}$

Exercise 4.1 (page 425)

1. exponential

2. 1

3. $(-\infty, \infty)$

4. base

5. $(0, \infty)$

6. y, $(0, 1)$

7. asymptote

8. 0, 1

9. increasing

10. $(1, b)$

11. 2.72

12. Pe^{rt}

13. increasing

14. $(1, e)$

15. $4^{\sqrt{3}} \approx 11.0357$

16. $5^{\sqrt{2}} \approx 9.7385$

17. $7^{\pi} \approx 451.8079$

18. $3^{-\pi} \approx 0.0317$

19. $5^{\sqrt{2}}5^{\sqrt{2}} = 5^{\sqrt{2}+\sqrt{2}} = 5^{2\sqrt{2}} = (5^2)^{\sqrt{2}} = 25^{\sqrt{2}}$

20. $\left(5^{\sqrt{2}}\right)^{\sqrt{2}} = 5^{\sqrt{2}\cdot\sqrt{2}} = 5^2 = 25$

21. $\left(a^{\sqrt{8}}\right)^{\sqrt{2}} = a^{\sqrt{8}\cdot\sqrt{2}} = a^{\sqrt{16}} = a^4$

22. $a^{\sqrt{12}}a^{\sqrt{3}} = a^{\sqrt{12}+\sqrt{3}} = a^{2\sqrt{3}+\sqrt{3}} = a^{3\sqrt{3}}$

23. $f(0) = 5^0 = 1$, $f(2) = 5^2 = 25$

24. $f(0) = 4^{-0} = 1$, $f(2) = 4^{-2} = \frac{1}{16}$

25. $f(0) = \left(\frac{1}{3}\right)^{-0} = 1$, $f(2) = \left(\frac{1}{3}\right)^{-2} = 9$

26. $f(0) = \left(\frac{1}{4}\right)^{0} = 1$, $f(2) = \left(\frac{1}{4}\right)^{2} = \frac{1}{16}$

27. $f(x) = 3^x$

points: (0, 1), (1, 3)

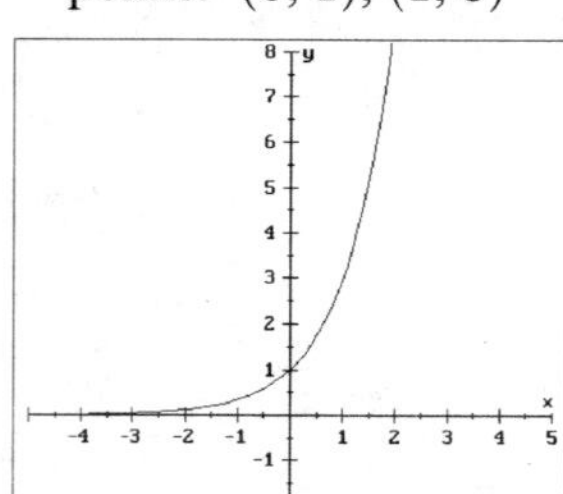

28. $f(x) = 5^x$

points: (0, 1), (1, 5)

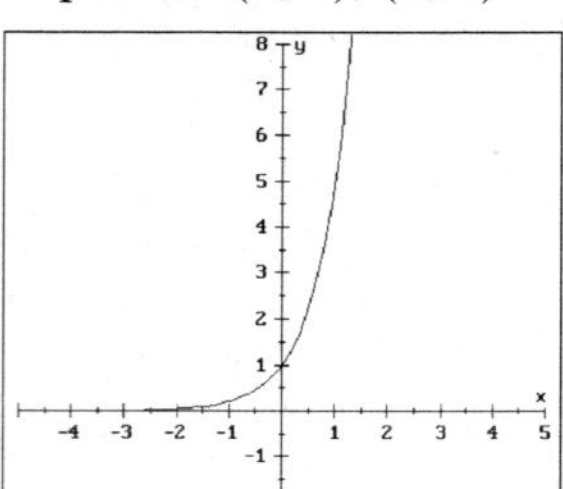

29. $f(x) = \left(\frac{1}{5}\right)^x$

points: (0, 1), $\left(1, \frac{1}{5}\right)$

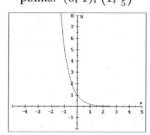

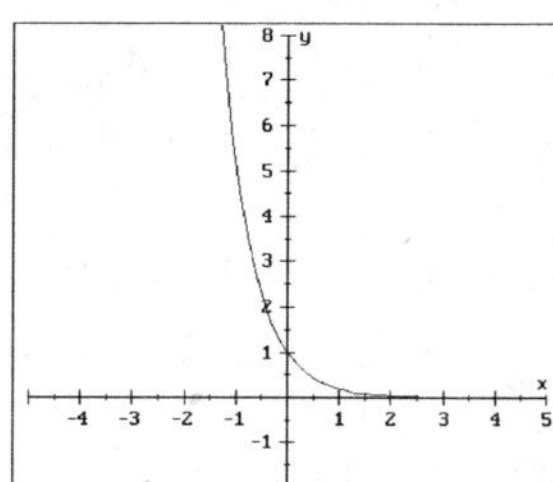

30. $f(x) = \left(\frac{1}{3}\right)^x$

points: (0, 1), $\left(1, \frac{1}{3}\right)$

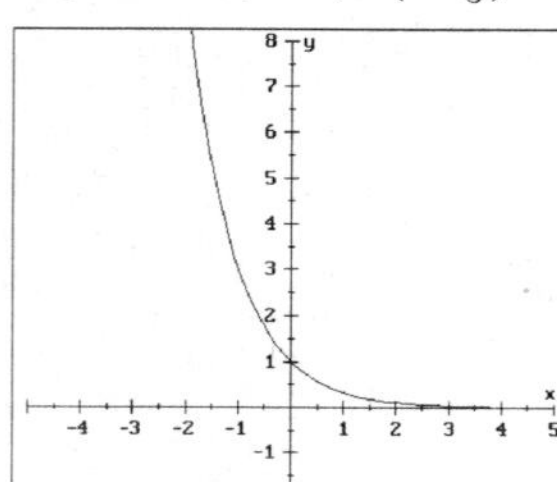

31. $f(x) = \left(\frac{3}{4}\right)^x$

points: (0, 1), $\left(1, \frac{3}{4}\right)$

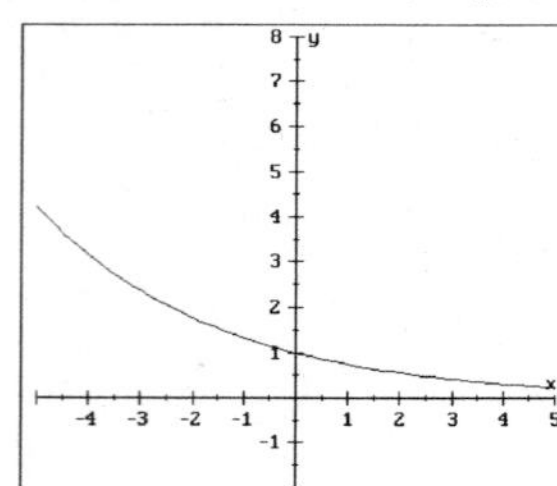

32. $f(x) = \left(\frac{4}{3}\right)^x$

points: (0, 1), $\left(1, \frac{4}{3}\right)$

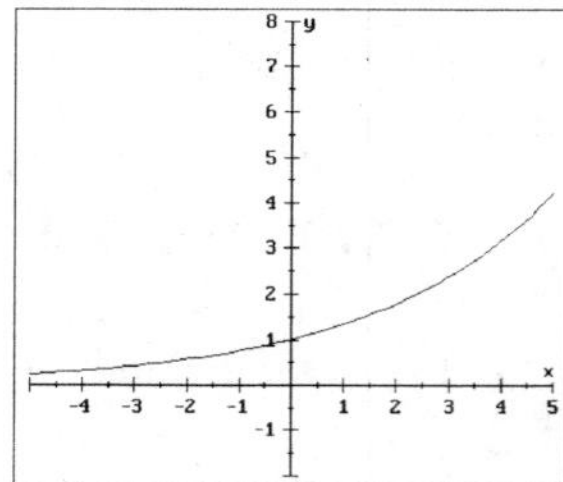

33. $f(x) = (1.5)^x$

points: (0, 1), (1, 1.5)

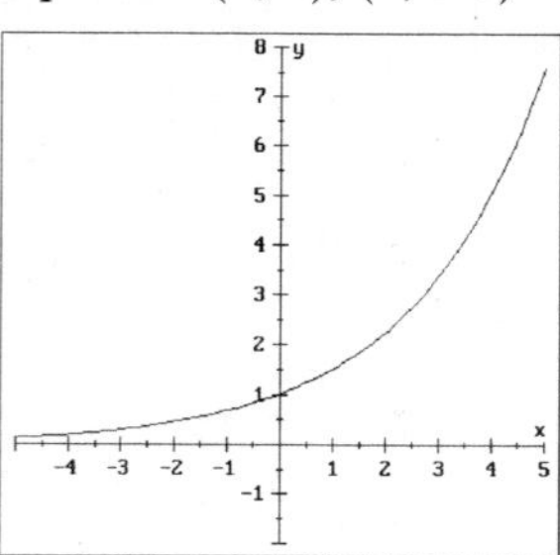

34. $f(x) = (0.3)^x$

points: (0, 1), (1, 0.3)

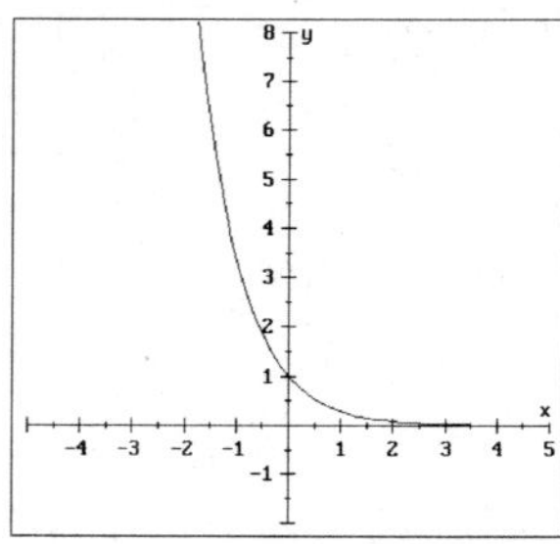

35. $f(x) = 3^{-x}$

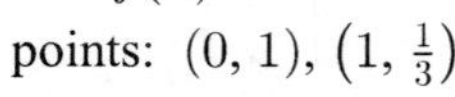

points: (0, 1), $\left(1, \frac{1}{3}\right)$

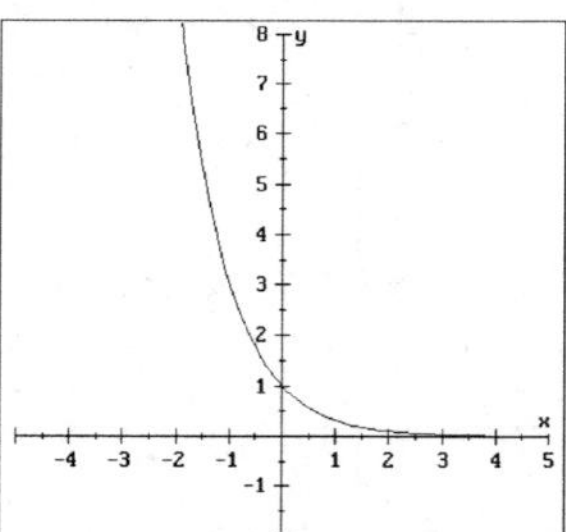

36. $f(x) = -5^x$
points: $(0, -1)$, $(1, -5)$

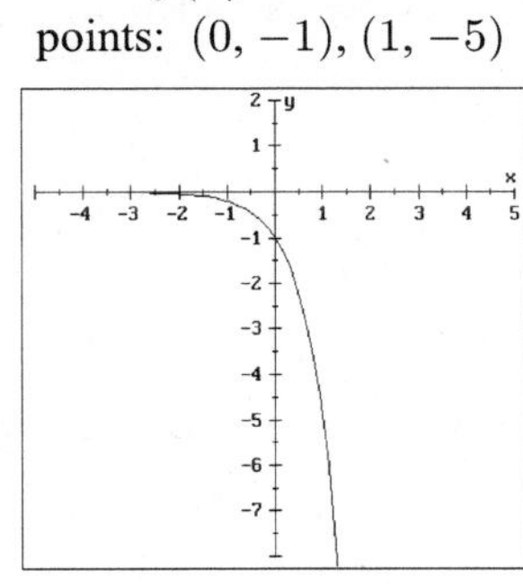

37. $f(x) = -\left(\frac{1}{5}\right)^x$
points: $(0, -1)$, $\left(1, -\frac{1}{5}\right)$

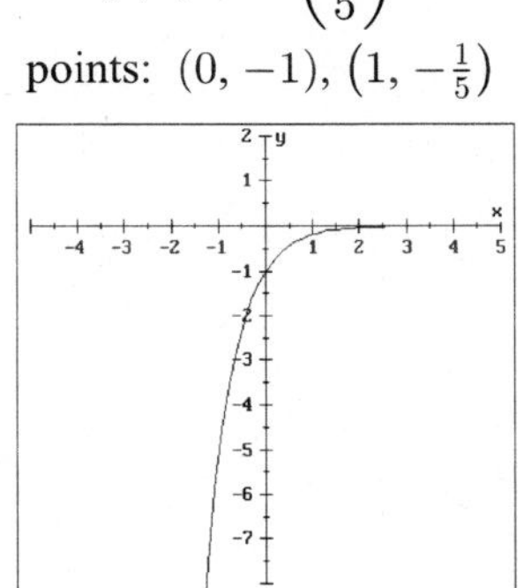

38. $f(x) = \left(\frac{1}{3}\right)^{-x}$
points: $(0, 1)$, $(1, 3)$

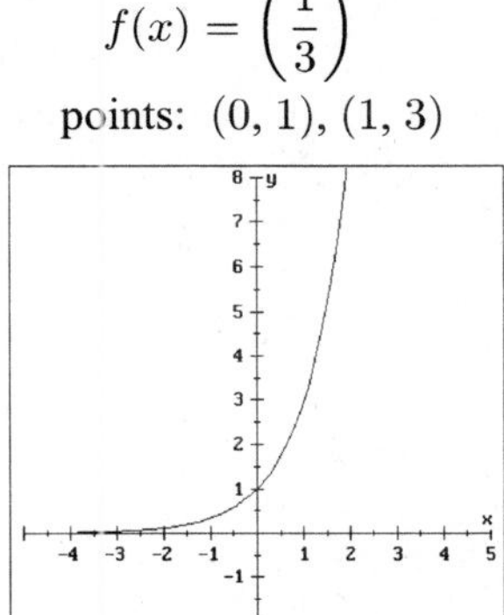

39. The graph passes through $(0, 1)$ and has the x-axis as an asymptote. YES

40. The graph does not pass through $(0, 1)$. NO

41. The graph does not pass through $(0, 1)$. NO

42. The graph passes through $(0, 1)$ and has the x-axis as an asymptote. YES

43. The graph passes through $(0, 1)$ and has the x-axis as an asymptote, so it could be an exponential function. It passes through the point $\left(1, \frac{1}{2}\right) = (1, b)$. $b = \frac{1}{2}$

44. The graph passes through $(0, 1)$ and has the x-axis as an asymptote, so it could be an exponential function. It passes through the point $(1, 7) = (1, b)$. $b = 7$

45. The graph does not pass through $(0, 1)$. It is not an exponential function.

46. The graph passes through $(0, 1)$ and has the x-axis as an asymptote, so it could be an exponential function. It passes through the point $(1, 3) = (1, b)$. $b = 3$

47. The graph passes through $(0, 1)$ and has the x-axis as an asymptote, so it could be an exponential function. It passes through the point $(1, 2) = (1, b)$. $b = 2$

48. The graph passes through $(0, 1)$ and has the x-axis as an asymptote, so it could be an exponential function.

$$\begin{aligned} y &= b^x \\ \frac{1}{3} &= b^{-1} \\ \left(\frac{1}{3}\right)^{-1} &= \left(b^{-1}\right)^{-1} \\ 3 &= b \end{aligned}$$

49. The graph passes through $(0, 1)$ and has the x-axis as an asymptote, so it could be an exponential function.

$$y = b^x$$
$$e^2 = b^2$$
$$e = b$$

50. The graph does not pass through $(0, 1)$. It is not an exponential function.

51. $f(x) = 3^x - 1$
Shift $y = 3^x$ D1.

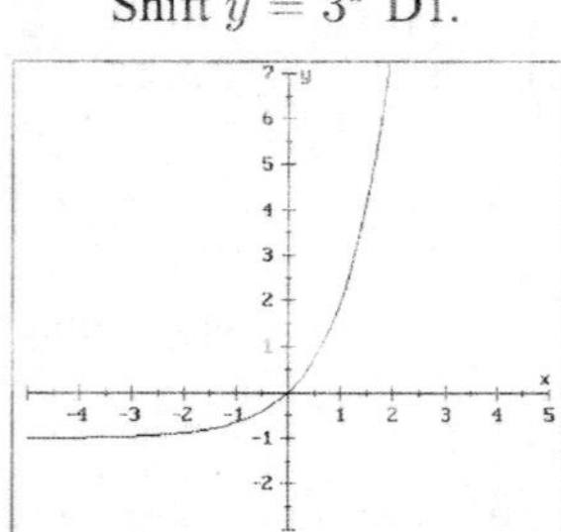

52. $f(x) = 2^x + 3$
Shift $y = 2^x$ U3.

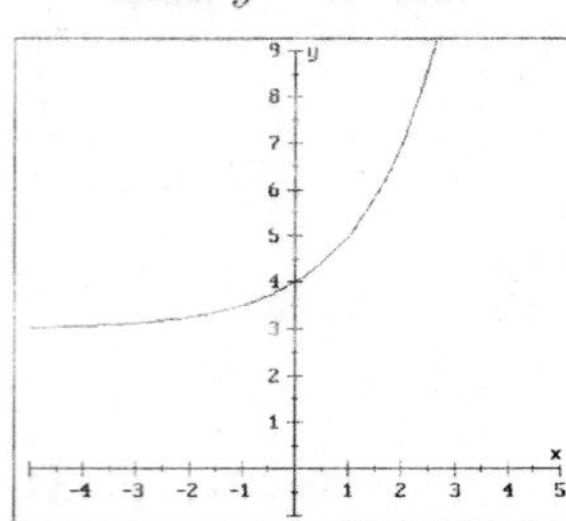

53. $f(x) = 2^x + 1$
Shift $y = 2^x$ U1.

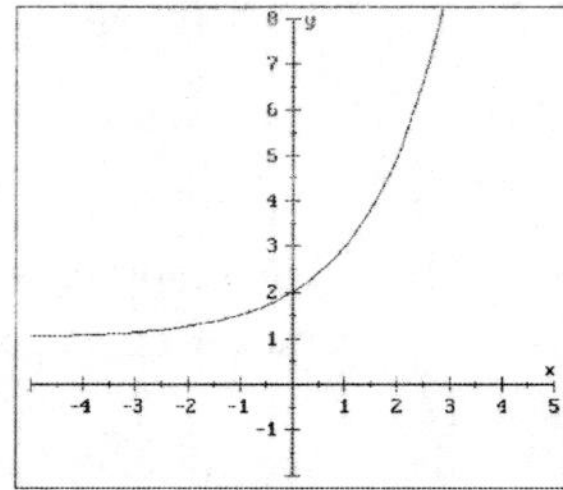

54. $f(x) = 4^x - 4$
Shift $y = 4^x$ D4.

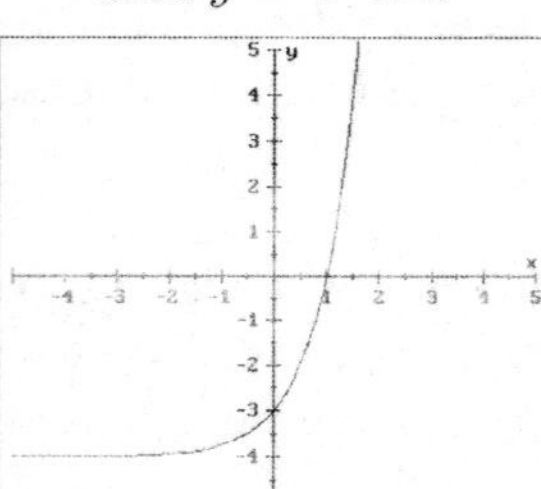

55. $f(x) = 3^{x-1}$
Shift $y = 3^x$ R1.

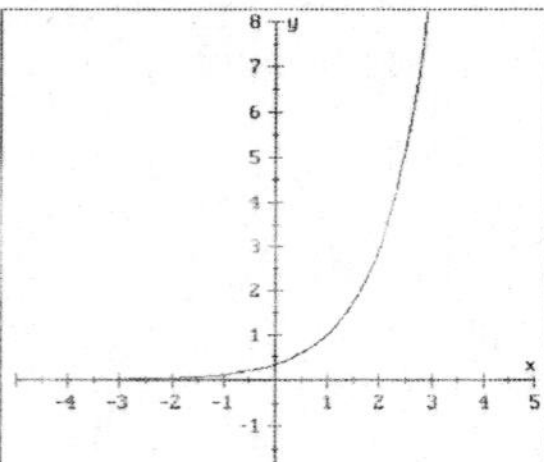

56. $f(x) = 2^{x+3}$
Shift $y = 2^x$ L3.

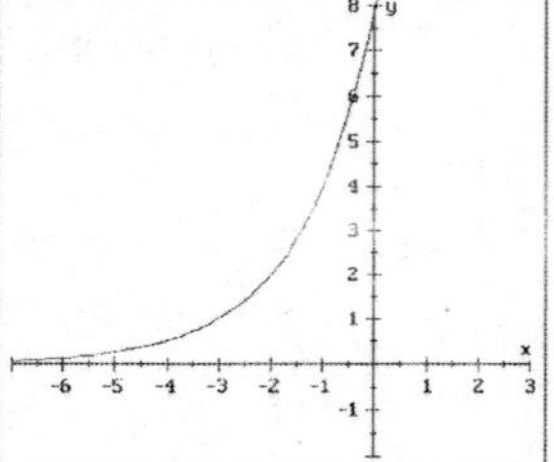

57. $f(x) = 3^{x+1}$
Shift $y = 3^x$ L1.

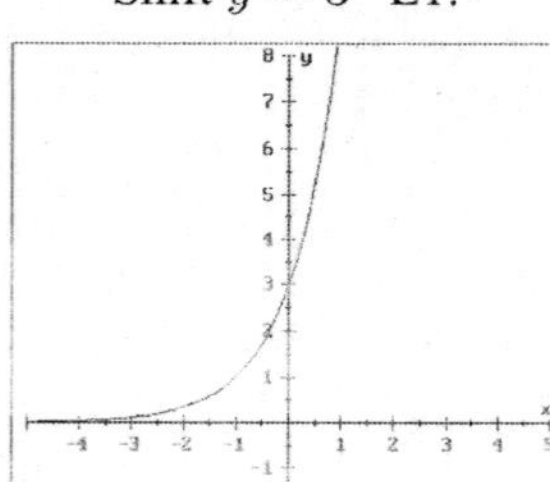

58. $f(x) = 2^{x-3}$
Shift $y = 2^x$ R3.

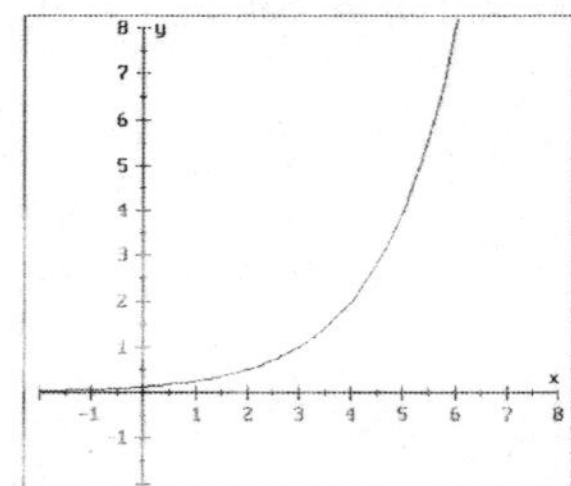

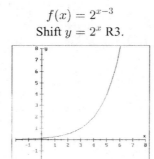

59. $f(x) = e^x - 4$
Shift $y = e^x$ D4.

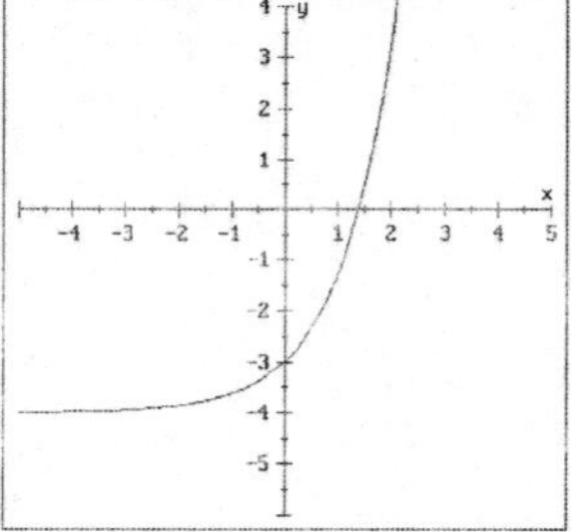

60. $f(x) = e^x + 2$
Shift $y = e^x$ U2.

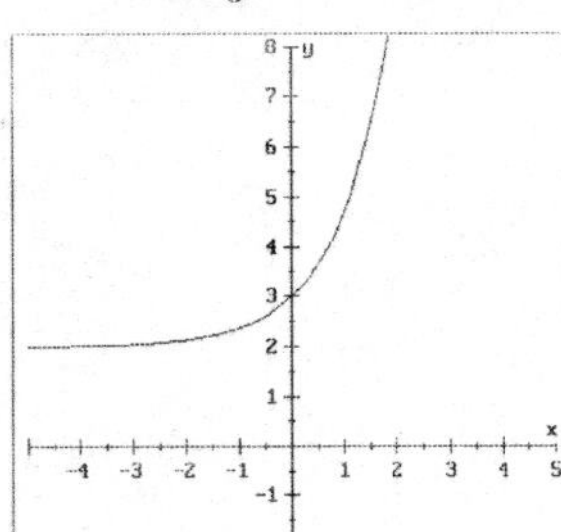

61. $f(x) = e^{x-2}$
Shift $y = e^x$ R2.

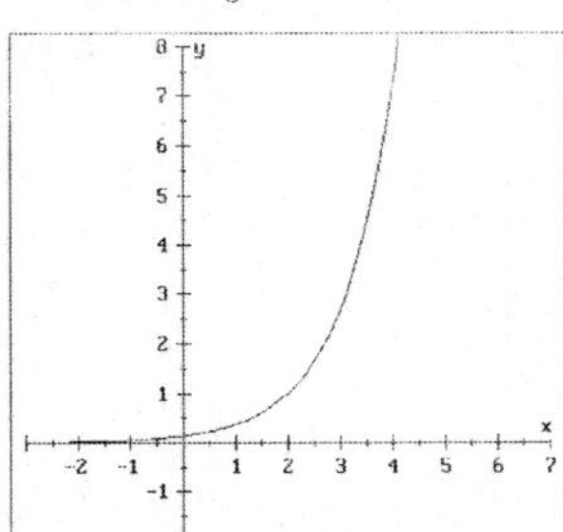

62. $f(x) = e^{x+3}$
Shift $y = e^x$ L3.

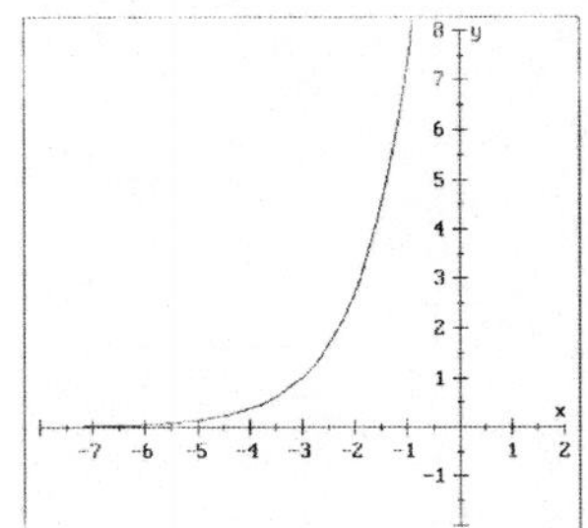

63. $f(x) = 2^{x+1} - 2$
Shift $y = 2^x$ L1, D2.

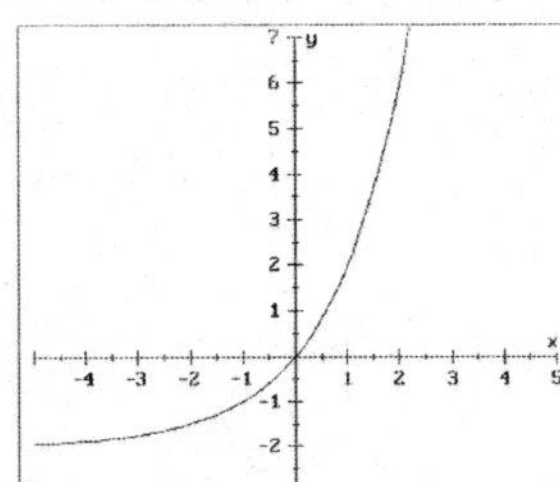

64. $f(x) = 3^{x-1} + 2$
Shift $y = 3^x$ R1, U2.

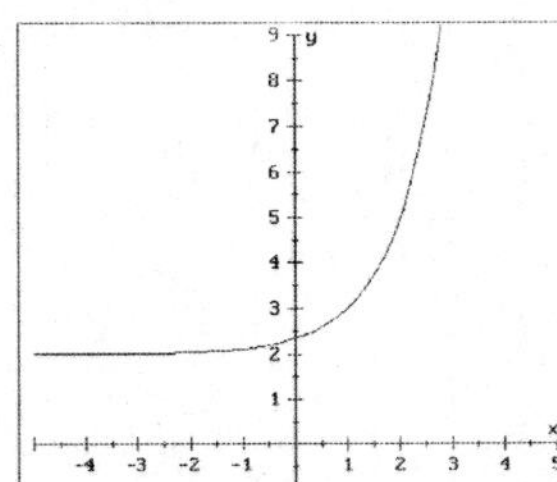

65. $f(x) = 3^{x-2} + 1$
Shift $y = 3^x$ R2, U1.

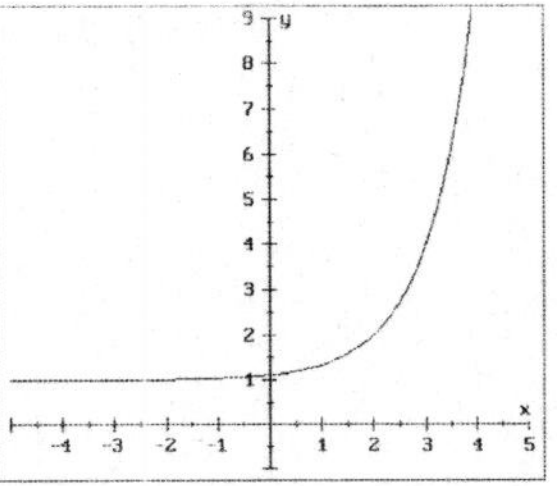

66. $f(x) = 3^{x+2} - 1$
Shift $y = 3^x$ L2, D1.

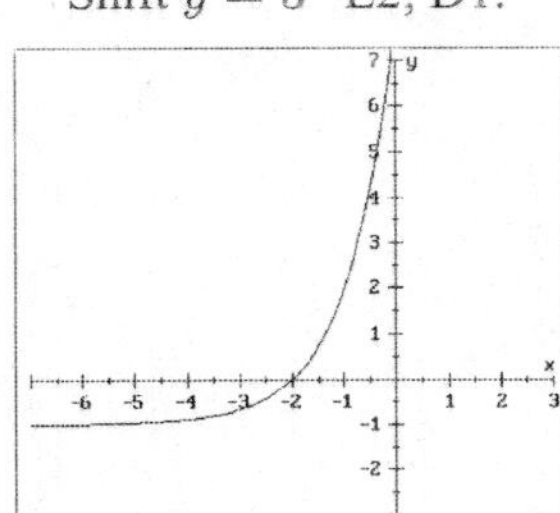

67. $f(x) = -3^x + 1$
Reflect $y = 3^x$ about x,
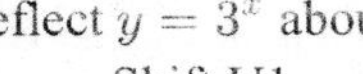
Shift U1

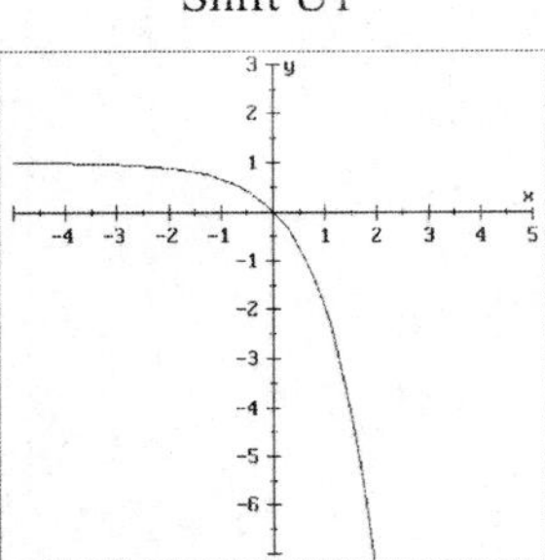

68. $f(x) = -2^x - 3$
Reflect $y = 2^x$ about x,
Shift D3

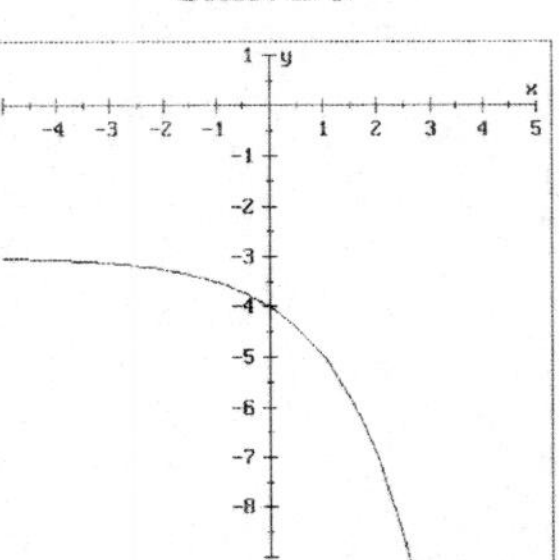

69. $f(x) = 2^{-x} - 3$
Reflect $y = 2^x$ about y,
Shift D3

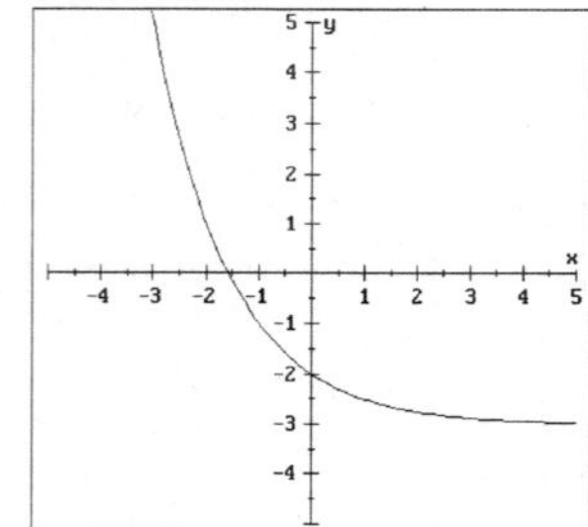

70. $f(x) = 4^{-x} + 4$
Reflect $y = 4^x$ about y,
Shift U4

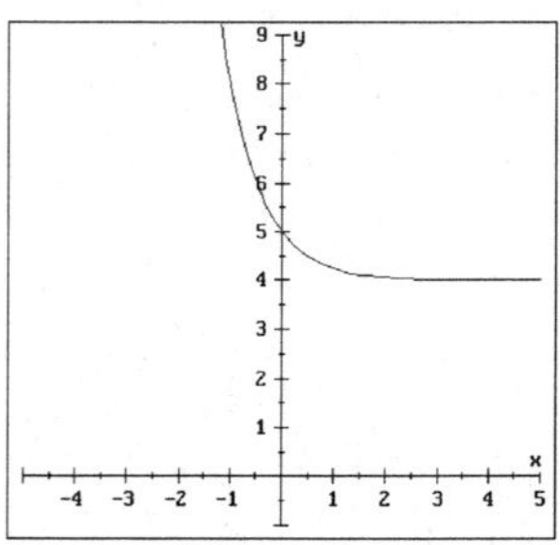

71. $f(x) = -e^x + 2$
Reflect $y = e^x$ about x,
Shift U2

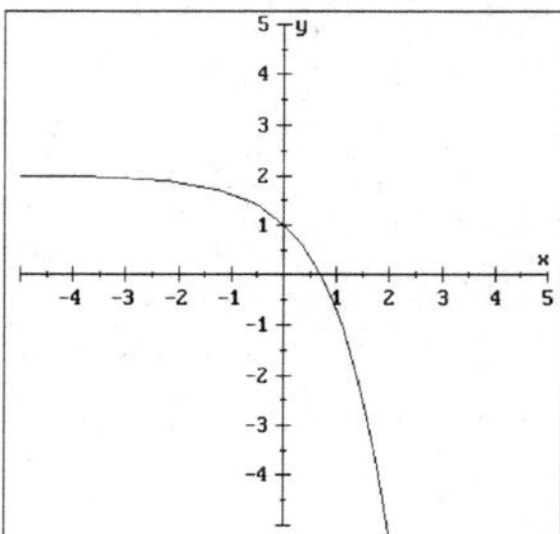

72. $f(x) = e^{-x} + 3$
Reflect $y = e^x$ about y,
Shift U3

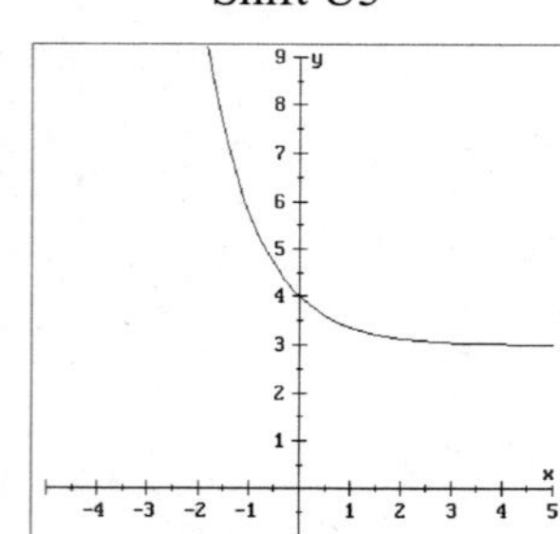

73. $y = 5(2^x)$

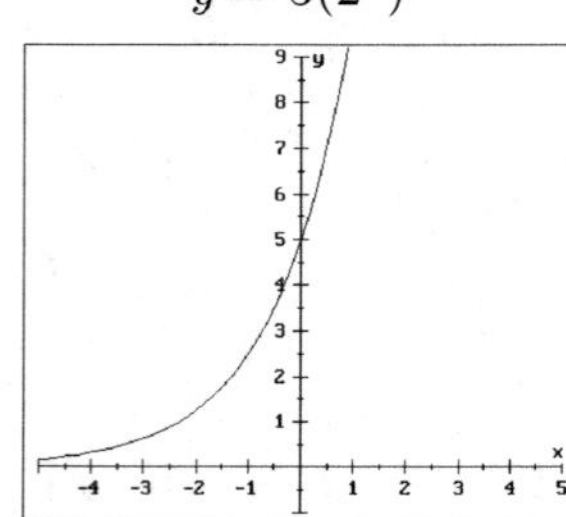

74. $y = 2(5^x)$

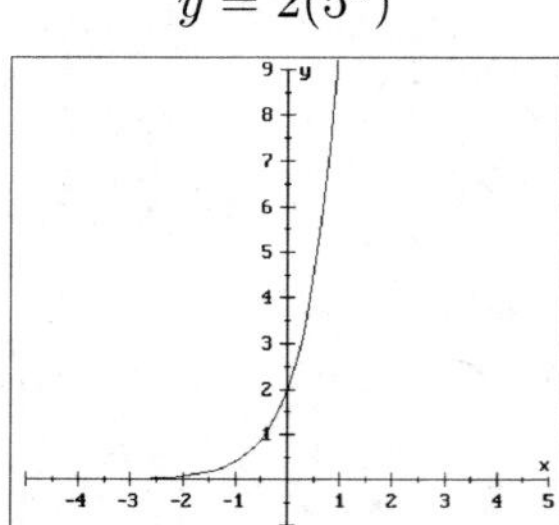

75. $y = 3^{-x}$

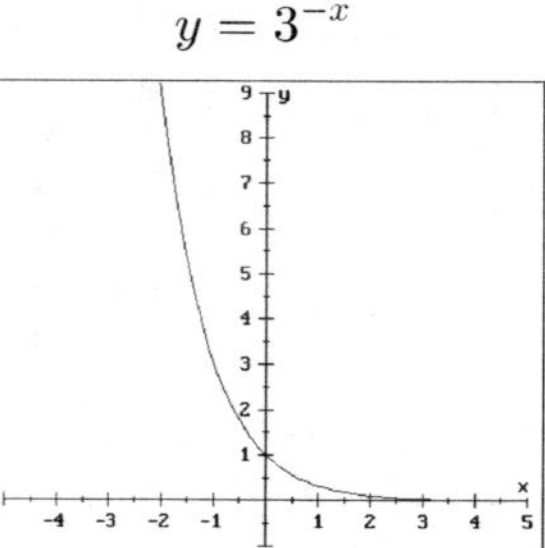

76. $y = 2^{-x}$

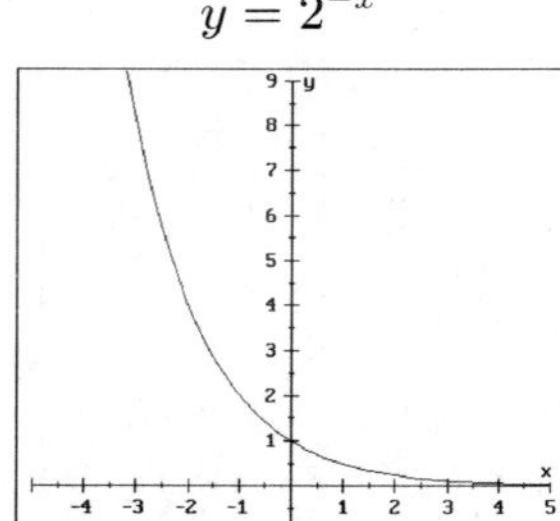

77. $y = 2e^x$

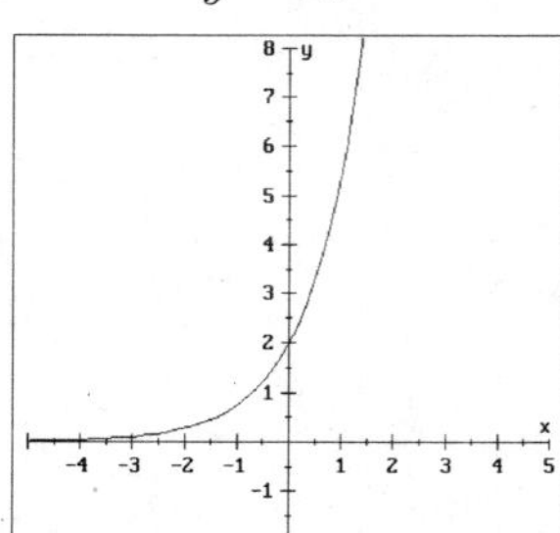

78. $y = 3e^{-x}$

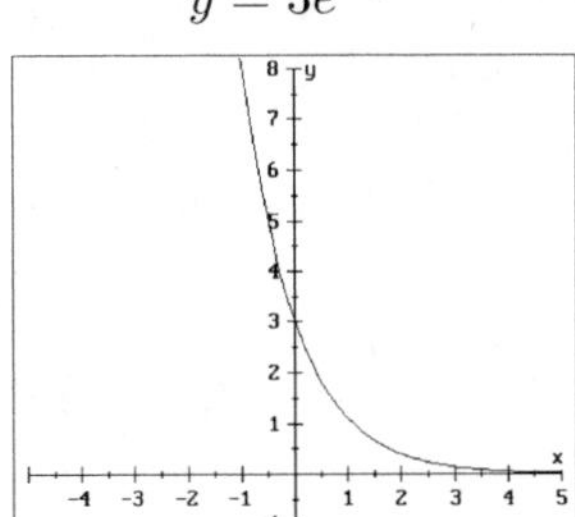

79. $y = 5e^{-0.5x}$

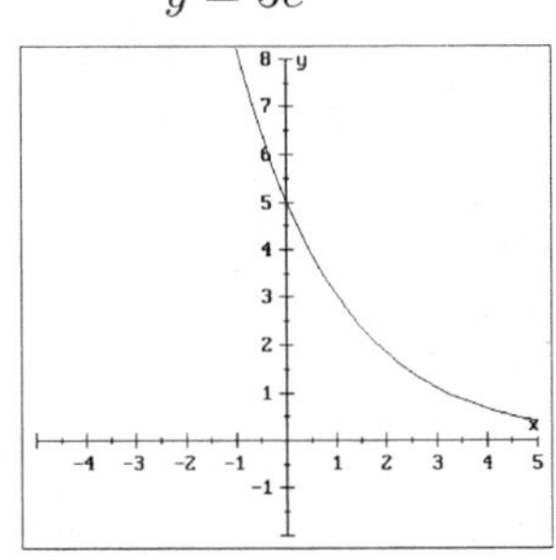

80. $y = -3e^{2x}$

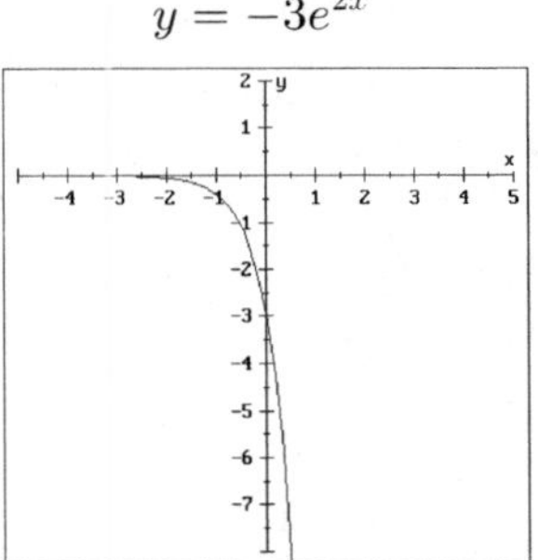

81.
$$\begin{aligned} A &= P\left(1+\frac{r}{k}\right)^{kt} \\ &= 10000\left(1+\frac{0.08}{4}\right)^{4(10)} \\ &\approx \$22{,}080.40 \end{aligned}$$

82.
$$\begin{aligned} A &= P\left(1+\frac{r}{k}\right)^{kt} \\ &= 1000\left(1+\frac{0.09}{12}\right)^{12(4.5)} \\ &\approx \$1497.04 \end{aligned}$$

83. 5% interest:
$$\begin{aligned} A &= P\left(1+\frac{r}{k}\right)^{kt} \\ &= 500\left(1+\frac{0.05}{2}\right)^{2(5)} \\ &\approx \$640.04 \end{aligned}$$

$5\frac{1}{2}$% interest:
$$\begin{aligned} A &= P\left(1+\frac{r}{k}\right)^{kt} \\ &= 500\left(1+\frac{0.055}{2}\right)^{2(5)} \\ &\approx \$655.83 \end{aligned}$$

$$\begin{aligned} \text{Difference} &= 655.83 - 640.04 \\ &= \$15.79 \text{ more} \end{aligned}$$

84. Assume 1 year for each account:

5.25% interest:
$$\begin{aligned} A &= P\left(1+\frac{r}{k}\right)^{kt} \\ &= P\left(1+\frac{0.0525}{12}\right)^{12(1)} \\ &\approx P(1.0538) \end{aligned}$$

5.35% interest:
$$\begin{aligned} A &= P\left(1+\frac{r}{k}\right)^{kt} \\ &= P\left(1+\frac{0.0535}{1}\right)^{1(1)} \\ &= P(1.0535) \end{aligned}$$

The 5.25% rate compounded monthly provides a better return.

85.
$$\begin{aligned} A &= P\left(1+\frac{r}{k}\right)^{kt} \\ &= 1\left(1+\frac{0.05}{1}\right)^{1(300)} \\ &\approx \$2{,}273{,}996.13 \end{aligned}$$

86.
$$\begin{aligned} A &= A_0\left(1+\frac{r}{360}\right)^{365t} \\ &= 1000\left(1+\frac{0.07}{360}\right)^{365(5)} \\ &\approx \$1425.93 \end{aligned}$$

87.
$$\begin{aligned} A &= P\left(1+\frac{r}{k}\right)^{kt} \\ &= 1100\left(1+\frac{0.0175}{1}\right)^{1(8)} \\ &\approx \$1263.77 \end{aligned}$$

88.
$$\begin{aligned} A &= P\left(1+\frac{r}{k}\right)^{kt} \\ &= 1500\left(1+\frac{0.21}{12}\right)^{12(1)} \\ &\approx \$1847.16 \end{aligned}$$

89.
$$\begin{aligned} A &= Pe^{rt} \\ &= 5000e^{0.082(12)} \\ &\approx \$13{,}375.68 \end{aligned}$$

90.
$$\begin{aligned} A &= Pe^{rt} = 2000e^{0.08(15)} \\ &\approx \$6640.23 \end{aligned}$$

91. Continuous:

$$A = Pe^{rt} = 5000e^{0.085(5)} \approx \$7647.95$$

Annually:

$$A = P\left(1+\frac{r}{k}\right)^{kt} = 5000\left(1+\frac{0.085}{1}\right)^{1(5)} \approx \$7518.28$$

92. Continuous:

$$A = Pe^{rt} = 30{,}000e^{0.08(20)} \approx \$148{,}590.97$$

Annually:

$$A = P\left(1+\frac{r}{k}\right)^{kt} = 30{,}000\left(1+\frac{0.08}{1}\right)^{1(20)} \approx \$139{,}828.71$$

93. Quarterly:

$$A = P\left(1+\frac{r}{k}\right)^{kt} = 10000\left(1+\frac{0.06}{4}\right)^{4(20)} \approx \$32{,}906.63$$

Daily:

$$A = P\left(1+\frac{r}{k}\right)^{kt} = 10000\left(1+\frac{0.06}{365}\right)^{365(20)} \approx \$33{,}197.90$$

Difference

$$33{,}197.90 - 32{,}906.63 = \boxed{\$291.27}$$

94.

$$\begin{aligned} A &= Pe^{rt} \\ 11{,}180 &= Pe^{0.07(7)} \\ \frac{11{,}180}{e^{0.07(7)}} &= P \\ \$6849.16 &\approx P \end{aligned}$$

95.

$$\begin{aligned} A &= P\left(1+\frac{r}{k}\right)^{kt} \\ 40{,}000 &= P\left(1+\frac{0.06}{4}\right)^{4(20)} \\ \frac{40{,}000}{\left(1+\frac{0.06}{4}\right)^{4(20)}} &= P \\ \$12{,}155.61 &\approx P \end{aligned}$$

96.

$$\begin{aligned} A &= Pe^{rt} \\ 40{,}000 &= Pe^{0.06(20)} \\ \frac{40{,}000}{e^{0.06(20)}} &= P \\ \$12{,}047.77 &\approx P \end{aligned}$$

97.

$$\begin{aligned} P(t) &= 1200e^{0.2t} \\ P(12) &= 1200e^{0.2(12)} \\ &\approx 13{,}228 \end{aligned}$$

98.

$$\begin{aligned} A(t) &= -1000e^{-0.3t} + 1250 \\ A(14) &= -1000e^{-0.3(14)} + 1250 \\ &\approx 1235 \text{ mg} \end{aligned}$$

99.

$$\begin{aligned} A &= P\left(1+\frac{r}{k}\right)^{kt} \\ P &= A(1+r)^n \\ \frac{P}{(1+r)^n} &= A \\ P(1+r)^{-n} &= A \end{aligned}$$

100.

$$\begin{aligned} 2^{t+4} &= k2^t \\ 2^t \cdot 2^4 &= 2^t \cdot k \\ 2^4 &= k \\ 16 &= k \end{aligned}$$

101.

$$\begin{aligned} 5^{3t} &= k^t \\ \left(5^3\right)^t &= k^t \\ 125^t &= k^t \\ 125 &= k \end{aligned}$$

102. **a.**
$$e^{t+3} = ke^t$$
$$e^t \cdot e^3 = e^t \cdot k$$
$$e^3 = k$$

b.
$$e^{3t} = k^t$$
$$\left(e^3\right)^t = k^t$$
$$e^3 = k$$

103. $x^2 + 9x^4 = x^2(1 + 9x^2)$

104. $x^2 - 9x^4 = x^2(1 - 9x^2) = x^2(1 + 3x)(1 - 3x)$

105. $x^2 + x - 12 = (x + 4)(x - 3)$

106. $x^3 + 27 = (x + 3)(x^2 - 3x + 9)$

Exercise 4.2 (page 435)

1. birth, death

2. population, linearly

3.
$$\begin{aligned} A &= A_0 2^{-t/h} \\ &= 50 \cdot 2^{-100/(12.4)} \\ &\approx 0.1868 \text{ grams} \end{aligned}$$

4.
$$\begin{aligned} A &= A_0 2^{-t/h} \\ &= 1000 \cdot 2^{-100/(30.17)} \\ &\approx 101 \text{ kg} \end{aligned}$$

5.
$$\begin{aligned} A &= A_0 2^{-t/h} \\ &= 1000 \cdot 2^{-200/(30.17)} \\ &\approx 10 \text{ kg} \end{aligned}$$

6.
$$\begin{aligned} A &= A_0 2^{-t/h} \\ &= A_0 \cdot 2^{-3000/5700} \\ &\approx A_0(0.694) \end{aligned}$$
About 69.4% will remain.

7. $A = A_0 2^{-t/h} = A_0 \cdot 2^{-60/40} \approx A_0(0.354) \Rightarrow$ About 35.4% will remain.

8. ^{162}Ho:
$$\begin{aligned} A &= A_0 2^{-t/h} \\ &= A_0 \cdot 2^{-60/22} \\ &\approx A_0(0.151) \end{aligned}$$
About 15.1% will remain.

^{164}Ho:
$$\begin{aligned} A &= A_0 2^{-t/h} \\ &= A_0 \cdot 2^{-60/37} \\ &\approx A_0(0.325) \end{aligned}$$
About 32.5% will remain.

$$\frac{\text{amt. of } ^{162}\text{Ho}}{\text{amt. of } ^{164}\text{Ho}} = \frac{0.151}{0.325} = 0.465$$

9.
$$\begin{aligned} A &= A_0 2^{-t/h} \\ &= 1 \cdot 2^{-12/(4.5)} \\ &\approx 0.1575 \text{ unit} \end{aligned}$$

10.
$$\begin{aligned} A &= A_0 2^{-t/h} \\ &= 1 \cdot 2^{-12/8} \\ &\approx 0.3536 \text{ unit} \end{aligned}$$

11.
$$\begin{aligned} I &= I_0 k^x \\ &= 8(0.5)^2 \\ &= 2 \text{ lumens} \end{aligned}$$

12.
$$\begin{aligned} I &= I_0 k^x \\ &= 14(0.7)^{12} \\ &\approx 0.194 \text{ lumens} \end{aligned}$$

13.
$$\begin{aligned} I &= I_0 k^x \\ 1 &= I_0(0.5)^3 \\ \frac{1}{(0.5)^3} &= I_0 \\ 8 \text{ lumens} &= I_0 \end{aligned}$$

14.
$$\begin{aligned} I &= I_0 k^x \\ 2 &= I_0(0.2)^2 \\ \frac{2}{(0.2)^2} &= I_0 \\ 50 \text{ lumens} &\approx I_0 \end{aligned}$$

15.
$$\begin{aligned} P &= P_0 2^{t/2} \\ &= 10{,}000 \cdot 2^{5/2} \\ &\approx 56{,}570 \text{ fish} \end{aligned}$$

16.
$$\begin{aligned} P &= 375(1.3)^t \\ &= 375(1.3)^3 \\ &\approx 824 \text{ people} \end{aligned}$$

17.
$$\begin{aligned} T &= 40 + 60(0.75)^t \\ &= 40 + 60(0.75)^{3.5} \\ &\approx 61.9^\circ \text{ C} \end{aligned}$$

18. $P = (6 \times 10^6)(2.3)^t$
$= (6 \times 10^6)(2.3)^4$
$\approx 167{,}904{,}600$

19. $P = 173e^{0.03t}$
$= 173e^{0.03(20)}$
≈ 315

20. $P = 1.2 \times 10^6 e^{-0.008t}$
$= 1.2 \times 10^6 e^{-0.008(30)}$
$\approx 9.44 \times 10^5$

21. $P = P_0 e^{0.27t}$
$= 2e^{0.27(7)}$
$\approx$ 13 cases

22. $P = 0.3(1 - e^{-0.05t})$
$= 0.3(1 - e^{-0.05(30)})$
$\approx 0.233 = 23.3\%$

23. $P = P_0 e^{kt}$
$= 6e^{0.019(30)}$
$\approx$ 10.6 billion

24. $P = P_0 e^{kt}$
$= 6e^{0.019(40)}$
$\approx$ 12.8 billion

25. $P = P_0 e^{kt}$
$= 6e^{0.019(50)}$
$\approx$ 15.5 billion
$\frac{15.5}{6} \approx$ a factor of 2.6

26. $P = P_0 e^{kt}$
$= 6e^{0.019(100)}$
$\approx$ 40.1 billion
$\frac{40.1}{6} \approx$ a factor of 6.7

27. $P = e^{-0.3t}$
$= e^{-0.3(24)}$
≈ 0.0007
$= 0.07\%$

28. $x = 0.08(1 - e^{-0.1t})$
$= 0.08(1 - e^{-0.1(30)})$
≈ 0.076

29. Let $t = 0$:
$x = 0.08(1 - e^{-0.1t})$
$= 0.08(1 - e^{-0.1(0)})$
$= 0.08(1 - e^0) = 0.08(1 - 1) = 0$

30. $N = P(1 - e^{-0.1t})$
$= 50{,}000(1 - e^{-0.1(1)})$
≈ 4758
$N = 50{,}000(1 - e^{-0.1(2)})$
≈ 9063
$9063 - 4758 = 4305$

31. $N = P(1 - e^{-0.1t})$
$= 50{,}000(1 - e^{-0.1(10)})$
$\approx 31{,}606$
$50{,}000 - 31{,}606 = 18{,}394$

32. $P = \frac{1{,}200{,}000}{1 + (1200 - 1)e^{-0.4t}}$
$= \frac{1{,}200{,}000}{1 + (1200 - 1)e^{-0.4(5)}}$
$\approx$ 7350 people

33. $P = \frac{1{,}200{,}000}{1 + (1200 - 1)e^{-0.4t}}$
$= \frac{1{,}200{,}000}{1 + (1200 - 1)e^{-0.4(8)}}$
$\approx$ 24,060 people

34. $P = \frac{450{,}000}{1 + (450 - 1)e^{-0.2t}}$
$= \frac{450{,}000}{1 + (450 - 1)e^{-0.2(6)}}$
$\approx$ 3303 people

35. $P = \frac{55{,}000}{1 + (550 - 1)e^{-0.8t}}$
$= \frac{55{,}000}{1 + (550 - 1)e^{-0.8(2)}}$
$\approx$ 492 people

36. $I = 78.5(1.001)^x$
$= 78.5(1.001)^{50}$
$\approx$ 82.5 years

SECTION 4.2

37. $w = 1.54e^{0.503n}$
$= 1.54e^{0.503(5)}$
≈ 19.0 mm

38. $v = 50(1 - e^{-0.2t})$
$= 50(1 - e^{-0.2(0)})$
$= 50(1 - e^{0})$
$= 0$ meters/second

39. $v = 50(1 - e^{-0.2t})$
$= 50(1 - e^{-0.2(20)})$
≈ 49 meters/second

40. $v = 50(1 - e^{-0.2t})$
$= 50(1 - e^{-0.2(2)})$
$\approx$ 16.5 meters/second

$v = 50(1 - e^{-0.3t})$
$= 50(1 - e^{-0.3(2)})$
$\approx$ 22.6 meters/second

This object will be falling faster.

41. Males
$P = P_0e^{kt}$
$= 133e^{0.01t}$
$= 133e^{0.01(20)}$
≈ 162.4 million

Females
$P = P_0e^{kt}$
$= 139e^{0.01t}$
$= 139e^{0.01(20)}$
≈ 169.8 million

There will be about 7 million more females.

42. Males
$P = P_0e^{kt}$
$= 133e^{0.01t}$
$= 133e^{0.01(50)}$
≈ 219.3 million

Females
$P = P_0e^{kt}$
$= 139e^{0.01t}$
$= 139e^{0.01(50)}$
≈ 229.2 million

There will be about 10 million more females.

43. Find where these graphs meet:
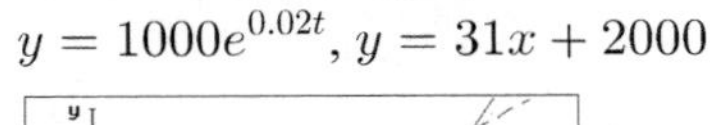
$y = 1000e^{0.02t}$, $y = 31x + 2000$

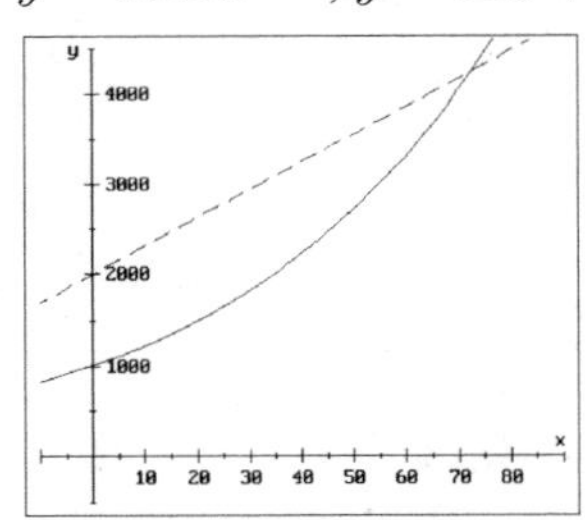

It will take about 72.2 years.

44. Find where these graphs meet:
$y = 1000e^{0.01t}$, $y = 30.624x + 2000$

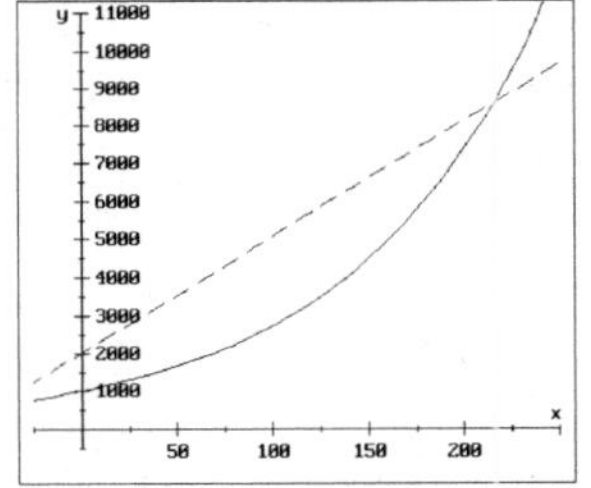

It will take about 215 years.

45. $1 + 1 + \frac{1}{2} + \frac{1}{2\cdot 3} + \frac{1}{2\cdot 3\cdot 4} + \frac{1}{2\cdot 3\cdot 4\cdot 5} \approx 2.71\overline{6}$; $e \approx 2.718$: accurate to 2 places

46. $y = \dfrac{e^{x} + e^{-x}}{2}$

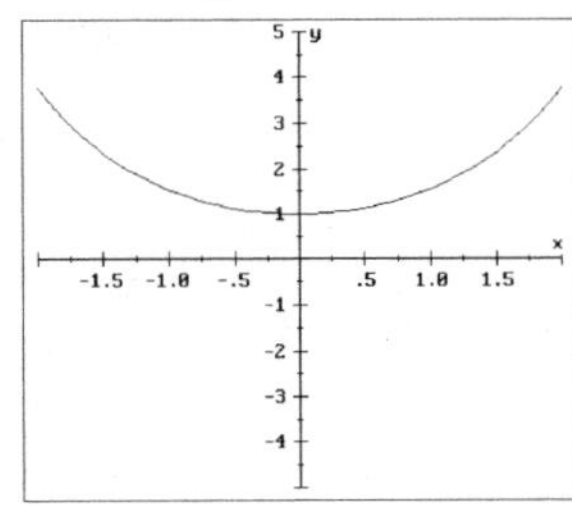

47. $P = \dfrac{1{,}200{,}000}{1 + 1199e^{-0.4t}}$

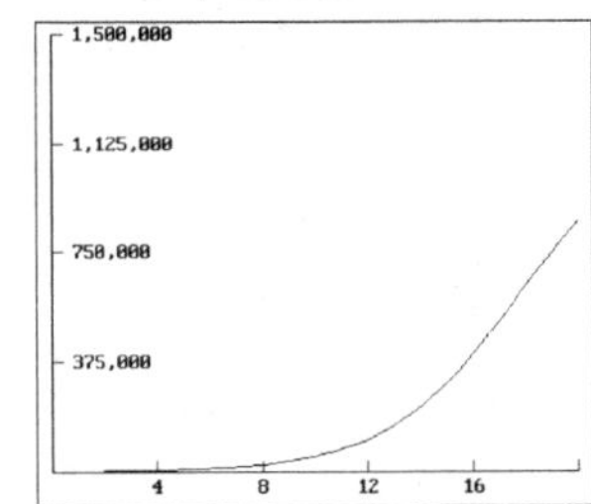

48. **Answers may vary.**

49. $2^3 = x$
$8 = x$

50. $3^x = 9$
$x = 2$

51. $x^3 = 27$
$x = 3$

52. $3^{-2} = x$
$\frac{1}{9} = x$

53. $x^{-3} = \frac{1}{8}$
$\frac{1}{x^3} = \frac{1}{8}$
$x = 2$

54. $3^x = \frac{1}{3}$
$3^x = 3^{-1}$
$x = -1$

55. $9^{1/2} = x$
$3 = x$

56. $x^{1/3} = 3$
$\left(x^{1/3}\right)^3 = 3^3$
$x = 27$

Exercise 4.3 (page 448)

1. $x = b^y$

2. $(0, \infty)$

3. range

4. x

5. inverse

6. logarithmic

7. exponent

8. asymptote

9. $(b, 1), (1, 0)$

10. x

11. $\log_e x$

12. $(0, \infty)$

13. $(-\infty, \infty)$

14. y-axis

15. 10

16. e

17. $8^2 = 64$
$\log_8 64 = 2$

18. $10^3 = 1000$
$\log_{10} 1000 = 3$

19. $4^{-2} = \frac{1}{16}$
$\log_4 \frac{1}{16} = -2$

20. $3^{-4} = \frac{1}{81}$
$\log_3 \frac{1}{81} = -4$

21. $\left(\frac{1}{2}\right)^{-5} = 32$
$\log_{1/2} 32 = -5$

22. $\left(\frac{1}{3}\right)^{-3} = 27$
$\log_{1/3} 27 = -3$

23. $x^y = z$
$\log_x z = y$

24. $m^n = p$
$\log_m p = n$

25. $\log_3 81 = 4$
$3^4 = 81$

26. $\log_7 7 = 1$
$7^1 = 7$

27. $\log_{1/2} \frac{1}{8} = 3$
$\left(\frac{1}{2}\right)^3 = \frac{1}{8}$

28. $\log_{1/5} 1 = 0$
$\left(\frac{1}{5}\right)^0 = 1$

29. $\log_4 \frac{1}{64} = -3$
$4^{-3} = \frac{1}{64}$

30. $\log_6 \frac{1}{36} = -2$
$6^{-2} = \frac{1}{36}$

31. $\log_\pi \pi = 1$
$\pi^1 = \pi$

32. $\log_7 \frac{1}{49} = -2$
$7^{-2} = \frac{1}{49}$

33. $\log_2 8 = x$
$2^x = 8$
$x = 3$

34. $\log_3 9 = x$
$3^x = 9$
$x = 2$

35. $\log_4 64 = x$
$4^x = 64$
$x = 3$

36. $\log_6 216 = x$
$6^x = 216$
$x = 3$

37. $\log_{1/2} \frac{1}{8} = x$

$\left(\frac{1}{2}\right)^x = \frac{1}{8}$

$x = 3$

38. $\log_{1/3} \frac{1}{81} = x$

$\left(\frac{1}{3}\right)^x = \frac{1}{81}$

$x = 4$

39. $\log_9 3 = x$

$9^x = 3$

$x = \frac{1}{2}$

40. $\log_{125} 5 = x$

$125^x = 5$

$x = \frac{1}{3}$

41. $\log_{1/2} 8 = x$

$\left(\frac{1}{2}\right)^x = 8$

$x = -3$

42. $\log_{1/2} 16 = x$

$\left(\frac{1}{2}\right)^x = 16$

$x = -4$

43. $\log_8 x = 2$

$8^2 = x$

$64 = x$

44. $\log_7 x = 0$

$7^0 = x$

$1 = x$

45. $\log_7 x = 1$

$7^1 = x$

$7 = x$

46. $\log_2 x = 8$

$2^8 = x$

$256 = x$

47. $\log_{25} x = \frac{1}{2}$

$25^{1/2} = x$

$5 = x$

48. $\log_4 x = \frac{1}{2}$

$4^{1/2} = x$

$2 = x$

49. $\log_5 x = -2$

$5^{-2} = x$

$\frac{1}{5^2} = x$

$\frac{1}{25} = x$

50. $\log_3 x = -4$

$3^{-4} = x$

$\frac{1}{3^4} = x$

$\frac{1}{81} = x$

51. $\log_{36} x = -\frac{1}{2}$

$36^{-1/2} = x$

$\frac{1}{36^{1/2}} = x$

$\frac{1}{6} = x$

52. $\log_{27} x = -\frac{1}{3}$

$27^{-1/3} = x$

$\frac{1}{27^{1/3}} = x$

$\frac{1}{3} = x$

53. $\log_x 5^3 = 3$

$x^3 = 5^3$

$x = 5$

54. $\log_x 5 = 1$

$x^1 = 5$

$x = 5$

55. $\log_x \frac{9}{4} = 2$

$x^2 = \frac{9}{4}$

$x = \frac{3}{2}$

56. $\log_x \frac{\sqrt{3}}{3} = \frac{1}{2}$

$x^{1/2} = \frac{\sqrt{3}}{3}$

$\left(x^{1/2}\right)^2 = \left(\frac{\sqrt{3}}{3}\right)^2$

$x = \frac{3}{9} = \frac{1}{3}$

57. $\log_x \frac{1}{64} = -3$

$x^{-3} = \frac{1}{64}$

$\frac{1}{x^3} = \frac{1}{4^3}$

$x = 4$

58. $\log_x \frac{1}{100} = -2$

$x^{-2} = \frac{1}{100}$

$\frac{1}{x^2} = \frac{1}{10^2}$

$x = 10$

59.
$$\log_x \frac{9}{4} = -2$$
$$x^{-2} = \frac{9}{4}$$
$$\left(x^{-2}\right)^{-1} = \left(\frac{9}{4}\right)^{-1}$$
$$x^2 = \frac{4}{9}$$
$$x = \frac{2}{3}$$

60.
$$\log_x \frac{\sqrt{3}}{3} = -\frac{1}{2}$$
$$x^{-1/2} = \frac{\sqrt{3}}{3}$$
$$\left(x^{-1/2}\right)^{-2} = \left(\frac{\sqrt{3}}{3}\right)^{-2}$$
$$x = \left(\frac{3}{\sqrt{3}}\right)^{2}$$
$$x = \frac{9}{3} = 3$$

61. From the definition:
$2^{\log_2 5} = 5$

62. From the definition:
$3^{\log_3 4} = 4$

63. From the definition:
$x^{\log_4 6} = 6 \Rightarrow x = 4$

64. From the definition:
$x^{\log_3 8} = 8 \Rightarrow x = 3$

65. $\log 3.25 \approx 0.5119$

66. $\log 0.57 \approx -0.2441$

67. $\log 0.00467 \approx -2.3307$

68. $\log 375.876 \approx 2.5750$

69. $\ln 45.7 \approx 3.8221$

70. $\ln 0.005 \approx -5.2983$

71. $\ln \frac{2}{3} \approx -0.4055$

72. $\ln \frac{12}{7} \approx 0.5390$

73. $\ln 35.15 \approx 3.5596$

74. $\ln 0.675 \approx -0.3930$

75. $\ln 7.896 \approx 2.0664$

76. $\ln 0.00465 \approx -5.3709$

77. $\log(\ln 1.7) \approx -0.2752$

78. $\ln(\log 9.8) \approx -0.0088$

79. $\ln(\log 0.1)$: undefined

80. $\log(\ln 0.01)$: undefined

81.
$$\log y = 1.4023$$
$$y \approx 25.2522$$

82.
$$\log y = 0.926$$
$$y \approx 8.4333$$

83.
$$\log y = -3.71$$
$$y \approx 1.9498 \times 10^{-4}$$

84.
$$\log y = \log \pi$$
$$y \approx 3.1416$$

85.
$$\ln y = 1.4023$$
$$y \approx 4.0645$$

86.
$$\ln y = 2.6490$$
$$y \approx 14.1399$$

87.
$$\ln y = 4.24$$
$$y \approx 69.4079$$

88.
$$\ln y = 0.926$$
$$y \approx 2.5244$$

89.
$$\ln y = -3.71$$
$$y \approx 0.0245$$

90.
$$\ln y = -0.28$$
$$y \approx 0.7558$$

91.
$$\log y = \ln 8$$
$$y \approx 120.0719$$

92.
$$\ln y = \log 7$$
$$y \approx 2.3282$$

93.
$$\log 10{,}000 = x$$
$$10^x = 10{,}000$$
$$x = 4$$
$$\log 10{,}000 = 4$$

94.
$$\log 1{,}000{,}000 = x$$
$$10^x = 1{,}000{,}000$$
$$x = 6$$
$$\log 1{,}000{,}000 = 6$$

95. $\log 0.001 = x$
$10^x = 0.001$
$x = -3$
$\log 0.001 = -3$

96. $\log \frac{1}{100{,}000} = x$
$10^x = \frac{1}{100{,}000}$
$x = -5$
$\log \frac{1}{100{,}000} = -5$

97. From the definition:
$e^{\ln 7} = 7$

98. From the definition:
$e^{\ln 9} = 9$

99. From the definition:
$\ln\left(e^4\right) = 4$

100. From the definition:
$\ln\left(e^{-6}\right) = -6$

101. The graph passes through the point $(b, 1) = (2, 1)$. $\Rightarrow b = 2$

102. The graph passes through the point $(b, 1) = \left(\frac{1}{2}, 1\right)$. $\Rightarrow b = \frac{1}{2}$

103.
$$y = \log_b x$$
$$b^y = x$$
$$b^{-1} = \tfrac{1}{2}$$
$$\left(b^{-1}\right)^{-1} = \left(\tfrac{1}{2}\right)^{-1}$$
$$b = 2$$

104.
$$y = \log_b x$$
$$b^y = x$$
$$b^{-1} = 2$$
$$\left(b^{-1}\right)^{-1} = (2)^{-1}$$
$$b = \tfrac{1}{2}$$

105. $f(x) = \log_3 x$
points: $(1, 0)$, $(3, 1)$

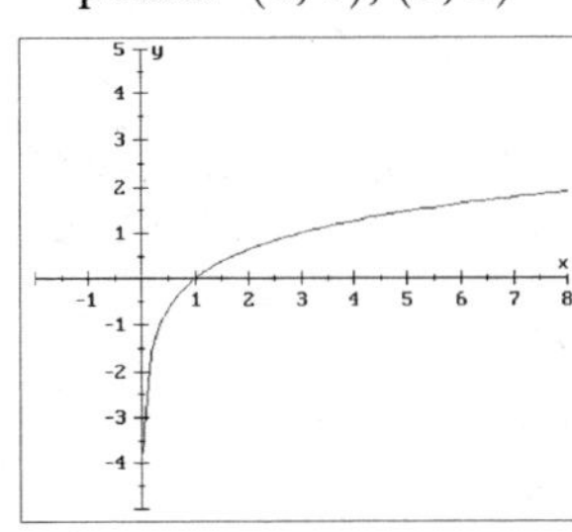

106. $f(x) = \log_4 x$
points: $(1, 0)$, $(4, 1)$

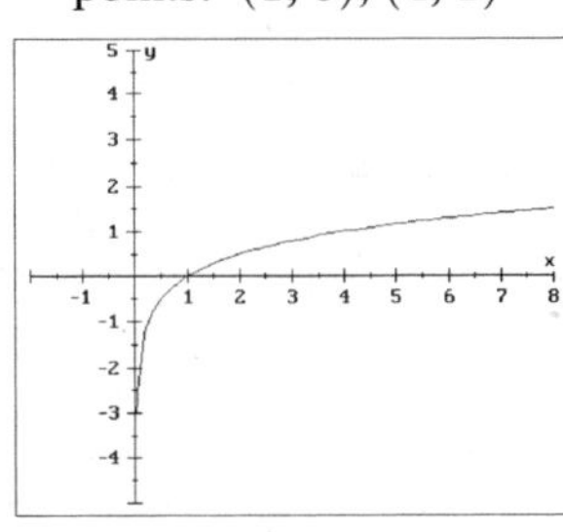

107. $f(x) = \log_{1/3} x$
points: $(1, 0)$, $\left(\frac{1}{3}, 1\right)$

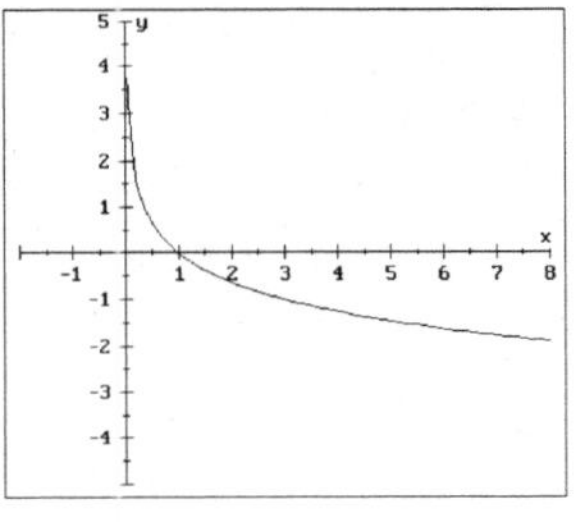

108. $f(x) = \log_{1/4} x$
points: $(1, 0)$, $\left(\frac{1}{4}, 1\right)$

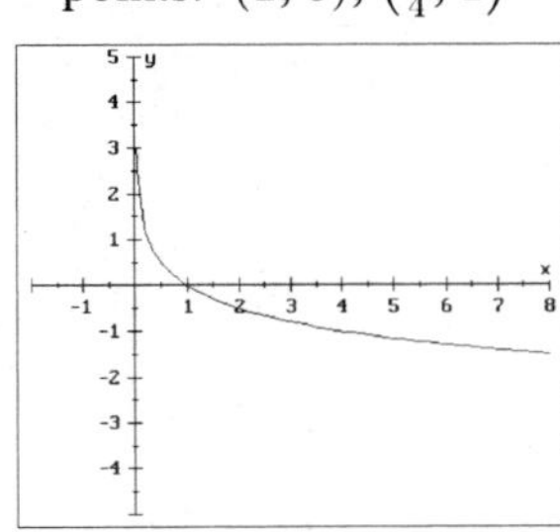

109. $f(x) = -\log_5 x$
Reflect $y = \log_5 x$ about x

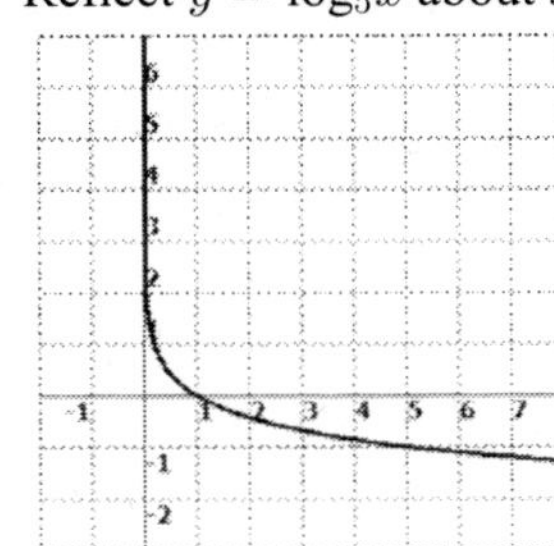

110. $f(x) = -\log_2 x$
Reflect $y = \log_2 x$ about x

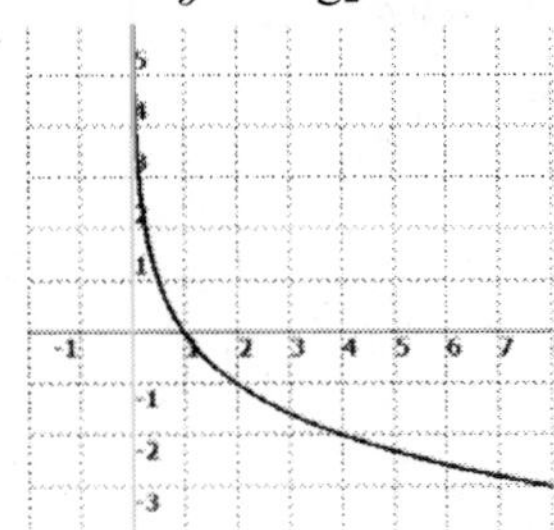

111. $f(x) = 2 + \log_2 x$
Shift $y = \log_2 x$ U2.

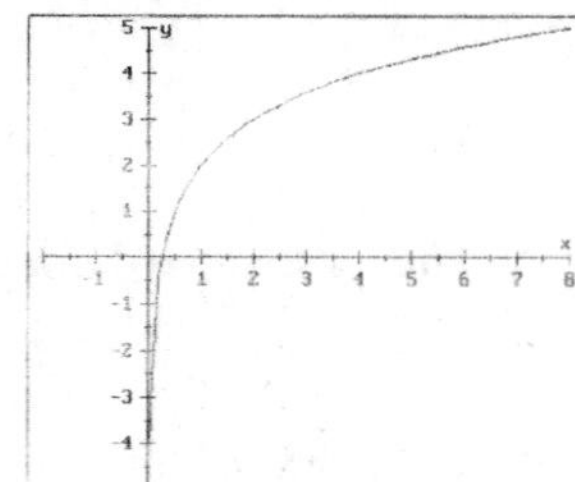

112. $f(x) = \log_2 (x - 1)$
Shift $y = \log_2 x$ R1.

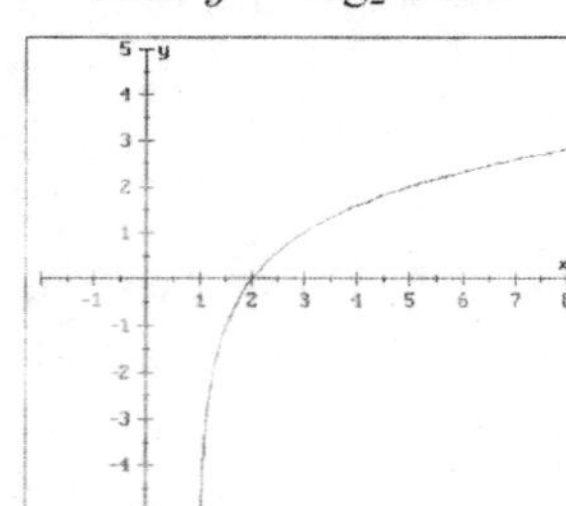

113. $f(x) = \log_3 (x + 2)$
Shift $y = \log_3 x$ L2.

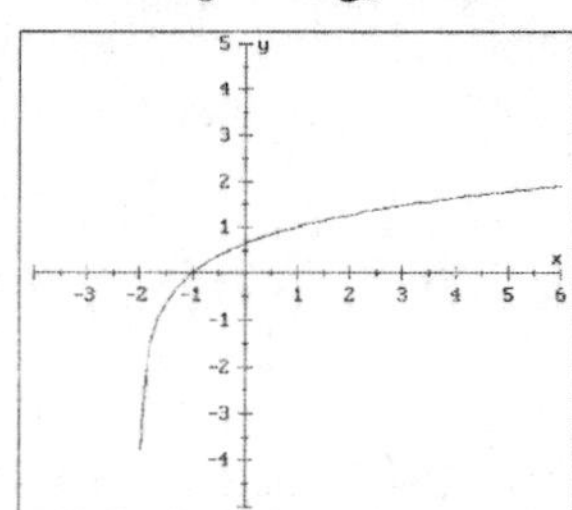

114. $f(x) = -3 + \log_3 x$
Shift $y = \log_3 x$ D3.

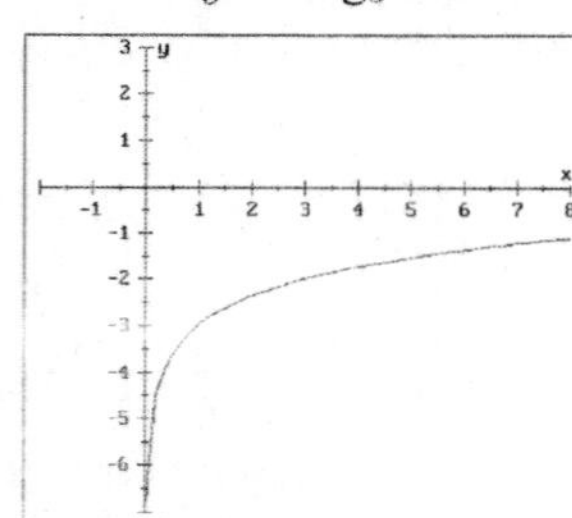

115. $f(x) = 3 + \log_3(x + 1)$
Shift $y = \log_3 x$ U3, L1.

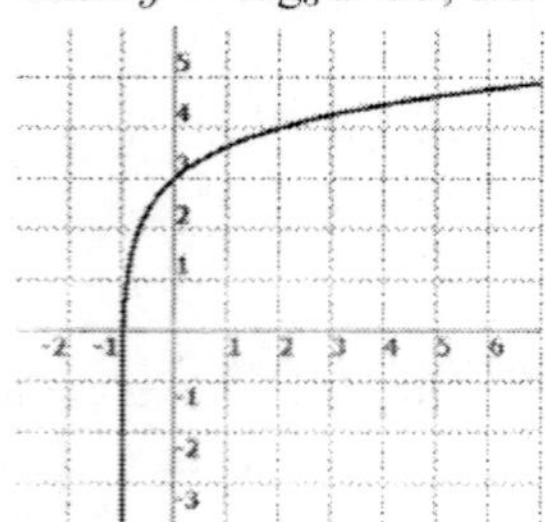

116. $f(x) = -3 + \log_3(x + 1)$
Shift $y = \log_3 x$ D3, L1.

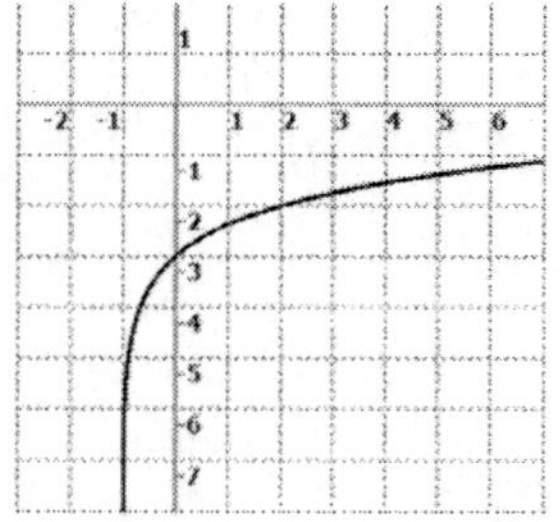

117. $f(x) = -3 + \ln x$
Shift $y = \ln x$ D3.

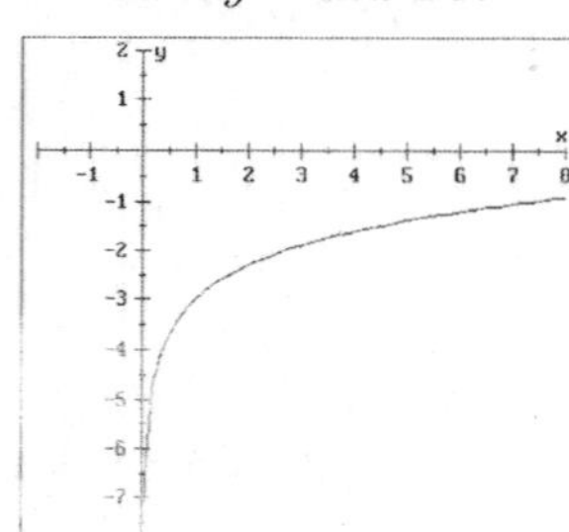

118. $f(x) = \ln (x + 1)$
Shift $y = \ln x$ L1.

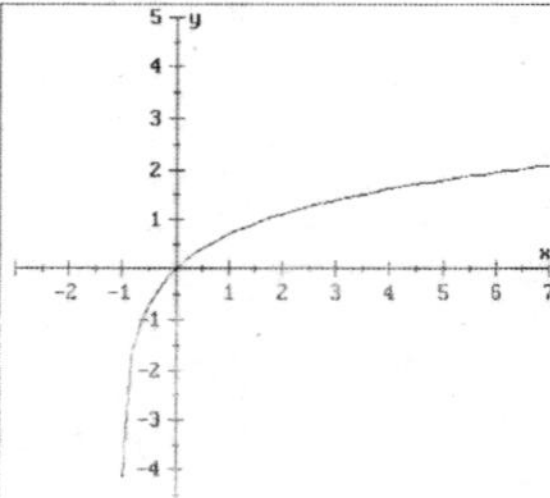

119. $f(x) = \ln (x - 4)$
Shift $y = \ln x$ R4.

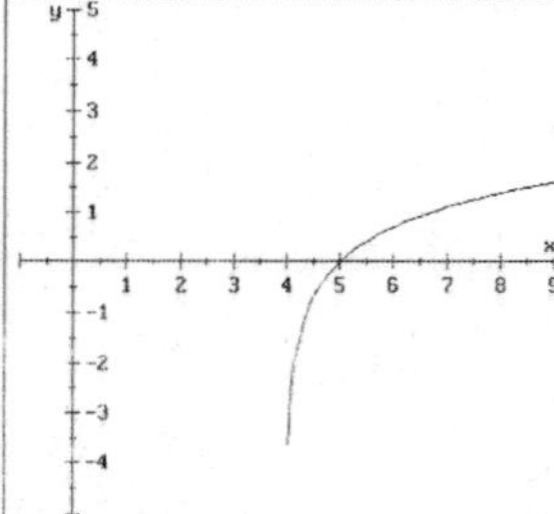

120. $f(x) = 2 + \ln x$
Shift $y = \ln x$ U2.

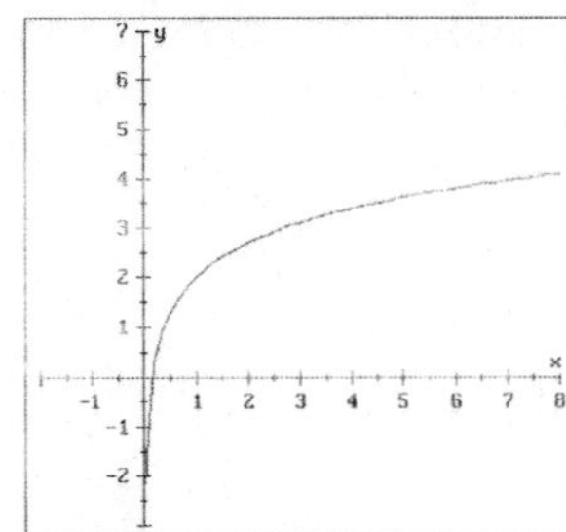

121. $f(x) = 1 - \ln x$
Reflect $y = \ln x$ about x, shift U1.

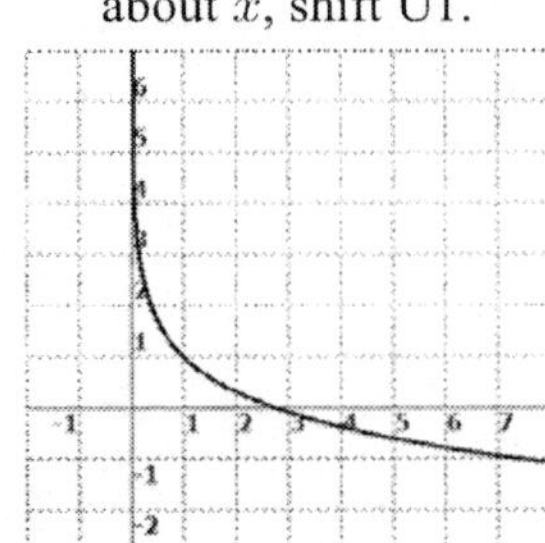

122. $f(x) = 2 - \ln x$
Reflect $y = \ln x$ about x, shift U2.

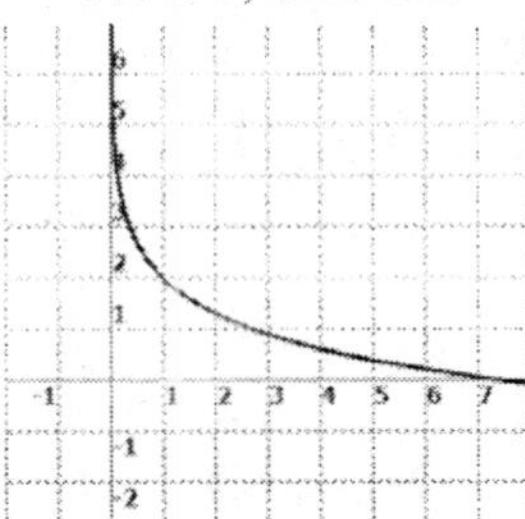

123. $f(x) = \log(3x)$

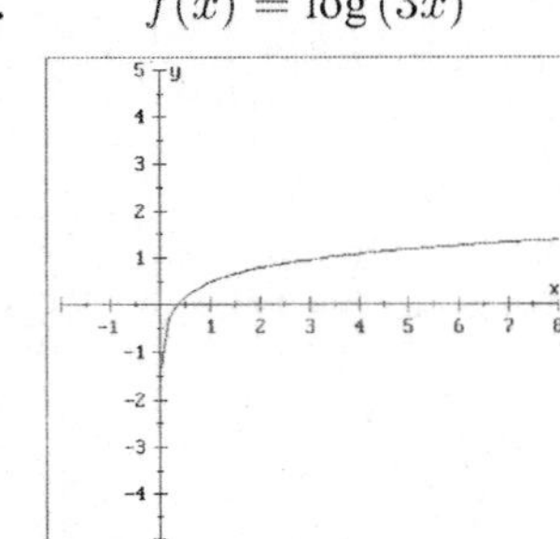

124. $f(x) = \log\left(\frac{x}{3}\right)$

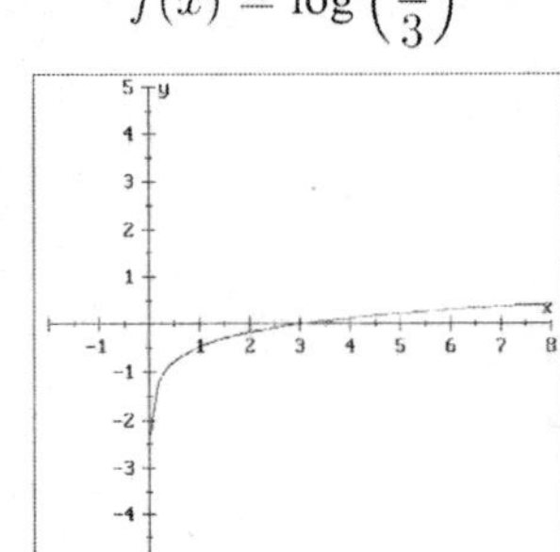

125. $f(x) = \log(-x)$

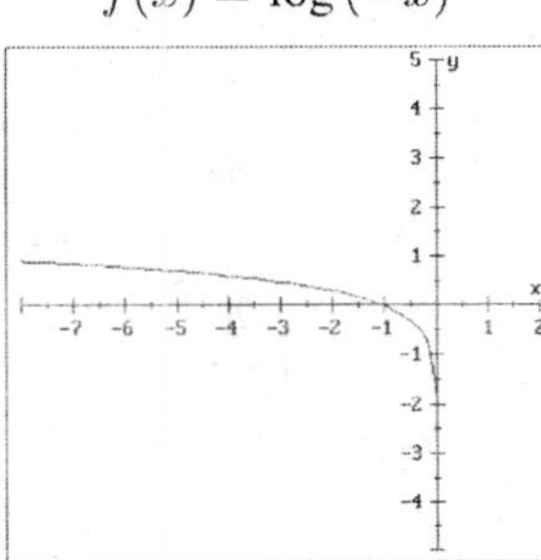

126. $f(x) = -\log x$

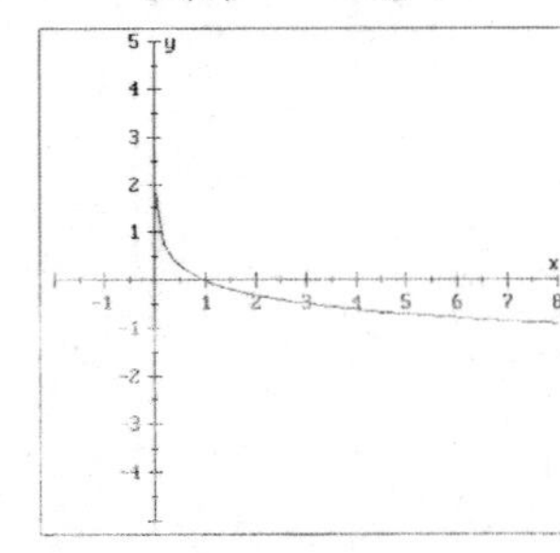

127. $f(x) = \ln\left(\frac{1}{2}x\right)$

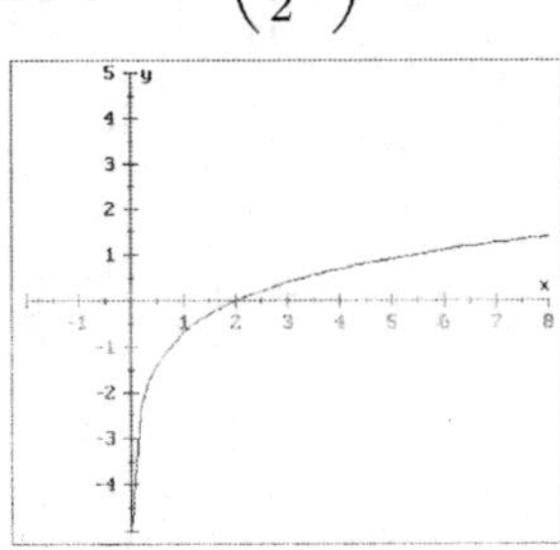

128. $f(x) = \ln x^2$

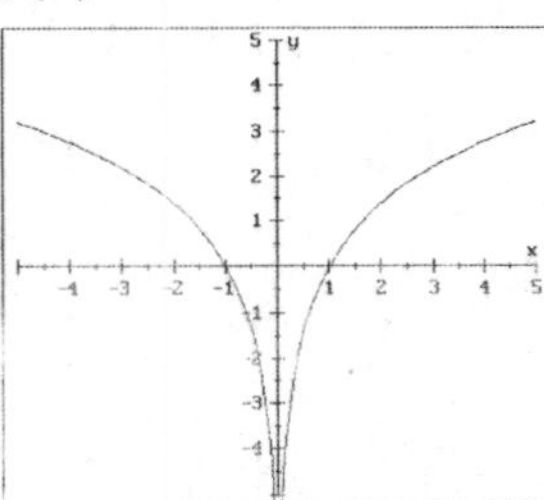

129. $f(x) = \ln(-x)$

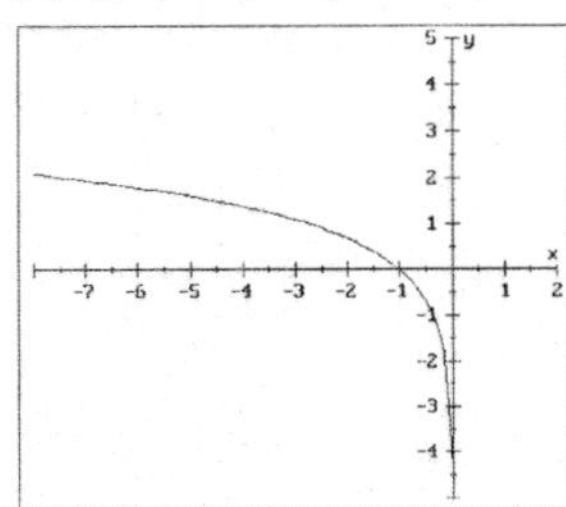

130. $f(x) = \ln(3x)$

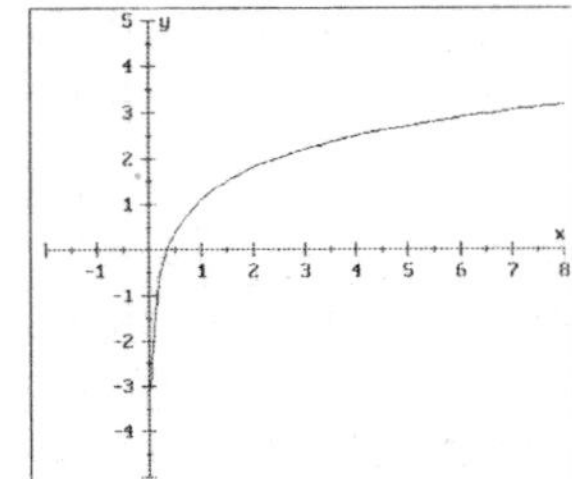

131-133. Answers may vary.

134. $\log_a b = 7$
$a^7 = b$
$(a^7)^{1/7} = b^{1/7}$
$a = b^{1/7}$
$\log_b a = \frac{1}{7}$

135. $y = x^2 + 7x + 3;\ a = 1, b = 7, c = 3$
$x = -\frac{b}{2a} = -\frac{7}{2(1)} = -\frac{7}{2}$
$y = x^2 + 7x + 3$
$= \left(-\frac{7}{2}\right)^2 + 7\left(-\frac{7}{2}\right) + 3 = -\frac{37}{4}$
Vertex: $\left(-\frac{7}{2}, -\frac{37}{4}\right)$

136. $y = 3x^2 - 8x - 1;\ a = 3, b = -8, c = -1$
$x = -\frac{b}{2a} = -\frac{-8}{2(3)} = \frac{4}{3}$
$y = 3x^2 - 8x - 1$
$= 3\left(\frac{4}{3}\right)^2 - 8\left(\frac{4}{3}\right) - 1 = -\frac{19}{3}$
Vertex: $\left(\frac{4}{3}, -\frac{19}{3}\right)$

137. Let x = width. Then $\frac{3400 - 4x}{2}$ = length.
$A = x\left(\frac{3400 - 4x}{2}\right) = x(1700 - 2x)$
$= 1700x - 2x^2$
$= -2x^2 + 1700x$
$x = -\frac{b}{2a} = -\frac{1700}{2(-2)} = 425$
The dimensions are 425 feet by 850 feet.

138. Revenue = price · # sold
$= p(2200 - p)$
$= 2200p - p^2$
$= -p^2 + 2200p$
$x = -\frac{b}{2a} = -\frac{2200}{2(-1)} = 1100$
A price of \$1100 will maximize revenue.

139. $y = 5x - 8:\ m = 5$
Use $m = 5$:
$y - y_1 = m(x - x_1)$
$y - 0 = 5(x - 0)$
$y = 5x$

140. $y = \frac{2}{3}x - 12$ $\quad y - y_1 = m(x - x_1)$
$m = \frac{2}{3}$ $\quad y - 2 = -\frac{3}{2}(x - 3)$
Use $m = -\frac{3}{2}$. $\quad y - 2 = -\frac{3}{2}x + \frac{9}{2} \Rightarrow \boxed{y = -\frac{3}{2}x + \frac{13}{2}}$

Exercise 4.4 (page 455)

1. $20 \log \frac{E_O}{E_I}$

2. $\log \frac{A}{P}$

3. $t = -\frac{1}{k} \ln\left(1 - \frac{C}{M}\right)$

4. $\frac{\ln 2}{r}$

5. $E = RT \ln\left(\frac{V_f}{V_i}\right)$

6. undefined

7. $\text{db gain} = 20 \log \dfrac{E_0}{E_I}$
$= 20 \log \dfrac{17}{0.03}$
$\approx 55 \text{ db}$

8. $\text{db gain} = 20 \log \dfrac{E_0}{E_I}$
$= 20 \log \dfrac{4.7}{4.9}$
$\approx -0.36 \text{ db gain}$
$\approx 0.36 \text{ db loss}$

9. $\text{db gain} = 20 \log \dfrac{E_0}{E_I}$
$= 20 \log \dfrac{20}{0.71}$
$\approx 29 \text{ db}$

10. $\text{db gain} = 20 \log \dfrac{E_0}{E_I}$
$= 20 \log \dfrac{2.8}{0.05}$
$\approx 35 \text{ db}$

11. $\text{db gain} = 20 \log \dfrac{E_0}{E_I}$
$= 20 \log \dfrac{30}{0.1}$
$\approx 49.5 \text{ db}$

12. $\text{db gain} = 20 \log \dfrac{E_0}{E_I}$
$= 20 \log \dfrac{80}{0.12}$
$\approx 56.5 \text{ db}$

13. $R = \log \dfrac{A}{P}$
$= \log \dfrac{5000}{0.2}$
≈ 4.4

14. $R = \log \dfrac{A}{P}$
$= \log \dfrac{8000}{0.008}$
$= 6$

15. $R = \log \dfrac{A}{P}$
$= \log \dfrac{2500}{\frac{1}{4}}$
$= 4$

16. $R = \log \dfrac{A}{P}$
$= \log \dfrac{50{,}000}{\frac{1}{2}}$
$= 5$

17. $R = \log \dfrac{A}{P}$
$= \log \dfrac{6000}{0.3}$
$\approx 4.3 \Rightarrow \text{no damage}$

18. $R = \log \dfrac{A}{P}$
$= \log \dfrac{1985000}{0.1}$
$\approx 7.3 \Rightarrow \text{damage}$

19. $t = -\dfrac{1}{k} \ln \left(1 - \dfrac{C}{M}\right)$
$t = -\dfrac{1}{0.116} \ln \left(1 - \dfrac{0.9M}{M}\right)$
$t = -\dfrac{1}{0.116} \ln(1 - 0.9) \approx 19.8 \text{ minutes}$

20. $t = -\dfrac{1}{k} \ln \left(1 - \dfrac{C}{M}\right)$
$t = -\dfrac{1}{0.201} \ln \left(1 - \dfrac{0.4M}{M}\right)$
$t = -\dfrac{1}{0.201} \ln(1 - 0.4) \approx 2.5 \text{ minutes}$

21. $t = \dfrac{\ln 2}{r} = \dfrac{\ln 2}{0.12} \approx 5.8 \text{ years}$

22. $t = \dfrac{\ln 2}{r} = \dfrac{\ln 2}{0.25} \approx 2.8 \text{ years}$

23. $t = \dfrac{\ln 3}{r} = \dfrac{\ln 3}{0.12} \approx 9.2 \text{ years}$

24. $t = \dfrac{\ln 3}{r} = \dfrac{\ln 3}{0.25} \approx 4.4 \text{ years}$

25. $E = RT \ln \left(\dfrac{V_f}{V_i}\right)$
$E = (8.314)(400) \ln \left(\dfrac{3V_i}{V_i}\right)$
$E = (8.314)(400) \ln (3)$
$E \approx 3654 \text{ joules}$

26. $E = RT \ln \left(\dfrac{V_f}{V_i}\right)$
$E = (8.314)(300) \ln \left(\dfrac{2V_i}{V_i}\right)$
$E = (8.314)(300) \ln (2)$
$E \approx 1729 \text{ joules}$

27. $r = \frac{1}{t}\ln\frac{P}{P_0}$
$= \frac{1}{7}\ln\frac{10{,}400{,}000}{10{,}400}$
$\approx 0.99 \Rightarrow$ about 99% per year

28. $r = \frac{1}{t}\ln\frac{P}{P_0}$
$= \frac{1}{4}\ln\frac{237{,}000}{5{,}000}$
$\approx 0.96 \Rightarrow$ about 96% per year

29. $n = \frac{\log V - \log C}{\log\left(1 - \frac{2}{N}\right)}$
$= \frac{\log 8000 - \log 37{,}000}{\log\left(1 - \frac{2}{5}\right)}$
≈ 3 years old

30. $n = \frac{\log V - \log C}{\log\left(1 - \frac{2}{N}\right)}$
$= \frac{\log 189 - \log 470}{\log\left(1 - \frac{2}{12}\right)}$
≈ 5 years old

31. $n = \frac{\log\left[\frac{Ar}{P} + 1\right]}{\log(1 + r)}$
$= \frac{\log\left[\frac{20000(0.12)}{1000} + 1\right]}{\log(1 + 0.12)}$
≈ 10.8 years

32. $n = \frac{\log\left[\frac{Ar}{P} + 1\right]}{\log(1 + r)}$
$= \frac{\log\left[\frac{50000(0.08)}{5000} + 1\right]}{\log(1 + 0.08)}$
≈ 7.6 years

33. $V = ER_1 \ln\frac{R_2}{R_1}$
$V = (400{,}000)(0.25)\ln\left(\frac{2}{0.25}\right)$
$V \approx 208{,}000$ V

34. $V = ER_1 \ln\frac{R_2}{R_1}$
$V = (400{,}000)(0.25)\ln\left(\frac{4}{0.25}\right)$
$V \approx 277{,}000$ V

35. $f(x) = 12 \Rightarrow \ln x = 12 \Rightarrow x \approx 162755 \Rightarrow$ You would go out 162,755 cm.
$162{,}755\text{ cm} = \frac{162{,}755\text{ cm}}{1} \cdot \frac{1\text{ in}}{2.54\text{ cm}} \cdot \frac{1\text{ ft}}{12\text{ in}} \cdot \frac{1\text{ mi}}{5280\text{ ft}} \approx 1$ mile

36. $f(x) = 12 \Rightarrow \log x = 12 \Rightarrow x = 10^{12}\text{ cm} \Rightarrow$ You would go out 10^{12} cm.
$10^{12}\text{ cm} = \frac{10^{12}\text{ cm}}{1} \cdot \frac{1\text{ in}}{2.54\text{ cm}} \cdot \frac{1\text{ ft}}{12\text{ in}} \cdot \frac{1\text{ mi}}{5280\text{ ft}} \approx 6{,}214{,}000$ mile
It is bigger because ln has a base of $e \approx 2.72$ while log has a base of 10.

37. Set $x = 0$:
$y = \frac{1}{1 + e^{-2(0)}}$
$= \frac{1}{1 + e^0}$
$= \frac{1}{1 + 1} = \frac{1}{2}$
y-intercept: $\left(0, \frac{1}{2}\right)$

38. **Explanations may vary.**

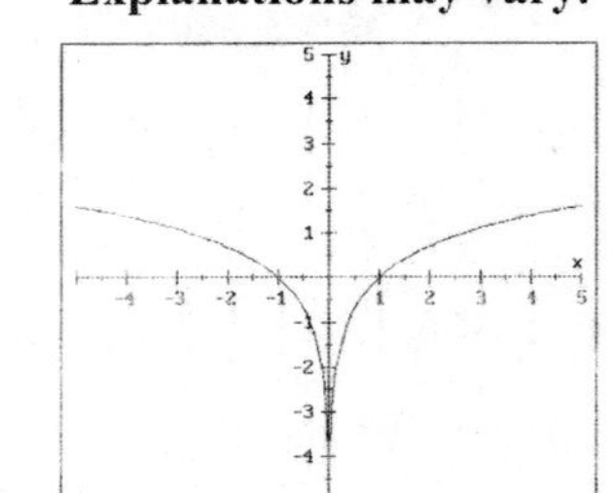

SECTION 4.4

39. $y = mx + b$
$y = 7x + 3$

40. $3x + 2y = 9$
$y = -\frac{3}{2}x + \frac{9}{2}$
$m = -\frac{3}{2}$
Use $m = -\frac{3}{2}$.

$y - y_1 = m(x - x_1)$
$y - 5 = -\frac{3}{2}(x + 3)$
$y - 5 = -\frac{3}{2}x - \frac{9}{2}$
$\boxed{y = -\frac{3}{2}x + \frac{1}{2}}$
$\boxed{\text{or } 3x + 2y = 1}$

41. Vertical through (2, 3): $x = 2$

42. Horizontal through (2, 3): $y = 3$

43. $\frac{2(x+2)-1}{4x^2-9} = \frac{2x+4-1}{(2x+3)(2x-3)} = \frac{2x+3}{(2x+3)(2x-3)} = \frac{1}{2x-3}$

44. $\frac{x+1}{x} + \frac{x-1}{x+1} = \frac{(x+1)(x+1)}{x(x+1)} + \frac{(x-1)\cdot x}{(x+1)\cdot x} = \frac{x^2+2x+1+x^2-x}{x(x+1)} = \frac{2x^2+x+1}{x(x+1)}$

45. $\frac{x^2+3x+2}{3x+9} \cdot \frac{x+3}{x^2-4} = \frac{(x+2)(x+1)}{3(x+3)} \cdot \frac{x+3}{(x+2)(x-2)} = \frac{x+1}{3(x-2)}$

46. $\frac{1+\frac{y}{x}}{\frac{y}{x}-1} = \frac{1+\frac{y}{x}}{\frac{y}{x}-1} \cdot \frac{x}{x} = \frac{x+y}{y-x}$

Exercise 4.5 (page 468)

1. 0
2. 1
3. M, N
4. x
5. x, y
6. $-$
7. x
8. x
9. $\neq$
10. $=$

11. $\log_4 1 = 0$

12. $\log_4 4 = 1$

13. $\log_4 4^7 = 7\log_4 4 = 7$

14. $4^{\log_4 8} = 8$

15. $5^{\log_5 10} = 10$

16. $\log_5 5^2 = 2\log_5 5 = 2$

17. $\log_5 5 = 1$

18. $\log_5 1 = 0$

19-24. Answers may vary.

25. $\log_b 2xy = \log_b 2 + \log_b x + \log_b y$

26. $\log_b 3xz = \log_b 3 + \log_b x + \log_b z$

27. $\log_b \frac{2x}{y} = \log_b 2x - \log_b y$
$= \log_b 2 + \log_b x - \log_b y$

28. $\log_b \frac{x}{yz} = \log_b x - \log_b yz$
$= \log_b x - (\log_b y + \log_b z)$
$= \log_b x - \log_b y - \log_b z$

29. $\log_b x^2y^3 = \log_b x^2 + \log_b y^3$
$= 2\log_b x + 3\log_b y$

30. $\log_b x^3y^2z = \log_b x^3 + \log_b y^2 + \log_b z$
$= 3\log_b x + 2\log_b y + \log_b z$

31. $\log_b (xy)^{1/3} = \dfrac{1}{3}\log_b xy$
$= \dfrac{1}{3}(\log_b x + \log_b y)$

32. $\log_b x^{1/2}y^3 = \log_b x^{1/2} + \log_b y^3$
$= \dfrac{1}{2}\log_b x + 3\log_b y$

33. $\log_b x\sqrt{z} = \log_b xz^{1/2}$
$= \log_b x + \log_b z^{1/2}$
$= \log_b x + \dfrac{1}{2}\log_b z$

34. $\log_b \sqrt{xy} = \log_b (xy)^{1/2}$
$= \dfrac{1}{2}\log_b xy$
$= \dfrac{1}{2}(\log_b x + \log_b y)$

35. $\log_b \dfrac{\sqrt[3]{x}}{\sqrt[3]{yz}} = \log_b \sqrt[3]{x} - \log_b \sqrt[3]{yz} = \log_b x^{1/3} - \log_b (yz)^{1/3} = \dfrac{1}{3}\log_b x - \dfrac{1}{3}\log_b yz$
$= \dfrac{1}{3}\log_b x - \dfrac{1}{3}(\log_b y + \log_b z)$
$= \dfrac{1}{3}\log_b x - \dfrac{1}{3}\log_b y - \dfrac{1}{3}\log_b z$

36. $\log_b \sqrt[4]{\dfrac{x^3y^2}{z^4}} = \log_b \left(\dfrac{x^3y^2}{z^4}\right)^{1/4} = \dfrac{1}{4}\log_b \dfrac{x^3y^2}{z^4} = \dfrac{1}{4}(\log_b x^3y^2 - \log_b z^4)$
$= \dfrac{1}{4}(\log_b x^3 + \log_b y^2 - \log_b z^4)$
$= \dfrac{1}{4}(3\log_b x + 2\log_b y - 4\log_b z)$
$= \dfrac{3}{4}\log_b x + \dfrac{1}{2}\log_b y - \log_b z$

37. $\ln x^7y^8 = \ln x^7 + \ln y^8$
$= 7\ln x + 8\ln y$

38. $\ln \dfrac{4x}{y} = \ln 4x - \ln y$
$= \ln 4 + \ln x - \ln y$

39. $\ln \dfrac{x}{y^4z} = \ln x - \ln y^4z$
$= \ln x - (\ln y^4 + \ln z)$
$= \ln x - (4\ln y + \ln z)$
$= \ln x - 4\ln y - \ln z$

40. $\ln x\sqrt{y} = \ln xy^{1/2}$
$= \ln x + \ln y^{1/2}$
$= \ln x + \dfrac{1}{2}\ln y$

41. $\log_b (x+1) - \log_b x = \log_b \dfrac{x+1}{x}$

42. $\log_b x + \log_b (x+2) - \log_b 8 = \log_b x(x+2) - \log_b 8 = \log_b \dfrac{x(x+2)}{8}$

43. $2\log_b x + \dfrac{1}{3}\log_b y = \log_b x^2 + \log_b y^{1/3} = \log_b x^2y^{1/3} = \log_b x^2\sqrt[3]{y}$

44. $-2\log_b x - 3\log_b y + \log_b z = \log_b x^{-2} + \log_b y^{-3} + \log_b z = \log_b x^{-2}y^{-3}z = \log_b \dfrac{z}{x^2y^3}$

45. $-3\log_b x - 2\log_b y + \dfrac{1}{2}\log_b z = \log_b x^{-3} + \log_b y^{-2} + \log_b z^{1/2} = \log_b x^{-3}y^{-2}\sqrt{z} = \log_b \dfrac{\sqrt{z}}{x^3y^2}$

46. $3\log_b(x+1) - 2\log_b(x+2) + \log_b x = \log_b(x+1)^3 + \log_b(x+2)^{-2} + \log_b x = \log_b \dfrac{x(x+1)^3}{(x+2)^2}$

47. $\log_b\left(\dfrac{x}{z} + x\right) - \log_b\left(\dfrac{y}{z} + y\right) = \log_b \dfrac{\frac{x}{z} + x}{\frac{y}{z} + y} = \log_b \dfrac{z(\frac{x}{z} + x)}{z(\frac{y}{z} + y)} = \log_b \dfrac{x + xz}{y + yz} = \log_b \dfrac{x}{y}$

48. $\log_b(xy + y^2) - \log_b(xz + yz) + \log_b z = \log_b \dfrac{(xy + y^2)z}{xz + yz} = \log_b \dfrac{(x+y)yz}{z(x+y)} = \log_b y$

49. $\ln x + \ln(x+5) - \ln 9 = \ln x(x+5) - \ln 9 = \ln \dfrac{x(x+5)}{9}$

50. $5\ln x + \frac{1}{5}\ln y = \ln x^5 + \ln y^{1/5} = \ln x^5\sqrt[5]{y}$

51. $-6\ln x - 2\ln y + \ln z = \ln x^{-6} + \ln y^{-2} + \ln z = \ln x^{-6}y^{-2}z = \ln \dfrac{z}{x^6y^2}$

52. $-2\ln x - 3\ln y + \frac{1}{3}\ln z = \ln x^{-2} + \ln y^{-3} + \ln z^{1/3} = \ln x^{-2}y^{-3}z^{1/3} = \ln \dfrac{\sqrt[3]{z}}{x^2y^3}$

53. $\log_b ab = \log_b a + \log_b b = \log_b a + 1$
TRUE

54. $\log_b \dfrac{1}{a} = \log_b a^{-1} = -\log_b a$
TRUE

55. $\log_b 0$ is undefined.
FALSE

56. $\log_b 2 = \log_2 b$
FALSE (except for $b = 2$)

57. $\log_b(x \cdot y) = \log_b x + \log_b y$, so
$\log_b(x + y) \neq \log_b x + \log_b y$
TRUE (unless $x \cdot y = x + y$)

58. $\log_b(x \cdot y) = \log_b x + \log_b y$, so
$\log_b(xy) \neq (\log_b x)(\log_b y)$
FALSE

59. If $\log_a b = c$, then $\log_b a = c$
FALSE

60. If $\log_a b = c$, then $\log_b a = \dfrac{1}{c}$

$\log_a b = c \Rightarrow a^c = b$

$(a^c)^{1/c} = b^{1/c}$

$a = b^{1/c} \Rightarrow \log_b a = \dfrac{1}{c}$

TRUE

61. $\log_7 7^7 = 7 \Rightarrow 7^7 = 7^7$
TRUE

62. $7^{\log_7 7} = 7$
TRUE

63. $-\log_b x = \log_b x^{-1} = \log_b \frac{1}{x}$
FALSE

64. $\log_b a^p = p \log_b a = pc$
TRUE

65. $\log_b \left(\frac{A}{B}\right) = \log_b A - \log_b B$, so
$\frac{\log_b (A)}{\log_b (B)} \neq \log_b A - \log_b B$
FALSE

66. $\log_b (A - B) = \frac{\log_b (A)}{\log_b (B)}$
FALSE

67. $\log_b \frac{1}{5} = \log_b 5^{-1} = -\log_b 5$
TRUE

68. $3 \log_b \sqrt[3]{a} = 3 \log_b a^{1/3} = 3 \cdot \frac{1}{3} \log_b a$
$= \log_b a$
TRUE

69. $\frac{1}{3} \log_b a^3 = \frac{1}{3} \cdot 3 \log_b a = \log_b a$
TRUE

70. Let $\log_{4/3} y = c$.
Then $\left(\frac{4}{3}\right)^c = y$.
$\left(\left(\frac{3}{4}\right)^{-1}\right)^c = y$
$\left(\frac{3}{4}\right)^{-c} = y \Rightarrow \log_{3/4} y = -c$.
Thus, $\log_{4/3} y = c = -\log_{3/4} y$. $\Rightarrow$ TRUE

71. Let $\log_{1/b} y = c$.
Then $\left(\frac{1}{b}\right)^c = y$.
$\left(\left(\frac{b}{1}\right)^{-1}\right)^c = y$
$(b)^{-c} = y \Rightarrow \log_b y = -c$.
$\log_{1/b} y + \log_b y = c + (-c) = 0$.
TRUE

72. $\log_{10} 10^3 = 3$
$3\left(10^{\log_{10} 3}\right) = 3(3) = 9$
$\log_{10} 10^3 \neq 3\left(10^{\log_{10} 3}\right)$
FALSE

73. $\ln (xy) = \ln x + \ln y$, so
$\ln (xy) \neq (\ln x)(\ln y)$
FALSE

74. $\ln A - \ln B = \ln \frac{A}{B}$, so
$\ln A - \ln B \neq \frac{\ln A}{\ln B}$
FALSE

75. $\frac{1}{5} \ln a^5 = \frac{1}{5} \cdot 5 \ln a = \ln a$
TRUE

76. $-\ln \frac{1}{y} = -\ln y^{-1} = -(-1) \ln y = \ln y$
TRUE

77. $\log_{10} 28 = \log_{10} (4 \cdot 7)$
$= \log_{10} 4 + \log_{10} 7$
$= 0.6021 + 0.8451 = 1.4472$

78. $\log_{10} \left(\frac{7}{4}\right) = \log_{10} 7 - \log_{10} 4$
$= 0.8451 - 0.6021 = 0.2430$

79. $\log_{10} 2.25 = \log_{10} \left(\frac{9}{4}\right)$
$= \log_{10} 9 - \log_{10} 4$
$= 0.9542 - 0.6021 = 0.3521$

80. $\log_{10} 36 = \log_{10} (4 \cdot 9)$
$= \log_{10} 4 + \log_{10} 9$
$= 0.6021 + 0.9542 = 1.5563$

81. $\log_{10} \left(\frac{63}{4}\right) = \log_{10} 63 - \log_{10} 4$
$= \log_{10} (7 \cdot 9) - \log_{10} 4$
$= \log_{10} 7 + \log_{10} 9 - \log_{10} 4$
$= 0.8451 + 0.9542 - 0.6021$
$= 1.1972$

82. $\log_{10} \left(\frac{4}{63}\right) = \log_{10} 4 - \log_{10} 63$
$= \log_{10} 4 - \log_{10} (7 \cdot 9)$
$= \log_{10} 4 - \log_{10} 7 - \log_{10} 9$
$= 0.6021 - 0.8451 - 0.9542$
$= -1.1972$

83. $\log_{10} 252 = \log_{10} (4 \cdot 63)$
$= \log_{10} (4 \cdot 7 \cdot 9)$
$= \log_{10} 4 + \log_{10} 7 + \log_{10} 9$
$= 0.6021 + 0.8451 + 0.9542$
$= 2.4014$

84. $\log_{10} 49 = \log_{10} 7^2 = 2 \log_{10} 7$
$= 2(0.8451)$
$= 1.6902$

85. $\log_{10} 112 = \log_{10} (4 \cdot 28)$
$= \log_{10} (4 \cdot 7 \cdot 4)$
$= \log_{10} 4 + \log_{10} 7 + \log_{10} 4$
$= 0.6021 + 0.8451 + 0.6021$
$= 2.0493$

86. $\log_{10} 324 = \log_{10} (4 \cdot 81)$
$= \log_{10} (4 \cdot 9 \cdot 9)$
$= \log_{10} 4 + \log_{10} 9 + \log_{10} 9$
$= 0.6021 + 0.9542 + 0.9542$
$= 2.5105$

87. $\log_{10} \left(\frac{144}{49}\right) = \log_{10} 144 - \log_{10} 49$
$= \log_{10} (4 \cdot 4 \cdot 9) - \log_{10} (7 \cdot 7)$
$= \log_{10} 4 + \log_{10} 4 + \log_{10} 9 - \log_{10} 7 - \log_{10} 7$
$= 0.6021 + 0.6021 + 0.9542 - 0.8451 - 0.8451$
$= 0.4682$

88. $\log_{10} \left(\frac{324}{63}\right) = \log_{10} 324 - \log_{10} 63$
$= \log_{10} (4 \cdot 9 \cdot 9) - \log_{10} (7 \cdot 9)$
$= \log_{10} 4 + \log_{10} 9 + \log_{10} 9 - \log_{10} 7 - \log_{10} 9$
$= 0.6021 + 0.9542 + 0.9542 - 0.8451 - 0.9542$
$= 0.7112$

89. $\log_3 7 = \frac{\log_{10} 7}{\log_{10} 3} \approx 1.7712$

90. $\log_7 3 = \frac{\log_{10} 3}{\log_{10} 7} \approx 0.5646$

91. $\log_\pi 3 = \dfrac{\log_{10} 3}{\log_{10} \pi} \approx 0.9597$

92. $\log_3 \pi = \dfrac{\log_{10} \pi}{\log_{10} 3} \approx 1.0420$

93. $\log_3 8 = \dfrac{\log_e 8}{\log_e 3} \approx 1.8928$

94. $\log_5 10 = \dfrac{\log_e 10}{\log_e 5} \approx 1.4307$

95. $\log_{\sqrt{2}} \sqrt{5} = \dfrac{\log_e \sqrt{5}}{\log_e \sqrt{2}} \approx 2.3219$

96. $\log_\pi e = \dfrac{\log_e e}{\log_e \pi} \approx 0.8736$

97.
$$\begin{aligned} \text{pH} &= -\log\left[\text{H}^+\right] \\ &= -\log\left(6.3 \times 10^{-8}\right) \\ &\approx 7.20 \end{aligned}$$

98.
$$\begin{aligned} \text{pH} &= -\log\left[\text{H}^+\right] \\ &= -\log\left(1.6 \times 10^{-7}\right) \\ &\approx 6.80 \Rightarrow \text{not ideal} \end{aligned}$$

99.
$$\begin{aligned} \text{pH} &= -\log\left[\text{H}^+\right] \\ &= -\log\left(1.7 \times 10^{-5}\right) \\ &\approx 4.77 \end{aligned}$$

100.
$$\begin{aligned} \text{pH} &= -\log\left[\text{H}^+\right] \\ 13.2 &= -\log\left[\text{H}^+\right] \\ -13.2 &= \log\left[\text{H}^+\right] \\ 6.3 \times 10^{-14} &\approx \left[\text{H}^+\right] \end{aligned}$$

101.
$$\begin{aligned} \text{pH} &= -\log\left[\text{H}^+\right] \\ 2.9 &= -\log\left[\text{H}^+\right] \\ -2.9 &= \log\left[\text{H}^+\right] \\ 1.26 \times 10^{-3} &\approx \left[\text{H}^+\right] \end{aligned} \qquad \begin{aligned} \text{pH} &= -\log\left[\text{H}^+\right] \\ 3.3 &= -\log\left[\text{H}^+\right] \\ -3.3 &= \log\left[\text{H}^+\right] \\ 5.01 \times 10^{-4} &\approx \left[\text{H}^+\right] \end{aligned}$$

The hydrogen ion concentration can range from 5.01×10^{-4} to 1.26×10^{-3}.

102.
$$\begin{aligned} \text{pH} &= -\log\left[\text{H}^+\right] \\ &= -\log\left(6.31 \times 10^{-4}\right) \\ &\approx 3.2 \end{aligned}$$

103.
$$\begin{aligned} \text{db gain} &= 10 \log \frac{P_O}{P_I} \\ &= 10 \log \frac{40}{\frac{1}{2}} \\ &\approx 19 \text{ db} \end{aligned}$$

104.
$$\begin{aligned} \text{db gain} &= 10 \log \frac{P_O}{P_I} \\ &= 10 \log \frac{3}{12} \\ &\approx -6 \text{ db} \end{aligned}$$

105. $L = k \ln I$

$4L = 4k \ln I = k \cdot 4 \ln I = k \ln I^4$

The original intensity must be raised to the fourth power.

106. $L = k \ln I$

$\frac{1}{2}L = \frac{1}{2}k \ln I = k \cdot \frac{1}{2} \ln I = k \ln I^{1/2}$

The original intensity must be raised to the one-half power (take the square root).

107. $E = 8300 \ln V$

$2E = 2 \cdot 8300 \ln V = 8300 \ln V^2$

The original volume is squared.

SECTION 4.5

108. $R = \log \frac{A}{P}$; $R + 1 = \log \frac{A}{P} + 1 = \log \frac{A}{P} + \log 10 = \log\left(\frac{A}{P} \cdot 10\right) = \log \frac{10A}{P}$

The amplitude must be multiplied by a factor of 10.

109. $3^{4\log_3 2} + 5^{\frac{1}{2}\log_5 25} = 3^{\log_3 2^4} + 5^{\log_5 25^{1/2}} = 2^4 + 25^{1/2} = 16 + 5 = 21$

110. $5\log x + \frac{1}{3}\log y - \frac{1}{2}\log x - \frac{5}{6}\log y = \log x^5 + \log y^{1/3} + \log x^{-1/2} + \log y^{-5/6}$

$= \log x^5 y^{1/3} x^{-1/2} y^{-5/6} = \log x^{9/2} y^{-1/2}$

$a = \frac{9}{2}, b = -\frac{1}{2} \Rightarrow a - b = \frac{9}{2} - \left(-\frac{1}{2}\right) = \frac{10}{2} = 5$

111. Let $\log_b M = x$ and $\log_b N = y$.
Then $b^x = M$ and $b^y = N$.

$\frac{M}{N} = \frac{b^x}{b^y} = b^{x-y}$.

So $\log_b \frac{M}{N} = x - y$, or

$\log_b \frac{M}{N} = \log_b M - \log_b N$.

112.

$$\begin{aligned} -\log_b x = Q \quad &\Rightarrow & b^Q &= x^{-1} \\ \log_b x^{-1} = Q \quad & & \left(b^Q\right)^{-1} &= \left(x^{-1}\right)^{-1} \\ & & b^{-Q} &= x \\ & & \left(b^{-1}\right)^Q &= x \\ & & \left(\tfrac{1}{b}\right)^Q &= x \\ & & \log_{1/b} x &= Q \end{aligned}$$

Thus, $-\log_b x = Q = \log_{1/b} x$.

113. $e^{x\ln a} = e^{\ln a^x} = a^x$

114. $\ln x = M \Rightarrow e^M = x$, by definition.
Thus, $e^{\ln x} = e^M = x$.

115. $\ln\left(e^x\right) = x\ln e = x(1) = x$

116.

$$\begin{aligned} \log_b 3x &= 1 + \log_b x \\ \log_b 3 + \log_b x &= 1 + \log_b x \\ \log_b 3 &= 1 \\ b^1 &= 3 \Rightarrow b = 3 \end{aligned}$$

117. $\log(0.9) < 0$, so $\ln(\log(0.9))$ is undefined.

118. $\ln 1 = 0$, so $\log_b(\ln 1)$ is undefined.

119. Answers may vary.

120. Answers may vary.

121. $y = 3x - 1 \Rightarrow$ function

122. $y = \frac{x+3}{x-1} \Rightarrow$ function

123. $y^2 = 4x$

$y = \pm\sqrt{4x} \Rightarrow$ not a function

124. $y = 4x^2 \Rightarrow$ function

125. $f(x) = x^2 - 4$; domain $= (-\infty, \infty)$

126. $f(x) = \frac{1}{x^2 - 4} = \frac{1}{(x+2)(x-2)}$

domain $= (-\infty, -2) \cup (-2, 2) \cup (2, \infty)$

127. $f(x) = \sqrt{x^2 + 4}$; domain $= (-\infty, \infty)$

128. $f(x) = \sqrt{x^2 - 4}$

$x^2 - 4 \geq 0 \Rightarrow x \leq -2$ or $x \geq 2$

domain $= (-\infty, -2] \cup [2, \infty)$

Exercise 4.6 (page 482)

1. exponential

2. logarithmic

3. $A_0 2^{-t/h}$

4. $P_0 e^{kt}$

5.
$$\begin{aligned} 2^{3x+2} &= 16^x \\ 2^{3x+2} &= \left(2^4\right)^x \\ 2^{3x+2} &= 2^{4x} \\ 3x+2 &= 4x \\ 2 &= x \end{aligned}$$

6.
$$\begin{aligned} 32^{x+2} &= 2^{7x+12} \\ \left(2^5\right)^{x+2} &= 2^{7x+12} \\ 2^{5x+10} &= 2^{7x+12} \\ 5x+10 &= 7x+12 \\ -2 &= 2x \\ -1 &= x \end{aligned}$$

7.
$$\begin{aligned} 27^{x+1} &= 3^{2x+1} \\ \left(3^3\right)^{x+1} &= 3^{2x+1} \\ 3^{3x+3} &= 3^{2x+1} \\ 3x+3 &= 2x+1 \\ x &= -2 \end{aligned}$$

8.
$$\begin{aligned} 3^{x-1} &= 9^{2x} \\ 3^{x-1} &= \left(3^2\right)^{2x} \\ 3^{x-1} &= 3^{4x} \\ x-1 &= 4x \\ -1 &= 3x \\ -\tfrac{1}{3} &= x \end{aligned}$$

9.
$$\begin{aligned} 5^{4x+1} &= 25^{-x-2} \\ 5^{4x+1} &= \left(5^2\right)^{-x-2} \\ 5^{4x+1} &= 5^{-2x-4} \\ 4x+1 &= -2x-4 \\ 6x &= -5 \\ x &= -\frac{5}{6} \end{aligned}$$

10.
$$\begin{aligned} 5^{2x+1} &= 125^x \\ 5^{2x+1} &= \left(5^3\right)^x \\ 5^{2x+1} &= 5^{3x} \\ 2x+1 &= 3x \\ 1 &= x \end{aligned}$$

11.
$$\begin{aligned} 4^{x-2} &= 8^x \\ \left(2^2\right)^{x-2} &= \left(2^3\right)^x \\ 2^{2x-4} &= 2^{3x} \\ 2x-4 &= 3x \\ -4 &= x \end{aligned}$$

12.
$$\begin{aligned} 16^{x+1} &= 8^{2x+1} \\ \left(2^4\right)^{x+1} &= \left(2^3\right)^{2x+1} \\ 2^{4x+4} &= 2^{6x+3} \\ 4x+4 &= 6x+3 \\ 1 &= 2x \\ \frac{1}{2} &= x \end{aligned}$$

13.
$$\begin{aligned} 81^{2x} &= 27^{2x-5} \\ \left(3^4\right)^{2x} &= \left(3^3\right)^{2x-5} \\ 3^{8x} &= 3^{6x-15} \\ 8x &= 6x-15 \\ 2x &= -15 \\ x &= -\frac{15}{2} \end{aligned}$$

14.
$$\begin{aligned} 625^{x-9} &= 125^{x-12} \\ \left(5^4\right)^{x-9} &= \left(5^3\right)^{x-12} \\ 5^{4x-36} &= 5^{3x-36} \\ 4x-36 &= 3x-36 \\ x &= 0 \end{aligned}$$

15.
$$\begin{aligned} 2^{x^2-2x} &= 8 \\ 2^{x^2-2x} &= 2^3 \\ x^2-2x &= 3 \\ x^2-2x-3 &= 0 \\ (x-3)(x+1) &= 0 \end{aligned}$$
$x-3=0$ **or** $x+1=0$
$x=3$ $\quad$ $x=-1$

16.
$$\begin{aligned} 5^{x^2-3x} &= 625 \\ 5^{x^2-3x} &= 5^4 \\ x^2-3x &= 4 \\ x^2-3x-4 &= 0 \\ (x-4)(x+1) &= 0 \end{aligned}$$
$x-4=0$ **or** $x+1=0$
$x=4$ $\quad$ $x=-1$

17.
$$\begin{aligned} 36^{x^2} &= 216^{x^2-3} \\ \left(6^2\right)^{x^2} &= \left(6^3\right)^{x^2-3} \\ 6^{2x^2} &= 6^{3x^2-9} \\ 2x^2 &= 3x^2 - 9 \\ 9 &= x^2 \\ \pm 3 &= x \end{aligned}$$

18.
$$\begin{aligned} 25^{x^2-5x} &= 3125^{4x} \\ \left(5^2\right)^{x^2-5x} &= \left(5^5\right)^{4x} \\ 5^{2x^2-10x} &= 5^{20x} \\ 2x^2 - 10x &= 20x \\ 2x^2 - 30x &= 0 \\ 2x(x-15) &= 0 \\ x = 0 &\text{ or } x = 15 \end{aligned}$$

19.
$$\begin{aligned} 7^{x^2+3x} &= \frac{1}{49} \\ 7^{x^2+3x} &= 7^{-2} \\ x^2 + 3x &= -2 \\ x^2 + 3x + 2 &= 0 \\ (x+2)(x+1) &= 0 \\ x + 2 = 0 \quad &\textbf{or} \quad x + 1 = 0 \\ x = -2 \quad & \quad x = -1 \end{aligned}$$

20.
$$\begin{aligned} 3^{x^2+4x} &= \frac{1}{81} \\ 3^{x^2+4x} &= 3^{-4} \\ x^2 + 4x &= -4 \\ x^2 + 4x + 4 &= 0 \\ (x+2)(x+2) &= 0 \\ x + 2 = 0 \quad &\text{or} \quad x + 2 = 0 \\ x = -2 \quad & \quad x = -2 \end{aligned}$$

21.
$$\begin{aligned} e^{-x+6} &= e^x \\ -x + 6 &= x \\ 6 &= 2x \\ 3 &= x \end{aligned}$$

22.
$$\begin{aligned} e^{2x+1} &= e^{3x-11} \\ 2x + 1 &= 3x - 11 \\ 12 &= x \end{aligned}$$

23.
$$\begin{aligned} e^{x^2-1} &= e^{24} \\ x^2 - 1 &= 24 \\ x^2 - 25 &= 0 \\ (x-5)(x+5) &= 0 \\ x - 5 = 0 \quad &\textbf{or} \quad x + 5 = 0 \\ x = -5 \quad & \quad x = 5 \end{aligned}$$

24.
$$\begin{aligned} e^{x^2+7x} &= \frac{1}{e^{12}} \\ e^{x^2+7x} &= e^{-12} \\ x^2 + 7x &= -12 \\ x^2 + 7x + 12 &= 0 \\ (x+3)(x+4) &= 0 \\ x + 3 = 0 \quad &\textbf{or} \quad x + 4 = 0 \\ x = -3 \quad & \quad x = -4 \end{aligned}$$

25.
$$\begin{aligned} 4^x &= 5 \\ \log 4^x &= \log 5 \\ x \log 4 &= \log 5 \\ x &= \frac{\log 5}{\log 4} \\ x &\approx 1.1610 \end{aligned}$$

26.
$$\begin{aligned} 7^x &= 12 \\ \log 7^x &= \log 12 \\ x \log 7 &= \log 12 \\ x &= \frac{\log 12}{\log 7} \\ x &\approx 1.2770 \end{aligned}$$

27.

$$\begin{aligned} 13^{x-1} &= 2 \\ \log 13^{x-1} &= \log 2 \\ (x-1)\log 13 &= \log 2 \\ x\log 13 - \log 13 &= \log 2 \\ x\log 13 &= \log 2 + \log 13 \\ x &= \frac{\log 2 + \log 13}{\log 13} \\ x &\approx 1.2702 \end{aligned}$$

28.

$$\begin{aligned} 5^{x+1} &= 3 \\ \log 5^{x+1} &= \log 3 \\ (x+1)\log 5 &= \log 3 \\ x\log 5 + \log 5 &= \log 3 \\ x\log 5 &= \log 3 - \log 5 \\ x &= \frac{\log 3 - \log 5}{\log 5} \\ x &\approx -0.3174 \end{aligned}$$

29.

$$\begin{aligned} 2^{x+1} &= 3^x \\ \log 2^{x+1} &= \log 3^x \\ (x+1)\log 2 &= x\log 3 \\ x\log 2 + \log 2 &= x\log 3 \\ x\log 2 - x\log 3 &= -\log 2 \\ x(\log 2 - \log 3) &= -\log 2 \\ x &= \frac{-\log 2}{\log 2 - \log 3} \\ x &\approx 1.7095 \end{aligned}$$

30.

$$\begin{aligned} 5^{x-3} &= 3^{2x} \\ \log 5^{x-3} &= \log 3^{2x} \\ (x-3)\log 5 &= 2x\log 3 \\ x\log 5 - 3\log 5 &= 2x\log 3 \\ x\log 5 - 2x\log 3 &= 3\log 5 \\ x(\log 5 - 2\log 3) &= 3\log 5 \\ x &= \frac{3\log 5}{\log 5 - 2\log 3} \\ x &\approx -8.2144 \end{aligned}$$

31.

$$\begin{aligned} 2^x &= 3^x \\ \log 2^x &= \log 3^x \\ x\log 2 &= x\log 3 \\ x\log 2 - x\log 3 &= 0 \\ x(\log 2 - \log 3) &= 0 \\ x &= \frac{0}{\log 2 - \log 3} = 0 \end{aligned}$$

32.

$$\begin{aligned} 3^{2x} &= 4^x \\ \log 3^{2x} &= \log 4^x \\ 2x\log 3 &= x\log 4 \\ 2x\log 3 - x\log 4 &= 0 \\ x(2\log 3 - \log 4) &= 0 \\ x &= \frac{0}{2\log 3 - \log 4} = 0 \end{aligned}$$

33.

$$\begin{aligned} 7^{x^2} &= 10 \\ \log 7^{x^2} &= \log 10 \\ x^2\log 7 &= \log 10 \\ x^2 &= \frac{\log 10}{\log 7} \\ x &= \pm\sqrt{\frac{\log 10}{\log 7}} \\ x &\approx \pm 1.0878 \end{aligned}$$

34.

$$\begin{aligned} 8^{x^2} &= 11 \\ \log 8^{x^2} &= \log 11 \\ x^2\log 8 &= \log 11 \\ x^2 &= \frac{\log 11}{\log 8} \\ x &= \pm\sqrt{\frac{\log 11}{\log 8}} \\ x &\approx \pm 1.0738 \end{aligned}$$

35.
$$\begin{aligned}
8^{x^2} &= 9^x\\
\log 8^{x^2} &= \log 9^x\\
x^2\log 8 &= x\log 9\\
x^2\log 8 - x\log 9 &= 0\\
x(x\log 8 - \log 9) &= 0\\
x = 0 \quad \textbf{or} \quad x\log 8 - \log 9 &= 0\\
x = 0 \qquad\qquad x\log 8 &= \log 9\\
x = 0 \qquad\qquad x &= \frac{\log 9}{\log 8}\\
x = 0 \qquad\qquad x &\approx 1.0566
\end{aligned}$$

36.
$$\begin{aligned}
5^{x^2} &= 2^{5x}\\
\log 5^{x^2} &= \log 2^{5x}\\
x^2\log 5 &= 5x\log 2\\
x^2\log 5 - 5x\log 2 &= 0\\
x(x\log 5 - 5\log 2) &= 0\\
x = 0 \quad \textbf{or} \quad x\log 5 - 5\log 2 &= 0\\
x = 0 \qquad\qquad x\log 5 &= 5\log 2\\
x = 0 \qquad\qquad x &= \frac{5\log 2}{\log 5}\\
x = 0 \qquad\qquad x &\approx 2.1534
\end{aligned}$$

37.
$$\begin{aligned}
e^x &= 10\\
\ln e^x &= \ln 10\\
x\ln e &= \ln 10\\
x &= \ln 10
\end{aligned}$$

38.
$$\begin{aligned}
8e^x &= 16\\
e^x &= 2\\
\ln e^x &= \ln 2\\
x\ln e &= \ln 2\\
x &= \ln 2
\end{aligned}$$

39.
$$\begin{aligned}
4e^{2x} &= 24\\
e^{2x} &= 6\\
\ln e^{2x} &= \ln 6\\
2x\ln e &= \ln 6\\
2x &= \ln 6\\
x &= \frac{\ln 6}{2}
\end{aligned}$$

40.
$$\begin{aligned}
2e^{5x} &= 18\\
e^{5x} &= 9\\
\ln e^{5x} &= \ln 9\\
5x\ln e &= \ln 9\\
5x &= \ln 9\\
x &= \frac{\ln 9}{5}
\end{aligned}$$

41.
$$\begin{aligned}
4^{x+2} - 4^x &= 15\\
4^x4^2 - 4^x &= 15\\
16\cdot 4^x - 4^x &= 15\\
15\cdot 4^x &= 15\\
4^x &= 1\\
x &= 0
\end{aligned}$$

42.
$$\begin{aligned}
3^{x+3} + 3^x &= 84\\
3^x3^3 + 3^x &= 84\\
27\cdot 3^x + 3^x &= 84\\
28\cdot 3^x &= 84\\
3^x &= 3\\
x &= 1
\end{aligned}$$

43.
$$\begin{aligned}
2(3^x) &= 6^{2x}\\
\log\,[2(3^x)] &= \log 6^{2x}\\
\log 2 + \log 3^x &= 2x\log 6\\
\log 2 + x\log 3 &= 2x\log 6\\
x\log 3 - 2x\log 6 &= -\log 2\\
x(\log 3 - 2\log 6) &= -\log 2\\
x &= \frac{-\log 2}{\log 3 - 2\log 6}\\
x &\approx 0.2789
\end{aligned}$$

44.
$$\begin{aligned} 2(3^{x+1}) &= 3(2^{x-1}) \\ \log\left[2(3^{x+1})\right] &= \log\left[3(2^{x-1})\right] \\ \log 2 + \log 3^{x+1} &= \log 3 + \log 2^{x-1} \\ \log 2 + (x+1)\log 3 &= \log 3 + (x-1)\log 2 \\ \log 2 + x\log 3 + \log 3 &= \log 3 + x\log 2 - \log 2 \\ x\log 3 - x\log 2 &= -2\log 2 \\ x(\log 3 - \log 2) &= -2\log 2 \\ x &= \frac{-2\log 2}{\log 3 - \log 2} \\ x &\approx -3.4190 \end{aligned}$$

45.
$$\begin{aligned} 2^{2x} - 10(2^x) + 16 &= 0 \\ y^2 - 10y + 16 &= 0 \\ (y-2)(y-8) &= 0 \\ y - 2 = 0 \quad &\textbf{or} \quad y - 8 = 0 \\ y = 2 \quad &\quad y = 8 \\ 2^x = 2 \quad &\quad 2^x = 8 \\ x = 1 \quad &\quad x = 3 \end{aligned}$$

46.
$$\begin{aligned} 3^{2x} - 10(3^x) + 9 &= 0 \\ y^2 - 10y + 9 &= 0 \\ (y-1)(y-9) &= 0 \\ y - 1 = 0 \quad &\textbf{or} \quad y - 9 = 0 \\ y = 1 \quad &\quad y = 9 \\ 3^x = 1 \quad &\quad 3^x = 9 \\ x = 0 \quad &\quad x = 2 \end{aligned}$$

47.
$$\begin{aligned} 2^{2x+1} - 2^x &= 1 \\ 2^{2x}2^1 - 2^x - 1 &= 0 \\ 2(2^{2x}) - 2^x - 1 &= 0 \\ (2(2^x) + 1)(2^x - 1) &= 0 \\ 2(2^x) + 1 = 0 \quad &\textbf{or} \quad 2^x - 1 = 0 \\ 2(2^x) = -1 \quad &\quad 2^x = 1 \\ 2^x = -\tfrac{1}{2} \quad &\quad x = 0 \\ \text{impossible} \quad & \end{aligned}$$

48.
$$\begin{aligned} 3^{2x+1} - 10(3^x) + 3 &= 0 \\ 3^{2x}3^1 - 10(3^x) + 3 &= 0 \\ 3(3^{2x}) - 10(3^x) + 3 &= 0 \\ (3(3^x) - 1)(3^x - 3) &= 0 \\ 3(3^x) - 1 = 0 \quad &\textbf{or} \quad 3^x - 3 = 0 \\ 3(3^x) = 1 \quad &\quad 3^x = 3 \\ 3^x = \tfrac{1}{3} \quad &\quad x = 1 \\ x = -1 \quad & \end{aligned}$$

49.
$$\begin{aligned} \log x^2 &= 2 \\ x^2 &= 10^2 \\ x^2 &= 100 \\ x &= \pm\sqrt{100} = \pm 10 \end{aligned}$$

50.
$$\begin{aligned} \log x^3 &= 3 \\ x^3 &= 10^3 \\ x^3 &= 1000 \\ x &= \sqrt[3]{1000} = 10 \end{aligned}$$

51.
$$\begin{aligned} \log\frac{4x+1}{2x+9} &= 0 \\ 10^0 &= \frac{4x+1}{2x+9} \\ 1 &= \frac{4x+1}{2x+9} \\ 2x + 9 &= 4x + 1 \\ 8 &= 2x \\ 4 &= x \end{aligned}$$

52.
$$\begin{aligned} \log\frac{5x+2}{2(x+7)} &= 0 \\ 10^0 &= \frac{5x+2}{2(x+7)} \\ 1 &= \frac{5x+2}{2x+14} \\ 2x + 14 &= 5x + 2 \\ -3x &= -12 \\ x &= 4 \end{aligned}$$

53. $\ln x = 6$
$e^6 = x$

54. $\ln x = 3$
$e^3 = x$

55. $\ln(2x-7) = 4$
$$e^4 = 2x - 7$$
$$e^4 + 7 = 2x$$
$$\frac{e^4+7}{2} = x, \text{ or } x = \frac{1}{2}(e^4+7)$$

56. $\ln(3x-5) = 7$
$$e^7 = 3x - 5$$
$$e^7 + 5 = 3x$$
$$\frac{e^7+5}{3} = x, \text{ or } x = \frac{1}{3}(e^7+5)$$

57. $\log(2x-3) = \log(x+4)$
$$2x - 3 = x + 4$$
$$x = 7$$

58. $\log(3x+5) - \log(2x+6) = 0$
$$\log(3x+5) = \log(2x+6)$$
$$3x+5 = 2x+6$$
$$x = 1$$

59.
$$\log x + \log(x-48) = 2$$
$$\log x(x-48) = 2$$
$$x(x-48) = 10^2$$
$$x^2 - 48x - 100 = 0$$
$$(x-50)(x+2) = 0$$
$x - 50 = 0$ **or** $x + 2 = 0$
$x = 50$ $\quad x = -2$: extraneous

60.
$$\log x + \log(x+9) = 1$$
$$\log x(x+9) = 1$$
$$x(x+9) = 10^1$$
$$x^2 + 9x - 10 = 0$$
$$(x-1)(x+10) = 0$$
$x - 1 = 0$ **or** $x + 10 = 0$
$x = 1$ $\quad x = -10$: extraneous

61.
$$\log x + \log(x-15) = 2$$
$$\log x(x-15) = 2$$
$$x(x-15) = 10^2$$
$$x^2 - 15x - 100 = 0$$
$$(x-20)(x+5) = 0$$
$x - 20 = 0$ **or** $x + 5 = 0$
$x = 20$ $\quad x = -5$: extraneous

62.
$$\log x + \log(x+21) = 2$$
$$\log x(x+21) = 2$$
$$x(x+21) = 10^2$$
$$x^2 + 21x - 100 = 0$$
$$(x-4)(x+25) = 0$$
$x - 4 = 0$ **or** $x + 25 = 0$
$x = 4$ $\quad x = -25$: extraneous

63.
$$\log(x+90) = 3 - \log x$$
$$\log x + \log(x+90) = 3$$
$$\log x(x+90) = 3$$
$$x(x+90) = 10^3$$
$$x^2 + 90x - 1000 = 0$$
$$(x-10)(x+100) = 0$$
$x - 10 = 0$ **or** $x + 100 = 0$
$x = 10$ $\quad x = -100$
extraneous

64. $\log(x-3) - \log 6 = 2$
$$\log\frac{x-3}{6} = 2$$
$$\frac{x-3}{6} = 10^2$$
$$x - 3 = 600$$
$$x = 603$$

65. $$\begin{aligned}\log 5000 - \log(x-2) &= 3\\ \log\frac{5000}{x-2} &= 3\\ \frac{5000}{x-2} &= 10^3\\ 5000 &= 1000(x-2)\\ 5000 &= 1000x - 2000\\ 7000 &= 1000x\\ 7 &= x\end{aligned}$$

66. $$\begin{aligned}\log(2x-3) - \log(x-1) &= 0\\ \log(2x-3) &= \log(x-1)\\ 2x-3 &= x-1\\ x &= 2\end{aligned}$$

67. $$\begin{aligned}\log_7 x + \log_7(x-5) &= \log_7 6\\ \log_7 x(x-5) &= \log_7 6\\ x(x-5) &= 6\\ x^2 - 5x - 6 &= 0\\ (x-6)(x+1) &= 0\end{aligned}$$

$x - 6 = 0$ **or** $x + 1 = 0$

$x = 6$ $\quad$ $x = -1$

extraneous

68. $$\begin{aligned}\ln x + \ln(x-2) &= \ln 120\\ \ln x(x-2) &= \ln 120\\ x(x-2) &= 120\\ x^2 - 2x - 120 &= 0\\ (x-12)(x+10) &= 0\end{aligned}$$

$x - 12 = 0$ **or** $x + 10 = 0$

$x = 12$ $\quad$ $x = -10$

extraneous

69. $$\begin{aligned}\ln 15 - \ln(x-2) &= \ln x\\ \ln\frac{15}{x-2} &= \ln x\\ \frac{15}{x-2} &= x\\ 15 &= x(x-2)\\ 0 &= x^2 - 2x - 15\\ 0 &= (x-5)(x+3)\end{aligned}$$

$x - 5 = 0$ **or** $x + 3 = 0$

$x = 5$ $\quad$ $x = -3$

extraneous

70. $$\begin{aligned}\ln 10 - \ln(x-3) &= \ln x\\ \ln\frac{10}{x-3} &= \ln x\\ \frac{10}{x-3} &= x\\ 10 &= x(x-3)\\ 0 &= x^2 - 3x - 10\\ 0 &= (x-5)(x+2)\end{aligned}$$

$x - 5 = 0$ **or** $x + 2 = 0$

$x = 5$ $\quad$ $x = -2$

extraneous

71. $$\begin{aligned}\log_6 8 - \log_6 x &= \log_6(x-2)\\ \log_6\frac{8}{x} &= \log_6(x-2)\\ \frac{8}{x} &= x-2\\ 8 &= x(x-2)\\ 0 &= x^2 - 2x - 8\\ 0 &= (x-4)(x+2)\end{aligned}$$

$x - 4 = 0$ **or** $x + 2 = 0$

$x = 4$ $\quad$ $x = -2$

extraneous

72. $$\begin{aligned}\log(x-6) - \log(x-2) &= \log\frac{5}{x}\\ \log\frac{x-6}{x-2} &= \log\frac{5}{x}\\ \frac{x-6}{x-2} &= \frac{5}{x}\\ x(x-6) &= 5(x-2)\\ x^2 - 6x &= 5x - 10\\ x^2 - 11x + 10 &= 0\\ (x-1)(x-10) &= 0\end{aligned}$$

$x - 1 = 0$ **or** $x - 10 = 0$

$x = 1$ $\quad$ $x = 10$

extraneous

73.
$$\begin{aligned} \log(x-1) - \log 6 &= \log(x-2) - \log x \\ \log \tfrac{x-1}{6} &= \log \tfrac{x-2}{x} \\ \tfrac{x-1}{6} &= \tfrac{x-2}{x} \\ x(x-1) &= 6(x-2) \\ x^2 - x &= 6x - 12 \\ x^2 - 7x + 12 &= 0 \\ (x-3)(x-4) &= 0 \end{aligned}$$
$$x - 3 = 0 \quad \textbf{or} \quad x - 4 = 0$$
$$x = 3 \qquad\qquad x = 4$$

74.
$$\begin{aligned} \log x^2 &= (\log x)^2 \\ 2\log x &= (\log x)^2 \\ 0 &= (\log x)^2 - 2\log x \\ 0 &= \log x\,(\log x - 2) \end{aligned}$$
$$\log x = 0 \quad \textbf{or} \quad \log x - 2 = 0$$
$$x = 1 \qquad\qquad \log x = 2$$
$$x = 1 \qquad\qquad x = 100$$

75.
$$\begin{aligned} \log(\log x) &= 1 \\ \log x &= 10^1 \\ \log x &= 10 \\ x &= 10^{10} \end{aligned}$$

76.
$$\begin{aligned} \log_3(\log_3 x) &= 1 \\ \log_3 x &= 3^1 \\ \log_3 x &= 3 \\ x &= 3^3 = 27 \end{aligned}$$

77.
$$\begin{aligned} \frac{\log(3x-4)}{\log x} &= 2 \\ \log(3x-4) &= 2\log x \\ \log(3x-4) &= \log x^2 \\ 3x - 4 &= x^2 \\ 0 &= x^2 - 3x + 4 \end{aligned}$$
No real solutions

78.
$$\begin{aligned} \frac{\ln(8x-7)}{\ln x} &= 2 \\ \ln(8x-7) &= 2\ln x \\ \ln(8x-7) &= \ln x^2 \\ 8x - 7 &= x^2 \\ 0 &= x^2 - 8x + 7 \\ 0 &= (x-7)(x-1) \end{aligned}$$
$$x - 7 = 0 \quad \textbf{or} \quad x - 1 = 0$$
$$x = 7 \qquad\qquad x = 1$$
extraneous

79.
$$\begin{aligned} \tfrac{\ln(5x+6)}{2} &= \ln x \\ \ln(5x+6) &= 2\ln x \\ \ln(5x+6) &= \ln x^2 \\ 5x + 6 &= x^2 \\ 0 &= x^2 - 5x - 6 \\ 0 &= (x-6)(x+1) \end{aligned}$$
$$x - 6 = 0 \quad \textbf{or} \quad x + 1 = 0$$
$$x = 6 \qquad\qquad x = -1$$
extraneous

80.
$$\begin{aligned} \tfrac{1}{2}\log(4x+5) &= \log x \\ \log(4x+5) &= 2\log x \\ \log(4x+5) &= \log x^2 \\ 4x + 5 &= x^2 \\ 0 &= x^2 - 4x - 5 \\ 0 &= (x-5)(x+1) \end{aligned}$$
$$x - 5 = 0 \quad \textbf{or} \quad x + 1 = 0$$
$$x = 5 \qquad\qquad x = -1$$
extraneous

81.
$$\begin{aligned}\log_3 x &= \log_3\left(\frac{1}{x}\right)+4\\ \log_3 x &= \log_3 x^{-1}+4\\ \log_3 x &= -\log_3 x+4\\ 2\log_3 x &= 4\\ \log_3 x &= 2\\ x &= 9\end{aligned}$$

82.
$$\begin{aligned}\log_5(7+x)+\log_5(8-x)-\log_5 2 &= 2\\ \log_5\tfrac{(7+x)(8-x)}{2} &= 2\\ \tfrac{(7+x)(8-x)}{2} &= 5^2\\ (7+x)(8-x) &= 50\\ -x^2+x+56 &= 50\\ x^2-x-6 &= 0\\ (x-3)(x+2) &= 0\end{aligned}$$
$x-3=0$ **or** $x+2=0$
$x=3$ $\quad x=-2$

83.
$$\begin{aligned}2\log_2 x &= 3+\log_2(x-2)\\ \log_2 x^2-\log_2(x-2) &= 3\\ \log_2\tfrac{x^2}{x-2} &= 3\\ \tfrac{x^2}{x-2} &= 2^3\\ x^2 &= 8(x-2)\\ x^2-8x+16 &= 0\\ (x-4)(x-4) &= 0\end{aligned}$$
$x-4=0$ **or** $x-4=0$
$x=4$ $\quad x=4$

84.
$$\begin{aligned}2\log_3 x-\log_3(x-4) &= 2+\log_3 2\\ \log_3 x^2-\log_3(x-4)-\log_3 2 &= 2\\ \log_3\tfrac{x^2}{2(x-4)} &= 2\\ \tfrac{x^2}{2x-8} &= 3^2\\ x^2 &= 9(2x-8)\\ x^2-18x+72 &= 0\\ (x-12)(x-6) &= 0\end{aligned}$$
$x-12=0$ **or** $x-6=0$
$x=12$ $\quad x=6$

85.
$$\begin{aligned}\ln(7y+1) &= 2\ln(y+3)-\ln 2\\ \ln(7y+1) &= \ln\tfrac{(y+3)^2}{2}\\ 7y+1 &= \tfrac{y^2+6y+9}{2}\\ 14y+2 &= y^2+6y+9\\ 0 &= y^2-8y+7\\ 0 &= (y-7)(y-1)\end{aligned}$$
$y-7=0$ **or** $y-1=0$
$y=7$ $\quad y=1$

86.
$$\begin{aligned}2\log(y+2) &= \log(y+2)-\log 12\\ \log(y+2)^2 &= \log\tfrac{(y+2)}{12}\\ y^2+4y+4 &= \tfrac{y+2}{12}\\ 12y^2+48y+48 &= y+2\\ 12y^2+47y+46 &= 0\\ (12y+23)(y+2) &= 0\end{aligned}$$
$12y+23=0$ **or** $y+2=0$
$12y=-23$ $\quad y=-2$
$y=-\frac{23}{12}$ $\quad$ extraneous

87. Graph $y = \log x + \log(x - 15)$ and $y = 2$ and find the x-coordinate of the point(s) of intersection: $x = 20$

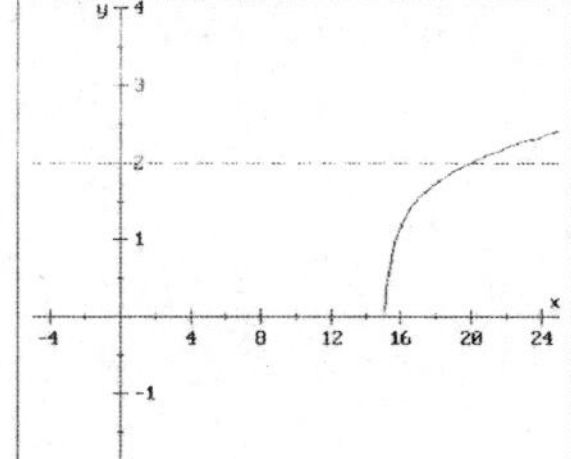

88. Graph $y = \log x + \log(x + 3)$ and $y = 1$ and find the x-coordinate of the point(s) of intersection: $x = 2$

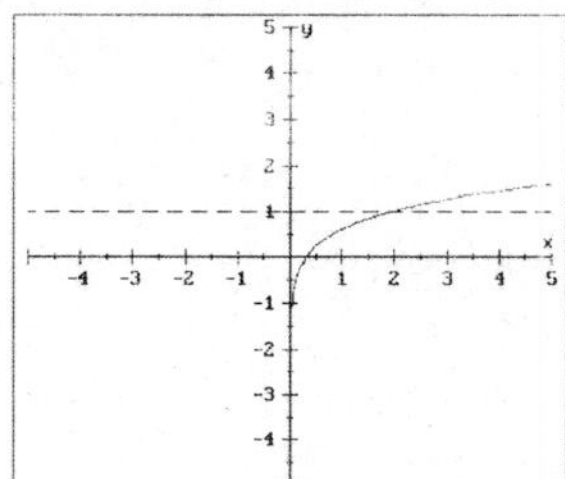

89. Graph $y = 2^{x+1}$ and $y = 7$ and find the x-coordinate of the point(s) of intersection: $x \approx 1.81$

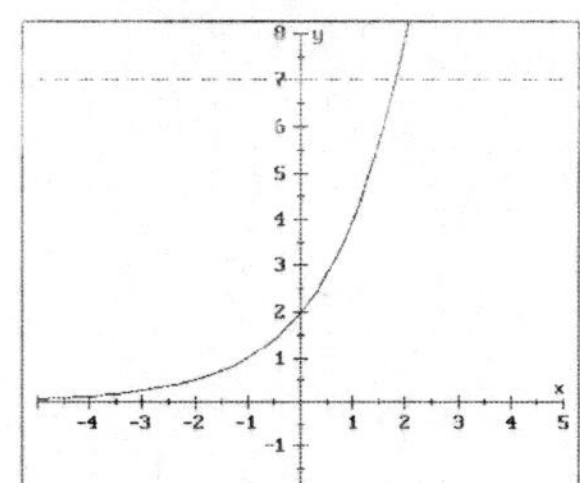

90. Graph $y = \ln(2x + 5) - \ln 3$ and $y = \ln(x - 1)$ and find the x-coordinate of the point(s) of intersection: $x = 8$

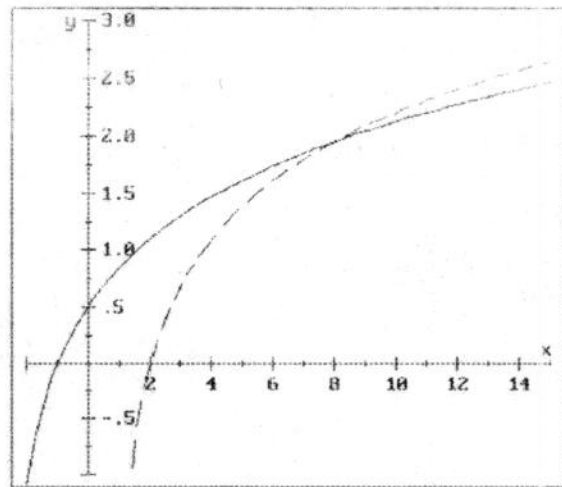

91.

$$
\begin{aligned}
A &= A_0 2^{-t/h} \\
0.75A_0 &= A_0 \cdot 2^{-t/(12.4)} \\
0.75 &= 2^{-t/12.4} \\
\log(0.75) &= \log\left(2^{-t/12.4}\right) \\
\log(0.75) &= -\frac{t}{12.4}\log 2 \\
-\frac{12.4\log(0.75)}{\log 2} &= t \\
5.1 \text{ years} &\approx t
\end{aligned}
$$

92.

$$
\begin{aligned}
A &= A_0 2^{-t/h} \\
0.80A_0 &= A_0 \cdot 2^{-2/h} \\
0.80 &= 2^{-2/h} \\
\log(0.80) &= \log\left(2^{-2/h}\right) \\
\log(0.80) &= -\frac{2}{h}\log 2 \\
h\log(0.80) &= -2\log 2 \\
h &= \frac{-2\log 2}{\log(0.80)} \\
h &\approx 6.2 \text{ years}
\end{aligned}
$$

93.
$$\begin{aligned} A &= A_0 2^{-t/h} \\ 0.20A_0 &= A_0 \cdot 2^{-t/(18.4)} \\ 0.20 &= 2^{-t/18.4} \\ \log(0.20) &= \log\left(2^{-t/18.4}\right) \\ \log(0.20) &= -\frac{t}{18.4}\log 2 \\ -\frac{18.4\log(0.20)}{\log 2} &= t \\ 42.7 \text{ days} &\approx t \end{aligned}$$

94.
$$\begin{aligned} A &= A_0 2^{-t/h} \\ 1.3A_0 &= A_0 \cdot 2^{-t/(8.4)} \\ 1.3 &= 2^{-t/8.4} \\ \log(1.3) &= \log\left(2^{-t/8.4}\right) \\ \log(1.3) &= -\frac{t}{8.4}\log 2 \\ -\frac{8.4\log(1.3)}{\log 2} &= t \\ -3.2 \text{ hours} &\approx t \Rightarrow \text{About 3.2 hours ago} \end{aligned}$$

95.
$$\begin{aligned} A &= A_0 2^{-t/h} \\ 0.70A_0 &= A_0 \cdot 2^{-t/5700} \\ 0.70 &= 2^{-t/5700} \\ \log(0.70) &= \log\left(2^{-t/5700}\right) \\ \log(0.70) &= -\frac{t}{5700}\log 2 \\ -\frac{5700\log(0.70)}{\log 2} &= t \\ 2900 \text{ years} &\approx t \end{aligned}$$

96.
$$\begin{aligned} A &= A_0 2^{-t/h} \\ 0.25A_0 &= A_0 \cdot 2^{-t/5700} \\ 0.25 &= 2^{-t/5700} \\ \log(0.25) &= \log\left(2^{-t/5700}\right) \\ \log(0.25) &= -\frac{t}{5700}\log 2 \\ -\frac{5700\log(0.25)}{\log 2} &= t \\ 11{,}000 \text{ years} &\approx t \end{aligned}$$

97.
$$\begin{aligned} A &= P\left(1+\frac{r}{k}\right)^{kt} \\ 800 &= 500\left(1+\frac{0.085}{2}\right)^{2t} \\ \frac{8}{5} &= (1.0425)^{2t} \\ \log\left(\frac{8}{5}\right) &= \log(1.0425)^{2t} \\ \log 8 - \log 5 &= 2t\log(1.0425) \\ \frac{\log 8 - \log 5}{2\log(1.0425)} &= t \\ 5.6 \text{ years} &\approx t \end{aligned}$$

98.
$$\begin{aligned} A &= Pe^{rt} \\ 800 &= 500e^{0.085t} \\ \frac{8}{5} &= e^{0.085t} \\ \ln\left(\frac{8}{5}\right) &= \ln e^{0.085t} \\ \ln 8 - \ln 5 &= 0.085t \\ \frac{\ln 8 - \ln 5}{0.085} &= t \\ 5.5 \text{ years} &\approx t \end{aligned}$$

99.

$$\begin{aligned} A &= P\left(1+\frac{r}{k}\right)^{kt} \\ 2100 &= 1300\left(1+\frac{0.09}{4}\right)^{4t} \\ \frac{21}{13} &= (1.0225)^{4t} \\ \log\left(\frac{21}{13}\right) &= \log(1.0225)^{4t} \\ \log 21 - \log 13 &= 4t\log(1.0225) \\ \frac{\log 21 - \log 13}{4\log(1.0225)} &= t \\ 5.4 \text{ years} &\approx t \end{aligned}$$

100.

$$\begin{aligned} A &= P\left(1+\frac{r}{k}\right)^{kt} \\ 7000 &= 5000\left(1+\frac{r}{1}\right)^{1(5)} \\ \frac{7}{5} &= (1+r)^5 \\ \sqrt[5]{\frac{7}{5}} &= \sqrt[5]{(1+r)^5} \\ \sqrt[5]{\frac{7}{5}} &= 1+r \\ \sqrt[5]{\frac{7}{5}} - 1 &= r \Rightarrow r \approx 0.696 = 6.96\% \end{aligned}$$

101.

$$\begin{aligned} A &= Pe^{rt} \\ 2P &= Pe^{rt} \\ 2 &= e^{rt} \\ \ln 2 &= \ln e^{rt} \\ \ln 2 &= rt \\ \frac{\ln 2}{r} &= t \\ \frac{0.70}{r} &\approx t \\ \frac{70}{(100\cdot r)\%} &\approx t \end{aligned}$$

102.

$$\begin{aligned} I &= I_0 e^{kx} \\ 0.70I_0 &= I_0 e^{k(6)} \\ 0.7 &= e^{6k} \\ \ln 0.7 &= \ln e^{6k} \\ \ln 0.7 &= 6k \\ \frac{\ln 0.7}{6} &= k \\ -0.05944 &\approx k \end{aligned}$$

$$\begin{aligned} I &= I_0 e^{kx} \\ 0.20I_0 &= I_0 e^{-0.05944x} \\ 0.2 &= e^{-0.05944x} \\ \ln 0.2 &= \ln e^{-0.05944x} \\ \ln 0.2 &= -0.05944x \\ \frac{\ln 0.2}{-0.05944} &= x \\ 27 \text{ meters} &\approx x \end{aligned}$$

103.

$$\begin{aligned} P &= P_0 a^t \\ 3P_0 &= P_0 a^5 \\ 3 &= a^5 \\ 3^{1/5} &= \left(a^5\right)^{1/5} \\ 3^{1/5} &= a \end{aligned}$$

$$\begin{aligned} P &= P_0 a^t \\ 2P_0 &= P_0\left(3^{1/5}\right)^t \\ 2 &= 3^{t/5} \\ \log 2 &= \log 3^{t/5} \\ \log 2 &= \frac{t}{5}\log 3 \\ \frac{5\log 2}{\log 3} &= t \\ 3.2 \text{ days} &\approx t \end{aligned}$$

104.

$$\begin{aligned} P &= P_0e^{kt} \\ 60{,}000 &= 30{,}000e^{k(5)} \\ 2 &= e^{5k} \\ \ln 2 &= \ln e^{5k} \\ \ln 2 &= 5k \\ \frac{\ln 2}{5} &= k \end{aligned}$$

$$\begin{aligned} P &= P_0e^{kt} \\ 1{,}000{,}000 &= 30{,}000e^{\frac{\ln 2}{5}t} \\ \frac{100}{3} &= e^{\frac{\ln 2}{5}t} \\ \ln\frac{100}{3} &= \ln e^{\frac{\ln 2}{5}t} \\ \ln 100 - \ln 3 &= \frac{\ln 2}{5}t \\ \frac{5(\ln 100 - \ln 3)}{\ln 2} &= t \Rightarrow t \approx 25.3 \text{ years} \end{aligned}$$

105.

$$\begin{aligned} T &= 70 + 110e^{-0.2t} \\ 80 &= 70 + 110e^{-0.2t} \\ 10 &= 110e^{-0.2t} \\ \tfrac{1}{11} &= e^{-0.2t} \\ \ln\left(\tfrac{1}{11}\right) &= \ln e^{-0.2t} \\ \ln\left(\tfrac{1}{11}\right) &= -0.2t \\ \tfrac{\ln\left(\frac{1}{11}\right)}{-0.2} &= t \\ 12 &\approx t \Rightarrow t \approx 12 \text{ minutes} \end{aligned}$$

106.

$$\begin{aligned} T(t) &= 17e^{-0.0626t} + 20 \\ 30 &= 17e^{-0.0626t} + 20 \\ 10 &= 17e^{-0.0626t} \\ \tfrac{10}{17} &= e^{-0.0626t} \\ \ln\left(\tfrac{10}{17}\right) &= \ln e^{-0.0626t} \\ \ln\left(\tfrac{10}{17}\right) &= -0.0626t \\ \tfrac{\ln\left(\frac{10}{17}\right)}{-0.0626} &= t \\ 8.5 &\approx t \Rightarrow \text{time of death: midnight} \end{aligned}$$

107.

$$\begin{aligned} T &= 60 + 40e^{kt} \\ 90 &= 60 + 40e^{k(3)} \\ 30 &= 40e^{3k} \\ 0.75 &= e^{3k} \\ \ln(0.75) &= \ln e^{3k} \\ \ln(0.75) &= 3k \\ \tfrac{\ln(0.75)}{3} &= k \end{aligned}$$

108. From #107, $k = \frac{\ln(0.75)}{3}$.

$$\begin{aligned} T &= 60 + 40e^{\frac{\ln 0.75}{3}t} \\ 70 &= 60 + 40e^{\frac{\ln 0.75}{3}t} \\ 10 &= 40e^{\frac{\ln 0.75}{3}t} \\ 0.25 &= e^{\frac{\ln 0.75}{3}t} \\ \ln 0.25 &= \ln e^{\frac{\ln 0.75}{3}t} \\ \ln 0.25 &= \frac{\ln 0.75}{3}t \\ \frac{3\ln 0.25}{\ln 0.75} &= t \Rightarrow t \approx 14.5 \text{ minutes} \end{aligned}$$

109.
$$\begin{aligned} T &= 300 - 300e^{kt} \\ 100 &= 300 - 300e^{k(5)} \\ -200 &= -300e^{5k} \\ \frac{2}{3} &= e^{5k} \\ \ln\left(\frac{2}{3}\right) &= \ln e^{5k} \\ \ln\left(\frac{2}{3}\right) &= 5k \\ \frac{\ln\left(\frac{2}{3}\right)}{5} &= k \end{aligned}$$

110. From **#109**, $k = \dfrac{\ln\left(\frac{2}{3}\right)}{5}$.
$$\begin{aligned} T &= 300 - 300e^{\frac{\ln(2/3)}{5}t} \\ 200 &= 300 - 300e^{\frac{\ln(2/3)}{5}t} \\ -100 &= -300e^{\frac{\ln(2/3)}{5}t} \\ \frac{1}{3} &= e^{\frac{\ln(2/3)}{5}t} \\ \ln(1/3) &= \ln e^{\frac{\ln(2/3)}{5}t} \\ \ln(1/3) &= \frac{\ln(2/3)}{5}t \\ \frac{5\ln(1/3)}{\ln(2/3)} &= t \Rightarrow t \approx 13.5 \text{ minutes} \end{aligned}$$

111. **Answers may vary.**

112.
$$\begin{aligned} P &= P_0e^{rt} \\ 2P_0 &= P_0e^{rt} \\ 2 &= e^{rt} \\ \ln 2 &= \ln e^{rt} \\ \ln 2 &= rt \\ \frac{\ln 2}{r} &= t \end{aligned}$$

113.
$$\begin{aligned} P &= P_0e^{rt} \\ 3P_0 &= P_0e^{rt} \\ 3 &= e^{rt} \\ \ln 3 &= \ln e^{rt} \\ \ln 3 &= rt \\ \frac{\ln 3}{r} &= t \end{aligned}$$

114. **Answers may vary.**

115.
$$\begin{aligned} \log_2(\log_5(\log_7 x)) &= 2 \\ \log_5(\log_7 x) &= 2^2 = 4 \\ \log_7 x &= 5^4 = 625 \\ x &= 7^{625} \end{aligned}$$

116.
$$\begin{aligned} \log_8\left(16\sqrt[3]{4096}\right)^{1/6} &= x \\ 8^x &= \left(16\sqrt[3]{4096}\right)^{1/6} \\ 8^x &= \left[2^4 \cdot \left(2^{12/3}\right)\right]^{1/6} \\ \left(2^3\right)^x &= 2^{4/3} \\ 3x &= \tfrac{4}{3} \Rightarrow x = \tfrac{4}{9} \end{aligned}$$

117.
$$\begin{aligned} y &= 3x + 2 \\ x &= 3y + 2 \\ x - 2 &= 3y \\ \frac{x-2}{3} &= f^{-1}(x) = y \end{aligned}$$

118.
$$\begin{aligned} y &= \frac{1}{x-3} \\ x &= \frac{1}{y-3} \\ x(y-3) &= 1 \\ xy - 3x &= 1 \\ xy &= 3x + 1 \\ y = f^{-1}(x) &= \frac{3x+1}{x} = \frac{1}{x} + 3 \end{aligned}$$

119. $(f \circ g)(2) = f(g(2)) = f(2^2) = f(4) = 5(4) - 1 = 19$

120. $(g \circ f)(2) = g(f(2)) = g(5(2) - 1) = g(9) = 9^2 = 81$

121. $(f \circ g)(x) = f(g(x)) = f(x^2) = 5x^2 - 1$

122. $(g \circ f)(x) = g(f(x)) = g(5x - 1) = (5x - 1)^2$

Chapter 4 Review (page 486)

1. $5^{\sqrt{2}}5^{\sqrt{2}} = 5^{\sqrt{2}+\sqrt{2}} = 5^{2\sqrt{2}}$

2. $\left(2^{\sqrt{5}}\right)^{\sqrt{2}} = 2^{\sqrt{5}\cdot\sqrt{2}} = 2^{\sqrt{10}}$

3. $f(x) = 3^x$: $(0, 1)$, $(1, 3)$

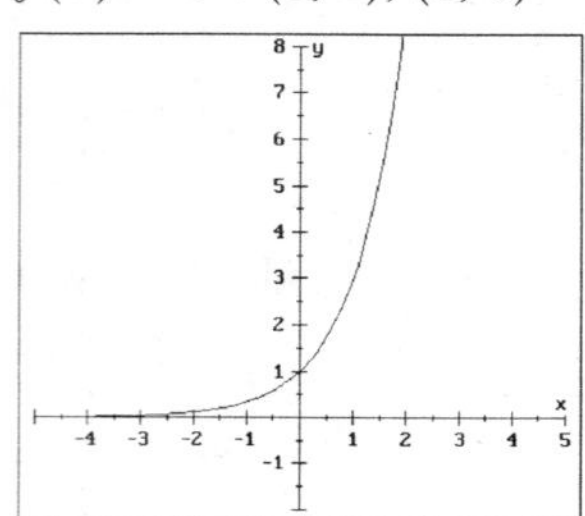

4. $f(x) = \left(\frac{1}{3}\right)^x$: $(0, 1)$, $\left(1, \frac{1}{3}\right)$

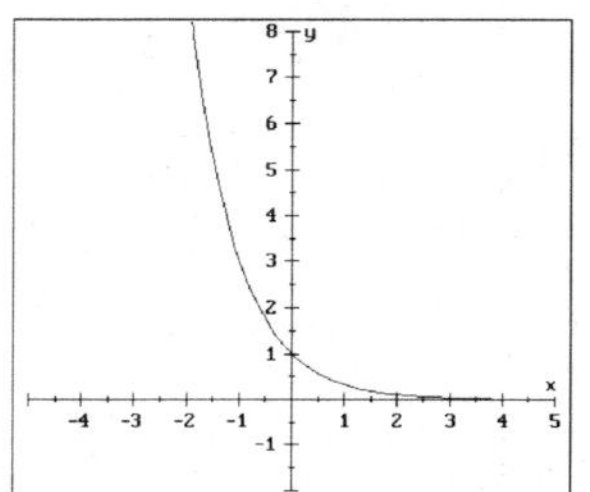

5. $f(x) = 7^x$: goes through $(0, 1)$ and $(1, 7)$
$p = 1, q = 7$

6. $y = b^x$: domain $= (-\infty, \infty)$; range $= (0, \infty)$

7. $f(x) = \left(\frac{1}{2}\right)^x - 2$

Shift $y = \left(\frac{1}{2}\right)^x$ down 2:

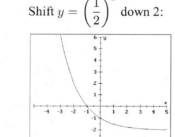

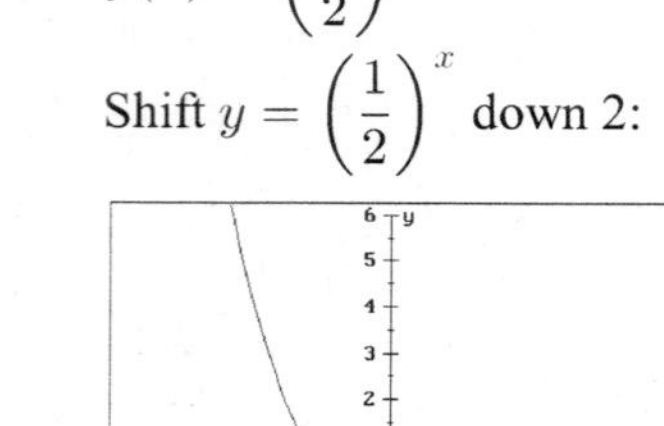

8. $f(x) = \left(\frac{1}{2}\right)^{x+2}$

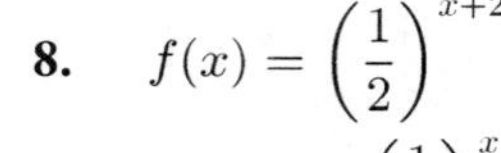

Shift $y = \left(\frac{1}{2}\right)^x$ left 2:

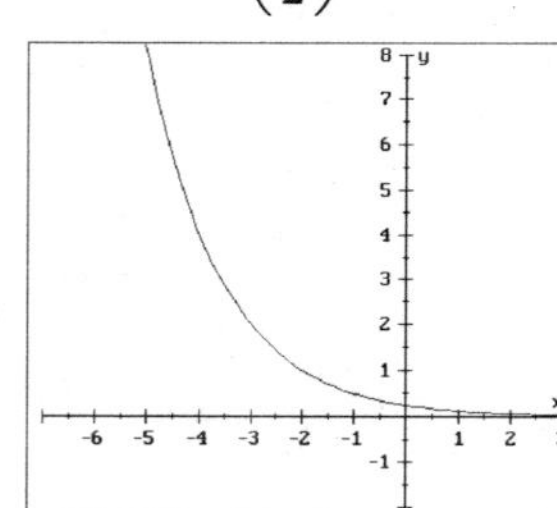

9. $f(x) = -5^x$
Reflect $y = 5^x$ about x-axis.

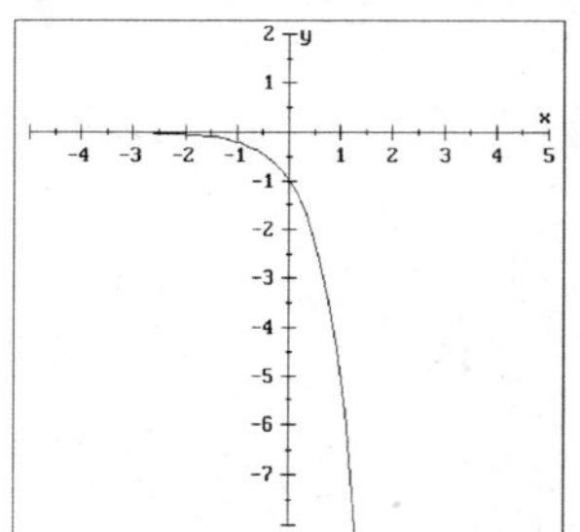

10. $f(x) = -5^x + 4$; Reflect $y = 5^x$ about x-axis. Shift U4.

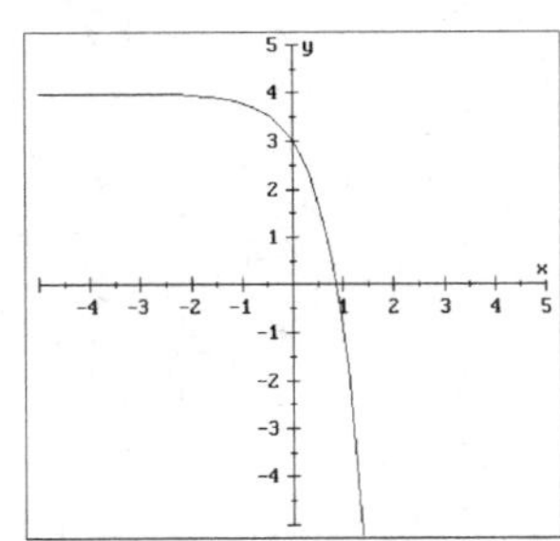

11. $f(x) = e^x + 1$
Shift $y = e^x$ up 1:

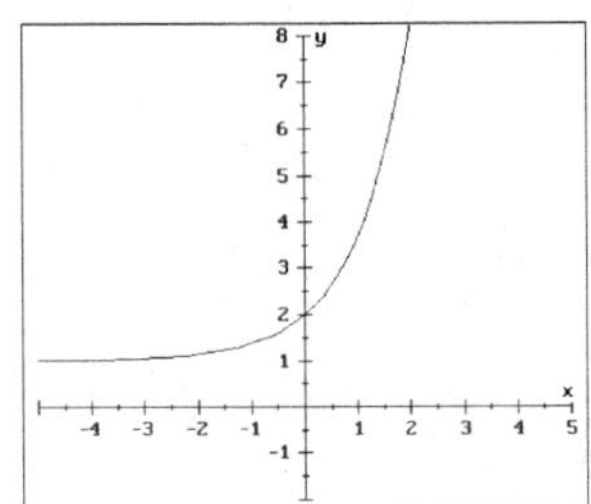

12. $f(x) = e^{x-3}$
Shift $y = e^x$ right 3:

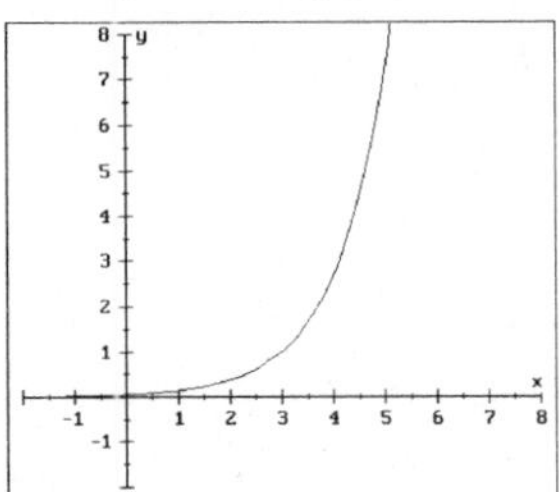

13. $$A = P\left(1 + \frac{r}{k}\right)^{kt} = 10{,}500\left(1 + \frac{0.09}{4}\right)^{4(60)} \approx \$2{,}189{,}703.45$$

14. $$A = Pe^{rt} = 10{,}500e^{0.09(60)} \approx 2{,}324{,}767.37$$

15. $$A = A_0 2^{-t/h} = A_0 \cdot 2^{-20/34.2} \approx 0.6667A_0$$
about $\frac{2}{3}$ of the original

16. $$I = I_0 k^x = 14(0.7)^{12} \approx 0.19 \text{ lumens}$$

17. $$P = P_0 e^{kt}$$
$$P = 300{,}000{,}000e^{0.015(50)}$$
$$P \approx 635{,}000{,}000 \text{ people}$$

18. $$P = \frac{450{,}000}{1 + (450 - 1)e^{-0.2t}} = \frac{450{,}000}{1 + (450 - 1)e^{-0.2(5)}} \approx 2708 \text{ people}$$

19. domain $= (0, \infty)$; range $= (-\infty, \infty)$

20. domain $= (0, \infty)$; range $= (-\infty, \infty)$

21. $\log_3 9 = ?$
$3^? = 9$
$\log_3 9 = 2$

22. $\log_9 \frac{1}{3} = ?$
$9^? = \frac{1}{3}$
$\log_9 \frac{1}{3} = -\frac{1}{2}$

23. $\log_x 1 = ?$
$x^? = 1$
$\log_x 1 = 0$

24. $\log_5 0.04 = ?$
$5^? = 0.04 = \frac{1}{25}$
$\log_5 0.04 = -2$

25. $\log_a \sqrt{a} = ?$
$a^? = \sqrt{a}$
$\log_a \sqrt{a} = \frac{1}{2}$

26. $\log_a \sqrt[3]{a} = ?$
$a^? = \sqrt[3]{a}$
$\log_a \sqrt[3]{a} = \frac{1}{3}$

27. $\log_2 x = 5$
$2^5 = x$
$32 = x$

28. $\log_{\sqrt{3}} x = 4$
$\left(\sqrt{3}\right)^4 = x$
$9 = x$

29. $\log_{\sqrt{2}} x = 6$
$\left(\sqrt{2}\right)^6 = x$
$8 = x$

30. $\log_{0.1} 10 = x$
$(0.1)^x = 10$
$\left(\frac{1}{10}\right)^x = 10$
$x = -1$

31. $\log_x 2 = -\frac{1}{3}$
$x^{-1/3} = 2$
$\left(x^{-1/3}\right)^{-3} = 2^{-3}$
$x = \frac{1}{8}$

32. $\log_x 32 = 5$
$x^5 = 32$
$x = 2$

33. $\log_{0.25} x = -1$
$(0.25)^{-1} = x$
$\left(\frac{1}{4}\right)^{-1} = x$
$4 = x$

34. $\log_{0.125} x = -\frac{1}{3}$
$(0.125)^{-1/3} = x$
$\left(\frac{1}{8}\right)^{-1/3} = x$
$2 = x$

35. $\log_{\sqrt{2}} 32 = x$
$\left(\sqrt{2}\right)^x = 32$
$\left(2^{1/2}\right)^x = 2^5$
$\frac{1}{2}x = 5$
$x = 10$

36. $\log_{\sqrt{5}} x = -4$
$\left(\sqrt{5}\right)^{-4} = x$
$\frac{1}{25} = x$

37. $\log_{\sqrt{3}} 9\sqrt{3} = x$
$\left(\sqrt{3}\right)^x = 9\sqrt{3}$
$\left(3^{1/2}\right)^x = 3^{5/2}$
$\frac{1}{2}x = \frac{5}{2}$
$x = 5$

38. $\log_{\sqrt{5}} 5\sqrt{5} = x$
$\left(\sqrt{5}\right)^x = 5\sqrt{5}$
$\left(5^{1/2}\right)^x = 5^{3/2}$
$\frac{1}{2}x = \frac{3}{2}$
$x = 3$

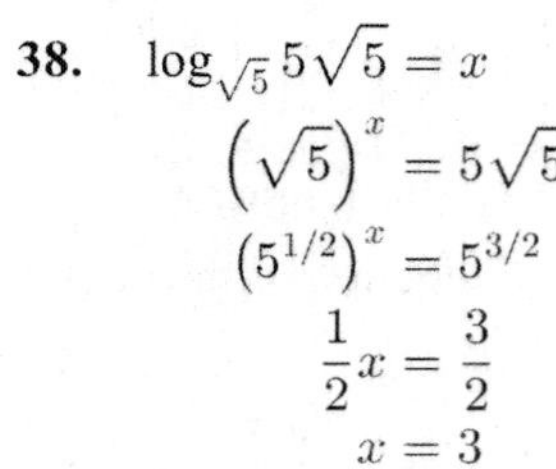

39. $f(x) = \log(x-2)$; Shift $y = \log x$ right 2:

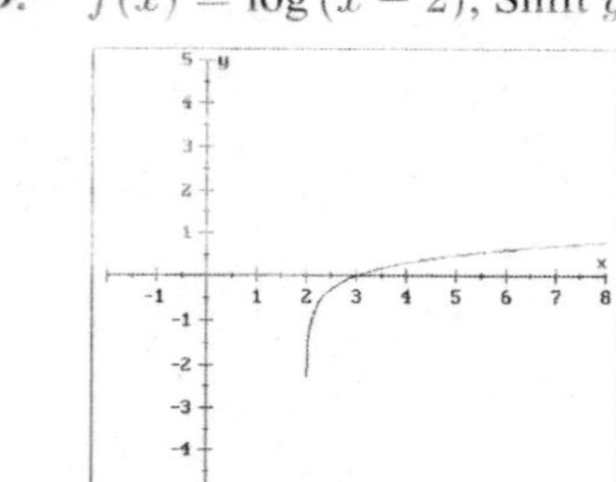

40. $f(x) = 3 + \log x$; Shift $y = \log x$ up 3:

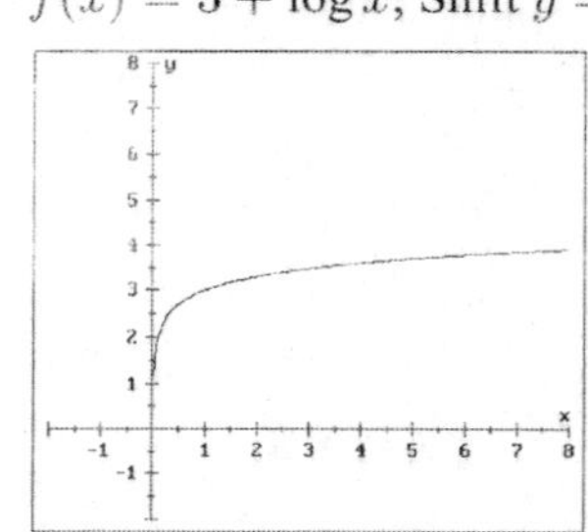

41. $y = 4^x; y = \log_4 x$

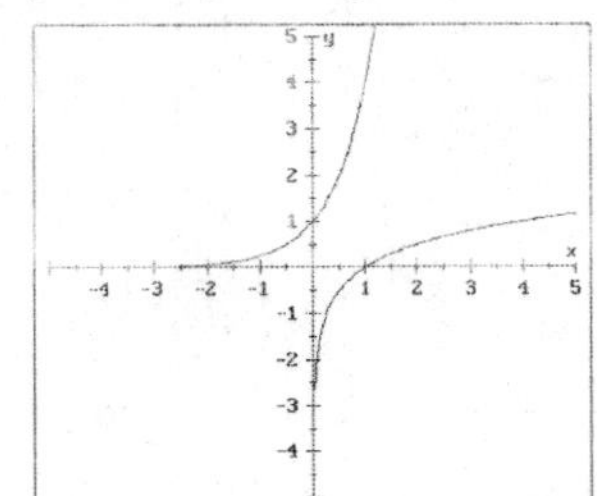

42. $y = \left(\frac{1}{3}\right)^x; y = \log_{1/3} x$

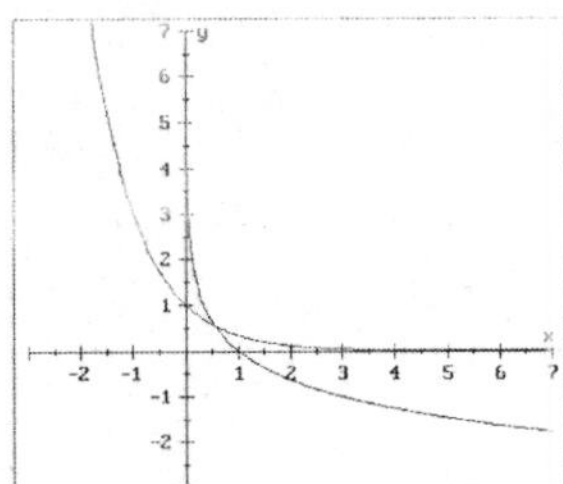

43. $\ln 452 \approx 6.1137$

44. $\ln(\log 7.85) \approx -0.1111$

45. $\ln x = 2.336$
$x \approx 10.3398$

46. $\ln x = \log 8.8$
$x \approx 2.5715$

47. $y = f(x) = 1 + \ln x$
Shift $y = \ln x$ up 1:

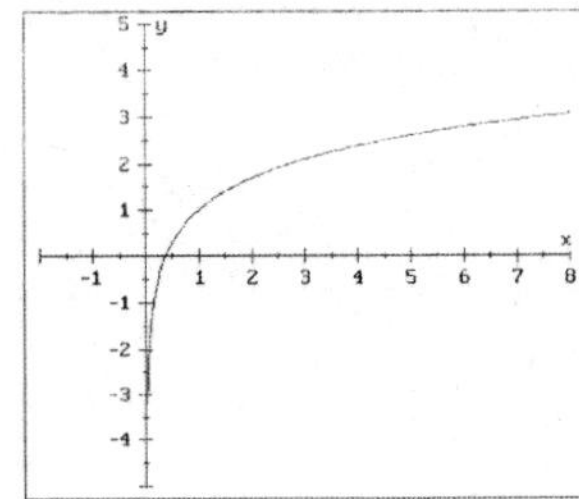

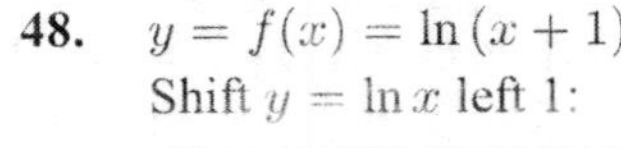

48. $y = f(x) = \ln(x+1)$
Shift $y = \ln x$ left 1:

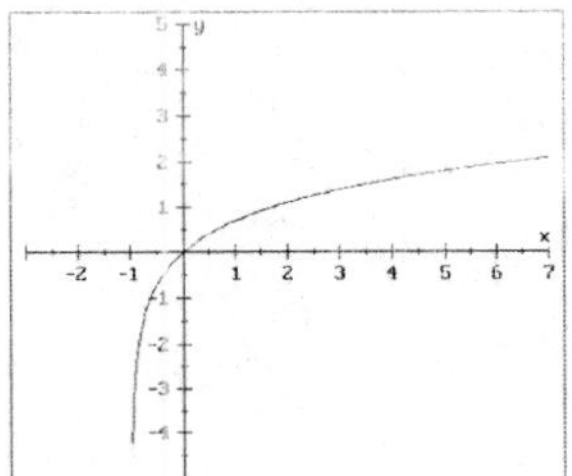

49. $\ln(e^{12}) = 12 \ln e = 12$

50. $e^{\ln 14x} = 14x$

51.
$$\begin{aligned} \text{db gain} &= 20 \log \frac{E_0}{E_I} \\ &= 20 \log \frac{18}{0.04} \\ &\approx 53 \text{ db gain} \end{aligned}$$

52.
$$\begin{aligned} R &= \log \frac{A}{P} \\ &= \log \frac{7500}{0.3} \\ &\approx 4.4 \end{aligned}$$

53.
$$t = -\frac{1}{k} \ln\left(1 - \frac{C}{M}\right)$$
$$t = -\frac{1}{0.17} \ln\left(1 - \frac{0.8M}{M}\right)$$
$$t = -\frac{1}{0.17} \ln(1 - 0.8) \approx 9.5 \text{ minutes}$$

54. $t = \dfrac{\ln 2}{r} = \dfrac{\ln 2}{0.03} \approx 23$ years

55. $E = RT \ln\left(\frac{V_f}{V_i}\right) = (8.314)(350) \ln\left(\frac{2V_i}{V_i}\right) = (8.314)(350) \ln(2) \approx 2017$ joules

56. $\log_7 1 = 0$

57. $\log_7 7 = 1$

58. $\log_7 7^3 = 3$

59. $7^{\log_7 4} = 4$

60. $\ln e^4 = 4 \ln e = 4$

61. $\ln 1 = 0$

62. $10^{\log_{10} 7} = 7$

63. $e^{\ln 3} = e^{\log_e 3} = 3$

64. $\log_b b^4 = 4\log_b b = 4$

65. $\ln e^9 = 9\ln e = 9$

66. $$\log_b \frac{x^2y^3}{z^4} = \log_b\left(x^2y^3\right) - \log_b\left(z^4\right) = \log_b x^2 + \log_b y^3 - \log_b z^4 = 2\log_b x + 3\log_b y - 4\log_b z$$

67. $$\log_b\sqrt{\frac{x}{yz^2}} = \log_b\left(\frac{x}{yz^2}\right)^{1/2} = \frac{1}{2}\log_b\left(\frac{x}{yz^2}\right) = \frac{1}{2}\left(\log_b x - \log_b yz^2\right) = \frac{1}{2}(\log_b x - \log_b y - 2\log_b z)$$

68. $$\ln\frac{x^4}{y^5z^6} = \ln x^4 - \ln y^5z^6 = \ln x^4 - \left(\ln y^5 + \ln z^6\right) = 4\ln x - (5\ln y + 6\ln z) = 4\ln x - 5\ln y - 6\ln z$$

69. $$\ln\sqrt[3]{xyz} = \ln(xyz)^{1/3} = \frac{1}{3}\ln xyz = \frac{1}{3}(\ln x + \ln y + \ln z)$$

70. $$3\log_b x - 5\log_b y + 7\log_b z = \log_b x^3 + \log_b y^{-5} + \log_b z^7 = \log_b\frac{x^3z^7}{y^5}$$

71. $$\frac{1}{2}(\log_b x + 3\log_b y) - 7\log_b z = \frac{1}{2}\left(\log_b x + \log_b y^3\right) + \log_b z^{-7} = \frac{1}{2}\log_b xy^3 + \log_b z^{-7} = \log_b\sqrt{xy^3} + \log_b z^{-7} = \log_b\frac{\sqrt{xy^3}}{z^7}$$

72. $$4\ln x - 5\ln y - 6\ln z = \ln x^4 + \ln y^{-5} + \ln z^{-6} = \ln\frac{x^4}{y^5z^6}$$

73. $$\frac{1}{2}\ln x + 3\ln y - \frac{1}{3}\ln z = \ln x^{1/2} + \ln y^3 + \ln z^{-1/3} = \ln\frac{y^3\sqrt{x}}{\sqrt[3]{z}}$$

74. $\log abc = \log a + \log b + \log c = 0.6 + 0.36 + 2.4 = 3.36$

75. $\log a^2b = \log a^2 + \log b = 2\log a + \log b = 2(0.6) + 0.36 = 1.56$

76. $\log\frac{ac}{b} = \log a + \log c - \log b = 0.6 + 2.4 - 0.36 = 2.64$

77. $$\log\frac{a^2}{c^3b^2} = \log a^2 - \log c^3b^2 = \log a^2 - \log c^3 - \log b^2 = 2\log a - 3\log c - 2\log b = 2(0.6) - 3(2.4) - 2(0.36) = -6.72$$

78. $\log_5 17 = \dfrac{\log 17}{\log 5} \approx 1.7604$

79.
$$\begin{aligned} \text{pH} &= -\log\,[\text{H}^+] \\ 3.1 &= -\log\,[\text{H}^+] \\ -3.1 &= \log\,[\text{H}^+] \\ 7.94 \times 10^{-4} &\approx [\text{H}^+] \end{aligned}$$

80. $L = k \ln I$

$k \ln \dfrac{I}{2} = k\,(\ln I - \ln 2) = k \ln I - k \ln 2 \Rightarrow$ The loudness decreases by $k \ln 2$.

81.
$$\begin{aligned} 81^{x+2} &= 27 \\ \left(3^4\right)^{x+2} &= 3^3 \\ 3^{4x+8} &= 3^3 \\ 4x + 8 &= 3 \\ 4x &= -5 \\ x &= -\frac{5}{4} \end{aligned}$$

82.
$$\begin{aligned} 2^{x^2+4x} &= \frac{1}{8} \\ 2^{x^2+4x} &= 2^{-3} \\ x^2 + 4x &= -3 \\ x^2 + 4x + 3 &= 0 \\ (x+1)(x+3) &= 0 \end{aligned}$$
$$x + 1 = 0 \quad \textbf{or} \quad x + 3 = 0$$
$$x = -1 \qquad\qquad x = -3$$

83.
$$\begin{aligned} e^x &= e^{-6x+14} \\ x &= -6x + 14 \\ 7x &= 14 \\ x &= 2 \end{aligned}$$

84.
$$\begin{aligned} e^{2x^2} &= e^{18} \\ 2x^2 &= 18 \\ x^2 &= 9 \\ x &= \pm 3 \end{aligned}$$

85.
$$\begin{aligned} 3^x &= 7 \\ \log 3^x &= \log 7 \\ x \log 3 &= \log 7 \\ x &= \frac{\log 7}{\log 3} \\ x &\approx 1.7712 \end{aligned}$$

86.
$$\begin{aligned} 2^x &= 3^{x-1} \\ \log 2^x &= \log 3^{x-1} \\ x \log 2 &= (x-1)\log 3 \\ x \log 2 &= x \log 3 - \log 3 \\ x \log 2 - x \log 3 &= -\log 3 \\ x(\log 2 - \log 3) &= -\log 3 \\ x &= \frac{-\log 3}{\log 2 - \log 3} \\ x &\approx 2.7095 \end{aligned}$$

87.
$$\begin{aligned} 2e^x &= 16 \\ e^x &= 8 \\ \ln e^x &= \ln 8 \\ x \ln e &= \ln 8 \\ x &= \ln 8 \approx 2.0794 \end{aligned}$$

88.
$$\begin{aligned} -5e^x &= -35 \\ e^x &= 7 \\ \ln e^x &= \ln 7 \\ x \ln e &= \ln 7 \\ x &= \ln 7 \approx 1.9459 \end{aligned}$$

89.
$$\begin{aligned} \log_7(-7x + 2) &= \log_7(3x + 32) \\ -7x + 2 &= 3x + 32 \\ -30 &= 10x \\ -3 &= x \end{aligned}$$

90.
$$\begin{aligned} \ln(x + 3) &= \ln(-5x + 51) \\ x + 3 &= -5x + 51 \\ 6x &= 48 \\ x &= 8 \end{aligned}$$

91.
$$\begin{aligned}\log x + \log(29 - x) &= 2\\ \log x(29 - x) &= 2\\ x(29 - x) &= 10^2\\ -x^2 + 29x - 100 &= 0\\ x^2 - 29x + 100 &= 0\\ (x - 25)(x - 4) &= 0\end{aligned}$$
$x - 25 = 0$ **or** $x - 4 = 0$
$x = 25$ $\quad$ $x = 4$

92.
$$\begin{aligned}\log_2 x + \log_2(x - 2) &= 3\\ \log_2 x(x - 2) &= 3\\ x(x - 2) &= 2^3\\ x^2 - 2x - 8 &= 0\\ (x - 4)(x + 2) &= 0\end{aligned}$$
$x - 4 = 0$ **or** $x + 2 = 0$
$x = 4$ $\quad$ $x = -2$
extraneous

93.
$$\begin{aligned}\log_2(x + 2) + \log_2(x - 1) &= 2\\ \log_2(x + 2)(x - 1) &= 2\\ (x + 2)(x - 1) &= 2^2\\ x^2 + x - 2 &= 4\\ x^2 + x - 6 &= 0\\ (x - 2)(x + 3) &= 0\end{aligned}$$
$x - 2 = 0$ **or** $x + 3 = 0$
$x = 2$ $\quad$ $x = -3$
extraneous

94.
$$\begin{aligned}\frac{\log(7x - 12)}{\log x} &= 2\\ \log(7x - 12) &= 2\log x\\ \log(7x - 12) &= \log x^2\\ 7x - 12 &= x^2\\ 0 &= x^2 - 7x + 12\\ 0 &= (x - 3)(x - 4)\\ x &= 3,\ x = 4\end{aligned}$$

95.
$$\begin{aligned}\ln x + \ln(x - 5) &= \ln 6\\ \ln x(x - 5) &= \ln 6\\ x(x - 5) &= 6\\ x^2 - 5x &= 6\\ x^2 - 5x - 6 &= 0\\ (x - 6)(x + 1) &= 0\end{aligned}$$
$x - 6 = 0$ **or** $x + 1 = 0$
$x = 6$ $\quad$ $x = -1$
extraneous

96.
$$\begin{aligned}\log 3 - \log(x - 1) &= -1\\ \log\frac{3}{x - 1} &= -1\\ \frac{3}{x - 1} &= 10^{-1}\\ \frac{3}{x - 1} &= \frac{1}{10}\\ 30 &= x - 1\\ 31 &= x\end{aligned}$$

97.
$$\begin{aligned}e^{x\ln 2} &= 9\\ \ln e^{x\ln 2} &= \ln 9\\ x\ln 2\ln e &= \ln 9\\ x\ln 2 &= \ln 9\\ x &= \frac{\ln 9}{\ln 2} \approx 3.1699\end{aligned}$$

98.
$$\begin{aligned}\ln x &= \ln(x - 1)\\ x &= x - 1\end{aligned}$$
no solution

99. $\ln x - 3 = 4$
$\ln x = 7$
$x = e^7 \approx 1096.6332$

100.
$$\ln x = \ln(x-1) + 1$$
$$\ln x - \ln(x-1) = 1$$
$$\ln \frac{x}{x-1} = 1$$
$$\frac{x}{x-1} = e^1$$
$$\frac{x}{x-1} = \frac{e}{1}$$
$$x = e(x-1)$$
$$\frac{e}{e-1} = x, \text{ or } x \approx 1.5820$$

101. Note: $\log_{10} x = \dfrac{\ln x}{\ln 10}$
$$\ln x = \log_{10} x$$
$$\ln x = \frac{\ln x}{\ln 10}$$
$$\ln x \ln 10 = \ln x$$
$$\ln x \ln 10 - \ln x = 0$$
$$\ln x(\ln 10 - 1) = 0$$
$$\ln x = 0 \Rightarrow x = 1$$

102.
$$A = A_0 2^{-t/h}$$
$$\frac{2}{3}A_0 = A_0 \cdot 2^{-t/5700}$$
$$\frac{2}{3} = 2^{-t/5700}$$
$$\log(2/3) = \log\left(2^{-t/5700}\right)$$
$$\log(2/3) = -\frac{t}{5700}\log 2$$
$$-\frac{5700\log(2/3)}{\log 2} = t \Rightarrow t \approx 3300 \text{ years}$$

Chapter 4 Test (page 497)

1. $f(x) = 2^x + 1 \Rightarrow$ Shift $y = 2^x$ up 1.

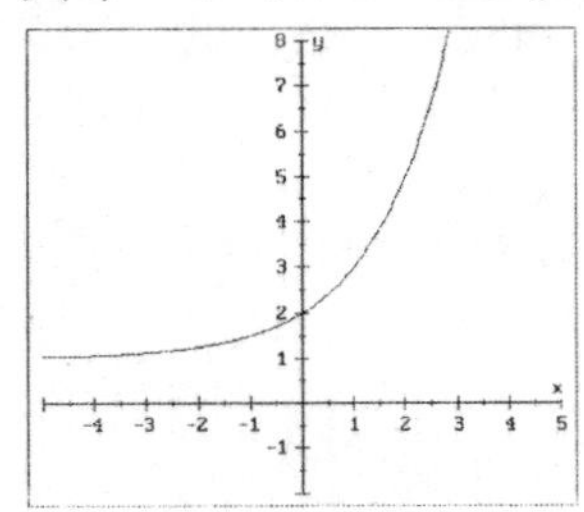

2. $f(x) = e^{x-2} \Rightarrow$ Shift $y = e^x$ right 2.

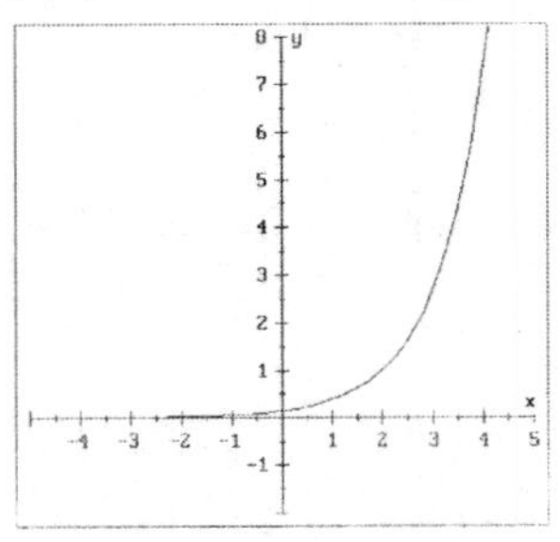

3. $A = 3(2)^{-6} = 3 \cdot \frac{1}{64} = \frac{3}{64}$ gram

4. $A = 1000\left(1 + \frac{0.06}{2}\right)^{2(1)} \approx \$1060.90$

5. $A = 2000e^{0.08(10)} \approx \$4451.08$

6. $\log_7 343 = \log_7 7^3 = 3$

7. $\log_3 \dfrac{1}{27} = \log_3 3^{-3} = -3$

8. $\log_{10} 10^{12} + 10^{\log_{10} 5} = 12 + 5 = 17$

9. $\log_{3/2} \frac{9}{4} = \log_{3/2}\left(\frac{3}{2}\right)^2 = 2$

10. $\log_{2/3} \frac{27}{8} = \log_{2/3}\left(\frac{2}{3}\right)^{-3} = -3$

11. $f(x) = \log(x-1)$; Shift $y = \log x$ right 1.

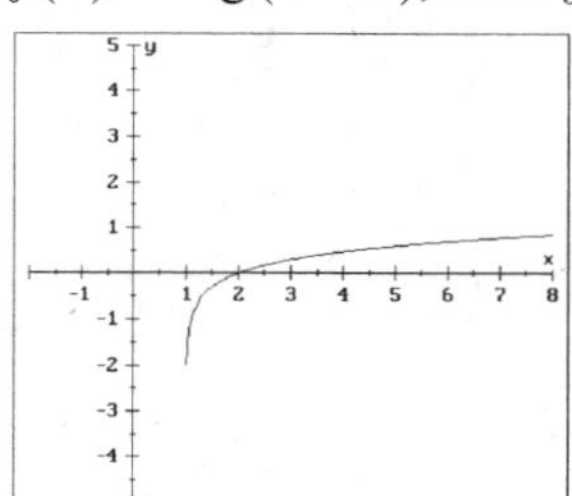

12. $f(x) = 2 + \ln x$; Shift $y = \ln x$ up 2.

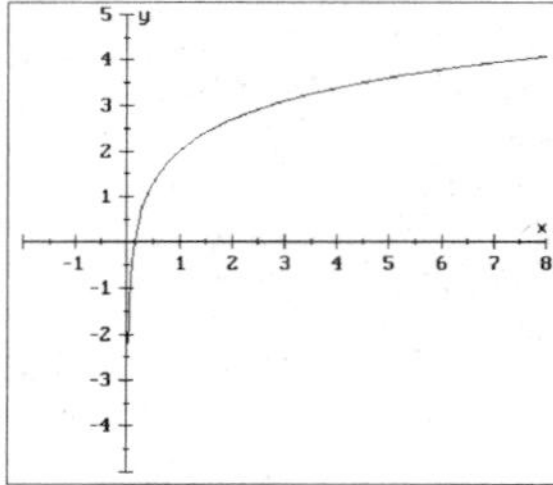

13. $\log a^2bc^3 = \log a^2 + \log b + \log c^3 = 2\log a + \log b + 3\log c$

14. $\ln\sqrt{\dfrac{a}{b^2c}} = \ln\left(\dfrac{a}{b^2c}\right)^{1/2} = \dfrac{1}{2}\ln\dfrac{a}{b^2c} = \dfrac{1}{2}\left(\ln a - \ln b^2 - \ln c\right) = \dfrac{1}{2}(\ln a - 2\ln b - \ln c)$

15. $\dfrac{1}{2}\log(a+2) + \log b - 2\log c = \log\sqrt{a+2} + \log b - \log c^2 = \log\dfrac{b\sqrt{a+2}}{c^2}$

16. $\dfrac{1}{3}(\ln a - 2\ln b) - \ln c = \dfrac{1}{3}\ln\dfrac{a}{b^2} - \ln c = \ln\sqrt[3]{\dfrac{a}{b^2}} - \ln c = \ln\dfrac{\sqrt[3]{\frac{a}{b^2}}}{c}$

17. $\log 24 = \log 8\cdot 3 = \log 2^3\cdot 3 = 3\log 2 + \log 3 = 3(0.3010) + 0.4771 = 1.3801$

18. $\log\dfrac{8}{3} = \log\dfrac{2^3}{3} = 3\log 2 - \log 3 = 3(0.3010) - 0.4771 = 0.4259$

19. $\log_7 3 = \dfrac{\log 3}{\log 7}$ or $\dfrac{\ln 3}{\ln 7}$

20. $\log_\pi e = \dfrac{\log e}{\log \pi}$ or $\dfrac{\ln e}{\ln \pi} = \dfrac{1}{\ln \pi}$

21. $\log_a ab = \log_a a + \log_a b = 1 + \log_a b$
TRUE

22. $\log\dfrac{a}{b} = \log a - \log b$
FALSE

23. $\text{pH} = -\log[\text{H}^+]$
$= -\log\left(3.7\times 10^{-7}\right)$
≈ 6.4

24. $\text{db gain} = 20\log\dfrac{E_O}{E_I}$
$= 20\log\dfrac{60}{0.3}$
≈ 46 db gain

25.
$$\begin{aligned} 3^{x^2-2x} &= 27 \\ 3^{x^2-2x} &= 3^3 \\ x^2-2x &= 3 \\ x^2-2x-3 &= 0 \\ (x-3)(x+1) &= 0 \\ x-3=0 \quad \textbf{or} &\quad x+1=0 \\ x=3 \qquad &\qquad x=-1 \end{aligned}$$

26.
$$\begin{aligned} 3^{x-1} &= 100^x \\ \log 3^{x-1} &= \log 100^x \\ (x-1)\log 3 &= x\log 100 \\ x\log 3 - \log 3 &= 2x \\ x\log 3 - 2x &= \log 3 \\ x(\log 3 - 2) &= \log 3 \\ x &= \frac{\log 3}{\log 3 - 2} \\ x &\approx -0.3133 \end{aligned}$$

27.
$$\begin{aligned} 5e^x &= 45 \\ e^x &= 9 \\ \ln e^x &= \ln 9 \\ x\ln e &= \ln 9 \\ x &= \ln 9 \approx 2.1972 \end{aligned}$$

28.
$$\begin{aligned} \ln(5x+2) &= \ln(2x+5) \\ 5x+2 &= 2x+5 \\ 3x &= 3 \\ x &= 1 \end{aligned}$$

29.
$$\begin{aligned} \log x + \log(x-9) &= 1 \\ \log x(x-9) &= 1 \\ x(x-9) &= 10^1 \\ x^2-9x-10 &= 0 \\ (x-10)(x+1) &= 0 \\ x-10=0 \quad \textbf{or} &\quad x+1=0 \\ x=10 \qquad &\qquad x=-1 \\ &\qquad \text{extraneous} \end{aligned}$$

30.
$$\begin{aligned} \log_6 18 - \log_6(x-3) &= \log_6 3 \\ \log_6 \frac{18}{x-3} &= \log_6 3 \\ \frac{18}{x-3} &= 3 \\ 18 &= 3x-9 \\ 27 &= 3x \\ 9 &= x \end{aligned}$$

Exercises 5.1 (page 508)

1. whole

2. $P(r)=0$

3. any

4. $x-r$

5. factor

6. synthetic

7.
$$\begin{array}{r|l} & 4x^2 + 2x + 1 + \frac{2}{x-1} \\ \hline x-1 & 4x^3 - 2x^2 - x + 1 \\ & \underline{4x^3 - 4x^2} \\ & \quad 2x^2 - x \\ & \quad \underline{2x^2 - 2x} \\ & \qquad x + 1 \\ & \qquad \underline{x - 1} \\ & \qquad\quad 2 \end{array}$$

8.
$$\begin{array}{r|l} & 2x^2 - 3x + 4 + \frac{-11}{x+3} \\ \hline x+3 & 2x^3 + 3x^2 - 5x + 1 \\ & \underline{2x^3 + 6x^2} \\ & \quad -3x^2 - 5x \\ & \quad \underline{-3x^2 - 9x} \\ & \qquad 4x + 1 \\ & \qquad \underline{4x + 12} \\ & \qquad\quad -11 \end{array}$$

9.

$$\begin{array}{r|l} & 2x^3 - 3x^2 + 8x - 1 + \frac{-3}{x+2} \\ \hline x+2 & 2x^4 + x^3 + 2x^2 + 15x - 5 \\ & \underline{2x^4 + 4x^3} \\ & -3x^3 + 2x^2 \\ & \underline{-3x^3 - 6x^2} \\ & 8x^2 + 15x \\ & \underline{8x^2 + 16x} \\ & -x - 5 \\ & \underline{-x - 2} \\ & -3 \end{array}$$

10.

$$\begin{array}{r|l} & x^3 + 7x^2 + 5x + 6 + \frac{5}{x-1} \\ \hline x-1 & x^4 + 6x^3 - 2x^2 + x - 1 \\ & \underline{x^4 - x^3} \\ & 7x^3 - 2x^2 \\ & \underline{7x^3 - 7x^2} \\ & 5x^2 + x \\ & \underline{5x^2 - 5x} \\ & 6x - 1 \\ & \underline{6x - 6} \\ & 5 \end{array}$$

11.

$$\begin{aligned} P(2) &= 3(2)^3 - 2(2)^2 - 5(2) - 7 \\ &= 3(8) - 2(4) - 5(2) - 7 \\ &= 24 - 8 - 10 - 7 = \boxed{-1} \end{aligned}$$

$$\begin{array}{r|l} & 3x^2 + 4x + 3 \\ \hline x-2 & 3x^3 - 2x^2 - 5x - 7 \\ & \underline{3x^3 - 6x^2} \\ & 4x^2 - 5x \\ & \underline{4x^2 - 8x} \\ & 3x - 7 \\ & \underline{3x - 6} \\ & \boxed{-1} \end{array}$$

12.

$$\begin{aligned} P(-2) &= 5(-2)^3 + 4(-2)^2 + (-2) - 1 \\ &= 5(-8) + 4(4) - 2 - 1 \\ &= -40 + 16 - 2 - 1 = \boxed{-27} \end{aligned}$$

$$\begin{array}{r|l} & 5x^2 - 6x + 13 \\ \hline x+2 & 5x^3 + 4x^2 + x - 1 \\ & \underline{5x^3 + 10x^2} \\ & -6x^2 + x \\ & \underline{-6x^2 - 12x} \\ & 13x - 1 \\ & \underline{13x + 26} \\ & \boxed{-27} \end{array}$$

13.

$$\begin{aligned} P(-1) &= 7(-1)^4 + 2(-1)^3 + 5(-1)^2 - 1 \\ &= 7(1) + 2(-1) + 5(1) - 1 \\ &= 7 - 2 + 5 - 1 = \boxed{9} \end{aligned}$$

$$\begin{array}{r|l} & 7x^3 - 5x^2 + 10x - 10 \\ \hline x+1 & 7x^4 + 2x^3 + 5x^2 + 0x - 1 \\ & \underline{7x^4 + 7x^3} \\ & -5x^3 + 5x^2 \\ & \underline{-5x^3 - 5x^2} \\ & 10x^2 + 0x \\ & \underline{10x^2 + 10x} \\ & -10x - 1 \\ & \underline{-10x - 10} \\ & \boxed{9} \end{array}$$

14.

$$\begin{aligned} P(2) &= 2(2)^4 - 2(2)^3 + 5(2)^2 - 1 \\ &= 2(16) - 2(8) + 5(4) - 1 \\ &= 32 - 16 + 20 - 1 = \boxed{35} \end{aligned}$$

$$\begin{array}{r|l} & 2x^3 + 2x^2 + 9x + 18 \\ \hline x-2 & 2x^4 - 2x^3 + 5x^2 + 0x - 1 \\ & \underline{2x^4 - 4x^3} \\ & 2x^3 + 5x^2 \\ & \underline{2x^3 - 4x^2} \\ & 9x^2 + 0x \\ & \underline{9x^2 - 18x} \\ & 18x - 1 \\ & \underline{18x - 36} \\ & \boxed{35} \end{array}$$

15.

$$\begin{aligned} P(1) &= 2(1)^5 + (1)^4 - (1)^3 - 2(1) + 3 \\ &= 2(1) + (1) - (1) - 2 + 3 \\ &= 2 + 1 - 1 - 2 + 3 = \boxed{3} \end{aligned}$$

$$\begin{array}{r|l} & 2x^4 + 3x^3 + 2x^2 + 2x \\ \hline x-1 & 2x^5 + x^4 - x^3 + 0x^2 - 2x + 3 \\ & \underline{2x^5 - 2x^4} \\ & 3x^4 - x^3 \\ & \underline{3x^4 - 3x^3} \\ & 2x^3 + 0x^2 \\ & \underline{2x^3 - 2x^2} \\ & 2x^2 - 2x \\ & \underline{2x^2 - 2x} \\ & 0x + \boxed{3} \end{array}$$

16. $$\begin{aligned} P(-2) &= 3(-2)^5 + (-2)^4 - 3(-2)^2 + 5(-2) + 7 \\ &= 3(-32) + (16) - 3(4) - 10 + 7 \\ &= -96 + 16 - 12 - 10 + 7 = \boxed{-95} \end{aligned}$$

$$\begin{array}{r|llllll} & 3x^4 & -\,5x^3 & +\,10x^2 & -\,23x & +\,51 & \\ \hline x+2 & 3x^5 + & x^4 + & 0x^3 - & 3x^2 + & 5x + & 7 \\ & 3x^5 + 6x^4 & & & & & \\ \cline{2-3} & & -\,5x^4 + 0x^3 & & & & \\ & & -\,5x^4 - 10x^3 & & & & \\ \cline{3-4} & & & 10x^3 - 3x^2 & & & \\ & & & 10x^3 + 20x^2 & & & \\ \cline{4-5} & & & & -\,23x^2 + 5x & & \\ & & & & -\,23x^2 - 46x & & \\ \cline{5-6} & & & & & 51x + & 7 \\ & & & & & 51x + & 102 \\ \cline{6-7} & & & & & & \boxed{-95} \end{array}$$

17. $$\begin{aligned} \text{remainder} = P(-2) &= 3(-2)^4 + 5(-2)^3 - 4(-2)^2 - 2(-2) + 1 \\ &= 3(16) + 5(-8) - 4(4) - 2(-2) + 1 = 48 - 40 - 16 + 4 + 1 = -3 \end{aligned}$$

18. $$\begin{aligned} \text{remainder} = P(1) &= 3(1)^4 + 5(1)^3 - 4(1)^2 - 2(1) + 1 \\ &= 3(1) + 5(1) - 4(1) - 2(1) + 1 = 3 + 5 - 4 - 2 + 1 = 3 \end{aligned}$$

19. $$\begin{aligned} \text{remainder} = P(2) &= 3(2)^4 + 5(2)^3 - 4(2)^2 - 2(2) + 1 \\ &= 3(16) + 5(8) - 4(4) - 2(2) + 1 = 48 + 40 - 16 - 4 + 1 = 69 \end{aligned}$$

20. $$\begin{aligned} \text{remainder} = P(-1) &= 3(-1)^4 + 5(-1)^3 - 4(-1)^2 - 2(-1) + 1 \\ &= 3(1) + 5(-1) - 4(1) - 2(-1) + 1 = 3 - 5 - 4 + 2 + 1 = -3 \end{aligned}$$

21. $$\begin{aligned} \text{remainder} = P(12) &= 3(12)^4 + 5(12)^3 - 4(12)^2 - 2(12) + 1 \\ &= 3(20{,}736) + 5(1728) - 4(144) - 2(12) + 1 \\ &= 62{,}208 + 8640 - 576 - 24 + 1 = 70{,}249 \end{aligned}$$

22. $$\begin{aligned} \text{remainder} = P(-15) &= 3(-15)^4 + 5(-15)^3 - 4(-15)^2 - 2(-15) + 1 \\ &= 3(50{,}625) + 5(-3375) - 4(225) - 2(-15) + 1 \\ &= 151{,}875 - 16{,}875 - 900 + 30 + 1 = 134{,}131 \end{aligned}$$

23. $$\begin{aligned} \text{remainder} = P(-3.25) &= 3(-3.25)^4 + 5(-3.25)^3 - 4(-3.25)^2 - 2(-3.25) + 1 \\ &= 3(111.56640625) + 5(-34.328125) - 4(10.5625) - 2(-3.25) + 1 \\ &= 334.69921875 - 171.640625 - 42.25 + 6.5 + 1 = 128.3085938 \end{aligned}$$

24. $$\begin{aligned} \text{remainder} = P(7.12) &= 3(7.12)^4 + 5(7.12)^3 - 4(7.12)^2 - 2(7.12) + 1 \\ &= 3(2569.92219136) + 5(360.944128) - 4(50.6944) - 2(7.12) + 1 \\ &= 7709.76657408 + 1804.72064 - 202.7776 - 14.24 + 1 = 9298.469614 \end{aligned}$$

25. $(x-1)$ is a factor if $P(1)=0$.
$P(1)=1^7-1=0$: true

26. $(x-2)$ is a factor if $P(2)=0$.
$P(2)=2^3-2^2+2(2)-8=0$: true

27. $(x-1)$ is a factor if $P(1)=0$.
$P(1)=3(1)^5+4(1)^2-7=0$: true

28. $(x+1)$ is a factor if $P(-1)=0$.
$P(-1)=3(-1)^5+4(-1)^2-7=-6$: false

29. $(x+3)$ is a factor if $P(-3)=0$.
$P(-3)=2(-3)^3-2(-3)^2+1$
$=-71$: false

30. $(x-3)$ is a factor if $P(3)=0$.
$P(3)=3(3)^5-3(3)^4+5(3)^2-13(3)-6$
$=486$: false

31. $(x-1)$ is a factor if $P(1)=0$. $P(1)=(1)^{1984}-(1)^{1776}+(1)^{1492}-(1)^{1066}=0$: true

32. $(x+1)$ is a factor if $P(-1)=0$. $P(1)=(-1)^{1984}+(-1)^{1776}-(-1)^{1492}-(-1)^{1066}=0$: true

33.
$$\begin{array}{r|rrrr} 1 & 3 & -2 & -6 & -4 \\ & & 3 & 1 & -5 \\ \hline & 3 & 1 & -5 & -9 \end{array}$$
$(x-1)(3x^2+x-5)-9$

34.
$$\begin{array}{r|rrrr} 2 & 3 & -2 & -6 & -4 \\ & & 6 & 8 & 4 \\ \hline & 3 & 4 & 2 & 0 \end{array}$$
$(x-2)(3x^2+4x+2)+0$

35.
$$\begin{array}{r|rrrr} 3 & 3 & -2 & -6 & -4 \\ & & 9 & 21 & 45 \\ \hline & 3 & 7 & 15 & 41 \end{array}$$
$(x-3)(3x^2+7x+15)+41$

36.
$$\begin{array}{r|rrrr} 4 & 3 & -2 & -6 & -4 \\ & & 12 & 40 & 136 \\ \hline & 3 & 10 & 34 & 132 \end{array}$$
$(x-4)(3x^2+10x+34)+132$

37.
$$\begin{array}{r|rrrr} -1 & 3 & -2 & -6 & -4 \\ & & -3 & 5 & 1 \\ \hline & 3 & -5 & -1 & -3 \end{array}$$
$(x+1)(3x^2-5x-1)-3$

38.
$$\begin{array}{r|rrrr} -2 & 3 & -2 & -6 & -4 \\ & & -6 & 16 & -20 \\ \hline & 3 & -8 & 10 & -24 \end{array}$$
$(x+2)(3x^2-8x+10)-24$

39.
$$\begin{array}{r|rrrr} -3 & 3 & -2 & -6 & -4 \\ & & -9 & 33 & -81 \\ \hline & 3 & -11 & 27 & -85 \end{array}$$
$(x+3)(3x^2-11x+27)-85$

40.
$$\begin{array}{r|rrrr} -4 & 3 & -2 & -6 & -4 \\ & & -12 & 56 & -200 \\ \hline & 3 & -14 & 50 & -204 \end{array}$$
$(x+4)(3x^2-14x+50)-204$

41.
$$\begin{array}{r|rrrr} 1 & 1 & 1 & 1 & -3 \\ & & 1 & 2 & 3 \\ \hline & 1 & 2 & 3 & 0 \end{array}$$
x^2+2x+3

42.
$$\begin{array}{r|rrrr} 2 & 1 & -1 & -5 & 6 \\ & & 2 & 2 & -6 \\ \hline & 1 & 1 & -3 & 0 \end{array}$$
x^2+x-3

43. $\begin{array}{r|rrrr} -1 & 7 & -3 & -5 & 1 \\ & & -7 & 10 & -5 \\ \hline & 7 & -10 & 5 & -4 \end{array}$

$7x^2 - 10x + 5 + \dfrac{-4}{x+1}$

44. $\begin{array}{r|rrrr} 3 & 2 & 4 & -3 & 8 \\ & & 6 & 30 & 81 \\ \hline & 2 & 10 & 27 & 89 \end{array}$

$2x^2 + 10x + 27 + \dfrac{89}{x-3}$

45. $\begin{array}{r|rrrrr} 3 & 4 & -3 & 0 & -1 & 5 \\ & & 12 & 27 & 81 & 240 \\ \hline & 4 & 9 & 27 & 80 & 245 \end{array}$

$4x^3 + 9x^2 + 27x + 80 + \dfrac{245}{x-3}$

46. $\begin{array}{r|rrrrr} -1 & 1 & 5 & -2 & 1 & -1 \\ & & -1 & -4 & 6 & -7 \\ \hline & 1 & 4 & -6 & 7 & -8 \end{array}$

$x^3 + 4x^2 - 6x + 7 + \dfrac{-8}{x+1}$

47. $\begin{array}{r|rrrrrr} 4 & 3 & 0 & 0 & 0 & -768 & 0 \\ & & 12 & 48 & 192 & 768 & 0 \\ \hline & 3 & 12 & 48 & 192 & 0 & 0 \end{array}$

$3x^4 + 12x^3 + 48x^2 + 192x$

48. $\begin{array}{r|rrrrrr} -3 & 1 & 0 & 0 & -4 & 4 & 4 \\ & & -3 & 9 & -27 & 93 & -291 \\ \hline & 1 & -3 & 9 & -31 & 97 & -287 \end{array}$

$x^4 - 3x^3 + 9x^2 - 31x + 97 + \dfrac{-287}{x+3}$

49. $\begin{array}{r|rrrr} 2 & 5 & 2 & -1 & 1 \\ & & 10 & 24 & 46 \\ \hline & 5 & 12 & 23 & 47 \end{array}$ $P(2) = 47$

50. $\begin{array}{r|rrrr} -2 & 5 & 2 & -1 & 1 \\ & & -10 & 16 & -30 \\ \hline & 5 & -8 & 15 & -29 \end{array}$ $P(-2) = -29$

51. $\begin{array}{r|rrrr} -5 & 5 & 2 & -1 & 1 \\ & & -25 & 115 & -570 \\ \hline & 5 & -23 & 114 & -569 \end{array}$

$P(-5) = -569$

52. $\begin{array}{r|rrrr} 3 & 5 & 2 & -1 & 1 \\ & & 15 & 51 & 150 \\ \hline & 5 & 17 & 50 & 151 \end{array}$ $P(3) = 151$

53. $\begin{array}{r|rrrr} i & 5 & 2 & -1 & 1 \\ & & 5i & -5+2i & -2-6i \\ \hline & 5 & 2+5i & -6+2i & -1-6i \end{array}$

$P(i) = -1 - 6i$

54. $\begin{array}{r|rrrr} -i & 5 & 2 & -1 & 1 \\ & & -5i & -5-2i & -2+6i \\ \hline & 5 & 2-5i & -6-2i & -1+6i \end{array}$

$P(i) = -1 + 6i$

55. $\begin{array}{r|rrrrr} \frac{1}{2} & 2 & 0 & -1 & 0 & 2 \\ & & 1 & \frac{1}{2} & -\frac{1}{4} & -\frac{1}{8} \\ \hline & 2 & 1 & -\frac{1}{2} & -\frac{1}{4} & \frac{15}{8} \end{array}$ $P\left(\frac{1}{2}\right) = \frac{15}{8}$

56. $\begin{array}{r|rrrrr} \frac{1}{3} & 2 & 0 & -1 & 0 & 2 \\ & & \frac{2}{3} & \frac{2}{9} & -\frac{7}{27} & -\frac{7}{81} \\ \hline & 2 & \frac{2}{3} & -\frac{7}{9} & -\frac{7}{27} & \frac{155}{81} \end{array}$ $P\left(\frac{1}{3}\right) = \frac{155}{81}$

57. $\begin{array}{r|rrrrr} i & 2 & 0 & -1 & 0 & 2 \\ & & 2i & -2 & -3i & 3 \\ \hline & 2 & 2i & -3 & -3i & 5 \end{array}$ $P(i) = 5$

58. $\begin{array}{r|rrrrr} -i & 2 & 0 & -1 & 0 & 2 \\ & & -2i & -2 & 3i & 3 \\ \hline & 2 & -2i & -3 & 3i & 5 \end{array}$ $P(-i) = 5$

59. $\begin{array}{r|rrrrr} 1 & 1 & -8 & 14 & 8 & -15 \\ & & 1 & -7 & 7 & 15 \\ \hline & 1 & -7 & 7 & 15 & 0 \end{array}$ $P(1) = 0$

60. $\begin{array}{r|rrrrr} 0 & 1 & -8 & 14 & 8 & -15 \\ & & 0 & 0 & 0 & 0 \\ \hline & 1 & -8 & 14 & 8 & -15 \end{array}$ $P(0) = -15$

61. $$\begin{array}{r|rrrrr} -3 & 1 & -8 & 14 & 8 & -15 \\ & & -3 & 33 & -141 & 399 \\ \hline & 1 & -11 & 47 & -133 & 384 \end{array}$$
$P(-3) = 384$

62. $$\begin{array}{r|rrrrr} -1 & 1 & -8 & 14 & 8 & -15 \\ & & -1 & 9 & -23 & 15 \\ \hline & 1 & -9 & 23 & -15 & 0 \end{array}$$
$P(-1) = 0$

63. $$\begin{array}{r|rrrrr} -i & 1 & -8 & 14 & 8 & -15 \\ & & -i & -1+8i & 8-13i & -13-16i \\ \hline & 1 & -8-i & 13+8i & 16-13i & -28-16i \end{array}$$
$P(-i) = -28 - 16i$

64. $$\begin{array}{r|rrrrr} i & 1 & -8 & 14 & 8 & -15 \\ & & i & -1-8i & 8+13i & -13+16i \\ \hline & 1 & -8+i & 13-8i & 16+13i & -28+16i \end{array}$$
$P(i) = -28 + 16i$

65. $$\begin{array}{r|rrrrrr} i & 1 & 0 & -1 & -8 & 0 & 8 \\ & & i & -1 & -2i & 2-8i & 8+2i \\ \hline & 1 & i & -2 & -8-2i & 2-8i & 16+2i \end{array}$$
$P(i) = 16 + 2i$

66. $$\begin{array}{r|rrrrrr} -i & 1 & 0 & -1 & -8 & 0 & 8 \\ & & -i & -1 & 2i & 2+8i & 8-2i \\ \hline & 1 & -i & -2 & -8+2i & 2+8i & 16-2i \end{array}$$
$P(-i) = 16 - 2i$

67. $$\begin{array}{r|rrrrrr} -2i & 1 & 0 & -1 & -8 & 0 & 8 \\ & & -2i & -4 & 10i & 20+16i & 32-40i \\ \hline & 1 & -2i & -5 & -8+10i & 20+16i & 40-40i \end{array}$$
$P(-2i) = 40 - 40i$

68. $$\begin{array}{r|rrrrrr} 2i & 1 & 0 & -1 & -8 & 0 & 8 \\ & & 2i & -4 & -10i & 20-16i & 32+40i \\ \hline & 1 & 2i & -5 & -8-10i & 20-16i & 40+40i \end{array}$$
$P(2i) = 40 + 40i$

69. $x = -1$ is a solution, so $(x + 1)$ is a factor. Use synthetic division to divide by $(x + 1)$.

$$\begin{array}{r|rrrr} -1 & 1 & 3 & -13 & -15 \\ & & -1 & -2 & 15 \\ \hline & 1 & 2 & -15 & 0 \end{array}$$

$$x^3 + 3x^2 - 13x - 15 = 0$$
$$(x + 1)\left(x^2 + 2x - 15\right) = 0$$
$$(x + 1)(x + 5)(x - 3) = 0$$

Solution set: $\{-1, -5, 3\}$

70. $x = 1$ is a solution, so $(x - 1)$ is a factor. Use synthetic division to divide by $(x - 1)$.

$$\begin{array}{r|rrrr} 1 & 1 & 6 & 5 & -12 \\ & & 1 & 7 & 12 \\ \hline & 1 & 7 & 12 & 0 \end{array}$$

$$x^3 + 6x^2 + 5x - 12 = 0$$
$$(x - 1)\left(x^2 + 7x + 12\right) = 0$$
$$(x - 1)(x + 3)(x + 4) = 0$$

Solution set: $\{1, -3, -4\}$

71. $x = -\frac{1}{2}$ is a solution, so $\left(x + \frac{1}{2}\right)$ is a factor.
Use synthetic division to divide by $\left(x + \frac{1}{2}\right)$.

$$\begin{array}{r|rrrr} -\frac{1}{2} & 2 & 1 & -18 & -9 \\ & & -1 & 0 & 9 \\ \hline & 2 & 0 & -18 & 0 \end{array}$$

$$\begin{aligned} 2x^3 + x^2 - 18x - 9 &= 0 \\ \left(x + \tfrac{1}{2}\right)(2x^2 - 18) &= 0 \\ 2\left(x + \tfrac{1}{2}\right)(x^2 - 9) &= 0 \\ 2\left(x + \tfrac{1}{2}\right)(x + 3)(x - 3) &= 0 \end{aligned}$$

Solution set: $\left\{-\frac{1}{2}, -3, 3\right\}$

72. $x = \frac{1}{2}$ is a solution, so $\left(x - \frac{1}{2}\right)$ is a factor.
Use synthetic division to divide by $\left(x - \frac{1}{2}\right)$.

$$\begin{array}{r|rrrr} \frac{1}{2} & 2 & -3 & -11 & 6 \\ & & 1 & -1 & -6 \\ \hline & 2 & -2 & -12 & 0 \end{array}$$

$$\begin{aligned} 2x^3 - 3x^2 - 11x + 6 &= 0 \\ \left(x - \tfrac{1}{2}\right)(2x^2 - 2x - 12) &= 0 \\ 2\left(x - \tfrac{1}{2}\right)(x^2 - x - 6) &= 0 \\ 2\left(x - \tfrac{1}{2}\right)(x + 2)(x - 3) &= 0 \end{aligned}$$

Solution set: $\left\{\frac{1}{2}, -2, 3\right\}$

73. $x = 2$ is a solution, so $(x - 2)$ is a factor.
Use synthetic division to divide by $(x - 2)$.

$$\begin{array}{r|rrrr} 2 & 1 & -6 & 7 & 2 \\ & & 2 & -8 & -2 \\ \hline & 1 & -4 & -1 & 0 \end{array}$$

$$\begin{aligned} x^3 - 6x^2 + 7x + 2 &= 0 \\ (x - 2)(x^2 - 4x - 1) &= 0 \end{aligned}$$

Use the quadratic formula to finish.

Solution set: $\left\{2, 2 + \sqrt{5}, 2 - \sqrt{5}\right\}$

74. $x = -3$ is a solution, so $(x + 3)$ is a factor.
Use synthetic division to divide by $(x + 3)$.

$$\begin{array}{r|rrrr} -3 & 1 & 1 & -8 & -6 \\ & & -3 & 6 & 6 \\ \hline & 1 & -2 & -2 & 0 \end{array}$$

$$\begin{aligned} x^3 + x^2 - 8x - 6 &= 0 \\ (x + 3)(x^2 - 2x - 2) &= 0 \end{aligned}$$

Use the quadratic formula to finish.

Solution set: $\left\{-3, 1 + \sqrt{3}, 1 - \sqrt{3}\right\}$

75. $x = -3$ is a solution, so $(x + 3)$ is a factor.
Use synthetic division to divide by $(x + 3)$.

$$\begin{array}{r|rrrr} -3 & 1 & -3 & 1 & 57 \\ & & -3 & 18 & -57 \\ \hline & 1 & -6 & 19 & 0 \end{array}$$

$$\begin{aligned} x^3 - 3x^2 + x + 57 &= 0 \\ (x + 3)(x^2 - 6x + 19) &= 0 \end{aligned}$$

Use the quadratic formula to finish.

Solution set: $\left\{-3, 3 \pm \sqrt{10}\,i\right\}$

76. $x = 1$ is a solution, so $(x - 1)$ is a factor.
Use synthetic division to divide by $(x - 1)$.

$$\begin{array}{r|rrrr} 1 & 2 & -1 & 1 & -2 \\ & & 2 & 1 & 2 \\ \hline & 2 & 1 & 2 & 0 \end{array}$$

$$\begin{aligned} 2x^3 - x^2 + x - 2 &= 0 \\ (x - 1)(2x^2 + x + 2) &= 0 \end{aligned}$$

Use the quadratic formula to finish.

Solution set: $\left\{1, -\frac{1}{4} \pm \frac{\sqrt{15}}{4}\,i\right\}$

77. $x = 1$ is a solution, so $(x - 1)$ is a factor.
Use synthetic division to divide by $(x - 1)$.

$$\begin{array}{r|rrrrr} 1 & 1 & -2 & -2 & 6 & -3 \\ & & 1 & -1 & -3 & 3 \\ \hline & 1 & -1 & -3 & 3 & 0 \end{array}$$

$$x^4 - 2x^3 - 2x^2 + 6x - 3 = 0$$
$$(x - 1)(x^3 - x^2 - 3x + 3) = 0$$

Use the fact that $x = 1$ is a double root and divide the depressed polynomial by $(x - 1)$:

$$\begin{array}{r|rrrr} 1 & 1 & -1 & -3 & 3 \\ & & 1 & 0 & -3 \\ \hline & 1 & 0 & -3 & 0 \end{array}$$

$$(x - 1)(x^3 - x^2 - 3x + 3) = 0$$
$$(x - 1)(x - 1)(x^2 - 3) = 0$$

Solution set: $\{1, 1, \sqrt{3}, -\sqrt{3}\}$

78. $x = -2$ is a solution, so $(x + 2)$ is a factor.
Use synthetic division to divide by $(x + 2)$.

$$\begin{array}{r|rrrrrr} -2 & 1 & 4 & 4 & -1 & -4 & -4 \\ & & -2 & -4 & 0 & 2 & 4 \\ \hline & 1 & 2 & 0 & -1 & -2 & 0 \end{array}$$

$$x^5 + 4x^4 + 4x^3 - x^2 - 4x - 4 = 0$$
$$(x + 2)(x^4 + 2x^3 - x - 2) = 0$$

Use the fact that $x = -2$ is a double root and divide the depressed polynomial by $(x + 2)$:

$$\begin{array}{r|rrrrr} -2 & 1 & 2 & 0 & -1 & -2 \\ & & -2 & 0 & 0 & 2 \\ \hline & 1 & 0 & 0 & -1 & 0 \end{array}$$

$$(x + 2)(x^4 + 2x^3 - x - 2) = 0$$
$$(x + 2)(x + 2)(x^3 - 1) = 0$$

Use the fact that $x = 1$ is a solution and divide the depressed polynomial by $(x - 1)$:

$$\begin{array}{r|rrrr} 1 & 1 & 0 & 0 & -1 \\ & & 1 & 1 & 1 \\ \hline & 1 & 1 & 1 & 0 \end{array}$$

$$(x + 2)(x + 2)(x^3 - 1) = 0$$
$$(x + 2)(x + 2)(x - 1)(x^2 + x + 1) = 0$$

[Use the quadratic formula to finish.]

Solution set: $\left\{-2, -2, 1, -\frac{1}{2} \pm \frac{\sqrt{3}}{2}i\right\}$

79. $x = 2$ is a solution, so $(x - 2)$ is a factor.
Use synthetic division to divide by $(x - 2)$.

$$\begin{array}{r|rrrrr} 2 & 1 & -5 & 7 & -5 & 6 \\ & & 2 & -6 & 2 & -6 \\ \hline & 1 & -3 & 1 & -3 & 0 \end{array}$$

$$x^4 - 5x^3 + 7x^2 - 5x + 6 = 0$$
$$(x - 2)(x^3 - 3x^2 + x - 3) = 0$$

$x = 3$ is a root, so $(x - 3)$ is a factor.
Use synthetic division to divide by $(x - 3)$.

$$\begin{array}{r|rrrr} 3 & 1 & -3 & 1 & -3 \\ & & 3 & 0 & 3 \\ \hline & 1 & 0 & 1 & 0 \end{array}$$

$$(x - 2)(x^3 - 3x^2 + x - 3) = 0$$
$$(x - 2)(x - 3)(x^2 + 1) = 0$$
$$x^2 + 1 = 0 \Rightarrow x^2 = -1 \Rightarrow x = \pm i$$

Solution set: $\{2, 3, \pm i\}$

80. $x = 1$ is a solution, so $(x - 1)$ is a factor.
Use synthetic division to divide by $(x - 1)$.

$$\begin{array}{r|rrrrr} 1 & 1 & 2 & -3 & -4 & 4 \\ & & 1 & 3 & 0 & -4 \\ \hline & 1 & 3 & 0 & -4 & 0 \end{array}$$

$$x^4 + 2x^3 - 3x^2 - 4x + 4 = 0$$
$$(x - 1)(x^3 + 3x^2 - 4) = 0$$

$x = -2$ is a root, so $(x + 2)$ is a factor.
Use synthetic division to divide by $(x + 2)$.

$$\begin{array}{r|rrrr} -2 & 1 & 3 & 0 & -4 \\ & & -2 & -2 & 4 \\ \hline & 1 & 1 & -2 & 0 \end{array}$$

$$(x - 1)(x^3 + 3x^2 - 4) = 0$$
$$(x - 1)(x + 2)(x^2 + x - 2) = 0$$
$$(x - 1)(x + 2)(x + 2)(x - 1) = 0$$

Solution set: $\{1, -2, 1, -2\}$

81. $(x - 4)(x - 5) = x^2 - 9x + 20$

82. $(x + 3)(x - 5) = x^2 - 2x - 15$

83. $(x-1)(x-1)(x-1)=(x^2-2x+1)(x-1)=x^3-3x^2+3x-1$

84. $(x-1)(x-0)(x+1)=(x^2-x)(x+1)=x^3-x$

85. $(x-2)(x-4)(x-5)=(x^2-6x+8)(x-5)=x^3-11x^2+38x-40$

86. $(x-7)(x-6)(x-3)=(x^2-13x+42)(x-3)=x^3-16x^2+81x-126$

87. $(x-1)(x+1)\left(x-\sqrt{2}\right)\left(x+\sqrt{2}\right)=(x^2-1)(x^2-2)=x^4-3x^2+2$

88. $(x-0)(x-0)(x-0)\left(x-\sqrt{3}\right)\left(x+\sqrt{3}\right)=x^3(x^2-3)=x^5-3x^3$

89. $\left(x-\sqrt{2}\right)(x-i)(x+i)=\left(x-\sqrt{2}\right)(x^2-i^2)=\left(x-\sqrt{2}\right)(x^2+1)=x^3-\sqrt{2}x^2+x-\sqrt{2}$

90.
$$\begin{aligned}(x-i)(x-i)(x-2)=\left(x^2-2ix+i^2\right)(x-2)&=\left(x^2-2ix-1\right)(x-2)\\&=x^3-2x^2-2ix^2+4ix-x+2\\&=x^3-(2+2i)x^2-(1-4i)x+2\end{aligned}$$

91.
$$\begin{aligned}(x-0)[x-(1+i)][x-(1-i)]&=x\left[x^2-(1-i)x-(1+i)x+(1+i)(1-i)\right]\\&=x\left[x^2-x+ix-x-ix+1-i^2\right]\\&=x\left[x^2-2x+2\right]=x^3-2x^2+2x\end{aligned}$$

92.
$$\begin{aligned}(x-i)[x-(2+i)][x-(2-i)]&=(x-i)\left[x^2-(2-i)x-(2+i)x+(2+i)(2-i)\right]\\&=(x-i)\left[x^2-2x+ix-2x-ix+4-i^2\right]\\&=(x-i)\left[x^2-4x+5\right]\\&=x^3-4x^2+5x-ix^2+4ix-5i\\&=x^3-(4+i)x^2+(5+4i)x-5i\end{aligned}$$

93.
$$\begin{aligned}P(0)&=0\\a_n(0)^n+a_{n-1}(0)^{n-1}+\cdots+a_1(0)+a_0&=0\\0+0+\cdots+0+a_0&=0\\a_0&=0\end{aligned}$$

94. From **#93**, $a_0=0$. Then,
$P(x)=a_nx^n+a_{n-1}x^{n-1}+\cdots+a_1x=x\left(a_nx^{n-1}+a_{n-1}x^{n-2}+\cdots+a_2x+a_1\right)$.
If 0 is a double root, then it is a root of the depressed polynomial, so
$a_n(0)^{n-1}+a_{n-1}(0)^{n-2}+\cdots+a_2(0)+a_1=0\Rightarrow a_1=0$ (as in **#93**).

95. $P(2) = 0 \Rightarrow (x-2)$ is a factor. $P(-2) = 0 \Rightarrow (x+2)$ is a factor. The product of two factors will also be a factor, so $(x-2)(x+2) = x^2 - 4$ is a factor of the polynomial $P(x)$.

96.
$$\begin{aligned} P(2) &= 11 \\ 2^4 - 3(2)^3 + k(2)^2 + 4(2) - 1 &= 11 \\ 16 - 3(8) + 4k + 8 - 1 &= 11 \\ 4k - 1 &= 11 \\ 4k &= 12 \\ k &= 3 \end{aligned}$$

97. $P(3, -2)$: QIV

98. $Q(-2, -5)$: QIII

99. $R(8, \pi)$: QI

100. $S(-9, 9)$: QII

101. $d = \sqrt{(3-(-5))^2 + (-3-3)^2} = \sqrt{(8)^2 + (-6)^2} = \sqrt{64+36} = \sqrt{100} = 10$

102. $d = \sqrt{(-8-2)^2 + (2-(-22))^2} = \sqrt{(-10)^2 + (24)^2} = \sqrt{100+576} = \sqrt{676} = 26$

103. $m = \dfrac{-3-5}{-5-3} = \dfrac{-8}{-8} = 1$

104. $m = \dfrac{1 - \frac{3}{5}}{-\frac{3}{5} - 3} = \dfrac{\frac{2}{5}}{-\frac{18}{5}} = -\dfrac{1}{9}$

Exercises 5.2 (page 518)

1. zero

2. Fundamental Theorem of Algebra

3. conjugate

4. 2

5. $(-x)^3 - (-x)^2 - 4$
$= -x^3 - x^2 - 4$
0 variations

6. 2 variations $\Rightarrow$ at most 2 positive roots

7. $7x^4 + 5x^3 - 2x + 1 \Rightarrow 7(-x)^4 + 5(-x)^3 - 2(-x) + 1$
$\Rightarrow 7x^4 - 5x^3 + 2x + 1 \Rightarrow$ 2 variations $\Rightarrow$ at most 2 negative roots

8. conjugate

9. lower bound

10. upper bound

11. $x^{10} = 1$
$x^{10} - 1 = 0 \Rightarrow$ 10 roots

12. $x^{40} = 1$
$x^{40} - 1 = 0 \Rightarrow$ 40 roots

13. $3x^4 - 4x^2 - 2x = -7$
$3x^4 - 4x^2 - 2x + 7 = 0 \Rightarrow$ 4 roots

14. $-32x^{111} - x^5 = 1$
$-32x^{111} - x^5 - 1 = 0 \Rightarrow$ 111 roots

15. $x(3x^4 - 2) = 12x$
$3x^5 - 14x = 0$
5 total roots $\Rightarrow$ $\boxed{\text{4 other roots}}$

16. $3x^2(x^7 - 14x + 3) = 0$
$3x^9 - 42x^3 + 9x^2 = 0$
9 total roots $\Rightarrow$ $\boxed{\text{7 other roots}}$

17. $P(x) = x^4 - 81$
4 linear factors, 4 zeros

18. $P(x) = x^{40} + x^{39}$
40 linear factors, 40 zeros

19. $P(x) = 4x^5 + 8x^3$
5 linear factors, 5 zeros

20. $P(x) = x^3 + 144x$
3 linear factors, 3 zeros

21. If $2i$ is a root, then $-2i$ is a root also:
$$\begin{aligned}(x-2i)(x+2i) &= 0\\ x^2-4i^2 &= 0\\ x^2+4 &= 0\end{aligned}$$

22. If $-3i$ is a root, then $3i$ is a root also:
$$\begin{aligned}(x+3i)(x-3i) &= 0\\ x^2-9i^2 &= 0\\ x^2+9 &= 0\end{aligned}$$

23. If $3-i$ is a root, then $3+i$ is a root also:
$$\begin{aligned}[x-(3-i)][x-(3+i)] &= 0\\ x^2-(3+i)x-(3-i)x+(3-i)(3+i) &= 0\\ x^2-3x-ix-3x+ix+9-i^2 &= 0\\ x^2-6x+10 &= 0\end{aligned}$$

24. If $4+2i$ is a root, then $4-2i$ is a root also:
$$\begin{aligned}[x-(4+2i)][x-(4-2i)] &= 0\\ x^2-(4-2i)x-(4+2i)x+(4+2i)(4-2i) &= 0\\ x^2-4x+2ix-4x-2ix+16-4i^2 &= 0\\ x^2-8x+20 &= 0\end{aligned}$$

25. If $-i$ is a root, then i is a root also:
$$\begin{aligned}(x-3)(x+i)(x-i) &= 0\\ (x-3)\left(x^2-i^2\right) &= 0\\ (x-3)\left(x^2+1\right) &= 0\\ x^3-3x^2+x-3 &= 0\end{aligned}$$

26. If i is a root, then $-i$ is a root also:
$$\begin{aligned}(x-1)(x-i)(x+i) &= 0\\ (x-1)\left(x^2-i^2\right) &= 0\\ (x-1)\left(x^2+1\right) &= 0\\ x^3-x^2+x-1 &= 0\end{aligned}$$

27. If $2+i$ is a root, then $2-i$ is a root also:
$$\begin{aligned}(x-2)[x-(2+i)][x-(2-i)] &= 0\\ (x-2)\left[x^2-(2-i)x-(2+i)x+(2+i)(2-i)\right] &= 0\\ (x-2)\left[x^2-2x+ix-2x-ix+4-i^2\right] &= 0\\ (x-2)\left[x^2-4x+5\right] &= 0\\ x^3-6x^2+13x-10 &= 0\end{aligned}$$

28. If $3-i$ is a root, then $3+i$ is a root also:
$$\begin{aligned}(x+2)[x-(3-i)][x-(3+i)] &= 0\\ (x+2)\left[x^2-(3+i)x-(3-i)x+(3-i)(3+i)\right] &= 0\\ (x+2)\left[x^2-3x-ix-3x+ix+9-i^2\right] &= 0\\ (x+2)\left[x^2-6x+10\right] &= 0\\ x^3-4x^2-2x+20 &= 0\end{aligned}$$

29. If i is a root, then $-i$ is a root also:

$$(x-3)(x-2)(x-i)(x+i)=0$$
$$\left(x^2-5x+6\right)\left(x^2-i^2\right)=0$$
$$\left(x^2-5x+6\right)\left(x^2+1\right)=0$$
$$x^4-5x^3+7x^2-5x+6=0$$

30. If $1+i$ is a root, then $1-i$ is a root also:

$$(x-1)(x-2)[x-(1+i)][x-(1-i)]=0$$
$$\left(x^2-3x+2\right)\left[x^2-(1-i)x-(1+i)x+(1+i)(1-i)\right]=0$$
$$\left(x^2-3x+2\right)\left[x^2-x+ix-x-ix+1-i^2\right]=0$$
$$\left(x^2-3x+2\right)\left[x^2-2x+2\right]=0$$
$$x^4-5x^3+10x^2-10x+4=0$$

31. If i and $1-i$ are roots, then $-i$ and $1+i$ are roots also:

$$(x-i)(x+i)[x-(1-i)][x-(1+i)]=0$$
$$\left(x^2-i^2\right)\left[x^2-(1+i)x-(1-i)x+(1-i)(1+i)\right]=0$$
$$\left(x^2+1\right)\left[x^2-x-ix-x+ix+1-i^2\right]=0$$
$$\left(x^2+1\right)\left[x^2-2x+2\right]=0$$
$$x^4-2x^3+3x^2-2x+2=0$$

32. If i and $2-i$ are roots, then $-i$ and $2+i$ are roots also:

$$(x-i)(x+i)[x-(2-i)][x-(2+i)]=0$$
$$\left(x^2-i^2\right)\left[x^2-(2+i)x-(2-i)x+(2-i)(2+i)\right]=0$$
$$\left(x^2+1\right)\left[x^2-2x-ix-2x+ix+4-i^2\right]=0$$
$$\left(x^2+1\right)\left[x^2-4x+5\right]=0$$
$$x^4-4x^3+6x^2-4x+5=0$$

33. If $2i$ is a double root, then there are two factors of $(x-2i)$. [The problem does not specify real coefficients, so we do not include $-2i$ as a root.]

$$(x-2i)(x-2i)=0$$
$$x^2-4ix+4i^2=0$$
$$x^2-4ix-4=0$$

34. If $-2i$ is a double root, then there are two factors of $(x+2i)$. [The problem does not specify real coefficients, so we do not include $2i$ as a root.]

$$(x+2i)(x+2i)=0$$
$$x^2+4ix+4i^2=0$$
$$x^2+4ix-4=0$$

35. $P(x) = 3x^3 + 5x^2 - 4x + 3$

2 sign variations $\Rightarrow$ 2 or 0 positive roots

$P(-x) = 3(-x)^3 + 5(-x)^2 - 4(-x) + 3$
$= -3x^3 + 5x^2 + 4x + 3$

1 sign variation $\Rightarrow$ 1 negative root

# pos	# neg	# nonreal
2	1	0
0	1	2

36. $P(x) = 3x^3 - 5x^2 - 4x - 3$

1 sign variation $\Rightarrow$ 1 positive root

$P(-x) = 3(-x)^3 - 5(-x)^2 - 4(-x) - 3$
$= -3x^3 - 5x^2 + 4x - 3$

2 sign variations $\Rightarrow$ 2 or 0 negative roots

# pos	# neg	# nonreal
1	2	0
1	0	2

37. $P(x) = 2x^3 + 7x^2 + 5x + 5$

0 sign variations $\Rightarrow$ 0 positive roots

$P(-x) = 2(-x)^3 + 7(-x)^2 + 5(-x) + 3$
$= -2x^3 + 7x^2 - 5x + 3$

3 sign variations $\Rightarrow$ 3 or 1 negative roots

# pos	# neg	# nonreal
0	3	0
0	1	2

38. $P(x) = -2x^3 - 7x^2 - 5x - 4$

0 sign variations $\Rightarrow$ 0 positive roots

$P(-x) = -2(-x)^3 - 7(-x)^2 - 5(-x) - 4$
$= 2x^3 - 7x^2 + 5x - 4$

3 sign variations $\Rightarrow$ 3 or 1 negative roots

# pos	# neg	# nonreal
0	3	0
0	1	2

39. $P(x) = 8x^4 + 5$

0 sign variations $\Rightarrow$ 0 positive roots

$P(-x) = 8(-x)^4 + 5$
$= 8x^4 + 5$

0 sign variations $\Rightarrow$ 0 negative roots

# pos	# neg	# nonreal
0	0	4

40. $P(x) = -3x^3 + 5$

1 sign variation $\Rightarrow$ 1 positive root

$P(-x) = -3(-x)^3 + 5$
$= 3x^3 + 5$

0 sign variations $\Rightarrow$ 0 negative roots

# pos	# neg	# nonreal
1	0	2

41. $P(x) = x^4 + 8x^2 - 5x - 10$: 1 sign variation $\Rightarrow$ 1 positive root

$P(-x) = (-x)^4 + 8(-x)^2 - 5(-x) - 10$
$= x^4 + 8x^2 + 5x - 10$: 1 sign variation $\Rightarrow$ 1 negative root

# pos	# neg	# nonreal
1	1	2

42. $P(x) = 5x^7 + 3x^6 - 2x^5 + 3x^4 + 9x^3 + x^2 + 1$: 2 sign variations $\Rightarrow$ 2 or 0 positive roots

$P(-x) = 5(-x)^7 + 3(-x)^6 - 2(-x)^5 + 3(-x)^4 + 9(-x)^3 + (-x)^2 + 1$
$= -5x^7 + 3x^6 + 2x^5 + 3x^4 - 9x^3 + x^2 + 1$: 3 sign variations $\Rightarrow$ 3 or 1 negative roots

# pos	# neg	# nonreal
2	3	2
2	1	4
0	3	4
0	1	6

43. $P(x) = -x^{10} - x^8 - x^6 - x^4 - x^2 - 1$: 0 sign variations $\Rightarrow$ 0 positive roots
$P(-x) = -(-x)^{10} - (-x)^8 - (-x)^6 - (-x)^4 - (-x)^2 - 1$
$= -x^{10} - x^8 - x^6 - x^4 - x^2 - 1$: 0 sign variations $\Rightarrow$ 0 negative roots

# pos	# neg	# nonreal
0	0	10

44. $P(x) = x^{10} + x^8 + x^6 + x^4 + x^2 + 1$: 0 sign variations $\Rightarrow$ 0 positive roots
$P(-x) = (-x)^{10} + (-x)^8 + (-x)^6 + (-x)^4 + (-x)^2 + 1$
$= x^{10} + x^8 + x^6 + x^4 + x^2 + 1$: 0 sign variations $\Rightarrow$ 0 negative roots

# pos	# neg	# nonreal
0	0	10

45. $P(x) = x^9 + x^7 + x^5 + x^3 + x = x(x^8 + x^6 + x^4 + x^2 + 1)$: 0 sign variations $\Rightarrow$ 0 positive roots
$P(-x) = (-x)\left[(-x)^8 + (-x)^6 + (-x)^4 + (-x)^2 + 1\right]$
$= -x\left[x^8 + x^6 + x^4 + x^2 + 1\right]$: 0 sign variations $\Rightarrow$ 0 negative roots

# pos	# neg	# zero	# nonreal
0	0	1	8

46. $P(x) = -x^9 - x^7 - x^5 - x^3 - x = -x(x^8 + x^6 + x^4 + x^2 + 1)$: 0 sign var $\Rightarrow$ 0 positive roots
$P(-x) = -(-x)\left[(-x)^8 + (-x)^6 + (-x)^4 + (-x)^2 + 1\right]$
$= x\left[x^8 + x^6 + x^4 + x^2 + 1\right]$: 0 sign variations $\Rightarrow$ 0 negative roots

# pos	# neg	# zero	# nonreal
0	0	1	8

47. $P(x) = -2x^4 - 3x^2 + 2x + 3$: 1 sign variation $\Rightarrow$ 1 positive root
$P(-x) = -2(-x)^4 - 3(-x)^2 + 2(-x) + 3$
$= -2x^4 - 3x^2 - 2x + 3$: 1 sign variation $\Rightarrow$ 1 negative root

# pos	# neg	# nonreal
1	1	2

48. $P(x) = -7x^5 - 6x^4 + 3x^3 - 2x^2 + 7x - 4$: 4 sign variations $\Rightarrow$ 4 or 2 or 0 positive roots
$P(-x) = -7(-x)^5 - 6(-x)^4 + 3(-x)^3 - 2(-x)^2 + 7(-x) - 4$
$= 7x^5 - 6x^4 - 3x^3 - 2x^2 - 7x - 4$: 1 sign variation $\Rightarrow$ 1 negative root

# pos	# neg	# nonreal
4	1	0
2	1	2
0	1	4

49. $P(x) = x^2 - 2x - 4$

$$\begin{array}{r|rrr} 4 & 1 & -2 & -4 \\ & & 4 & 8 \\ \hline & 1 & 2 & 4 \end{array} \qquad \begin{array}{r|rrr} -2 & 1 & -2 & -4 \\ & & -2 & 8 \\ \hline & 1 & -4 & 4 \end{array}$$

Upper bound: 4 Lower bound: -2

50. $P(x) = 9x^2 - 6x - 1$

$$\begin{array}{r|rrr} 1 & 9 & -6 & -1 \\ & & 9 & 3 \\ \hline & 9 & 3 & 2 \end{array} \qquad \begin{array}{r|rrr} -1 & 9 & -6 & -1 \\ & & -9 & 15 \\ \hline & 9 & -15 & 14 \end{array}$$

Upper bound: 1 Lower bound: -1

51. $P(x) = 18x^2 - 6x - 1$

$$\begin{array}{r|rrr} 1 & 18 & -6 & -1 \\ & & 18 & 12 \\ \hline & 18 & 12 & 11 \end{array}$$

Upper bound: 1

$$\begin{array}{r|rrr} -1 & 18 & -6 & -1 \\ & & -18 & 24 \\ \hline & 18 & -24 & 23 \end{array}$$

Lower bound: -1

52. $P(x) = 2x^2 - 10x - 9$

$$\begin{array}{r|rrr} 6 & 2 & -10 & -9 \\ & & 12 & 12 \\ \hline & 2 & 2 & 3 \end{array}$$

Upper bound: 6

$$\begin{array}{r|rrr} -1 & 2 & -10 & -9 \\ & & -2 & 12 \\ \hline & 2 & -12 & 3 \end{array}$$

Lower bound: -1

53. $P(x) = 6x^3 - 13x^2 - 110x$

$$\begin{array}{r|rrrr} 6 & 6 & -13 & -110 & 0 \\ & & 36 & 138 & 168 \\ \hline & 6 & 23 & 28 & 168 \end{array}$$

Upper bound: 6

$$\begin{array}{r|rrrr} -4 & 6 & -13 & -110 & 0 \\ & & -24 & 148 & -152 \\ \hline & 6 & -37 & 38 & -152 \end{array}$$

Lower bound: -4

54. $P(x) = 12x^3 + 20x^2 - x - 6$

$$\begin{array}{r|rrrr} 1 & 12 & 20 & -1 & -6 \\ & & 12 & 32 & 31 \\ \hline & 12 & 32 & 31 & 25 \end{array}$$

Upper bound: 1

$$\begin{array}{r|rrrr} -2 & 12 & 20 & -1 & -6 \\ & & -24 & 8 & -14 \\ \hline & 12 & -4 & 7 & -20 \end{array}$$

Lower bound: -2

55. $P(x) = x^5 + x^4 - 8x^3 - 8x^2 + 15x + 15$

$$\begin{array}{r|rrrrrr} 3 & 1 & 1 & -8 & -8 & 15 & 15 \\ & & 3 & 12 & 12 & 12 & 81 \\ \hline & 1 & 4 & 4 & 4 & 27 & 96 \end{array}$$

Upper bound: 3

$$\begin{array}{r|rrrrrr} -4 & 1 & 1 & -8 & -8 & 15 & 15 \\ & & -4 & 12 & -16 & 96 & -444 \\ \hline & 1 & -3 & 4 & -24 & 111 & -429 \end{array}$$

Lower bound: -4

56. $P(x) = 3x^4 - 5x^3 - 9x^2 + 15x$

$$\begin{array}{r|rrrrr} 3 & 3 & -5 & -9 & 15 & 0 \\ & & 9 & 12 & 9 & 72 \\ \hline & 3 & 4 & 3 & 24 & 72 \end{array}$$

Upper bound: 3

$$\begin{array}{r|rrrrr} -2 & 3 & -5 & -9 & 15 & 0 \\ & & -6 & 22 & -26 & 22 \\ \hline & 3 & -11 & 13 & -11 & 22 \end{array}$$

Lower bound: -2

57. $P(x) = 3x^5 - 11x^4 - 2x^3 + 38x^2 - 21x - 15$

$$\begin{array}{r|rrrrrr} 4 & 3 & -11 & -2 & 38 & -21 & -15 \\ & & 12 & 4 & 8 & 184 & 652 \\ \hline & 3 & 1 & 2 & 46 & 163 & 637 \end{array} \qquad \begin{array}{r|rrrrrr} -2 & 3 & -11 & -2 & 38 & -21 & -15 \\ & & -6 & 34 & -64 & 52 & -62 \\ \hline & 3 & -17 & 32 & -26 & 31 & -77 \end{array}$$

Upper bound: 4 Lower bound: -2

58. $P(x) = 3x^6 - 4x^5 - 21x^4 + 4x^3 + 8x^2 + 8x + 32$

4	3	−4	−21	4	8	8	32
		12	32	44	192	800	3232
	3	8	11	48	200	808	3264

Upper bound: 4

−3	3	−4	−21	4	8	8	32
		−9	39	−54	150	−474	1398
	3	−13	18	−50	158	−466	1430

Lower bound: −3

59. **Answers may vary.**

60. **Answers may vary.**

61. The number of nonreal roots must occur in conjugate pairs, so the number of nonreal roots will always be even. Since a polynomial of odd degree has an odd number of roots, at least one root must not be nonreal. Thus, at least one root of such a polynomial will be real.

62. According to Descartes' Rule of Signs, the polynomial will have 1 positive root and 1 negative root. Since the polynomial has a total of 4 roots, the other 2 roots must be nonreal (and conjugates).

63. k units to the right

64. k units downward

65. reflected about the y-axis

66. reflected about the x-axis

67. stretched vertically by a factor of k

68. shrunk horizontally by a factor of $\frac{1}{k}$

Exercises 5.3 (page 528)

1. -7

2. 5

3. root

4. $5x^2 + 8x + 21 = 0$

5. num: $\pm 1, \pm 2, \pm 3, \pm 4, \pm 6, \pm 12$; den: ± 1
possible roots: $\pm 1, \pm 2, \pm 3, \pm 4, \pm 6, \pm 12$

6. num: $\pm 1, \pm 2, \pm 4, \pm 8$; den: ± 1
possible roots: $\pm 1, \pm 2, \pm 4, \pm 8$

7. num: $\pm 1, \pm 2, \pm 3, \pm 6$; den: $\pm 1, \pm 2$
possible roots: $\pm 1, \pm 2, \pm 3, \pm 6, \pm \frac{1}{2}, \pm \frac{3}{2}$

8. num: $\pm 1, \pm 2, \pm 4, \pm 8$; den: $\pm 1, \pm 3$
possible roots: $\pm 1, \pm 2, \pm 4, \pm 8, \pm \frac{1}{3}, \pm \frac{2}{3}, \pm \frac{4}{3}, \pm \frac{8}{3}$

9. num: $\pm 1, \pm 2, \pm 5, \pm 10$; den: $\pm 1, \pm 2, \pm 4$
possible roots: $\pm 1, \pm 2, \pm 5, \pm 10, \pm \frac{1}{2}, \pm \frac{5}{2}, \pm \frac{1}{4}, \pm \frac{5}{4}$

10. num: $\pm 1, \pm 3$; den: $\pm 1, \pm 2, \pm 3, \pm 6$
possible roots: $\pm 1, \pm 3, \pm \frac{1}{2}, \pm \frac{3}{2}, \pm \frac{1}{3}, \pm \frac{1}{6}$

11. $x^3 - 5x^2 - x + 5 = 0$

Possible rational roots: $\pm 1, \pm 5$

Descartes' Rule of Signs:

# pos	# neg	# nonreal
2	1	0
0	1	2

Test $x = -1$:

$$\begin{array}{r|rrrr} -1 & 1 & -5 & -1 & 5 \\ & & -1 & 6 & -5 \\ \hline & 1 & -6 & 5 & 0 \end{array}$$

$$x^3 - 5x^2 - x + 5 = 0$$
$$(x+1)(x^2 - 6x + 5) = 0$$
$$(x+1)(x-5)(x-1) = 0$$

Solution set: $\{-1, 5, 1\}$

12. $x^3 + 7x^2 - x - 7 = 0$

Possible rational roots: $\pm 1, \pm 7$

Descartes' Rule of Signs:

# pos	# neg	# nonreal
1	2	0
1	0	2

Test $x = 1$:

$$\begin{array}{r|rrrr} 1 & 1 & 7 & -1 & -7 \\ & & 1 & 8 & 7 \\ \hline & 1 & 8 & 7 & 0 \end{array}$$

$$x^3 + 7x^2 - x - 7 = 0$$
$$(x-1)(x^2 + 8x + 7) = 0$$
$$(x-1)(x+1)(x+7) = 0$$

Solution set: $\{1, -1, -7\}$

13. $x^3 - 2x^2 - x + 2 = 0$

Possible rational roots

$\pm 1, \pm 2$

Descartes' Rule of Signs

# pos	# neg	# nonreal
2	1	0
0	1	2

Test $x = -1$:

$$\begin{array}{r|rrrr} -1 & 1 & -2 & -1 & 2 \\ & & -1 & 3 & -2 \\ \hline & 1 & -3 & 2 & 0 \end{array}$$

$$x^3 - 2x^2 - x + 2 = 0$$
$$(x+1)(x^2 - 3x + 2) = 0$$
$$(x+1)(x-1)(x-2) = 0$$

Solution set: $\{-1, 1, 2\}$

14. $x^3 + x^2 - 4x - 4 = 0$

Possible rational roots

$\pm 1, \pm 2, \pm 4$

Descartes' Rule of Signs

# pos	# neg	# nonreal
1	2	0
1	0	2

Test $x = -1$:

$$\begin{array}{r|rrrr} -1 & 1 & 1 & -4 & -4 \\ & & -1 & 0 & 4 \\ \hline & 1 & 0 & -4 & 0 \end{array}$$

$$x^3 + x^2 - 4x - 4 = 0$$
$$(x+1)(x^2 - 4) = 0$$
$$(x+1)(x+2)(x-2) = 0$$

Solution set: $\{-1, -2, 2\}$

15. $x^3 - x^2 - 4x + 4 = 0$

Possible rational roots

$\pm 1, \pm 2, \pm 4$

Descartes' Rule of Signs

# pos	# neg	# nonreal
2	1	0
0	1	2

Test $x = 1$:

$$\begin{array}{r|rrrr} 1 & 1 & -1 & -4 & 4 \\ & & 1 & 0 & -4 \\ \hline & 1 & 0 & -4 & 0 \end{array}$$

$$x^3 - x^2 - 4x + 4 = 0$$
$$(x-1)(x^2-4) = 0$$
$$(x-1)(x+2)(x-2) = 0$$

Solution set: $\{1, -2, 2\}$

16. $x^3 + 2x^2 - x - 2 = 0$

Possible rational roots

$\pm 1, \pm 2$

Descartes' Rule of Signs

# pos	# neg	# nonreal
1	2	0
1	0	2

Test $x = 1$:

$$\begin{array}{r|rrrr} 1 & 1 & 2 & -1 & -2 \\ & & 1 & 3 & 2 \\ \hline & 1 & 3 & 2 & 0 \end{array}$$

$$x^3 + 2x^2 - x - 2 = 0$$
$$(x-1)(x^2+3x+2) = 0$$
$$(x-1)(x+1)(x+2) = 0$$

Solution set: $\{1, -1, -2\}$

17. $x^3 - 2x^2 - 9x + 18 = 0$

Possible rational roots:

$\pm 1, \pm 2, \pm 3, \pm 6, \pm 9, \pm 18$

Descartes' Rule of Signs:

# pos	# neg	# nonreal
2	1	0
0	1	2

Test $x = 2$:

$$\begin{array}{r|rrrr} 2 & 1 & -2 & -9 & 18 \\ & & 2 & 0 & -18 \\ \hline & 1 & 0 & -9 & 0 \end{array}$$

$$x^3 - 2x^2 - 9x + 18 = 0$$
$$(x-2)(x^2-9) = 0$$
$$(x-2)(x+3)(x-3) = 0$$

Solution set: $\{2, -3, 3\}$

18. $x^3 + 3x^2 - 4x - 12 = 0$

Possible rational roots:

$\pm 1, \pm 2, \pm 3, \pm 4, \pm 6, \pm 12$

Descartes' Rule of Signs:

# pos	# neg	# nonreal
1	2	0
1	0	2

Test $x = 2$:

$$\begin{array}{r|rrrr} 2 & 1 & 3 & -4 & -12 \\ & & 2 & 10 & 12 \\ \hline & 1 & 5 & 6 & 0 \end{array}$$

$$x^3 + 3x^2 - 4x - 12 = 0$$
$$(x-2)(x^2+5x+6) = 0$$
$$(x-2)(x+3)(x+2) = 0$$

Solution set: $\{2, -3, -2\}$

19. Possible rational roots

$\pm 1, \pm \frac{1}{2}$

Descartes' Rule of Signs

# pos	# neg	# nonreal
2	1	0
0	1	2

Test $x = 1$:

$$\begin{array}{r|rrrr} 1 & 2 & -1 & -2 & 1 \\ & & 2 & 1 & -1 \\ \hline & 2 & 1 & -1 & 0 \end{array}$$

$$2x^3 - x^2 - 2x + 1 = 0$$
$$(x-1)(2x^2+x-1) = 0$$
$$(x-1)(2x-1)(x+1) = 0$$

Solution set: $\{1, \frac{1}{2}, -1\}$

20. $3x^3 + x^2 - 3x - 1 = 0$

Possible rational roots:

$\pm 1, \ \pm \frac{1}{3}$

Descartes' Rule of Signs:

# pos	# neg	# nonreal
1	2	0
1	0	2

Test $x = 1$:

$$\begin{array}{r|rrrr} 1 & 3 & 1 & -3 & -1 \\ & & 3 & 4 & 1 \\ \hline & 3 & 4 & 1 & 0 \end{array}$$

$$3x^3 + x^2 - 3x - 1 = 0$$
$$(x-1)\left(3x^2 + 4x + 1\right) = 0$$
$$(x-1)(3x+1)(x+1) = 0$$

Solution set: $\left\{1, -\frac{1}{3}, -1\right\}$

21. $3x^3 + 5x^2 + x - 1 = 0$

Possible rational roots:

$\pm 1, \ \pm \frac{1}{3}$

Descartes' Rule of Signs:

# pos	# neg	# nonreal
1	2	0
1	0	2

Test $x = -1$:

$$\begin{array}{r|rrrr} -1 & 3 & 5 & 1 & -1 \\ & & -3 & -2 & 1 \\ \hline & 3 & 2 & -1 & 0 \end{array}$$

$$3x^3 + 5x^2 + x - 1 = 0$$
$$(x+1)\left(3x^2 + 2x - 1\right) = 0$$
$$(x+1)(3x-1)(x+1) = 0$$

Solution set: $\left\{-1, \frac{1}{3}, -1\right\}$

22. Possible rational roots

$\pm 1, \ \pm \frac{1}{2}$

Test $x = 1$:

$$\begin{array}{r|rrrr} 1 & 2 & -3 & 0 & 1 \\ & & 2 & -1 & -1 \\ \hline & 2 & -1 & -1 & 0 \end{array}$$

Descartes' Rule of Signs

# pos	# neg	# nonreal
2	1	0
0	1	2

$$2x^3 - 3x^2 + 1 = 0$$
$$(x-1)\left(2x^2 - x - 1\right) = 0$$
$$(x-1)(2x+1)(x-1) = 0$$

Solution set: $\left\{1, -\frac{1}{2}, 1\right\}$

23. Possible rational roots

$\pm 1, \pm 2, \pm 3, \pm 6,$
$\pm 9, \pm 18, \pm \frac{1}{2}, \pm \frac{3}{2},$
$\pm \frac{9}{2}, \pm \frac{1}{3}, \pm \frac{2}{3}, \pm \frac{1}{5},$
$\pm \frac{2}{5}, \pm \frac{3}{5}, \pm \frac{6}{5}, \pm \frac{9}{5},$
$\pm \frac{18}{5}, \pm \frac{1}{6}, \pm \frac{1}{10}, \pm \frac{3}{10},$
$\pm \frac{9}{10}, \pm \frac{1}{15}, \pm \frac{2}{15}, \pm \frac{1}{30}$

Descartes' Rule of Signs

# pos	# neg	# nonreal
2	1	0
0	1	2

Test $x = \frac{2}{3}$:

$$\begin{array}{r|rrrr} \frac{2}{3} & 30 & -47 & -9 & 18 \\ & & 20 & -18 & -18 \\ \hline & 30 & -27 & -27 & 0 \end{array}$$

$$30x^3 - 47x^2 - 9x + 18 = 0$$
$$\left(x - \tfrac{2}{3}\right)\left(30x^2 - 27x - 27\right) = 0$$
$$3\left(x - \tfrac{2}{3}\right)\left(10x^2 - 9x - 9\right) = 0$$
$$(3x-2)(2x-3)(5x+3) = 0$$

Solution set: $\left\{\frac{2}{3}, \frac{3}{2}, -\frac{3}{5}\right\}$

24. Possible rational roots

$\pm 1, \pm 2, \pm 3, \pm 6,$
$\pm 9, \pm 18, \pm \frac{1}{2}, \pm \frac{3}{2},$
$\pm \frac{9}{2}, \pm \frac{1}{4}, \pm \frac{3}{4}, \pm \frac{9}{4},$
$\pm \frac{1}{5}, \pm \frac{2}{5}, \pm \frac{3}{5}, \pm \frac{6}{5},$
$\pm \frac{9}{5}, \pm \frac{18}{5}, \pm \frac{1}{10}, \pm \frac{3}{10},$
$\pm \frac{9}{10}, \pm \frac{1}{20}, \pm \frac{3}{20}, \pm \frac{9}{20}$

Descartes' Rule of Signs

# pos	# neg	# nonreal
2	1	0
0	1	2

Test $x = 3$:

$$\begin{array}{r|rrrr} 3 & 20 & -53 & -27 & 18 \\ & & 60 & 21 & -18 \\ \hline & 20 & 7 & -6 & 0 \end{array}$$

$$20x^3 - 53x^2 - 27x + 18 = 0$$
$$(x-3)\left(20x^2 + 7x - 6\right) = 0$$
$$(x-3)(4x+3)(5x-2) = 0$$

Solution set: $\left\{3, -\frac{3}{4}, \frac{2}{5}\right\}$

25.

Possible rational roots

$\pm 1, \pm 2, \pm 3, \pm 4,$
$\pm 6, \pm 8, \pm 12, \pm 24,$
$\pm \frac{1}{3}, \pm \frac{2}{3}, \pm \frac{4}{3}, \pm \frac{8}{3},$
$\pm \frac{1}{5}, \pm \frac{2}{5}, \pm \frac{3}{5}, \pm \frac{4}{5},$
$\pm \frac{6}{5}, \pm \frac{8}{5}, \pm \frac{12}{5}, \pm \frac{24}{5},$
$\pm \frac{1}{15}, \pm \frac{2}{15}, \pm \frac{4}{15}, \pm \frac{8}{15}$

Descartes' Rule of Signs

# pos	# neg	# nonreal
2	1	0
0	1	2

Test $x = 4$:

$$\begin{array}{r|rrrr} 4 & 15 & -61 & -2 & 24 \\ & & 60 & -4 & -24 \\ \hline & 15 & -1 & -6 & 0 \end{array}$$

$15x^3 - 61x^2 - 2x + 24 = 0$
$(x-4)(15x^2 - x - 6) = 0$
$(x-4)(3x-2)(5x+3) = 0$
Solution set: $\{4, \frac{2}{3}, -\frac{3}{5}\}$

26.

Possible rational roots

$\pm 1, \pm 2, \pm 3, \pm 6,$
$\pm 9, \pm 18, \pm \frac{1}{2}, \pm \frac{3}{2},$
$\pm \frac{9}{2}, \pm \frac{1}{4}, \pm \frac{3}{4}, \pm \frac{9}{4},$
$\pm \frac{1}{5}, \pm \frac{2}{5}, \pm \frac{3}{5}, \pm \frac{6}{5},$
$\pm \frac{9}{5}, \pm \frac{18}{5}, \pm \frac{1}{10}, \pm \frac{3}{10},$
$\pm \frac{9}{10}, \pm \frac{1}{20}, \pm \frac{3}{20}, \pm \frac{9}{20}$

Descartes' Rule of Signs

# pos	# neg	# nonreal
2	1	0
0	1	2

Test $x = \frac{3}{2}$:

$$\begin{array}{r|rrrr} \frac{3}{2} & 20 & -44 & 9 & 18 \\ & & 30 & -21 & -18 \\ \hline & 20 & -14 & -12 & 0 \end{array}$$

$20x^3 - 44x^2 + 9x + 18 = 0$
$(x - \frac{3}{2})(20x^2 - 14x - 12) = 0$
$2(x - \frac{3}{2})(10x^2 - 7x - 6) = 0$
$(2x-3)(2x+1)(5x-6) = 0$
Solution set: $\{\frac{3}{2}, -\frac{1}{2}, \frac{6}{5}\}$

27.

Possible rational roots

$\pm 1, \pm 2, \pm 3, \pm 5,$
$\pm 6, \pm 10, \pm 15, \pm 30,$
$\pm \frac{1}{2}, \pm \frac{3}{2}, \pm \frac{5}{2}, \pm \frac{15}{2},$
$\pm \frac{1}{3}, \pm \frac{2}{3}, \pm \frac{5}{3}, \pm \frac{10}{3},$
$\pm \frac{1}{4}, \pm \frac{3}{4}, \pm \frac{5}{4}, \pm \frac{15}{4},$
$\pm \frac{1}{6}, \pm \frac{5}{6}, \pm \frac{1}{8}, \pm \frac{3}{8},$
$\pm \frac{5}{8}, \pm \frac{15}{8}, \pm \frac{1}{12}, \pm \frac{5}{12},$
$\pm \frac{1}{24}, \pm \frac{5}{24}$

Descartes' Rule of Signs

# pos	# neg	# nonreal
3	0	0
1	0	2

Test $x = \frac{3}{2}$:

$$\begin{array}{r|rrrr} \frac{3}{2} & 24 & -82 & 89 & -30 \\ & & 36 & -69 & 30 \\ \hline & 24 & -46 & 20 & 0 \end{array}$$

$24x^3 - 82x^2 + 89x - 30 = 0$
$(x - \frac{3}{2})(24x^2 - 46x + 20) = 0$
$2(x - \frac{3}{2})(12x^2 - 23x + 10) = 0$
$(2x-3)(4x-5)(3x-2) = 0$
Solution set: $\{\frac{3}{2}, \frac{5}{4}, \frac{2}{3}\}$

28.

Possible rational roots

$\pm 1, \pm 2, \pm 4, \pm 8,$
$\pm \frac{1}{3}, \pm \frac{2}{3}, \pm \frac{4}{3}, \pm \frac{8}{3}$

Test $x = \frac{2}{3}$:

$$\begin{array}{r|rrrr} \frac{2}{3} & 3 & -2 & 12 & -8 \\ & & 2 & 0 & 8 \\ \hline & 3 & 0 & 12 & 0 \end{array}$$

Descartes' Rule of Signs

# pos	# neg	# nonreal
3	0	0
1	0	2

$3x^3 - 2x^2 + 12x - 8 = 0$
$(x - \frac{2}{3})(3x^2 + 12) = 0$
$3x^2 + 12$ does not factor rationally.
Rational solution: $\{\frac{2}{3}\}$

29. Possible rational roots: $\pm 1, \pm 2, \pm 3, \pm 4, \pm 6, \pm 8, \pm 12, \pm 24$

Descartes' Rule of Signs

# pos	# neg	# nonreal
4	0	0
2	0	2
0	0	4

$$x^4 - 10x^3 + 35x^2 - 50x + 24 = 0$$
$$(x-1)(x^3 - 9x^2 + 26x - 24) = 0$$
$$(x-1)(x-2)(x^2 - 7x + 12) = 0$$
$$(x-1)(x-2)(x-3)(x-4) = 0$$

Solution set: $\{1, 2, 3, 4\}$

Test $x = 1$:

$$\begin{array}{r|rrrrr} 1 & 1 & -10 & 35 & -50 & 24 \\ & & 1 & -9 & 26 & -24 \\ \hline & 1 & -9 & 26 & -24 & 0 \end{array}$$

Test $x = 2$:

$$\begin{array}{r|rrrr} 2 & 1 & -9 & 26 & -24 \\ & & 2 & -14 & 24 \\ \hline & 1 & -7 & 12 & 0 \end{array}$$

30. Possible rational roots: ± 1

Descartes' Rule of Signs

# pos	# neg	# nonreal
0	4	0
0	2	2
0	0	4

$$x^4 + 4x^3 + 6x^2 + 4x + 1 = 0$$
$$(x+1)(x^3 + 3x^2 + 3x + 1) = 0$$
$$(x+1)(x+1)(x^2 + 2x + 1) = 0$$
$$(x+1)(x+1)(x+1)(x+1) = 0$$

Solution set: $\{-1, -1, -1, -1\}$

Test $x = -1$:

$$\begin{array}{r|rrrrr} -1 & 1 & 4 & 6 & 4 & 1 \\ & & -1 & -3 & -3 & -1 \\ \hline & 1 & 3 & 3 & 1 & 0 \end{array}$$

Test $x = -1$:

$$\begin{array}{r|rrrr} -1 & 1 & 3 & 3 & 1 \\ & & -1 & -2 & -1 \\ \hline & 1 & 2 & 1 & 0 \end{array}$$

31. Possible rational roots: $\pm 1, \pm 2, \pm 3, \pm 5, \pm 6, \pm 10, \pm 15, \pm 30$

Descartes' Rule of Signs

# pos	# neg	# nonreal
2	2	0
2	0	2
0	2	2
0	0	4

$$x^4 + 3x^3 - 13x^2 - 9x + 30 = 0$$
$$(x-2)(x^3 + 5x^2 - 3x - 15) = 0$$
$$(x-2)(x+5)(x^2 - 3) = 0$$

$x^2 - 3$ does not factor rationally.

Rational solutions: $\{2, -5\}$

Test $x = 2$:

$$\begin{array}{r|rrrrr} 2 & 1 & 3 & -13 & -9 & 30 \\ & & 2 & 10 & -6 & -30 \\ \hline & 1 & 5 & -3 & -15 & 0 \end{array}$$

Test $x = -5$:

$$\begin{array}{r|rrrr} -5 & 1 & 5 & -3 & -15 \\ & & -5 & 0 & 15 \\ \hline & 1 & 0 & -3 & 0 \end{array}$$

32. Possible rational roots: $\pm 1, \pm 3, \pm 5, \pm 15$

Descartes' Rule of Signs

# pos	# neg	# nonreal
3	1	0
1	1	2

$$x^4 - 8x^3 + 14x^2 + 8x - 15 = 0$$
$$(x+1)(x^3 - 9x^2 + 23x - 15) = 0$$
$$(x+1)(x-1)(x^2 - 8x + 15) = 0$$
$$(x+1)(x-1)(x-3)(x-5) = 0$$

Solution set: $\{-1, 1, 3, 5\}$

Test $x = -1$:

$$\begin{array}{r|rrrrr} -1 & 1 & -8 & 14 & 8 & -15 \\ & & -1 & 9 & -23 & 15 \\ \hline & 1 & -9 & 23 & -15 & 0 \end{array}$$

Test $x = 1$:

$$\begin{array}{r|rrrr} 1 & 1 & -9 & 23 & -15 \\ & & 1 & -8 & 15 \\ \hline & 1 & -8 & 15 & 0 \end{array}$$

33. Possible rational roots

$\pm 1, \pm 3, \pm \frac{1}{2}, \pm \frac{3}{2}, \pm \frac{1}{4}, \pm \frac{3}{4}$

Descartes' Rule of Signs

# pos	# neg	# nonreal
3	1	0
1	1	2

$$4x^4 - 8x^3 - x^2 + 8x - 3 = 0$$
$$(x+1)(4x^3 - 12x^2 + 11x + 3) = 0$$
$$(x+1)(x-1)(4x^2 - 8x + 3) = 0$$
$$(x+1)(x-1)(2x-3)(2x-1) = 0$$

Solution set: $\{-1, 1, \frac{3}{2}, \frac{1}{2}\}$

Test $x = -1$:

-1	4	-8	-1	8	-3
		-4	12	-11	3
	4	-12	11	-3	0

Test $x = 1$:

1	4	-12	11	-3
		4	-8	3
	4	-8	3	0

34. Possible rational roots

$\pm 1, \pm 2, \pm 3, \pm 4, \pm 6, \pm 12, \pm \frac{1}{3}, \pm \frac{2}{3}, \pm \frac{4}{3}$

Descartes' Rule of Signs

# pos	# neg	# nonreal
3	1	0
1	1	2

$$3x^4 - 14x^3 + 11x^2 + 16x - 12 = 0$$
$$(x+1)(3x^3 - 17x^2 + 28x - 12) = 0$$
$$(x+1)(x-2)(3x^2 - 11x + 6) = 0$$
$$(x+1)(x-2)(3x-2)(x-3) = 0$$

Solution set: $\{-1, 2, \frac{2}{3}, 3\}$

Test $x = -1$:

-1	3	-14	11	16	-12
		-3	17	-28	12
	3	-17	28	-12	0

Test $x = 2$:

2	3	-17	28	-12
		6	-22	12
	3	-11	6	0

35. Possible rational roots

$\pm 1, \pm 2, \pm 4, \pm 5, \pm 8, \pm 10, \pm 20, \pm 40, \pm \frac{1}{2}, \pm \frac{5}{2}$

Descartes' Rule of Signs

# pos	# neg	# nonreal
1	3	0
1	1	2

$$2x^4 - x^3 - 2x^2 - 4x - 40 = 0$$
$$(x+2)(2x^3 - 5x^2 + 8x - 20) = 0$$
$$(x+2)(x - \tfrac{5}{2})(2x^2 + 8) = 0$$

$2x^2 + 8$ does not factor rationally.

Rational Solutions: $\{-2, \frac{5}{2}\}$

Test $x = -2$:

-2	2	-1	-2	-4	-40
		-4	10	-16	40
	2	-5	8	-20	0

Test $x = \frac{5}{2}$:

$\frac{5}{2}$	2	-5	8	-20
		5	0	20
	2	0	8	0

36. Possible rational roots

$\pm 1, \pm 3, \pm \frac{1}{2}, \pm \frac{3}{2}, \pm \frac{1}{3}, \pm \frac{1}{4}, \pm \frac{3}{4}, \pm \frac{1}{6}, \pm \frac{1}{12}$

Descartes' Rule of Signs

# pos	# neg	# nonreal
3	1	0
1	1	2

$$12x^4 + 20x^3 - 41x^2 + 20x - 3 = 0$$
$$(x+3)(12x^3 - 16x^2 + 7x - 1) = 0$$
$$(x+3)(x - \tfrac{1}{2})(12x^2 - 10x + 2) = 0$$
$$2(x+3)(x - \tfrac{1}{2})(6x^2 - 5x + 1) = 0$$
$$(x+3)(2x-1)(3x-1)(2x-1) = 0$$

Solution set: $\{-3, \frac{1}{2}, \frac{1}{3}, \frac{1}{2}\}$

Test $x = -3$:

-3	12	20	-41	20	-3
		-36	48	-21	3
	12	-16	7	-1	0

Test $x = \frac{1}{2}$:

$\frac{1}{2}$	12	-16	7	-1
		6	-5	1
	12	-10	2	0

37. Possible rational roots

$\pm 1, \pm \frac{1}{2}, \pm \frac{1}{3}, \pm \frac{1}{4},$
$\pm \frac{1}{6}, \pm \frac{1}{9}, \pm \frac{1}{12}, \pm \frac{1}{18}$
$\pm \frac{1}{36}$

Descartes' Rule of Signs

# pos	# neg	# nonreal
3	1	0
1	1	2

$$36x^4 - x^2 + 2x - 1 = 0$$
$$\left(x + \tfrac{1}{2}\right)\left(36x^3 - 18x^2 + 8x - 2\right) = 0$$
$$\left(x + \tfrac{1}{2}\right)\left(x - \tfrac{1}{3}\right)\left(36x^2 - 6x + 6\right) = 0$$

$36x^2 - 6x + 6$ does not factor rationally. Rational Solutions: $\left\{-\frac{1}{2}, \frac{1}{3}\right\}$

Test $x = -\frac{1}{2}$:

$$\begin{array}{r|rrrrr} -\frac{1}{2} & 36 & 0 & -1 & 2 & -1 \\ & & -18 & 9 & -4 & 1 \\ \hline & 36 & -18 & 8 & -2 & 0 \end{array}$$

Test $x = \frac{1}{3}$:

$$\begin{array}{r|rrrr} \frac{1}{3} & 36 & -18 & 8 & -2 \\ & & 12 & -2 & 2 \\ \hline & 36 & -6 & 6 & 0 \end{array}$$

38. Possible rational roots

$\pm 1, \pm 2, \pm 3, \pm 4,$
$\pm 6, \pm 8, \pm 12, \pm 24$
$\pm \frac{1}{2}, \pm \frac{3}{2}, \pm \frac{1}{3}, \pm \frac{2}{3},$
$\pm \frac{4}{3}, \pm \frac{8}{3}, \pm \frac{1}{4}, \pm \frac{3}{4},$
$\pm \frac{1}{6}, \pm \frac{1}{12}$

Descartes' Rule of Signs

# pos	# neg	# nonreal
1	3	0
1	1	2

$$12x^4 + x^3 + 42x^2 + 4x - 24 = 0$$
$$\left(x + \tfrac{3}{4}\right)\left(12x^3 - 8x^2 + 48x - 32\right) = 0$$
$$\left(x + \tfrac{3}{4}\right)\left(x - \tfrac{2}{3}\right)\left(12x^2 + 48\right) = 0$$

$12x^2 + 48$ does not factor rationally.

Rational Solutions: $\left\{-\frac{3}{4}, \frac{2}{3}\right\}$

Test $x = -\frac{3}{4}$:

$$\begin{array}{r|rrrrr} -\frac{3}{4} & 12 & 1 & 42 & 4 & -24 \\ & & -9 & 6 & -36 & 24 \\ \hline & 12 & -8 & 48 & -32 & 0 \end{array}$$

Test $x = \frac{2}{3}$:

$$\begin{array}{r|rrrr} \frac{2}{3} & 12 & -8 & 48 & -32 \\ & & 8 & 0 & 32 \\ \hline & 12 & 0 & 48 & 0 \end{array}$$

39. Possible rat. roots

$\pm 1, \pm 2, \pm 3,$
$\pm 4, \pm 6, \pm 12$

Descartes' Rule of Signs

# pos	# neg	# nonreal
2	3	0
2	1	2
0	3	2
0	1	4

$$x^5 + 3x^4 - 5x^3 - 15x^2 + 4x + 12 = 0$$
$$(x+1)\left(x^4 + 2x^3 - 7x^2 - 8x + 12\right) = 0$$
$$(x+1)(x-1)\left(x^3 + 3x^2 - 4x - 12\right) = 0$$
$$(x+1)(x-1)(x-2)\left(x^2 + 5x + 6\right) = 0$$
$$(x+1)(x-1)(x-2)(x+2)(x+3) = 0$$

Solution set: $\{-1, 1, 2, -2, -3\}$

Test $x = -1$:

$$\begin{array}{r|rrrrrr} -1 & 1 & 3 & -5 & -15 & 4 & 12 \\ & & -1 & -2 & 7 & 8 & -12 \\ \hline & 1 & 2 & -7 & -8 & 12 & 0 \end{array}$$

Test $x = 1$:

$$\begin{array}{r|rrrrr} 1 & 1 & 2 & -7 & -8 & 12 \\ & & 1 & 3 & -4 & -12 \\ \hline & 1 & 3 & -4 & -12 & 0 \end{array}$$

Test $x = 2$:

$$\begin{array}{r|rrrr} 2 & 1 & 3 & -4 & -12 \\ & & 2 & 10 & 12 \\ \hline & 1 & 5 & 6 & 0 \end{array}$$

40.

Possible rat. roots

$\pm 1,\ \pm 2,\ \pm 3,\ \pm 4,\ \pm 6,\ \pm 12$

Descartes' Rule of Signs

# pos	# neg	# nonreal
3	2	0
3	0	2
1	2	2
1	0	4

$$x^5 - 3x^4 - 5x^3 + 15x^2 + 4x - 12 = 0$$
$$(x-1)\left(x^4 - 2x^3 - 7x^2 + 8x + 12\right) = 0$$
$$(x-1)(x+1)\left(x^3 - 3x^2 - 4x + 12\right) = 0$$
$$(x-1)(x+1)(x-2)\left(x^2 - x - 6\right) = 0$$
$$(x-1)(x+1)(x-2)(x+2)(x-3) = 0$$

Solution set: $\{1, -1, 2, -2, 3\}$

Test $x = 1$:

$$\begin{array}{r|rrrrrr} 1 & 1 & -3 & -5 & 15 & 4 & -12 \\ & & 1 & -2 & -7 & 8 & 12 \\ \hline & 1 & -2 & -7 & 8 & 12 & 0 \end{array}$$

Test $x = -1$:

$$\begin{array}{r|rrrrr} -1 & 1 & -2 & -7 & 8 & 12 \\ & & -1 & 3 & 4 & -12 \\ \hline & 1 & -3 & -4 & 12 & 0 \end{array}$$

Test $x = 2$:

$$\begin{array}{r|rrrr} 2 & 1 & -3 & -4 & 12 \\ & & 2 & -2 & -12 \\ \hline & 1 & -1 & -6 & 0 \end{array}$$

41.

Possible rat. roots

$\pm 1,\ \pm 2,\ \pm 3,\ \pm 4,\ \pm 6,\ \pm 12,\ \pm \frac{1}{2},\ \pm \frac{3}{2},\ \pm \frac{1}{4},\ \pm \frac{3}{4}$

Descartes' Rule of Signs

# pos	# neg	# nonreal
4	1	0
2	1	2
0	1	4

Test $x = 3$:

$$\begin{array}{r|rrrrrr} 3 & 4 & -12 & 15 & -45 & -4 & 12 \\ & & 12 & 0 & 45 & 0 & -12 \\ \hline & 4 & 0 & 15 & 0 & -4 & 0 \end{array}$$

Test $x = -\frac{1}{2}$:

$$\begin{array}{r|rrrrr} -\frac{1}{2} & 4 & 0 & 15 & 0 & -4 \\ & & -2 & 1 & -8 & 4 \\ \hline & 4 & -2 & 16 & -8 & 0 \end{array}$$

Test $x = \frac{1}{2}$:

$$\begin{array}{r|rrrr} \frac{1}{2} & 4 & -2 & 16 & -8 \\ & & 2 & 0 & 8 \\ \hline & 4 & 0 & 16 & 0 \end{array}$$

$$4x^5 - 12x^4 + 15x^3 - 45x^2 - 4x + 12 = 0$$
$$(x-3)\left(4x^4 + 15x^2 - 4\right) = 0$$
$$(x-3)\left(x+\tfrac{1}{2}\right)\left(4x^3 - 2x^2 + 16x - 8\right) = 0$$
$$(x-3)\left(x+\tfrac{1}{2}\right)\left(x-\tfrac{1}{2}\right)\left(4x^2 + 16\right) = 0$$

$4x^2 + 16$ does not factor rationally. Rational Solutions: $\left\{3, -\frac{1}{2}, \frac{1}{2}\right\}$

42.

Possible rat. roots

$\pm 1,\ \pm 2,\ \pm 3,\ \pm 4,\ \pm 6,\ \pm 12,\ \pm \frac{1}{2},\ \pm \frac{3}{2},\ \pm \frac{1}{3},\ \pm \frac{2}{3},\ \pm \frac{4}{3},\ \pm \frac{1}{6}$

Descartes' Rule of Signs

# pos	# neg	# nonreal
3	2	0
3	0	2
1	2	2
1	0	4

Test $x = 2$:

$$\begin{array}{r|rrrrrr} 2 & 6 & -7 & -48 & 81 & -4 & -12 \\ & & 12 & 10 & -76 & 10 & 12 \\ \hline & 6 & 5 & -38 & 5 & 6 & 0 \end{array}$$

Test $x = -3$:

$$\begin{array}{r|rrrrr} -3 & 6 & 5 & -38 & 5 & 6 \\ & & -18 & 39 & -3 & -6 \\ \hline & 6 & -13 & 1 & 2 & 0 \end{array}$$

Test $x = 2$:

$$\begin{array}{r|rrrr} 2 & 6 & -13 & 1 & 2 \\ & & 12 & -2 & -2 \\ \hline & 6 & -1 & -1 & 0 \end{array}$$

$$6x^5 - 7x^4 - 48x^3 + 81x^2 - 4x - 12 = 0$$
$$(x-2)\left(6x^4 + 5x^3 - 38x^2 + 5x + 6\right) = 0$$
$$(x-2)(x+3)\left(6x^3 - 13x^2 + x + 2\right) = 0$$
$$(x-2)(x+3)(x-2)\left(6x^2 - x - 1\right) = 0$$
$$(x-2)(x+3)(x-2)(2x-1)(3x+1) = 0$$

Solution set: $\left\{2, -3, 2, \frac{1}{2}, -\frac{1}{3}\right\}$

43. First, factor out the common factor of x: $x^7-12x^5+48x^3-64x=x\left(x^6-12x^4+48x^2-64\right)$

Possible rat. roots

$\pm 1,\ \pm 2,\ \pm 4,\ \pm 8,\ \pm 16,\ \pm 32,\ \pm 64$

Descartes' Rule of Signs

# pos	# neg	# zero	# nonreal
3	3	1	0
3	1	1	2
1	3	1	2
1	1	1	4

Test $x=2$:

$$\begin{array}{r|rrrrrrr} 2 & 1 & 0 & -12 & 0 & 48 & 0 & -64 \\ & & 2 & 4 & -16 & -32 & 32 & 64 \\ \hline & 1 & 2 & -8 & -16 & 16 & 32 & 0 \end{array}$$

Test $x=2$:

$$\begin{array}{r|rrrrrr} 2 & 1 & 2 & -8 & -16 & 16 & 32 \\ & & 2 & 8 & 0 & -32 & -32 \\ \hline & 1 & 4 & 0 & -16 & -16 & 0 \end{array}$$

Test $x=2$:

$$\begin{array}{r|rrrrr} 2 & 1 & 4 & 0 & -16 & -16 \\ & & 2 & 12 & 24 & 16 \\ \hline & 1 & 6 & 12 & 8 & 0 \end{array}$$

Test $x=-2$:

$$\begin{array}{r|rrrr} -2 & 1 & 6 & 12 & 8 \\ & & -2 & -8 & -8 \\ \hline & 1 & 4 & 4 & 0 \end{array}$$

$$\begin{aligned} x^7-12x^5+48x^3-64x &= 0 \\ x\left(x^6-12x^4+48x^2-64\right) &= 0 \\ x(x-2)\left(x^5+2x^4-8x^3-16x^2+16x+32\right) &= 0 \\ x(x-2)(x-2)\left(x^4+4x^3-16x-16\right) &= 0 \\ x(x-2)(x-2)(x-2)\left(x^3+6x^2+12x+8\right) &= 0 \\ x(x-2)(x-2)(x-2)(x+2)\left(x^2+4x+4\right) &= 0 \\ x(x-2)(x-2)(x-2)(x+2)(x+2)(x+2) &= 0 \Rightarrow \text{Sol. set} = \{0, 2, 2, 2, -2, -2, -2\} \end{aligned}$$

44. Possible rat. roots

± 1

Descartes' Rule of Signs

# pos	# neg	# nonreal
0	7	0
0	5	2
0	3	4
0	1	6

Test $x=-1$:

$$\begin{array}{r|rrrrrrrr} -1 & 1 & 7 & 21 & 35 & 35 & 21 & 7 & 1 \\ & & -1 & -6 & -15 & -20 & -15 & -6 & -1 \\ \hline & 1 & 6 & 15 & 20 & 15 & 6 & 1 & 0 \end{array}$$

Test $x=-1$:

$$\begin{array}{r|rrrrrrr} -1 & 1 & 6 & 15 & 20 & 15 & 6 & 1 \\ & & -1 & -5 & -10 & -10 & -5 & -1 \\ \hline & 1 & 5 & 10 & 10 & 5 & 1 & 0 \end{array}$$

Test $x=-1$:

$$\begin{array}{r|rrrrrr} -1 & 1 & 5 & 10 & 10 & 5 & 1 \\ & & -1 & -4 & -6 & -4 & -1 \\ \hline & 1 & 4 & 6 & 4 & 1 & 0 \end{array}$$

continued on next page

44. continued

Test $x = -1$:

-1	1	4	6	4	1
		-1	-3	-3	-1
	1	3	3	1	0

Test $x = -1$:

-1	1	3	3	1
		-1	-2	-1
	1	2	1	0

$$x^7 + 7x^6 + 21x^5 + 35x^4 + 35x^3 + 21x^2 + 7x + 1 = 0$$
$$(x+1)\left(x^6 + 6x^5 + 15x^4 + 20x^3 + 15x^2 + 6x + 1\right) = 0$$
$$(x+1)(x+1)\left(x^5 + 5x^4 + 10x^3 + 10x^2 + 5x + 1\right) = 0$$
$$(x+1)(x+1)(x+1)\left(x^4 + 4x^3 + 6x^2 + 4x + 1\right) = 0$$
$$(x+1)(x+1)(x+1)(x+1)\left(x^3 + 3x^2 + 3x + 1\right) = 0$$
$$(x+1)(x+1)(x+1)(x+1)(x+1)\left(x^2 + 2x + 1\right) = 0$$
$$(x+1)(x+1)(x+1)(x+1)(x+1)(x+1)(x+1) = 0$$

Solution set $= \{-1, -1, -1, -1, -1, -1, -1\}$

45. Possible rational roots

$\pm 1,\ \pm 2,\ \pm 3,\ \pm 6$

Test $x = 3$:

3	1	-3	-2	6
		3	0	-6
	1	0	-2	0

Descartes' Rule of Signs

# pos	# neg	# nonreal
2	1	0
0	1	2

$$x^3 - 3x^2 - 2x + 6 = 0$$
$$(x-3)\left(x^2 - 2\right) = 0$$
$x - 3 = 0$ **or** $x^2 - 2 = 0$

$x = 3$ $\qquad$ $x = \pm\sqrt{2}$

Solution set: $\left\{3, -\sqrt{2}, \sqrt{2}\right\}$

46. Possible rational roots

$\pm 1,\ \pm 3,\ \pm 9$

Test $x = -3$:

-3	1	3	-3	-9
		-3	0	0
	1	0	-3	0

Descartes' Rule of Signs

# pos	# neg	# nonreal
1	2	0
1	0	2

$$x^3 + 3x^2 - 3x - 9 = 0$$
$$(x+3)\left(x^2 - 3\right) = 0$$
$x + 3 = 0$ **or** $x^2 - 3 = 0$

$x = -3$ $\qquad$ $x = \pm\sqrt{3}$

Solution set: $\left\{3, -\sqrt{3}, \sqrt{3}\right\}$

47. Possible rational roots

$\pm 1,\ \pm \frac{1}{2}$

Test $x = \frac{1}{2}$:

$\frac{1}{2}$	2	-1	2	-1
		1	0	1
	2	0	2	0

Descartes' Rule of Signs

# pos	# neg	# nonreal
3	0	0
1	0	2

$$2x^3 - x^2 + 2x - 1 = 0$$
$$\left(x - \tfrac{1}{2}\right)\left(2x^2 + 2\right) = 0$$
$x - \frac{1}{2} = 0$ **or** $2x^2 + 2 = 0$

$x = \frac{1}{2}$ $\qquad$ $x = \pm\sqrt{-1}$

$x = \pm i$

Solution set: $\left\{\frac{1}{2}, -i, i\right\}$

48. Possible rational roots

$\pm 1, \pm \frac{1}{3}$

Test $x = -\frac{1}{3}$:

$$\begin{array}{r|rrrr} -\frac{1}{3} & 3 & 1 & 3 & 1 \\ & & -1 & 0 & -1 \\ \hline & 3 & 0 & 3 & 0 \end{array}$$

Descartes' Rule of Signs

# pos	# neg	# nonreal
0	3	0
0	1	2

$3x^3 + x^2 + 3x + 1 = 0$

$\left(x + \frac{1}{3}\right)\left(3x^2 + 3\right) = 0$

$x + \frac{1}{3} = 0$ **or** $3x^2 + 3 = 0$

$x = -\frac{1}{3}$ $\quad x = \pm\sqrt{-1}$

$x = \pm i$

Solution set: $\left\{-\frac{1}{3}, -i, i\right\}$

49. Possible rational roots

$\pm 1, \pm 2, \pm 4, \pm 8$

± 16

Descartes' Rule of Signs

# pos	# neg	# nonreal
2	2	0
2	0	2
0	2	2
0	0	4

$x^4 - 2x^3 - 8x^2 + 8x + 16 = 0$

$(x-2)\left(x^3 - 8x - 8\right) = 0$

$(x-2)(x+2)\left(x^2 - 2x - 4\right) = 0$

Use the quadratic formula.

Solution set: $\left\{2, -2, 1 \pm \sqrt{5}\right\}$

Test $x = 2$:

$$\begin{array}{r|rrrrr} 2 & 1 & -2 & -8 & 8 & 16 \\ & & 2 & 0 & -16 & -16 \\ \hline & 1 & 0 & -8 & -8 & 0 \end{array}$$

Test $x = -2$:

$$\begin{array}{r|rrrr} -2 & 1 & 0 & -8 & -8 \\ & & -2 & 4 & 8 \\ \hline & 1 & -2 & -4 & 0 \end{array}$$

50. Possible rational roots

± 1

Descartes' Rule of Signs

# pos	# neg	# nonreal
2	2	0
2	0	2
0	2	2
0	0	4

$x^4 - 2x^3 - 2x^2 + 2x + 1 = 0$

$(x-1)\left(x^3 - x^2 - 3x - 1\right) = 0$

$(x-1)(x+1)\left(x^2 - 2x - 1\right) = 0$

Use the quadratic formula.

Solution set: $\left\{1, -1, 1 \pm \sqrt{2}\right\}$

Test $x = 1$:

$$\begin{array}{r|rrrrr} 1 & 1 & -2 & -2 & 2 & 1 \\ & & 1 & -1 & -3 & -1 \\ \hline & 1 & -1 & -3 & -1 & 0 \end{array}$$

Test $x = -1$:

$$\begin{array}{r|rrrr} -1 & 1 & -1 & -3 & -1 \\ & & -1 & 2 & 1 \\ \hline & 1 & -2 & -1 & 0 \end{array}$$

51. Possible rational roots

$\pm 1, \pm 3, \pm 9, \pm \frac{1}{2}$

$\pm \frac{3}{2}, \pm \frac{9}{2}$

Descartes' Rule of Signs

# pos	# neg	# nonreal
1	3	0
1	1	2

$2x^4 + x^3 + 17x^2 + 9x - 9 = 0$

$(x+1)\left(2x^3 - x^2 + 18x - 9\right) = 0$

$(x+1)\left(x - \frac{1}{2}\right)\left(2x^2 + 18\right) = 0$

$2x^2 + 18 = 0 \Rightarrow x = \pm\sqrt{-9}$

Solution set: $\left\{-1, \frac{1}{2}, \pm 3i\right\}$

Test $x = -1$:

$$\begin{array}{r|rrrrr} -1 & 2 & 1 & 17 & 9 & -9 \\ & & -2 & 1 & -18 & 9 \\ \hline & 2 & -1 & 18 & -9 & 0 \end{array}$$

Test $x = \frac{1}{2}$:

$$\begin{array}{r|rrrr} \frac{1}{2} & 2 & -1 & 18 & -9 \\ & & 1 & 0 & 9 \\ \hline & 2 & 0 & 18 & 0 \end{array}$$

52. Possible rational roots

$\pm 1, \pm 2, \pm 4, \pm \frac{1}{2}$

Descartes' Rule of Signs

# pos	# neg	# nonreal
3	1	0
1	1	2

$$2x^4 - 4x^3 + 2x^2 + 4x - 4 = 0$$
$$(x-1)(2x^3 - 2x^2 + 4) = 0$$
$$(x-1)(x+1)(2x^2 - 4x + 4) = 0$$

Use the quadratic formula.

Solution set: $\{1, -1, 1 \pm i\}$

Test $x = 1$:

$$\begin{array}{r|rrrrr} 1 & 2 & -4 & 2 & 4 & -4 \\ & & 2 & -2 & 0 & 4 \\ \hline & 2 & -2 & 0 & 4 & 0 \end{array}$$

Test $x = -1$:

$$\begin{array}{r|rrrr} -1 & 2 & -2 & 0 & 4 \\ & & -2 & 4 & -4 \\ \hline & 2 & -4 & 4 & 0 \end{array}$$

53. Possible rat. roots

$\pm 1, \pm 5, \pm 25$

Descartes' Rule of Signs

# pos	# neg	# nonreal
5	0	0
3	0	2
1	0	4

$$x^5 - 3x^4 + 28x^3 - 76x^2 + 75x - 25 = 0$$
$$(x-1)(x^4 - 2x^3 + 26x^2 - 50x + 25) = 0$$
$$(x-1)(x-1)(x^3 - x^2 + 25x - 25) = 0$$
$$(x-1)(x-1)(x-1)(x^2 + 25) = 0$$
$$x^2 + 25 = 0 \Rightarrow x = \pm\sqrt{-25}$$

Solution set: $\{1, 1, 1, \pm 5i\}$

Test $x = 1$:

$$\begin{array}{r|rrrrrr} 1 & 1 & -3 & 28 & -76 & 75 & -25 \\ & & 1 & -2 & 26 & -50 & 25 \\ \hline & 1 & -2 & 26 & -50 & 25 & 0 \end{array}$$

Test $x = 1$:

$$\begin{array}{r|rrrrr} 1 & 1 & -2 & 26 & -50 & 25 \\ & & 1 & -1 & 25 & -25 \\ \hline & 1 & -1 & 25 & -25 & 0 \end{array}$$

Test $x = 1$:

$$\begin{array}{r|rrrr} 1 & 1 & -1 & 25 & -25 \\ & & 1 & 0 & 25 \\ \hline & 1 & 0 & 25 & 0 \end{array}$$

54. Possible rat. roots

$\pm 1, \pm 5$

Descartes' Rule of Signs

# pos	# neg	# nonreal
1	4	0
1	2	2
1	0	4

$$x^5 + 3x^4 - 2x^3 - 14x^2 - 15x - 5 = 0$$
$$(x+1)(x^4 + 2x^3 - 4x^2 - 10x - 5) = 0$$
$$(x+1)(x+1)(x^3 + x^2 - 5x - 5) = 0$$
$$(x+1)(x+1)(x+1)(x^2 - 5) = 0$$
$$x^2 - 5 = 0 \Rightarrow x = \pm\sqrt{5}$$

Solution set: $\left\{-1, -1, -1, \pm\sqrt{5}\right\}$

Test $x = -1$:

$$\begin{array}{r|rrrrrr} -1 & 1 & 3 & -2 & -14 & -15 & -5 \\ & & -1 & -2 & 4 & 10 & 5 \\ \hline & 1 & 2 & -4 & -10 & -5 & 0 \end{array}$$

Test $x = -1$:

$$\begin{array}{r|rrrrr} -1 & 1 & 2 & -4 & -10 & -5 \\ & & -1 & -1 & 5 & 5 \\ \hline & 1 & 1 & -5 & -5 & 0 \end{array}$$

Test $x = -1$:

$$\begin{array}{r|rrrr} -1 & 1 & 1 & -5 & -5 \\ & & -1 & 0 & 5 \\ \hline & 1 & 0 & -5 & 0 \end{array}$$

55.

Possible rat. roots
$\pm 1, \pm 2, \pm 3,$
$\pm 4, \pm 6, \pm 12,$
$\pm \frac{1}{2}, \pm \frac{3}{2}$

Descartes' Rule of Signs

# pos	# neg	# nonreal
4	1	0
2	1	2
0	1	4

$$2x^5 - 3x^4 + 6x^3 - 9x^2 - 8x + 12 = 0$$
$$(x-1)(2x^4 - x^3 + 5x^2 - 4x - 12) = 0$$
$$(x-1)(x+1)(2x^3 - 3x^2 + 8x - 12) = 0$$
$$(x-1)(x+1)(x - \tfrac{3}{2})(2x^2 + 8) = 0$$
$$2x^2 + 8 = 0 \Rightarrow x = \pm\sqrt{-4}$$

Solution set: $\{1, -1, \frac{3}{2}, \pm 2i\}$

Test $x = 1$:

$$\begin{array}{c|cccccc} 1 & 2 & -3 & 6 & -9 & -8 & 12 \\ & & 2 & -1 & 5 & -4 & -12 \\ \hline & 2 & -1 & 5 & -4 & -12 & 0 \end{array}$$

Test $x = -1$:

$$\begin{array}{c|ccccc} -1 & 2 & -1 & 5 & -4 & -12 \\ & & -2 & 3 & -8 & 12 \\ \hline & 2 & -3 & 8 & -12 & 0 \end{array}$$

Test $x = \frac{3}{2}$:

$$\begin{array}{c|cccc} \frac{3}{2} & 2 & -3 & 8 & -12 \\ & & 3 & 0 & 12 \\ \hline & 2 & 0 & 8 & 0 \end{array}$$

56.

Possible rat. roots
$\pm 1, \pm 2, \pm 4,$
$\pm 8, \pm 16, \pm 32,$
$\pm 64, \pm \frac{1}{3}, \pm \frac{2}{3},$
$\pm \frac{4}{3}, \pm \frac{8}{3}, \pm \frac{16}{3},$
$\pm \frac{32}{3}, \pm \frac{64}{3}$

Descartes' Rule of Signs

# pos	# neg	# nonreal
4	1	0
2	1	2
0	1	4

$$3x^5 - x^4 + 36x^3 - 12x^2 - 192x + 64 = 0$$
$$(x-2)(3x^4 + 5x^3 + 46x^2 + 80x - 32) = 0$$
$$(x-2)(x+2)(3x^3 - x^2 + 48x - 16) = 0$$
$$(x-2)(x+2)(x - \tfrac{1}{3})(3x^2 + 48) = 0$$
$$3x^2 + 48 = 0 \Rightarrow x = \pm\sqrt{-16}$$

Solution set: $\{2, -2, \frac{1}{3}, \pm 4i\}$

Test $x = 2$:

$$\begin{array}{c|cccccc} 2 & 3 & -1 & 36 & -12 & -192 & 64 \\ & & 6 & 10 & 92 & 160 & -64 \\ \hline & 3 & 5 & 46 & 80 & -32 & 0 \end{array}$$

Test $x = -2$:

$$\begin{array}{c|ccccc} -2 & 3 & 5 & 46 & 80 & -32 \\ & & -6 & 2 & -96 & 32 \\ \hline & 3 & -1 & 48 & -16 & 0 \end{array}$$

Test $x = \frac{1}{3}$:

$$\begin{array}{c|cccc} \frac{1}{3} & 3 & -1 & 48 & -16 \\ & & 1 & 0 & 16 \\ \hline & 3 & 0 & 48 & 0 \end{array}$$

57. If $(1+i)$ is a root, then so is $(1-i)$, and $x - (1+i)$ and $x - (1-i)$ are factors. Then $[x - (1+i)][x - (1-i)] = x^2 - 2x + 2$ is a factor. Divide it out:

$$\begin{array}{r} x - 3 \\ x^2 - 2x + 2 \overline{\big)\, x^3 - 5x^2 + 8x - 6} \\ \underline{x^3 - 2x^2 + 2x} \\ -3x^2 + 6x - 6 \\ \underline{-3x^2 + 6x - 6} \\ 0 \end{array}$$

$$x^3 - 5x^2 + 8x - 6 = 0$$
$$(x^2 - 2x + 2)(x - 3) = 0$$

Solution set: $\{1+i, 1-i, 3\}$

58. If $(1+i)$ is a root, then so is $(1-i)$, and $x-(1+i)$ and $x-(1-i)$ are factors. Then $[x-(1+i)][x-(1-i)] = x^2-2x+2$ is a factor. Divide it out:

$$\begin{array}{r|l} & x + 2 \\ \hline x^2-2x+2 & x^3+0x^2-2x+4 \\ & x^3-2x^2+2x \\ \hline & \quad 2x^2-4x+4 \\ & \quad 2x^2-4x+4 \\ \hline & \qquad 0 \end{array}$$

$$x^3-2x+4=0$$
$$(x^2-2x+2)(x+2)=0$$

Solution set: $\{1+i, 1-i, -2\}$

59. If $(1+i)$ is a root, then so is $(1-i)$, and $x-(1+i)$ and $x-(1-i)$ are factors. Then $[x-(1+i)][x-(1-i)] = x^2-2x+2$ is a factor. Divide it out:

$$\begin{array}{r|l} & x^2 - 9 \\ \hline x^2-2x+2 & x^4-2x^3-7x^2+18x-18 \\ & x^4-2x^3+2x^2 \\ \hline & \quad -9x^2+18x-18 \\ & \quad -9x^2+18x-18 \\ \hline & \qquad 0 \end{array}$$

$$x^4-2x^3-7x^2+18x-18=0$$
$$(x^2-2x+2)(x^2-9)=0$$
$$(x^2-2x+2)(x+3)(x-3)=0$$

Solution set: $\{1+i, 1-i, -3, 3\}$

60. If $(1+i)$ is a root, then so is $(1-i)$, and $x-(1+i)$ and $x-(1-i)$ are factors. Then $[x-(1+i)][x-(1-i)] = x^2-2x+2$ is a factor. Divide it out:

$$\begin{array}{r|l} & x^2 - 4 \\ \hline x^2-2x+2 & x^4-2x^3-2x^2+8x-8 \\ & x^4-2x^3+2x^2 \\ \hline & \quad -4x^2+8x-8 \\ & \quad -4x^2+8x-8 \\ \hline & \qquad 0 \end{array}$$

$$x^4-2x^3-2x^2+8x-8=0$$
$$(x^2-2x+2)(x^2-4)=0$$
$$(x^2-2x+2)(x+2)(x-2)=0$$

Solution set: $\{1+i, 1-i, -2, 2\}$

61. Possible rational roots

$\pm 1, \pm 2, \pm 3, \pm 6, \pm\frac{1}{3}, \pm\frac{2}{3}$

Descartes' Rule of Signs

# pos	# neg	# nonreal
1	2	0
1	0	2

Test $x=-1$:

$$\begin{array}{r|rrrr} -1 & 3 & -4 & -13 & -6 \\ & & -3 & 7 & 6 \\ \hline & 3 & -7 & -6 & 0 \end{array}$$

$$x^3-\frac{4}{3}x^2-\frac{13}{3}x-2=0$$
$$3x^3-4x^2-13x-6=0$$
$$(x+1)(3x^2-7x-6)=0$$
$$(x+1)(3x+2)(x-3)=0$$

Solution set: $\{-1, -\frac{2}{3}, 3\}$

62. Possible rational roots

$\pm 1, \pm 2, \pm 3, \pm 6, \pm\frac{1}{2}, \pm\frac{3}{2}, \pm\frac{1}{3}, \pm\frac{2}{3}, \pm\frac{1}{6}$

Descartes' Rule of Signs

# pos	# neg	# nonreal
2	1	0
0	1	2

Test $x=3$:

$$\begin{array}{r|rrrr} 3 & 6 & -19 & 1 & 6 \\ & & 18 & -3 & -6 \\ \hline & 6 & -1 & -2 & 0 \end{array}$$

$$x^3-\frac{19}{6}x^2+\frac{1}{6}x+1=0$$
$$6x^3-19x^2+x+6=0$$
$$(x-3)(6x^2-x-2)=0$$
$$(x-3)(3x-2)(2x+1)=0$$

Solution set: $\{3, \frac{2}{3}, -\frac{1}{2}\}$

63. $x^{-5} - 8x^{-4} + 25x^{-3} - 38x^{-2} + 28x^{-1} - 8 = 0$

$$x^5\left(x^{-5} - 8x^{-4} + 25x^{-3} - 38x^{-2} + 28x^{-1} - 8\right) = x^5(0)$$

$$1 - 8x + 25x^2 - 38x^3 + 28x^4 - 8x^5 = 0$$

Possible rat. roots: $\pm 1, \pm\frac{1}{2}, \pm\frac{1}{4}, \pm\frac{1}{8}$

Descartes' Rule of Signs

# pos	# neg	# nonreal
5	0	0
3	0	2
1	0	4

Test $x = 1$:

$$\begin{array}{r|rrrrrr} 1 & 8 & -28 & 38 & -25 & 8 & -1 \\ & & 8 & -20 & 18 & -7 & 1 \\ \hline & 8 & -20 & 18 & -7 & 1 & 0 \end{array}$$

Test $x = 1$:

$$\begin{array}{r|rrrrr} 1 & 8 & -20 & 18 & -7 & 1 \\ & & 8 & -12 & 6 & -1 \\ \hline & 8 & -12 & 6 & -1 & 0 \end{array}$$

Test $x = \frac{1}{2}$:

$$\begin{array}{r|rrrr} \frac{1}{2} & 8 & -12 & 6 & -1 \\ & & 4 & -4 & 1 \\ \hline & 8 & -8 & 2 & 0 \end{array}$$

$$8x^5 - 28x^4 + 38x^3 - 25x^2 + 8x - 1 = 0$$
$$(x-1)\left(8x^4 - 20x^3 + 18x^2 - 7x + 1\right) = 0$$
$$(x-1)(x-1)\left(8x^3 - 12x^2 + 6x - 1\right) = 0$$
$$(x-1)(x-1)\left(x - \tfrac{1}{2}\right)\left(8x^2 - 8x + 2\right) = 0$$
$$(x-1)(x-1)\left(x - \tfrac{1}{2}\right)(4x-2)(2x-1) = 0$$

Solution set: $\left\{1, 1, \frac{1}{2}, \frac{1}{2}, \frac{1}{2}\right\}$

64. $1 - x^{-1} - x^{-2} - 2x^{-3} = 0$

$$x^3\left(1 - x^{-1} - x^{-2} - 2x^{-3}\right) = x^3(0) \Rightarrow x^3 - x^2 - x - 2 = 0$$

Possible rat. roots: $\pm 1, \pm 2$

Descartes' Rule of Signs

# pos	# neg	# nonreal
1	2	0
1	0	2

Test $x = 2$:

$$\begin{array}{r|rrrr} 2 & 1 & -1 & -1 & -2 \\ & & 2 & 2 & 2 \\ \hline & 1 & 1 & 1 & 0 \end{array}$$

$$x^3 - x^2 - x - 2 = 0$$
$$(x-2)\left(x^2 + x + 1\right) = 0$$

Use the quadratic formula on the second factor.

Sol. set: $\left\{2, -\frac{1}{2} + \frac{\sqrt{3}}{2}i, -\frac{1}{2} - \frac{\sqrt{3}}{2}i\right\}$

65. Let $x = R_1$. Then $x + 10 = R_2$ and $x + 50 = R_3$.

$$\frac{1}{R} = \frac{1}{R_1} + \frac{1}{R_2} + \frac{1}{R_3}$$
$$\frac{1}{6} = \frac{1}{x} + \frac{1}{x+10} + \frac{1}{x+50}$$
$$6x(x+10)(x+50)\cdot\frac{1}{6} = 6x(x+10)(x+50)\left(\frac{1}{x} + \frac{1}{x+10} + \frac{1}{x+50}\right)$$
$$x(x+10)(x+50) = 6(x+10)(x+50) + 6x(x+50) + 6x(x+10)$$
$$x^3 + 60x^2 + 500x = 6x^2 + 360x + 3000 + 6x^2 + 300x + 6x^2 + 60x$$
$$x^3 + 42x^2 - 220x - 3000 = 0$$
$$(x-10)\left(x^2 + 52x + 300\right) = 0$$

$$\begin{array}{r|rrrr} 10 & 1 & 42 & -220 & -3000 \\ & & 10 & 520 & 3000 \\ \hline & 1 & 52 & 300 & 0 \end{array}$$

Use the quadratic formula on the second factor. The two solutions from that factor are negative. The only solution that makes sense is $x = 10$. The resistances are 10, 20 and 60 ohms.

66. The volume is $(12-2x)(14-2x)x = 4x^3 - 52x^2 + 168x$.

$$4x^3 - 52x^2 + 168x = 160$$
$$4x^3 - 52x^2 + 168x - 160 = 0$$
$$4(x^3 - 13x^2 + 42x - 40) = 0$$
$$x^3 - 13x^2 + 42x - 40 = 0$$
$$(x-2)(x^2 - 11x + 20) = 0$$
$$(x-2)(x-2)(x-9) = 0$$

Test $x = 2$:

2	1	−13	42	−40
		2	−22	40
	1	−11	20	0

The only solution that makes sense is $x = 2$.
2 inch by 2 inch squares should be cut from the corners.

67. Let $x =$ the height. Then $x+7 =$ the length, and $x+4 =$ the width.
The volume is $x(x+7)(x+4) = x^3 + 11x^2 + 28x$.

$$x^3 + 11x^2 + 28x = 4420$$
$$x^3 + 11x^2 + 28x - 4420 = 0$$
$$(x-13)(x^2 + 24x + 340) = 0$$

Test $x = 13$:

13	1	11	28	−4420
		13	312	4420
	1	24	340	0

The only real solution is $x = 13$.
The height is 13 inches.

68. Let $x =$ the radius. Then $x+9 =$ the height.
The volume is $\pi r^2 h = \pi x^2(x+9) = \pi(x^3 + 9x^2)$.

$$\pi(x^3 + 9x^2) = 108\pi$$
$$x^3 + 9x^2 = 108$$
$$x^3 + 9x^2 - 108 = 0$$
$$(x-3)(x^2 + 12x + 36) = 0$$
$$(x-3)(x+6)(x+6) = 0$$

Test $x = 3$:

3	1	9	0	−108
		3	36	108
	1	12	36	0

The only solution that makes sense is $x = 3$.
The radius is 3 inches.

69. Possible rat'l roots

$\pm 1, \pm 2, \pm 3,$
$\pm 5, \pm 6, \pm 9,$
$\pm 10, \pm 15, \pm 18,$
$\pm 25, \pm 30, \pm 45,$
$\pm 50, \pm 75, \pm 90,$
$\pm 150, \pm 225,$
± 450

Descartes' Rule of Signs

# pos	# neg	# nonreal
3	1	0
1	1	2

$$-x^4 + 5x^3 + 91x^2 - 545x + 550 = 100$$
$$x^4 - 5x^3 - 91x^2 + 545x - 450 = 0$$
$$(x-1)(x^3 - 4x^2 - 95x + 450) = 0$$
$$(x-1)(x-5)(x^2 + x - 90) = 0$$
$$(x-1)(x-5)(x-9)(x+10) = 0$$

Solution set: $\{1, 5, 9, -10\}$

Test $x = 1$:

1	1	−5	−91	545	−450
		1	−4	−95	450
	1	−4	−95	450	0

Test $x = 5$:

5	1	−4	−95	450
		5	5	−450
	1	1	−90	0

The only solutions between 0 and 9 are 1, 5, and 9 miles.

70. Possible rational roots

$\pm 1, \pm 2, \pm 4, \pm 5, \pm 8, \pm 10, \pm 16, \pm 20, \pm 25, \pm 32, \pm 40, \pm 50, \pm 80, \pm 100, \pm 160, \pm 200, \pm 400, \pm 800,$

Descartes' Rule of Signs

# pos	# neg	# nonreal
3	0	0
1	0	2

Test $t = 4$:

$$\begin{array}{r|rrrr} 4 & 1 & -34 & 320 & -800 \\ & & 4 & -120 & 800 \\ \hline & 1 & -30 & 200 & 0 \end{array}$$

$$-t^3 + 34t^2 - 320t + 850 = 50$$
$$t^3 - 34t^2 + 320t - 800 = 0$$
$$(t-4)(t^2 - 30t + 200) = 0$$
$$(t-4)(t-10)(t-20) = 0$$

Solution set: $\{4, 10, 20\}$; After 4, 10, and 20 minutes.

71. Answers may vary.

72. Answers may vary.

73. A coordinate of a point on the parabola has coordinates $(x, 16 - x^2)$.
Thus, the area of the rectangle is $A = 2x(16 - x^2) = 32x - 2x^3$.

$$32x - 2x^3 = 42$$
$$-2x^3 + 32x - 42 = 0$$
$$x^3 - 16x + 21 = 0$$
$$(x-3)(x^2 + 3x - 7) = 0$$

Test $x = 3$:

$$\begin{array}{r|rrrr} 3 & 1 & 0 & -16 & 21 \\ & & 3 & 9 & -21 \\ \hline & 1 & 3 & --7 & 0 \end{array}$$

Using the quadratic formula on the second factor yields the solutions $x = \dfrac{-3 \pm \sqrt{37}}{2} \approx 1.54$ or -4.54.
The only solutions that make sense are $x = 3$ or $x = 1.54$.
Points: $(3, 7)$ or $(1.54, 13.63)$

74. A coordinate of a point on the curve has coordinates $(x, x^3 - 2x^2)$.
Thus, the area of the rectangle is $A = x(x^3 - 2x^2) = x^4 - 2x^3$.

$$x^4 - 2x^3 = 27$$
$$x^4 - 2x^3 - 27 = 0$$
$$(x-3)(x^3 + x^2 + 3x + 9) = 0$$

Test $x = 3$:

$$\begin{array}{r|rrrrr} 3 & 1 & -2 & 0 & 0 & -27 \\ & & 3 & 3 & 9 & 27 \\ \hline & 1 & 1 & 3 & 9 & 0 \end{array}$$

Since the coefficients of the second factor are all positive, Descartes' Rule of Signs indicates that there are no more positive solutions. Thus, $x = 3$: $(3, 9)$.

75. $\sqrt{72a^3b^5c} = \sqrt{36a^2b^4}\sqrt{2abc} = 6ab^2\sqrt{2abc}$

76. $\dfrac{5a}{\sqrt{5a}} = \dfrac{5a\sqrt{5a}}{\sqrt{5a}\cdot\sqrt{5a}} = \dfrac{5a\sqrt{5a}}{5a} = \sqrt{5a}$

77. $\sqrt{18a^2b} + a\sqrt{50b} = \sqrt{9a^2}\sqrt{2b} + a\sqrt{25}\sqrt{2b} = 3a\sqrt{2b} + 5a\sqrt{2b} = 8a\sqrt{2b}$

78. $\left(\sqrt{3}+\sqrt{5b}\right)\left(\sqrt{12}-\sqrt{45b}\right) = \sqrt{36}-\sqrt{135b}+\sqrt{60b}-\sqrt{225b^2}$
$= 6-\sqrt{9}\sqrt{15b}+\sqrt{4}\sqrt{15b}-15b$
$= 6-3\sqrt{15b}+2\sqrt{15b}-15b = 6-\sqrt{15b}-15b$

79. $\frac{2}{\sqrt{3}-1} = \frac{2\left(\sqrt{3}+1\right)}{\left(\sqrt{3}-1\right)\left(\sqrt{3}+1\right)} = \frac{2\left(\sqrt{3}+1\right)}{\left(\sqrt{3}\right)^2-1^2} = \frac{2\left(\sqrt{3}+1\right)}{3-1} = \frac{2\left(\sqrt{3}+1\right)}{2} = \sqrt{3}+1$

80. $\frac{\sqrt{11}+\sqrt{x}}{\sqrt{11}-\sqrt{x}} = \frac{\left(\sqrt{11}+\sqrt{x}\right)\left(\sqrt{11}+\sqrt{x}\right)}{\left(\sqrt{11}-\sqrt{x}\right)\left(\sqrt{11}+\sqrt{x}\right)} = \frac{11+2\sqrt{11x}+x}{11-x}$

Exercises 5.4 (page 535)

1. $P(a)$ and $P(b)$

2. $P(r) = 0$

3. x_l and x_r

4. continuous

5. $x^4-4 = \left(\sqrt{2}\right)^4-4 = 4-4 = 0;$
The only possible rational roots are ± 1, ± 2, ± 4. None of these satisfy the equation, so $\sqrt{2}$ is irrational.

6. $x^4-36 = \left(\sqrt{6}\right)^4-36 = 36-36 = 0;$
The only possible rational roots are $\pm 1, \pm 2, \pm 3, \pm 4, \pm 6, \pm 9, \pm 12, \pm 18, \pm 36$. None of these satisfy the equation, so $\sqrt{6}$ is irrational.

7. $x^4-49 = \left(\sqrt{7}\right)^4-49 = 49-49 = 0;$
The only possible rational roots are ± 1, ± 7, ± 49. None of these satisfy the equation, so $\sqrt{7}$ is irrational.

8. $x^4-64 = \left(-2\sqrt{2}\right)^4-64 = 64-64 = 0;$
The only possible rational roots are $\pm 1, \pm 2, \pm 4, \pm 8, \pm 16, \pm 32, \pm 64$. None of these satisfy the equation, so $-2\sqrt{2}$ is irrational.

9. $P(x) = 2x^2+x-3$
$P(-2) = 3; P(-1) = -2$
Thus, there is a root between -2 and -1.

10. $P(x) = 2x^3+17x^2+31x-20$
$P(-1) = -36; P(2) = 126$
Thus, there is a root between -1 and 2.

11. $P(x) = 3x^3-11x^2-14x$
$P(4) = -40; P(5) = 30$
Thus, there is a root between 4 and 5.

12. $P(x) = 2x^3-3x^2+2x-3$
$P(1) = -2; P(2) = 5$
Thus, there is a root between 1 and 2.

13. $P(x) = x^4-8x^2+15$
$P(1) = 8; P(2) = -1$
Thus, there is a root between 1 and 2.

14. $P(x) = x^4-8x^2+15$
$P(2) = -1; P(3) = 24$
Thus, there is a root between 2 and 3.

15. $30x^3 + 10 = 61x^2 + 39x$
$30x^3 - 61x^2 - 39x + 10 = 0$
$P(x) = 30x^3 - 61x^2 - 39x + 10$
$P(2) = -72; P(3) = 154$
Thus, there is a root between 2 and 3.

16. $30x^3 + 10 = 61x^2 + 39x$
$30x^3 - 61x^2 - 39x + 10 = 0$
$P(x) = 30x^3 - 61x^2 - 39x + 10$
$P(-1) = -42; P(0) = 10$
Thus, there is a root between -1 and 0.

17. $30x^3 + 10 = 61x^2 + 39x$
$30x^3 - 61x^2 - 39x + 10 = 0$
$P(x) = 30x^3 - 61x^2 - 39x + 10$
$P(0) = 10; P(1) = -60$
Thus, there is a root between 0 and 1.

18. $P(x) = 5x^3 - 9x^2 - 4x + 9$
$P(-1) = -1; P(0) = 9$
Thus, there is a root between -1 and 0.

19. $P(x) = x^2 - 3$. Note that $P(1) = -2$ and $P(2) = 1$. There is a root between 1 and 2.

STEP	x_l	c	x_r	$P(x_l)$	$P(x_c)$	$P(x_r)$
0	1	1.5	2	-2.0	-0.75	1.0
1	1.5	1.75	2	-0.75	0.0625	1.0
2	1.5	1.625	1.75	-0.75	-0.3594	0.0625
3	1.625	1.6875	1.75	-0.3594	-0.1523	0.0625
4	1.6875	1.71875	1.75	-0.1523	-0.0459	0.0625
5	1.71875	1.734375	1.75			

To the nearest tenth, the solution is $x = 1.7$.

20. $P(x) = x^2 - 3$. Note that $P(-2) = 1$ and $P(-1) = -2$. There is a root between -2 and -1.

STEP	x_l	c	x_r	$P(x_l)$	$P(x_c)$	$P(x_r)$
0	-2	-1.5	-1	1.0	-0.75	-2.0
1	-2	-1.75	-1.5	1.0	0.0625	-0.75
2	-1.75	-1.625	-1.5	0.0625	-0.3594	-0.75
3	-1.75	-1.6875	-1.625	0.0625	-0.1523	-0.3594
4	-1.75	-1.71875	-1.6875	0.0625	-0.0459	-0.1523
5	-1.75	-1.734375	-1.71875			

To the nearest tenth, the solution is $x = -1.7$.

21. $P(x) = x^2 - 5$. Note that $P(-3) = 4$ and $P(-2) = -1$. There is a root between -3 and -2.

STEP	x_l	c	x_r	$P(x_l)$	$P(x_c)$	$P(x_r)$
0	-3	-2.5	-2	4.0	1.25	-1.0
1	-2.5	-2.25	-2	1.25	0.0625	-1.0
2	-2.25	-2.125	-2	0.0625	-0.4844	-1.0
3	-2.25	-2.1875	-2.125	0.0625	-0.2148	-0.4844
4	-2.25	-2.21875	-2.1875	0.0625	-0.0771	-0.2148
5	-2.25	-2.234375	-2.21875			

To the nearest tenth, the solution is $x = -2.2$.

22. $P(x) = x^2 - 5$. Note that $P(2) = -1$ and $P(3) = 4$. There is a root between 2 and 3.

STEP	x_l	c	x_r	$P(x_l)$	$P(x_c)$	$P(x_r)$
0	2	2.5	3	−1.0	1.25	4.0
1	2	2.25	2.5	−1.0	0.0625	1.25
2	2	2.125	2.25	−1.0	−0.4844	0.0625
3	2.125	2.1875	2.25	−0.4844	−0.2148	0.0625
4	2.1875	2.21875	2.25	−0.2148	−0.0771	0.0625
5	2.21875	2.234375	2.25			

To the nearest tenth, the solution is $x = 2.2$.

23. $P(x) = x^3 - x^2 - 2$. Note that $P(1) = -2$ and $P(2) = 2$. There is a root between 1 and 2.

STEP	x_l	c	x_r	$P(x_l)$	$P(x_c)$	$P(x_r)$
0	1	1.5	2	−2.0	−0.875	2.0
1	1.5	1.75	2	−0.875	0.2969	2.0
2	1.5	1.625	1.75	−0.875	−0.3496	0.2969
3	1.625	1.6875	1.75	−0.3496	−0.0422	0.2969
4	1.6875	1.71875	1.75	−0.0422	0.1233	0.2969
5	1.6875	1.703125	1.71875			

To the nearest tenth, the solution is $x = 1.7$.

24. $P(x) = x^3 - x + 2$. Note that $P(-2) = -4$ and $P(-1) = 2$. There is a root between -2 and -1.

STEP	x_l	c	x_r	$P(x_l)$	$P(x_c)$	$P(x_r)$
0	−2	−1.5	−1	−4.0	−0.125	2.0
1	−1.5	−1.25	−1	−0.125	1.2969	2.0
2	−1.5	−1.375	−1.25	−0.125	0.7754	1.2969
3	−1.5	−1.4375	−1.375	−0.125	0.4670	0.7754
4	−1.5	−1.46875	−1.4375	−0.125	0.3003	0.4670
5	−1.5	−1.484375	−1.46875			

To the nearest tenth, the solution is $x = -1.5$.

25. $P(x) = 3x^4 + 3x^3 - x^2 - 4x - 4$. Note that $P(-2) = 24$ and $P(-1) = -1$.
There is a root between -2 and -1.

STEP	x_l	c	x_r	$P(x_l)$	$P(x_c)$	$P(x_r)$
0	−2	−1.5	−1	24.0	4.8125	−1.0
1	−1.5	−1.25	−1	4.8125	0.9023	−1.0
2	−1.25	−1.125	−1	0.9023	−0.2317	−1.0
3	−1.25	−1.1875	−1.125	0.9023	0.2818	−0.2317
4	−1.1875	−1.15625	−1.125	0.2818	0.0127	−0.2317
5	−1.15625	−1.140625	−1.125	0.0127	−0.1125	−0.2317
6	−1.15625	−1.1484375	−1.140625	0.0127	−0.0507	−0.1125
7	−1.15625	−1.15234375	−1.1484375	0.0127	−0.0192	−0.0507
8	−1.15625	−1.154296875	−1.15234375			

To the nearest tenth, the solution is $x = -1.2$.

26. $P(x) = x^5 + x^4 - 4x^3 - 4x^2 - 5x - 5$. Note that $P(2) = -15$ and $P(3) = 160$. There is a root between 2 and 3.

STEP	x_l	c	x_r	$P(x_l)$	$P(x_c)$	$P(x_r)$
0	2	2.5	3	−15.0	31.7188	160.0
1	2	2.25	2.5	−15.0	1.2314	31.7188
2	2	2.125	2.25	−15.0	−8.3488	1.2314
3	2.125	2.1875	2.25	−8.3488	−3.9618	1.2314
4	2.1875	2.21875	2.25	−3.9618	−1.4708	1.2314
5	2.21875	2.234375	2.25	−1.4708	−0.1467	1.2314
6	2.234375	2.2421875	2.25	−0.1467	0.5355	1.2314
7	2.234275	2.23823125	2.2421875			

To the nearest tenth, the solution is $x = 2.2$.

27. Find the x-coordinates of any x-intercepts:

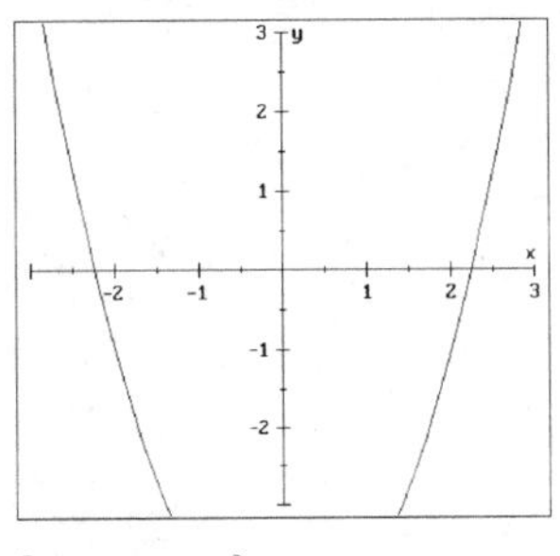

$\{-2.2, 2.2\}$

28. Find the x-coordinates of any x-intercepts:

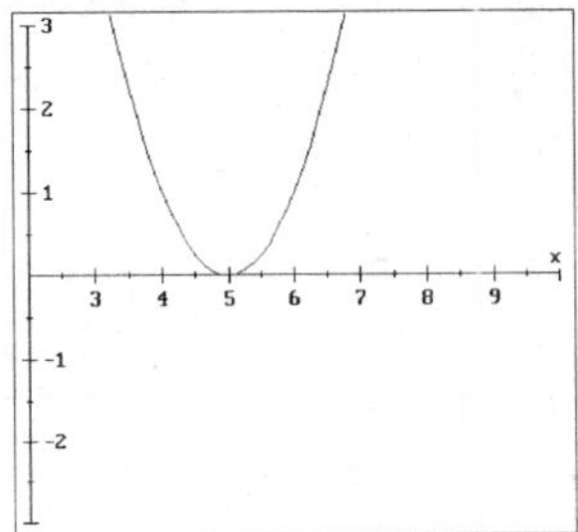

$\{5\}$: Bisection fails since the solution cannot be bracketed by a negative y-coordinate and a positive y-coordinate.

29. Find the x-coordinates of any x-intercepts:

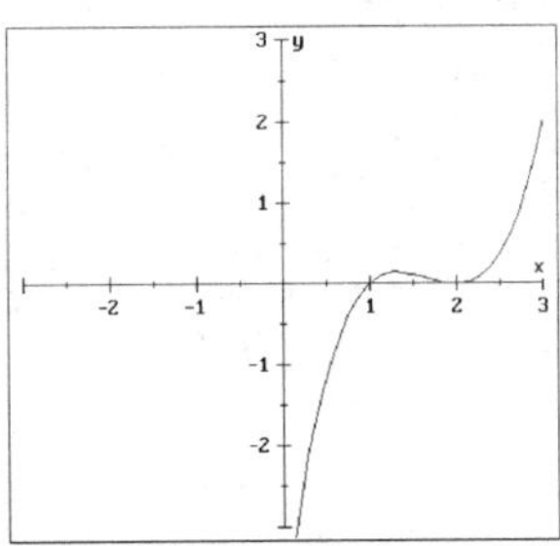

$\{1, 2\}$: Bisection fails for $x = 2$ since the solution cannot be bracketed by a negative y-coordinate and a positive y-coordinate.

30. Find the x-coordinates of any x-intercepts:

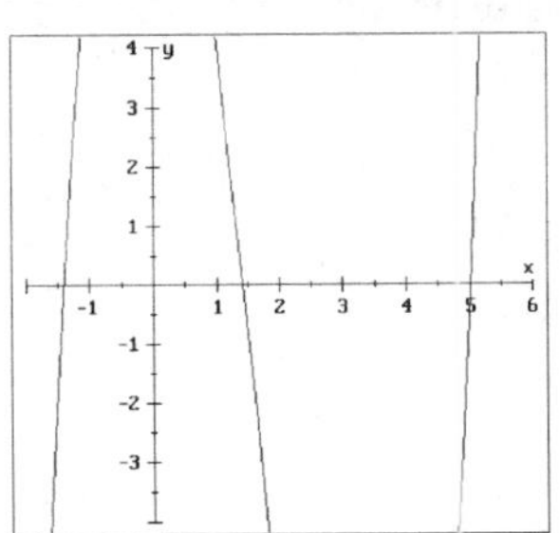

$\{-1.4, 1.4, 5\}$

31. Let h = the height of the box. Then the volume of the box is $16(10)h$, or$160h$.
$160h = 1000 \Rightarrow 160h - 1000 = 0$
Let $f(h) = 160h - 1000$. $f(4) = -360$ while $f(8) = 280$, so there is a solution between $h = 4$ and $h = 8$.

32. Let r = the radius of a lollipop. Then the volume of a lollipop is $\frac{4}{3}\pi r^3$.
$\frac{4}{3}\pi r^3 = 200 \Rightarrow \frac{4}{3}\pi r^3 - 200 = 0$
Let $f(r) = \frac{4}{3}\pi r^3 - 200$. $f(1) \approx -196$ while $f(4) \approx 68$, so there is a solution between $r = 1$ and $r = 4$.

33. A point on the graph has coordinates (x, x^3). Then the distance to the origin is found by the distance formula:

$$d = \sqrt{(x-0)^2 + (x^3-0)^2} = \sqrt{x^2 + x^6} = 1$$

$$\sqrt{x^2 + x^6} = 1$$

$$x^2 + x^6 = 1$$

$x^2 + x^6 - 1 = 0$: Graph and find intercepts. The x-coordinates are about 0.83 and -0.83. Find the y-coordinates using $y = x^3$. The points are $(0.83, 0.56)$ and $(-0.83, -0.56)$.

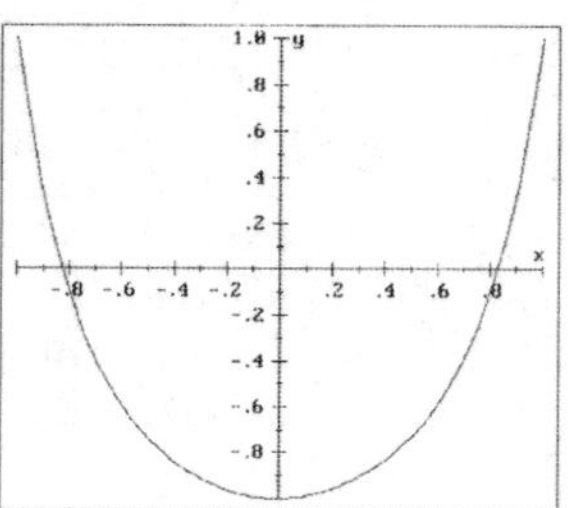

34. Let x = the length. Then $x - 2$ = the height and $x - 5$ = the width.

$$x(x-2)(x-5) = 170$$

$x^3 - 7x^2 + 10x - 170 = 0$: Graph and find intercepts. The x-coordinate is about 8.2, so the height is abut 3.2 feet.

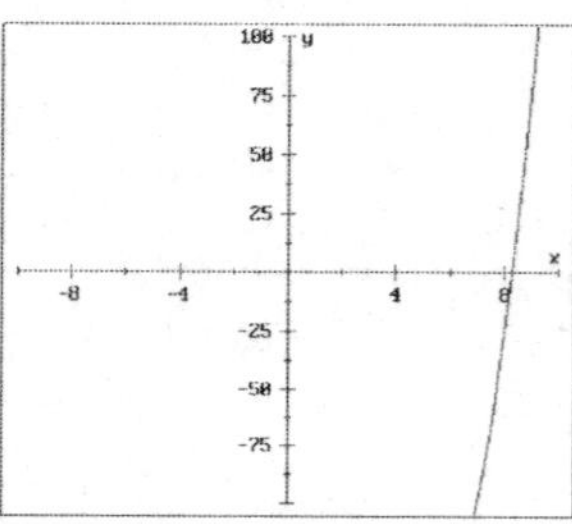

35. **Answers may vary.**

36. **Answers may vary.**

37. $y = \dfrac{5x-3}{x^2-4} = \dfrac{5x-3}{(x+2)(x-2)}$
vertical: $x = -2$, $x = 2$
horizontal: $y = 0$
slant: none

38. $y = \dfrac{5x^2-3}{x^2-25} = \dfrac{5x^2-3}{(x+5)(x-5)}$
vertical: $x = -5$, $x = 5$
horizontal: $y = \dfrac{5}{1} \Rightarrow y = 5$
slant: none

39. $y = \dfrac{x^2}{x-2} = x + 2 + \dfrac{4}{x-2}$
vertical: $x = 2$
horizontal: none
slant: $y = x + 2$

40. $y = \dfrac{x+1}{x^2+1}$
vertical: none
horizontal: $y = 0$
slant: none

Chapter 5 Review (page 539)

1. $P(1) = 4(1)^4 + 2(1)^3 - 3(1)^2 - 2 = 1$
The remainder is 1.

2. $P(2) = 4(2)^4 + 2(2)^3 - 3(2)^2 - 2 = 66$
The remainder is 66.

3. $P(-3) = 4(-3)^4 + 2(-3)^3 - 3(-3)^2 - 2 = 241 \Rightarrow$ The remainder is 241.

4. $P(-2) = 4(-2)^4 + 2(-2)^3 - 3(-2)^2 - 2 = 34 \Rightarrow$ The remainder is 34.

5. $P(2) = (2)^3 + 4(2)^2 - 2(2) + 4 = 24 \Rightarrow$ The remainder is 24. $\Rightarrow$ not a factor

6. $P(-3) = 2(-3)^4 + 10(-3)^3 + 4(-3)^2 + 7(-3) + 21 = -72 \Rightarrow$ The remainder is -72.
$\Rightarrow$ not a factor

7. $P(5) = (5)^5 - 3125 = 0$
The remainder is 0. $\Rightarrow$ factor

8. $P(6) = (6)^5 - 6(6)^4 - 4(6) + 24 = 0$
The remainder is 0. $\Rightarrow$ factor

9.
$$\begin{array}{r|rrrrr} 3 & 3 & 0 & 2 & 3 & 7 \\ & & 9 & 27 & 87 & 270 \\ \hline & 3 & 9 & 29 & 90 & 277 \end{array}$$
$$3x^3 + 9x^2 + 29x + 90 + \frac{277}{x-3}$$

10.
$$\begin{array}{r|rrrrr} 2 & 2 & 0 & -3 & 3 & -1 \\ & & 4 & 8 & 10 & 26 \\ \hline & 2 & 4 & 5 & 13 & 25 \end{array}$$
$$2x^3 + 4x^2 + 5x + 13 + \frac{25}{x-2}$$

11.
$$\begin{array}{r|rrrrrr} -2 & 5 & -4 & 3 & -2 & 1 & -1 \\ & & -10 & 28 & -62 & 128 & -258 \\ \hline & 5 & -14 & 31 & -64 & 129 & -259 \end{array}$$
$$5x^4 - 14x^3 + 31x^2 - 64x + 129 + \frac{-259}{x+2}$$

12.
$$\begin{array}{r|rrrrrr} -1 & 4 & 2 & -1 & 3 & 2 & 1 \\ & & -4 & 2 & -1 & -2 & 0 \\ \hline & 4 & -2 & 1 & 2 & 0 & 1 \end{array}$$
$$4x^4 - 2x^3 + x^2 + 2x + \frac{1}{x+1}$$

13.
$$\begin{array}{r|rrrr} 3 & 5 & 2 & -1 & 1 \\ & & 15 & 51 & 150 \\ \hline & 5 & 17 & 50 & 151 \end{array} \quad P(3) = 151$$

14.
$$\begin{array}{r|rrrr} -3 & 5 & 2 & -1 & 1 \\ & & -15 & 39 & -114 \\ \hline & 5 & -13 & 38 & -113 \end{array}$$
$$P(-3) = -113$$

15.
$$\begin{array}{r|rrrr} \frac{1}{2} & 5 & 2 & -1 & 1 \\ & & \frac{5}{2} & \frac{9}{4} & \frac{5}{8} \\ \hline & 5 & \frac{9}{2} & \frac{5}{4} & \frac{13}{8} \end{array} \quad P\left(\tfrac{1}{2}\right) = \tfrac{13}{8}$$

16.
$$\begin{array}{r|rrrr} i & 5 & 2 & -1 & 1 \\ & & 5i & -5+2i & -2-6i \\ \hline & 5 & 2+5i & -6+2i & -1-6i \end{array}$$
$$P(i) = -1 - 6i$$

17. $x = 3$ is a solution, so $(x-3)$ is a factor.
Use synthetic division to divide by $(x-3)$.
$$\begin{array}{r|rrrr} 3 & 2 & -3 & -11 & 6 \\ & & 6 & 9 & -6 \\ \hline & 2 & 3 & -2 & 0 \end{array}$$

$$2x^3 - 3x^2 - 11x + 6 = 0$$
$$(x-3)\left(2x^2 + 3x - 2\right) = 0$$
$$(x-3)(2x-1)(x+2) = 0$$
Solution set: $\left\{3, \frac{1}{2}, -2\right\}$

18. $x = -2$ is a solution, so $(x+2)$ is a factor. Use synthetic division to divide by $(x+2)$.

$$\begin{array}{r|rrrrr} -2 & 1 & 4 & -1 & -20 & -20 \\ & & -2 & -4 & 10 & 20 \\ \hline & 1 & 2 & -5 & -10 & 0 \end{array}$$

$$x^4 + 4x^3 - x^2 - 20x - 20 = 0$$
$$(x+2)\left(x^3 + 2x^2 - 5x - 10\right) = 0$$

Use the fact that $x = -2$ is a double root and divide the depressed polynomial by $(x+2)$:

$$\begin{array}{r|rrrr} -2 & 1 & 2 & -5 & -10 \\ & & -2 & 0 & 10 \\ \hline & 1 & 0 & -5 & 0 \end{array}$$

$$(x+2)\left(x^3 + 2x^2 - 5x - 10\right) = 0$$
$$(x+2)(x+2)\left(x^2 - 5\right) = 0$$

Solution set: $\left\{-2, -2, \sqrt{5}, -\sqrt{5}\right\}$

19. $2(x+1)(x-2)\left(x-\frac{3}{2}\right) = 2(x^2 - x - 2)\left(x - \frac{3}{2}\right) = 2\left(x^3 - \frac{5}{2}x^2 - \frac{1}{2}x + 3\right)$
$= 2x^3 - 5x^2 - x + 6$

20. $2(x-1)(x+3)\left(x-\frac{1}{2}\right) = 2(x^2 + 2x - 3)\left(x - \frac{1}{2}\right) = 2\left(x^3 + \frac{3}{2}x^2 - 4x + \frac{3}{2}\right)$
$= 2x^3 + 3x^2 - 8x + 3$

21. $(x-2)(x+5)(x-i)(x+i) = \left(x^2 + 3x - 10\right)\left(x^2 - i^2\right) = \left(x^2 + 3x - 10\right)\left(x^2 + 1\right)$
$= x^4 + 3x^3 - 9x^2 + 3x - 10$

22. $(x+3)(x-2)(x-i)(x+i) = \left(x^2 + x - 6\right)\left(x^2 - i^2\right) = \left(x^2 + x - 6\right)\left(x^2 + 1\right)$
$= x^4 + x^3 - 5x^2 + x - 6$

23. $3x^6 - 4x^5 + 3x + 2 = 0$
6 roots

24. $2x^6 - 5x^4 + 5x^3 - 4x^2 + x - 12 = 0$
6 roots

25. $3x^{65} - 4x^{50} + 3x^{17} + 2x = 0$
65 roots

26. $x^{1984} - 12 = 0$
1984 roots

27. $P(x) = x^4 - 16$
4 linear factors, 4 zeros

28. $P(x) = x^{40} + x^{30}$
40 linear factors, 40 zeros

29. $P(x) = 4x^5 + 2x^3$
5 linear factors, 5 zeros

30. $P(x) = x^3 - 64x$
3 linear factors, 3 zeros

31. $2 - i$ is also a root.

32. $-i = 0 - i$, so $0 + i = i$ is also a root.

33. If $-i$ is a root, then i is a root also:
$$(x-4)(x+i)(x-i) = 0$$
$$(x-4)\left(x^2 - i^2\right) = 0$$
$$(x-4)\left(x^2 + 1\right) = 0$$
$$x^3 - 4x^2 + x - 4 = 0$$

34. If i is a root, then $-i$ is a root also:
$$(x+5)(x-i)(x+i) = 0$$
$$(x+5)\left(x^2 - i^2\right) = 0$$
$$(x+5)\left(x^2 + 1\right) = 0$$
$$x^3 + 5x^2 + x + 5 = 0$$

35. $P(x) = 3x^4 + 2x^3 - 4x + 2$: 2 sign variations $\Rightarrow$ 2 or 0 positive roots
$P(-x) = 3(-x)^4 + 2(-x)^3 - 4(-x) + 2$
$= 3x^4 - 2x^3 + 4x + 2$: 2 sign variations $\Rightarrow$ 2 or 0 negative roots

# pos	# neg	# nonreal
2	2	0
2	0	2
0	2	2
0	0	4

36. $P(x) = 2x^4 - 3x^3 + 5x^2 + x - 5$: 3 sign variations $\Rightarrow$ 3 or 1 positive roots
$P(-x) = 2(-x)^4 - 3(-x)^3 + 5(-x)^2 + (-x) - 5$
$= 2x^4 + 3x^3 + 5x^2 - x - 5$: 1 sign variation $\Rightarrow$ 1 negative root

# pos	# neg	# nonreal
3	1	0
1	1	2

37. $4x^5 + 3x^4 + 2x^3 + x^2 + x = 7$
$4x^5 + 3x^4 + 2x^3 + x^2 + x - 7 = 0$
$P(x) = 4x^5 + 3x^4 + 2x^3 + x^2 + x - 7$: 1 sign variation $\Rightarrow$ 1 positive root
$P(-x) = 4(-x)^5 + 3(-x)^4 + 2(-x)^3 + (-x)^2 + (-x) - 7$
$= -4x^5 + 3x^4 - 2x^3 + x^2 - x - 7$: 4 sign variations $\Rightarrow$ 4 or 2 or 0 negative roots

# pos	# neg	# nonreal
1	4	0
1	2	2
1	0	4

38. $P(x) = 3x^7 - 4x^5 + 3x^3 + x - 4$: 3 sign variations $\Rightarrow$ 3 or 1 positive roots
$P(-x) = 3(-x)^7 - 4(-x)^5 + 3(-x)^3 + (-x) - 4$
$= -3x^7 + 4x^5 - 3x^3 - x - 4$: 2 sign variations $\Rightarrow$ 2 or 0 negative roots

# pos	# neg	# nonreal
3	2	2
3	0	4
1	2	4
1	0	6

39. $P(x) = x^4 + x^2 + 24{,}567$: 0 sign variations $\Rightarrow$ 0 positive roots
$P(-x) = (-x)^4 + (-x)^2 + 24{,}567$
$= x^4 + x^2 + 24{,}567$: 0 sign variations $\Rightarrow$ 0 negative roots

# pos	# neg	# nonreal
0	0	4

40. $P(x) = -x^7 - 5$: 0 sign variations $\Rightarrow$ 0 positive roots
$P(-x) = -(-x)^7 - 5$
$= x^7 - 5$: 1 sign variation $\Rightarrow$ 1 negative root

# pos	# neg	# nonreal
0	1	6

41. $P(x) = 5x^3 - 4x^2 - 2x + 4$

$$\begin{array}{r|rrrr} 2 & 5 & -4 & -2 & 4 \\ & & 10 & 12 & 20 \\ \hline & 5 & 6 & 10 & 24 \end{array}$$

Upper bound: 2

$$\begin{array}{r|rrrr} -1 & 5 & -4 & -2 & 4 \\ & & -5 & 9 & -7 \\ \hline & 5 & -9 & 7 & -3 \end{array}$$

Lower bound: -1

42. $P(x) = x^4 + 3x^3 - 5x^2 - 9x + 1$

$$\begin{array}{r|rrrrr} 2 & 1 & 3 & -5 & -9 & 1 \\ & & 2 & 10 & 10 & 2 \\ \hline & 1 & 5 & 5 & 1 & 3 \end{array}$$

Upper bound: 2

$$\begin{array}{r|rrrrr} -5 & 1 & 3 & -5 & -9 & 1 \\ & & -5 & 10 & -25 & 170 \\ \hline & 1 & -2 & 5 & -34 & 171 \end{array}$$

Lower bound: -5

43. num: $\pm 1, \pm 2, \pm 3, \pm 6$; den: $\pm 1, \pm 2$
possible roots: $\pm 1, \pm 2, \pm 3, \pm 6, \pm \frac{1}{2}, \pm \frac{3}{2}$

44. num: $\pm 1, \pm 2, \pm 5, \pm 10$; den: $\pm 1, \pm 2, \pm 4$
possible roots: $\pm 1, \pm 2, \pm 5, \pm 10, \pm \frac{1}{2}, \pm \frac{5}{2}, \pm \frac{1}{4}, \pm \frac{5}{4}$

45. $x^3 - 10x^2 + 29x - 20 = 0$
Possible rational roots
$\pm 1, \pm 2, \pm 4, \pm 5, \pm 10, \pm 20$
Descartes' Rule of Signs

# pos	# neg	# nonreal
3	0	0
1	0	2

Test $x = 1$:

$$\begin{array}{r|rrrr} 1 & 1 & -10 & 29 & -20 \\ & & 1 & -9 & 20 \\ \hline & 1 & -9 & 20 & 0 \end{array}$$

$x^3 - 10x^2 + 29x - 20 = 0$
$(x-1)(x^2 - 9x + 20) = 0$
$(x-1)(x-5)(x-4) = 0$
Solution set: $\{1, 5, 4\}$

46. $x^3 - 8x^2 - x + 8 = 0$
Possible rational roots
$\pm 1, \pm 2, \pm 4, \pm 8$
Descartes' Rule of Signs

# pos	# neg	# nonreal
2	1	0
0	1	2

Test $x = 1$:

$$\begin{array}{r|rrrr} 1 & 1 & -8 & -1 & 8 \\ & & 1 & -7 & -8 \\ \hline & 1 & -7 & -8 & 0 \end{array}$$

$x^3 - 8x^2 - x + 8 = 0$
$(x-1)(x^2 - 7x - 8) = 0$
$(x-1)(x-8)(x+1) = 0$
Solution set: $\{1, 8, -1\}$

47. Possible rational roots

$\pm 1, \pm 2, \pm 3, \pm 5,$
$\pm 6, \pm 10, \pm 15, \pm 30,$
$\pm \frac{1}{2}, \pm \frac{3}{2}, \pm \frac{5}{2}, \pm \frac{15}{2}$

Descartes' Rule of Signs

# pos	# neg	# nonreal
0	3	0
0	1	2

Test $x = -2$:

$$\begin{array}{r|rrrr} -2 & 2 & 17 & 41 & 30 \\ & & -4 & -26 & -30 \\ \hline & 2 & 13 & 15 & 0 \end{array}$$

$$2x^3 + 17x^2 + 41x + 30 = 0$$
$$(x+2)(2x^2 + 13x + 15) = 0$$
$$(x+2)(2x+3)(x+5) = 0$$

Solution set: $\{-2, -\frac{3}{2}, -5\}$

48. Possible rational roots

$\pm 1, \pm \frac{1}{3}$

Descartes' Rule of Signs

# pos	# neg	# nonreal
1	2	0
1	0	2

Test $x = \frac{1}{3}$:

$$\begin{array}{r|rrrr} \frac{1}{3} & 3 & 2 & 2 & -1 \\ & & 1 & 1 & 1 \\ \hline & 3 & 3 & 3 & 0 \end{array}$$

$$3x^3 + 2x^2 + 2x - 1 = 0$$
$$(x - \tfrac{1}{3})(3x^2 + 3x + 3) = 0$$

$3x^2 + 3x + 3$ does not factor rationally.

Rational solutions: $\{\frac{1}{3}\}$

49. Possible rat. roots

$\pm 1, \pm 2, \pm 3, \pm 4,$
$\pm 6, \pm 9, \pm 12,$
$\pm 18, \pm 36, \pm \frac{1}{2},$
$\pm \frac{3}{2}, \pm \frac{9}{2}, \pm \frac{1}{4},$
$\pm \frac{3}{4}, \pm \frac{9}{4}$

Descartes' Rule of Signs

# pos	# neg	# nonreal
2	2	0
2	0	2
0	2	2
0	0	4

$$4x^4 - 25x^2 + 36 = 0$$
$$(x-2)(4x^3 + 8x^2 - 9x - 18) = 0$$
$$(x-2)(x+2)(4x^2 - 9) = 0$$
$$(x-2)(x+2)(2x+3)(2x-3) = 0$$

Solution set: $\{2, -2, -\frac{3}{2}, \frac{3}{2}\}$

Test $x = 2$:

$$\begin{array}{r|rrrrr} 2 & 4 & 0 & -25 & 0 & 36 \\ & & 8 & 16 & -18 & -36 \\ \hline & 4 & 8 & -9 & -18 & 0 \end{array}$$

Test $x = -2$:

$$\begin{array}{r|rrrr} -2 & 4 & 8 & -9 & -18 \\ & & -8 & 0 & 18 \\ \hline & 4 & 0 & -9 & 0 \end{array}$$

50. Possible rat. roots

$\pm 1, \pm 2, \pm 4,$
$\pm 8, \pm 16, \pm 32,$
$\pm \frac{1}{2}$

Descartes' Rule of Signs

# pos	# neg	# nonreal
2	2	0
2	0	2
0	2	2
0	0	4

$$2x^4 - 11x^3 - 6x^2 + 64x + 32 = 0$$
$$(x-4)(2x^3 - 3x^2 - 18x - 8) = 0$$
$$(x-4)(x-4)(2x^2 + 5x + 2) = 0$$
$$(x-4)(x-4)(2x+1)(x+2) = 0$$

Solution set: $\{4, 4, -\frac{1}{2}, -2\}$

Test $x = 4$:

$$\begin{array}{r|rrrrr} 4 & 2 & -11 & -6 & 64 & 32 \\ & & 8 & -12 & -72 & -32 \\ \hline & 2 & -3 & -18 & -8 & 0 \end{array}$$

Test $x = 4$:

$$\begin{array}{r|rrrr} 4 & 2 & -3 & -18 & -8 \\ & & 8 & 20 & 8 \\ \hline & 2 & 5 & 2 & 0 \end{array}$$

51. Possible rational roots

$\pm 1, \pm 2, \pm 4, \pm 8$
$\pm 16, \pm \frac{1}{3}, \pm \frac{2}{3}, \pm \frac{4}{3}$
$\pm \frac{8}{3}, \pm \frac{16}{3}$

Test $x = \frac{1}{3}$:

$$\begin{array}{r|rrrr} \frac{1}{3} & 3 & -1 & 48 & -16 \\ & & 1 & 0 & 16 \\ \hline & 3 & 0 & 48 & 0 \end{array}$$

Descartes' Rule of Signs

# pos	# neg	# nonreal
3	0	0
1	0	2

$3x^3 - x^2 + 48x - 16 = 0$
$\left(x - \frac{1}{3}\right)\left(3x^2 + 48\right) = 0$
$x = \frac{1}{3}$ **or** $x = \pm\sqrt{-16}$
$x = \pm 4i$

Solution set: $\left\{\frac{1}{3}, -4i, 4i\right\}$

52. Possible rational roots

$\pm 1, \pm 2, \pm 4, \pm 5$
$\pm 10, \pm 20$

Descartes' Rule of Signs

# pos	# neg	# nonreal
2	2	0
2	0	2
0	2	2
0	0	4

$x^4 - 2x^3 - 9x^2 + 8x + 20 = 0$
$(x-2)\left(x^3 - 9x - 10\right) = 0$
$(x-2)(x-2)\left(x^2 - 2x - 5\right) = 0$
Use the quadratic formula.
Solution set: $\left\{2, -2, 1 \pm \sqrt{6}\right\}$

Test $x = 2$:

$$\begin{array}{r|rrrrr} 2 & 1 & -2 & -9 & 8 & 20 \\ & & 2 & 0 & -18 & -20 \\ \hline & 1 & 0 & -9 & -10 & 0 \end{array}$$

Test $x = -2$:

$$\begin{array}{r|rrrr} -2 & 1 & 0 & -9 & -10 \\ & & -2 & 4 & 10 \\ \hline & 1 & -2 & -5 & 0 \end{array}$$

53. $P(x) = 5x^3 + 37x^2 + 59x + 18$
$P(-1) = -9$; $P(0) = 18$

54. $P(x) = 6x^3 - x^2 - 10x - 3$
$P(1) = -8$; $P(2) = 21$

55. $P(x) = x^3 - 2x^2 - 9x - 2$. Note that $P(4) = -6$ and $P(5) = 28$.
There is a root between 4 and 5.

STEP	x_l	c	x_r	$P(x_l)$	$P(x_c)$	$P(x_r)$
0	4	4.5	5	−8.0	8.125	21.0
1	4	4.25	4.5	−8.0	0.3906	8.125
2	4	4.125	4.25	−8.0	−2.9668	0.3906
3	4.125	4.1875	4.25	−2.9668	−1.3293	0.3906
4	4.1875	4.21875	4.25	−1.3293	−0.4798	0.3906
5	4.21875	4.234375	4.25	−0.4798	−0.0472	0.3906
6	4.234375	4.2421875	2.25	−0.0472	0.1711	0.3906
7	4.234275	4.23823125	4.2421875			

To the nearest tenth, the solution is $x = 4.2$.

56. $P(x) = 6x^2 - 13x - 5$. Note that $P(2) = -7$ and $P(3) = 10$.
There is a root between 2 and 3.

STEP	x_l	c	x_r	$P(x_l)$	$P(x_c)$	$P(x_r)$
0	2	2.5	3	−7.0	0	10.0

The solution is exactly $x = 2.5$.

57. Find the x-coordinates of any positive x-intercepts:

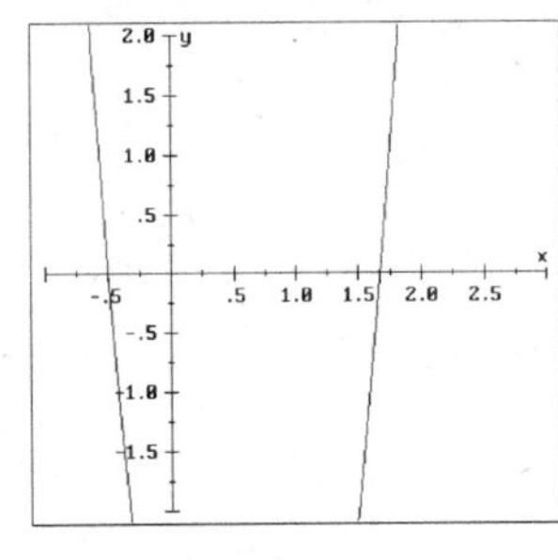

$x = 1.67$

58. Find the x-coordinates of any positive x-intercepts:

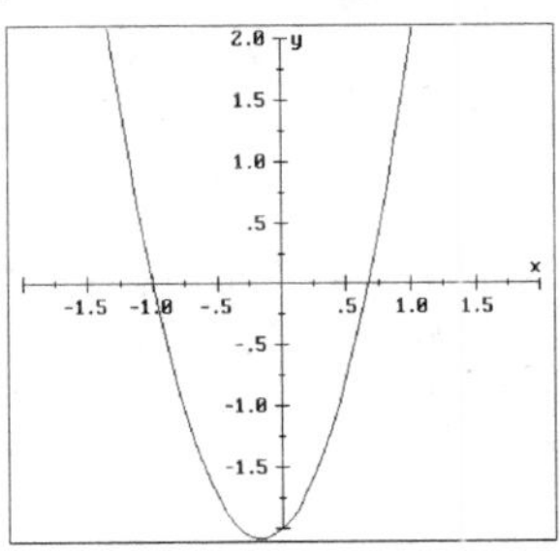

$x = 0.67$

59. Let $x =$ the length of the shortest panel. Then $x + 2$ and $x + 5$ are the lengths of the other panels. Since each panel has an area of 60, the widths are $\frac{60}{x}$, $\frac{60}{x+2}$ and $\frac{60}{x+5}$, respectively.

$$
\begin{aligned}
15 &= \frac{60}{x} + \frac{60}{x+2} + \frac{60}{x+5} \\
x(x+2)(x+5)(15) &= x(x+2)(x+5)\left(\frac{60}{x} + \frac{60}{x+2} + \frac{60}{x+5}\right) \\
15x(x+2)(x+5) &= 60(x+2)(x+5) + 60x(x+5) + 60x(x+2) \\
15x^3 + 105x^2 + 150x &= 60x^2 + 420x + 600 + 60x^2 + 300x + 60x^2 + 120x \\
15x^3 - 75x^2 - 690x - 600 &= 0 \\
15\left(x^3 - 5x^2 - 46x - 40\right) &= 0 \\
x^3 - 5x^2 - 46x - 40 &= 0 \\
(x-10)\left(x^2 + 5x + 4\right) &= 0 \\
(x-10)(x+4)(x+1) &= 0
\end{aligned}
$$

Test $x = 10$:

$$
\begin{array}{r|rrrr}
10 & 1 & -5 & -46 & -40 \\
 & & 10 & 50 & 40 \\
\hline
 & 1 & 5 & 4 & 0
\end{array}
$$

The positive solution $x = 10$ is the only one that makes sense.
The dimensions are 10 m by 6 m, 12 m by 5 m, and 15 m by 4 m.

60. Let $x =$ the radius. Then $x + 3$ is the height.

$$
\begin{aligned}
\pi r^2 h &= V \\
r^2 h &= \frac{V}{\pi} \\
x^2(x+3) &= \frac{19000}{\pi} \\
x^3 + 3x^2 &= 6047.89 \\
x^3 + 3x^2 - 6047.89 &= 0
\end{aligned}
$$

Graph $y = x^3 + 3x^2 - 6047.89$ and find the x-coordinates of any x-intercepts:

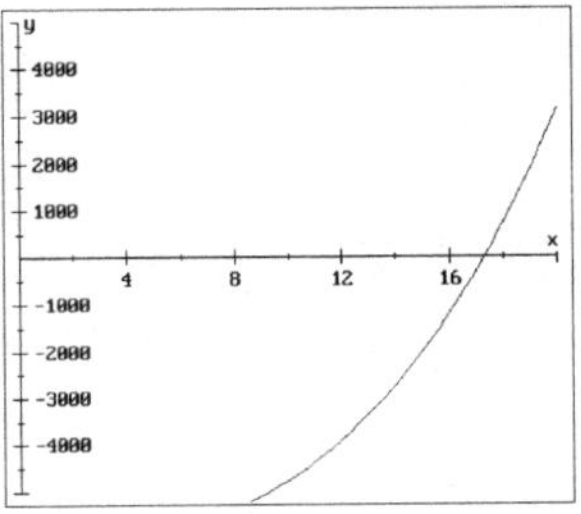

The radius should be about 17.27 feet.

Chapter 5 Test (page 546)

1. $P(-2) = (-2)^2 + 5(-2) + 6 = 4 - 10 + 6 = 0$; -2 is a zero of $P(x)$.

2. $P(2) = 3(2)^3 - 9(2) - 5$
$= 3(8) - 18 - 5 = \boxed{1}$

$$\begin{array}{rl} & 3x^2 + 6x + 3 \\ x-2 & \overline{)\,3x^3 + 0x^2 - 9x - 5} \\ & \underline{3x^3 - 6x^2} \\ & \quad 6x^2 - 9x \\ & \quad \underline{6x^2 - 12x} \\ & \qquad 3x - 5 \\ & \qquad \underline{3x - 6} \\ & \qquad\quad \boxed{1} \end{array}$$

3. $P(-2) = (-2)^5 + 2$
$= -32 + 2 = \boxed{-30}$

$$\begin{array}{rl} & x^4 - 2x^3 + 4x^2 - 8x + 16 \\ x+2 & \overline{)\,x^5 + 0x^4 + 0x^3 + 0x^2 + 0x + 2} \\ & \underline{x^5 + 2x^4} \\ & \quad -2x^4 + 0x^3 \\ & \quad \underline{-2x^4 - 4x^3} \\ & \qquad 4x^3 + 0x^2 \\ & \qquad \underline{4x^3 + 8x^2} \\ & \qquad\quad -8x^2 + 0x \\ & \qquad\quad \underline{-8x^2 - 16x} \\ & \qquad\qquad 16x + 2 \\ & \qquad\qquad \underline{16x + 32} \\ & \qquad\qquad\quad \boxed{-30} \end{array}$$

4. $P(3) = 2(3)^4 - 10(3)^3 + 4(3^2) + 7(3) + 21 = -30 \Rightarrow \text{remainder} = -30$
$x - 3$ is not a factor of the polynomial.

5.
$$\begin{array}{r|rrrr} 2 & 2 & -3 & -4 & -1 \\ & & 4 & 2 & -4 \\ \hline & 2 & 1 & -2 & -5 \end{array}$$
$(x-2)(2x^2 + x - 2) - 5$

6.
$$\begin{array}{r|rrrr} -1 & 2 & -3 & -4 & -1 \\ & & -2 & 5 & -1 \\ \hline & 2 & -5 & 1 & -2 \end{array}$$
$(x+1)(2x^2 - 5x + 1) - 2$

7.
$$\begin{array}{r|rrr} 5 & 2 & -7 & -15 \\ & & 10 & 15 \\ \hline & 2 & 3 & 0 \end{array} \quad \boxed{2x+3}$$

8.
$$\begin{array}{r|rrrr} -2 & 3 & 7 & 2 & 0 \\ & & -6 & -2 & 0 \\ \hline & 3 & 1 & 0 & 0 \end{array} \quad \boxed{3x^2 + x}$$

9.
$$\begin{array}{r|rrrr} 1 & 3 & -2 & 0 & 4 \\ & & 3 & 1 & 1 \\ \hline & 3 & 1 & 1 & 5 \end{array} \quad P(1) = 5$$

10.
$$\begin{array}{r|rrrr} -2 & 3 & -2 & 0 & 4 \\ & & -6 & 16 & -32 \\ \hline & 3 & -8 & 16 & -28 \end{array} \quad P(-2) = -28$$

11.
$$\begin{array}{r|rrrr} -\frac{1}{3} & 3 & -2 & 0 & 4 \\ & & -1 & 1 & -\frac{1}{3} \\ \hline & 3 & -3 & 1 & \frac{11}{3} \end{array} \quad P\left(-\tfrac{1}{3}\right) = \tfrac{11}{3}$$

12.
$$\begin{array}{r|rrrr} i & 3 & -2 & 0 & 4 \\ & & 3i & -3-2i & 2-3i \\ \hline & 3 & -2+3i & -3-2i & 6-3i \end{array}$$
$P(i) = 6 - 3i$

13. $(x-5)(x+1)(x-0) = (x^2 - 4x - 5)x = x^3 - 4x^2 - 5x$

14. $(x-i)(x+i)\left(x-\sqrt{3}\right)\left(x+\sqrt{3}\right) = (x^2 - i^2)(x^2 - 3) = (x^2+1)(x^2-3) = x^4 - 2x^2 - 3$

15. If i is a root, then $-i$ is a root also:

$$(x-2)(x-i)(x+i)=0$$
$$(x-2)\left(x^2-i^2\right)=0$$
$$(x-2)\left(x^2+1\right)=0$$
$$x^3-2x^2+x-2=0$$

16. If $2+i$ is a root, then $2-i$ is a root also:

$$(x-1)[x-(2+i)][x-(2-i)]=0$$
$$(x-1)\left[x^2-(2-i)x-(2+i)x+(2+i)(2-i)\right]=0$$
$$(x-1)\left[x^2-2x+ix-2x-ix+4-i^2\right]=0$$
$$(x-1)\left[x^2-4x+5\right]=0$$
$$x^3-5x^2+9x-5=0$$

17. $P(x)=3x^3+2x^2-4x+1$
3 linear factors, 3 zeros

18. If $3-2i$ is a root, then $3+2i$ is also a root.

19. $P(x)=3x^5-2x^4+2x^2-x-3$: 3 sign variations $\Rightarrow$ 3 or 1 positive roots
$P(-x)=3(-x)^5-2(-x)^4+2(-x)^2-(-x)-3$
$=-3x^5-2x^4+2x^2+x-4$: 2 sign variations $\Rightarrow$ 2 or 0 negative roots

# pos	# neg	# nonreal
3	2	0
3	0	2
1	2	2
1	0	4

20. $P(x)=2x^3-5x^2-2x-1$: 1 sign variation $\Rightarrow$ 1 positive root
$P(-x)=2(-x)^3-5(-x)^2-2(-x)-1$
$=-2x^3-5x^2+2x-1$: 2 sign variations $\Rightarrow$ 2 or 0 negative roots

# pos	# neg	# nonreal
1	2	0
1	0	2

21. $P(x)=x^5-x^4-5x^3+5x^2+4x-5$

$$\begin{array}{r|rrrrrr} 3 & 1 & -1 & -5 & 5 & 4 & -5 \\ & & 3 & 6 & 3 & 24 & 84 \\ \hline & 1 & 2 & 1 & 8 & 28 & 79 \end{array}$$

Upper bound: 3

$$\begin{array}{r|rrrrrr} -3 & 1 & -1 & -5 & 5 & 4 & -5 \\ & & -3 & 12 & -21 & 48 & -156 \\ \hline & 1 & -4 & 7 & -16 & 52 & -161 \end{array}$$

Lower bound: -3

22. $P(x)=2x^3-11x^2+10x+3$

$$\begin{array}{r|rrrr} 6 & 2 & -11 & 10 & 3 \\ & & 12 & 6 & 96 \\ \hline & 2 & 1 & 16 & 99 \end{array}$$

Upper bound: 6

$$\begin{array}{r|rrrr} -1 & 2 & -11 & 10 & 3 \\ & & -2 & 13 & -23 \\ \hline & 2 & -13 & 23 & -20 \end{array}$$

Lower bound: -1

CHAPTER 5 TEST

23. num: $\pm 1, \pm 2, \pm 4, \pm 8$; den: ± 1; possible roots: $\pm 1, \pm 2, \pm 4, \pm 8$

24. num: $\pm 1, \pm 2$; den: $\pm 1, \pm 5$; possible roots: $\pm 1, \pm 2, \pm \frac{1}{5}, \pm \frac{2}{5}$

25. Possible rational roots

$\pm 1, \pm 2, \pm 3, \pm 6,$
$\pm \frac{1}{2}, \pm \frac{3}{2}$

Test $x = 2$:

$$\begin{array}{r|rrrr} 2 & 2 & 3 & -11 & -6 \\ & & 4 & 14 & 6 \\ \hline & 2 & 7 & 3 & 0 \end{array}$$

Descartes' Rule of Signs

# pos	# neg	# nonreal
1	2	0
1	0	2

$$2x^3 + 3x^2 - 11x - 6 = 0$$
$$(x-2)\left(2x^2 + 7x + 3\right) = 0$$
$$(x-2)(2x+1)(x+3) = 0$$
Solution set: $\left\{2, -\frac{1}{2}, -3\right\}$

26. Possible rational roots

$\pm 1, \pm 2$

Test $x = 2$:

$$\begin{array}{r|rrrr} 2 & 1 & -2 & 1 & -2 \\ & & 2 & 0 & 2 \\ \hline & 1 & 0 & 1 & 0 \end{array}$$

Descartes' Rule of Signs

# pos	# neg	# nonreal
3	0	0
1	0	2

$$x^3 - 2x^2 + x - 2 = 0$$
$$(x-2)\left(x^2+1\right) = 0$$
$x - 2 = 0$ **or** $x^2 + 1 = 0$
$x = 2$ $\quad x = \pm\sqrt{-1}$
$x = \pm i$

Solution set: $\{2, -i, i\}$

27. Possible rational roots

$\pm 1, \pm 2, \pm 3, \pm 6,$
$\pm 9, \pm 18, \pm 27, \pm 54$

Descartes' Rule of Signs

# pos	# neg	# nonreal
1	3	0
1	1	2

$$x^4 + x^3 + 3x^2 + 9x - 54 = 0$$
$$(x-2)\left(x^3 + 3x^2 + 9x + 27\right) = 0$$
$$(x-2)(x+3)\left(x^2+9\right) = 0$$
$$x^2 + 9 = 0 \Rightarrow x^2 = -9 \Rightarrow x = \pm 3i$$
Solution set: $\{2, -3, \pm 3i\}$

Test $x = 2$:

$$\begin{array}{r|rrrrr} 2 & 1 & 1 & 3 & 9 & -54 \\ & & 2 & 6 & 18 & 54 \\ \hline & 1 & 3 & 9 & 27 & 0 \end{array}$$

Test $x = -3$:

$$\begin{array}{r|rrrr} -3 & 1 & 3 & 9 & 27 \\ & & -3 & 0 & -27 \\ \hline & 1 & 0 & 9 & 0 \end{array}$$

28. Possible rat. roots

$\pm 1, \pm 2, \pm 4,$
± 8

Descartes' Rule of Signs

# pos	# neg	# nonreal
1	4	0
1	2	2
1	0	4

$$x^5 + 2x^4 + 3x^3 + 6x^2 - 4x - 8 = 0$$
$$(x-1)\left(x^4 + 3x^3 + 6x^2 + 12x + 8\right) = 0$$
$$(x-1)(x+1)\left(x^3 + 2x^2 + 4x + 8\right) = 0$$
$$(x-1)(x+1)(x+2)\left(x^2+4\right) = 0$$
$$x^2 + 4 = 0 \Rightarrow x = \pm\sqrt{-4}$$
Solution set: $\{1, -1, -2, \pm 2i\}$

Test $x = 1$:

$$\begin{array}{r|rrrrrr} 1 & 1 & 2 & 3 & 6 & -4 & -8 \\ & & 1 & 3 & 6 & 12 & 8 \\ \hline & 1 & 3 & 6 & 12 & 8 & 0 \end{array}$$

Test $x = -1$:

$$\begin{array}{r|rrrrr} -1 & 1 & 3 & 6 & 12 & 8 \\ & & -1 & -2 & -4 & -8 \\ \hline & 1 & 2 & 4 & 8 & 0 \end{array}$$

Test $x = -2$:

$$\begin{array}{r|rrrr} -2 & 1 & 2 & 4 & 8 \\ & & -2 & 0 & -8 \\ \hline & 1 & 0 & 4 & 0 \end{array}$$

29. $P(1) = 5$, $P(2) = 28$; The Intermediate Value Theorem does not guarantee a zero between 1 and 2.

30. $P(x) = x^2 - 11$. Note that $P(3) = -2$ and $P(4) = 5$. There is a root between 3 and 4.

STEP	x_l	c	x_r	$P(x_l)$	$P(x_c)$	$P(x_r)$
0	3	3.5	4	-2.0	1.25	5.0
1	3	3.25	3.5	-2.0	-0.4375	1.25
2	3.25	3.375	3.5	-0.4375	0.3906	1.25
3	3.25	3.3125	3.375	-0.4375	-0.0273	0.3906
4	3.3125	3.34375	3.375			

To the nearest tenth, the solution is $x = 3.3$.

Cumulative Review Exercises (page 547)

1. $f(x) = 3^x - 2$; Shift $y = 3^x$ D2.

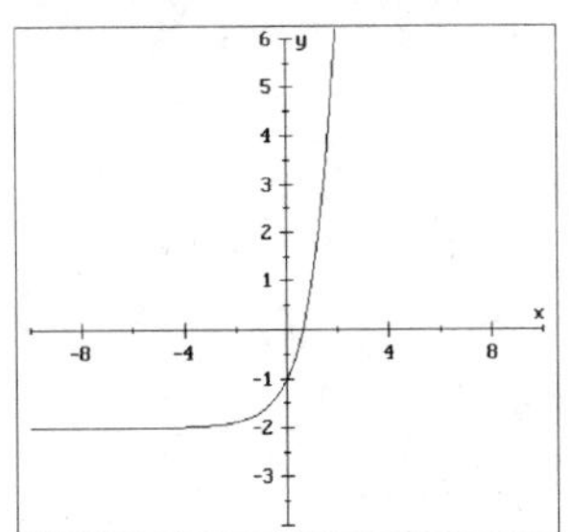

2. $f(x) = 2e^x$; Stretch $y = e^x$ vertically by a factor of 2.

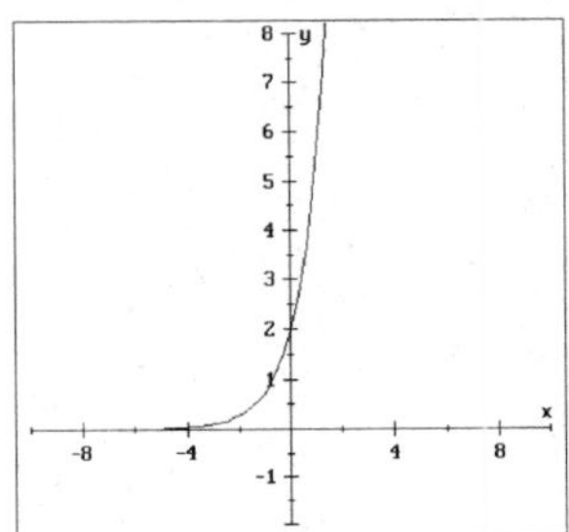

3. $f(x) = \log_3 x$

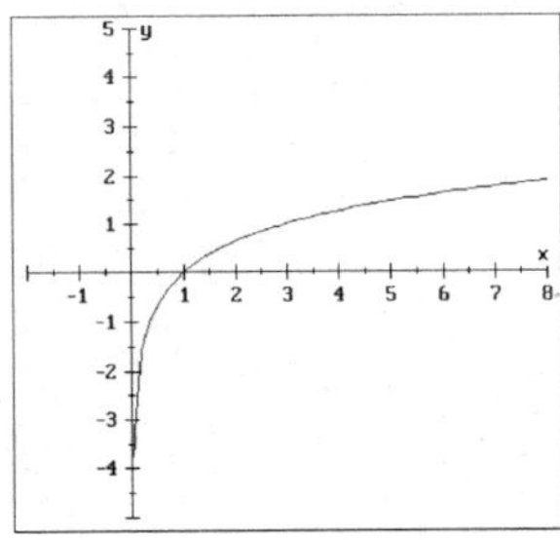

4. $f(x) = \ln(x-2)$; Shift $y = \ln x$ R2.

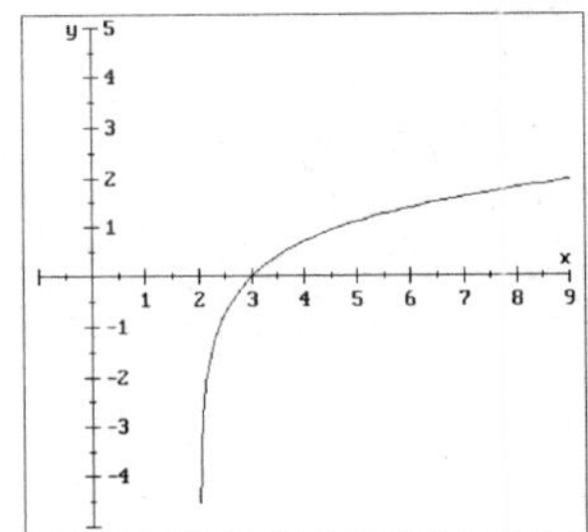

5. $\log_2 64 = 6$ (because $2^6 = 64$)

6. $\log_{1/2} 8 = -3$ $\left(\text{because } \left(\frac{1}{2}\right)^{-3} = 8\right)$

7. $\ln e^3 = 3 \ln e = 3$

8. $2^{\log_2 2} = 2$

9. $\log abc = \log a + \log b + \log c$

10. $$\begin{aligned} \log \frac{a^2b}{c} &= \log a^2b - \log c \\ &= \log a^2 + \log b - \log c \\ &= 2\log a + \log b - \log c \end{aligned}$$

11. $\log\sqrt{\frac{ab}{c^3}} = \log\left(\frac{ab}{c^3}\right)^{1/2} = \frac{1}{2}\log\left(\frac{ab}{c^3}\right) = \frac{1}{2}(\log ab - \log c^3) = \frac{1}{2}(\log a + \log b - 3\log c)$

12. $\ln\frac{\sqrt{ab^2}}{c} = \ln\frac{(ab^2)^{1/2}}{c} = \ln(ab^2)^{1/2} - \ln c = \frac{1}{2}\ln(ab^2) - \ln c = \frac{1}{2}(\ln a + \ln b^2) - \ln c = \frac{1}{2}(\ln a + 2\ln b) - \ln c = \frac{1}{2}\ln a + \ln b - \ln c$

13. $3\ln a - 3\ln b = \ln a^3 - \ln b^3 = \ln\frac{a^3}{b^3}$

14. $\frac{1}{2}\log a + 3\log b - \frac{2}{3}\log c = \log a^{1/2} + \log b^3 - \log c^{2/3} = \log\frac{a^{1/2}b^3}{c^{2/3}} = \log\frac{\sqrt{a}\,b^3}{\sqrt[3]{c^2}}$

15.
$$\begin{aligned} 3^{x+1} &= 8 \\ \log 3^{x+1} &= \log 8 \\ (x+1)\log 3 &= \log 8 \\ x+1 &= \frac{\log 8}{\log 3} \\ x &= \frac{\log 8}{\log 3} - 1 \end{aligned}$$

16.
$$\begin{aligned} 3^{x-1} &= 3^{2x} \\ x-1 &= 2x \\ -1 &= x \end{aligned}$$

17.
$$\begin{aligned} \log x + \log 2 &= 3 \\ \log 2x &= 3 \\ 10^3 &= 2x \\ 1000 &= 2x \\ 500 &= x \end{aligned}$$

18.
$$\begin{aligned} \log(x+1) + \log(x-1) &= 1 \\ \log(x+1)(x-1) &= 1 \\ \log(x^2-1) &= 1 \\ 10^1 &= x^2 - 1 \\ 10 &= x^2 - 1 \\ 11 &= x^2 \\ \pm\sqrt{11} &= x \end{aligned}$$

Only the positive answer, $x = \sqrt{11}$, checks.

19.
$$\begin{array}{r|rrrr} 1 & 4 & 0 & 3 & 2 \\ & & 4 & 4 & 7 \\ \hline & 4 & 4 & 7 & 9 \end{array} \quad P(1) = 9$$

20.
$$\begin{array}{r|rrrr} -2 & 4 & 0 & 3 & 2 \\ & & -8 & 16 & -38 \\ \hline & 4 & -8 & 19 & -36 \end{array} \quad P(-2) = -36$$

21.
$$\begin{array}{r|rrrr} \frac{1}{2} & 4 & 0 & 3 & 2 \\ & & 2 & 1 & 2 \\ \hline & 4 & 2 & 4 & 4 \end{array} \quad P(\tfrac{1}{2}) = 4$$

22.
$$\begin{array}{r|rrrr} i & 4 & 0 & 3 & 2 \\ & & 4i & -4 & -i \\ \hline & 4 & 4i & -1 & 2-i \end{array} \quad P(i) = 2 - i$$

23.
$$\begin{array}{r|rrrr} -1 & 1 & 2 & -1 & -2 \\ & & -1 & -1 & 2 \\ \hline & 1 & 1 & -2 & 0 \end{array} \quad \text{factor}$$

24.
$$\begin{array}{r|rrrr} 2 & 1 & 2 & -1 & -2 \\ & & 2 & 8 & 14 \\ \hline & 1 & 4 & 7 & 12 \end{array} \quad \text{not a factor}$$

25. $\begin{array}{r|rrrr} 1 & 1 & 2 & -1 & -2 \\ & & 1 & 3 & 2 \\ \hline & 1 & 3 & 2 & 0 \end{array}$ factor

26. $\begin{array}{r|rrrr} -2 & 1 & 2 & -1 & -2 \\ & & -2 & 0 & 2 \\ \hline & 1 & 0 & -1 & 0 \end{array}$ factor

27. $x^{12} - 4x^8 + 2x^4 + 12 = 0 \Rightarrow 12$ roots

28. $x^{2000} - 1 = 0 \Rightarrow 2000$ roots

29. $P(x) = x^4 + 2x^3 - 3x^2 + x + 2$: 2 sign variations $\Rightarrow$ 2 or 0 positive roots
$P(-x) = (-x)^4 + 2(-x)^3 - 3(-x)^2 + (-x) + 2$
$= x^4 - 2x^3 - 3x^2 - x + 2$: 2 sign variations $\Rightarrow$ 2 or 0 negative roots

# pos	# neg	# nonreal
2	2	0
2	0	2
0	2	2
0	0	4

30. $P(x) = x^4 - 3x^3 - 2x^2 - 3x - 5$
1 sign variation $\Rightarrow$ 1 positive root
$P(-x) = (-x)^4 - 3(-x)^3 - 2(-x)^2 - 3(-x) - 5$
$= x^4 + 3x^3 - 2x^2 + 3x - 3$
3 sign variations $\Rightarrow$ 3 or 1 negative roots

# pos	# neg	# nonreal
1	3	0
1	1	2

31. Possible rational roots
$\pm 1, \pm 3, \pm 9$

Descartes' Rule of Signs

# pos	# neg	# nonreal
1	2	0
1	0	2

Test $x = -1$: $\begin{array}{r|rrrr} -1 & 1 & 1 & -9 & -9 \\ & & -1 & 0 & 9 \\ \hline & 1 & 0 & -9 & 0 \end{array}$

$x^3 + x^2 - 9x - 9 = 0$
$(x + 1)(x^2 - 9) = 0$
$(x + 1)(x + 3)(x - 3) = 0$
Solution set: $\{-1, -3, 3\}$

32. Possible rational roots
$\pm 1, \pm 2$

Descartes' Rule of Signs

# pos	# neg	# nonreal
2	1	0
0	1	2

Test $x = -1$: $\begin{array}{r|rrrr} -1 & 1 & -2 & -1 & 2 \\ & & -1 & 3 & -2 \\ \hline & 1 & -3 & 2 & 0 \end{array}$

$x^3 - 2x^2 - x + 2 = 0$
$(x + 1)(x^2 - 3x + 2) = 0$
$(x + 1)(x - 1)(x - 2) = 0$
Solution set: $\{-1, 1, 2\}$

Exercises 6.1 (page 560)

1.	system	**2.**	solution	**3.**	consistent	**4.**	inconsistent
5.	independent	**6.**	dependent	**7.**	consistent	**8.**	inconsistent
9.	dependent	**10.**	independent	**11.**	is	**12.**	is

13. $\begin{cases} y = -3x + 5 \\ x - 2y = -3 \end{cases}$

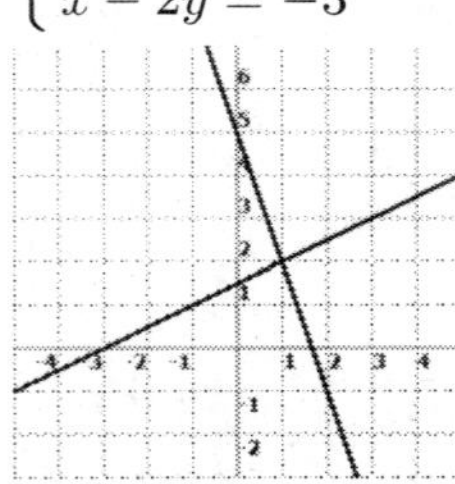

solution: $(1, 2)$

14. $\begin{cases} x - 2y = -3 \\ 3x + y = -9 \end{cases}$

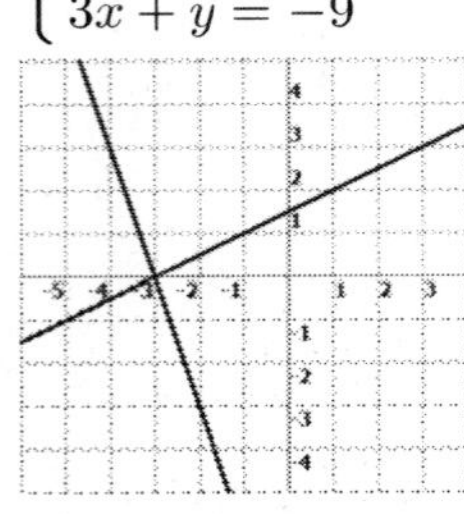

solution: $(-3, 0)$

15. $\begin{cases} 3x + 2y = 2 \\ -2x + 3y = 16 \end{cases}$

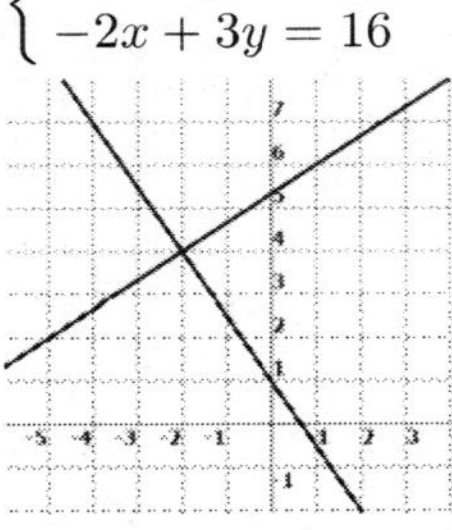

solution: $(-2, 4)$

16. 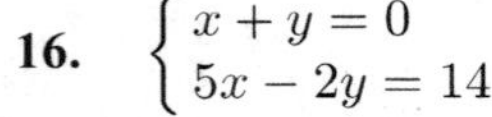 $\begin{cases} x + y = 0 \\ 5x - 2y = 14 \end{cases}$

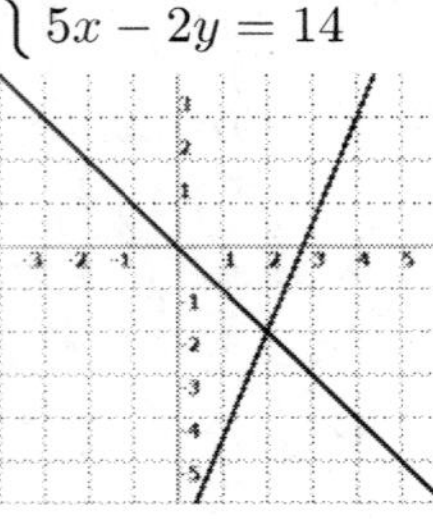

solution: $(2, -2)$

17. $\begin{cases} y = -x + 5 \\ 3x + 3y = 27 \end{cases}$

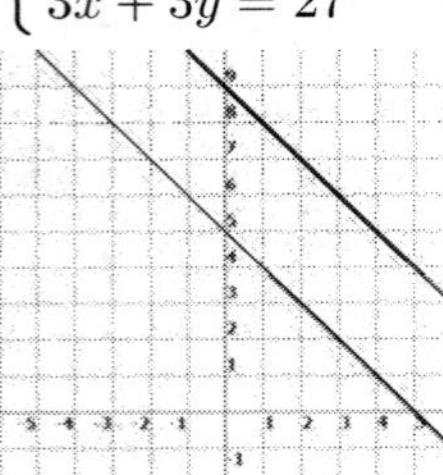

no solution
inconsistent system

18. $\begin{cases} x - 3y = -3 \\ 2x - 6y = 12 \end{cases}$

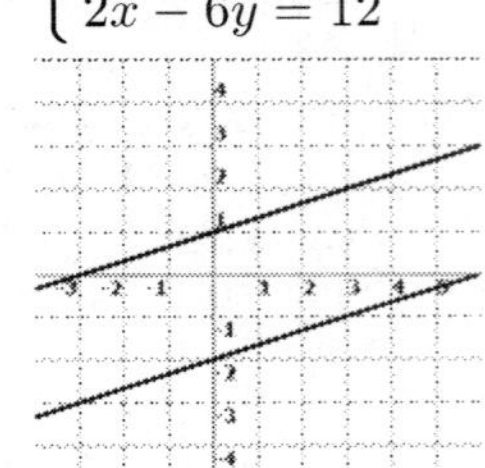

no solution
inconsistent system

19. $\begin{cases} y = -x + 6 \\ 5x + 5y = 30 \end{cases}$

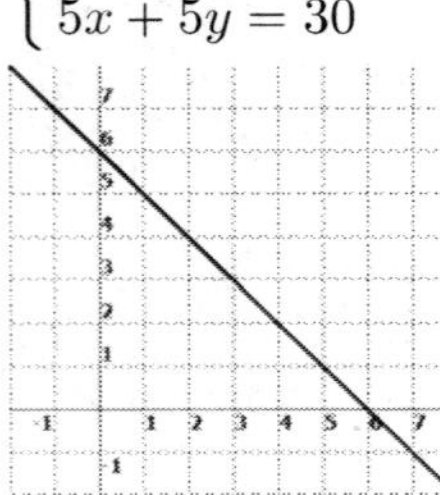

dependent equations
infinitely many solutions

20. $\begin{cases} 2x - y = -3 \\ 8x - 4y = -12 \end{cases}$

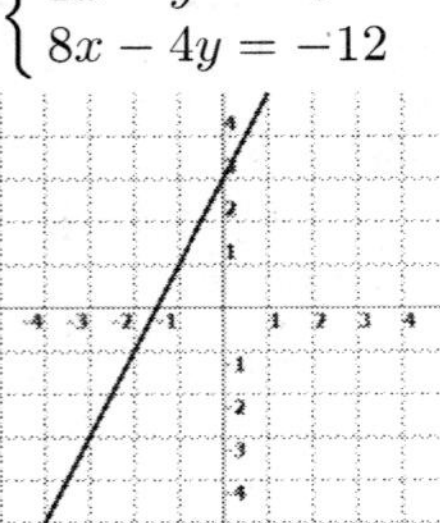

dependent equations
infinitely many solutions

21. $\begin{cases} y = -5.7x + 7.8 \\ y = 37.2 - 19.1x \end{cases}$

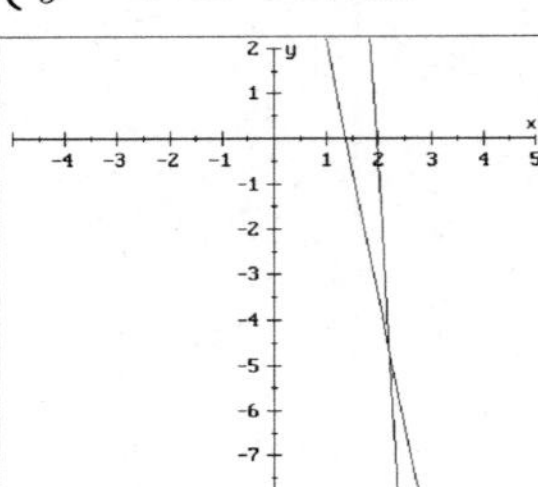

solution: $(2.2, -4.7)$

22. $\begin{cases} y = 3.4x - 1 \\ y = -7.1x + 3.1 \end{cases}$

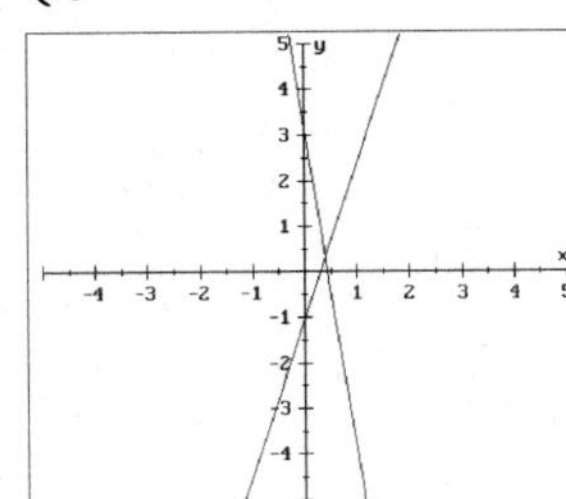

solution: $(0.4, 0.3)$

23. $\begin{cases} y = \dfrac{5.5 - 2.7x}{3.5} \\ 5.3x - 9.2y = 6.0 \end{cases}$

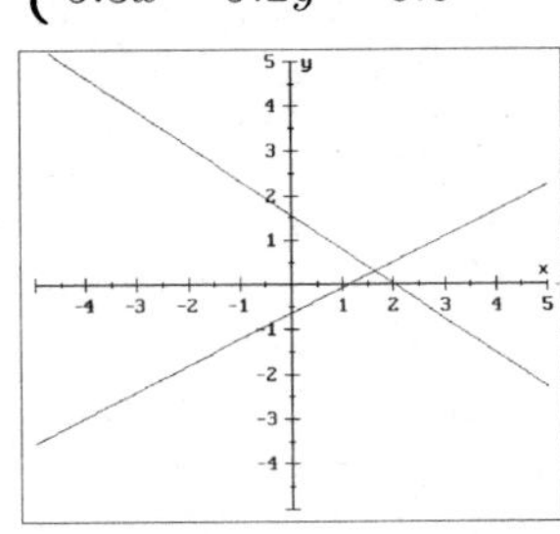

solution: $(1.7, 0.3)$

24. $\begin{cases} 29x + 17y = 7 \\ -17x + 23y = 19 \end{cases}$

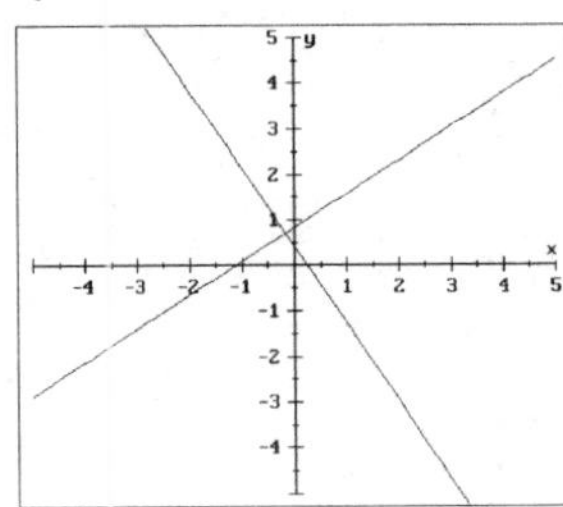

solution: $(-0.2, 0.7)$

25. $\begin{cases} (1) \quad y = x - 1 \\ (2) \quad y = 2x \end{cases}$

Substitute $y = x - 1$ from (1) into (2):

$$\begin{aligned} y &= 2x \\ x - 1 &= 2x \\ -1 &= x \end{aligned}$$

Substitute and solve for y:

$y = 2x$

$y = 2(-1) = -2$

$(-1, -2)$

26. $\begin{cases} (1) \quad y = 2x - 1 \\ (2) \quad x + y = 5 \end{cases}$

Substitute $y = 2x - 1$ from (1) into (2):

$$\begin{aligned} x + y &= 5 \\ x + 2x - 1 &= 5 \\ 3x &= 6 \\ x &= 2 \end{aligned}$$

Substitute and solve for y:

$y = 2x - 1$

$y = 2(2) - 1 = 3$

$(2, 3)$

27. $\begin{cases} (1) \quad 2x + 3y = 0 \\ (2) \quad y = 3x - 11 \end{cases}$

Substitute $y = 3x - 11$ from (2) into (1):

$$\begin{aligned} 2x + 3y &= 0 \\ 2x + 3(3x - 11) &= 0 \\ 2x + 9x - 33 &= 0 \\ 11x &= 33 \\ x &= 3 \end{aligned}$$

Substitute and solve for y:

$y = 3x - 11$

$y = 3(3) - 11 = -2$

$(3, -2)$

28. $\begin{cases} (1) \quad 2x + y = 3 \\ (2) \quad y = 5x - 11 \end{cases}$

Substitute $y = 5x - 11$ from (2) into (1):

$$\begin{aligned} 2x + y &= 3 \\ 2x + 5x - 11 &= 3 \\ 7x &= 14 \\ x &= 2 \end{aligned}$$

Substitute and solve for y:

$y = 5x - 11$

$y = 5(2) - 11 = -1$

$(2, -1)$

29. $\begin{cases} (1) & 4x + 3y = 3 \\ (2) & 2x - 6y = -1 \end{cases}$

Substitute $y = \dfrac{3-4x}{3}$ from (1) into (2):

$$\begin{aligned} 2x - 6y &= -1 \\ 2x - 6 \cdot \frac{3-4x}{3} &= -1 \\ 2x - 2(3-4x) &= -1 \\ 2x - 6 + 8x &= -1 \\ 10x &= 5 \\ x &= \tfrac{1}{2} \end{aligned}$$

Substitute and solve for y:

$$\begin{aligned} 4x + 3y &= 3 \\ 4\left(\tfrac{1}{2}\right) + 3y &= 3 \\ 2 + 3y &= 3 \\ 3y &= 1 \\ y &= \tfrac{1}{3} \end{aligned}$$

Solution: $\left(\tfrac{1}{2}, \tfrac{1}{3}\right)$

30. $\begin{cases} (1) & 4x + 5y = 4 \\ (2) & 8x - 15y = 3 \end{cases}$

Substitute $y = \dfrac{4-4x}{5}$ from (1) into (2):

$$\begin{aligned} 8x - 15y &= 3 \\ 8x - 15 \cdot \frac{4-4x}{5} &= 3 \\ 8x - 3(4-4x) &= 3 \\ 8x - 12 + 12x &= 3 \\ 20x &= 15 \\ x &= \tfrac{3}{4} \end{aligned}$$

Substitute and solve for y:

$$\begin{aligned} 4x + 5y &= 4 \\ 4\left(\tfrac{3}{4}\right) + 5y &= 4 \\ 3 + 5y &= 4 \\ 5y &= 1 \\ y &= \tfrac{1}{5} \end{aligned}$$

Solution: $\left(\tfrac{3}{4}, \tfrac{1}{5}\right)$

31. $\begin{cases} (1) & x + 3y = 1 \\ (2) & 2x + 6y = 3 \end{cases}$

Substitute $x = 1 - 3y$ from (1) into (2):

$$\begin{aligned} 2x + 6y &= 3 \\ 2(1-3y) + 6y &= 3 \\ 2 - 6y + 6y &= 3 \\ 2 &\neq 3 \end{aligned}$$

Inconsistent system $\Rightarrow$ No solution

32. $\begin{cases} (1) & x - 3y = 14 \\ (2) & 3(x-12) = 9y \end{cases}$

Substitute $x = 3y + 14$ from (1) into (2):

$$\begin{aligned} 3(x-12) &= 9y \\ 3(3y + 14 - 12) &= 9y \\ 3(3y+2) &= 9y \\ 9y + 6 &= 9y \\ 6 &\neq 0 \end{aligned}$$

Inconsistent system $\Rightarrow$ No solution

33. $\begin{cases} (1) & y = 3x - 6 \\ (2) & x = \tfrac{1}{3}y + 2 \end{cases}$

Substitute $x = \tfrac{1}{3}y + 2$ from (2) into (1):

$$\begin{aligned} &y = 3x - 6 \\ &y = 3\left(\tfrac{1}{3}y + 2\right) - 6 \\ &y = y + 6 - 6 \\ &0 = 0 \end{aligned}$$

Dependent equations

General solution: $(x, 3x - 6)$

34. $\begin{cases} (1) & 3x - y = 12 \\ (2) & y = 3x - 12 \end{cases}$

Substitute $y = 3x - 12$ from (2) into (1):

$$\begin{aligned} 3x - (3x - 12) &= 12 \\ 3x - 3x + 12 &= 12 \\ 0 &= 0 \end{aligned}$$

Dependent equations

General solution: $(x, 3x - 12)$

35.
$$\begin{array}{l} 5x - 3y = 12 \Rightarrow \times\ (-1) \\ \underline{2x - 3y = \ \ 3} \end{array} \quad \begin{array}{rcr} -5x + 3y &=& -12 \\ \underline{2x - 3y} &\underline{=}& \underline{3} \\ -3x &=& -9 \\ x &=& 3 \end{array} \quad \begin{array}{r} 2x - 3y = 3 \\ 2(3) - 3y = 3 \\ 6 - 3y = 3 \\ -3y = -3 \\ y = 1 \end{array}$$
Solution: $(3, 1)$

36.
$$\begin{array}{l} 2x + 3y = \ \ 8 \\ \underline{-5x + \ \ y = -3} \Rightarrow \times\ (-3) \end{array} \quad \begin{array}{rcr} 2x + 3y &=& 8 \\ \underline{15x - 3y} &\underline{=}& \underline{9} \\ 17x &=& 17 \\ x &=& 1 \end{array} \quad \begin{array}{r} 2x + 3y = 8 \\ 2(1) + 3y = 8 \\ 2 + 3y = 8 \\ 3y = 6 \\ y = 2 \end{array}$$
Solution: $(1, 2)$

37.
$$\begin{array}{l} x - 7y = -11 \Rightarrow \times\ (-8) \\ \underline{8x + 2y = \ \ 28} \end{array} \quad \begin{array}{rcr} -8x + 56y &=& 88 \\ \underline{8x + \ \ 2y} &\underline{=}& \underline{28} \\ 58y &=& 116 \\ y &=& 2 \end{array} \quad \begin{array}{r} x - 7y = -11 \\ x - 7(2) = -11 \\ x - 14 = -11 \\ x = 3 \end{array}$$
Solution: $(3, 2)$

38.
$$\begin{array}{l} 3x + 9y = \ \ 9 \\ \underline{-x + 5y = -3} \Rightarrow \times\ (3) \end{array} \quad \begin{array}{rcr} 3x + \ \ 9y &=& 9 \\ \underline{-3x + 15y} &\underline{=}& \underline{-9} \\ 24y &=& 0 \\ y &=& 0 \end{array} \quad \begin{array}{r} 3x + 9y = 9 \\ 3x + 9(0) = 9 \\ 3x + 0 = 9 \\ 3x = 9 \\ x = 3 \end{array}$$
Solution: $(3, 0)$

39.
$$\begin{array}{l} 3(x - y) = y - 9 \Rightarrow 3x - 3y = y - 9 \Rightarrow 3x - 4y = \ \ -9 \Rightarrow \times\ (5) \\ \underline{5(x + y) = \ \ -15} \Rightarrow \underline{5x + 5y = \ \ -15} \Rightarrow \underline{5x + 5y = -15} \Rightarrow \times\ (4) \end{array} \quad \begin{array}{rcr} 15x - 20y &=& -45 \\ \underline{20x + 20y} &\underline{=}& \underline{-60} \\ 35x &=& -105 \\ x &=& -3 \end{array}$$
$$\begin{array}{r} 5x + 5y = -15 \\ 5(-3) + 5y = -15 \\ -15 + 5y = -15 \\ 5y = 0 \\ y = 0 \end{array}$$
Solution: $(-3, 0)$

40.
$$\begin{array}{l} 2(x + y) = y + 1 \Rightarrow 2x + 2y = y + 1 \Rightarrow 2x + y = \ \ 1 \\ \underline{3(x + 1) = y - 3} \Rightarrow \ \underline{3x + 3 = y - 3} \Rightarrow \underline{3x - y = -6} \\ \qquad\qquad\qquad\qquad\qquad\qquad\qquad\qquad 5x \ \ = -5 \\ \qquad\qquad\qquad\qquad\qquad\qquad\qquad\qquad x \ \ = -1 \end{array} \quad \begin{array}{r} 2x + y = 1 \\ 2(-1) + y = 1 \\ -2 + y = 1 \\ y = 3 \end{array}$$
Solution: $(-1, 3)$

41.
$$\begin{array}{l} 2 = \dfrac{1}{x + y} \Rightarrow 2(x + y) = 1 \Rightarrow 2x + 2y = 1 \\ \underline{2 = \dfrac{3}{x - y}} \Rightarrow \underline{2(x - y) = 3} \Rightarrow \underline{2x - 2y = 3} \\ \qquad\qquad\qquad\qquad\qquad\qquad 4x \ \ = 4 \\ \qquad\qquad\qquad\qquad\qquad\qquad x \ \ = 1 \end{array} \quad \begin{array}{r} 2x + 2y = 1 \\ 2(1) + 2y = 1 \\ 2 + 2y = 1 \\ 2y = -1 \\ y = -\frac{1}{2} \end{array}$$
Solution: $(1, -\frac{1}{2})$

42.

$$\begin{array}{rcl} \dfrac{1}{x+y} = 12 \Rightarrow 1 = 12(x+y) \Rightarrow -12x - 12y = -1 & & -12x - 12y = -1 \\ \dfrac{3x}{y} = -4 \Rightarrow 3x = -4y \Rightarrow 3x + 4y = 0 \Rightarrow \times\ (4) & & 12x + 16y = 0 \\ & & 4y = -1 \\ & & y = -\frac{1}{4} \end{array}$$

$$\begin{aligned} 3x &= -4y \\ 3x &= -4\left(-\tfrac{1}{4}\right) \\ 3x &= 1 \\ x &= \tfrac{1}{3} \end{aligned}$$

Solution: $\left(\frac{1}{3}, -\frac{1}{4}\right)$

43.

$$\begin{array}{rcl} y + 2x = 5 \Rightarrow 2x + y = 5 & & 2x + y = 5 \\ 0.5y = 2.5 - x \Rightarrow x + 0.5y = 2.5 \Rightarrow \times\ (-2) & & -2x - y = -5 \\ & & 0 = 0 \end{array}$$

Dependent Equations

$$\begin{aligned} 2x + y &= 5 \\ y &= -2x + 5 \end{aligned}$$

Gen. sol.: $(x, -2x + 5)$

44.

$$\begin{array}{rcl} -0.3x + 0.1y = -0.1 \Rightarrow \times\ (20) & & -6x + 2y = -2 \\ 6x - 2y = 2 & & 6x - 2y = 2 \\ & & 0 = 0 \end{array}$$

Dependent Equations

$$\begin{aligned} 6x - 2y &= 2 \\ -2y &= 2 - 6x \\ y &= -1 + 3x = 3x - 1 \end{aligned}$$

General solution: $(x, 3x - 1)$

45.

$$\begin{array}{rcl} x + 2(x-y) = 2 \Rightarrow x + 2x - 2y = 2 \Rightarrow & & 3x - 2y = 2 \\ 3(y-x) - y = 5 \Rightarrow 3y - 3x - y = 5 \Rightarrow & & -3x + 2y = 5 \\ & & 0 \neq 7 \end{array}$$

No Solution

Inconsistent system

46.

$$\begin{array}{rcl} 3x = 4(2-y) \Rightarrow 3x = 8 - 4y \Rightarrow 3x + 4y = 8 & & 3x + 4y = 8 \\ 3(x-2) + 4y = 0 \Rightarrow 3x - 6 + 4y = 0 \Rightarrow 3x + 4y = 6 \Rightarrow \times\ (-1) & & -3x - 4y = -6 \\ & & 0 \neq 2 \end{array}$$

No Solution $\Rightarrow$ Inconsistent System

47.

$$\begin{array}{rcl} x + \dfrac{y}{3} = \dfrac{5}{3} \Rightarrow \times\ (3)\ \ 3x + y = 5 \Rightarrow 3x + y = 5 & & 3x + y = 5 \\ \dfrac{x+y}{3} = 3 - x \Rightarrow \times\ (3)\ \ x + y = 9 - 3x \Rightarrow 4x + y = 9 \Rightarrow \times\ (-1) & & -4x - y = -9 \\ & & -x = -4 \\ & & x = 4 \end{array}$$

$$\begin{aligned} 3x + y &= 5 \\ 3(4) + y &= 5 \\ 12 + y &= 5 \\ y &= -7 \end{aligned}$$

Solution: $(4, -7)$

48. $3x - y = 0.25 \Rightarrow$ $\quad$ $3x - y = 0.25 \Rightarrow \times (3)$ $\quad$ $9x - 3y = 0.75$

$\underline{x + \frac{3}{2}y = 2.375} \Rightarrow \times (2)$ $\quad$ $\underline{2x + 3y = 4.75} \Rightarrow$ $\quad$ $\underline{2x + 3y = 4.75}$

$11x = 5.5$

$x = 0.5$

$3x - y = 0.25$

$3(0.5) - y = 0.25$

$1.5 - y = 0.25$

$1.25 = y$

Solution: $(0.5, 1.25)$

49. $\frac{3}{2}x + \frac{1}{3}y = 2 \Rightarrow \times (6)$ $\quad$ $9x + 2y = 12 \Rightarrow$ $\quad$ $9x + 2y = 12$

$\underline{\frac{2}{3}x + \frac{1}{9}y = 1} \Rightarrow \times (9)$ $\quad$ $\underline{6x + y = 9} \Rightarrow \times (-2)$ $\quad$ $\underline{-12x - 2y = -18}$

$-3x = -6$

$x = 2$

$6x + y = 9$

$6(2) + y = 9$

$12 + y = 9$

$y = -3$

Solution: $(2, -3)$

50. $\frac{x+y}{2} + \frac{x-y}{5} = 2 \Rightarrow \times (10)$ $\quad$ $5(x+y) + 2(x-y) = 20 \Rightarrow 5x + 5y + 2x - 2y = 20$

$\underline{x = \frac{y}{2} + 1} \Rightarrow \times (2)$ $\quad$ $\underline{2x = y + 2} \Rightarrow$ $\quad$ $\underline{2x - y = 2}$

$7x + 3y = 20$

$\underline{2x - y = 2} \Rightarrow \times (3)$

$7x + 3y = 20$

$\underline{6x - 3y = 6}$

$13x = 26$

$x = 2$

$7x + 3y = 20$

$7(2) + 3y = 20$

$14 + 3y = 20$

$3y = 6$

$y = 2$

Solution: $(2, 2)$

51. $\frac{x-y}{5} + \frac{x+y}{2} = 6 \Rightarrow \times (10)$ $\quad$ $2(x-y) + 5(x+y) = 60 \Rightarrow 2x - 2y + 5x + 5y = 60$

$\underline{\frac{x-y}{2} - \frac{x+y}{4} = 3} \Rightarrow \times (8)$ $\quad$ $\underline{4(x-y) - 2(x+y) = 24} \Rightarrow \underline{4x - 4y - 2x - 2y = 24}$

$7x + 3y = 60 \Rightarrow \times (2)$

$\underline{2x - 6y = 24}$

$14x + 6y = 120$

$\underline{2x - 6y = 24}$

$16x = 144$

$x = 9$

$7x + 3y = 60$

$7(9) + 3y = 60$

$63 + 3y = 60$

$3y = -3$

$y = -1$

Solution: $(9, -1)$

52.
$$\begin{array}{l} \frac{x-2}{5}+\frac{y+3}{2}=5 \Rightarrow \times(10) \quad 2(x-2)+5(y+3)=50 \Rightarrow 2x-4+5y+15=50 \\ \frac{x+3}{2}+\frac{y-2}{3}=6 \Rightarrow \times(6) \quad 3(x+3)+2(y-2)=36 \Rightarrow 3x+9+2y-4=36 \end{array}$$

$$\begin{array}{llll} 2x+5y=39 \Rightarrow \times(-2) & -4x-10y=-78 & 3x+2y=31 & \text{Solution:} \\ 3x+2y=31 \Rightarrow \times(5) & 15x+10y=155 & 3(7)+2y=31 & (7,5) \\ & 11x=77 & 2y=10 & \\ & x=7 & y=5 & \end{array}$$

53.
$$\begin{array}{lll} (1)\ x+y+z=3 & \text{Add (1) and (3):} & \text{Add equations (2) and (3):} \\ (2)\ 2x+y+z=4 & (1)\ x+y+z=3 & (2)\ 2x+y+z=4 \\ (3)\ 3x+y-z=5 & (3)\ 3x+y-z=5 & (3)\ 3x+y-z=5 \\ & (4)\ 4x+2y=8 & (5)\ 5x+2y=9 \end{array}$$

Solve the system of two equations and two unknowns formed by equations (4) and (5):

$$\begin{array}{lllll} 4x+2y=8 \Rightarrow \times(-1) & -4x-2y=-8 & 4x+2y=8 & x+y+z=3 & \text{Solution:} \\ 5x+2y=9 \Rightarrow & 5x+2y=9 & 4(1)+2y=8 & 1+2+z=3 & (1,2,0) \\ & x=1 & 2y=4 & 3+z=3 & \\ & & y=2 & z=0 & \end{array}$$

54.
$$\begin{array}{lll} (1)\ x-y-z=0 & \text{Add (1) and (3):} & \text{Add equations (2) and (3):} \\ (2)\ x+y-z=0 & (1)\ x-y-z=0 & (2)\ x+y-z=0 \\ (3)\ x-y+z=2 & (3)\ x-y+z=2 & (3)\ x-y+z=2 \\ & (4)\ 2x-2y=2 & (5)\ 2x=2 \\ & & x=1 \end{array}$$

Solve the system of two equations and two unknowns formed by equations (4) and (5):

$$\begin{array}{lll} 2x-2y=2 & x-y+z=2 & \text{Solution:} \\ 2(1)-2y=2 & 1-0+z=2 & (1,0,1) \\ -2y=0 & 1+z=2 & \\ y=0 & z=1 & \end{array}$$

55.
$$\begin{array}{lll} (1)\ x-y+z=0 & \text{Add (1) and (2):} & \text{Add equations (2) and (3):} \\ (2)\ x+y+2z=-1 & (1)\ x-y+z=0 & (2)\ x+y+2z=-1 \\ (3)\ -x-y+z=0 & (2)\ x+y+2z=-1 & (3)\ -x-y+z=0 \\ & (4)\ 2x+3z=-1 & (5)\ 3z=-1 \\ & & z=-\frac{1}{3} \end{array}$$

Solve the system of two equations and two unknowns formed by equations (4) and (5):

$$\begin{array}{lll} 2x+3z=-1 & x-y+z=0 & \text{Solution:} \\ 2x+3\left(-\frac{1}{3}\right)=-1 & 0-y+\left(-\frac{1}{3}\right)=0 & \left(0,-\frac{1}{3},-\frac{1}{3}\right) \\ 2x=0 & -y=\frac{1}{3} & \\ x=0 & y=-\frac{1}{3} & \end{array}$$

56. (1) $2x + y - z = 7$ (2) $x - y + z = 2$ (3) $x + y - 3z = 2$

Add (1) and (2):

$$\begin{array}{ll} (1) & 2x + y - z = 7 \\ (3) & \underline{x - y + z = 2} \\ (4) & 3x \qquad\quad = 9 \\ & x \qquad\quad = 3 \end{array}$$

Add equations (2) and (3):

$$\begin{array}{ll} (2) & x - y + \ z = 2 \\ (3) & \underline{x + y - 3z = 2} \\ (5) & 2x \qquad - 2z = 4 \end{array}$$

Solve the system of two equations and two unknowns formed by equations (4) and (5):

$$\begin{aligned} 2x - 2z &= 4 \\ 2(3) - 2z &= 4 \\ -2z &= -2 \\ z &= 1 \end{aligned} \qquad \begin{aligned} x + y - 3z &= 2 \\ 3 + y - 3(1) &= 2 \\ y &= 2 \end{aligned}$$

Solution: $(3, 2, 1)$

57. (1) $2x + y = 4$ (2) $x - z = 2$ (3) $y + z = 1$

Add (2) and (3):

$$\begin{array}{ll} (2) & x \qquad - z = 2 \\ (3) & \underline{\qquad y + z = 1} \\ (4) & x + y \qquad = 3 \end{array}$$

Solve the system of two equations and two unknowns formed by equations (1) and (4):

$$\begin{aligned} 2x + y = 4 &\Rightarrow \times(-1) \\ \underline{x + y = 3} &\Rightarrow \end{aligned} \qquad \begin{aligned} -2x - y &= -4 \\ \underline{x + y} &\underline{= \ \ 3} \\ -x \quad &= -1 \\ x \quad &= \ \ 1 \end{aligned} \qquad \begin{aligned} x + y &= 3 \\ 1 + y &= 3 \\ y &= 2 \end{aligned} \qquad \begin{aligned} y + z &= 1 \\ 2 + z &= 1 \\ z &= -1 \end{aligned}$$

Solution: $(1, 2, -1)$

58. (1) $3x + y + z = 0$ (2) $2x - y + z = 0$ (3) $2x + y + z = 0$

Add (1) and (2):

$$\begin{array}{ll} (1) & 3x + y + \ z = 0 \\ (2) & \underline{2x - y + \ z = 0} \\ (4) & 5x \qquad + 2z = 0 \end{array}$$

Add equations (2) and (3):

$$\begin{array}{ll} (2) & 2x - y + \ z = 0 \\ (3) & \underline{2x + y + \ z = 0} \\ (5) & 4x \qquad + 2z = 0 \end{array}$$

Solve the system of two equations and two unknowns formed by equations (4) and (5):

$$\begin{aligned} 5x + 2z = 0 &\Rightarrow \times(-1) \\ \underline{4x + 2z = 0} &\Rightarrow \end{aligned} \qquad \begin{aligned} -5x - 2z &= 0 \\ \underline{4x + 2z} &\underline{= 0} \\ -x \quad &= 0 \\ x \quad &= 0 \end{aligned} \qquad \begin{aligned} 4x + 2z &= 0 \\ 4(0) + 2z &= 0 \\ 2z &= 0 \\ z &= 0 \end{aligned} \qquad \begin{aligned} 3x + y + z &= 0 \\ 3(0) + y + 0 &= 9 \\ y &= 0 \end{aligned}$$

Solution: $(0, 0, 0)$

59. (1) $x + y + z = 6$ (2) $2x + y + 3z = 17$ (3) $x + y + 2z = 11$

Add (1) and $-(2)$:

$$\begin{array}{ll} (1) & x + y + \ z = \quad 6 \\ -(2) & \underline{-2x - y - 3z = -17} \\ (4) & -x \qquad - 2z = -11 \end{array}$$

Add equations (1) and $-(3)$:

$$\begin{array}{ll} (1) & x + y + \ z = \quad 6 \\ -(3) & \underline{-x - y - 2z = -11} \\ (5) & \qquad\quad - z = \ -5 \\ & \qquad\qquad z = \quad 5 \end{array}$$

Solve the system of two equations and two unknowns formed by equations (4) and (5):

$$\begin{aligned} -x - 2z &= -11 \\ -x - 2(5) &= -11 \\ -x &= -1 \\ x &= 1 \end{aligned} \qquad \begin{aligned} x + y + z &= 6 \\ 1 + y + 5 &= 6 \\ y &= 0 \end{aligned}$$

Solution: $(1, 0, 5)$

60. (1) $x + y + z = 3$
(2) $2x + y + z = 6$
(3) $x + 2y + 3z = 2$

Add $-(1)$ and (2):

$$\begin{array}{lrcl} -(1) & -x - y - z & = & -3 \\ (2) & 2x + y + z & = & 6 \\ \hline (4) & x & = & 3 \end{array}$$

Add equations $-2 \cdot (1)$ and (3):

$$\begin{array}{lrcl} -2 \cdot (1) & -2x - 2y - 2z & = & -6 \\ (3) & x + 2y + 3z & = & 2 \\ \hline (5) & -x \quad\quad + z & = & -4 \end{array}$$

Solve the system of two equations and two unknowns formed by equations (4) and (5):

$$\begin{array}{rcl} -x + z & = & -4 \\ -3 + z & = & -4 \\ z & = & -1 \end{array} \qquad \begin{array}{rcl} x + y + z & = & 3 \\ 3 + y + (-1) & = & 3 \\ y & = & 1 \end{array}$$

Solution: $(3, 1, -1)$

61. (1) $x + y + z = 3$
(2) $x + z = 2$
(3) $2x + 2y + 2z = 3$

Add $-2 \cdot (1)$ and (3):

$$\begin{array}{lrcl} -2 \cdot (1) & -2x - 2y - 2z & = & -6 \\ (3) & 2x + 2y + 2z & = & 3 \\ \hline (4) & 0 & \neq & -3 \end{array}$$

No solution; inconsistent system

62. (1) $x + y + z = 3$
(2) $x + z = 2$
(3) $2x + y + 2z = 5$

Add (1) and $-(2)$:

$$\begin{array}{lrcl} (1) & x + y + z & = & 3 \\ -(2) & -x \quad\quad - z & = & -2 \\ \hline (4) & y & = & 1 \end{array}$$

Add equations $-2 \cdot (1)$ and (3):

$$\begin{array}{lrcl} -2(1) & -2x - 2y - 2z & = & -6 \\ (3) & 2x + y + 2z & = & 5 \\ \hline (5) & -y & = & -1 \end{array}$$

Since both additions resulted in the same equation, the equations are dependent. Thus, y must equal 1, but x and z can be any real numbers that satisfy the equations. Notice that if the value $y = 1$ is substituted into any of the equations, $x + z = 2$ is the result. So $y = 1$, and x and z must satisfy $x + z = 2$. Solution: $x =$ any real number, $y = 1$, $z = 2 - x \Rightarrow \boxed{(x, 1, 2 - x)}$

63. (1) $x + 2y - z = 2$
(2) $2x - y = -1$
(3) $3x + y + z = 1$

Add (1) and (3):

$$\begin{array}{lrcl} (1) & x + 2y - z & = & 2 \\ (3) & 3x + y + z & = & 1 \\ \hline (4) & 4x + 3y & = & 3 \end{array}$$

Solve the system of two equations and two unknowns formed by equations (2) and (4):

$$\begin{array}{rcl} 2x - y & = & -1 \Rightarrow \times (3) \\ 4x + 3y & = & 3 \Rightarrow \end{array} \qquad \begin{array}{rcl} 6x - 3y & = & -3 \\ 4x + 3y & = & 3 \\ \hline 10x & = & 0 \\ x & = & 0 \end{array} \qquad \begin{array}{rcl} 2x - y & = & -1 \\ 2(0) - y & = & -1 \\ -y & = & -1 \\ y & = & 1 \end{array} \qquad \begin{array}{rcl} 3x + y + z & = & 1 \\ 3(0) + 1 + z & = & 1 \\ z & = & 0 \end{array}$$

Solution: $(0, 1, 0)$

64. (1) $x + y = 2$
(2) $y + z = 2$
(3) $3x + 3y = 2$

Add $-3 \cdot (1)$ and (3):

$$\begin{array}{lrcl} -3 \cdot (1) & -3x - 3y & = & -6 \\ (3) & 3x + 3y & = & 2 \\ \hline (4) & 0 & \neq & -4 \end{array}$$

$\boxed{\text{Inconsistent system} \Rightarrow \text{No solution}}$

65. (1) $3x + 4y + 2z = 4$
(2) $6x - 2y + z = 4$
(3) $3x - 8y - 6z = -3$

Add (1) and $2 \cdot (2)$:

$$\begin{array}{rl} (1) & 3x + 4y + 2z = 4 \\ 2\cdot(2) & 12x - 4y + 2z = 8 \\ \hline (4) & 15x \qquad + 4z = 12 \end{array}$$

Add equations $2 \cdot (1)$ and (3):

$$\begin{array}{rl} 2\cdot(1) & 6x + 8y + 4z = 8 \\ (3) & 3x - 8y - 6z = -3 \\ \hline (5) & 9x \qquad - 2z = 5 \end{array}$$

Solve the system of two equations and two unknowns formed by equations (4) and (5):

$$\begin{array}{rl} 15x + 4z = 12 \Rightarrow & 15x + 4z = 12 \\ 9x - 2z = 5 \Rightarrow \times(2) & 18x - 4z = 10 \\ \hline & 33x = 22 \\ & x = \frac{2}{3} \end{array}$$

$$\begin{aligned} 15x + 4z &= 12 \\ 15\left(\tfrac{2}{3}\right) + 4z &= 12 \\ 4z &= 2 \\ z &= \tfrac{1}{2} \end{aligned}$$

$$\begin{aligned} 3x + 4y + 2z &= 4 \\ 3\left(\tfrac{2}{3}\right) + 4y + 2\left(\tfrac{1}{2}\right) &= 4 \\ 4y &= 1 \\ y &= \tfrac{1}{4} \end{aligned}$$

Solution: $\left(\frac{2}{3}, \frac{1}{4}, \frac{1}{2}\right)$

66. (1) $x + y = 2$
(2) $y + z = 2$
(3) $x - z = 0$

Add (1) and $-(3)$:

$$\begin{array}{rl} (1) & x + y \qquad = 2 \\ -(3) & -x \qquad + z = 0 \\ \hline (4) & y + z = 2 \end{array}$$

Since (4) is the same as (2), the equations are dependent. Let $x =$ any real number. Then, from (1), $y = 2 - x$. Finally, substituting for y in (2) yields $z = 2 - y = 2 - (2 - x) = x$.

Solution: $\boxed{(x, 2 - x, x)}$

67. (1) $2x - y - z = 0$
(2) $x - 2y - z = -1$
(3) $x - y - 2z = -1$

Add (1) and $-2 \cdot (2)$:

$$\begin{array}{rl} (1) & 2x - y - z = 0 \\ -2\cdot(2) & -2x + 4y + 2z = 2 \\ \hline (4) & 3y + z = 2 \end{array}$$

Add equations (1) and $-2 \cdot (3)$:

$$\begin{array}{rl} (1) & 2x - y - z = 0 \\ (3) & -2x + 2y + 4z = 2 \\ \hline (5) & y + 3z = 2 \end{array}$$

Solve the system of two equations and two unknowns formed by equations (4) and (5):

$$\begin{array}{rl} 3y + z = 2 \Rightarrow & 3y + z = 2 \\ y + 3z = 2 \Rightarrow \times(-3) & -3y - 9z = -6 \\ \hline & -8z = -4 \\ & z = \frac{1}{2} \end{array}$$

$$\begin{aligned} y + 3z &= 2 \\ y + 3\left(\tfrac{1}{2}\right) &= 2 \\ y &= \tfrac{1}{2} \end{aligned}$$

$$\begin{aligned} x - y - 2z &= -1 \\ x - \tfrac{1}{2} - 2\left(\tfrac{1}{2}\right) &= -1 \\ x &= \tfrac{1}{2} \end{aligned}$$

Solution: $\left(\frac{1}{2}, \frac{1}{2}, \frac{1}{2}\right)$

68. (1) $x + 3y - z = 5$
(2) $3x - y + z = 2$
(3) $2x + y = 1$

Add (1) and (2):

$$\begin{array}{rl} (1) & x + 3y - z = 5 \\ (2) & 3x - y + z = 2 \\ \hline (4) & 4x + 2y \qquad = 7 \end{array}$$

Add equations $-2 \cdot (3)$ and (4):

$$\begin{array}{rl} -2\cdot(3) & -4x - 2y = -2 \\ (4) & 4x + 2y = 7 \\ \hline (5) & 0 \neq 5 \end{array}$$

$\boxed{\text{No solution}}$ $\boxed{\text{Inconsistent System}}$

69. (1) $(x + y) + (y + z) + (z + x) = 6 \Rightarrow 2x + 2y + 2z = 6$
(2) $(x - y) + (y - z) + (z - x) = 0 \Rightarrow 0 = 0$
(3) $x + y + 2z = 4 \Rightarrow x + y + 2z = 4$

Add (1) and $-2 \cdot (3)$:

$$\begin{array}{rl} (1) & 2x + 2y + 2z = 6 \\ -2\cdot(3) & -2x - 2y - 4z = -8 \\ \hline (4) & -2z = -2 \\ & z = 1 \end{array}$$

Since (2) is always true, the equations are dependent. z must equal 1. Then, from (3), $x + y = 2$. Let $x =$ any real #. Then $y = 2 - x$. Solution: $\boxed{(x, 2 - x, 1)}$

70. (1) $(x+y)+(y+z)=1 \Rightarrow x+2y+z=1$
(2) $(x+z)+(x+z)=3 \Rightarrow 2x+2z=3$
(3) $(x-y)-(x-z)=-1 \Rightarrow -y+z=-1$

Add $-2\cdot(1)$ and (2):

$$\begin{array}{rrcrcl} -2\cdot(1) & -2x & -4y & -2z & = & -2 \\ (2) & 2x & & +2z & = & 3 \\ \hline (4) & & -4y & & = & 1 \\ & & y & & = & -\frac{1}{4} \end{array}$$

$$\begin{aligned} -y+z&=-1 \\ -\left(-\tfrac{1}{4}\right)+z&=-1 \\ z&=-\tfrac{5}{4} \end{aligned} \qquad \begin{aligned} 2x+2z&=3 \\ 2x+2\left(-\tfrac{5}{4}\right)&=3 \\ 2x&=\tfrac{22}{4} \\ x&=\tfrac{11}{4} \end{aligned}$$

Solution: $\left(\frac{11}{4},-\frac{1}{4},-\frac{5}{4}\right)$

71. Let x = cost of a hamburger and let y = cost of the fries. Then $\begin{cases} (1) & 2x+4y=8 \\ (2) & 3x+2y=8 \end{cases}$

$$\begin{aligned} 2x+4y&=8 \\ 3x+2y&=8 \Rightarrow \times(-2) \end{aligned} \qquad \begin{array}{rcl} 2x+4y &=& 8 \\ -6x-4y &=& -16 \\ \hline -4x &=& -8 \\ x &=& 2 \end{array} \qquad \begin{aligned} 2x+4y&=8 \\ 2(2)+4y&=8 \\ 4y&=4 \\ y&=1 \end{aligned}$$

A hamburger costs \$2, while an order of fries costs \$1.

72. Let x = cost of a racket and let y = cost of a can of balls. Then $\begin{cases} (1) & 2x+4y=102 \\ (2) & 3x+2y=141 \end{cases}$

$$\begin{aligned} 2x+4y&=102 \\ 3x+2y&=141 \Rightarrow \times(-2) \end{aligned} \qquad \begin{array}{rcl} 2x+4y &=& 102 \\ -6x-4y &=& -282 \\ \hline -4x &=& -180 \\ x &=& 45 \end{array} \qquad \begin{aligned} 2x+4y&=102 \\ 2(45)+4y&=102 \\ 4y&=12 \\ y&=3 \end{aligned}$$

A racket costs \$45, while a can of balls costs \$3.

73. Let x = acres of corn and let y = acres of soybeans. Then $\begin{cases} (1) & x+y=350 \\ (2) & x=y+100 \end{cases}$

Substitute $x=y+100$ from (2) into (1):

$$\begin{aligned} x+y&=350 \\ y+100+y&=350 \\ 2y&=250 \\ y&=125 \end{aligned}$$

Substitute and solve for x:

$$\begin{aligned} x&=y+100 \\ &=125+100=225 \end{aligned}$$

The farmer should plant 225 acres of corn and 125 acres of soybeans.

74. Let x = the initiation fee and let y = the monthly dues. Then the following system applies:

$$\begin{aligned} x+7y&=3025 \Rightarrow \times(-1) \\ x+18y&=3850 \end{aligned} \qquad \begin{array}{rcl} -x-7y &=& -3025 \\ x+18y &=& 3850 \\ \hline 11y &=& 825 \\ y &=& 75 \end{array} \qquad \begin{aligned} x+7y&=3025 \\ x+7(75)&=3025 \\ x&=2500 \end{aligned}$$

The initiation fee is \$2500 and dues are \$75 per month.

75. Let b = speed in still water. Let c = the speed of the current. Then the following system applies:

$$\begin{aligned} 3(b+c)&=30 \\ 5(b-c)&=30 \end{aligned} \qquad \begin{aligned} 3b+3c&=30 \Rightarrow \times(5) \\ 5b-5c&=30 \Rightarrow \times(3) \end{aligned} \qquad \begin{array}{rcl} 15b+15c &=& 150 \\ 15b-15c &=& 90 \\ \hline 30b &=& 240 \\ b &=& 8 \end{array}$$

The boat has a speed of 8 kilometers per hour in still water.

76. Let w = width and let l = length. Then $\begin{cases} (1) & 2w + 2l = 1900 \\ (2) & w = l - 250 \end{cases}$

Substitute $w = l - 250$ from (2) into (1):

$$\begin{aligned} 2w + 2l &= 1900 \\ 2(l - 250) + 2l &= 1900 \\ 2l - 500 + 2l &= 1900 \\ 4l &= 2400 \\ l &= 600 \end{aligned}$$

Substitute and solve for w:

$$\begin{aligned} w &= l - 250 \\ &= 600 - 250 = 350 \end{aligned}$$

Area $= lw = (600 \text{ cm})(350 \text{ cm})$

The area is 210,000 cm^2.

77. Let x = grams of 9% alloy. Let y = grams of 84% alloy. Then the following system applies: (note: 34% of 60 is $0.34 \times 60 = 20.4$)

$$\begin{aligned} x + y &= 60 \Rightarrow \times(-9) & -9x - 9y &= -540 \\ 0.09x + 0.84y &= 20.4 \Rightarrow \times(100) & 9x + 84y &= 2040 \\ & & 75y &= 1500 \\ & & y &= 20 \end{aligned}$$

She must use 40 grams of the 9% and 20 grams of the 84% alloy.

78.

$$\begin{aligned} 2w_1 &= 3w_2 & \Rightarrow 2w_1 - 3w_2 &= 0 \Rightarrow \times(-2) & -4w_1 + 6w_2 &= 0 \\ 3w_1 &= 2(w_2 + 5) & \Rightarrow 3w_1 - 2w_2 &= 10 \Rightarrow \times(3) & 9w_1 - 6w_2 &= 30 \\ & & & & 5w_1 &= 30 \\ & & & & w_1 &= 6 \end{aligned}$$

The weights are 6 and 4 pounds.

79.

$$\begin{aligned} 448x &= 112y & \Rightarrow 448x - 112y &= 0 \Rightarrow \times(-1) & -448x + 112y &= 0 \\ 448(x + 1) &= 192(y - 1) & \Rightarrow 448x - 192y &= -640 \Rightarrow & 448x - 192y &= -640 \\ & & & & -80y &= -640 \\ & & & & y &= 8 \end{aligned}$$

$$\begin{aligned} 448x &= 112y \\ 448x &= 112(8) \\ x &= 2 \end{aligned}$$

The lever has a length of 10 feet.

80.

$$\begin{aligned} a(x + 2y) - b(2x - y) &= ax + 2ay - 2bx + by \\ &= (a - 2b)x + (2a + b)y \end{aligned}$$

$$\begin{aligned} a - 2b &= -3 \Rightarrow \times(-2) & -2a + 4b &= 6 \\ 2a + b &= 9 & 2a + b &= 9 \\ & & 5b &= 15 \\ & & b &= 3 \end{aligned}$$

$$\begin{aligned} a - 2b &= -3 \\ a - 2(3) &= -3 \\ a &= 3 \end{aligned}$$

Solution: $a = 3, b = 3$

81.

$$\begin{aligned} E(x) &= 43.53x + 742.72 \\ R(x) &= 89.95x \end{aligned}$$

$$\begin{aligned} E(x) &= R(x) \\ 43.53x + 742.72 &= 89.95x \\ 742.72 &= 46.42x \\ 16 &= x \Rightarrow \end{aligned}$$

Daily production should be 16 pairs.

82.

$$\begin{aligned} S_1(x) &= 326 + 0.035x \\ S_2(x) &= 200 + 0.0425x \end{aligned}$$

$$\begin{aligned} S_1(x) &= S_2(x) \\ 326 + 0.035x &= 200 + 0.0425x \\ 126 &= 0.0075x \\ 16{,}800 &= x \end{aligned}$$

The salary would be the same at a sales level of \$16,800.

83. Let $x =$ hours at fast food restaurant, $y =$ hours at gas station and $z =$ janitorial hours.

$$\begin{array}{ll} (1) & x = 15 \\ (2) & x + y + z = 30 \\ (3) & 5.7x + 6.3y + 10z = 198.50 \end{array}$$

Substitute $x = 15$ into (2) and (3):

$$\begin{array}{ll} (2) & 15 + y + z = 30 \\ (3) & 5.7(15) + 6.3y + 10z = 198.5 \end{array}$$

Solve the system of two equations and two unknowns formed by equations (2) and (3):

$$\begin{array}{lll} y + z = 15 \Rightarrow \times(-10) & -10y - 10z = -150 & y + z = 15 \\ 6.3y + 10z = 113 \Rightarrow \times(-3) & 6.3y + 10z = 113 & 10 + z = 15 \\ & -3.7y = -37 & z = 5 \\ & y = 10 & \end{array}$$

He spends 15 hours cooking, 10 hours at the gas station and 5 hours doing janitorial work.

84. Let $x =$ amount at 5%, $y =$ amount at 6% and $z =$ amount at 7%.

$$\begin{array}{ll} (1) & x + y + z = 22000 \\ (2) & y = x + 2000 \\ (3) & 0.05x + 0.06y + 0.07z = 1370 \end{array}$$

Add (1) and (2):

$$\begin{array}{ll} (1) & x + y + z = 22000 \\ (2) & -x + y = 2000 \\ (4) & 2y + z = 24000 \end{array}$$

Add $-0.05(1)$ and (3):

$$\begin{array}{ll} -0.05(1) & -0.05x - 0.05y - 0.05z = -1100 \\ (3) & 0.05x + 0.06y + 0.07z = 1370 \\ (5) & 0.01y + 0.02z = 270 \end{array}$$

Solve the system of two equations and two unknowns formed by equations (4) and (5):

$$\begin{array}{llll} 2y + z = 24000 \Rightarrow & 2y + z = 24000 \Rightarrow \times(-2) & -4y - 2z = -48000 \\ 0.01y + 0.02z = 270 \Rightarrow \times(100) & y + 2z = 27000 \Rightarrow & y + 2z = 27000 \\ & & -3y = -21000 \\ & & y = 7000 \end{array}$$

She invested \$5000 at 5%, \$7000 at 6% and \$10,000 at 7%.

85. Let $x =$ # between 0-14, $y =$ # between 15-49 and $z =$ # 50 or over.

$$\begin{array}{ll} (1) & x + y + z = 3 \\ (2) & x + y = 2.61 \\ (3) & y + z = 1.95 \end{array}$$

Add (1) and $-(2)$:

$$\begin{array}{ll} (1) & x + y + z = 3 \\ -(2) & -x - y = -2.61 \\ & z = 0.39 \end{array}$$

Substitute $z = 0.39$ into (3):

$$\begin{array}{l} y + z = 1.95 \\ y + 0.39 = 1.95 \\ y = 1.56 \end{array}$$

Substitute $y = 1.56$ into (2):

$$\begin{array}{l} x + y = 2.61 \\ x + 1.56 = 2.61 \\ x = 1.05 \end{array}$$

There are 1.05 million between 0-14, 1.56 million between 15-49 and 0.39 million over 50.

86. Points on the parabola: $(0, 0)$, $(10, 22.5)$ and $(40, 0)$. Substitute each into the equation:

$$y = ax^2 + bx + c \qquad y = ax^2 + bx + c \qquad y = ax^2 + bx + c$$
$$0 = a(0)^2 + b(0) + c \qquad 22.5 = a(10)^2 + b(10) + c \qquad 0 = a(40)^2 + b(40) + c$$
$$(1)\ 0 = c \qquad (2)\ 22.5 = 100a + 10b + c \qquad (3)\ 0 = 1600a + 40b + c$$

Substitute $c = 0$ into (2) and (3) and solve the resulting system of equations:

$$\begin{aligned} 100a + 10b &= 22.5 \Rightarrow \times\ (-4) \\ 1600a + 40b &= 0 \end{aligned} \qquad \begin{aligned} -400a - 40b &= -90 \\ 1600a + 40b &= 0 \\ \hline 1200a &= -90 \\ a &= -\tfrac{3}{40} \end{aligned} \qquad \begin{aligned} 1600a + 40b &= 0 \\ 1600\left(-\tfrac{3}{40}\right) + 40b &= 0 \\ -120 + 40b &= 0 \\ b &= 3 \end{aligned}$$

Solution: $\boxed{a = -\frac{3}{40},\ b = 3,\ c = 0}$

87. Let $x =$ the smallest angle, $y =$ the middle angle and $z =$ the largest angle.

$$\begin{aligned} &(1)\ x + y + z = 180 \\ &(2)\ z = x + y + 20 \\ &(3)\ z = 3x + 10 \end{aligned} \qquad \begin{aligned} &\text{Substitute (3) into (1):} \\ &x + y + 3x + 10 = 180 \\ &4x + y = 170\ (4) \end{aligned} \qquad \begin{aligned} &\text{Substitute (3) and (2):} \\ &3x + 10 = x + y + 20 \\ &2x - y = 10\ (5) \end{aligned}$$

Solve the system of two equations and two unknowns formed by equations (4) and (5):

$$\begin{aligned} 4x + y &= 170 \\ 2x - y &= 10 \\ \hline 6x &= 180 \\ x &= 30 \end{aligned} \qquad \begin{aligned} 4x + y &= 170 \\ 4(30) + y &= 170 \\ 120 + y &= 170 \\ y &= 50 \end{aligned} \qquad \begin{aligned} z &= 3x + 10 \\ z &= 3(30) + 10 \\ z &= 90 + 10 \\ z &= 100 \end{aligned}$$

Solution: **The angles have measures of 30°, 50° and 100°.**

88. Points on the parabola: $(0, 0)$, $(8, 12)$ and $(12, 15)$. Substitute each into the equation:

$$y = ax^2 + bx + c \qquad y = ax^2 + bx + c \qquad y = ax^2 + bx + c$$
$$0 = a(0)^2 + b(0) + c \qquad 12 = a(8)^2 + b(8) + c \qquad 15 = a(12)^2 + b(12) + c$$
$$(1)\ 0 = c \qquad (2)\ 12 = 64a + 8b + c \qquad (3)\ 15 = 144a + 12b + c$$

Substitute $c = 0$ into (2) and (3) and solve the resulting system of equations:

$$\begin{aligned} 64a + 8b &= 12 \Rightarrow \times\ (-3) \\ 144a + 12b &= 15 \Rightarrow \times\ (2) \end{aligned} \qquad \begin{aligned} -192a - 24b &= -36 \\ 288a + 24b &= 30 \\ \hline 96a &= -6 \\ a &= -\tfrac{1}{16} \end{aligned} \qquad \begin{aligned} 64a + 8b &= 12 \\ 64\left(-\tfrac{1}{16}\right) + 8b &= 12 \\ -4 + 8b &= 12 \\ 8b &= 16 \\ b &= 2 \end{aligned}$$

Solution: $\boxed{a = -\frac{1}{16},\ b = 2,\ c = 0}$

89-94. Answers may vary.

95. $y = 3^x$; points: $(0, 1)$, $(1, 3)$

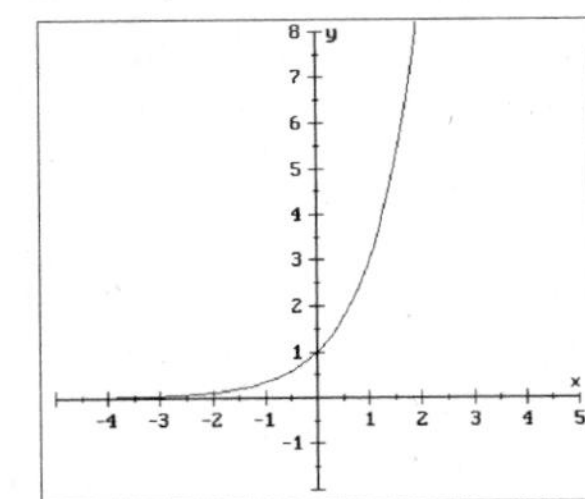

96. $y = \log_2 x$; points: $(1, 0)$, $(2, 1)$

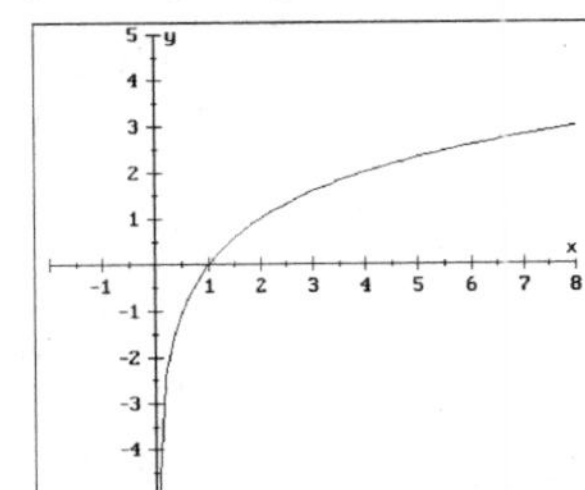

97. $3 = \log_2 x$
$2^3 = x$
$8 = x$

98. $x = \log_5 \frac{1}{25}$
$5^x = \frac{1}{25}$
$x = -2$

99. $\log \frac{x}{y^2 z} = \log x - \log\left(y^2 z\right) = \log x - \left(\log y^2 + \log z\right) = \log x - 2\log y - \log z$

100. $\ln x(y^z) = \ln x + \ln y^z = \ln x + z \ln y$

101. $\log x + 3\log y - \frac{1}{2}\log z = \log x + \log y^3 + \log z^{-1/2} = \log x + \log y^3 + \log \frac{1}{\sqrt{z}} = \log \frac{xy^3}{\sqrt{z}}$

102. $\frac{1}{2}(\ln A - 3\ln B) = \frac{1}{2}\left(\ln A - \ln B^3\right) = \frac{1}{2}\ln \frac{A}{B^3} = \ln \sqrt{\frac{A}{B^3}}$

Exercises 6.2 (page 574)

1. matrix
2. 3, 5
3. coefficient
4. system, augmented
5. equation
6. row operations
7. row equivalent
8. same solutions
9. interchanged
10. multiplied
11. adding, multiple
12. lead entry

13. $\begin{cases} (1) & x + y = 5 \\ (2) & x - 2y = -4 \end{cases} \Rightarrow \begin{cases} (1) & x + y = 5 \\ (2) & -3y = -9 \end{cases} \Rightarrow \begin{cases} (1) & x + y = 5 \\ (2) & y = 3 \end{cases}$

$-(1) + (2) \Rightarrow (2)$ $\quad -\frac{1}{3}(2) \Rightarrow (2)$

From (2): $y = 3$

From (1): $x + y = 5$, $x + 3 = 5$, $x = 2$

Solution: $(2, 3)$

14. $\begin{cases} (1) & x + 3y = 8 \\ (2) & 2x - 5y = 5 \end{cases} \Rightarrow \begin{cases} (1) & x + 3y = 8 \\ (2) & -11y = -11 \end{cases} \Rightarrow \begin{cases} (1) & x + 3y = 8 \\ (2) & y = 1 \end{cases}$

$-2(1) + (2) \Rightarrow (2)$ $\quad -\frac{1}{11}(2) \Rightarrow (2)$

From (2): $y = 1$

From (1): $x + 3y = 8$, $x + 3(1) = 8$, $x = 5$

Solution: $(5, 1)$

15. $\begin{cases}(1) & x-y=1\\(2) & 2x-y=8\end{cases} \Rightarrow \begin{cases}(1) & x-y=1\\(2) & y=6\end{cases}$

$-2(1)+(2)\Rightarrow(2)$

From (2): $y=6$ From (1): $x-y=1$, $x-6=1$, $x=7$ Solution: $(7,6)$

16. $\begin{cases}(1) & x-5y=4\\(2) & 2x+3y=21\end{cases} \Rightarrow \begin{cases}(1) & x-5y=4\\(2) & 13y=13\end{cases} \Rightarrow \begin{cases}(1) & x-5y=4\\(2) & y=1\end{cases}$

$-2(1)+(2)\Rightarrow(2)$ $\quad \frac{1}{13}(2)\Rightarrow(2)$

From (2): $y=1$ From (1): $x-5y=4$, $x-5(1)=4$, $x=9$ Solution: $(9,1)$

17. $\begin{cases}(1) & x+2y-z=2\\(2) & x-3y+2z=1\\(3) & x+y-3z=-6\end{cases} \Rightarrow \begin{cases}(1) & x+2y-z=2\\(2) & -5y+3z=-1\\(3) & -y-2z=-8\end{cases} \Rightarrow \begin{cases}(1) & x+2y-z=2\\(2) & -5y+3z=-1\\(3) & 13z=39\end{cases} \Rightarrow$

$-(1)+(2)\Rightarrow(2)$, $-(1)+(3)\Rightarrow(3)$ $\quad -5(3)+(2)\Rightarrow(3)$

$\begin{cases}(1) & x+2y-z=2\\(2) & y-\frac{3}{5}z=\frac{1}{5}\\(3) & z=3\end{cases}$

$-\frac{1}{5}(2)\Rightarrow(2)$, $\frac{1}{13}(3)\Rightarrow(3)$

From (3): $z=3$

From (2): $y-\frac{3}{5}z=\frac{1}{5}$, $y-\frac{3}{5}(3)=\frac{1}{5}$, $y=2$

From (1): $x+2y-z=2$, $x+2(2)-(3)=2$, $x=1$

Solution: $(1,2,3)$

18. $\begin{cases}(1) & x+5y-z=2\\(2) & x+2y+z=3\\(3) & x+y+z=2\end{cases} \Rightarrow \begin{cases}(1) & x+5y-z=2\\(2) & 3y-2z=-1\\(3) & 4y-2z=0\end{cases} \Rightarrow \begin{cases}(1) & x+5y-z=2\\(2) & y-\frac{2}{3}z=-\frac{1}{3}\\(3) & 4y-2z=0\end{cases} \Rightarrow$

$-(2)+(1)\Rightarrow(2)$, $-(3)+(1)\Rightarrow(3)$ $\quad \frac{1}{3}(2)\Rightarrow(2)$

$\begin{cases}(1) & x+5y-z=2\\(2) & y-\frac{2}{3}z=-\frac{1}{3}\\(3) & \frac{2}{3}z=\frac{4}{3}\end{cases} \Rightarrow \begin{cases}(1) & x+5y-z=2\\(2) & y-\frac{2}{3}z=-\frac{1}{3}\\(3) & z=2\end{cases}$

$-4(2)+(3)\Rightarrow(3)$ $\quad \frac{3}{2}(3)\Rightarrow(3)$

From (3): $z=2$ From (2): $y-\frac{2}{3}z=-\frac{1}{3}$, $y-\frac{2}{3}(2)=-\frac{1}{3}$, $y=1$ From (1): $x+5y-z=2$, $x+5(1)-2=2$, $x=-1$

Solution: $(-1,1,2)$

19. $\begin{cases}(1)\ x-y-z=-3\\(2)\ 5x+y=6\\(3)\ y+z=4\end{cases}\Rightarrow\begin{cases}(1)\ x-y-z=-3\\(2)\ 6y+5z=21\\(3)\ y+z=4\end{cases}\Rightarrow\begin{cases}(1)\ x-y-z=-3\\(2)\ y+\frac{5}{6}z=\frac{7}{2}\\(3)\ -z=-3\end{cases}\Rightarrow$

$-5(1)+(2)\Rightarrow(2)$ $\quad\frac{1}{6}(2)\Rightarrow(2)$, $-6(3)+(2)\Rightarrow(3)$

$\begin{cases}(1)\ x-y-z=-3\\(2)\ y+\frac{5}{6}z=\frac{7}{2}\\(3)\ z=3\end{cases}\Rightarrow$ $\quad -(3)\Rightarrow(3)$

From (3): $z=3$

From (2): $y+\frac{5}{6}z=\frac{7}{2}$
$y+\frac{5}{6}(3)=\frac{7}{2}$
$y=1$

From (1): $x-y-z=-3$
$x-(1)-(3)=-3$
$x=1$

Solution: $(1,1,3)$

20. $\begin{cases}(1)\ x+y=1\\(2)\ x+z=3\\(3)\ y+z=2\end{cases}\Rightarrow\begin{cases}(1)\ x+y=1\\(2)\ -y+z=2\\(3)\ y+z=2\end{cases}\Rightarrow\begin{cases}(1)\ x+y=1\\(2)\ y-z=-2\\(3)\ 2z=4\end{cases}\Rightarrow$

$-(1)+(2)\Rightarrow(2)$ $\quad -(2)\Rightarrow(2)$, $(2)+(3)\Rightarrow(3)$

$\begin{cases}(1)\ x+y=1\\(2)\ y-z=-2\\(3)\ z=2\end{cases}\Rightarrow$ $\quad \frac{1}{2}(3)\Rightarrow(3)$

From (3): $z=2$

From (2): $y-z=-2$
$y-(2)=-2$
$y=0$

From (1): $x+y=1$
$x+(0)=1$
$x=1$

Solution: $(1,0,2)$

21. row echelon form **22.** row echelon form **23.** reduced row echelon form **24.** reduced row echelon form

25. $\left[\begin{array}{cc|c}2&1&3\\1&-3&5\end{array}\right]\Rightarrow\left[\begin{array}{cc|c}1&-3&5\\2&1&3\end{array}\right]\Rightarrow\left[\begin{array}{cc|c}1&-3&5\\0&7&-7\end{array}\right]\Rightarrow\left[\begin{array}{cc|c}1&-3&5\\0&1&-1\end{array}\right]$

$R_1\Leftrightarrow R_2$ $\quad -2R_1+R_2\Rightarrow R_2$ $\quad \frac{1}{7}R_2\Rightarrow R_2$

From R_2: $y=-1$ From R_1: $x-3y=5$
$x-3(-1)=5$
$x+3=5$
$x=2$

Solution: $(2,-1)$

26. $\left[\begin{array}{cc|c}1&2&-1\\3&-5&19\end{array}\right]\Rightarrow\left[\begin{array}{cc|c}1&2&-1\\0&-11&22\end{array}\right]\Rightarrow\left[\begin{array}{cc|c}1&2&-1\\0&1&-2\end{array}\right]$

$-3R_1+R_2\Rightarrow R_2$ $\quad -\frac{1}{11}R_2\Rightarrow R_2$

From R_2: $y=-2$ From R_1: $x+2y=-1$
$x+2(-2)=-1$
$x=3$

Solution: $(3,-2)$

27. $\left[\begin{array}{cc|c} 1 & -7 & -2 \\ 5 & -2 & -10 \end{array}\right] \Rightarrow \left[\begin{array}{cc|c} 1 & -7 & -2 \\ 0 & 33 & 0 \end{array}\right] \Rightarrow \left[\begin{array}{cc|c} 1 & -7 & -2 \\ 0 & 1 & 0 \end{array}\right]$

$-5R_1 + R_2 \Rightarrow R_2$ $\quad \frac{1}{33}R_2 \Rightarrow R_2$

From R_2: $y = 0$ From R_1: $x - 7y = -2$ Solution: $(-2, 0)$

$$x - 7(0) = -2$$
$$x = -2$$

28. $\left[\begin{array}{cc|c} 3 & -1 & 3 \\ 2 & 1 & -3 \end{array}\right] \Rightarrow \left[\begin{array}{cc|c} 3 & -1 & 3 \\ 0 & -\frac{5}{2} & \frac{15}{2} \end{array}\right] \Rightarrow \left[\begin{array}{cc|c} 1 & -\frac{1}{3} & 1 \\ 0 & 1 & -3 \end{array}\right]$

$-\frac{3}{2}R_2 + R_1 \Rightarrow R_2$ $\quad \frac{1}{3}R_1 \Rightarrow R_1$, $-\frac{2}{5}R_2 \Rightarrow R_2$

From R_2: $y = -3$ From R_1: $x - \frac{1}{3}y = 1$ Solution: $(0, -3)$

$$x - \tfrac{1}{3}(-3) = 1$$
$$x + 1 = 1$$
$$x = 0$$

29. $\left[\begin{array}{cc|c} 2 & -1 & 5 \\ 1 & 3 & 6 \end{array}\right] \Rightarrow \left[\begin{array}{cc|c} 1 & 3 & 6 \\ 2 & -1 & 5 \end{array}\right] \Rightarrow \left[\begin{array}{cc|c} 1 & 3 & 6 \\ 0 & -7 & -7 \end{array}\right] \Rightarrow \left[\begin{array}{cc|c} 1 & 3 & 6 \\ 0 & 1 & 1 \end{array}\right]$

$R_1 \Leftrightarrow R_2$ $\quad -2R_1 + R_2 \Rightarrow R_2$ $\quad -\frac{1}{7}R_2 \Rightarrow R_2$

From R_2: $y = 1$ From R_1: $x + 3y = 6$ Solution: $(3, 1)$

$$x + 3(1) = 6$$
$$x = 3$$

30. $\left[\begin{array}{cc|c} 3 & -5 & -25 \\ 2 & 1 & 5 \end{array}\right] \Rightarrow \left[\begin{array}{cc|c} 3 & -5 & -25 \\ 0 & -\frac{13}{2} & -\frac{65}{2} \end{array}\right] \Rightarrow \left[\begin{array}{cc|c} 1 & -\frac{5}{3} & -\frac{25}{3} \\ 0 & 1 & 5 \end{array}\right]$

$-\frac{3}{2}R_2 + R_1 \Rightarrow R_2$ $\quad \frac{1}{3}R_1 \Rightarrow R_1$, $-\frac{2}{13}R_2 \Rightarrow R_2$

From R_2: $y = 5$ From R_1: $x - \frac{5}{3}y = -\frac{25}{3}$ Solution: $(0, 5)$

$$x - \tfrac{5}{3}(5) = -\tfrac{25}{3}$$
$$x - \tfrac{25}{3} = -\tfrac{25}{3}$$
$$x = 0$$

31. $\left[\begin{array}{cc|c} 1 & -2 & 3 \\ -2 & 4 & 6 \end{array}\right] \Rightarrow \left[\begin{array}{cc|c} 1 & -2 & 3 \\ 0 & 0 & 12 \end{array}\right] \Rightarrow$ From R_2, $0x + 0y = 12$. This is impossible.

$2R_1 + R_2 \Rightarrow R_2$ $\quad$ No solution $\Rightarrow$ inconsistent system

32. $2(2y - x) = 6 \quad \Rightarrow 4y - 2x = 6 \quad \Rightarrow -2x + 4y = 6$

$4y = 2(x+3) \Rightarrow \quad 4y = 2x + 6 \Rightarrow -2x + 4y = 6$

$$\left[\begin{array}{cc|c} -2 & 4 & 6 \\ -2 & 4 & 6 \end{array}\right] \Rightarrow \underset{-R_1 + R_2 \Rightarrow R_2}{\left[\begin{array}{cc|c} -2 & 4 & 6 \\ 0 & 0 & 0 \end{array}\right]} \Rightarrow \text{Dependent equations}$$

From R_1: $-2x + 4y = 6$ Solution: $\left(x, \frac{1}{2}x + \frac{3}{2}\right)$

$4y = 2x + 6$

$y = \frac{1}{2}x + \frac{3}{2}$

33. $$\left[\begin{array}{cc|c} 2 & -1 & 7 \\ -1 & \frac{1}{3} & -\frac{7}{3} \end{array}\right] \Rightarrow \underset{R_1 \Leftrightarrow -R_2}{\left[\begin{array}{cc|c} 1 & -\frac{1}{3} & \frac{7}{3} \\ 2 & -1 & 7 \end{array}\right]} \Rightarrow \underset{-2R_1 + R_2 \Rightarrow R_2}{\left[\begin{array}{cc|c} 1 & -\frac{1}{3} & \frac{7}{3} \\ 0 & -\frac{1}{3} & \frac{7}{3} \end{array}\right]} \Rightarrow \underset{-3R_2 \Rightarrow R_2}{\left[\begin{array}{cc|c} 1 & -\frac{1}{3} & \frac{7}{3} \\ 0 & 1 & -7 \end{array}\right]}$$

From R_2: $y = -7$ From R_1: $x - \frac{1}{3}y = \frac{7}{3}$ Solution: $(0, -7)$

$x - \frac{1}{3}(-7) = \frac{7}{3}$

$x + \frac{7}{3} = \frac{7}{3}$

$x = 0$

34. $$\left[\begin{array}{cc|c} 45 & -6 & 60 \\ 30 & 15 & 63.75 \end{array}\right] \Rightarrow \underset{R_1 \Leftrightarrow \frac{1}{30}R_2}{\left[\begin{array}{cc|c} 1 & 0.5 & 2.125 \\ 45 & -6 & 60 \end{array}\right]} \Rightarrow \underset{-45R_1 + R_2 \Rightarrow R_2}{\left[\begin{array}{cc|c} 1 & 0.5 & 2.125 \\ 0 & -28.5 & -35.625 \end{array}\right]} \Rightarrow \underset{-\frac{1}{28.5}R_2 \Rightarrow R_2}{\left[\begin{array}{cc|c} 1 & 0.5 & 2.125 \\ 0 & 1 & 1.25 \end{array}\right]}$$

From R_2: $y = 1.25$ From R_1: $x + 0.5y = 2.125$ Solution: $(1.5, 1.25)$

$x + 0.5(1.25) = 2.125$

$x + 0.625 = 2.125$

$x = 1.5$

35. $$\left[\begin{array}{ccc|c} 1 & -1 & 1 & 3 \\ 2 & -1 & 1 & 4 \\ 1 & 2 & -1 & -1 \end{array}\right] \Rightarrow \underset{\substack{-2R_1 + R_2 \Rightarrow R_2 \\ -R_1 + R_3 \Rightarrow R_3}}{\left[\begin{array}{ccc|c} 1 & -1 & 1 & 3 \\ 0 & 1 & -1 & -2 \\ 0 & 3 & -2 & -4 \end{array}\right]} \Rightarrow \underset{-3R_2 + R_3 \Rightarrow R_3}{\left[\begin{array}{ccc|c} 1 & -1 & 1 & 3 \\ 0 & 1 & -1 & -2 \\ 0 & 0 & 1 & 2 \end{array}\right]} \Rightarrow$$

From R_3: $z = 2$ From R_1: $x - y + z = 3$

From R_2: $y - z = -2$ $\quad x - (0) + (2) = 3$

$y - (2) = -2$ $\quad x = 1$

$y = 0$ Solution: $(1, 0, 2)$

36. $\left[\begin{array}{ccc|c} 2 & 1 & -1 & 1 \\ 1 & 1 & -1 & 0 \\ 3 & 1 & 2 & 2 \end{array}\right] \Rightarrow \left[\begin{array}{ccc|c} 2 & 1 & -1 & 1 \\ 0 & -1 & 1 & 1 \\ 0 & -2 & 5 & 2 \end{array}\right] \Rightarrow \left[\begin{array}{ccc|c} 2 & 1 & -1 & 1 \\ 0 & 1 & -1 & -1 \\ 0 & 0 & 3 & 0 \end{array}\right] \Rightarrow \left[\begin{array}{ccc|c} 1 & \frac{1}{2} & -\frac{1}{2} & \frac{1}{2} \\ 0 & 1 & -1 & -1 \\ 0 & 0 & 1 & 0 \end{array}\right]$

$-2R_2 + R_1 \Rightarrow R_2$, $-3R_2 + R_3 \Rightarrow R_3$; $-R_2 \Rightarrow R_2$, $-2R_2 + R_3 \Rightarrow R_3$; $\frac{1}{3}R_3 \Rightarrow R_3$, $\frac{1}{2}R_1 \Rightarrow R_1$

From (3): $z = 0$

From (2): $y - z = -1$

$y - (0) = -1$

$y = -1$

From (1): $x + \frac{1}{2}y - \frac{1}{2}z = \frac{1}{2}$

$x + \frac{1}{2}(-1) - \frac{1}{2}(0) = \frac{1}{2}$

$x - \frac{1}{2} = \frac{1}{2}$

$x = 1$

Solution: $(1, -1, 0)$

37. $\left[\begin{array}{ccc|c} 1 & 1 & -1 & -1 \\ 3 & 1 & 0 & 4 \\ 0 & 1 & -2 & -4 \end{array}\right] \Rightarrow \left[\begin{array}{ccc|c} 1 & 1 & -1 & -1 \\ 0 & -2 & 3 & 7 \\ 0 & 1 & -2 & -4 \end{array}\right] \Rightarrow \left[\begin{array}{ccc|c} 1 & 1 & -1 & -1 \\ 0 & 1 & -\frac{3}{2} & -\frac{7}{2} \\ 0 & 0 & -1 & -1 \end{array}\right] \Rightarrow \left[\begin{array}{ccc|c} 1 & 1 & -1 & -1 \\ 0 & 1 & -\frac{3}{2} & -\frac{7}{2} \\ 0 & 0 & 1 & 1 \end{array}\right]$

$-3R_1 + R_2 \Rightarrow R_2$; $-\frac{1}{2}R_2 \Rightarrow R_2$, $R_2 + 2R_3 \Rightarrow R_3$; $-R_3 \Rightarrow R_3$

From (3): $z = 1$

From (2): $y - \dfrac{3}{2}z = -\dfrac{7}{2}$

$y - \dfrac{3}{2}(1) = -\dfrac{7}{2}$

$y = -2$

From (1): $x + y - z = -1$

$x + (-2) - (1) = -1$

$x = 2$

Solution: $(2, -2, 1)$

38. $\left[\begin{array}{ccc|c} 3 & 1 & 0 & 7 \\ 1 & 0 & -1 & 0 \\ 0 & 1 & -2 & -8 \end{array}\right] \Rightarrow \left[\begin{array}{ccc|c} 1 & \frac{1}{3} & 0 & \frac{7}{3} \\ 0 & 1 & 3 & 7 \\ 0 & 1 & -2 & -8 \end{array}\right] \Rightarrow \left[\begin{array}{ccc|c} 1 & \frac{1}{3} & 0 & \frac{7}{3} \\ 0 & 1 & 3 & 7 \\ 0 & 0 & 5 & 15 \end{array}\right] \Rightarrow \left[\begin{array}{ccc|c} 1 & \frac{1}{3} & 0 & \frac{7}{3} \\ 0 & 1 & 3 & 7 \\ 0 & 0 & 1 & 3 \end{array}\right]$

$-3R_2 + R_1 \Rightarrow R_2$, $\frac{1}{3}R_1 \Rightarrow R_1$; $-R_3 + R_2 \Rightarrow R_3$; $\frac{1}{5}R_3 \Rightarrow R_3$

From (3): $z = 3$

From (2): $y + 3z = 7$

$y + 3(3) = 7$

$y = -2$

From (1): $x + \frac{1}{3}y = \frac{7}{3}$

$x + \frac{1}{3}(-2) = \frac{7}{3}$

$x = 3$

Solution: $(3, -2, 3)$

39. $\left[\begin{array}{ccc|c} 1 & -1 & 1 & 2 \\ 2 & 1 & 1 & 5 \\ 3 & 0 & -4 & -5 \end{array}\right] \Rightarrow \left[\begin{array}{ccc|c} 1 & -1 & 1 & 2 \\ 0 & 3 & -1 & 1 \\ 0 & 3 & -7 & -11 \end{array}\right] \Rightarrow \left[\begin{array}{ccc|c} 1 & -1 & 1 & 2 \\ 0 & 1 & -\frac{1}{3} & \frac{1}{3} \\ 0 & 0 & 6 & 12 \end{array}\right] \Rightarrow$

$-2R_1 + R_2 \Rightarrow R_2$, $-3R_1 + R_3 \Rightarrow R_3$; $\frac{1}{3}R_2 \Rightarrow R_2$, $-R_3 + R_2 \Rightarrow R_3$

$\left[\begin{array}{ccc|c} 1 & -1 & 1 & 2 \\ 0 & 1 & -\frac{1}{3} & \frac{1}{3} \\ 0 & 0 & 1 & 2 \end{array}\right]$

$\frac{1}{6}R_3 \Rightarrow R_3$

From (3): $z = 2$

From (2): $y - \frac{1}{3}z = \frac{1}{3}$

$y - \frac{1}{3}(2) = \frac{1}{3}$

$y = 1$

From (1): $x - y + z = 2$

$x - (1) + (2) = 2$

$x = 1$

Solution: $(1, 1, 2)$

40. $\left[\begin{array}{ccc|c} 1 & 0 & 1 & -1 \\ 3 & 1 & 0 & 2 \\ 2 & 1 & 5 & 3 \end{array}\right] \Rightarrow \left[\begin{array}{ccc|c} 1 & 0 & 1 & -1 \\ 0 & 1 & -3 & 5 \\ 0 & 1 & 3 & 5 \end{array}\right] \Rightarrow \left[\begin{array}{ccc|c} 1 & 0 & 1 & -1 \\ 0 & 1 & -3 & 5 \\ 0 & 0 & 6 & 0 \end{array}\right] \Rightarrow \left[\begin{array}{ccc|c} 1 & 0 & 1 & -1 \\ 0 & 1 & -3 & 5 \\ 0 & 0 & 1 & 0 \end{array}\right]$

$-3R_1 + R_2 \Rightarrow R_2$, $-2R_1 + R_3 \Rightarrow R_3$; $-R_2 + R_3 \Rightarrow R_3$; $\frac{1}{6}R_3 \Rightarrow R_3$

From (3): $z = 0$

From (2): $y - 3z = 5$, $y - 3(0) = 5$, $y = 5$

From (1): $x + z = -1$, $x + (0) = -1$, $x = -1$

Solution: $(-1, 5, 0)$

41. $\left[\begin{array}{ccc|c} 1 & 1 & -1 & 5 \\ 1 & 1 & 1 & 2 \\ 3 & 3 & -1 & 12 \end{array}\right] \Rightarrow \left[\begin{array}{ccc|c} 1 & 1 & -1 & 5 \\ 0 & 0 & 2 & -3 \\ 0 & 0 & 2 & -3 \end{array}\right] \Rightarrow \left[\begin{array}{ccc|c} 1 & 1 & -1 & 5 \\ 0 & 0 & 1 & -\frac{3}{2} \\ 0 & 0 & 1 & -\frac{3}{2} \end{array}\right]$

$-R_1 + R_2 \Rightarrow R_2$, $-3R_1 + R_3 \Rightarrow R_3$; $\frac{1}{2}R_2 \Rightarrow R_2$, $\frac{1}{2}R_3 \Rightarrow R_3$

From R_2: $z = -\frac{3}{2}$

From R_1: $x + y - z = 5$, $x + y - \left(-\frac{3}{2}\right) = 5$, $y = -x + \frac{7}{2}$

Solution: $\left(x, -x + \frac{7}{2}, -\frac{3}{2}\right)$

42. $\left[\begin{array}{ccc|c} 1 & 1 & 2 & 4 \\ -1 & -1 & -3 & -5 \\ 2 & 1 & 1 & 2 \end{array}\right] \Rightarrow \left[\begin{array}{ccc|c} 1 & 1 & 2 & 4 \\ 0 & 0 & -1 & -1 \\ 0 & -1 & -3 & -6 \end{array}\right] \Rightarrow \left[\begin{array}{ccc|c} 1 & 1 & 2 & 4 \\ 0 & -1 & -3 & -6 \\ 0 & 0 & -1 & -1 \end{array}\right] \Rightarrow \left[\begin{array}{ccc|c} 1 & 1 & 2 & 4 \\ 0 & 1 & 3 & 6 \\ 0 & 0 & 1 & 1 \end{array}\right]$

$R_1 + R_2 \Rightarrow R_2$, $-2R_1 + R_3 \Rightarrow R_3$; $R_2 \Leftrightarrow R_3$; $-R_2 \Rightarrow R_2$, $-R_3 \Rightarrow R_3$

From (3): $z = 1$

From (2): $y + 3z = 6$, $y + 3(1) = 6$, $y = 3$

From (1): $x + y + 2z = 4$, $x + (3) + 2(1) = 4$, $x = -1$

Solution: $(-1, 3, 1)$

43. $\left[\begin{array}{ccc|c} 2 & -1 & 1 & 6 \\ 3 & 1 & -1 & 2 \\ -1 & 3 & -3 & 8 \end{array}\right] \Rightarrow \left[\begin{array}{ccc|c} -1 & 3 & -3 & 8 \\ 3 & 1 & -1 & 2 \\ 2 & -1 & 1 & 6 \end{array}\right] \Rightarrow \left[\begin{array}{ccc|c} -1 & 3 & -3 & 8 \\ 0 & 10 & -10 & 26 \\ 0 & 5 & -5 & 22 \end{array}\right] \Rightarrow$

$R_1 \Leftrightarrow R_3$; $3R_1 + R_2 \Rightarrow R_2$, $2R_1 + R_3 \Rightarrow R_3$

$\left[\begin{array}{ccc|c} -1 & 3 & -3 & 8 \\ 0 & 10 & -10 & 26 \\ 0 & 0 & 0 & -18 \end{array}\right]$

$-2R_3 + R_2 \Rightarrow R_3$

R_3 indicates $0x + 0y + 0z = -18$. This is impossible.

No solution $\Rightarrow$ inconsistent system

44. $\left[\begin{array}{ccc|c} -1 & 3 & 2 & -10 \\ 3 & -2 & -2 & 7 \\ -2 & 1 & -1 & -10 \end{array}\right] \Rightarrow \left[\begin{array}{ccc|c} -1 & 3 & 2 & -10 \\ 0 & 7 & 4 & -23 \\ 0 & -5 & -5 & 10 \end{array}\right] \Rightarrow \left[\begin{array}{ccc|c} 1 & -3 & -2 & 10 \\ 0 & 1 & 1 & -2 \\ 0 & 7 & 4 & -23 \end{array}\right] \Rightarrow$

$3R_1 + R_2 \Rightarrow R_2$, $-2R_1 + R_3 \Rightarrow R_3$; $-R_1 \Rightarrow R_1$, $R_2 \Rightarrow R_3$, $-\frac{1}{5}R_3 \Rightarrow R_2$

$\left[\begin{array}{ccc|c} 1 & -3 & -2 & 10 \\ 0 & 1 & 1 & -2 \\ 0 & 0 & -3 & -9 \end{array}\right] \Rightarrow \left[\begin{array}{ccc|c} 1 & -3 & -2 & 10 \\ 0 & 1 & 1 & -2 \\ 0 & 0 & 1 & 3 \end{array}\right]$

$-7R_2 + R_3 \Rightarrow R_3$; $-\frac{1}{3}R_3 \Rightarrow R_3$

From (3): $z = 3$

From (2): $y + z = -2$
$y + 3 = -2$
$y = -5$

From (1): $x - 3y - 2z = 10$
$x - 3(-5) - 2(3) = 10$
$x + 15 - 6 = 10$
$x = 1$

Solution: $(1, -5, 3)$

45. $\left[\begin{array}{cc|c} 1 & -2 & 7 \\ 0 & 1 & 3 \end{array}\right] \Rightarrow \left[\begin{array}{cc|c} 1 & 0 & 13 \\ 0 & 1 & 3 \end{array}\right] \Rightarrow$ Solution: $(13, 3)$

$2R_2 + R_1 \Rightarrow R_1$

46. $\left[\begin{array}{cc|c} 1 & -2 & 7 \\ 0 & 1 & 8 \end{array}\right] \Rightarrow \left[\begin{array}{cc|c} 1 & 0 & 23 \\ 0 & 1 & 8 \end{array}\right] \Rightarrow$ Solution: $(23, 8)$

$2R_2 + R_1 \Rightarrow R_1$

47. $\left[\begin{array}{ccc|c} 1 & 2 & -1 & 3 \\ 0 & 1 & 3 & 1 \\ 0 & 0 & 1 & -2 \end{array}\right] \Rightarrow \left[\begin{array}{ccc|c} 1 & 0 & -7 & 1 \\ 0 & 1 & 3 & 1 \\ 0 & 0 & 1 & -2 \end{array}\right] \Rightarrow \left[\begin{array}{ccc|c} 1 & 0 & 0 & -13 \\ 0 & 1 & 0 & 7 \\ 0 & 0 & 1 & -2 \end{array}\right]$ Solution: $(-13, 7, -2)$

$-2R_2 + R_1 \Rightarrow R_1$; $7R_3 + R_1 \Rightarrow R_1$, $-3R_3 + R_2 \Rightarrow R_2$

48. $\left[\begin{array}{ccc|c} 1 & -3 & 2 & -1 \\ 0 & 1 & -2 & 3 \\ 0 & 0 & 1 & 5 \end{array}\right] \Rightarrow \left[\begin{array}{ccc|c} 1 & 0 & -4 & 8 \\ 0 & 1 & -2 & 3 \\ 0 & 0 & 1 & 5 \end{array}\right] \Rightarrow \left[\begin{array}{ccc|c} 1 & 0 & 0 & 28 \\ 0 & 1 & 0 & 13 \\ 0 & 0 & 1 & 5 \end{array}\right]$ Solution: $(28, 13, 5)$

$3R_2 + R_1 \Rightarrow R_1$; $4R_3 + R_1 \Rightarrow R_1$, $2R_3 + R_2 \Rightarrow R_2$

49. $\left[\begin{array}{cc|c} 1 & -1 & 7 \\ 1 & 1 & 13 \end{array}\right] \Rightarrow \left[\begin{array}{cc|c} 1 & -1 & 7 \\ 0 & 2 & 6 \end{array}\right] \Rightarrow \left[\begin{array}{cc|c} 1 & -1 & 7 \\ 0 & 1 & 3 \end{array}\right] \Rightarrow \left[\begin{array}{cc|c} 1 & 0 & 10 \\ 0 & 1 & 3 \end{array}\right]$ Solution: $(10, 3)$

$-R_1 + R_2 \Rightarrow R_2$; $\frac{1}{2}R_2 \Rightarrow R_2$; $R_2 + R_1 \Rightarrow R_1$

50. $\left[\begin{array}{cc|c} 1 & 2 & 7 \\ 2 & -1 & -1 \end{array}\right] \Rightarrow \left[\begin{array}{cc|c} 1 & 2 & 7 \\ 0 & -5 & -15 \end{array}\right] \Rightarrow \left[\begin{array}{cc|c} 1 & 2 & 7 \\ 0 & 1 & 3 \end{array}\right] \Rightarrow \left[\begin{array}{cc|c} 1 & 0 & 1 \\ 0 & 1 & 3 \end{array}\right]$ Solution: $(1, 3)$

$-2R_1 + R_2 \Rightarrow R_2$; $-\frac{1}{5}R_2 \Rightarrow R_2$; $-2R_2 + R_1 \Rightarrow R_1$

51. $$\left[\begin{array}{cc|c} 1 & -\frac{1}{2} & 0 \\ 1 & 2 & 0 \end{array}\right] \Rightarrow \underset{-R_1 + R_2 \Rightarrow R_2}{\left[\begin{array}{cc|c} 1 & -\frac{1}{2} & 0 \\ 0 & \frac{5}{2} & 0 \end{array}\right]} \Rightarrow \underset{\frac{2}{5}R_2 \Rightarrow R_2}{\left[\begin{array}{cc|c} 1 & -\frac{1}{2} & 0 \\ 0 & 1 & 0 \end{array}\right]} \Rightarrow \underset{\frac{1}{2}R_2 + R_1 \Rightarrow R_1}{\left[\begin{array}{cc|c} 1 & 0 & 0 \\ 0 & 1 & 0 \end{array}\right]}$$

Solution: $(0, 0)$

52. $$\left[\begin{array}{cc|c} 1 & -1 & 5 \\ -1 & \frac{1}{5} & -9 \end{array}\right] \Rightarrow \underset{R_1 + R_2 \Rightarrow R_2}{\left[\begin{array}{cc|c} 1 & -1 & 5 \\ 0 & -\frac{4}{5} & -4 \end{array}\right]} \Rightarrow \underset{-\frac{5}{4}R_2 \Rightarrow R_2}{\left[\begin{array}{cc|c} 1 & -1 & 5 \\ 0 & 1 & 5 \end{array}\right]} \Rightarrow \underset{R_2 + R_1 \Rightarrow R_1}{\left[\begin{array}{cc|c} 1 & 0 & 10 \\ 0 & 1 & 5 \end{array}\right]}$$

Solution: $(10, 5)$

53. $$\left[\begin{array}{ccc|c} 1 & 1 & 2 & 0 \\ 1 & 1 & 1 & 2 \\ 1 & 0 & 1 & 1 \end{array}\right] \Rightarrow \underset{\substack{-R_1 + R_2 \Rightarrow R_2 \\ -R_1 + R_3 \Rightarrow R_3}}{\left[\begin{array}{ccc|c} 1 & 1 & 2 & 0 \\ 0 & 0 & -1 & 2 \\ 0 & -1 & -1 & 1 \end{array}\right]} \Rightarrow \underset{R_2 \Leftrightarrow R_3}{\left[\begin{array}{ccc|c} 1 & 1 & 2 & 0 \\ 0 & -1 & -1 & 1 \\ 0 & 0 & -1 & 2 \end{array}\right]} \Rightarrow \underset{\substack{-R_2 \Rightarrow R_2 \\ -R_3 \Rightarrow R_3}}{\left[\begin{array}{ccc|c} 1 & 1 & 2 & 0 \\ 0 & 1 & 1 & -1 \\ 0 & 0 & 1 & -2 \end{array}\right]}$$

$$\underset{-R_2 + R_1 \Rightarrow R_1}{\left[\begin{array}{ccc|c} 1 & 0 & 1 & 1 \\ 0 & 1 & 1 & -1 \\ 0 & 0 & 1 & -2 \end{array}\right]} \Rightarrow \underset{\substack{-R_3 + R_1 \Rightarrow R_1 \\ -R_3 + R_2 \Rightarrow R_2}}{\left[\begin{array}{ccc|c} 1 & 0 & 0 & 3 \\ 0 & 1 & 0 & 1 \\ 0 & 0 & 1 & -2 \end{array}\right]}$$

Solution: $(3, 1, -2)$

54. $$\left[\begin{array}{ccc|c} 1 & 2 & 0 & -3 \\ 1 & 4 & 0 & -2 \\ 2 & 0 & 1 & -8 \end{array}\right] \Rightarrow \underset{\substack{-R_1 + R_2 \Rightarrow R_2 \\ -2R_1 + R_3 \Rightarrow R_3}}{\left[\begin{array}{ccc|c} 1 & 2 & 0 & -3 \\ 0 & 2 & 0 & 1 \\ 0 & -4 & 1 & -2 \end{array}\right]} \Rightarrow \underset{\substack{-R_2 + R_1 \Rightarrow R_1 \\ 2R_2 + R_3 \Rightarrow R_3}}{\left[\begin{array}{ccc|c} 1 & 0 & 0 & -4 \\ 0 & 2 & 0 & 1 \\ 0 & 0 & 1 & 0 \end{array}\right]} \Rightarrow \underset{\frac{1}{2}R_2 \Rightarrow R_2}{\left[\begin{array}{ccc|c} 1 & 0 & 0 & -4 \\ 0 & 1 & 0 & \frac{1}{2} \\ 0 & 0 & 1 & 0 \end{array}\right]}$$

Solution: $\left(-4, \frac{1}{2}, 0\right)$

55. $$\left[\begin{array}{ccc|c} 2 & 1 & -2 & 1 \\ -1 & 1 & -3 & 0 \\ 4 & 3 & 0 & 4 \end{array}\right] \Rightarrow \underset{\substack{R_1 + 2R_2 \Rightarrow R_2 \\ -2R_1 + R_3 \Rightarrow R_3}}{\left[\begin{array}{ccc|c} 2 & 1 & -2 & 1 \\ 0 & 3 & -8 & 1 \\ 0 & 1 & 4 & 2 \end{array}\right]} \Rightarrow \underset{\substack{-3R_1 + R_2 \Rightarrow R_1 \\ -3R_3 + R_2 \Rightarrow R_3}}{\left[\begin{array}{ccc|c} -6 & 0 & -2 & -2 \\ 0 & 3 & -8 & 1 \\ 0 & 0 & -20 & -5 \end{array}\right]} \Rightarrow \underset{-\frac{1}{20}R_3 \Rightarrow R_3}{\left[\begin{array}{ccc|c} -6 & 0 & -2 & -2 \\ 0 & 3 & -8 & 1 \\ 0 & 0 & 1 & \frac{1}{4} \end{array}\right]}$$

$$\underset{\substack{2R_3 + R_1 \Rightarrow R_1 \\ 8R_3 + R_2 \Rightarrow R_2}}{\left[\begin{array}{ccc|c} -6 & 0 & 0 & -\frac{3}{2} \\ 0 & 3 & 0 & 3 \\ 0 & 0 & 1 & \frac{1}{4} \end{array}\right]} \Rightarrow \underset{\substack{-\frac{1}{6}R_1 \Rightarrow R_1 \\ \frac{1}{3}R_2 \Rightarrow R_2}}{\left[\begin{array}{ccc|c} 1 & 0 & 0 & \frac{1}{4} \\ 0 & 1 & 0 & 1 \\ 0 & 0 & 1 & \frac{1}{4} \end{array}\right]}$$

Solution: $\left(\frac{1}{4}, 1, \frac{1}{4}\right)$

56. $$\left[\begin{array}{ccc|c} 3 & 1 & 0 & 3 \\ 3 & 1 & -1 & 2 \\ 6 & 0 & 1 & 5 \end{array}\right] \Rightarrow \underset{\substack{-R_1 + R_2 \Rightarrow R_2 \\ -2R_1 + R_3 \Rightarrow R_3}}{\left[\begin{array}{ccc|c} 3 & 1 & 0 & 3 \\ 0 & 0 & -1 & -1 \\ 0 & -2 & 1 & -1 \end{array}\right]} \Rightarrow \underset{R_2 \Leftrightarrow R_3}{\left[\begin{array}{ccc|c} 3 & 1 & 0 & 3 \\ 0 & -2 & 1 & -1 \\ 0 & 0 & -1 & -1 \end{array}\right]} \Rightarrow \underset{\substack{2R_1 + R_2 \Rightarrow R_1 \\ -R_3 \Rightarrow R_3}}{\left[\begin{array}{ccc|c} 6 & 0 & 1 & 5 \\ 0 & -2 & 1 & -1 \\ 0 & 0 & 1 & 1 \end{array}\right]}$$

continued on next page...

56. continued

$$\begin{bmatrix} 6 & 0 & 0 & 4 \\ 0 & -2 & 0 & -2 \\ 0 & 0 & 1 & 1 \end{bmatrix} \Rightarrow \begin{bmatrix} 1 & 0 & 0 & \frac{2}{3} \\ 0 & 1 & 0 & 1 \\ 0 & 0 & 1 & 1 \end{bmatrix} \quad \text{Solution: } \left(\tfrac{2}{3}, 1, 1\right)$$

$-R_3 + R_1 \Rightarrow R_1$, $-R_3 + R_2 \Rightarrow R_2$; $\frac{1}{6}R_1 \Rightarrow R_1$, $\frac{1}{2}R_2 \Rightarrow R_2$

57.

$$\begin{bmatrix} 2 & -2 & 3 & 1 & 2 \\ 1 & 1 & 1 & 1 & 5 \\ -1 & 2 & -3 & 2 & 2 \\ 1 & 1 & 2 & -1 & 4 \end{bmatrix} \Rightarrow \begin{bmatrix} 2 & -2 & 3 & 1 & 2 \\ 0 & -4 & 1 & -1 & -8 \\ 0 & 2 & -3 & 5 & 6 \\ 0 & -4 & -1 & 3 & -6 \end{bmatrix} \Rightarrow \begin{bmatrix} -4 & 0 & -5 & -3 & -12 \\ 0 & -4 & 1 & -1 & -8 \\ 0 & 0 & -5 & 9 & 4 \\ 0 & 0 & 2 & -4 & -2 \end{bmatrix}$$

$-2R_2 + R_1 \Rightarrow R_2$, $2R_3 + R_1 \Rightarrow R_3$, $-2R_4 + R_1 \Rightarrow R_4$; $-2R_1 + R_2 \Rightarrow R_1$, $2R_3 + R_2 \Rightarrow R_3$, $-R_4 + R_2 \Rightarrow R_4$

$$\begin{bmatrix} -4 & 0 & -5 & -3 & -12 \\ 0 & -4 & 1 & -1 & -8 \\ 0 & 0 & -5 & 9 & 4 \\ 0 & 0 & 1 & -2 & -1 \end{bmatrix} \Rightarrow \begin{bmatrix} 4 & 0 & 0 & 12 & 16 \\ 0 & -20 & 0 & 4 & -36 \\ 0 & 0 & -5 & 9 & 4 \\ 0 & 0 & 0 & -1 & -1 \end{bmatrix} \Rightarrow \begin{bmatrix} 1 & 0 & 0 & 3 & 4 \\ 0 & -5 & 0 & 1 & -9 \\ 0 & 0 & -5 & 9 & 4 \\ 0 & 0 & 0 & 1 & 1 \end{bmatrix}$$

$\frac{1}{2}R_4 \Rightarrow R_4$; $-R_1 + R_3 \Rightarrow R_1$, $5R_2 + R_3 \Rightarrow R_2$, $5R_4 + R_3 \Rightarrow R_4$; $\frac{1}{4}R_1 \Rightarrow R_1$, $\frac{1}{4}R_2 \Rightarrow R_2$, $-R_4 \Rightarrow R_4$

$$\Rightarrow \begin{bmatrix} 1 & 0 & 0 & 0 & 1 \\ 0 & -5 & 0 & 0 & -10 \\ 0 & 0 & -5 & 0 & -5 \\ 0 & 0 & 0 & 1 & 1 \end{bmatrix} \Rightarrow \begin{bmatrix} 1 & 0 & 0 & 0 & 1 \\ 0 & 1 & 0 & 0 & 2 \\ 0 & 0 & 1 & 0 & 1 \\ 0 & 0 & 0 & 1 & 1 \end{bmatrix} \quad \text{Solution: } (1, 2, 1, 1)$$

$-3R_4 + R_1 \Rightarrow R_1$, $-R_4 + R_2 \Rightarrow R_2$, $-9R_4 + R_3 \Rightarrow R_3$; $-\frac{1}{5}R_2 \Rightarrow R_2$, $-\frac{1}{5}R_3 \Rightarrow R_3$

58.

$$\begin{bmatrix} 1 & 1 & 2 & 1 & 1 \\ 1 & 2 & 1 & 1 & 2 \\ 2 & 1 & 1 & 1 & 4 \\ 1 & 1 & 1 & 2 & 3 \end{bmatrix} \Rightarrow \begin{bmatrix} 1 & 1 & 2 & 1 & 1 \\ 0 & 1 & -1 & 0 & 1 \\ 0 & -1 & -3 & -1 & 2 \\ 0 & 0 & -1 & 1 & 2 \end{bmatrix} \Rightarrow \begin{bmatrix} 1 & 0 & -1 & 0 & 3 \\ 0 & 1 & -1 & 0 & 1 \\ 0 & 0 & -4 & -1 & 3 \\ 0 & 0 & -1 & 1 & 2 \end{bmatrix} \Rightarrow$$

$-R_1 + R_2 \Rightarrow R_2$, $-2R_1 + R_3 \Rightarrow R_3$, $-R_1 + R_4 \Rightarrow R_4$; $R_3 + R_1 \Rightarrow R_1$, $R_3 + R_2 \Rightarrow R_3$

$$\begin{bmatrix} 1 & 0 & -1 & 0 & 3 \\ 0 & 1 & -1 & 0 & 1 \\ 0 & 0 & 1 & \frac{1}{4} & -\frac{3}{4} \\ 0 & 0 & -1 & 1 & 2 \end{bmatrix} \Rightarrow \begin{bmatrix} 1 & 0 & 0 & \frac{1}{4} & \frac{9}{4} \\ 0 & 1 & 0 & \frac{1}{4} & \frac{1}{4} \\ 0 & 0 & 1 & \frac{1}{4} & -\frac{3}{4} \\ 0 & 0 & 0 & \frac{5}{4} & \frac{5}{4} \end{bmatrix} \Rightarrow \begin{bmatrix} -5 & 0 & 0 & 0 & -10 \\ 0 & -5 & 0 & 0 & 0 \\ 0 & 0 & -5 & 0 & 5 \\ 0 & 0 & 0 & \frac{5}{4} & \frac{5}{4} \end{bmatrix} \Rightarrow$$

$-\frac{1}{4}R_3 \Rightarrow R_3$; $R_1 + R_3 \Rightarrow R_1$, $R_2 + R_3 \Rightarrow R_2$, $R_4 + R_3 \Rightarrow R_4$; $-5R_1 + R_4 \Rightarrow R_1$, $-5R_2 + R_4 \Rightarrow R_2$, $-5R_3 + R_4 \Rightarrow R_3$

continued on next page...

58. **continued**

$$\begin{matrix} -\frac{1}{5}R_1 \Rightarrow R_1 \\ -\frac{1}{5}R_2 \Rightarrow R_2 \\ -\frac{1}{5}R_3 \Rightarrow R_3 \\ \frac{4}{5}R_4 \Rightarrow R_4 \end{matrix} \left[\begin{array}{cccc|c} 1 & 0 & 0 & 0 & 2 \\ 0 & 1 & 0 & 0 & 0 \\ 0 & 0 & 1 & 0 & -1 \\ 0 & 0 & 0 & 1 & 1 \end{array}\right]$$

Solution: $(2, 0, -1, 1)$

59.

$$\left[\begin{array}{cccc|c} 1 & 1 & 0 & 1 & 4 \\ 1 & 0 & 1 & 1 & 2 \\ 2 & 2 & 1 & 2 & 8 \\ 1 & -1 & 1 & -1 & -2 \end{array}\right] \Rightarrow \left[\begin{array}{cccc|c} 1 & 1 & 0 & 1 & 4 \\ 0 & 1 & -1 & 0 & 2 \\ 0 & 0 & 1 & 0 & 0 \\ 0 & 2 & -1 & 2 & 6 \end{array}\right] \Rightarrow \left[\begin{array}{cccc|c} 1 & 0 & 1 & 1 & 2 \\ 0 & 1 & -1 & 0 & 2 \\ 0 & 0 & 1 & 0 & 0 \\ 0 & 0 & 1 & 2 & 2 \end{array}\right] \Rightarrow$$

$-R_2 + R_1 \Rightarrow R_2$, $-2R_1 + R_3 \Rightarrow R_3$, $-R_4 + R_1 \Rightarrow R_4$; $-R_2 + R_1 \Rightarrow R_1$, $-2R_2 + R_4 \Rightarrow R_4$

$$\left[\begin{array}{cccc|c} 1 & 0 & 0 & 1 & 2 \\ 0 & 1 & 0 & 0 & 2 \\ 0 & 0 & 1 & 0 & 0 \\ 0 & 0 & 0 & 2 & 2 \end{array}\right] \Rightarrow \left[\begin{array}{cccc|c} 1 & 0 & 0 & 0 & 1 \\ 0 & 1 & 0 & 0 & 2 \\ 0 & 0 & 1 & 0 & 0 \\ 0 & 0 & 0 & 1 & 1 \end{array}\right]$$

Solution: $(1, 2, 0, 1)$

$-R_3 + R_1 \Rightarrow R_1$, $R_3 + R_2 \Rightarrow R_2$, $-R_3 + R_4 \Rightarrow R_4$; $-\frac{1}{2}R_4 + R_1 \Rightarrow R_1$, $\frac{1}{2}R_4 \Rightarrow R_4$

60.

$$\left[\begin{array}{cccc|c} 1 & -1 & 2 & 1 & 3 \\ 3 & -2 & -1 & -1 & 4 \\ 2 & 1 & 2 & -1 & 10 \\ 1 & 2 & 1 & -3 & 8 \end{array}\right] \Rightarrow \left[\begin{array}{cccc|c} 1 & -1 & 2 & 1 & 3 \\ 0 & 1 & -7 & -4 & -5 \\ 0 & 3 & -2 & -3 & 4 \\ 0 & 3 & -1 & -4 & 5 \end{array}\right] \Rightarrow \left[\begin{array}{cccc|c} 1 & 0 & -5 & -3 & -2 \\ 0 & 1 & -7 & -4 & -5 \\ 0 & 0 & 19 & 9 & 19 \\ 0 & 0 & 20 & 8 & 20 \end{array}\right]$$

$-3R_1 + R_2 \Rightarrow R_2$, $-2R_1 + R_3 \Rightarrow R_3$, $-R_1 + R_4 \Rightarrow R_4$; $R_2 + R_1 \Rightarrow R_1$, $-3R_2 + R_3 \Rightarrow R_3$, $-3R_2 + R_4 \Rightarrow R_4$

$$\left[\begin{array}{cccc|c} 1 & 0 & -5 & -3 & -2 \\ 0 & 1 & -7 & -4 & -5 \\ 0 & 0 & 1 & \frac{9}{19} & 1 \\ 0 & 0 & 1 & \frac{2}{5} & 1 \end{array}\right] \Rightarrow \left[\begin{array}{cccc|c} 1 & 0 & 0 & -\frac{12}{19} & 3 \\ 0 & 1 & 0 & -\frac{13}{19} & 2 \\ 0 & 0 & 1 & \frac{9}{19} & 1 \\ 0 & 0 & 0 & \frac{7}{95} & 0 \end{array}\right] \Rightarrow \left[\begin{array}{cccc|c} 1 & 0 & 0 & -\frac{12}{19} & 3 \\ 0 & 1 & 0 & -\frac{13}{19} & 2 \\ 0 & 0 & 1 & \frac{9}{19} & 1 \\ 0 & 0 & 0 & 1 & 0 \end{array}\right] \Rightarrow$$

$\frac{1}{19}R_3 \Rightarrow R_3$, $\frac{1}{20}R_4 \Rightarrow R_4$; $5R_3 + R_1 \Rightarrow R_1$, $7R_3 + R_2 \Rightarrow R_2$, $-R_4 + R_3 \Rightarrow R_4$; $\frac{95}{7}R_4 \Rightarrow R_4$

$$\Rightarrow \left[\begin{array}{cccc|c} 1 & 0 & 0 & 0 & 3 \\ 0 & 1 & 0 & 0 & 2 \\ 0 & 0 & 1 & 0 & 1 \\ 0 & 0 & 0 & 1 & 0 \end{array}\right]$$

Solution: $(3, 2, 1, 0)$

$\frac{12}{19}R_4 + R_1 \Rightarrow R_1$, $\frac{13}{19}R_4 + R_2 \Rightarrow R_2$, $-\frac{9}{19}R_4 + R_3 \Rightarrow R_3$

61. $\left[\begin{array}{ccc|c} \frac{1}{3} & \frac{3}{4} & -\frac{2}{3} & -2 \\ 1 & \frac{1}{2} & \frac{1}{3} & 1 \\ \frac{1}{6} & -\frac{1}{8} & -1 & 0 \end{array}\right] \Rightarrow \left[\begin{array}{ccc|c} 1 & \frac{9}{4} & -2 & -6 \\ 6 & 3 & 2 & 6 \\ 4 & -3 & -24 & 0 \end{array}\right] \Rightarrow \left[\begin{array}{ccc|c} 1 & \frac{9}{4} & -2 & -6 \\ 0 & -\frac{21}{2} & 14 & 42 \\ 0 & -12 & -16 & 24 \end{array}\right] \Rightarrow$

$3R_1 \Rightarrow R_1$
$6R_2 \Rightarrow R_2$
$24R_3 \Rightarrow R_3$

$-6R_1 + R_2 \Rightarrow R_2$
$-4R_1 + R_3 \Rightarrow R_3$

$\left[\begin{array}{ccc|c} 1 & \frac{9}{4} & -2 & -6 \\ 0 & 1 & -\frac{4}{3} & -4 \\ 0 & 3 & 4 & -6 \end{array}\right] \Rightarrow \left[\begin{array}{ccc|c} 1 & 0 & 1 & 3 \\ 0 & 1 & -\frac{4}{3} & -4 \\ 0 & 0 & 8 & 6 \end{array}\right] \Rightarrow \left[\begin{array}{ccc|c} 1 & 0 & 0 & \frac{9}{4} \\ 0 & 1 & 0 & -3 \\ 0 & 0 & 1 & \frac{3}{4} \end{array}\right]$ Solution: $\left(\frac{9}{4}, -3, \frac{3}{4}\right)$

$-\frac{2}{21}R_2 \Rightarrow R_2$
$-\frac{1}{4}R_3 \Rightarrow R_3$

$-\frac{9}{4}R_2 + R_1 \Rightarrow R_1$
$-3R_2 + R_3 \Rightarrow R_3$

$-\frac{1}{8}R_3 + R_1 \Rightarrow R_1$
$\frac{1}{6}R_3 + R_2 \Rightarrow R_2$
$\frac{1}{8}R_3 \Rightarrow R_3$

62. $\left[\begin{array}{ccc|c} \frac{1}{4} & 1 & 3 & 1 \\ \frac{1}{2} & -4 & 6 & -1 \\ \frac{1}{3} & -2 & -2 & -1 \end{array}\right] \Rightarrow \left[\begin{array}{ccc|c} 1 & 4 & 12 & 4 \\ 1 & -8 & 12 & -2 \\ 1 & -6 & -6 & -3 \end{array}\right] \Rightarrow \left[\begin{array}{ccc|c} 1 & 4 & 12 & 4 \\ 0 & 12 & 0 & 6 \\ 0 & 10 & 18 & 7 \end{array}\right] \Rightarrow$

$4R_1 \Rightarrow R_1, 2R_2 \Rightarrow R_2$
$3R_3 \Rightarrow R_3$

$-R_2 + R_1 \Rightarrow R_2$
$-R_3 + R_1 \Rightarrow R_3$

$\left[\begin{array}{ccc|c} 1 & 4 & 12 & 4 \\ 0 & 1 & 0 & \frac{1}{2} \\ 0 & 10 & 18 & 7 \end{array}\right] \Rightarrow \left[\begin{array}{ccc|c} 1 & 0 & 12 & 2 \\ 0 & 1 & 0 & \frac{1}{2} \\ 0 & 0 & 18 & 2 \end{array}\right] \Rightarrow \left[\begin{array}{ccc|c} 1 & 0 & 0 & \frac{2}{3} \\ 0 & 1 & 0 & \frac{1}{2} \\ 0 & 0 & 1 & \frac{1}{9} \end{array}\right]$ Solution: $\left(\frac{2}{3}, \frac{1}{2}, \frac{1}{9}\right)$

$\frac{1}{12}R_2 \Rightarrow R_2$

$-4R_2 + R_1 \Rightarrow R_1$
$-10R_2 + R_3 \Rightarrow R_3$

$-\frac{2}{3}R_3 + R_1 \Rightarrow R_1$
$\frac{1}{18}R_3 \Rightarrow R_3$

63. $\left[\begin{array}{ccc|c} \frac{1}{2} & \frac{1}{4} & -1 & 2 \\ \frac{2}{3} & \frac{1}{4} & \frac{1}{2} & \frac{3}{2} \\ \frac{2}{3} & 0 & 1 & -\frac{1}{3} \end{array}\right] \Rightarrow \left[\begin{array}{ccc|c} 1 & \frac{1}{2} & -2 & 4 \\ 8 & 3 & 6 & 18 \\ 2 & 0 & 3 & -1 \end{array}\right] \Rightarrow \left[\begin{array}{ccc|c} 1 & \frac{1}{2} & -2 & 4 \\ 0 & -1 & 22 & -14 \\ 0 & -1 & 7 & -9 \end{array}\right] \Rightarrow$

$2R_1 \Rightarrow R_1, 12R_2 \Rightarrow R_2$
$3R_3 \Rightarrow R_3$

$-8R_1 + R_2 \Rightarrow R_2$
$-2R_1 + R_3 \Rightarrow R_3$

$\left[\begin{array}{ccc|c} 1 & \frac{1}{2} & -2 & 4 \\ 0 & 1 & -22 & 14 \\ 0 & -1 & 7 & -9 \end{array}\right] \Rightarrow \left[\begin{array}{ccc|c} 1 & 0 & 9 & -3 \\ 0 & 1 & -22 & 14 \\ 0 & 0 & -15 & 5 \end{array}\right] \Rightarrow \left[\begin{array}{ccc|c} 1 & 0 & 9 & -3 \\ 0 & 1 & -22 & 14 \\ 0 & 0 & 1 & -\frac{1}{3} \end{array}\right] \Rightarrow$

$-R_2 \Rightarrow R_2$

$-\frac{1}{2}R_2 + R_1 \Rightarrow R_1$
$R_2 + R_3 \Rightarrow R_3$

$-\frac{1}{15}R_3 \Rightarrow R_3$

$\left[\begin{array}{ccc|c} 1 & 0 & 0 & 0 \\ 0 & 1 & 0 & \frac{20}{3} \\ 0 & 0 & 1 & -\frac{1}{3} \end{array}\right]$ Solution: $\left(0, \frac{20}{3}, -\frac{1}{3}\right)$

$-9R_3 + R_1 \Rightarrow R_1$
$22R_3 + R_2 \Rightarrow R_2$

64. $$\left[\begin{array}{ccc|c} \frac{5}{7} & -\frac{1}{3} & 1 & 0 \\ \frac{2}{7} & 1 & \frac{1}{8} & 9 \\ 6 & 4 & -\frac{27}{4} & 20 \end{array}\right] \Rightarrow \left[\begin{array}{ccc|c} 1 & -\frac{7}{15} & \frac{7}{5} & 0 \\ 16 & 56 & 7 & 504 \\ 24 & 16 & -27 & 80 \end{array}\right] \Rightarrow \left[\begin{array}{ccc|c} 1 & -\frac{7}{15} & \frac{7}{5} & 0 \\ 0 & \frac{952}{15} & -\frac{77}{5} & 504 \\ 0 & \frac{408}{15} & -\frac{303}{5} & 80 \end{array}\right] \Rightarrow$$

$\frac{7}{5}R_1 \Rightarrow R_1,\ 56R_2 \Rightarrow R_2$
$4R_3 \Rightarrow R_3$

$-16R_1 + R_2 \Rightarrow R_2$
$-24R_1 + R_3 \Rightarrow R_3$

$$\left[\begin{array}{ccc|c} 1 & -\frac{7}{15} & \frac{7}{5} & 0 \\ 0 & 1 & -\frac{33}{136} & \frac{135}{17} \\ 0 & 1 & -\frac{303}{136} & \frac{150}{51} \end{array}\right] \Rightarrow \left[\begin{array}{ccc|c} 1 & 0 & \frac{175}{136} & \frac{63}{17} \\ 0 & 1 & -\frac{33}{136} & \frac{135}{17} \\ 0 & 0 & \frac{135}{68} & 5 \end{array}\right] \Rightarrow \left[\begin{array}{ccc|c} 1 & 0 & \frac{175}{136} & \frac{63}{17} \\ 0 & 1 & -\frac{33}{136} & \frac{135}{17} \\ 0 & 0 & 1 & \frac{68}{27} \end{array}\right] \Rightarrow$$

$\frac{15}{952}R_2 \Rightarrow R_2$
$\frac{15}{408}R_3 \Rightarrow R_3$

$\frac{7}{15}R_2 + R_1 \Rightarrow R_1$
$-R_3 + R_2 \Rightarrow R_3$

$\frac{68}{135}R_3 \Rightarrow R_3$

$$\left[\begin{array}{ccc|c} 1 & 0 & 0 & \frac{427}{918} \\ 0 & 1 & 0 & \frac{2617}{306} \\ 0 & 0 & 1 & \frac{68}{27} \end{array}\right]$$

Solution: $\left(\frac{427}{918}, \frac{2617}{306}, \frac{68}{27}\right)$

$-\frac{175}{136}R_3 + R_1 \Rightarrow R_1$
$\frac{33}{136}R_3 + R_2 \Rightarrow R_2$

65. $$\left[\begin{array}{ccc|c} 3 & -6 & 9 & 18 \\ 2 & -4 & 3 & 12 \\ 1 & -2 & 3 & 6 \end{array}\right] \Rightarrow \left[\begin{array}{ccc|c} 1 & -2 & 3 & 6 \\ 2 & -4 & 3 & 12 \\ 3 & -6 & 9 & 18 \end{array}\right] \Rightarrow \left[\begin{array}{ccc|c} 1 & -2 & 3 & 6 \\ 0 & 0 & -3 & 0 \\ 0 & 0 & 0 & 0 \end{array}\right] \Rightarrow \left[\begin{array}{ccc|c} 1 & -2 & 3 & 6 \\ 0 & 0 & 1 & 0 \\ 0 & 0 & 0 & 0 \end{array}\right]$$

$R_1 \Leftrightarrow R_3$

$-2R_1 + R_2 \Rightarrow R_2$
$-3R_1 + R_3 \Rightarrow R_3$

$-\frac{1}{3}R_2 \Rightarrow R_2$

From (2): $z = 0$

From (1):
$x - 2y + 3z = 6$
$x - 2y + 3(0) = 6$
$2y = -x + 6$
$y = -\frac{1}{2}x - 3$

Solution: $\left(x, -\frac{1}{2}x - 3, 0\right)$

66. $$\left[\begin{array}{ccc|c} 1 & 2 & -1 & 7 \\ 2 & -1 & 1 & 2 \\ 3 & -4 & 3 & -3 \end{array}\right] \Rightarrow \left[\begin{array}{ccc|c} 1 & 2 & -1 & 7 \\ 0 & -5 & 3 & -12 \\ 0 & -10 & 6 & -24 \end{array}\right] \Rightarrow \left[\begin{array}{ccc|c} 1 & 2 & -1 & 7 \\ 0 & -5 & 3 & -12 \\ 0 & 0 & 0 & 0 \end{array}\right] \Rightarrow$$

$-2R_1 + R_2 \Rightarrow R_2$
$-3R_1 + R_3 \Rightarrow R_3$

$-2R_2 + R_3 \Rightarrow R_3$

$$\left[\begin{array}{ccc|c} 1 & 2 & -1 & 7 \\ 0 & -5 & 3 & -12 \\ 0 & 0 & 0 & 0 \end{array}\right] \Rightarrow \left[\begin{array}{ccc|c} 1 & 2 & -1 & 7 \\ 0 & 1 & -\frac{3}{5} & \frac{12}{5} \\ 0 & 0 & 0 & 0 \end{array}\right] \Rightarrow \left[\begin{array}{ccc|c} 1 & 0 & \frac{1}{5} & \frac{11}{5} \\ 0 & 1 & -\frac{3}{5} & \frac{12}{5} \\ 0 & 0 & 0 & 0 \end{array}\right]$$

$-\frac{1}{5}R_2 \Rightarrow R_2$

$-2R_2 + R_1 \Rightarrow R_1$

From (2): $y - \frac{3}{5}z = \frac{12}{5}$
$y = \frac{3}{5}z + \frac{12}{5}$

From (1): $x + \frac{1}{5}z = \frac{11}{5}$
$x = -\frac{1}{5}z + \frac{11}{5}$

Solution: $\left(-\frac{1}{5}z + \frac{11}{5}, \frac{3}{5}z + \frac{12}{5}, z\right)$

67. $\left[\begin{array}{cc|c}1&1&-2\\3&-1&6\\2&2&-4\\1&-1&4\end{array}\right] \Rightarrow \left[\begin{array}{cc|c}1&1&-2\\0&-4&12\\0&0&0\\0&-2&6\end{array}\right] \Rightarrow \left[\begin{array}{cc|c}1&1&-2\\0&1&-3\\0&-2&6\\0&0&0\end{array}\right] \Rightarrow \left[\begin{array}{cc|c}1&0&1\\0&1&-3\\0&0&0\\0&0&0\end{array}\right]$ Solution: $(1,-3)$

$-3R_1+R_2 \Rightarrow R_2$, $-2R_1+R_3 \Rightarrow R_3$, $-R_1+R_4 \Rightarrow R_4$; $-\frac{1}{4}R_2 \Rightarrow R_2$, $R_3 \Leftrightarrow R_4$; $-R_2+R_1 \Rightarrow R_1$, $2R_2+R_3 \Rightarrow R_3$

68. $\left[\begin{array}{cc|c}1&-1&-3\\2&1&-3\\3&-1&-7\\4&1&-7\end{array}\right] \Rightarrow \left[\begin{array}{cc|c}1&-1&-3\\0&3&3\\0&2&2\\0&5&5\end{array}\right] \Rightarrow \left[\begin{array}{cc|c}1&-1&-3\\0&1&1\\0&2&2\\0&5&5\end{array}\right] \Rightarrow \left[\begin{array}{cc|c}1&0&-2\\0&1&1\\0&0&0\\0&0&0\end{array}\right]$ Solution: $(-2,1)$

$-2R_1+R_2 \Rightarrow R_2$, $-3R_1+R_3 \Rightarrow R_3$, $-4R_1+R_4 \Rightarrow R_4$; $\frac{1}{3}R_2 \Rightarrow R_2$, $R_3 \Leftrightarrow R_4$; $R_2+R_1 \Rightarrow R_1$, $-2R_2+R_3 \Rightarrow R_3$, $-5R_2+R_4 \Rightarrow R_4$

69. $\left[\begin{array}{ccc|c}1&2&1&4\\3&-1&-1&2\end{array}\right] \Rightarrow \left[\begin{array}{ccc|c}1&2&1&4\\0&-7&-4&-10\end{array}\right] \Rightarrow \left[\begin{array}{ccc|c}1&2&1&4\\0&1&\frac{4}{7}&\frac{10}{7}\end{array}\right] \Rightarrow \left[\begin{array}{ccc|c}1&0&-\frac{1}{7}&\frac{8}{7}\\0&1&\frac{4}{7}&\frac{10}{7}\end{array}\right]$

$-3R_1+R_2 \Rightarrow R_2$; $-\frac{1}{7}R_2 \Rightarrow R_2$; $-2R_2+R_1 \Rightarrow R_1$

From R_1: $x-\frac{1}{7}z=\frac{8}{7}$, $x=\frac{8}{7}+\frac{1}{7}z$

From R_2: $y+\frac{4}{7}z=\frac{10}{7}$, $y=\frac{10}{7}-\frac{4}{7}z$

Solution: $x=\frac{8}{7}+\frac{1}{7}z$, $y=\frac{10}{7}-\frac{4}{7}z$, $z=$ any real number

70. $\left[\begin{array}{ccc|c}1&2&-3&-5\\5&1&-1&-11\end{array}\right] \Rightarrow \left[\begin{array}{ccc|c}1&2&-3&-5\\0&-9&14&14\end{array}\right] \Rightarrow \left[\begin{array}{ccc|c}1&2&-3&-5\\0&1&-\frac{14}{9}&-\frac{14}{9}\end{array}\right] \Rightarrow \left[\begin{array}{ccc|c}1&0&\frac{1}{9}&-\frac{17}{9}\\0&1&-\frac{14}{9}&-\frac{14}{9}\end{array}\right]$

$-5R_1+R_2 \Rightarrow R_2$; $-\frac{1}{9}R_2 \Rightarrow R_2$; $-2R_2+R_1 \Rightarrow R_1$

From R_1: $x+\frac{1}{9}z=-\frac{17}{9}$, $x=-\frac{17}{9}-\frac{1}{9}z$

From R_2: $y-\frac{14}{9}z=-\frac{14}{9}$, $y=-\frac{14}{9}+\frac{14}{9}z$

Solution: $x=-\frac{17}{9}-\frac{1}{9}z$, $y=-\frac{14}{9}+\frac{14}{9}z$, $z=$ any real number

71. $\left[\begin{array}{cccc|c}1&1&0&0&1\\1&0&1&0&0\\0&1&0&1&0\end{array}\right] \Rightarrow \left[\begin{array}{cccc|c}1&1&0&0&1\\0&1&-1&0&1\\0&1&0&1&0\end{array}\right] \Rightarrow \left[\begin{array}{cccc|c}1&0&1&0&0\\0&1&-1&0&1\\0&0&1&1&-1\end{array}\right] \Rightarrow$

$-R_2+R_1 \Rightarrow R_2$; $-R_2+R_1 \Rightarrow R_1$, $-R_2+R_3 \Rightarrow R_3$

$\left[\begin{array}{cccc|c}1&0&0&-1&1\\0&1&0&1&0\\0&0&1&1&-1\end{array}\right] \Rightarrow$ From R_1: $w-z=1$, $w=1+z$; From R_2: $x+z=0$, $x=-z$; From R_3: $y+z=-1$, $y=-1-z$

$-R_3+R_1 \Rightarrow R_1$, $R_3+R_2 \Rightarrow R_2$

Solution: $w=1+z$, $x=-z$, $y=-1-z$, $z=$ any real #

72. $\left[\begin{array}{cccc|c} 1 & 1 & -1 & 1 & 2 \\ 2 & -1 & -2 & 1 & 0 \\ 1 & -2 & -1 & 1 & -1 \end{array}\right] \Rightarrow \left[\begin{array}{cccc|c} 1 & 1 & -1 & 1 & 2 \\ 0 & -3 & 0 & -1 & -4 \\ 0 & 3 & 0 & 0 & 3 \end{array}\right] \Rightarrow \left[\begin{array}{cccc|c} 3 & 0 & -3 & 2 & 2 \\ 0 & 0 & 0 & -1 & -1 \\ 0 & 1 & 0 & 0 & 1 \end{array}\right] \Rightarrow$

$-2R_1 + R_2 \Rightarrow R_2$; $-R_3 + R_1 \Rightarrow R_3$ — $3R_1 + R_2 \Rightarrow R_1$; $R_2 + R_3 \Rightarrow R_2$; $\frac{1}{3}R_3 \Rightarrow R_3$

$\left[\begin{array}{cccc|c} 3 & 0 & -3 & 0 & 0 \\ 0 & 0 & 0 & 1 & 1 \\ 0 & 1 & 0 & 0 & 1 \end{array}\right] \Rightarrow \left[\begin{array}{cccc|c} 1 & 0 & -1 & 0 & 0 \\ 0 & 0 & 0 & 1 & 1 \\ 0 & 1 & 0 & 0 & 1 \end{array}\right]$ From R_1: $w - y = 0$, $w = y$

$2R_2 + R_1 \Rightarrow R_1$; $-R_2 \Rightarrow R_2$ — $\frac{1}{3}R_1 \Rightarrow R_1$

Solution: $w = y$, $x = 1$, $y =$ any real #, $z = 1$

73. $\left[\begin{array}{cc|c} 1 & 1 & 3 \\ 2 & 1 & 1 \\ 3 & 2 & 2 \end{array}\right] \Rightarrow \left[\begin{array}{cc|c} 1 & 1 & 3 \\ 0 & -1 & -5 \\ 0 & -1 & -7 \end{array}\right] \Rightarrow \left[\begin{array}{cc|c} 1 & 1 & 3 \\ 0 & -1 & -5 \\ 0 & 0 & -2 \end{array}\right]$

$-2R_1 + R_2 \Rightarrow R_2$; $-3R_1 + R_3 \Rightarrow R_3$ — $-R_2 + R_3 \Rightarrow R_3$

R_3 indicates that $0x + 0y = -2$. This is impossible. The system is inconsistent. $\Rightarrow$ no solution

74. $\left[\begin{array}{ccc|c} 1 & 2 & 1 & 4 \\ 1 & -1 & 1 & 1 \\ 2 & 1 & 2 & 2 \\ 3 & 0 & 3 & 6 \end{array}\right] \Rightarrow \left[\begin{array}{ccc|c} 1 & 2 & 1 & 4 \\ 0 & -3 & 0 & -3 \\ 0 & -3 & 0 & -6 \\ 0 & -6 & 0 & -6 \end{array}\right] \Rightarrow \left[\begin{array}{ccc|c} 1 & 2 & 1 & 4 \\ 0 & -3 & 0 & -3 \\ 0 & 0 & 0 & -3 \\ 0 & -6 & 0 & -6 \end{array}\right]$

$-R_1 + R_2 \Rightarrow R_2$; $-2R_1 + R_3 \Rightarrow R_3$; $-3R_1 + R_4 \Rightarrow R_4$ — $-R_2 + R_3 \Rightarrow R_3$

R_3 indicates that $0x + 0y + 0z = -3$. This is impossible. The system is inconsistent. $\Rightarrow$ no solution

75. Let $p =$ speed with no wind. Let $w =$ the speed of the wind. Then the following system applies:

$\begin{cases} p + w = 300 \\ p - w = 220 \end{cases}$ $\left[\begin{array}{cc|c} 1 & 1 & 300 \\ 1 & -1 & 220 \end{array}\right] \Rightarrow \left[\begin{array}{cc|c} 1 & 1 & 300 \\ 0 & 2 & 80 \end{array}\right] \Rightarrow \left[\begin{array}{cc|c} 1 & 1 & 300 \\ 0 & 1 & 40 \end{array}\right] \Rightarrow \left[\begin{array}{cc|c} 1 & 0 & 260 \\ 0 & 1 & 40 \end{array}\right]$

$-R_2 + R_1 \Rightarrow R_2$ — $\frac{1}{2}R_2 \Rightarrow R_2$ — $-R_2 + R_1 \Rightarrow R_1$

The plane has a speed of 260 miles per hour with no wind, so it could travel 1300 miles in 5 hours.

76. Let $T =$ gallons for Triple A. Let $U =$ gallons for UnityAir. Then the following system applies:

$\begin{cases} T + U = 120000 \\ T = 2U \end{cases}$ $\begin{cases} T + U = 120000 \\ T - 2U = 0 \end{cases}$ $\left[\begin{array}{cc|c} 1 & 1 & 120000 \\ 1 & -2 & 0 \end{array}\right] \Rightarrow \left[\begin{array}{cc|c} 1 & 1 & 120000 \\ 0 & 3 & 120000 \end{array}\right] \Rightarrow$

$-R_2 + R_1 \Rightarrow R_2$

$\left[\begin{array}{cc|c} 1 & 1 & 120000 \\ 0 & 1 & 40000 \end{array}\right] \Rightarrow \left[\begin{array}{cc|c} 1 & 0 & 80000 \\ 0 & 1 & 40000 \end{array}\right]$ Triple A should be allocated 80,000 gallons.

$\frac{1}{3}R_2 \Rightarrow R_2$ — $-R_2 + R_1 \Rightarrow R_1$

77. Let $d =$ width of a dictionary, $a =$ width of an atlas and $t =$ width of a thesaurus.

$$\begin{cases} 3d+5a+t=35 \\ 6d+2t=35 \\ 2d+4a+3t=35 \end{cases} \quad \left[\begin{array}{ccc|c} 3 & 5 & 1 & 35 \\ 6 & 0 & 2 & 35 \\ 2 & 4 & 3 & 35 \end{array}\right] \Rightarrow \left[\begin{array}{ccc|c} 3 & 5 & 1 & 35 \\ 0 & -10 & 0 & -35 \\ 0 & \frac{2}{3} & \frac{7}{3} & \frac{35}{3} \end{array}\right] \Rightarrow \left[\begin{array}{ccc|c} 3 & 5 & 1 & 35 \\ 0 & 1 & 0 & 3.5 \\ 0 & 2 & 7 & 35 \end{array}\right]$$

$-2R_1 + R_2 \Rightarrow R_2$, $-\frac{2}{3}R_1 + R_3 \Rightarrow R_3$; $-\frac{1}{10}R_2 \Rightarrow R_2$, $3R_3 \Rightarrow R_3$

$$\Rightarrow \left[\begin{array}{ccc|c} 3 & 0 & 1 & 17.5 \\ 0 & 1 & 0 & 3.5 \\ 0 & 0 & 7 & 28 \end{array}\right] \Rightarrow \left[\begin{array}{ccc|c} 3 & 0 & 0 & 13.5 \\ 0 & 1 & 0 & 3.5 \\ 0 & 0 & 1 & 4 \end{array}\right] \Rightarrow \left[\begin{array}{ccc|c} 1 & 0 & 0 & 4.5 \\ 0 & 1 & 0 & 3.5 \\ 0 & 0 & 1 & 4 \end{array}\right]$$

$-5R_2 + R_1 \Rightarrow R_1$, $-2R_2 + R_3 \Rightarrow R_3$; $-\frac{1}{7}R_3 + R_1 \Rightarrow R_1$, $\frac{1}{7}R_3 \Rightarrow R_3$; $\frac{1}{3}R_1 \Rightarrow R_1$

Dictionaries are 4.5 in. wide. Atlases are 3.5 in. wide. Thesauruses are 4 in. wide.

78. Let A, B and C represent the number of copies per minute each copier can make.

$$\begin{cases} A+B=100 \\ A+C=140 \\ A+B+C=180 \end{cases} \quad \left[\begin{array}{ccc|c} 1 & 1 & 0 & 100 \\ 1 & 0 & 1 & 140 \\ 1 & 1 & 1 & 180 \end{array}\right] \Rightarrow \left[\begin{array}{ccc|c} 1 & 1 & 0 & 100 \\ 0 & -1 & 1 & 40 \\ 0 & 0 & 1 & 80 \end{array}\right] \Rightarrow$$

$-R_1 + R_2 \Rightarrow R_2$, $-R_1 + R_3 \Rightarrow R_3$

$$\left[\begin{array}{ccc|c} 1 & 0 & 1 & 140 \\ 0 & 1 & -1 & -40 \\ 0 & 0 & 1 & 80 \end{array}\right] \Rightarrow \left[\begin{array}{ccc|c} 1 & 0 & 0 & 60 \\ 0 & 1 & 0 & 40 \\ 0 & 0 & 1 & 80 \end{array}\right]$$

$R_2 + R_1 \Rightarrow R_1$, $-R_2 \Rightarrow R_2$; $-R_3 + R_1 \Rightarrow R_1$, $R_3 + R_2 \Rightarrow R_2$

Copier A can make 60 copies per minute. Copier B can make 40 copies per minute. Copier C can make 80 copies per minute.

79. Let A, B and C represent the number of ounces of each food.

$$\begin{cases} A+2B+2C=22 \\ A+B+C=12 \\ 2A+B+2C=20 \end{cases} \quad \left[\begin{array}{ccc|c} 1 & 2 & 2 & 22 \\ 1 & 1 & 1 & 12 \\ 2 & 1 & 2 & 20 \end{array}\right] \Rightarrow \left[\begin{array}{ccc|c} 1 & 2 & 2 & 22 \\ 0 & -1 & -1 & -10 \\ 0 & -3 & -2 & -24 \end{array}\right] \Rightarrow$$

$-R_1 + R_2 \Rightarrow R_2$, $-2R_1 + R_3 \Rightarrow R_3$

$$\left[\begin{array}{ccc|c} 1 & 0 & 0 & 2 \\ 0 & 1 & 1 & 10 \\ 0 & 0 & 1 & 6 \end{array}\right] \Rightarrow \left[\begin{array}{ccc|c} 1 & 0 & 0 & 2 \\ 0 & 1 & 0 & 4 \\ 0 & 0 & 1 & 6 \end{array}\right]$$

$2R_2 + R_1 \Rightarrow R_1$, $-3R_2 + R_3 \Rightarrow R_3$, $-R_2 \Rightarrow R_2$; $-R_3 + R_2 \Rightarrow R_2$

2 ounces of Food A, 4 ounces of Food B, and 6 ounces of Food C should be used.

80. Let A, B and C represent the numbers of poles, bears, and deer made.

$$\begin{cases} 2A+2B+C=14 \\ A+2B+2C=15 \\ 3A+2B+2C=21 \end{cases} \quad \left[\begin{array}{ccc|c} 2 & 2 & 1 & 14 \\ 1 & 2 & 2 & 15 \\ 3 & 2 & 2 & 21 \end{array}\right] \Rightarrow \left[\begin{array}{ccc|c} 1 & 2 & 2 & 15 \\ 0 & -2 & -3 & -16 \\ 0 & -4 & -4 & -24 \end{array}\right] \Rightarrow$$

$-2R_2 + R_1 \Rightarrow R_2$, $-3R_2 + R_3 \Rightarrow R_3$, $R_2 \Rightarrow R_1$

continued on next page...

80. continued

$$\left[\begin{array}{ccc|c} 1 & 0 & -1 & -1 \\ 0 & 2 & 3 & 16 \\ 0 & 0 & 2 & 8 \end{array}\right] \Rightarrow \left[\begin{array}{ccc|c} 1 & 0 & 0 & 3 \\ 0 & 2 & 0 & 4 \\ 0 & 0 & 1 & 4 \end{array}\right] \Rightarrow \left[\begin{array}{ccc|c} 1 & 0 & 0 & 3 \\ 0 & 1 & 0 & 2 \\ 0 & 0 & 1 & 4 \end{array}\right]$$

$R_2 + R_1 \Rightarrow R_1$, $-2R_2 + R_3 \Rightarrow R_3$, $-R_2 \Rightarrow R_2$; $\frac{1}{2}R_3 + R_1 \Rightarrow R_1$, $-\frac{3}{2}R_3 + R_2 \Rightarrow R_2$, $\frac{1}{2}R_3 \Rightarrow R_3$; $\frac{1}{2}R_2 \Rightarrow R_2$

3 poles, 2 bears, and 4 deer should be made.

81-84. Answers may vary.

85.

$$\left[\begin{array}{ccc|c} 1 & 1 & 1 & 14 \\ 2 & 3 & -2 & -7 \\ 1 & -5 & 1 & 8 \end{array}\right] \Rightarrow \left[\begin{array}{ccc|c} 1 & 1 & 1 & 14 \\ 0 & 1 & -4 & -35 \\ 0 & -6 & 0 & -6 \end{array}\right] \Rightarrow \left[\begin{array}{ccc|c} 1 & 1 & 1 & 14 \\ 0 & -6 & 0 & -6 \\ 0 & 1 & -4 & -35 \end{array}\right] \Rightarrow$$

$-2R_1 + R_2 \Rightarrow R_2$, $-R_1 + R_3 \Rightarrow R_3$; $R_2 \Leftrightarrow R_3$

$$\left[\begin{array}{ccc|c} 1 & 0 & 1 & 13 \\ 0 & -6 & 0 & -6 \\ 0 & 0 & -4 & -36 \end{array}\right] \Rightarrow \left[\begin{array}{ccc|c} 1 & 0 & 0 & 4 \\ 0 & 1 & 0 & 1 \\ 0 & 0 & 1 & 9 \end{array}\right]$$

$\frac{1}{6}R_2 + R_1 \Rightarrow R_1$, $\frac{1}{6}R_2 + R_3 \Rightarrow R_3$; $\frac{1}{4}R_3 + R_1 \Rightarrow R_1$, $-\frac{1}{6}R_2 \Rightarrow R_2$, $-\frac{1}{4}R_3 \Rightarrow R_3$

$x^2 = 4 \Rightarrow \boxed{x = \pm 2}$

$y^2 = 1 \Rightarrow \boxed{y = \pm 1}$

$z^2 = 9 \Rightarrow \boxed{z = \pm 3}$

86.

$$\left[\begin{array}{ccc|c} 5 & 2 & 1 & 22 \\ 1 & 1 & -1 & 5 \\ 3 & -2 & -3 & 10 \end{array}\right] \Rightarrow \left[\begin{array}{ccc|c} 1 & 1 & -1 & 5 \\ 5 & 2 & 1 & 22 \\ 3 & -2 & -3 & 10 \end{array}\right] \Rightarrow \left[\begin{array}{ccc|c} 1 & 1 & -1 & 5 \\ 0 & -3 & 6 & -3 \\ 0 & -5 & 0 & -5 \end{array}\right] \Rightarrow$$

$R_1 \Leftrightarrow R_2$; $-5R_1 + R_2 \Rightarrow R_2$, $-3R_1 + R_3 \Rightarrow R_3$

$$\left[\begin{array}{ccc|c} 1 & 1 & -1 & 5 \\ 0 & -5 & 0 & -5 \\ 0 & -3 & 6 & -3 \end{array}\right] \Rightarrow \left[\begin{array}{ccc|c} 1 & 1 & -1 & 5 \\ 0 & 1 & 0 & 1 \\ 0 & -1 & 2 & -1 \end{array}\right] \Rightarrow \left[\begin{array}{ccc|c} 1 & 0 & -1 & 4 \\ 0 & 1 & 0 & 1 \\ 0 & 0 & 2 & 0 \end{array}\right] \Rightarrow \left[\begin{array}{ccc|c} 1 & 0 & 0 & 4 \\ 0 & 1 & 0 & 1 \\ 0 & 0 & 1 & 0 \end{array}\right]$$

$R_2 \Leftrightarrow R_3$; $-\frac{1}{5}R_2 \Rightarrow R_2$, $\frac{1}{3}R_3 \Rightarrow R_3$; $-R_2 + R_1 \Rightarrow R_1$, $R_2 + R_3 \Rightarrow R_3$; $\frac{1}{2}R_3 + R_1 \Rightarrow R_1$, $\frac{1}{2}R_3 \Rightarrow R_3$

$\sqrt{x} = 4 \Rightarrow \boxed{x = 16}$, $\sqrt{y} = 1 \Rightarrow \boxed{y = 1}$, $\sqrt{z} = 0 \Rightarrow \boxed{z = 0}$

87. $y = mx + b$

88. $y - y_1 = m(x - x_1)$

89. equal

90. perpendicular

91. $y = mx + b$
$y = 2x + 7$

92.
$$\begin{aligned} y - y_1 &= m(x - x_1) \\ y - (-3) &= -3(x - 2) \\ y + 3 &= -3x + 6 \\ y &= -3x + 3 \end{aligned}$$

93. $x = 2$

94. $y = -3$

Exercises 6.3 (page 588)

1. i, j

2. size, equal

3. corresponding

4. every element

5. columns, rows

6. 3×4

7. additive identity

8. multiplicative identity

9. $x = 2, y = 5$

10. $x = 0, y = 2$

11. $x + y = 3$
$3 + x = 4 \Rightarrow x = 1$
$5y = 10 \Rightarrow y = 2$

12. $x + y = -x \qquad x = -1$
$x - y = x - 2 \qquad y = 2$
$2x = -y$
$3y = 8 - y$

13. $A + B = \begin{bmatrix} 2 & 1 & -1 \\ -3 & 2 & 5 \end{bmatrix} + \begin{bmatrix} -3 & 1 & 2 \\ -3 & -2 & -5 \end{bmatrix} = \begin{bmatrix} -1 & 2 & 1 \\ -6 & 0 & 0 \end{bmatrix}$

14. $A + B = \begin{bmatrix} 3 & 2 & 1 \\ -2 & 3 & -3 \\ -4 & -2 & -1 \end{bmatrix} + \begin{bmatrix} -2 & 6 & -2 \\ 5 & 7 & -1 \\ -4 & -6 & 7 \end{bmatrix} = \begin{bmatrix} 1 & 8 & -1 \\ 3 & 10 & -4 \\ -8 & -8 & 6 \end{bmatrix}$

15. additive inverse of $A = \begin{bmatrix} -5 & 2 & -7 \\ 5 & 0 & -3 \\ 2 & -3 & 5 \end{bmatrix}$

16. additive inverse of $A = \begin{bmatrix} -3 & \frac{2}{3} & 5 & -\frac{1}{2} \end{bmatrix}$

17. $A - B = \begin{bmatrix} -3 & 2 & -2 \\ -1 & 4 & -5 \end{bmatrix} - \begin{bmatrix} 3 & -3 & -2 \\ -2 & 5 & -5 \end{bmatrix} = \begin{bmatrix} -6 & 5 & 0 \\ 1 & -1 & 0 \end{bmatrix}$

18. $A - B = \begin{bmatrix} 2 & 2 & 0 \\ -2 & 8 & 1 \\ 3 & -3 & -8 \end{bmatrix} - \begin{bmatrix} -4 & 3 & 7 \\ -1 & 2 & 0 \\ 1 & 4 & -1 \end{bmatrix} = \begin{bmatrix} 6 & -1 & -7 \\ -1 & 6 & 1 \\ 2 & -7 & -7 \end{bmatrix}$

19. $5A = 5\begin{bmatrix} 3 & -3 \\ 0 & -2 \end{bmatrix} = \begin{bmatrix} 15 & -15 \\ 0 & -10 \end{bmatrix}$

20. $5A = 5\begin{bmatrix} 3 & \frac{3}{5} \\ 0 & -1 \end{bmatrix} = \begin{bmatrix} 15 & 3 \\ 0 & -5 \end{bmatrix}$

21. $5A = 5\begin{bmatrix} 5 & 15 & -2 \\ -2 & -5 & 1 \end{bmatrix}$
$= \begin{bmatrix} 25 & 75 & -10 \\ -10 & -25 & 5 \end{bmatrix}$

22. $5A = 5\begin{bmatrix} -3 & 1 & 2 \\ -8 & -2 & -5 \end{bmatrix}$
$= \begin{bmatrix} -15 & 5 & 10 \\ -40 & -10 & -25 \end{bmatrix}$

23. $5A + 3B = 5\begin{bmatrix} 3 & 1 & -2 \\ -4 & 3 & -2 \end{bmatrix} + 3\begin{bmatrix} 1 & -2 & 2 \\ -5 & -5 & 3 \end{bmatrix} = \begin{bmatrix} 15 & 5 & -10 \\ -20 & 15 & -10 \end{bmatrix} + \begin{bmatrix} 3 & -6 & 6 \\ -15 & -15 & 9 \end{bmatrix}$
$= \begin{bmatrix} 18 & -1 & -4 \\ -35 & 0 & -1 \end{bmatrix}$

24. $5A+3B=5\begin{bmatrix}2&-5\\-5&2\end{bmatrix}+3\begin{bmatrix}5&-2\\2&-5\end{bmatrix}=\begin{bmatrix}10&-25\\-25&10\end{bmatrix}+\begin{bmatrix}15&-6\\6&-15\end{bmatrix}=\begin{bmatrix}25&-31\\-19&-5\end{bmatrix}$

25. $\begin{bmatrix}2&3\\3&-2\end{bmatrix}_{2\times2}\begin{bmatrix}1&2\\0&-2\end{bmatrix}_{2\times2}=\begin{bmatrix}(2)(1)+(3)(0)&(2)(2)+(3)(-2)\\(3)(1)+(-2)(0)&(3)(2)+(-2)(-2)\end{bmatrix}_{2\times2}=\begin{bmatrix}2&-2\\3&10\end{bmatrix}$

26. $\begin{bmatrix}-2&3\\3&-2\end{bmatrix}_{2\times2}\begin{bmatrix}2&4\\-5&7\end{bmatrix}_{2\times2}=\begin{bmatrix}(-2)(2)+(3)(-5)&(-2)(4)+(3)(7)\\(3)(2)+(-2)(-5)&(3)(4)+(-2)(7)\end{bmatrix}_{2\times2}=\begin{bmatrix}-19&13\\16&-2\end{bmatrix}$

27. $\begin{bmatrix}-4&-2\\21&0\end{bmatrix}_{2\times2}\begin{bmatrix}-5&6\\21&-1\end{bmatrix}_{2\times2}=\begin{bmatrix}(-4)(-5)+(-2)(21)&(-4)(6)+(-2)(-1)\\(21)(-5)+(0)(21)&(21)(6)+(0)(-1)\end{bmatrix}_{2\times2}$

$=\begin{bmatrix}-22&-22\\-105&126\end{bmatrix}$

28. $\begin{bmatrix}-5&4\\4&-5\end{bmatrix}_{2\times2}\begin{bmatrix}6&-2\\1&3\end{bmatrix}_{2\times2}=\begin{bmatrix}(-5)(6)+(4)(1)&(-5)(-2)+(4)(3)\\(4)(6)+(-5)(1)&(4)(-2)+(-5)(3)\end{bmatrix}_{2\times2}=\begin{bmatrix}-26&22\\19&-23\end{bmatrix}$

29. $\begin{bmatrix}2&1&3\\1&2&-1\\0&1&0\end{bmatrix}_{3\times3}\begin{bmatrix}1&2&3\\2&-2&1\\0&0&1\end{bmatrix}_{3\times3}$

$=\begin{bmatrix}(2)(1)+(1)(2)+(3)(0)&(2)(2)+(1)(-2)+(3)(0)&(2)(3)+(1)(1)+(3)(1)\\(1)(1)+(2)(2)+(-1)(0)&(1)(2)+(2)(-2)+(-1)(0)&(1)(3)+(2)(1)+(-1)(1)\\(0)(1)+(1)(2)+(0)(0)&(0)(2)+(1)(-2)+(0)(0)&(0)(3)+(1)(1)+(0)(1)\end{bmatrix}_{3\times3}$

$=\begin{bmatrix}4&2&10\\5&-2&4\\2&-2&1\end{bmatrix}$

30. $\begin{bmatrix}2&1&1\\1&1&2\\1&-2&-1\end{bmatrix}_{3\times3}\begin{bmatrix}1&2&3\\1&2&-3\\-1&-1&3\end{bmatrix}_{3\times3}$

$=\begin{bmatrix}(2)(1)+(1)(1)+(1)(-1)&(2)(2)+(1)(2)+(1)(-1)&(2)(3)+(1)(-3)+(1)(3)\\(1)(1)+(1)(1)+(2)(-1)&(1)(2)+(1)(2)+(2)(-1)&(1)(3)+(1)(-3)+(2)(3)\\1(1)+(-2)(1)+(-1)(-1)&1(2)+(-2)(2)+(-1)(-1)&1(3)+(-2)(-3)+(-1)(3)\end{bmatrix}$

$=\begin{bmatrix}2&5&6\\0&2&6\\0&-1&6\end{bmatrix}$

31. $\begin{bmatrix}1\\-2\\-3\end{bmatrix}_{3\times1}[4\quad -5\quad -6]_{1\times3}=\begin{bmatrix}(1)(4)&(1)(-5)&(1)(-6)\\(-2)(4)&(-2)(-5)&(-2)(-6)\\(-3)(4)&(-3)(-5)&(-3)(-6)\end{bmatrix}_{3\times3}=\begin{bmatrix}4&-5&-6\\-8&10&12\\-12&15&18\end{bmatrix}$

32. $\begin{bmatrix}1&-2&-3\\2&0&1\end{bmatrix}_{2\times3}\begin{bmatrix}4\\-5\\-6\end{bmatrix}_{3\times1}=\begin{bmatrix}(1)(4)+(-2)(-5)+(-3)(-6)\\(2)(4)+(0)(-5)+(1)(-6)\end{bmatrix}_{2\times1}=\begin{bmatrix}32\\2\end{bmatrix}$

33. $\begin{bmatrix} 1 & 2 & 3 \end{bmatrix}_{1\times 3} \begin{bmatrix} 4 & 5 & 6 \\ 7 & 8 & 9 \end{bmatrix}_{2\times 3}$

Not possible

34. $\begin{bmatrix} 2 & 5 \\ -1 & 7 \end{bmatrix}_{2\times 2} \begin{bmatrix} 3 & 5 & -8 \\ -2 & 7 & 5 \\ 3 & --6 & 2 \end{bmatrix}_{3\times 3}$

Not possible

35. $$\begin{bmatrix} 2 & 3 & 4 \\ 1 & 2 & 3 \\ -2 & 2 & 2 \end{bmatrix}_{3\times 3} \begin{bmatrix} -1 \\ 2 \\ 3 \end{bmatrix}_{3\times 1} = \begin{bmatrix} (2)(-1)+(3)(2)+(4)(3) \\ (1)(-1)+(2)(2)+(3)(3) \\ (-2)(-1)+(2)(2)+(2)(3) \end{bmatrix}_{3\times 1} = \begin{bmatrix} 16 \\ 12 \\ 12 \end{bmatrix}$$

36. $$\begin{bmatrix} 2 & 5 \\ -3 & 1 \\ 0 & -2 \\ 1 & -5 \end{bmatrix}_{4\times 2} \begin{bmatrix} 3 & -2 & 4 \\ -2 & -3 & 1 \end{bmatrix}_{2\times 3}$$

$$= \begin{bmatrix} (2)(3)+(5)(-2) & (2)(-2)+(5)(-3) & (2)(4)+(5)(1) \\ (-3)(3)+(1)(-2) & (-3)(-2)+(1)(-3) & (-3)(4)+(1)(1) \\ (0)(3)+(-2)(-2) & (0)(-2)+(-2)(-3) & (0)(4)+(-2)(1) \\ (1)(3)+(-5)(-2) & (1)(-2)+(-5)(-3) & (1)(4)+(-5)(1) \end{bmatrix}_{4\times 3} = \begin{bmatrix} -4 & -19 & 13 \\ -11 & 3 & -11 \\ 4 & 6 & -2 \\ 13 & 13 & -1 \end{bmatrix}$$

37. $\begin{bmatrix} 1 & 2 & 3 \\ 4 & 5 & 6 \\ 7 & 8 & 9 \end{bmatrix}_{3\times 3} \begin{bmatrix} 1 & 2 \\ 3 & 4 \end{bmatrix}_{2\times 2}$

Not possible

38. $$\begin{bmatrix} 1 & 4 & 0 & 0 \\ -4 & 1 & 0 & -2 \\ 0 & 0 & 1 & 0 \\ 0 & 2 & 0 & 1 \end{bmatrix}_{4\times 4} \begin{bmatrix} 1 \\ 2 \\ -2 \\ -1 \end{bmatrix}_{4\times 1} = \begin{bmatrix} (1)(1)+(4)(2)+(0)(-2)+(0)(-1) \\ (-4)(1)+(1)(2)+(0)(-2)+(-2)(-1) \\ (0)(1)+(0)(2)+(1)(-2)+(0)(-1) \\ (0)(1)+(2)(2)+(0)(-2)+(1)(-1) \end{bmatrix}_{4\times 1} = \begin{bmatrix} 9 \\ 0 \\ -2 \\ 3 \end{bmatrix}$$

39. $$AB = \begin{bmatrix} 2.3 & -1.7 & 3.1 \\ -2 & 3.5 & 1 \\ -8 & 4.7 & 9.1 \end{bmatrix} \begin{bmatrix} -2.5 \\ 5.2 \\ -7 \end{bmatrix} = \begin{bmatrix} -36.29 \\ 16.2 \\ -19.26 \end{bmatrix}$$

40. $$B + C = \begin{bmatrix} -2.5 \\ 5.2 \\ -7 \end{bmatrix} + \begin{bmatrix} -5.8 \\ 2.9 \\ 4.1 \end{bmatrix} = \begin{bmatrix} -8.3 \\ 8.1 \\ -2.9 \end{bmatrix}$$

41. $$A^2 = \begin{bmatrix} 2.3 & -1.7 & 3.1 \\ -2 & 3.5 & 1 \\ -8 & 4.7 & 9.1 \end{bmatrix} \begin{bmatrix} 2.3 & -1.7 & 3.1 \\ -2 & 3.5 & 1 \\ -8 & 4.7 & 9.1 \end{bmatrix} = \begin{bmatrix} -16.11 & 4.71 & 33.64 \\ -19.6 & 20.35 & 6.4 \\ -100.6 & 72.82 & 62.71 \end{bmatrix}$$

42. $$AB + C = \begin{bmatrix} 2.3 & -1.7 & 3.1 \\ -2 & 3.5 & 1 \\ -8 & 4.7 & 9.1 \end{bmatrix} \begin{bmatrix} -2.5 \\ 5.2 \\ -7 \end{bmatrix} + \begin{bmatrix} -5.8 \\ 2.9 \\ 4.1 \end{bmatrix} = \begin{bmatrix} -42.09 \\ 19.1 \\ -15.16 \end{bmatrix}$$

43. $A(B+C)=\begin{bmatrix}2&3\\1&3\end{bmatrix}\left(\begin{bmatrix}2&1&-5\\1&1&2\end{bmatrix}+\begin{bmatrix}-2&-1&6\\0&-1&-1\end{bmatrix}\right)=\begin{bmatrix}2&3\\1&3\end{bmatrix}\begin{bmatrix}0&0&1\\1&0&1\end{bmatrix}=\begin{bmatrix}3&0&5\\3&0&4\end{bmatrix}$

$$AB+AC=\begin{bmatrix}2&3\\1&3\end{bmatrix}\begin{bmatrix}2&1&-5\\1&1&2\end{bmatrix}+\begin{bmatrix}2&3\\1&3\end{bmatrix}\begin{bmatrix}-2&-1&6\\0&-1&-1\end{bmatrix}$$
$$=\begin{bmatrix}7&5&-4\\5&4&1\end{bmatrix}+\begin{bmatrix}-4&-5&9\\-2&-4&3\end{bmatrix}=\begin{bmatrix}3&0&5\\3&0&4\end{bmatrix}$$

44. $5(6A)=5\left(6\begin{bmatrix}2&3\\1&3\end{bmatrix}\right)=5\begin{bmatrix}12&18\\6&18\end{bmatrix}=\begin{bmatrix}60&90\\30&90\end{bmatrix}$

$(5\cdot 6)A=30A=30\begin{bmatrix}2&3\\1&3\end{bmatrix}=\begin{bmatrix}60&90\\30&90\end{bmatrix}$

45. $3(AB)=3\left(\begin{bmatrix}2&3\\1&3\end{bmatrix}\begin{bmatrix}2&1&-5\\1&1&2\end{bmatrix}\right)=3\begin{bmatrix}7&5&-4\\5&4&1\end{bmatrix}=\begin{bmatrix}21&15&-12\\15&12&3\end{bmatrix}$

$(3A)B=\left(3\begin{bmatrix}2&3\\1&3\end{bmatrix}\right)\begin{bmatrix}2&1&-5\\1&1&2\end{bmatrix}=\begin{bmatrix}6&9\\3&9\end{bmatrix}\begin{bmatrix}2&1&-5\\1&1&2\end{bmatrix}=\begin{bmatrix}21&15&-12\\15&12&3\end{bmatrix}$

46. $A(DE)=\begin{bmatrix}2&3\\1&3\end{bmatrix}\left(\begin{bmatrix}1&2\\1&3\end{bmatrix}\begin{bmatrix}1&-2\\2&3\end{bmatrix}\right)=\begin{bmatrix}2&3\\1&3\end{bmatrix}\begin{bmatrix}5&4\\7&7\end{bmatrix}=\begin{bmatrix}31&29\\26&25\end{bmatrix}$

$(AD)E=\left(\begin{bmatrix}2&3\\1&3\end{bmatrix}\begin{bmatrix}1&2\\1&3\end{bmatrix}\right)\begin{bmatrix}1&-2\\2&3\end{bmatrix}=\begin{bmatrix}5&13\\4&11\end{bmatrix}\begin{bmatrix}1&-2\\2&3\end{bmatrix}=\begin{bmatrix}31&29\\26&25\end{bmatrix}$

47. $A-BC=\begin{bmatrix}1&3\\2&5\end{bmatrix}-\begin{bmatrix}-1\\3\end{bmatrix}\begin{bmatrix}3&2\end{bmatrix}=\begin{bmatrix}1&3\\2&5\end{bmatrix}-\begin{bmatrix}-3&-2\\9&6\end{bmatrix}=\begin{bmatrix}4&5\\-7&-1\end{bmatrix}$

48. $AB+B=\begin{bmatrix}1&3\\2&5\end{bmatrix}\begin{bmatrix}-1\\3\end{bmatrix}+\begin{bmatrix}-1\\3\end{bmatrix}=\begin{bmatrix}8\\13\end{bmatrix}+\begin{bmatrix}-1\\3\end{bmatrix}=\begin{bmatrix}7\\16\end{bmatrix}$

49. $CB-AB=\begin{bmatrix}3&2\end{bmatrix}\begin{bmatrix}-1\\3\end{bmatrix}-\begin{bmatrix}1&3\\2&5\end{bmatrix}\begin{bmatrix}-1\\3\end{bmatrix}=\begin{bmatrix}3\end{bmatrix}-\begin{bmatrix}8\\13\end{bmatrix}\Rightarrow$ not possible

50. $CAB=\begin{bmatrix}3&2\end{bmatrix}\begin{bmatrix}1&3\\2&5\end{bmatrix}\begin{bmatrix}-1\\3\end{bmatrix}=\begin{bmatrix}7&19\end{bmatrix}\begin{bmatrix}-1\\3\end{bmatrix}=\begin{bmatrix}50\end{bmatrix}$

51. $ABC=\begin{bmatrix}1&3\\2&5\end{bmatrix}\begin{bmatrix}-1\\3\end{bmatrix}\begin{bmatrix}3&2\end{bmatrix}=\begin{bmatrix}8\\13\end{bmatrix}\begin{bmatrix}3&2\end{bmatrix}=\begin{bmatrix}24&16\\39&26\end{bmatrix}$

52. $CA+C=\begin{bmatrix}3&2\end{bmatrix}\begin{bmatrix}1&3\\2&5\end{bmatrix}+\begin{bmatrix}3&2\end{bmatrix}=\begin{bmatrix}7&19\end{bmatrix}+\begin{bmatrix}3&2\end{bmatrix}=\begin{bmatrix}10&21\end{bmatrix}$

53. $A^2B=\begin{bmatrix}1&3\\2&5\end{bmatrix}\begin{bmatrix}1&3\\2&5\end{bmatrix}\begin{bmatrix}-1\\3\end{bmatrix}=\begin{bmatrix}7&18\\12&31\end{bmatrix}\begin{bmatrix}-1\\3\end{bmatrix}=\begin{bmatrix}47\\81\end{bmatrix}$

54. $(BC)^2 = \left(\begin{bmatrix} -1 \\ 3 \end{bmatrix}\begin{bmatrix} 3 & 2 \end{bmatrix}\right)^2 = \left(\begin{bmatrix} -3 & -2 \\ 9 & 6 \end{bmatrix}\right)^2 = \begin{bmatrix} -3 & -2 \\ 9 & 6 \end{bmatrix}\begin{bmatrix} -3 & -2 \\ 9 & 6 \end{bmatrix} = \begin{bmatrix} -9 & -6 \\ 27 & 18 \end{bmatrix}$

55. $Q = \begin{bmatrix} 200 & 300 & 100 \\ 100 & 200 & 200 \end{bmatrix}, C = \begin{bmatrix} 5 \\ 2 \\ 4 \end{bmatrix}$

$QC = \begin{bmatrix} 200 & 300 & 100 \\ 100 & 200 & 200 \end{bmatrix}\begin{bmatrix} 5 \\ 2 \\ 4 \end{bmatrix} = \begin{bmatrix} 2000 \\ 1700 \end{bmatrix}$ Cost of balls from Supplier 1; Cost of balls from Supplier 2

56. $Q = \begin{bmatrix} 75 & 75 & 32 \\ 80 & 69 & 27 \\ 62 & 40 & 30 \end{bmatrix}, P = \begin{bmatrix} 1.50 \\ 1.75 \\ 3.00 \end{bmatrix}$

$QP = \begin{bmatrix} 75 & 75 & 32 \\ 80 & 69 & 27 \\ 62 & 40 & 30 \end{bmatrix}\begin{bmatrix} 1.50 \\ 1.75 \\ 3.00 \end{bmatrix} = \begin{bmatrix} 339.75 \\ 321.75 \\ 253.00 \end{bmatrix}$ \$ made by Store 1; \$ made by Store 2; \$ made by Store 3

57. $Q = \begin{bmatrix} 217 & 23 & 319 \\ 347 & 24 & 340 \\ 3 & 97 & 750 \end{bmatrix}, P = \begin{bmatrix} 0.75 \\ 1.00 \\ 1.25 \end{bmatrix}$

$QP = \begin{bmatrix} 217 & 23 & 319 \\ 347 & 24 & 340 \\ 3 & 97 & 750 \end{bmatrix}\begin{bmatrix} 0.75 \\ 1.00 \\ 1.25 \end{bmatrix} = \begin{bmatrix} 584.50 \\ 709.25 \\ 1036.75 \end{bmatrix}$ \$ spent by adult males; \$ spent by adult females; \$ spent by children

58. $\begin{bmatrix} 19 & 23 & 27 \\ 17 & 21 & 22 \\ 21 & 18 & 20 \\ 27 & 25 & 22 \end{bmatrix}\begin{bmatrix} 1.20 & 1.35 \\ 0.75 & 0.85 \\ 3.50 & 3.70 \end{bmatrix} = \begin{bmatrix} 134.55 & 145.10 \\ 113.15 & 122.20 \\ 108.70 & 117.65 \\ 128.15 & 139.10 \end{bmatrix}$ Day/Night costs in Ashtabula; Day/Night costs in Boston; Day/Night costs in Chicago; Day/Night costs in Denver

59. $A^2 = \begin{bmatrix} 0 & 1 & 1 \\ 1 & 0 & 0 \\ 0 & 1 & 0 \end{bmatrix}^2 = \begin{bmatrix} 0 & 1 & 1 \\ 1 & 0 & 0 \\ 0 & 1 & 0 \end{bmatrix}\begin{bmatrix} 0 & 1 & 1 \\ 1 & 0 & 0 \\ 0 & 1 & 0 \end{bmatrix} = \begin{bmatrix} 1 & 1 & 0 \\ 0 & 1 & 1 \\ 1 & 0 & 0 \end{bmatrix}$

60. $A + A^2 = \begin{bmatrix} 0 & 1 & 1 \\ 1 & 0 & 0 \\ 0 & 1 & 0 \end{bmatrix} + \begin{bmatrix} 0 & 1 & 1 \\ 1 & 0 & 0 \\ 0 & 1 & 0 \end{bmatrix}^2 = \begin{bmatrix} 0 & 1 & 1 \\ 1 & 0 & 0 \\ 0 & 1 & 0 \end{bmatrix} + \begin{bmatrix} 1 & 1 & 0 \\ 0 & 1 & 1 \\ 1 & 0 & 0 \end{bmatrix} = \begin{bmatrix} 1 & 2 & 1 \\ 1 & 1 & 1 \\ 1 & 1 & 0 \end{bmatrix}$

The matrix $A + A^2$ contains the number of ways for a message to get from one person to another either directly or through one other person. The only 0 in the matrix is in the location which represents a message from Carl to himself. Thus, everybody is able to receive a letter from everyone else with at most one forwarding.

61. $A^2 = \begin{bmatrix} 0 & 2 & 1 & 0 \\ 2 & 0 & 1 & 0 \\ 1 & 1 & 0 & 2 \\ 0 & 0 & 2 & 0 \end{bmatrix}^2 = \begin{bmatrix} 0 & 2 & 1 & 0 \\ 2 & 0 & 1 & 0 \\ 1 & 1 & 0 & 2 \\ 0 & 0 & 2 & 0 \end{bmatrix}\begin{bmatrix} 0 & 2 & 1 & 0 \\ 2 & 0 & 1 & 0 \\ 1 & 1 & 0 & 2 \\ 0 & 0 & 2 & 0 \end{bmatrix} = \begin{bmatrix} 5 & 1 & 2 & 2 \\ 1 & 5 & 2 & 2 \\ 2 & 2 & 6 & 0 \\ 2 & 2 & 0 & 4 \end{bmatrix}$

A^2 represents the number of ways two cities can be linked through one intermediary.

62. $C^2 = \begin{bmatrix} 0 & 2 & 2 \\ 1 & 0 & 1 \\ 1 & 0 & 0 \end{bmatrix}^2 = \begin{bmatrix} 0 & 2 & 2 \\ 1 & 0 & 1 \\ 1 & 0 & 0 \end{bmatrix}\begin{bmatrix} 0 & 2 & 2 \\ 1 & 0 & 1 \\ 1 & 0 & 0 \end{bmatrix} = \begin{bmatrix} 4 & 0 & 2 \\ 1 & 2 & 2 \\ 0 & 2 & 2 \end{bmatrix}$

C^2 represents the number of ways two centers can be linked through one intermediary.

63. Let $A = \begin{bmatrix} 1 & 1 \\ 1 & 1 \end{bmatrix}$ and $B = \begin{bmatrix} 1 & 0 \\ 0 & 0 \end{bmatrix}$.

$(AB)^2 = \left(\begin{bmatrix} 1 & 1 \\ 1 & 1 \end{bmatrix}\begin{bmatrix} 1 & 0 \\ 0 & 0 \end{bmatrix}\right)^2 = \begin{bmatrix} 1 & 0 \\ 1 & 0 \end{bmatrix}^2 = \begin{bmatrix} 1 & 0 \\ 1 & 0 \end{bmatrix}\begin{bmatrix} 1 & 0 \\ 1 & 0 \end{bmatrix} = \begin{bmatrix} 1 & 0 \\ 1 & 0 \end{bmatrix}$

$A^2B^2 = \begin{bmatrix} 1 & 1 \\ 1 & 1 \end{bmatrix}^2\begin{bmatrix} 1 & 0 \\ 0 & 0 \end{bmatrix}^2 = \begin{bmatrix} 2 & 2 \\ 2 & 2 \end{bmatrix}\begin{bmatrix} 1 & 0 \\ 0 & 0 \end{bmatrix} = \begin{bmatrix} 2 & 0 \\ 2 & 0 \end{bmatrix}$. $(AB)^2 \neq A^2B^2$

64. Let $A = \begin{bmatrix} 1 & 0 \\ 0 & 0 \end{bmatrix}$, $B = \begin{bmatrix} 0 & 1 \\ 1 & 1 \end{bmatrix}$ and $C = \begin{bmatrix} 0 & 1 \\ 1 & 2 \end{bmatrix}$.

$AB = \begin{bmatrix} 1 & 0 \\ 0 & 0 \end{bmatrix}\begin{bmatrix} 0 & 1 \\ 1 & 1 \end{bmatrix} = \begin{bmatrix} 0 & 1 \\ 0 & 0 \end{bmatrix}$; $AC = \begin{bmatrix} 1 & 0 \\ 0 & 0 \end{bmatrix}\begin{bmatrix} 0 & 1 \\ 1 & 2 \end{bmatrix} = \begin{bmatrix} 0 & 1 \\ 0 & 0 \end{bmatrix}$

So $AB = AC$, but $B \neq C$.

65. Let $A = \begin{bmatrix} 1 & 2 \\ 1 & 2 \end{bmatrix}$ and $B = \begin{bmatrix} 2 & 2 \\ -1 & -1 \end{bmatrix}$. $AB = \begin{bmatrix} 1 & 2 \\ 1 & 2 \end{bmatrix}\begin{bmatrix} 2 & 2 \\ -1 & -1 \end{bmatrix} = \begin{bmatrix} 0 & 0 \\ 0 & 0 \end{bmatrix}$

66. Let $A = \begin{bmatrix} 1 & 0 \\ 0 & 0 \end{bmatrix}$ and $B = \begin{bmatrix} 0 & 1 \\ 0 & 0 \end{bmatrix}$.

$$(A+B)(A-B) = \left(\begin{bmatrix} 1 & 0 \\ 0 & 0 \end{bmatrix} + \begin{bmatrix} 0 & 1 \\ 0 & 0 \end{bmatrix}\right)\left(\begin{bmatrix} 1 & 0 \\ 0 & 0 \end{bmatrix} - \begin{bmatrix} 0 & 1 \\ 0 & 0 \end{bmatrix}\right)$$
$$= \begin{bmatrix} 1 & 1 \\ 0 & 0 \end{bmatrix}\begin{bmatrix} 1 & -1 \\ 0 & 0 \end{bmatrix} = \begin{bmatrix} 1 & -1 \\ 0 & 0 \end{bmatrix}$$

$$A^2 - B^2 = \begin{bmatrix} 1 & 0 \\ 0 & 0 \end{bmatrix}^2 - \begin{bmatrix} 0 & 1 \\ 0 & 0 \end{bmatrix}^2 = \begin{bmatrix} 1 & 0 \\ 0 & 0 \end{bmatrix}\begin{bmatrix} 1 & 0 \\ 0 & 0 \end{bmatrix} - \begin{bmatrix} 0 & 1 \\ 0 & 0 \end{bmatrix}\begin{bmatrix} 0 & 1 \\ 0 & 0 \end{bmatrix}$$
$$= \begin{bmatrix} 1 & 0 \\ 0 & 0 \end{bmatrix} - \begin{bmatrix} 0 & 0 \\ 0 & 0 \end{bmatrix} = \begin{bmatrix} 1 & 0 \\ 0 & 0 \end{bmatrix}$$

67. $(3x+2)(2x-3) - (2-x) = 6x^2 - 9x + 4x - 6 - 2 + x = 6x^2 - 4x - 8$

68. $\dfrac{x^2+3x-4}{2x+5-(x+1)} = \dfrac{(x-1)(x+4)}{2x+5-x-1} = \dfrac{(x-1)(x+4)}{x+4} = x-1$

69. $\dfrac{1+\frac{1}{x}}{1-\frac{1}{x}} = \dfrac{x\left(1+\frac{1}{x}\right)}{x\left(1-\frac{1}{x}\right)} = \dfrac{x+1}{x-1}$

70. $\dfrac{1-x^{-1}}{1+x^{-1}} = \dfrac{1-\frac{1}{x}}{1+\frac{1}{x}} = \dfrac{x\left(1-\frac{1}{x}\right)}{x\left(1+\frac{1}{x}\right)} = \dfrac{x-1}{x+1}$

71.
$$\begin{aligned} s &= \frac{n(a+l)}{2} \\ 2s &= n(a+l) \\ \frac{2s}{n} &= a+l \\ \frac{2s}{n} - l &= a \end{aligned}$$

72.
$$\begin{aligned} y-y_1 &= m(x-x_1) \\ \frac{y-y_1}{m} &= x-x_1 \\ x_1 &= x - \frac{y-y_1}{m} \end{aligned}$$

Exercises 6.4 (page 598)

1. $AB = BA = I$ 2. is 3. $[I \mid A^{-1}]$ 4. $X = A^{-1}B$

5. $\left[\begin{array}{cc|cc} 3 & -4 & 1 & 0 \\ -2 & 3 & 0 & 1 \end{array}\right] \Rightarrow \left[\begin{array}{cc|cc} 1 & -\frac{4}{3} & \frac{1}{3} & 0 \\ -2 & 3 & 0 & 1 \end{array}\right] \Rightarrow \left[\begin{array}{cc|cc} 1 & -\frac{4}{3} & \frac{1}{3} & 0 \\ 0 & \frac{1}{3} & \frac{2}{3} & 1 \end{array}\right] \Rightarrow$

$\frac{1}{3}R_1 \Rightarrow R_1$ $\quad 2R_1 + R_2 \Rightarrow R_2$

$\left[\begin{array}{cc|cc} 1 & 0 & 3 & 4 \\ 0 & \frac{1}{3} & \frac{2}{3} & 1 \end{array}\right] \Rightarrow \left[\begin{array}{cc|cc} 1 & 0 & 3 & 4 \\ 0 & 1 & 2 & 3 \end{array}\right] \Rightarrow$ Inverse: $\begin{bmatrix} 3 & 4 \\ 2 & 3 \end{bmatrix}$

$4R_2 + R_1 \Rightarrow R_1$ $\quad 3R_2 \Rightarrow R_2$

6. $\left[\begin{array}{cc|cc} 2 & 3 & 1 & 0 \\ 3 & 5 & 0 & 1 \end{array}\right] \Rightarrow \left[\begin{array}{cc|cc} 1 & \frac{3}{2} & \frac{1}{2} & 0 \\ 3 & 5 & 0 & 1 \end{array}\right] \Rightarrow \left[\begin{array}{cc|cc} 1 & \frac{3}{2} & \frac{1}{2} & 0 \\ 0 & \frac{1}{2} & -\frac{3}{2} & 1 \end{array}\right] \Rightarrow$

$\frac{1}{2}R_1 \Rightarrow R_1$ $\quad -3R_1 + R_2 \Rightarrow R_2$

$\left[\begin{array}{cc|cc} 1 & 0 & 5 & -3 \\ 0 & \frac{1}{2} & -\frac{3}{2} & 1 \end{array}\right] \Rightarrow \left[\begin{array}{cc|cc} 1 & 0 & 5 & -3 \\ 0 & 1 & -3 & 2 \end{array}\right] \Rightarrow$ Inverse: $\begin{bmatrix} 5 & -3 \\ -3 & 2 \end{bmatrix}$

$-3R_2 + R_1 \Rightarrow R_1$ $\quad 2R_2 \Rightarrow R_2$

7. $\left[\begin{array}{cc|cc} 3 & 7 & 1 & 0 \\ 2 & 5 & 0 & 1 \end{array}\right] \Rightarrow \left[\begin{array}{cc|cc} 1 & \frac{7}{3} & \frac{1}{3} & 0 \\ 2 & 5 & 0 & 1 \end{array}\right] \Rightarrow \left[\begin{array}{cc|cc} 1 & \frac{7}{3} & \frac{1}{3} & 0 \\ 0 & \frac{1}{3} & -\frac{2}{3} & 1 \end{array}\right] \Rightarrow$

$\frac{1}{3}R_1 \Rightarrow R_1$ $\quad -2R_1 + R_2 \Rightarrow R_2$

$\left[\begin{array}{cc|cc} 1 & 0 & 5 & -7 \\ 0 & \frac{1}{3} & -\frac{2}{3} & 1 \end{array}\right] \Rightarrow \left[\begin{array}{cc|cc} 1 & 0 & 5 & -7 \\ 0 & 1 & -2 & 3 \end{array}\right] \Rightarrow$ Inverse: $\begin{bmatrix} 5 & -7 \\ -2 & 3 \end{bmatrix}$

$-7R_2 + R_1 \Rightarrow R_1$ $\quad 3R_2 \Rightarrow R_2$

8. $\left[\begin{array}{cc|cc} 1 & -2 & 1 & 0 \\ 2 & -5 & 0 & 1 \end{array}\right] \Rightarrow \left[\begin{array}{cc|cc} 1 & -2 & 1 & 0 \\ 0 & -1 & -2 & 1 \end{array}\right] \Rightarrow \left[\begin{array}{cc|cc} 1 & 0 & 5 & -2 \\ 0 & 1 & 2 & -1 \end{array}\right] \Rightarrow$ Inverse: $\begin{bmatrix} 5 & -2 \\ 2 & -1 \end{bmatrix}$

$-2R_1 + R_2 \Rightarrow R_2$ $\quad -2R_2 + R_1 \Rightarrow R_1$, $-R_2 \Rightarrow R_2$

9. $\left[\begin{array}{ccc|ccc} 1 & 0 & 3 & 1 & 0 & 0 \\ -1 & 1 & 3 & 0 & 1 & 0 \\ -2 & 1 & 1 & 0 & 0 & 1 \end{array}\right] \Rightarrow \left[\begin{array}{ccc|ccc} 1 & 0 & 3 & 1 & 0 & 0 \\ 0 & 1 & 6 & 1 & 1 & 0 \\ 0 & 1 & 7 & 2 & 0 & 1 \end{array}\right] \Rightarrow \left[\begin{array}{ccc|ccc} 1 & 0 & 3 & 1 & 0 & 0 \\ 0 & 1 & 6 & 1 & 1 & 0 \\ 0 & 0 & 1 & 1 & -1 & 1 \end{array}\right] \Rightarrow$

$R_1 + R_2 \Rightarrow R_2$, $2R_1 + R_3 \Rightarrow R_3$; $-R_2 + R_3 \Rightarrow R_3$

$\left[\begin{array}{ccc|ccc} 1 & 0 & 0 & -2 & 3 & -3 \\ 0 & 1 & 0 & -5 & 7 & -6 \\ 0 & 0 & 1 & 1 & -1 & 1 \end{array}\right] \Rightarrow \text{Inverse: } \begin{bmatrix} -2 & 3 & -3 \\ -5 & 7 & -6 \\ 1 & -1 & 1 \end{bmatrix}$

$-3R_3 + R_1 \Rightarrow R_1$, $-6R_3 + R_2 \Rightarrow R_2$

10. $\left[\begin{array}{ccc|ccc} 2 & 1 & -1 & 1 & 0 & 0 \\ 2 & 2 & -1 & 0 & 1 & 0 \\ -1 & -1 & 1 & 0 & 0 & 1 \end{array}\right] \Rightarrow \left[\begin{array}{ccc|ccc} 1 & 1 & -1 & 0 & 0 & -1 \\ 2 & 2 & -1 & 0 & 1 & 0 \\ 2 & 1 & -1 & 1 & 0 & 0 \end{array}\right] \Rightarrow \left[\begin{array}{ccc|ccc} 1 & 1 & -1 & 0 & 0 & -1 \\ 0 & 0 & 1 & 0 & 1 & 2 \\ 0 & -1 & 1 & 1 & 0 & 2 \end{array}\right]$

$-R_3 \Leftrightarrow R_1$; $-2R_1 + R_2 \Rightarrow R_2$, $-2R_1 + R_3 \Rightarrow R_3$

$\Rightarrow \left[\begin{array}{ccc|ccc} 1 & 1 & -1 & 0 & 0 & -1 \\ 0 & 1 & -1 & -1 & 0 & -2 \\ 0 & 0 & 1 & 0 & 1 & 2 \end{array}\right] \Rightarrow \left[\begin{array}{ccc|ccc} 1 & 0 & 0 & 1 & 0 & 1 \\ 0 & 1 & -1 & -1 & 0 & -2 \\ 0 & 0 & 1 & 0 & 1 & 2 \end{array}\right] \Rightarrow$

$-R_2 \Leftrightarrow R_3$; $-R_2 + R_1 \Rightarrow R_1$

$\left[\begin{array}{ccc|ccc} 1 & 0 & 0 & 1 & 0 & 1 \\ 0 & 1 & 0 & -1 & 1 & 0 \\ 0 & 0 & 1 & 0 & 1 & 2 \end{array}\right] \Rightarrow \text{Inverse} = \begin{bmatrix} 1 & 0 & 1 \\ -1 & 1 & 0 \\ 0 & 1 & 2 \end{bmatrix}$

$R_2 + R_3 \Rightarrow R_2$

11. $\left[\begin{array}{ccc|ccc} 3 & 2 & 1 & 1 & 0 & 0 \\ 1 & 1 & -1 & 0 & 1 & 0 \\ 4 & 3 & 1 & 0 & 0 & 1 \end{array}\right] \Rightarrow \left[\begin{array}{ccc|ccc} 1 & 1 & -1 & 0 & 1 & 0 \\ 3 & 2 & 1 & 1 & 0 & 0 \\ 4 & 3 & 1 & 0 & 0 & 1 \end{array}\right] \Rightarrow \left[\begin{array}{ccc|ccc} 1 & 1 & -1 & 0 & 1 & 0 \\ 0 & -1 & 4 & 1 & -3 & 0 \\ 0 & -1 & 5 & 0 & -4 & 1 \end{array}\right] \Rightarrow$

$R_1 \Leftrightarrow R_2$; $-3R_1 + R_2 \Rightarrow R_2$, $-4R_1 + R_3 \Rightarrow R_3$

$\left[\begin{array}{ccc|ccc} 1 & 1 & -1 & 0 & 1 & 0 \\ 0 & 1 & -4 & -1 & 3 & 0 \\ 0 & -1 & 5 & 0 & -4 & 1 \end{array}\right] \Rightarrow \left[\begin{array}{ccc|ccc} 1 & 0 & 3 & 1 & -2 & 0 \\ 0 & 1 & -4 & -1 & 3 & 0 \\ 0 & 0 & 1 & -1 & -1 & 1 \end{array}\right] \Rightarrow$

$-R_2 \Rightarrow R_2$; $-R_2 + R_1 \Rightarrow R_1$, $R_2 + R_3 \Rightarrow R_3$

$\left[\begin{array}{ccc|ccc} 1 & 0 & 0 & 4 & 1 & -3 \\ 0 & 1 & 0 & -5 & -1 & 4 \\ 0 & 0 & 1 & -1 & -1 & 1 \end{array}\right] \Rightarrow \text{Inverse} = \begin{bmatrix} 4 & 1 & -3 \\ -5 & -1 & 4 \\ -1 & -1 & 1 \end{bmatrix}$

$-3R_3 + R_1 \Rightarrow R_1$, $4R_3 + R_2 \Rightarrow R_2$

12. $\left[\begin{array}{ccc|ccc} -2 & 1 & -3 & 1 & 0 & 0 \\ 2 & 3 & 0 & 0 & 1 & 0 \\ 1 & 0 & 1 & 0 & 0 & 1 \end{array}\right] \Rightarrow \left[\begin{array}{ccc|ccc} 1 & 0 & 1 & 0 & 0 & 1 \\ 2 & 3 & 0 & 0 & 1 & 0 \\ -2 & 1 & -3 & 1 & 0 & 0 \end{array}\right] \Rightarrow \left[\begin{array}{ccc|ccc} 1 & 0 & 1 & 0 & 0 & 1 \\ 0 & 3 & -2 & 0 & 1 & -2 \\ 0 & 1 & -1 & 1 & 0 & 2 \end{array}\right] \Rightarrow$

$R_3 \Leftrightarrow R_1$ $\qquad$ $-2R_1 + R_2 \Rightarrow R_2$, $2R_1 + R_3 \Rightarrow R_3$

$\left[\begin{array}{ccc|ccc} 1 & 0 & 1 & 0 & 0 & 1 \\ 0 & 1 & -1 & 1 & 0 & 2 \\ 0 & 3 & -2 & 0 & 1 & -2 \end{array}\right] \Rightarrow \left[\begin{array}{ccc|ccc} 1 & 0 & 1 & 0 & 0 & 1 \\ 0 & 1 & -1 & 1 & 0 & 2 \\ 0 & 0 & 1 & -3 & 1 & -8 \end{array}\right] \Rightarrow$

$R_2 \Leftrightarrow R_3$ $\qquad$ $-3R_2 + R_3 \Rightarrow R_3$

$\left[\begin{array}{ccc|ccc} 1 & 0 & 0 & 3 & -1 & 9 \\ 0 & 1 & 0 & -2 & 1 & -6 \\ 0 & 0 & 1 & -3 & 1 & -8 \end{array}\right] \Rightarrow \text{Inverse} = \begin{bmatrix} 3 & -1 & 9 \\ -2 & 1 & -6 \\ -3 & 1 & -8 \end{bmatrix}$

$-R_3 + R_1 \Rightarrow R_1$, $R_3 + R_2 \Rightarrow R_2$

13. $\left[\begin{array}{ccc|ccc} 1 & 3 & 5 & 1 & 0 & 0 \\ 0 & 1 & 6 & 0 & 1 & 0 \\ 1 & 4 & 11 & 0 & 0 & 1 \end{array}\right] \Rightarrow \left[\begin{array}{ccc|ccc} 1 & 3 & 5 & 1 & 0 & 0 \\ 0 & 1 & 6 & 0 & 1 & 0 \\ 0 & 1 & 6 & -1 & 0 & 1 \end{array}\right] \Rightarrow \left[\begin{array}{ccc|ccc} 1 & 3 & 5 & 1 & 0 & 0 \\ 0 & 1 & 6 & 0 & 1 & 0 \\ 0 & 0 & 0 & -1 & -1 & 1 \end{array}\right]$

$-R_1 + R_3 \Rightarrow R_3$ $\qquad$ $-R_2 + R_3 \Rightarrow R_3$

Since the original matrix cannot be changed into the identity, there is no inverse matrix.

14. $\left[\begin{array}{ccc|ccc} 1 & 2 & 3 & 1 & 0 & 0 \\ 4 & 5 & 6 & 0 & 1 & 0 \\ 7 & 8 & 9 & 0 & 0 & 1 \end{array}\right] \Rightarrow \left[\begin{array}{ccc|ccc} 1 & 2 & 3 & 1 & 0 & 0 \\ 0 & -3 & -6 & -4 & 1 & 0 \\ 0 & -6 & -12 & -7 & 0 & 1 \end{array}\right] \Rightarrow \left[\begin{array}{ccc|ccc} 1 & 2 & 3 & 1 & 0 & 0 \\ 0 & -3 & -6 & -4 & 1 & 0 \\ 0 & 0 & 0 & 1 & -2 & 1 \end{array}\right]$

$-4R_1 + R_2 \Rightarrow R_2$, $-7R_1 + R_3 \Rightarrow R_3$ $\qquad$ $-2R_2 + R_3 \Rightarrow R_3$

Since the original matrix cannot be changed into the identity, there is no inverse matrix.

15. $\left[\begin{array}{ccc|ccc} 1 & 2 & 3 & 1 & 0 & 0 \\ 0 & 1 & 2 & 0 & 1 & 0 \\ 0 & 0 & 1 & 0 & 0 & 1 \end{array}\right] \Rightarrow \left[\begin{array}{ccc|ccc} 1 & 0 & -1 & 1 & -2 & 0 \\ 0 & 1 & 2 & 0 & 1 & 0 \\ 0 & 0 & 1 & 0 & 0 & 1 \end{array}\right] \Rightarrow \left[\begin{array}{ccc|ccc} 1 & 0 & 0 & 1 & -2 & 1 \\ 0 & 1 & 0 & 0 & 1 & -2 \\ 0 & 0 & 1 & 0 & 0 & 2 \end{array}\right] \Rightarrow$

$-2R_2 + R_1 \Rightarrow R_1$ $\qquad$ $R_3 + R_1 \Rightarrow R_1$, $-2R_3 + R_2 \Rightarrow R_2$

$\text{Inverse} = \begin{bmatrix} 1 & -2 & 1 \\ 0 & 1 & -2 \\ 0 & 0 & 1 \end{bmatrix}$

16. $\left[\begin{array}{ccc|ccc} 1 & 2 & 3 & 1 & 0 & 0 \\ 0 & 1 & 1 & 0 & 1 & 0 \\ 0 & -1 & 0 & 0 & 0 & 1 \end{array}\right] \Rightarrow \left[\begin{array}{ccc|ccc} 1 & 2 & 3 & 1 & 0 & 0 \\ 0 & -1 & 0 & 0 & 0 & 1 \\ 0 & 1 & 1 & 0 & 1 & 0 \end{array}\right] \Rightarrow \left[\begin{array}{ccc|ccc} 1 & 0 & 3 & 1 & 0 & 2 \\ 0 & 1 & 0 & 0 & 0 & -1 \\ 0 & 0 & 1 & 0 & 1 & 1 \end{array}\right] \Rightarrow$

$R_2 \Leftrightarrow R_3$ $\qquad$ $2R_2 + R_1 \Rightarrow R_1$, $R_2 + R_3 \Rightarrow R_3$, $-R_2 \Rightarrow R_2$

continued on next page...

16. continued

$$\left[\begin{array}{ccc|ccc} 1 & 0 & 0 & 1 & -3 & -1 \\ 0 & 1 & 0 & 0 & 0 & -1 \\ 0 & 0 & 1 & 0 & 1 & 1 \end{array}\right] \Rightarrow \text{Inverse} = \begin{bmatrix} 1 & -3 & -1 \\ 0 & 0 & -1 \\ 0 & 1 & 1 \end{bmatrix}$$

$-3R_3 + R_1 \Rightarrow R_1$

17. $$\left[\begin{array}{ccc|ccc} 1 & 6 & 4 & 1 & 0 & 0 \\ 1 & -2 & -5 & 0 & 1 & 0 \\ 2 & 4 & -1 & 0 & 0 & 1 \end{array}\right] \Rightarrow \left[\begin{array}{ccc|ccc} 1 & 6 & 4 & 1 & 0 & 0 \\ 0 & -8 & -9 & -1 & 1 & 0 \\ 0 & -8 & -9 & -2 & 0 & 1 \end{array}\right] \Rightarrow \left[\begin{array}{ccc|ccc} 1 & 6 & 4 & 1 & 0 & 0 \\ 0 & -8 & -9 & -1 & 1 & 0 \\ 0 & 0 & 0 & -1 & -1 & 1 \end{array}\right]$$

$-R_1 + R_2 \Rightarrow R_2$ $\quad -R_2 + R_3 \Rightarrow R_3$

$-2R_1 + R_3 \Rightarrow R_3$

Since the original matrix cannot be changed into the identity, there is no inverse matrix.

18. $$\left[\begin{array}{ccc|ccc} 1 & 1 & 1 & 1 & 0 & 0 \\ 1 & 0 & -1 & 0 & 1 & 0 \\ 1 & 2 & 3 & 0 & 0 & 1 \end{array}\right] \Rightarrow \left[\begin{array}{ccc|ccc} 1 & 1 & 1 & 1 & 0 & 0 \\ 0 & -1 & -2 & -1 & 1 & 0 \\ 0 & 1 & 2 & -1 & 0 & 1 \end{array}\right] \Rightarrow \left[\begin{array}{ccc|ccc} 1 & 1 & 1 & 1 & 0 & 0 \\ 0 & -1 & -2 & -1 & 1 & 0 \\ 0 & 0 & 0 & -2 & 1 & 1 \end{array}\right]$$

$-R_1 + R_2 \Rightarrow R_2$ $\quad R_2 + R_3 \Rightarrow R_3$

$-R_1 + R_3 \Rightarrow R_3$

Since the original matrix cannot be changed into the identity, there is no inverse matrix.

19. Inverse $= \begin{bmatrix} 1 & -2 & 1 & 0 \\ 0 & 1 & -2 & 1 \\ 0 & 0 & 1 & -2 \\ 0 & 0 & 0 & 1 \end{bmatrix}$

20. Inverse $= \begin{bmatrix} 1 & 0 & 0 & 0 \\ -1 & 1 & 0 & 0 \\ 0 & -1 & 1 & 0 \\ 1 & 0 & -2 & 1 \end{bmatrix}$

21. Inverse $= \begin{bmatrix} 8 & -2 & -6 \\ -5 & 2 & 4 \\ 2 & 0 & -2 \end{bmatrix}$

22. Inverse $= \begin{bmatrix} -0.2 & 1.2 & 1.6 \\ -0.2 & -0.8 & -0.4 \\ 0.4 & 1.6 & 2.8 \end{bmatrix}$

23. Inverse $= \begin{bmatrix} -2.5 & 5 & 3 & 5.5 \\ 5.5 & -8 & -6 & -9.5 \\ -1 & 3 & 1 & 3 \\ -5.5 & 9 & 6 & 10.5 \end{bmatrix}$

24. Inverse $= \begin{bmatrix} 1 & 0 & 0 & 0 \\ -2 & 1 & 0 & 0 \\ 1 & -2 & 1 & 0 \\ 0 & 1 & -2 & 1 \end{bmatrix}$

25. $\begin{bmatrix} 3 & -4 \\ -2 & 3 \end{bmatrix}\begin{bmatrix} x \\ y \end{bmatrix} = \begin{bmatrix} 1 \\ 5 \end{bmatrix}$

$$\begin{bmatrix} x \\ y \end{bmatrix} = \begin{bmatrix} 3 & -4 \\ -2 & 3 \end{bmatrix}^{-1}\begin{bmatrix} 1 \\ 5 \end{bmatrix}$$

$$\begin{bmatrix} x \\ y \end{bmatrix} = \begin{bmatrix} 3 & 4 \\ 2 & 3 \end{bmatrix}\begin{bmatrix} 1 \\ 5 \end{bmatrix}$$

$$\begin{bmatrix} x \\ y \end{bmatrix} = \begin{bmatrix} 23 \\ 17 \end{bmatrix}$$

26. $\begin{bmatrix} 3 & -4 \\ -2 & 3 \end{bmatrix}\begin{bmatrix} x \\ y \end{bmatrix} = \begin{bmatrix} -1 \\ 3 \end{bmatrix}$

$$\begin{bmatrix} x \\ y \end{bmatrix} = \begin{bmatrix} 3 & -4 \\ -2 & 3 \end{bmatrix}^{-1}\begin{bmatrix} -1 \\ 3 \end{bmatrix}$$

$$\begin{bmatrix} x \\ y \end{bmatrix} = \begin{bmatrix} 3 & 4 \\ 2 & 3 \end{bmatrix}\begin{bmatrix} -1 \\ 3 \end{bmatrix}$$

$$\begin{bmatrix} x \\ y \end{bmatrix} = \begin{bmatrix} 9 \\ 7 \end{bmatrix}$$

27. $\begin{bmatrix} 3 & -4 \\ -2 & 3 \end{bmatrix}\begin{bmatrix} x \\ y \end{bmatrix} = \begin{bmatrix} 0 \\ 0 \end{bmatrix}$

$$\begin{bmatrix} x \\ y \end{bmatrix} = \begin{bmatrix} 3 & -4 \\ -2 & 3 \end{bmatrix}^{-1}\begin{bmatrix} 0 \\ 0 \end{bmatrix}$$
$$\begin{bmatrix} x \\ y \end{bmatrix} = \begin{bmatrix} 3 & 4 \\ 2 & 3 \end{bmatrix}\begin{bmatrix} 0 \\ 0 \end{bmatrix}$$
$$\begin{bmatrix} x \\ y \end{bmatrix} = \begin{bmatrix} 0 \\ 0 \end{bmatrix}$$

28. $\begin{bmatrix} 3 & -4 \\ -2 & 3 \end{bmatrix}\begin{bmatrix} x \\ y \end{bmatrix} = \begin{bmatrix} -3 \\ -2 \end{bmatrix}$

$$\begin{bmatrix} x \\ y \end{bmatrix} = \begin{bmatrix} 3 & -4 \\ -2 & 3 \end{bmatrix}^{-1}\begin{bmatrix} -3 \\ -2 \end{bmatrix}$$
$$\begin{bmatrix} x \\ y \end{bmatrix} = \begin{bmatrix} 3 & 4 \\ 2 & 3 \end{bmatrix}\begin{bmatrix} -3 \\ -2 \end{bmatrix}$$
$$\begin{bmatrix} x \\ y \end{bmatrix} = \begin{bmatrix} -17 \\ -12 \end{bmatrix}$$

29. $\begin{bmatrix} 2 & 1 & -1 \\ 2 & 2 & -1 \\ -1 & -1 & 1 \end{bmatrix}\begin{bmatrix} x \\ y \\ z \end{bmatrix} = \begin{bmatrix} 2 \\ 4 \\ -1 \end{bmatrix}$

$$\begin{bmatrix} x \\ y \\ z \end{bmatrix} = \begin{bmatrix} 2 & 1 & -1 \\ 2 & 2 & -1 \\ -1 & -1 & 1 \end{bmatrix}^{-1}\begin{bmatrix} 2 \\ 4 \\ -1 \end{bmatrix}$$
$$\begin{bmatrix} x \\ y \\ z \end{bmatrix} = \begin{bmatrix} 1 & 0 & 1 \\ -1 & 1 & 0 \\ 0 & 1 & 2 \end{bmatrix}\begin{bmatrix} 2 \\ 4 \\ -1 \end{bmatrix} = \begin{bmatrix} 1 \\ 2 \\ 2 \end{bmatrix}$$

30. $\begin{bmatrix} 2 & 1 & -1 \\ 2 & 2 & -1 \\ -1 & -1 & 1 \end{bmatrix}\begin{bmatrix} x \\ y \\ z \end{bmatrix} = \begin{bmatrix} 3 \\ -1 \\ 4 \end{bmatrix}$

$$\begin{bmatrix} x \\ y \\ z \end{bmatrix} = \begin{bmatrix} 2 & 1 & -1 \\ 2 & 2 & -1 \\ -1 & -1 & 1 \end{bmatrix}^{-1}\begin{bmatrix} 3 \\ -1 \\ 4 \end{bmatrix}$$
$$\begin{bmatrix} x \\ y \\ z \end{bmatrix} = \begin{bmatrix} 1 & 0 & 1 \\ -1 & 1 & 0 \\ 0 & 1 & 2 \end{bmatrix}\begin{bmatrix} 3 \\ -1 \\ 4 \end{bmatrix} = \begin{bmatrix} 7 \\ -4 \\ 7 \end{bmatrix}$$

31. $\begin{bmatrix} -2 & 1 & -3 \\ 2 & 3 & 0 \\ 1 & 0 & 1 \end{bmatrix}\begin{bmatrix} x \\ y \\ z \end{bmatrix} = \begin{bmatrix} 2 \\ -3 \\ 5 \end{bmatrix}$

$$\begin{bmatrix} x \\ y \\ z \end{bmatrix} = \begin{bmatrix} -2 & 1 & -3 \\ 2 & 3 & 0 \\ 1 & 0 & 1 \end{bmatrix}^{-1}\begin{bmatrix} 2 \\ -3 \\ 5 \end{bmatrix}$$
$$\begin{bmatrix} x \\ y \\ z \end{bmatrix} = \begin{bmatrix} 3 & -1 & 9 \\ -2 & 1 & -6 \\ -3 & 1 & -8 \end{bmatrix}\begin{bmatrix} 2 \\ -3 \\ 5 \end{bmatrix} = \begin{bmatrix} 54 \\ -37 \\ -49 \end{bmatrix}$$

32. $\begin{bmatrix} -2 & 1 & -3 \\ 2 & 3 & 0 \\ 1 & 0 & 1 \end{bmatrix}\begin{bmatrix} x \\ y \\ z \end{bmatrix} = \begin{bmatrix} 5 \\ 1 \\ -2 \end{bmatrix}$

$$\begin{bmatrix} x \\ y \\ z \end{bmatrix} = \begin{bmatrix} -2 & 1 & -3 \\ 2 & 3 & 0 \\ 1 & 0 & 1 \end{bmatrix}^{-1}\begin{bmatrix} 5 \\ 1 \\ -2 \end{bmatrix}$$

$$\begin{bmatrix} x \\ y \\ z \end{bmatrix} = \begin{bmatrix} 3 & -1 & 9 \\ -2 & 1 & -6 \\ -3 & 1 & -8 \end{bmatrix}\begin{bmatrix} 5 \\ 1 \\ -2 \end{bmatrix} = \begin{bmatrix} -4 \\ 3 \\ 2 \end{bmatrix}$$

33. $\begin{bmatrix} 5 & 3 \\ -7 & 5 \end{bmatrix}\begin{bmatrix} x \\ y \end{bmatrix} = \begin{bmatrix} 13 \\ -9 \end{bmatrix}$

$$\begin{bmatrix} x \\ y \end{bmatrix} = \begin{bmatrix} 5 & 3 \\ -7 & 5 \end{bmatrix}^{-1}\begin{bmatrix} 13 \\ -9 \end{bmatrix}$$

$$\begin{bmatrix} x \\ y \end{bmatrix} = \begin{bmatrix} 2 \\ 1 \end{bmatrix}$$

34. $\begin{bmatrix} 8 & -3 \\ -3 & 2 \end{bmatrix}\begin{bmatrix} x \\ y \end{bmatrix} = \begin{bmatrix} 7 \\ 0 \end{bmatrix}$

$$\begin{bmatrix} x \\ y \end{bmatrix} = \begin{bmatrix} 8 & -3 \\ -3 & 2 \end{bmatrix}^{-1}\begin{bmatrix} 7 \\ 0 \end{bmatrix}$$

$$\begin{bmatrix} x \\ y \end{bmatrix} = \begin{bmatrix} 2 \\ 3 \end{bmatrix}$$

35. $\begin{bmatrix} 5 & 2 & 3 \\ 2 & 0 & 5 \\ 3 & 0 & 1 \end{bmatrix}\begin{bmatrix} x \\ y \\ z \end{bmatrix} = \begin{bmatrix} 12 \\ 7 \\ 4 \end{bmatrix}$

$$\begin{bmatrix} x \\ y \\ z \end{bmatrix} = \begin{bmatrix} 5 & 2 & 3 \\ 2 & 0 & 5 \\ 3 & 0 & 1 \end{bmatrix}^{-1}\begin{bmatrix} 12 \\ 7 \\ 4 \end{bmatrix} = \begin{bmatrix} 1 \\ 2 \\ 1 \end{bmatrix}$$

36. $\begin{bmatrix} 3 & 2 & -1 \\ 5 & -2 & 0 \\ 3 & 1 & 1 \end{bmatrix}\begin{bmatrix} x \\ y \\ z \end{bmatrix} = \begin{bmatrix} 0 \\ 5 \\ 6 \end{bmatrix}$

$$\begin{bmatrix} x \\ y \\ z \end{bmatrix} = \begin{bmatrix} 3 & 2 & -1 \\ 5 & -2 & 0 \\ 3 & 1 & 1 \end{bmatrix}^{-1}\begin{bmatrix} 0 \\ 5 \\ 6 \end{bmatrix} = \begin{bmatrix} 1 \\ 0 \\ 3 \end{bmatrix}$$

37. $\begin{bmatrix} 23 & 27 \\ 21 & 22 \end{bmatrix}\begin{bmatrix} x \\ y \end{bmatrix} = \begin{bmatrix} 127 \\ 108 \end{bmatrix}$

$$\begin{bmatrix} x \\ y \end{bmatrix} = \begin{bmatrix} 23 & 27 \\ 21 & 22 \end{bmatrix}^{-1}\begin{bmatrix} 127 \\ 108 \end{bmatrix}$$

$\begin{bmatrix} x \\ y \end{bmatrix} = \begin{bmatrix} 2 \\ 3 \end{bmatrix} \Rightarrow$ 2 of model A and 3 of model B can be made.

38. $\begin{bmatrix} \frac{1}{3} & \frac{1}{4} & \frac{1}{6} \\ 1 & \frac{1}{2} & \frac{2}{5} \\ \frac{1}{12} & \frac{1}{5} & \frac{1}{10} \end{bmatrix} \begin{bmatrix} x \\ y \\ z \end{bmatrix} = \begin{bmatrix} 115 \\ 280 \\ 65 \end{bmatrix}$

$$\begin{bmatrix} x \\ y \\ z \end{bmatrix} = \begin{bmatrix} \frac{1}{3} & \frac{1}{4} & \frac{1}{6} \\ 1 & \frac{1}{2} & \frac{2}{5} \\ \frac{1}{12} & \frac{1}{5} & \frac{1}{10} \end{bmatrix}^{-1} \begin{bmatrix} 115 \\ 280 \\ 65 \end{bmatrix} = \begin{bmatrix} 120 \\ 200 \\ 150 \end{bmatrix}$$ $\Rightarrow$ 120 coats, 200 shirts, and 150 slacks should be made.

39. $AB = \begin{bmatrix} 17 \\ 43 \end{bmatrix}$

$A^{-1}AB = IB = B$

$B = A^{-1}AB = \begin{bmatrix} 1 & 1 \\ 2 & 3 \end{bmatrix}^{-1} \begin{bmatrix} 17 \\ 43 \end{bmatrix}$

$= \begin{bmatrix} 8 \\ 9 \end{bmatrix}$ $\Rightarrow$ "HI"

40. $AY = \begin{bmatrix} 30 \\ 122 \\ 49 \end{bmatrix}$

$A^{-1}AY = IY = Y$

$Y = A^{-1}AY = \begin{bmatrix} 1 & 1 & 0 \\ 2 & 3 & 3 \\ 1 & 1 & 1 \end{bmatrix}^{-1} \begin{bmatrix} 30 \\ 122 \\ 49 \end{bmatrix}$

$= \begin{bmatrix} 25 \\ 5 \\ 19 \end{bmatrix}$ $\Rightarrow$ "YES"

41. No

42. Yes

43. $A^2 = \begin{bmatrix} -1 & -1 \\ 1 & 1 \end{bmatrix} \begin{bmatrix} -1 & -1 \\ 1 & 1 \end{bmatrix} = \begin{bmatrix} 0 & 0 \\ 0 & 0 \end{bmatrix}$

44. $I - A = \begin{bmatrix} 2 & 1 \\ -1 & 0 \end{bmatrix}, I + A = \begin{bmatrix} 0 & -1 \\ 1 & 2 \end{bmatrix};$

$(I - A)(I + A) = \begin{bmatrix} 2 & 1 \\ -1 & 0 \end{bmatrix} \begin{bmatrix} 0 & -1 \\ 1 & 2 \end{bmatrix} = \begin{bmatrix} 1 & 0 \\ 0 & 1 \end{bmatrix}$

Since the product is the identity, they are inverse matrices.

45. $\begin{bmatrix} 1 & 0 & 0 \\ -2 & -3 & -2 \\ 3 & 6 & 1 \end{bmatrix} \begin{bmatrix} x \\ y \\ z \end{bmatrix} = \begin{bmatrix} 0 \\ 0 \\ 0 \end{bmatrix}$

$$\begin{bmatrix} x \\ y \\ z \end{bmatrix} = \begin{bmatrix} 1 & 0 & 0 \\ -2 & -3 & -2 \\ 3 & 6 & 1 \end{bmatrix}^{-1} \begin{bmatrix} 0 \\ 0 \\ 0 \end{bmatrix} = \begin{bmatrix} 0 \\ 0 \\ 0 \end{bmatrix}$$

46. Cannot be solved using inverse matrix.

Solution is $\begin{bmatrix} 0 \\ 0 \\ 0 \end{bmatrix}$.

47.
$$AB = AC$$
$$A^{-1}AB = A^{-1}AC$$
$$IB = IC$$
$$B = C$$

48. $\left[\begin{array}{cc|cc} a & b & 1 & 0 \\ c & d & 0 & 1 \end{array}\right] \Rightarrow \left[\begin{array}{cc|cc} 1 & \frac{b}{a} & \frac{1}{a} & 0 \\ c & d & 0 & 1 \end{array}\right] \Rightarrow \left[\begin{array}{cc|cc} 1 & \frac{b}{a} & \frac{1}{a} & 0 \\ 0 & \frac{ad-bc}{a} & -\frac{c}{a} & 1 \end{array}\right] \Rightarrow$

$\frac{1}{a}R_1 \Rightarrow R_1$ $\quad -cR_1 + R_2 \Rightarrow R_2$

$\left[\begin{array}{cc|cc} 1 & \frac{b}{a} & \frac{1}{a} & 0 \\ 0 & 1 & -\frac{c}{ad-bc} & \frac{a}{ad-bc} \end{array}\right] \Rightarrow \left[\begin{array}{cc|cc} 1 & 0 & \frac{d}{ad-bc} & -\frac{b}{ad-bc} \\ 0 & 1 & -\frac{c}{ad-bc} & \frac{a}{ad-bc} \end{array}\right] \Rightarrow$ Inverse: $\begin{bmatrix} \frac{d}{ad-bc} & -\frac{b}{ad-bc} \\ -\frac{c}{ad-bc} & \frac{a}{ad-bc} \end{bmatrix}$

$\frac{a}{ad-bc}R_2 \Rightarrow R_2$ $\quad -\frac{b}{a}R_2 + R_1 \Rightarrow R_1$

The inverse will be defined if and only if the denominator, $ad - bc$, is not equal to 0.

49. $(I - B)(I + B) = I^2 + IB - BI - B^2$
$= I + B - B - B^2$
$= I - B^2$
$= I - \mathbf{0} = I \Rightarrow$ Thus, $I - B$ and $I + B$ are inverses.

50. $(I - C)(I + C + C^2) = I^2 + IC + IC^2 - CI - C^2 - C^3$
$= I + C + C^2 - C - C^2 - C^3$
$= I - C^3$
$= I - \mathbf{0} = I \Rightarrow$ Thus, $I - C$ and $I + C + C^2$ are inverses.

51. $y = \frac{3x-5}{x^2-4} = \frac{3x-5}{(x+2)(x-2)}$
domain: $(-\infty, -2) \cup (-2, 2) \cup (2, \infty)$

52. $y = \frac{3x-5}{x^2+4}$
domain: $(-\infty, \infty)$

53. $y = \frac{3x-5}{\sqrt{x^2+4}}$
domain: $(-\infty, \infty)$

54. $y = \frac{3x-5}{\sqrt{x^2-4}}$
domain: $(-\infty, -2) \cup (2, \infty)$

55. $y = x^2$; range: $[0, \infty)$

56. $y = x^3$; range: $(-\infty, \infty)$

57. $y = \log x$; range: all $(-\infty, \infty)$

58. $y = 2^x$; range: $(0, \infty)$

Exercises 6.5 (page 610)

1. $|A|$, det A

2. $ad - bc$

3. 0

4. $|A|$

5. 0

6. coefficient matrix

7. $\begin{vmatrix} 2 & 1 \\ -2 & 3 \end{vmatrix} = (2)(3) - (1)(-2)$
$= 6 - (-2) = 8$

8. $\begin{vmatrix} -3 & -6 \\ 2 & -5 \end{vmatrix} = (-3)(-5) - (-6)(2)$
$= 15 - (-12) = 27$

9. $\begin{vmatrix} 2 & -3 \\ -3 & 5 \end{vmatrix} = (2)(5) - (-3)(-3)$
$= 10 - 9 = 1$

10. $\begin{vmatrix} 5 & 8 \\ -6 & -2 \end{vmatrix} = (5)(-2) - (8)(-6)$
$= -10 - (-48) = 38$

11. $M_{21} = \begin{vmatrix} -2 & 3 \\ 8 & 9 \end{vmatrix} = (-2)(9) - (3)(8)$
$= -18 - 24 = -42$

12. $M_{13} = \begin{vmatrix} 4 & 5 \\ -7 & 8 \end{vmatrix} = (4)(8) - (5)(-7)$
$= 32 - (-35) = 67$

13. $M_{33} = \begin{vmatrix} 1 & -2 \\ 4 & 5 \end{vmatrix} = (1)(5) - (-2)(4)$
$= 5 + 8 = 13$

14. $M_{32} = \begin{vmatrix} 1 & 3 \\ 4 & -6 \end{vmatrix} = (1)(-6) - (3)(4)$
$= -6 - 12 = -18$

15. $C_{21} = -\begin{vmatrix} -2 & 3 \\ 8 & 9 \end{vmatrix} = -[(-2)(9) - (3)(8)]$
$= -[-18 - 24] = 42$

16. $C_{13} = \begin{vmatrix} 4 & 5 \\ -7 & 8 \end{vmatrix} = (4)(8) - (5)(-7)$
$= 32 - (-35) = 67$

17. $C_{33} = \begin{vmatrix} 1 & -2 \\ 4 & 5 \end{vmatrix} = (1)(5) - (-2)(4)$
$= 5 + 8 = 13$

18. $C_{32} = -\begin{vmatrix} 1 & 3 \\ 4 & -6 \end{vmatrix} = -[(1)(-6) - (3)(4)]$
$= -[-6 - 12] = 18$

19. $\begin{vmatrix} 2 & -3 & 5 \\ -2 & 1 & 3 \\ 1 & 3 & -2 \end{vmatrix} = 2\begin{vmatrix} 1 & 3 \\ 3 & -2 \end{vmatrix} - (-3)\begin{vmatrix} -2 & 3 \\ 1 & -2 \end{vmatrix} + 5\begin{vmatrix} -2 & 1 \\ 1 & 3 \end{vmatrix}$
$= 2(-11) + 3(1) + 5(-7) = -22 + 3 - 35 = -54$

20. $\begin{vmatrix} 1 & 3 & 1 \\ -2 & 5 & 3 \\ 3 & -2 & -2 \end{vmatrix} = 1\begin{vmatrix} 5 & 3 \\ -2 & -2 \end{vmatrix} - 3\begin{vmatrix} -2 & 3 \\ 3 & -2 \end{vmatrix} + 1\begin{vmatrix} -2 & 5 \\ 3 & -2 \end{vmatrix}$
$= 1(-4) - 3(-5) + 1(-11) = -4 + 15 - 11 = 0$

21. $\begin{vmatrix} 1 & -1 & 2 \\ 2 & 1 & 3 \\ 1 & 1 & -1 \end{vmatrix} = 1\begin{vmatrix} 1 & 3 \\ 1 & -1 \end{vmatrix} - (-1)\begin{vmatrix} 2 & 3 \\ 1 & -1 \end{vmatrix} + 2\begin{vmatrix} 2 & 1 \\ 1 & 1 \end{vmatrix}$
$= 1(-4) + 1(-5) + 2(1) = -4 - 5 + 2 = -7$

22. $\begin{vmatrix} 1 & 3 & 1 \\ 2 & 1 & -1 \\ 2 & -1 & 1 \end{vmatrix} = 1\begin{vmatrix} 1 & -1 \\ -1 & 1 \end{vmatrix} - 3\begin{vmatrix} 2 & -1 \\ 2 & 1 \end{vmatrix} + 1\begin{vmatrix} 2 & 1 \\ 2 & -1 \end{vmatrix}$
$= 1(0) - 3(4) + 1(-4) = 0 - 12 - 4 = -16$

23. $\begin{vmatrix} 2 & 1 & -1 \\ 1 & 3 & 5 \\ 2 & -5 & 3 \end{vmatrix} = 2\begin{vmatrix} 3 & 5 \\ -5 & 3 \end{vmatrix} - 1\begin{vmatrix} 1 & 5 \\ 2 & 3 \end{vmatrix} + (-1)\begin{vmatrix} 1 & 3 \\ 2 & -5 \end{vmatrix}$
$= 2(34) - 1(-7) - 1(-11) = 68 + 7 + 11 = 86$

24. $\begin{vmatrix} 3 & 1 & -2 \\ -3 & 2 & 1 \\ 1 & 3 & 0 \end{vmatrix} = 3\begin{vmatrix} 2 & 1 \\ 3 & 0 \end{vmatrix} - 1\begin{vmatrix} -3 & 1 \\ 1 & 0 \end{vmatrix} + (-2)\begin{vmatrix} -3 & 2 \\ 1 & 3 \end{vmatrix}$

$= 3(-3) - 1(-1) - 2(-11) = -9 + 1 + 22 = 14$

25. $\begin{vmatrix} 0 & 1 & -3 \\ -3 & 5 & 2 \\ 2 & -5 & 3 \end{vmatrix} = 0\begin{vmatrix} 5 & 2 \\ -5 & 3 \end{vmatrix} - 1\begin{vmatrix} -3 & 2 \\ 2 & 3 \end{vmatrix} + (-3)\begin{vmatrix} -3 & 5 \\ 2 & -5 \end{vmatrix}$

$= 0 - 1(-13) - 3(5) = 0 + 13 - 15 = -2$

26. $\begin{vmatrix} 1 & -7 & -2 \\ -2 & 0 & 3 \\ -1 & 7 & 1 \end{vmatrix} = 1\begin{vmatrix} 0 & 3 \\ 7 & 1 \end{vmatrix} - (-7)\begin{vmatrix} -2 & 3 \\ -1 & 1 \end{vmatrix} + (-2)\begin{vmatrix} -2 & 0 \\ -1 & 7 \end{vmatrix}$

$= 1(-21) + 7(1) - 2(-14) = -21 + 7 + 28 = 14$

27. $\begin{vmatrix} 0 & 0 & 1 & 0 \\ -2 & 1 & 0 & 1 \\ 1 & 0 & 1 & 2 \\ 2 & 0 & 1 & 2 \end{vmatrix} = 0(***) - 0(***) + 1\begin{vmatrix} -2 & 1 & 1 \\ 1 & 0 & 2 \\ 2 & 0 & 2 \end{vmatrix} - 0(***)$

$= 1\left(-2\begin{vmatrix} 0 & 2 \\ 0 & 2 \end{vmatrix} - 1\begin{vmatrix} 1 & 2 \\ 2 & 2 \end{vmatrix} + 1\begin{vmatrix} 1 & 0 \\ 2 & 0 \end{vmatrix}\right) = -2(0) - 1(-2) + 1(0) = 2$

28. Expand along 1st column...

$\begin{vmatrix} 1 & 0 & -2 & 1 \\ 0 & 1 & 0 & 1 \\ 0 & 3 & -1 & 2 \\ 0 & -1 & 0 & 1 \end{vmatrix} = 1\begin{vmatrix} 1 & 0 & 1 \\ 3 & -1 & 2 \\ -1 & 0 & 1 \end{vmatrix} - 0(***) + 0(***) - 0(***)$

$= 1\left(1\begin{vmatrix} -1 & 2 \\ 0 & 1 \end{vmatrix} - 0\begin{vmatrix} 3 & 2 \\ -1 & 1 \end{vmatrix} + 1\begin{vmatrix} 3 & -1 \\ -1 & 0 \end{vmatrix}\right) = 1(-1) - 0 + 1(-1) = -2$

29. $\begin{vmatrix} 10 & 20 & 10 & 30 \\ -2 & 1 & -3 & 1 \\ -1 & 0 & 1 & -2 \\ 2 & -1 & -1 & 3 \end{vmatrix} = \begin{vmatrix} 10 & 20 & 10 & 30 \\ 0 & 0 & -4 & 4 \\ 0 & 2 & 2 & 1 \\ 0 & -5 & -3 & -3 \end{vmatrix} \quad \begin{matrix} R_2 + R_4 \\ R_1 + R_3 \\ -2R_1 + R_4 \end{matrix}$

$= 10\begin{vmatrix} 0 & -4 & 4 \\ 2 & 2 & 1 \\ -5 & -3 & -3 \end{vmatrix}$ (expand along first column)

$= 10\left(0\begin{vmatrix} 2 & 1 \\ -3 & -3 \end{vmatrix} - (-4)\begin{vmatrix} 2 & 1 \\ -5 & -3 \end{vmatrix} + 4\begin{vmatrix} 2 & 2 \\ -5 & -3 \end{vmatrix}\right)$

$= 10[0 + 4(-1) + 4(4)] = 10(12) = 120$

30. $\begin{vmatrix} -1 & 3 & -2 & 5 \\ 2 & 1 & 0 & 1 \\ 1 & 3 & -2 & 5 \\ 2 & -1 & 0 & -1 \end{vmatrix} = \begin{vmatrix} -1 & 3 & -2 & 5 \\ 0 & 7 & -4 & 11 \\ 0 & 6 & -4 & 10 \\ 0 & 5 & -4 & 9 \end{vmatrix} \begin{matrix} \\ 2R_1 + R_2 \\ R_1 + R_3 \\ 2R_1 + R_4 \end{matrix}$

$= 1\begin{vmatrix} 7 & -4 & 11 \\ 6 & -4 & 10 \\ 5 & -4 & 9 \end{vmatrix}$ (expand along first column)

$= 1\left(7\begin{vmatrix} -4 & 11 \\ -4 & 10 \end{vmatrix} - (-4)\begin{vmatrix} 6 & 10 \\ 5 & 9 \end{vmatrix} + 11\begin{vmatrix} 6 & -4 \\ 5 & -4 \end{vmatrix}\right)$

$= 7(4) + 4(4) + 11(-4) = 0$

31. R_1 and R_2 have been switched. This multiplies the determinant by -1. TRUE

32. R_1 has been multiplied by $\frac{1}{2}$. This multiplies the determinant by $\frac{1}{2}$. FALSE

33. R_1 and R_2 have both been multiplied by -1. This multiplies the determinant by -1 twice. FALSE

34. R_1 has been added to R_2. This leaves the determinant unchanged. TRUE

35. R_1 and R_2 have been switched. This multiplies the determinant by -1. However, R_3 has been multiplied by -1, which also multiplies the determinant by -1. Thus, the determinant remains equal to 3.

36. R_1 has been multiplied by 5, which multiplies the determinant by 5. R_3 has been multiplied by 3, which multiplies the determinant by 3. R_2 has been multiplied by -1, which multiplies the determinant by -1. Thus, the determinant $= 5(3)(-1) \cdot 3 = -45$.

37. R_1 has been added to R_3. This leaves the determinant equal to 3.

38. R_1 and R_3 were switched, and then R_2 and the new R_3 were switched. Both switches multiply the determinant by -1. Thus, the determinant remains equal to 3.

39. $x = \dfrac{\begin{vmatrix} 7 & 2 \\ -4 & -3 \end{vmatrix}}{\begin{vmatrix} 3 & 2 \\ 2 & -3 \end{vmatrix}} = \dfrac{-13}{-13} = 1 \quad y = \dfrac{\begin{vmatrix} 3 & 7 \\ 2 & -4 \end{vmatrix}}{\begin{vmatrix} 3 & 2 \\ 2 & -3 \end{vmatrix}} = \dfrac{-26}{-13} = 2$

40. $x = \dfrac{\begin{vmatrix} -6 & -5 \\ -1 & 2 \end{vmatrix}}{\begin{vmatrix} 1 & -5 \\ 3 & 2 \end{vmatrix}} = \dfrac{-17}{17} = -1 \quad y = \dfrac{\begin{vmatrix} 1 & -6 \\ 3 & -1 \end{vmatrix}}{\begin{vmatrix} 1 & -5 \\ 3 & 2 \end{vmatrix}} = \dfrac{17}{17} = 1$

41. $x = \dfrac{\begin{vmatrix} 3 & -1 \\ 9 & -7 \end{vmatrix}}{\begin{vmatrix} 1 & -1 \\ 3 & -7 \end{vmatrix}} = \dfrac{-12}{-4} = 3 \quad y = \dfrac{\begin{vmatrix} 1 & 3 \\ 3 & 9 \end{vmatrix}}{\begin{vmatrix} 1 & -1 \\ 3 & -7 \end{vmatrix}} = \dfrac{0}{-4} = 0$

42. $x = \dfrac{\begin{vmatrix} -6 & -1 \\ 0 & 1 \end{vmatrix}}{\begin{vmatrix} 2 & -1 \\ 1 & 1 \end{vmatrix}} = \dfrac{-6}{3} = -2 \quad y = \dfrac{\begin{vmatrix} 2 & -6 \\ 1 & 0 \end{vmatrix}}{\begin{vmatrix} 2 & -1 \\ 1 & 1 \end{vmatrix}} = \dfrac{6}{3} = 2$

43. $x = \dfrac{\begin{vmatrix} 2 & 2 & 1 \\ 2 & -1 & 1 \\ 4 & 1 & 3 \end{vmatrix}}{\begin{vmatrix} 1 & 2 & 1 \\ 1 & -1 & 1 \\ 1 & 1 & 3 \end{vmatrix}} = \dfrac{-6}{-6} = 1 \quad y = \dfrac{\begin{vmatrix} 1 & 2 & 1 \\ 1 & 2 & 1 \\ 1 & 4 & 3 \end{vmatrix}}{\begin{vmatrix} 1 & 2 & 1 \\ 1 & -1 & 1 \\ 1 & 1 & 3 \end{vmatrix}} = \dfrac{0}{-6} = 0 \quad z = \dfrac{\begin{vmatrix} 1 & 2 & 2 \\ 1 & -1 & 2 \\ 1 & 1 & 4 \end{vmatrix}}{\begin{vmatrix} 1 & 2 & 1 \\ 1 & -1 & 1 \\ 1 & 1 & 3 \end{vmatrix}} = \dfrac{-6}{-6} = 1$

44. $x = \dfrac{\begin{vmatrix} -1 & 2 & -1 \\ 1 & 1 & -1 \\ 17 & -3 & -5 \end{vmatrix}}{\begin{vmatrix} 1 & 2 & -1 \\ 2 & 1 & -1 \\ 1 & -3 & -5 \end{vmatrix}} = \dfrac{4}{17} \quad y = \dfrac{\begin{vmatrix} 1 & -1 & -1 \\ 2 & 1 & -1 \\ 1 & 17 & -5 \end{vmatrix}}{\begin{vmatrix} 1 & 2 & -1 \\ 2 & 1 & -1 \\ 1 & -3 & -5 \end{vmatrix}} = \dfrac{-30}{17} \quad z = \dfrac{\begin{vmatrix} 1 & 2 & -1 \\ 2 & 1 & 1 \\ 1 & -3 & 17 \end{vmatrix}}{\begin{vmatrix} 1 & 2 & -1 \\ 2 & 1 & -1 \\ 1 & -3 & -5 \end{vmatrix}} = \dfrac{-39}{17}$

45. $x = \dfrac{\begin{vmatrix} 5 & -1 & 1 \\ 10 & -3 & 2 \\ 0 & 3 & 1 \end{vmatrix}}{\begin{vmatrix} 2 & -1 & 1 \\ 3 & -3 & 2 \\ 1 & 3 & 1 \end{vmatrix}} = \frac{-5}{-5} = 1 \quad y = \dfrac{\begin{vmatrix} 2 & 5 & 1 \\ 3 & 10 & 2 \\ 1 & 0 & 1 \end{vmatrix}}{\begin{vmatrix} 2 & -1 & 1 \\ 3 & -3 & 2 \\ 1 & 3 & 1 \end{vmatrix}} = \frac{5}{-5} = -1 \quad z = \dfrac{\begin{vmatrix} 2 & -1 & 5 \\ 3 & -3 & 10 \\ 1 & 3 & 0 \end{vmatrix}}{\begin{vmatrix} 2 & -1 & 1 \\ 3 & -3 & 2 \\ 1 & 3 & 1 \end{vmatrix}} = \frac{-10}{-5} = 2$

46. $x = \dfrac{\begin{vmatrix} 2 & -1 & -1 \\ 2 & 1 & 1 \\ -4 & -1 & 1 \end{vmatrix}}{\begin{vmatrix} 1 & -1 & -1 \\ 1 & 1 & 1 \\ -1 & -1 & 1 \end{vmatrix}} = \dfrac{8}{4} = 2 \qquad y = \dfrac{\begin{vmatrix} 1 & 2 & -1 \\ 1 & 2 & 1 \\ -1 & -4 & 1 \end{vmatrix}}{\begin{vmatrix} 1 & -1 & -1 \\ 1 & 1 & 1 \\ -1 & -1 & 1 \end{vmatrix}} = \dfrac{4}{4} = 1$

$z = \dfrac{\begin{vmatrix} 1 & -1 & 2 \\ 1 & 1 & 2 \\ -1 & -1 & -4 \end{vmatrix}}{\begin{vmatrix} 1 & -1 & -1 \\ 1 & 1 & 1 \\ -1 & -1 & 1 \end{vmatrix}} = \dfrac{-4}{4} = -1$

47. Rewrite system:

$$3x + 2y + 3z = 66$$
$$2x + 6y - z = 36$$
$$3x + 1y + 6z = 96$$

$$x = \frac{\begin{vmatrix} 66 & 2 & 3 \\ 36 & 6 & -1 \\ 96 & 1 & 6 \end{vmatrix}}{\begin{vmatrix} 3 & 2 & 3 \\ 2 & 6 & -1 \\ 3 & 1 & 6 \end{vmatrix}} = \frac{198}{33} = 6$$

$$y = \frac{\begin{vmatrix} 3 & 66 & 3 \\ 2 & 36 & -1 \\ 3 & 96 & 6 \end{vmatrix}}{\begin{vmatrix} 3 & 2 & 3 \\ 2 & 6 & -1 \\ 3 & 1 & 6 \end{vmatrix}} = \frac{198}{33} = 6 \qquad z = \frac{\begin{vmatrix} 3 & 2 & 66 \\ 2 & 6 & 36 \\ 3 & 1 & 96 \end{vmatrix}}{\begin{vmatrix} 3 & 2 & 3 \\ 2 & 6 & -1 \\ 3 & 1 & 6 \end{vmatrix}} = \frac{396}{33} = 12$$

48. Rewrite system:

$$15x + 6y + 10z = 510$$
$$2x + 5y + 2z = 320$$
$$6x + 2y + 3z = 180$$

$$x = \frac{\begin{vmatrix} 510 & 6 & 10 \\ 320 & 5 & 2 \\ 180 & 2 & 3 \end{vmatrix}}{\begin{vmatrix} 15 & 6 & 10 \\ 2 & 5 & 2 \\ 6 & 2 & 3 \end{vmatrix}} = \frac{-590}{-59} = 10$$

$$y = \frac{\begin{vmatrix} 15 & 510 & 10 \\ 2 & 320 & 2 \\ 6 & 180 & 3 \end{vmatrix}}{\begin{vmatrix} 15 & 6 & 10 \\ 2 & 5 & 2 \\ 6 & 2 & 3 \end{vmatrix}} = \frac{-3540}{-59} = 60 \qquad z = \frac{\begin{vmatrix} 15 & 6 & 510 \\ 2 & 5 & 320 \\ 6 & 2 & 180 \end{vmatrix}}{\begin{vmatrix} 15 & 6 & 10 \\ 2 & 5 & 2 \\ 6 & 2 & 3 \end{vmatrix}} = \frac{0}{-59} = 0$$

49.

$$p = \frac{\begin{vmatrix} 0 & -1 & 3 & -1 \\ -1 & 1 & 0 & -1 \\ 2 & 0 & -1 & 0 \\ 7 & -2 & 0 & 3 \end{vmatrix}}{\begin{vmatrix} 2 & -1 & 3 & -1 \\ 1 & 1 & 0 & -1 \\ 3 & 0 & -1 & 0 \\ 1 & -2 & 0 & 3 \end{vmatrix}} = \frac{-15}{-18} = \frac{5}{6} \qquad q = \frac{\begin{vmatrix} 2 & 0 & 3 & -1 \\ 1 & -1 & 0 & -1 \\ 3 & 2 & -1 & 0 \\ 1 & 7 & 0 & 3 \end{vmatrix}}{\begin{vmatrix} 2 & -1 & 3 & -1 \\ 1 & 1 & 0 & -1 \\ 3 & 0 & -1 & 0 \\ 1 & -2 & 0 & 3 \end{vmatrix}} = \frac{-12}{-18} = \frac{2}{3}$$

$$r = \frac{\begin{vmatrix} 2 & -1 & 0 & -1 \\ 1 & 1 & -1 & -1 \\ 3 & 0 & 2 & 0 \\ 1 & -2 & 7 & 3 \end{vmatrix}}{\begin{vmatrix} 2 & -1 & 3 & -1 \\ 1 & 1 & 0 & -1 \\ 3 & 0 & -1 & 0 \\ 1 & -2 & 0 & 3 \end{vmatrix}} = \frac{-9}{-18} = \frac{1}{2} \qquad s = \frac{\begin{vmatrix} 2 & -1 & 3 & 0 \\ 1 & 1 & 0 & -1 \\ 3 & 0 & -1 & 2 \\ 1 & -2 & 0 & 7 \end{vmatrix}}{\begin{vmatrix} 2 & -1 & 3 & -1 \\ 1 & 1 & 0 & -1 \\ 3 & 0 & -1 & 0 \\ 1 & -2 & 0 & 3 \end{vmatrix}} = \frac{-45}{-18} = \frac{5}{2}$$

50. $a = \dfrac{\begin{vmatrix} 8 & 1 & 1 & 1 \\ 7 & 1 & 1 & 2 \\ 3 & 1 & 2 & 3 \\ 4 & 2 & 3 & 4 \end{vmatrix}}{\begin{vmatrix} 1 & 1 & 1 & 1 \\ 1 & 1 & 1 & 2 \\ 1 & 1 & 2 & 3 \\ 1 & 2 & 3 & 4 \end{vmatrix}} = \dfrac{-7}{-1} = 7 \quad b = \dfrac{\begin{vmatrix} 1 & 8 & 1 & 1 \\ 1 & 7 & 1 & 2 \\ 1 & 3 & 2 & 3 \\ 1 & 4 & 3 & 4 \end{vmatrix}}{\begin{vmatrix} 1 & 1 & 1 & 1 \\ 1 & 1 & 1 & 2 \\ 1 & 1 & 2 & 3 \\ 1 & 2 & 3 & 4 \end{vmatrix}} = \dfrac{-5}{-1} = 5$

$c = \dfrac{\begin{vmatrix} 1 & 1 & 8 & 1 \\ 1 & 1 & 7 & 2 \\ 1 & 1 & 3 & 3 \\ 1 & 2 & 4 & 4 \end{vmatrix}}{\begin{vmatrix} 1 & 1 & 1 & 1 \\ 1 & 1 & 1 & 2 \\ 1 & 1 & 2 & 3 \\ 1 & 2 & 3 & 4 \end{vmatrix}} = \dfrac{3}{-1} = -3 \quad d = \dfrac{\begin{vmatrix} 1 & 1 & 1 & 8 \\ 1 & 1 & 1 & 7 \\ 1 & 1 & 2 & 3 \\ 1 & 2 & 3 & 4 \end{vmatrix}}{\begin{vmatrix} 1 & 1 & 1 & 1 \\ 1 & 1 & 1 & 2 \\ 1 & 1 & 2 & 3 \\ 1 & 2 & 3 & 4 \end{vmatrix}} = \dfrac{1}{-1} = -1$

51.

$$\begin{vmatrix} x & y & 1 \\ 0 & 0 & 1 \\ 4 & 6 & 1 \end{vmatrix} = 0$$

$$x\begin{vmatrix} 0 & 1 \\ 6 & 1 \end{vmatrix} - y\begin{vmatrix} 0 & 1 \\ 4 & 1 \end{vmatrix} + 1\begin{vmatrix} 0 & 0 \\ 4 & 6 \end{vmatrix} = 0$$

$$x(-6) - y(-4) + 1(0) = 0$$
$$-6x + 4y = 0$$
$$3x - 2y = 0$$

52.

$$\begin{vmatrix} x & y & 1 \\ 2 & 3 & 1 \\ 6 & 8 & 1 \end{vmatrix} = 0$$

$$x\begin{vmatrix} 3 & 1 \\ 8 & 1 \end{vmatrix} - y\begin{vmatrix} 2 & 1 \\ 6 & 1 \end{vmatrix} + 1\begin{vmatrix} 2 & 3 \\ 6 & 8 \end{vmatrix} = 0$$

$$x(-5) - y(-4) + 1(-2) = 0$$
$$-5x + 4y - 2 = 0$$
$$5x - 4y = -2$$

53.

$$\begin{vmatrix} x & y & 1 \\ -2 & 3 & 1 \\ 5 & -3 & 1 \end{vmatrix} = 0$$

$$x\begin{vmatrix} 3 & 1 \\ -3 & 1 \end{vmatrix} - y\begin{vmatrix} -2 & 1 \\ 5 & 1 \end{vmatrix} + 1\begin{vmatrix} -2 & 3 \\ 5 & -3 \end{vmatrix} = 0$$

$$x(6) - y(-7) + 1(-9) = 0$$
$$6x + 7y - 9 = 0$$
$$6x + 7y = 9$$

54.

$$\begin{vmatrix} x & y & 1 \\ 1 & -2 & 1 \\ -4 & 3 & 1 \end{vmatrix} = 0$$

$$x\begin{vmatrix} -2 & 1 \\ 3 & 1 \end{vmatrix} - y\begin{vmatrix} 1 & 1 \\ -4 & 1 \end{vmatrix} + 1\begin{vmatrix} 1 & -2 \\ -4 & 3 \end{vmatrix} = 0$$

$$x(-5) - y(5) + 1(-5) = 0$$
$$-5x - 5y - 5 = 0$$
$$x + y = -1$$

55. $\pm\dfrac{1}{2}\begin{vmatrix} 0 & 0 & 1 \\ 12 & 0 & 1 \\ 12 & 5 & 1 \end{vmatrix} = \pm\dfrac{1}{2}(60)$

$= 30$ square units

56. $\pm\dfrac{1}{2}\begin{vmatrix} 0 & 0 & 1 \\ 0 & 5 & 1 \\ 12 & 5 & 1 \end{vmatrix} = \pm\dfrac{1}{2}(-60)$

$= 30$ square units

57. $\pm\frac{1}{2}\begin{vmatrix} 2 & 3 & 1 \\ 10 & 8 & 1 \\ 0 & 20 & 1 \end{vmatrix} = \pm\frac{1}{2}(146)$

$= 73$ square units

58. $\pm\frac{1}{2}\begin{vmatrix} 1 & 1 & 1 \\ 6 & 6 & 1 \\ 2 & 10 & 1 \end{vmatrix} = \pm\frac{1}{2}(40)$

$= 20$ square units

59. $\begin{vmatrix} a & b \\ c & d \end{vmatrix} = ad - bc$

$\begin{vmatrix} b & a \\ d & c \end{vmatrix} = bc - ad = -(ad - bc)$

60. $\begin{vmatrix} a & b \\ c & d \end{vmatrix} = ad - bc$

$\begin{vmatrix} ka & b \\ kc & d \end{vmatrix} = kad - kbc = k(ad - bc)$

61. $\begin{vmatrix} a & b \\ c & d \end{vmatrix} = ad - bc$

$\begin{vmatrix} a & b + ka \\ c & d + kc \end{vmatrix} = a(d + kc) - (b + ka)c = ad + akc - bc - akc = ad - bc$

62.
$$\begin{aligned} ax + by = e &\Rightarrow \times(-c) & -acx - bcy &= -ec \\ cx + dy = f &\Rightarrow \times a & acx + ady &= fa \\ & & (ad - bc)y &= af - ec \\ & & y &= \frac{af - ec}{ad - bc} \end{aligned}$$

63. $\begin{vmatrix} 3 & x \\ 1 & 2 \end{vmatrix} = \begin{vmatrix} 2 & -1 \\ x & -5 \end{vmatrix}$

$$\begin{aligned} 6 - x &= -10 + x \\ -2x &= -16 \\ x &= 8 \end{aligned}$$

64. $\begin{vmatrix} 4 & x^2 \\ 1 & -1 \end{vmatrix} = \begin{vmatrix} x & 4 \\ 2 & 3 \end{vmatrix}$

$$\begin{aligned} -4 - x^2 &= 3x - 8 \\ 0 &= x^2 + 3x - 4 \\ 0 &= (x - 1)(x + 4) \\ x = 1 &\text{ or } x = -4 \end{aligned}$$

65. $\begin{vmatrix} 3 & x & 1 \\ x & 0 & -2 \\ 4 & 0 & 1 \end{vmatrix} = \begin{vmatrix} 2 & x \\ x & 4 \end{vmatrix}$

$$\begin{aligned} -x\begin{vmatrix} x & -2 \\ 4 & 1 \end{vmatrix} &= 8 - x^2 \\ -x(x + 8) &= 8 - x^2 \\ -x^2 - 8x &= -x^2 + 8 \\ x &= -1 \end{aligned}$$

66. $\begin{vmatrix} x & -1 & 2 \\ -2 & x & 3 \\ 4 & -3 & -1 \end{vmatrix} = \begin{vmatrix} 2 & 2 \\ 5 & x \end{vmatrix}$

$$\begin{aligned} x\begin{vmatrix} x & 3 \\ -3 & -1 \end{vmatrix} - (-1)\begin{vmatrix} -2 & 3 \\ 4 & -1 \end{vmatrix} + 2\begin{vmatrix} -2 & x \\ 4 & -3 \end{vmatrix} &= 2x - 10 \\ x(-x + 9) + 1(2 - 12) + 2(6 - 4x) &= 2x - 10 \\ -x^2 + 9x - 10 + 12 - 8x &= 2x - 10 \\ 0 &= x^2 + x - 12 \\ 0 &= (x + 4)(x - 3) \Rightarrow x = -4 \text{ or } x = 3 \end{aligned}$$

67. Let $x =$ \$ invested in HiTech, $y =$ \$ invested in SaveTel, and $z =$ \$ invested in OilCo.

$$\begin{cases} x+y+z=20{,}000 \\ y+z=3x \\ 0.10x+0.05y+0.06z=0.066(20{,}000) \end{cases} \qquad \begin{aligned} x+y+z&=20000 \\ -3x+y+z&=0 \\ 10x+5y+6z&=132000 \end{aligned}$$

$$x = \frac{\begin{vmatrix} 20000 & 1 & 1 \\ 0 & 1 & 1 \\ 132000 & 5 & 6 \end{vmatrix}}{\begin{vmatrix} 1 & 1 & 1 \\ -3 & 1 & 1 \\ 10 & 5 & 6 \end{vmatrix}} = \frac{20000}{4} = 5000,\ y = \frac{\begin{vmatrix} 1 & 20000 & 1 \\ -3 & 0 & 1 \\ 10 & 132000 & 6 \end{vmatrix}}{\begin{vmatrix} 1 & 1 & 1 \\ -3 & 1 & 1 \\ 10 & 5 & 6 \end{vmatrix}} = \frac{32000}{4} = 8000$$

$$z = \frac{\begin{vmatrix} 1 & 1 & 20000 \\ -3 & 1 & 0 \\ 10 & 5 & 132000 \end{vmatrix}}{\begin{vmatrix} 1 & 1 & 1 \\ -3 & 1 & 1 \\ 10 & 5 & 6 \end{vmatrix}} = \frac{28000}{4} = 7000 \Rightarrow$$ He should invest \$5000 in HiTech, \$8000 in SaveTel, and \$7000 in OilCo.

68. Let x, y, and z represent the radii of the circles.

$$\begin{cases} x+y=10 \\ x+z=18 \\ y+z=14 \end{cases} \quad x = \frac{\begin{vmatrix} 10 & 1 & 0 \\ 18 & 0 & 1 \\ 14 & 1 & 1 \end{vmatrix}}{\begin{vmatrix} 1 & 1 & 0 \\ 1 & 0 & 1 \\ 0 & 1 & 1 \end{vmatrix}} = \frac{-14}{-2} = 7,\ y = \frac{\begin{vmatrix} 1 & 10 & 0 \\ 1 & 18 & 1 \\ 0 & 14 & 1 \end{vmatrix}}{\begin{vmatrix} 1 & 1 & 0 \\ 1 & 0 & 1 \\ 0 & 1 & 1 \end{vmatrix}} = \frac{-6}{-2} = 3$$

$$z = \frac{\begin{vmatrix} 1 & 1 & 10 \\ 1 & 0 & 18 \\ 0 & 1 & 14 \end{vmatrix}}{\begin{vmatrix} 1 & 1 & 0 \\ 1 & 0 & 1 \\ 0 & 1 & 1 \end{vmatrix}} = \frac{-22}{-2} = 11 \Rightarrow$$ The radii are 7 yd, 3 yd, and 11 yd.

69. $\begin{vmatrix} 1 & 3 & 4 \\ 0 & 5 & 2 \\ 0 & 0 & 2 \end{vmatrix} = 10$

$1 \cdot 5 \cdot 2 = 10$

70. $\begin{vmatrix} 2 & 1 & -2 \\ 0 & 3 & 4 \\ 0 & 0 & -1 \end{vmatrix} = -6$

$2 \cdot 3 \cdot (-1) = -6$

71. $\begin{vmatrix} 1 & 2 & 4 & 3 \\ 0 & 2 & 2 & 1 \\ 0 & 0 & 3 & 2 \\ 0 & 0 & 0 & 4 \end{vmatrix} = 24$

$1 \cdot 2 \cdot 3 \cdot 4 = 24$

72. $\begin{vmatrix} 2 & 1 & -2 & 1 \\ 0 & 2 & 2 & -1 \\ 0 & 0 & 3 & 1 \\ 0 & 0 & 0 & 2 \end{vmatrix} = 24$

$2 \cdot 2 \cdot 3 \cdot 2 = 24$

73. $3(1)(1) + 2(-2)(1) + (-1)(2)(3) = -7$
$1(1)(-1) + 3(-2)(3) + 1(2)(2) = -15$
$-7 - (-15) = 8$

74. $0(5)(3) + 1(2)(2) + (-3)(-3)(-5) = -41$
$2(5)(-3) + (-5)(2)(0) + 3(-3)(1) = -39$
$-41 - (-39) = -2$

75-78. Answers may vary.

79. yes

80. no

81. $\begin{vmatrix} 2.3 & 5.7 & 6.1 \\ 3.4 & 6.2 & 8.3 \\ 5.8 & 8.2 & 9.2 \end{vmatrix} = 21.468$

82. $\begin{vmatrix} 0.32 & -7.4 & -6.7 \\ 3.3 & 5.5 & -0.27 \\ -8 & -0.13 & 5.47 \end{vmatrix} = -164.716332$

83. $x^2 + 3x - 4 = (x + 4)(x - 1)$

84. $2x^2 - 5x - 12 = (2x + 3)(x - 4)$

85. $9x^3 - x = x(9x^2 - 1)$
$= x(3x + 1)(3x - 1)$

86. $x^2 + 3x + 5$: prime

87. $\frac{1}{x-2} + \frac{2}{2x-1} = \frac{1(2x-1)}{(x-2)(2x-1)} + \frac{2(x-2)}{(2x-1)(x-2)} = \frac{2x-1+2x-4}{(x-2)(2x-1)} = \frac{4x-5}{(x-2)(2x-1)}$

88. $\frac{2}{x} + \frac{3}{x^2} - \frac{1}{x-1} = \frac{2x(x-1)}{x^2(x-1)} + \frac{3(x-1)}{x^2(x-1)} - \frac{x^2}{x^2(x-1)} = \frac{2x^2-2x+3x-3-x^2}{x^2(x-1)}$
$= \frac{x^2+x-3}{x^2(x-1)}$

89. $\frac{2}{x^2+1} + \frac{1}{x} = \frac{2x}{x(x^2+1)} + \frac{x^2+1}{x(x^2+1)}$
$= \frac{x^2+2x+1}{x(x^2+1)}$

90. $\frac{2x}{x^2+1} + \frac{1}{x} = \frac{2x^2}{x(x^2+1)} + \frac{x^2+1}{x(x^2+1)}$
$= \frac{3x^2+1}{x(x^2+1)}$

Exercises 6.6 (page 620)

1. first-degree, second-degree

2. prime

3. $\frac{3x-1}{x(x-1)} = \frac{A}{x} + \frac{B}{x-1}$
$\frac{3x-1}{x(x-1)} = \frac{A(x-1)}{x(x-1)} + \frac{Bx}{x(x-1)}$
$\frac{3x-1}{x(x-1)} = \frac{Ax-A+Bx}{x(x-1)}$
$\frac{3x-1}{x(x-1)} = \frac{(A+B)x-A}{x(x-1)}$

$\begin{cases} A + B = 3 \\ -A = -1 \end{cases} \Rightarrow A = 1, B = 2$
$\frac{3x-1}{x(x-1)} = \frac{1}{x} + \frac{2}{x-1}$

4. $\dfrac{4x+6}{x(x+2)} = \dfrac{A}{x} + \dfrac{B}{x+2}$

$\dfrac{4x+6}{x(x+2)} = \dfrac{A(x+2)}{x(x+2)} + \dfrac{Bx}{x(x+2)}$

$\dfrac{4x+6}{x(x+2)} = \dfrac{Ax+2A+Bx}{x(x+2)}$

$\dfrac{4x+6}{x(x+2)} = \dfrac{(A+B)x+2A}{x(x+2)}$

$\begin{cases} A+B=4 \\ 2A \quad\;\; =6 \end{cases} \Rightarrow A=3,\ B=1$

$\dfrac{4x+6}{x(x+2)} = \dfrac{3}{x} + \dfrac{1}{x+2}$

5. $\dfrac{2x-15}{x(x-3)} = \dfrac{A}{x} + \dfrac{B}{x-3}$

$\dfrac{2x-15}{x(x-3)} = \dfrac{A(x-3)}{x(x-3)} + \dfrac{Bx}{x(x-3)}$

$\dfrac{2x-15}{x(x-3)} = \dfrac{Ax-3A+Bx}{x(x-3)}$

$\dfrac{2x-15}{x(x-3)} = \dfrac{(A+B)x-3A}{x(x-3)}$

$\begin{cases} A+B= \quad 2 \\ -3A \quad\;\; =-15 \end{cases} \Rightarrow A=5,\ B=-3$

$\dfrac{2x-15}{x(x-3)} = \dfrac{5}{x} - \dfrac{3}{x-3}$

6. $\dfrac{5x+21}{x(x+7)} = \dfrac{A}{x} + \dfrac{B}{x+7}$

$\dfrac{5x+21}{x(x+7)} = \dfrac{A(x+7)}{x(x+7)} + \dfrac{Bx}{x(x+7)}$

$\dfrac{5x+21}{x(x+7)} = \dfrac{Ax+7A+Bx}{x(x+7)}$

$\dfrac{5x+21}{x(x+7)} = \dfrac{(A+B)x+7A}{x(x+7)}$

$\begin{cases} A+B= \;5 \\ 7A \quad\;\; =21 \end{cases} \Rightarrow A=3,\ B=2$

$\dfrac{5x+21}{x(x+7)} = \dfrac{3}{x} + \dfrac{2}{x+7}$

7. $\dfrac{3x+1}{(x+1)(x-1)} = \dfrac{A}{x+1} + \dfrac{B}{x-1}$

$\dfrac{3x+1}{(x+1)(x-1)} = \dfrac{A(x-1)}{(x+1)(x-1)} + \dfrac{B(x+1)}{(x+1)(x-1)}$

$\dfrac{3x+1}{(x+1)(x-1)} = \dfrac{Ax-A+Bx+B}{(x+1)(x-1)}$

$\dfrac{3x+1}{(x+1)(x-1)} = \dfrac{(A+B)x+(-A+B)}{(x+1)(x-1)}$

$\begin{cases} A+B=3 \\ -A+B=1 \end{cases} \Rightarrow A=1,\ B=2$

$\dfrac{3x+1}{(x+1)(x-1)} = \dfrac{1}{x+1} + \dfrac{2}{x-1}$

8. $\dfrac{9x-3}{(x+1)(x-2)} = \dfrac{A}{x+1} + \dfrac{B}{x-2}$

$\dfrac{9x-3}{(x+1)(x-2)} = \dfrac{A(x-2)}{(x+1)(x-2)} + \dfrac{B(x+1)}{(x+1)(x-2)}$

$\dfrac{9x-3}{(x+1)(x-2)} = \dfrac{Ax-2A+Bx+B}{(x+1)(x-2)}$

$\dfrac{9x-3}{(x+1)(x-2)} = \dfrac{(A+B)x+(-2A+B)}{(x+1)(x-2)}$

$\begin{cases} A+B= \;\;9 \\ -2A+B=-3 \end{cases} \Rightarrow A=4,\ B=5$

$\dfrac{9x-3}{(x+1)(x-2)} = \dfrac{4}{x+1} + \dfrac{5}{x-2}$

9.

$$\frac{-4}{x^2-2x}=$$
$$\frac{-4}{x(x-2)}=\frac{A}{x}+\frac{B}{x-2}$$
$$\frac{-4}{x(x-2)}=\frac{A(x-2)}{x(x-2)}+\frac{Bx}{x(x-2)}$$
$$\frac{-4}{x(x-2)}=\frac{Ax-2A+Bx}{x(x-2)}$$
$$\frac{-4}{x(x-2)}=\frac{(A+B)x-2A}{x(x-2)}$$
$$\begin{cases} A+B=0 \\ -2A=-4 \end{cases} \Rightarrow A=2,\ B=-2$$
$$\frac{4}{x^2-2x}=\frac{2}{x}-\frac{2}{x-2}$$

10.

$$\frac{1}{P^2-300P}=$$
$$\frac{1}{P(P-300)}=\frac{A}{P}+\frac{B}{P-300}$$
$$\frac{1}{P(P-300)}=\frac{A(P-300)}{P(P-300)}+\frac{BP}{P(P-300)}$$
$$\frac{1}{P(P-300)}=\frac{AP-300A+BP}{P(P-300)}$$
$$\frac{1}{P(P-300)}=\frac{(A+B)P-300A}{P(P-300)}$$
$$\begin{cases} A+B=0 \\ -300A=1 \end{cases} \Rightarrow A=-\frac{1}{300},\ B=\frac{1}{300}$$
$$\frac{1}{P^2-300P}=\frac{-\frac{1}{300}}{P}+\frac{\frac{1}{300}}{P-300}$$

11.

$$\frac{-2x+11}{(x+2)(x-3)}=\frac{A}{x+2}+\frac{B}{x-3}$$
$$\frac{-2x+11}{(x+2)(x-3)}=\frac{A(x-3)}{(x+2)(x-3)}+\frac{B(x+2)}{(x+2)(x-3)}$$
$$\frac{-2x+11}{(x+2)(x-3)}=\frac{Ax-3A+Bx+2B}{(x+2)(x-3)}$$
$$\frac{-2x+11}{(x+2)(x-3)}=\frac{(A+B)x+(-3A+2B)}{(x+2)(x-3)}$$
$$\frac{-2x+11}{x^2-x-6}=\frac{-2x+11}{(x+2)(x-3)}$$
$$\begin{cases} A+B=-2 \\ -3A+2B=11 \end{cases} \Rightarrow A=-3,\ B=1$$
$$\frac{-2x+11}{(x+2)(x-3)}=\frac{-3}{x+2}+\frac{1}{x-3}$$

12.

$$\frac{7x+2}{(x+2)(x-1)}=\frac{A}{x+2}+\frac{B}{x-1}$$
$$\frac{7x+2}{(x+2)(x-1)}=\frac{A(x-1)}{(x+2)(x-1)}+\frac{B(x+2)}{(x+2)(x-1)}$$
$$\frac{7x+2}{(x+2)(x-1)}=\frac{Ax-A+Bx+2B}{(x+2)(x-1)}$$
$$\frac{7x+2}{(x+2)(x-1)}=\frac{(A+B)x+(-A+2B)}{(x+2)(x-1)}$$
$$\frac{7x+2}{x^2+x-2}=\frac{7x+2}{(x+2)(x-1)}$$
$$\begin{cases} A+B=7 \\ -A+2B=2 \end{cases} \Rightarrow A=4,\ B=3$$
$$\frac{7x+2}{(x+2)(x-1)}=\frac{4}{x+2}+\frac{3}{x-1}$$

13.

$$\frac{3x-23}{(x+3)(x-1)}=\frac{A}{x+3}+\frac{B}{x-1}$$
$$\frac{3x-23}{(x+3)(x-1)}=\frac{A(x-1)}{(x+3)(x-1)}+\frac{B(x+3)}{(x+3)(x-1)}$$
$$\frac{3x-23}{(x+3)(x-1)}=\frac{Ax-A+Bx+3B}{(x+3)(x-1)}$$
$$\frac{3x-23}{(x+3)(x-1)}=\frac{(A+B)x+(-A+3B)}{(x+3)(x-1)}$$
$$\frac{3x-23}{x^2+2x-3}=\frac{3x-23}{(x+3)(x-1)}$$
$$\begin{cases} A+B=3 \\ -A+3B=-23 \end{cases} \Rightarrow A=8,\ B=-5$$
$$\frac{3x-23}{(x+3)(x-1)}=\frac{8}{x+3}-\frac{5}{x-1}$$

14. $\dfrac{-x-17}{(x+2)(x-3)} = \dfrac{A}{x+2} + \dfrac{B}{x-3}$

$\dfrac{-x-17}{(x+2)(x-3)} = \dfrac{A(x-3)}{(x+2)(x-3)} + \dfrac{B(x+2)}{(x+2)(x-3)}$

$\dfrac{-x-17}{(x+2)(x-3)} = \dfrac{Ax-3A+Bx+2B}{(x+2)(x-3)}$

$\dfrac{-x-17}{(x+2)(x-3)} = \dfrac{(A+B)x+(-3A+2B)}{(x+2)(x-3)}$

$\dfrac{-x-17}{x^2-x-6} = \dfrac{-x-17}{(x+2)(x-3)}$

$\begin{cases} A + B = -1 \\ -3A+2B = -17 \end{cases} \Rightarrow A = 3, B = -4$

$\dfrac{-x-17}{(x+2)(x-3)} = \dfrac{3}{x+2} - \dfrac{4}{x-3}$

15. $\dfrac{9x-31}{2x^2-13x+15} = \dfrac{9x-31}{(2x-3)(x-5)} = \dfrac{A}{2x-3} + \dfrac{B}{x-5}$

$\dfrac{9x-31}{(2x-3)(x-5)} = \dfrac{A(x-5)}{(2x-3)(x-5)} + \dfrac{B(2x-3)}{(2x-3)(x-5)}$

$\dfrac{9x-31}{(2x-3)(x-5)} = \dfrac{Ax-5A+2Bx-3B}{(2x-3)(x-5)}$

$\dfrac{9x-31}{(2x-3)(x-5)} = \dfrac{(A+2B)x+(-5A-3B)}{(2x-3)(x-5)}$

$\begin{cases} A+2B = 9 \\ -5A-3B = -31 \end{cases} \Rightarrow A = 5, B = 2 \quad \dfrac{9x-31}{(2x-3)(x-5)} = \dfrac{5}{2x-3} + \dfrac{2}{x-5}$

16. $\dfrac{-2x-6}{3x^2-7x+2} = \dfrac{-2x-6}{(3x-1)(x-2)} = \dfrac{A}{3x-1} + \dfrac{B}{x-2}$

$\dfrac{-2x-6}{(3x-1)(x-2)} = \dfrac{A(x-2)}{(3x-1)(x-2)} + \dfrac{B(3x-1)}{(3x-1)(x-2)}$

$\dfrac{-2x-6}{(3x-1)(x-2)} = \dfrac{Ax-2A+3Bx-B}{(3x-1)(x-2)}$

$\dfrac{-2x-6}{(3x-1)(x-2)} = \dfrac{(A+3B)x+(-2A-B)}{(3x-1)(x-2)}$

$\begin{cases} A+3B = -2 \\ -2A - B = -6 \end{cases} \Rightarrow A = 4, B = -2 \quad \dfrac{-2x-6}{(3x-1)(x-2)} = \dfrac{4}{3x-1} - \dfrac{2}{x-2}$

17. $\dfrac{4x^2+4x-2}{x(x^2-1)} = \dfrac{4x^2+4x-2}{x(x+1)(x-1)} = \dfrac{A}{x} + \dfrac{B}{x+1} + \dfrac{C}{x-1}$

$\dfrac{4x^2+4x-2}{x(x+1)(x-1)} = \dfrac{A(x+1)(x-1)}{x(x+1)(x-1)} + \dfrac{Bx(x-1)}{x(x+1)(x-1)} + \dfrac{Cx(x+1)}{x(x+1)(x-1)}$

$\dfrac{4x^2+4x-2}{x(x+1)(x-1)} = \dfrac{Ax^2-A+Bx^2-Bx+Cx^2+Cx}{x(x+1)(x-1)}$

$\dfrac{4x^2+4x-2}{x(x+1)(x-1)} = \dfrac{(A+B+C)x^2+(-B+C)x+(-A)}{x(x+1)(x-1)}$

$\begin{cases} A+B+C = 4 \\ -B+C = 4 \\ -A = -2 \end{cases} \Rightarrow \begin{matrix} A = 2 \\ B = -1 \\ C = 3 \end{matrix} \quad \dfrac{4x^2+4x-2}{x(x+1)(x-1)} = \dfrac{2}{x} - \dfrac{1}{x+1} + \dfrac{3}{x-1}$

18. $$\frac{x^2-6x-13}{(x+2)(x^2-1)} = \frac{x^2-6x-13}{(x+2)(x+1)(x-1)} = \frac{A}{x+2}+\frac{B}{x+1}+\frac{C}{x-1}$$
$$= \frac{A(x+1)(x-1)}{(x+2)(x+1)(x-1)} + \frac{B(x+2)(x-1)}{(x+2)(x+1)(x-1)} + \frac{C(x+2)(x+1)}{(x+2)(x+1)(x-1)}$$
$$= \frac{Ax^2-A+Bx^2+Bx-2B+Cx^2+3Cx+2C}{(x+2)(x+1)(x-1)}$$
$$= \frac{(A+B+C)x^2+(B+3C)x+(-A-2B+2C)}{(x+2)(x+1)(x-1)}$$

$$\begin{cases} A+B+C = 1 \\ B+3C = -6 \\ -A-2B+2C = -13 \end{cases} \Rightarrow \begin{array}{l} A=1 \\ B=3 \\ C=-3 \end{array} \qquad \frac{x^2-6x-13}{(x+2)(x+1)(x-1)} = \frac{1}{x+2}+\frac{3}{x+1}-\frac{3}{x-1}$$

19. $$\frac{x^2+x+3}{x(x^2+3)} = \frac{A}{x}+\frac{Bx+C}{x^2+3}$$
$$= \frac{A(x^2+3)}{x(x^2+3)}+\frac{(Bx+C)x}{x(x^2+3)}$$
$$= \frac{Ax^2+3A+Bx^2+Cx}{x(x^2+3)}$$
$$= \frac{(A+B)x^2+Cx+3A}{x(x^2+3)}$$

$$\begin{cases} A+B = 1 \\ C = 1 \\ 3A = 3 \end{cases} \Rightarrow \begin{array}{l} A=1 \\ B=0 \\ C=1 \end{array}$$
$$\frac{x^2+x+3}{x(x^2+3)} = \frac{1}{x}+\frac{1}{x^2+3}$$

20. $$\frac{5x^2+2x+2}{x(x^2+1)} = \frac{A}{x}+\frac{Bx+C}{x^2+1}$$
$$= \frac{A(x^2+1)}{x(x^2+1)}+\frac{(Bx+C)x}{x(x^2+1)}$$
$$= \frac{Ax^2+A+Bx^2+Cx}{x(x^2+1)}$$
$$= \frac{(A+B)x^2+Cx+A}{x(x^2+1)}$$

$$\begin{cases} A+B = 5 \\ C = 2 \\ A = 2 \end{cases} \Rightarrow \begin{array}{l} A=2 \\ B=3 \\ C=2 \end{array}$$
$$\frac{5x^2+2x+2}{x(x^2+1)} = \frac{2}{x}+\frac{3x+2}{x^2+1}$$

21. $$\frac{3x^2+8x+11}{(x+1)(x^2+2x+3)} = \frac{A}{x+1}+\frac{Bx+C}{x^2+2x+3}$$
$$\frac{3x^2+8x+11}{(x+1)(x^2+2x+3)} = \frac{A(x^2+2x+3)}{(x+1)(x^2+2x+3)}+\frac{(Bx+C)(x+1)}{(x+1)(x^2+2x+3)}$$
$$\frac{3x^2+8x+11}{(x+1)(x^2+2x+3)} = \frac{Ax^2+2Ax+3A+Bx^2+Bx+Cx+C}{(x+1)(x^2+2x+3)}$$
$$\frac{3x^2+8x+11}{(x+1)(x^2+2x+3)} = \frac{(A+B)x^2+(2A+B+C)x+(3A+C)}{(x+1)(x^2+2x+3)}$$

$$\begin{cases} A+B = 3 \\ 2A+B+C = 8 \\ 3A+C = 11 \end{cases} \Rightarrow \begin{array}{l} A=3 \\ B=0 \\ C=2 \end{array} \qquad \frac{3x^2+8x+11}{(x+1)(x^2+2x+3)} = \frac{3}{x+1}+\frac{2}{x^2+2x+3}$$

22. $$\frac{-3x^2+x-5}{(x+1)(x^2+2)}=\frac{A}{x+1}+\frac{Bx+C}{x^2+2}$$

$$\frac{-3x^2+x-5}{(x+1)(x^2+2)}=\frac{A(x^2+2)}{(x+1)(x^2+2)}+\frac{(Bx+C)(x+1)}{(x+1)(x^2+2)}$$

$$\frac{-3x^2+x-5}{(x+1)(x^2+2)}=\frac{Ax^2+2A+Bx^2+Bx+Cx+C}{(x+1)(x^2+2)}$$

$$\frac{-3x^2+x-5}{(x+1)(x^2+2)}=\frac{(A+B)x^2+(B+C)x+(2A+C)}{(x+1)(x^2+2)}$$

$$\begin{cases} A+B \quad\ = -3 \\ \quad B+C = 1 \\ 2A \quad +C = -5 \end{cases} \Rightarrow \begin{matrix} A=-3 \\ B=0 \\ C=1 \end{matrix} \qquad \frac{-3x^2+x-5}{(x+1)(x^2+2)}=\frac{-3}{x+1}+\frac{1}{x^2+2}$$

23. $$\frac{5x^2+9x+3}{x(x+1)^2}=\frac{A}{x}+\frac{B}{x+1}+\frac{C}{(x+1)^2}$$

$$=\frac{A(x+1)^2}{x(x+1)^2}+\frac{Bx(x+1)}{x(x+1)^2}+\frac{Cx}{x(x+1)^2}$$

$$=\frac{Ax^2+2Ax+A+Bx^2+Bx+Cx}{x(x+1)^2}$$

$$=\frac{(A+B)x^2+(2A+B+C)x+A}{x(x+1)^2}$$

$$\begin{cases} A+B \qquad\ = 5 \\ 2A+B+C = 9 \\ A \qquad\qquad = 3 \end{cases} \Rightarrow \begin{matrix} A=3 \\ B=2 \\ C=1 \end{matrix} \qquad \frac{5x^2+9x+3}{x(x+1)^2}=\frac{3}{x}+\frac{2}{x+1}+\frac{1}{(x+1)^2}$$

24. $$\frac{2x^2-7x+2}{x(x-1)^2}=\frac{A}{x}+\frac{B}{x-1}+\frac{C}{(x-1)^2}$$

$$=\frac{A(x-1)^2}{x(x-1)^2}+\frac{Bx(x-1)}{x(x-1)^2}+\frac{Cx}{x(x-1)^2}$$

$$=\frac{Ax^2-2Ax+A+Bx^2-Bx+Cx}{x(x-1)^2}$$

$$=\frac{(A+B)x^2+(-2A-B+C)x+A}{x(x-1)^2}$$

$$\begin{cases} A+B \qquad\quad = 2 \\ -2A-B+C = -7 \\ A \qquad\qquad\quad = 2 \end{cases} \Rightarrow \begin{matrix} A=2 \\ B=0 \\ C=-3 \end{matrix} \qquad \frac{2x^2-7x+2}{x(x-1)^2}=\frac{2}{x}-\frac{3}{(x-1)^2}$$

25. $$\frac{-2x^2+x-2}{x^2(x-1)} = \frac{A}{x}+\frac{B}{x^2}+\frac{C}{x-1}$$
$$= \frac{Ax(x-1)}{x^2(x-1)}+\frac{B(x-1)}{x^2(x-1)}+\frac{Cx^2}{x^2(x-1)}$$
$$= \frac{Ax^2-Ax+Bx-B+Cx^2}{x^2(x-1)}$$
$$= \frac{(A+C)x^2+(-A+B)x+(-B)}{x^2(x-1)}$$

$$\begin{cases} A \quad +C = -2 \\ -A+B \quad = 1 \\ \quad -B \quad = -2 \end{cases} \Rightarrow \begin{array}{l} A=1 \\ B=2 \\ C=-3 \end{array} \qquad \frac{-2x^2+x-2}{x^2(x-1)} = \frac{1}{x}+\frac{2}{x^2}-\frac{3}{x-1}$$

26. $$\frac{x^2+x+1}{x^3} = \frac{A}{x}+\frac{B}{x^2}+\frac{C}{x^3}$$
$$= \frac{Ax^2}{x^3}+\frac{Bx}{x^3}+\frac{C}{x^3}$$
$$= \frac{Ax^2+Bx+C}{x^3}$$

$$\begin{cases} A \quad = 1 \\ \quad B \quad = 1 \\ \quad\quad C = 1 \end{cases} \qquad \frac{x^2+x+1}{x^3} = \frac{1}{x}+\frac{1}{x^2}+\frac{1}{x^3}$$

27. $$\frac{3x^2-13x+18}{x^3-6x^2+9x} = \frac{3x^2-13x+18}{x(x-3)^2} = \frac{A}{x}+\frac{B}{x-3}+\frac{C}{(x-3)^2}$$
$$= \frac{A(x-3)^2}{x(x-3)^2}+\frac{Bx(x-3)}{x(x-3)^2}+\frac{Cx}{x(x-3)^2}$$
$$= \frac{Ax^2-6Ax+9A+Bx^2-3Bx+Cx}{x(x-3)^2}$$
$$= \frac{(A+B)x^2+(-6A-3B+C)x+9A}{x(x-3)^2}$$

$$\begin{cases} A+B \quad = 3 \\ -6A-3B+C = -13 \\ 9A \quad = 18 \end{cases} \Rightarrow \begin{array}{l} A=2 \\ B=1 \\ C=2 \end{array} \qquad \frac{3x^2-13x+18}{x(x-3)^2} = \frac{2}{x}+\frac{1}{x-3}+\frac{2}{(x-3)^2}$$

28. $$\frac{3x^2+13x+20}{x^3+4x^2+4x} = \frac{3x^2+13x+20}{x(x+2)^2} = \frac{A}{x} + \frac{B}{x+2} + \frac{C}{(x+2)^2}$$
$$= \frac{A(x+2)^2}{x(x+2)^2} + \frac{Bx(x+2)}{x(x+2)^2} + \frac{Cx}{x(x+2)^2}$$
$$= \frac{Ax^2+4Ax+4A+Bx^2+2Bx+Cx}{x(x+2)^2}$$
$$= \frac{(A+B)x^2+(4A+2B+C)x+4A}{x(x+2)^2}$$

$$\begin{cases} A+B = 3 \\ 4A+2B+C = 13 \\ 4A = 20 \end{cases} \Rightarrow \begin{matrix} A=5 \\ B=-2 \\ C=-3 \end{matrix} \qquad \frac{3x^2+13x+20}{x(x+2)^2} = \frac{5}{x} - \frac{2}{x+2} - \frac{3}{(x+2)^2}$$

29. $$\frac{x^2-2x-3}{(x-1)^3} = \frac{A}{x-1} + \frac{B}{(x-1)^2} + \frac{C}{(x-1)^3}$$
$$= \frac{A(x-1)^2}{(x-1)^3} + \frac{B(x-1)}{(x-1)^3} + \frac{C}{(x-1)^3}$$
$$= \frac{Ax^2-2Ax+A+Bx-B+C}{(x-1)^3}$$
$$= \frac{Ax^2+(-2A+B)x+(A-B+C)}{(x-1)^3}$$

$$\begin{cases} A = 1 \\ -2A+B = -2 \\ A-B+C = -3 \end{cases} \Rightarrow \begin{matrix} A=1 \\ B=0 \\ C=-4 \end{matrix} \qquad \frac{x^2-2x-3}{(x-1)^3} = \frac{1}{x-1} - \frac{4}{(x-1)^3}$$

30. $$\frac{x^2+8x+18}{(x+3)^3} = \frac{A}{x+3} + \frac{B}{(x+3)^2} + \frac{C}{(x+3)^3}$$
$$= \frac{A(x+3)^2}{(x+3)^3} + \frac{B(x+3)}{(x+3)^3} + \frac{C}{(x+3)^3}$$
$$= \frac{Ax^2+6Ax+9A+Bx+3B+C}{(x+3)^3}$$
$$= \frac{Ax^2+(6A+B)x+(9A+3B+C)}{(x+3)^3}$$

$$\begin{cases} A = 1 \\ 6A+B = 8 \\ 9A+3B+C = 18 \end{cases} \Rightarrow \begin{matrix} A=1 \\ B=2 \\ C=3 \end{matrix} \qquad \frac{x^2+8x+18}{(x+3)^3} = \frac{1}{x+3} + \frac{2}{(x+3)^2} + \frac{3}{(x+3)^3}$$

31. $$\frac{x^3+4x^2+2x+1}{x^4+x^3+x^2}=$$

$$\begin{aligned}\frac{x^3+4x^2+2x+1}{x^2(x^2+x+1)} &= \frac{A}{x}+\frac{B}{x^2}+\frac{Cx+D}{x^2+x+1}\\ &= \frac{Ax(x^2+x+1)}{x^2(x^2+x+1)}+\frac{B(x^2+x+1)}{x^2(x^2+x+1)}+\frac{(Cx+D)x^2}{x^2(x^2+x+1)}\\ &= \frac{Ax^3+Ax^2+Ax+Bx^2+Bx+B+Cx^3+Dx^2}{x^2(x^2+x+1)}\\ &= \frac{(A+C)x^3+(A+B+D)x^2+(A+B)x+B}{x^2(x^2+x+1)}\end{aligned}$$

$$\begin{cases}A \quad +C \quad =1\\ A+B \quad +D=4\\ A+B \quad =2\\ \quad B \quad =1\end{cases} \Rightarrow \begin{matrix}A=1\\ B=1\\ C=0\\ D=2\end{matrix} \quad \frac{x^3+4x^2+2x+1}{x^2(x^2+x+1)}=\frac{1}{x}+\frac{1}{x^2}+\frac{2}{x^2+x+1}$$

32. $$\begin{aligned}\frac{3x^3+5x^2+3x+1}{x^2(x^2+x+1)} &= \frac{A}{x}+\frac{B}{x^2}+\frac{Cx+D}{x^2+x+1}\\ &= \frac{Ax(x^2+x+1)}{x^2(x^2+x+1)}+\frac{B(x^2+x+1)}{x^2(x^2+x+1)}+\frac{(Cx+D)x^2}{x^2(x^2+x+1)}\\ &= \frac{Ax^3+Ax^2+Ax+Bx^2+Bx+B+Cx^3+Dx^2}{x^2(x^2+x+1)}\\ &= \frac{(A+C)x^3+(A+B+D)x^2+(A+B)x+B}{x^2(x^2+x+1)}\end{aligned}$$

$$\begin{cases}A \quad +C \quad =3\\ A+B \quad +D=5\\ A+B \quad =3\\ \quad B \quad =1\end{cases} \Rightarrow \begin{matrix}A=2\\ B=1\\ C=1\\ D=2\end{matrix} \quad \frac{3x^3+5x^2+3x+1}{x^2(x^2+x+1)}=\frac{2}{x}+\frac{1}{x^2}+\frac{x+2}{x^2+x+1}$$

33. $$\begin{aligned}\frac{4x^3+5x^2+3x+4}{x^2(x^2+1)} &= \frac{A}{x}+\frac{B}{x^2}+\frac{Cx+D}{x^2+1}\\ &= \frac{Ax(x^2+1)}{x^2(x^2+1)}+\frac{B(x^2+1)}{x^2(x^2+1)}+\frac{(Cx+D)x^2}{x^2(x^2+1)}\\ &= \frac{Ax^3+Ax+Bx^2+B+Cx^3+Dx^2}{x^2(x^2+1)}\\ &= \frac{(A+C)x^3+(B+D)x^2+Ax+B}{x^2(x^2+1)}\end{aligned}$$

$$\begin{cases}A \quad +C \quad =4\\ \quad B \quad +D=5\\ A \quad =3\\ \quad B \quad =4\end{cases} \Rightarrow \begin{matrix}A=3\\ B=4\\ C=1\\ D=1\end{matrix} \quad \frac{4x^3+5x^2+3x+4}{x^2(x^2+1)}=\frac{3}{x}+\frac{4}{x^2}+\frac{x+1}{x^2+1}$$

34. $$\frac{2x^2+1}{x^4+x^2}=\frac{2x^2+1}{x^2(x^2+1)}=\frac{A}{x}+\frac{B}{x^2}+\frac{Cx+D}{x^2+1}$$
$$=\frac{Ax(x^2+1)}{x^2(x^2+1)}+\frac{B(x^2+1)}{x^2(x^2+1)}+\frac{(Cx+D)x^2}{x^2(x^2+1)}$$
$$=\frac{Ax^3+Ax+Bx^2+B+Cx^3+Dx^2}{x^2(x^2+1)}$$
$$=\frac{(A+C)x^3+(B+D)x^2+Ax+B}{x^2(x^2+1)}$$

$$\begin{cases} A \quad +C \quad =0 \\ \quad B \quad +D=2 \\ A \quad\quad\quad =0 \\ \quad B \quad\quad =1 \end{cases} \Rightarrow \begin{array}{l} A=0 \\ B=1 \\ C=0 \\ D=1 \end{array} \quad \frac{2x^2+1}{x^2(x^2+1)}=\frac{1}{x^2}+\frac{1}{x^2+1}$$

35. $$\frac{-x^2-3x-5}{x^3+x^2+2x+2}=\frac{-x^2-3x-5}{x^2(x+1)+2(x+1)}=\frac{-x^2-3x-5}{(x+1)(x^2+2)}$$
$$\frac{-x^2-3x-5}{(x+1)(x^2+2)}=\frac{A}{x+1}+\frac{Bx+C}{x^2+2}$$
$$=\frac{A(x^2+2)}{(x+1)(x^2+2)}+\frac{(Bx+C)(x+1)}{(x+1)(x^2+2)}$$
$$=\frac{Ax^2+2A+Bx^2+Bx+Cx+C}{(x+1)(x^2+2)}$$
$$=\frac{(A+B)x^2+(B+C)x+(2A+C)}{(x+1)(x^2+2)}$$

$$\begin{cases} A+B \quad =-1 \\ \quad B+C=-3 \\ 2A \quad +C=-5 \end{cases} \Rightarrow \begin{array}{l} A=-1 \\ B=0 \\ C=-3 \end{array} \quad \frac{-x^2-3x-5}{(x+1)(x^2+2)}=\frac{-1}{x+1}-\frac{3}{x^2+2}$$

36. $$\frac{-2x^3+7x^2+6}{x^2(x^2+2)}=\frac{A}{x}+\frac{B}{x^2}+\frac{Cx+D}{x^2+2}$$
$$=\frac{Ax(x^2+2)}{x^2(x^2+2)}+\frac{B(x^2+2)}{x^2(x^2+2)}+\frac{(Cx+D)x^2}{x^2(x^2+2)}$$
$$=\frac{Ax^3+2Ax+Bx^2+2B+Cx^3+Dx^2}{x^2(x^2+2)}$$
$$=\frac{(A+C)x^3+(B+D)x^2+2Ax+2B}{x^2(x^2+2)}$$

$$\begin{cases} A \quad +C \quad =-2 \\ \quad B \quad +D=\ 7 \\ 2A \quad\quad\quad =\ 0 \\ \quad 2B \quad\quad =\ 6 \end{cases} \Rightarrow \begin{array}{l} A=0 \\ B=3 \\ C=-2 \\ D=4 \end{array} \quad \frac{-2x^3+7x^2+6}{x^2(x^2+2)}=\frac{3}{x^2}+\frac{-2x+4}{x^2+2}$$

37. $$\frac{x^3+4x^2+3x+6}{(x^2+2)(x^2+x+2)} = \frac{Ax+B}{x^2+2}+\frac{Cx+D}{x^2+x+2}$$
$$= \frac{(Ax+B)(x^2+x+2)}{(x^2+2)(x^2+x+2)}+\frac{(Cx+D)(x^2+2)}{(x^2+2)(x^2+x+2)}$$
$$= \frac{Ax^3+Ax^2+2Ax+Bx^2+Bx+2B+Cx^3+2Cx+Dx^2+2D}{(x^2+2)(x^2+x+2)}$$
$$= \frac{(A+C)x^3+(A+B+D)x^2+(2A+B+2C)x+(2B+2D)}{(x^2+2)(x^2+x+2)}$$

$$\begin{cases} A \quad + C \quad = 1 \\ A + B \quad + D = 4 \\ 2A + B + 2C \quad = 3 \\ 2B \quad + 2D = 6 \end{cases} \Rightarrow \begin{array}{l} A=1 \\ B=1 \\ C=0 \\ D=2 \end{array} \quad \frac{x^3+4x^2+3x+6}{(x^2+2)(x^2+x+2)} = \frac{x+1}{x^2+2}+\frac{2}{x^2+x+2}$$

38. $$\frac{x^3+3x^2+2x+4}{(x^2+1)(x^2+x+2)} = \frac{Ax+B}{x^2+1}+\frac{Cx+D}{x^2+x+2}$$
$$= \frac{(Ax+B)(x^2+x+2)}{(x^2+1)(x^2+x+2)}+\frac{(Cx+D)(x^2+1)}{(x^2+1)(x^2+x+2)}$$
$$= \frac{Ax^3+Ax^2+2Ax+Bx^2+Bx+2B+Cx^3+Cx+Dx^2+D}{(x^2+1)(x^2+x+2)}$$
$$= \frac{(A+C)x^3+(A+B+D)x^2+(2A+B+C)x+(2B+D)}{(x^2+1)(x^2+x+2)}$$

$$\begin{cases} A \quad + C \quad = 1 \\ A + B \quad + D = 3 \\ 2A + B + C \quad = 2 \\ 2B \quad + D = 4 \end{cases} \Rightarrow \begin{array}{l} A=0 \\ B=1 \\ C=1 \\ D=2 \end{array} \quad \frac{x^3+3x^2+2x+4}{(x^2+1)(x^2+x+2)} = \frac{1}{x^2+1}+\frac{x+2}{x^2+x+2}$$

39. $$\frac{2x^4+6x^3+20x^2+22x+25}{x(x^2+2x+5)^2}$$
$$= \frac{A}{x}+\frac{Bx+C}{x^2+2x+5}+\frac{Dx+E}{(x^2+2x+5)^2}$$
$$= \frac{A(x^2+2x+5)^2}{x(x^2+2x+5)^2}+\frac{(Bx+C)(x)(x^2+2x+5)}{x(x^2+2x+5)^2}+\frac{(Dx+E)x}{x(x^2+2x+5)^2}$$
$$= \frac{(A+B)x^4+(4A+2B+C)x^3+(14A+5B+2C+D)x^2+(20A+5C+E)x+(25A)}{x(x^2+2x+5)^2}$$

$$\begin{cases} A + B \quad = 2 \\ 4A + 2B + C \quad = 6 \\ 14A + 5B + 2C + D \quad = 20 \\ 20A \quad + 5C \quad + E = 22 \\ 25A \quad = 25 \end{cases} \Rightarrow \begin{array}{l} A=1 \\ B=1 \\ C=0 \\ D=1 \\ E=2 \end{array}$$

$$\frac{2x^4+6x^3+20x^2+22x+25}{x(x^2+2x+5)^2} = \frac{1}{x}+\frac{x}{x^2+2x+5}+\frac{x+2}{(x^2+2x+5)^2}$$

40. $$\frac{x^3+3x^2+6x+6}{(x^2+1)(x^2+x+5)} = \frac{Ax+B}{x^2+1}+\frac{Cx+D}{x^2+x+5}$$
$$= \frac{(Ax+B)(x^2+x+5)}{(x^2+1)(x^2+x+5)}+\frac{(Cx+D)(x^2+1)}{(x^2+1)(x^2+x+5)}$$
$$= \frac{Ax^3+Ax^2+5Ax+Bx^2+Bx+5B+Cx^3+Cx+Dx^2+D}{(x^2+1)(x^2+x+5)}$$
$$= \frac{(A+C)x^3+(A+B+D)x^2+(5A+B+C)x+(5B+D)}{(x^2+1)(x^2+x+5)}$$

$$\begin{cases} A \quad +C = 1 \\ A+B \quad +D = 3 \\ 5A+B+C = 6 \\ 5B \quad +D = 6 \end{cases} \Rightarrow \begin{matrix} A=1 \\ B=1 \\ C=0 \\ D=1 \end{matrix} \quad \frac{x^3+3x^2+6x+6}{(x^2+1)(x^2+x+5)} = \frac{x+1}{x^2+1}+\frac{1}{x^2+x+5}$$

41. Use long division first: $\frac{x^3}{x^2+3x+2} = x-3+\frac{7x+6}{x^2+3x+2} = x-3+\frac{7x+6}{(x+1)(x+2)}$

$$\frac{7x+6}{(x+1)(x+2)} = \frac{A}{x+1}+\frac{B}{x+2}$$
$$= \frac{A(x+2)}{(x+1)(x+2)}+\frac{B(x+1)}{(x+1)(x+2)}$$
$$= \frac{Ax+2A+Bx+B}{(x+1)(x+2)}$$
$$= \frac{(A+B)x+(2A+B)}{(x+1)(x+2)}$$

$$\begin{cases} A+B=7 \\ 2A+B=6 \end{cases} \Rightarrow A=-1, B=8 \quad x-3+\tfrac{7x+6}{(x+1)(x+2)} = x-3-\tfrac{1}{x+1}+\tfrac{8}{x+2}$$

42. Use long division first: $\frac{2x^3+6x^2+3x+2}{x^3+x^2} = 2+\frac{4x^2+3x+2}{x^3+x^2} = 2+\frac{4x^2+3x+2}{x^2(x+1)}$

$$\frac{4x^2+3x+2}{x^2(x+1)} = \frac{A}{x}+\frac{B}{x^2}+\frac{C}{x+1}$$
$$= \frac{Ax(x+1)}{x^2(x+1)}+\frac{B(x+1)}{x^2(x+1)}+\frac{Cx^2}{x^2(x+1)}$$
$$= \frac{Ax^2+Ax+Bx+B+Cx^2}{x^2(x+1)}$$
$$= \frac{(A+C)x^2+(A+B)x+(B)}{x^2(x+1)}$$

$$\begin{cases} A \quad +C = 4 \\ A+B \quad = 3 \\ B \quad = 2 \end{cases} \Rightarrow \begin{matrix} A=1 \\ B=2 \\ C=3 \end{matrix} \quad 2+\frac{4x^2+3x+2}{x^2(x+1)} = 2+\frac{1}{x}+\frac{2}{x^2}+\frac{3}{x+1}$$

43. Use long division first: $\dfrac{3x^3+3x^2+6x+4}{3x^3+x^2+3x+1} = 1 + \dfrac{2x^2+3x+3}{3x^3+x^2+3x+1} = 1 + \dfrac{2x^2+3x+3}{(3x+1)(x^2+1)}$

$$\begin{aligned}\frac{2x^2+3x+3}{(3x+1)(x^2+1)} &= \frac{A}{3x+1} + \frac{Bx+C}{x^2+1} \\ &= \frac{A(x^2+1)}{(3x+1)(x^2+1)} + \frac{(Bx+C)(3x+1)}{(3x+1)(x^2+1)} \\ &= \frac{Ax^2+A+3Bx^2+Bx+3Cx+C}{(3x+1)(x^2+1)} \\ &= \frac{(A+3B)x^2+(B+3C)x+(A+C)}{(3x+1)(x^2+1)}\end{aligned}$$

$$\begin{cases} A+3B = 2 \\ \phantom{A+{}}B+3C = 3 \\ A +C = 3 \end{cases} \Rightarrow \begin{array}{l} A=2 \\ B=0 \\ C=1 \end{array} \quad 1 + \frac{2x^2+3x+3}{(3x+1)(x^2+1)} = 1 + \frac{2}{3x+1} + \frac{1}{x^2+1}$$

44. Use long division first: $\dfrac{x^4+x^3+3x^2+x+4}{(x^2+1)^2} = 1 + \dfrac{x^3+x^2+x+3}{(x^2+1)^2}$

$$\begin{aligned}\frac{x^3+x^2+x+3}{(x^2+1)^2} &= \frac{Ax+B}{x^2+1} + \frac{Cx+D}{(x^2+1)^2} \\ &= \frac{(Ax+B)(x^2+1)}{(x^2+1)^2} + \frac{(Cx+D)}{(x^2+1)^2} \\ &= \frac{Ax^3+Ax+Bx^2+B+Cx+D}{(x^2+1)^2} \\ &= \frac{Ax^3+Bx^2+(A+C)x+(B+D)}{(x^2+1)^2}\end{aligned}$$

$$\begin{cases} A = 1 \\ B = 1 \\ A+C = 1 \\ B+D = 3 \end{cases} \Rightarrow \begin{array}{l} A=1 \\ B=1 \\ C=0 \\ D=2 \end{array} \quad 1 + \frac{x^3+x^2+x+3}{(x^2+1)^2} = 1 + \frac{x+1}{x^2+1} + \frac{2}{(x^2+1)^2}$$

45. Use long division first: $\dfrac{x^3+3x^2+2x+1}{x^3+x^2+x} = 1 + \dfrac{2x^2+x+1}{x^3+x^2+x} = 1 + \dfrac{2x^2+x+1}{x(x^2+x+1)}$

$$\begin{aligned}\frac{2x^2+x+1}{x(x^2+x+1)} &= \frac{A}{x} + \frac{Bx+C}{x^2+x+1} \\ &= \frac{A(x^2+x+1)}{x(x^2+x+1)} + \frac{(Bx+C)x}{x(x^2+x+1)} \\ &= \frac{Ax^2+Ax+A+Bx^2+Cx}{x(x^2+x+1)} \\ &= \frac{(A+B)x^2+(A+C)x+(A)}{x(x^2+x+1)}\end{aligned}$$

continued on next page...

45. continued

$$\frac{2x^2+x+1}{x(x^2+x+1)}=\frac{(A+B)x^2+(A+C)x+(A)}{x(x^2+x+1)}$$

$$\begin{cases} A+B = 2 \\ A + C = 1 \\ A = 1 \end{cases} \Rightarrow \begin{matrix} A=1 \\ B=1 \\ C=0 \end{matrix} \quad 1+\frac{2x^2+x+1}{x(x^2+x+1)}=1+\frac{1}{x}+\frac{x}{x^2+x+1}$$

46. Use long division first: $\dfrac{x^4-x^3+x^2-x+1}{(x^2+1)^2}=1+\dfrac{-x^3-x^2-x}{(x^2+1)^2}$

$$\begin{aligned}\frac{-x^3-x^2-x}{(x^2+1)^2}&=\frac{Ax+B}{x^2+1}+\frac{Cx+D}{(x^2+1)^2}\\&=\frac{(Ax+B)(x^2+1)}{(x^2+1)^2}+\frac{(Cx+D)}{(x^2+1)^2}\\&=\frac{Ax^3+Ax+Bx^2+B+Cx+D}{(x^2+1)^2}\\&=\frac{Ax^3+Bx^2+(A+C)x+(B+D)}{(x^2+1)^2}\end{aligned}$$

$$\begin{cases} A = -1 \\ B = -1 \\ A + C = -1 \\ B + D = 0 \end{cases} \Rightarrow \begin{matrix} A=-1 \\ B=-1 \\ C=0 \\ D=1 \end{matrix} \quad \begin{aligned}1+\frac{-x^3-x^2-x}{(x^2+1)^2}&=1+\frac{-x-1}{x^2+1}+\frac{1}{(x^2+1)^2}\\&=1-\frac{x+1}{x^2+1}+\frac{1}{(x^2+1)^2}\end{aligned}$$

47. Use long division first: $\dfrac{2x^4+2x^3+3x^2-1}{(x^2-x)(x^2+1)}=2+\dfrac{4x^3+x^2+2x-1}{x(x-1)(x^2+1)}$

$$\begin{aligned}\frac{4x^3+x^2+2x-1}{x(x-1)(x^2+1)}&=\frac{A}{x}+\frac{B}{x-1}+\frac{Cx+D}{x^2+1}\\&=\frac{A(x-1)(x^2+1)}{x(x-1)(x^2+1)}+\frac{Bx(x^2+1)}{x(x-1)(x^2+1)}+\frac{(Cx+D)(x)(x-1)}{x(x-1)(x^2+1)}\\&=\frac{Ax^3-Ax^2+Ax-A+Bx^3+Bx+Cx^3-Cx^2+Dx^2-Dx}{x(x-1)(x^2+1)}\\&=\frac{(A+B+C)x^3+(-A-C+D)x^2+(A+B-D)x+(-A)}{x(x-1)(x^2+1)}\end{aligned}$$

$$\begin{cases} A+B+C = 4 \\ -A - C + D = 1 \\ A+B - D = 2 \\ -A = -1 \end{cases} \Rightarrow \begin{matrix} A=1 \\ B=3 \\ C=0 \\ D=2 \end{matrix} \quad 2+\frac{4x^3+x^2+2x-1}{x(x-1)(x^2+1)}=2+\frac{1}{x}+\frac{3}{x-1}+\frac{2}{x^2+1}$$

48. Use long division first: $\dfrac{x^4 - x^3 + 5x^2 + x + 6}{(x^2+3)(x^2+1)} = 1 + \dfrac{-x^3 + x^2 + x + 3}{(x^2+3)(x^2+1)}$

$$\begin{aligned}\frac{-x^3 + x^2 + x + 3}{(x^2+3)(x^2+1)} &= \frac{Ax+B}{x^2+3} + \frac{Cx+D}{x^2+1}\\ &= \frac{(Ax+B)(x^2+1)}{(x^2+3)(x^2+1)} + \frac{(Cx+D)(x^2+3)}{(x^2+3)(x^2+1)}\\ &= \frac{Ax^3 + Ax + Bx^2 + B + Cx^3 + 3Cx + Dx^2 + 3D}{(x^2+3)(x^2+1)}\\ &= \frac{(A+C)x^3 + (B+D)x^2 + (A+3C)x + (B+3D)}{(x^2+3)(x^2+1)}\end{aligned}$$

$$\begin{cases} A + C = -1 \\ B + D = 1 \\ A + 3C = 1 \\ B + 3D = 3 \end{cases} \Rightarrow \begin{matrix} A = -2 \\ B = 0 \\ C = 1 \\ D = 1 \end{matrix} \qquad 1 + \frac{-x^3 + x^2 + x + 3}{(x^2+3)(x^2+1)} = 1 - \frac{2x}{x^2+3} + \frac{x+1}{x^2+1}$$

49. $x^3 + 1 = (x+1)(x^2 - x + 1) \Rightarrow$ not prime

50.
$$\begin{aligned}\frac{1}{x^3+1} = \frac{1}{(x+1)(x^2-x+1)} &= \frac{A}{x+1} + \frac{Bx+C}{x^2-x+1}\\ &= \frac{A(x^2-x+1)}{(x+1)(x^2-x+1)} + \frac{(Bx+C)(x+1)}{(x+1)(x^2-x+1)}\\ &= \frac{Ax^2 - Ax + A + Bx^2 + Bx + Cx + C}{(x+1)(x^2-x+1)}\\ &= \frac{(A+B)x^2 + (-A+B+C)x + (A+C)}{(x+1)(x^2-x+1)}\end{aligned}$$

$$\begin{cases} A + B = 0 \\ -A + B + C = 0 \\ A + C = 1 \end{cases} \Rightarrow \begin{matrix} A = \frac{1}{3} \\ B = -\frac{1}{3} \\ C = \frac{2}{3} \end{matrix} \qquad \frac{1}{x^3+1} = \frac{1}{(x+1)(x^2-x+1)} = \frac{\frac{1}{3}}{x+1} + \frac{-\frac{1}{3}x + \frac{2}{3}}{x^2-x+1}$$

51. $\sqrt{8a^3b} = \sqrt{4a^2}\sqrt{2ab} = 2|a|\sqrt{2ab}$

52. $\sqrt{x^2+6x+9} = \sqrt{(x+3)^2} = |x+3|$

53.
$$\begin{aligned}\sqrt{18x^5} + x^2\sqrt{50x} - 5x^2\sqrt{2x} &= \sqrt{9x^4}\sqrt{2x} + x^2\sqrt{25}\sqrt{2x} - 5x^2\sqrt{2x}\\ &= 3x^2\sqrt{2x} + 5x^2\sqrt{2x} - 5x^2\sqrt{2x} = 3x^2\sqrt{2x}\end{aligned}$$

54. $\dfrac{\sqrt{x^2y^3}}{\sqrt{xy^5}} = \sqrt{\dfrac{x^2y^3}{xy^5}} = \sqrt{\dfrac{x}{y^2}} = \dfrac{\sqrt{x}}{|y|}$

55.
$$\sqrt{x-5} = x-7$$
$$\left(\sqrt{x-5}\right)^2 = (x-7)^2$$
$$x-5 = x^2-14x+49$$
$$0 = x^2-15x+54$$
$$0 = (x-9)(x-6)$$
$$x=9 \quad \text{or} \quad x=6$$
$x=6$ does not check and is extraneous.

56.
$$x-5 = (x-7)^2$$
$$x-5 = x^2-14x+49$$
$$0 = x^2-15x+54$$
$$0 = (x-9)(x-6)$$
$$x=9 \quad \text{or} \quad x=6$$

Exercises 6.7 (page 629)

1. half-plane, boundary

2. excluded

3. is not

4. is

5. $2x+3y<12$

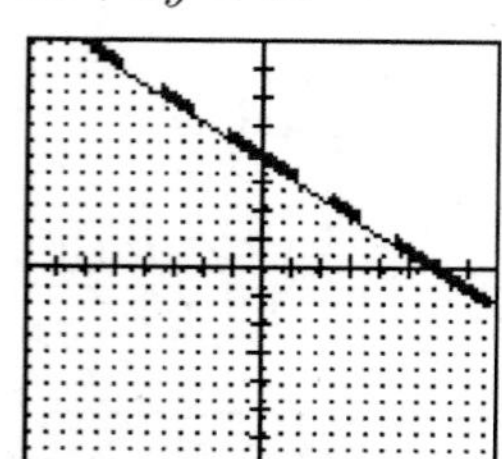

6. $4x-3y>6$

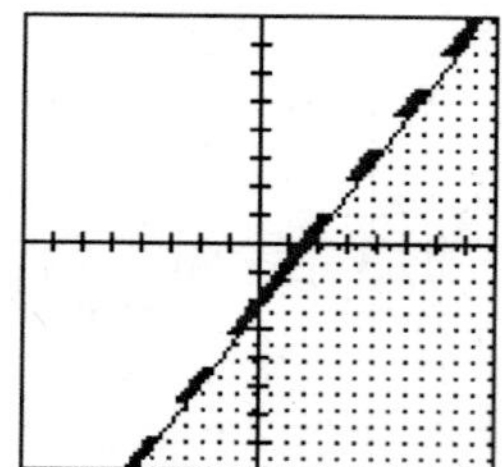

7. $x<3$

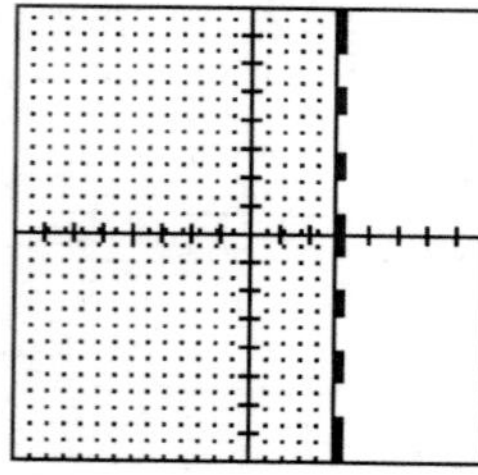

8. $y>-1$

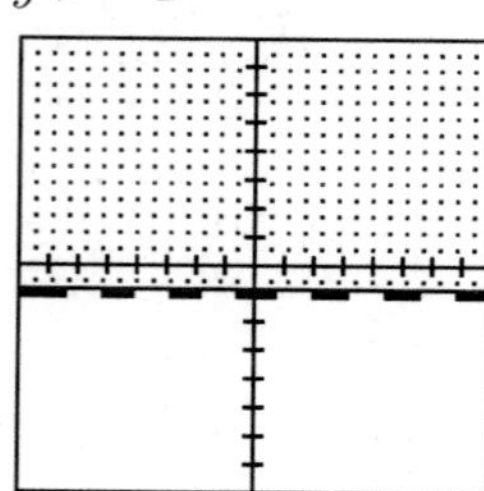

9. $4x-y>4$

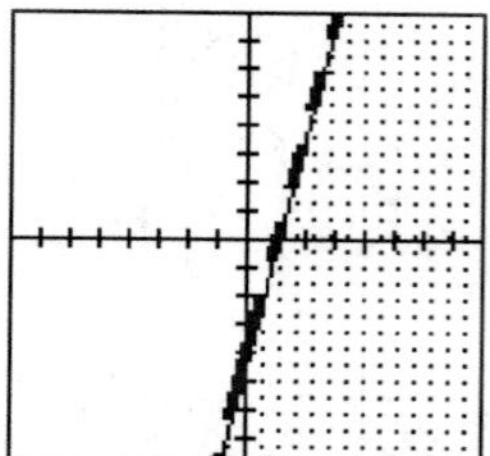

10. $x-2y<5$

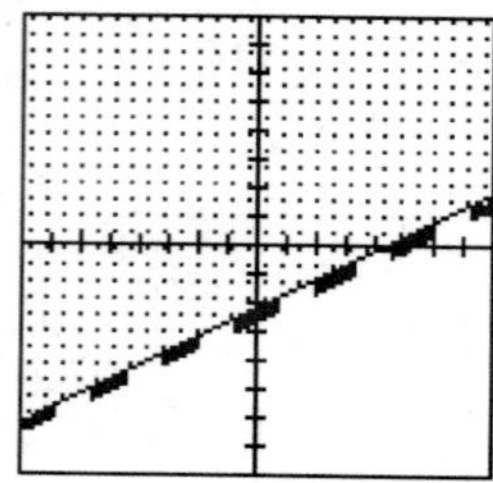

11. $y>2x$

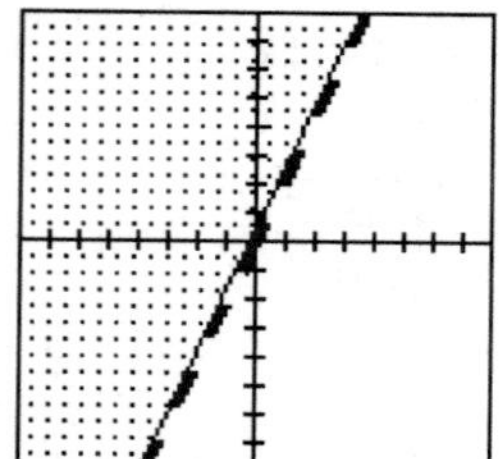

12. $y<3x$

SECTION 6.7

13. $y \le \frac{1}{2}x + 1$

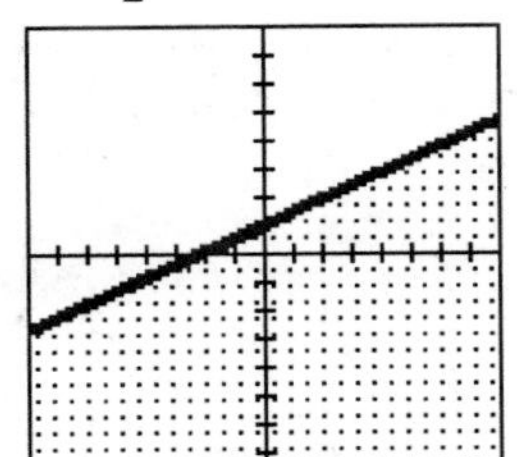

14. $y \ge \frac{1}{3}x - 1$

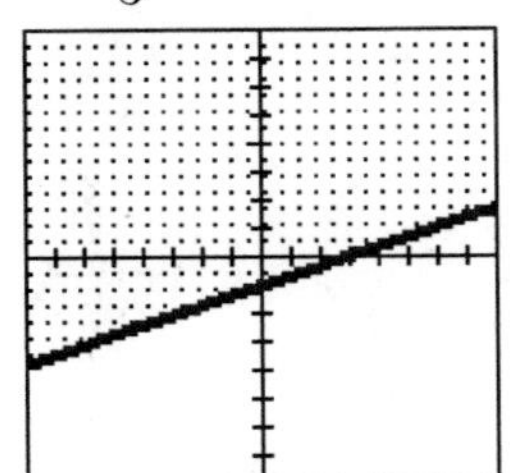

15. $2y \ge 3x - 2$

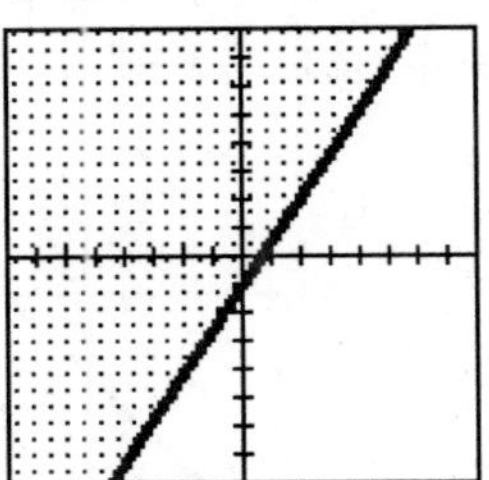

16. $3y \le 2x + 3$

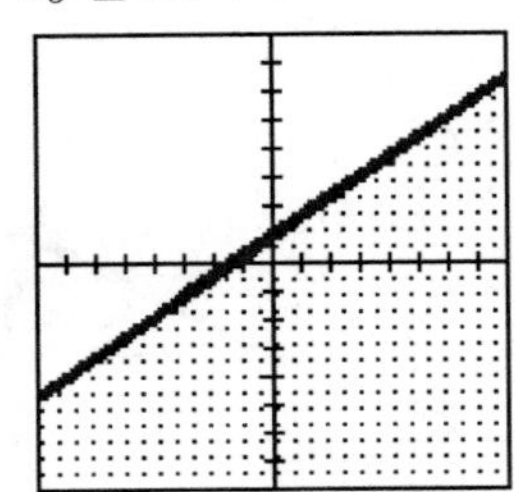

17. $y < x^2$

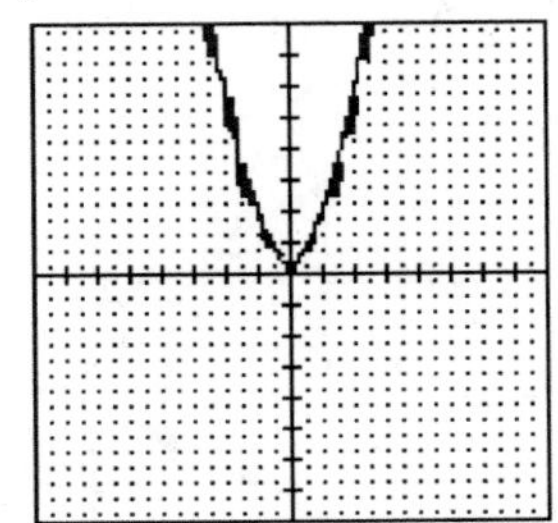

18. $y \ge |x|$

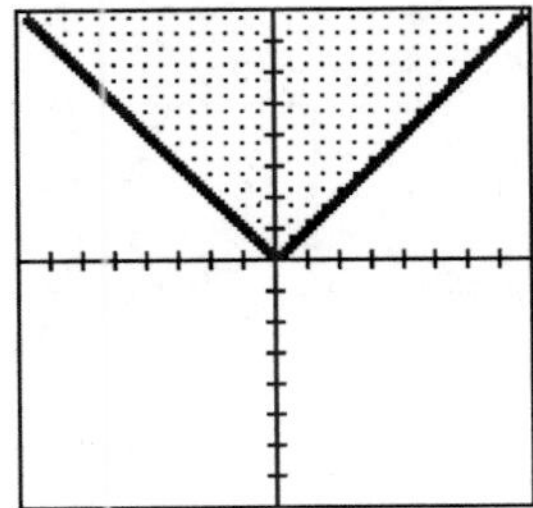

19. $x^2 + y^2 \le 4$

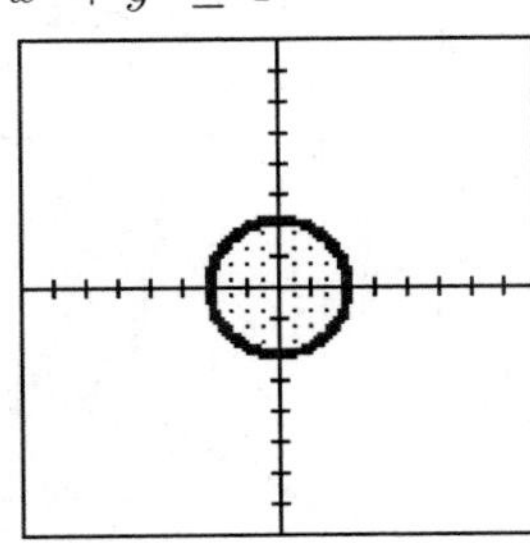

20. $x^2 + y^2 > 4$

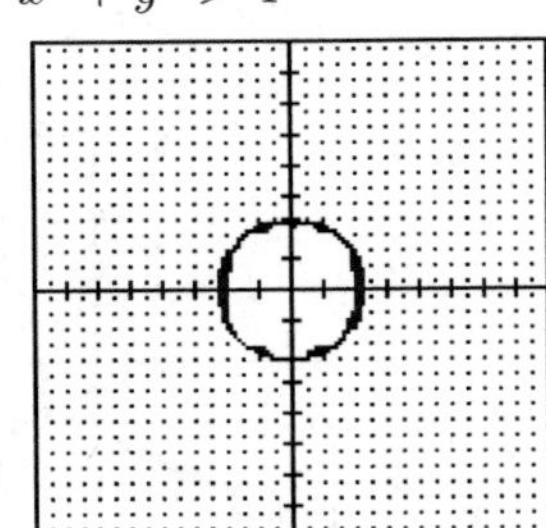

21. $\begin{cases} y < 3 \\ x \ge 2 \end{cases}$

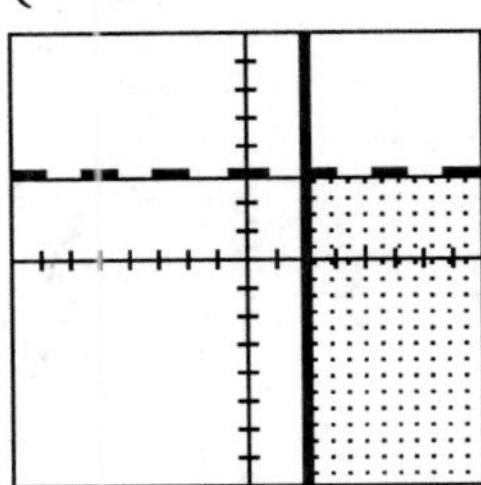

22. $\begin{cases} y \ge -2 \\ x < 0 \end{cases}$

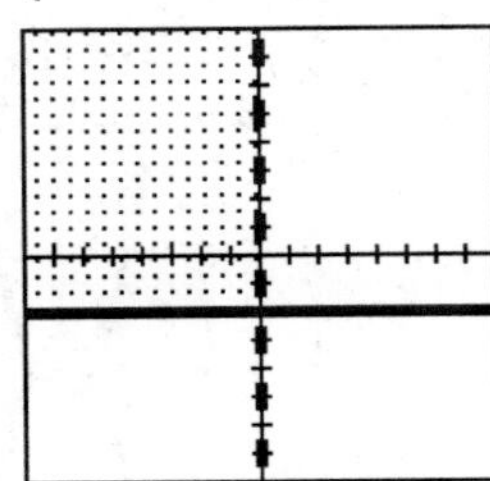

23. $\begin{cases} y \ge 1 \\ x < 2 \end{cases}$

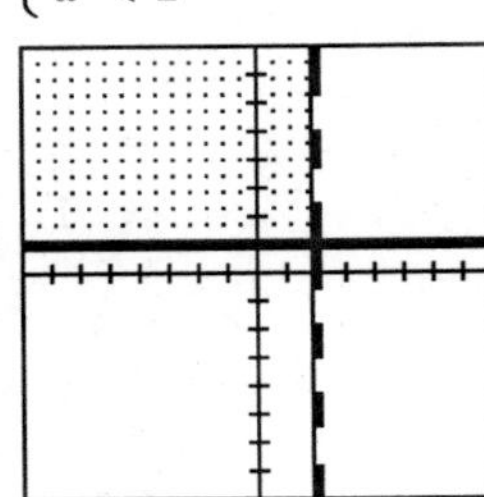

24. $\begin{cases} y \le -1 \\ x > -1 \end{cases}$

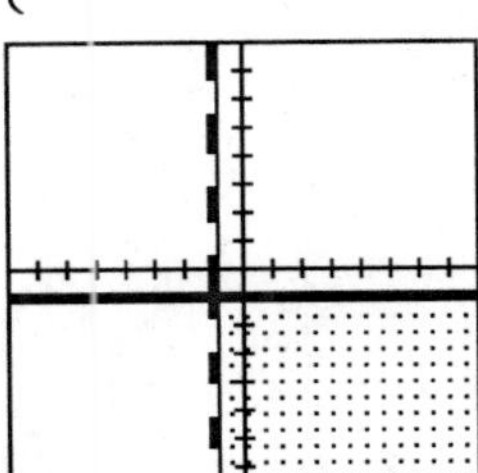

25. $\begin{cases} y \le x - 2 \\ y \ge 2x + 1 \end{cases}$

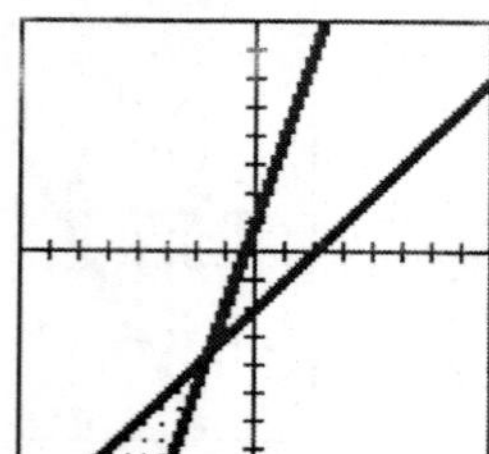

26. $\begin{cases} y < 3x + 2 \\ y < -2x + 3 \end{cases}$

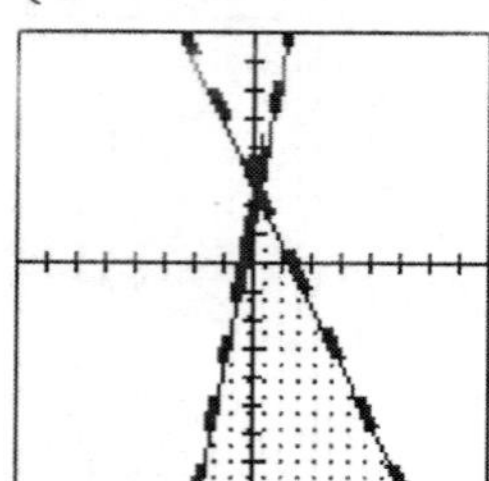

27. $\begin{cases} x + y < 2 \\ x + y \le 1 \end{cases}$

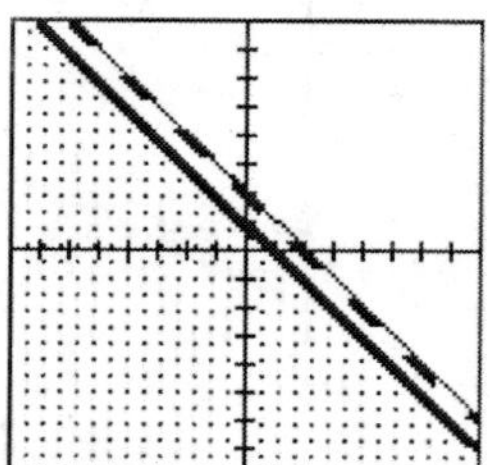

28. $\begin{cases} 3x + 2y \ge 6 \\ x + 3y \le 2 \end{cases}$

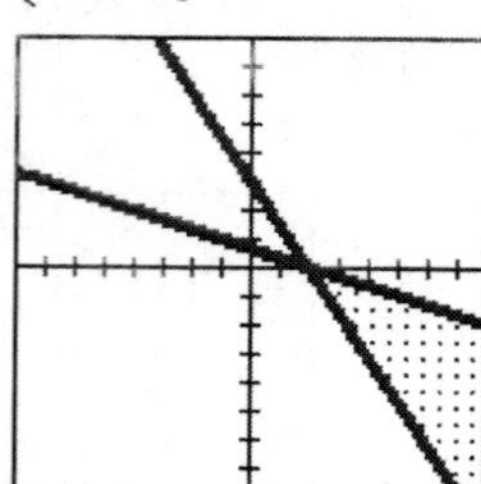

29. $\begin{cases} x + 2y < 3 \\ 2x - 4y < 8 \end{cases}$

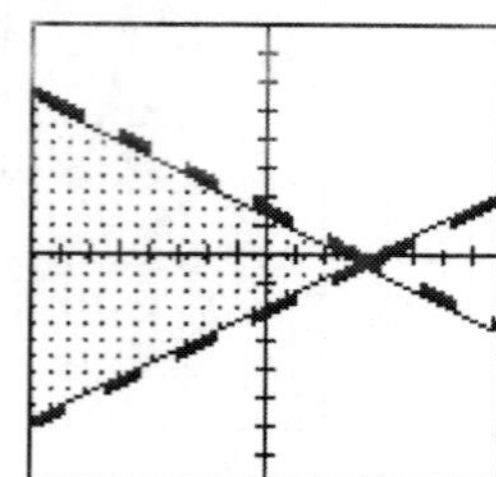

30. $\begin{cases} 3x + y \le 1 \\ -x + 2y \ge 9 \end{cases}$

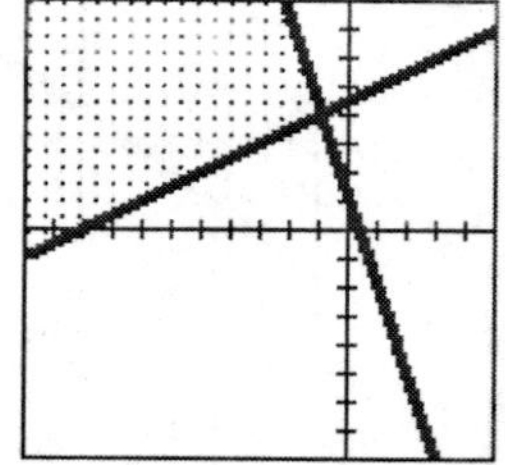

31. $\begin{cases} 2x - 3y \ge 6 \\ 3x + 2y < 6 \end{cases}$

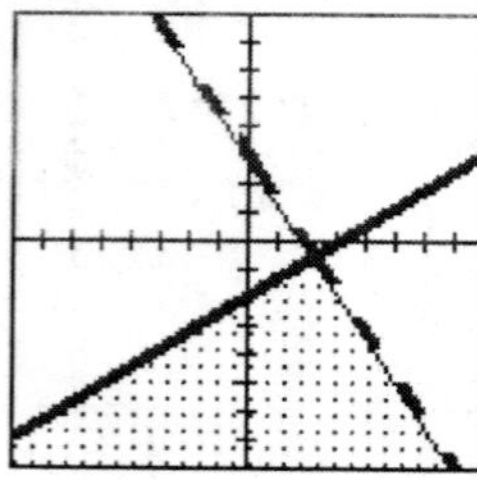

32. $\begin{cases} 4x + 2y \le 6 \\ 2x - 4y \ge 10 \end{cases}$

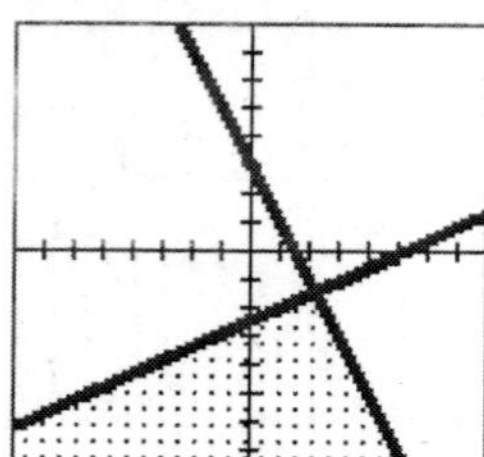

33. $\begin{cases} y \ge x^2 - 4 \\ y \le \frac{1}{2}x \end{cases}$

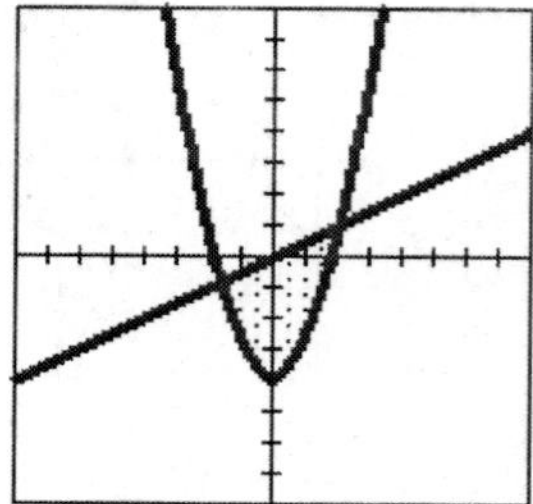

34. $\begin{cases} y \le -x^2 + 4 \\ y > -x - 1 \end{cases}$

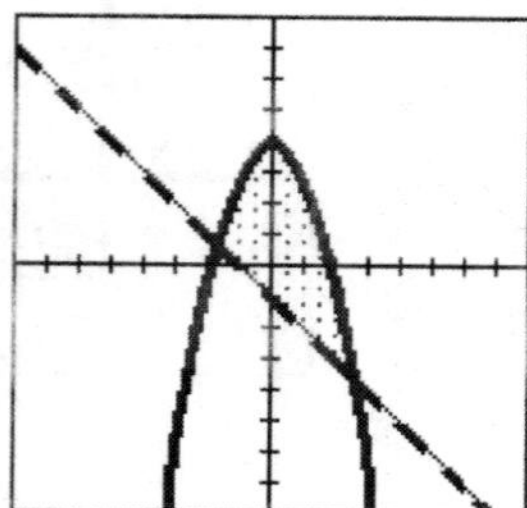

35. $\begin{cases} y \ge x^2 \\ y < 4 - x^2 \end{cases}$

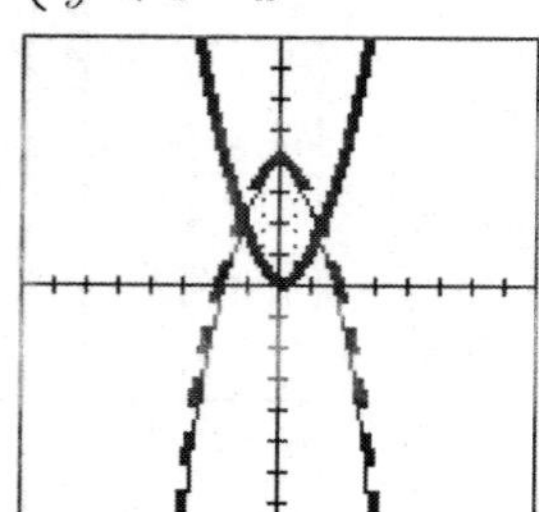

36. $\begin{cases} x^2 + y \le 1 \\ y - x^2 \ge -1 \end{cases}$

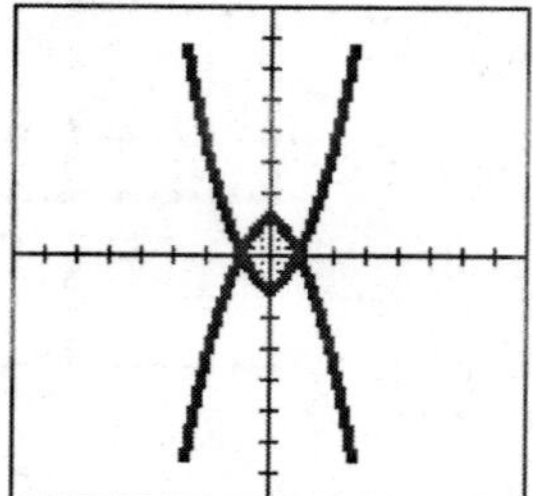

37. $\begin{cases} 2x - y \leq 0 \\ x + 2y \leq 10 \\ y \geq 0 \end{cases}$

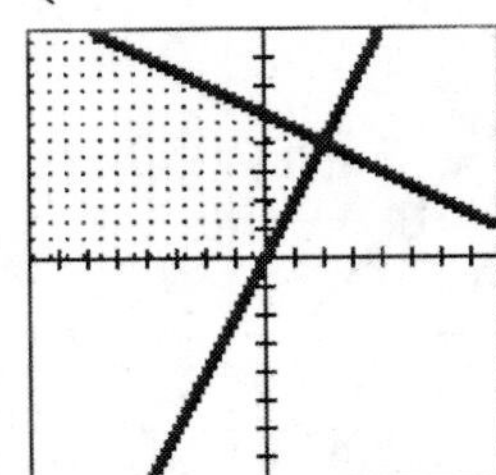

38. $\begin{cases} 3x - 2y \geq 5 \\ 2x + y \geq 8 \\ x \leq 5 \end{cases}$

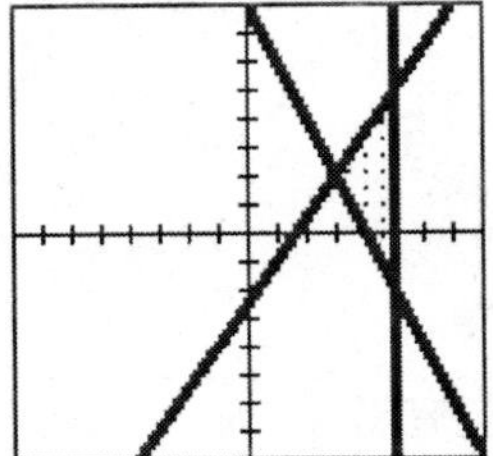

39. $\begin{cases} x - 2y \geq 0 \\ x - y \leq 2 \\ x \geq 0 \end{cases}$

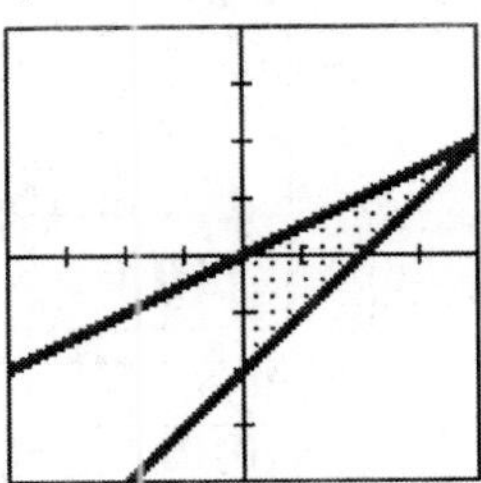

40. $\begin{cases} 2x + 3y \leq 6 \\ x - y \geq 4 \\ y \geq -4 \end{cases}$

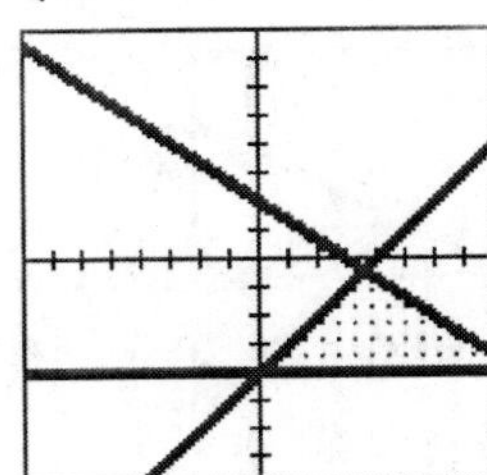

41. $\begin{cases} x + y \leq 4 \\ x - y \leq 4 \\ x \geq 0, y \geq 0 \end{cases}$

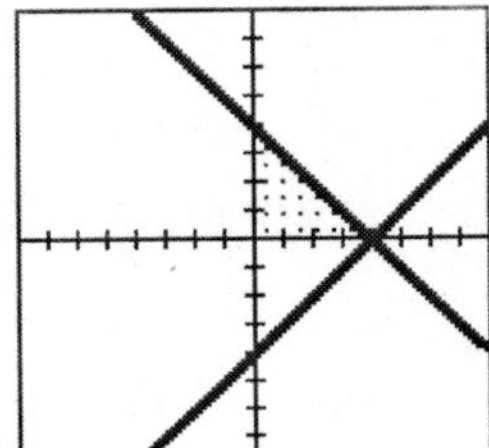

42. $\begin{cases} 2x + 3y \geq 12 \\ 2x - 3y \leq 6 \\ x \geq 0, y \leq 4 \end{cases}$

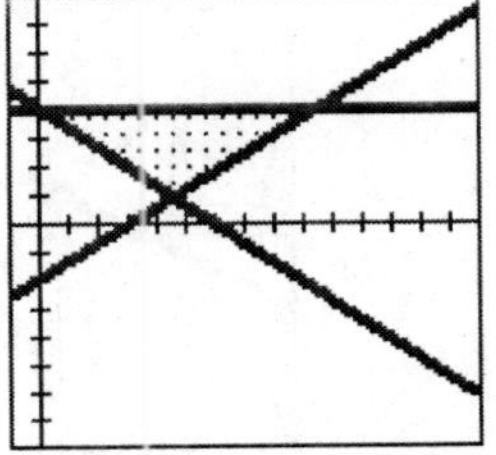

43. $\begin{cases} 3x - 2y \leq 6 \\ x + 2y \leq 10 \\ x \geq 0, y \geq 0 \end{cases}$

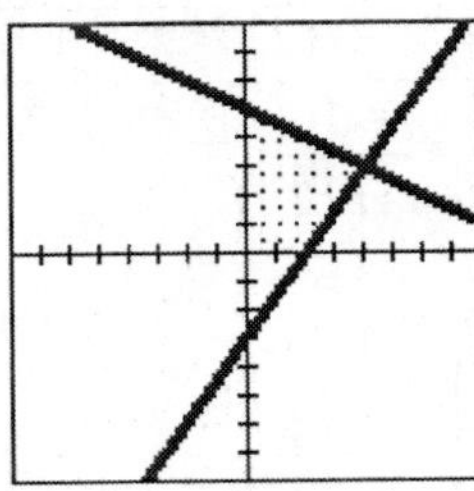

44. $\begin{cases} 3x + 2y \geq 12 \\ 5x - y \leq 15 \\ x \geq 0, y \leq 4 \end{cases}$

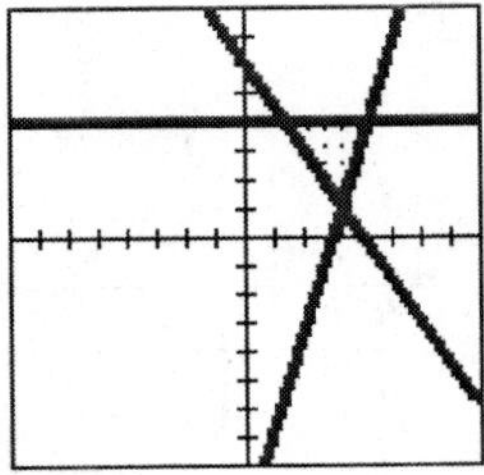

45. $\begin{cases} 6s + 4l \leq 60 \\ s \geq 0, l \geq 0 \end{cases}$

46. $\begin{cases} 5d + 6t \leq 90 \\ d \geq 0, t \geq 0 \end{cases}$

47-52. **Answers may vary.**

53. one, one

54. zero

55. 0

56. yes

Exercises 6.8 (page 639)

1. constraints

2. feasible

3. objective

4. corner, edge

5.

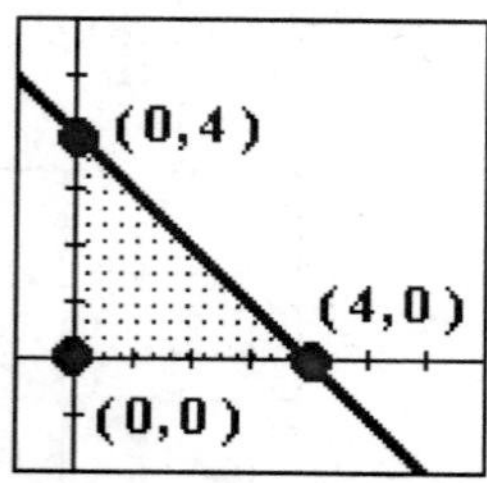

Point	$P = 2x + 3y$
(0, 0)	$= 2(0) + 3(0) = 0$
(0, 4)	$= 2(0) + 3(4) = 12$
(4, 0)	$= 2(4) + 3(0) = 8$

Max: $P = 12$ at $(0, 4)$

6.

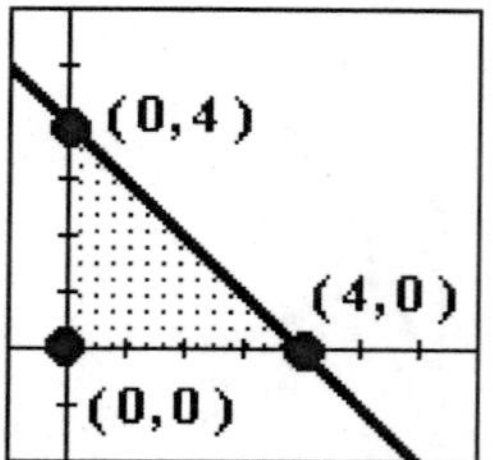

Point	$P = 3x + 2y$
(0, 0)	$= 3(0) + 2(0) = 0$
(0, 4)	$= 3(0) + 2(4) = 8$
(4, 0)	$= 3(4) + 2(0) = 12$

Max: $P = 12$ at $(4, 0)$

7.

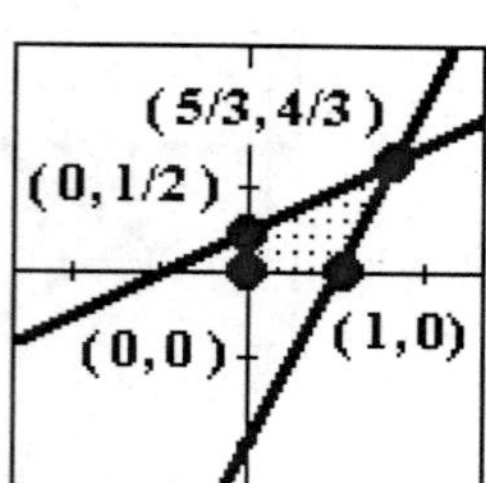

Point	$P = y + \frac{1}{2}x$
(0, 0)	$= 0 + \frac{1}{2}(0) = 0$
$(0, \frac{1}{2})$	$= \frac{1}{2} + \frac{1}{2}(0) = \frac{1}{2}$
$(\frac{5}{3}, \frac{4}{3})$	$= \frac{4}{3} + \frac{1}{2}(\frac{5}{3}) = \frac{13}{6}$
(1, 0)	$= 0 + \frac{1}{2}(1) = \frac{1}{2}$

Max: $P = \frac{13}{6}$ at $\left(\frac{5}{3}, \frac{4}{3}\right)$

8.

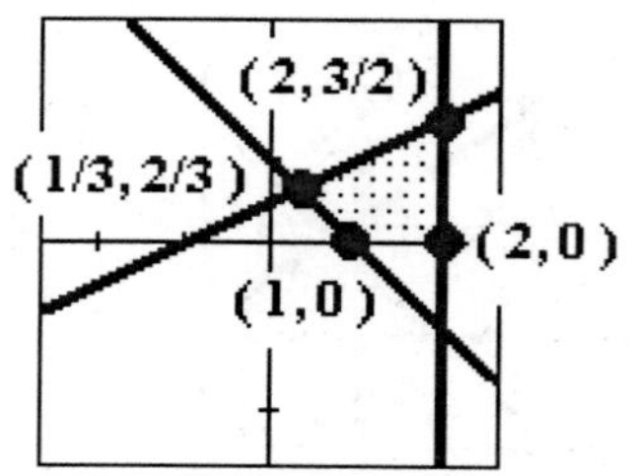

Point	$P = 4y - x$
(1, 0)	$= 4(0) - 1 = -1$
(2, 0)	$= 4(0) - 2 = -2$
$(2, \frac{3}{2})$	$= 4(\frac{3}{2}) - 2 = 4$
$(\frac{1}{3}, \frac{2}{3})$	$= 4(\frac{2}{3}) - \frac{1}{3} = \frac{7}{3}$

Max: $P = 4$ at $\left(2, \frac{3}{2}\right)$

9.

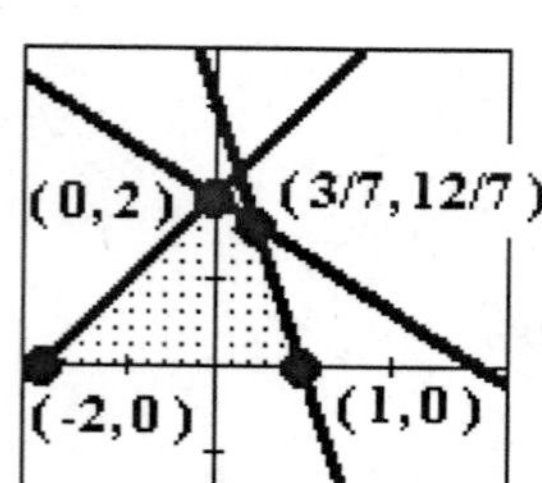

Point	$P = 2x + y$
(−2, 0)	$= 2(-2) + 0 = -4$
(1, 0)	$= 2(1) + 0 = 2$
$(\frac{3}{7}, \frac{12}{7})$	$= 2(\frac{3}{7}) + \frac{12}{7} = \frac{18}{7}$
(0, 2)	$= 2(0) + 2 = 2$

Max: $P = \frac{18}{7}$ at $\left(\frac{3}{7}, \frac{12}{7}\right)$

10.

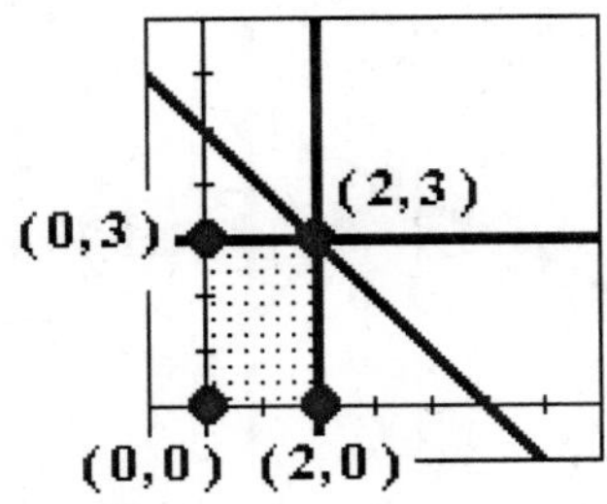

Point	$P = x - 2y$
$(0, 0)$	$= 0 - 2(0) = 0$
$(2, 0)$	$= 2 - 2(0) = 2$
$(2, 3)$	$= 2 - 2(3) = -4$
$(0, 3)$	$= 0 - 2(3) = -6$

Max: $P = 2$ at $(2, 0)$

11.

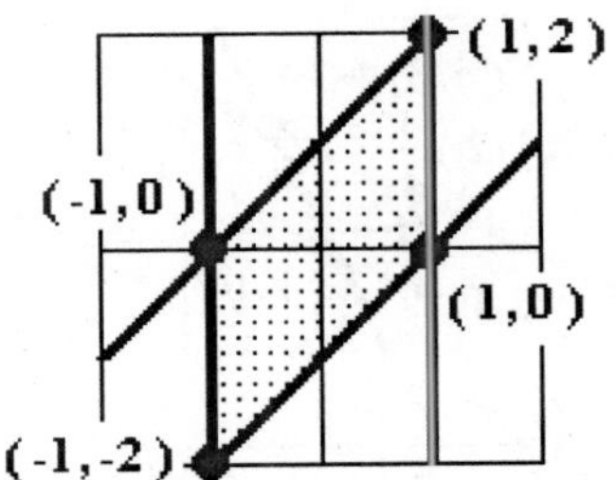

Point	$P = 3x - 2y$
$(1, 0)$	$= 3(1) - 2(0) = 3$
$(1, 2)$	$= 3(1) - 2(2) = -1$
$(-1, 0)$	$= 3(-1) - 2(0) = -3$
$(-1, -2)$	$= 3(-1) - 2(-2) = 1$

Max: $P = 3$ at $(1, 0)$

12.

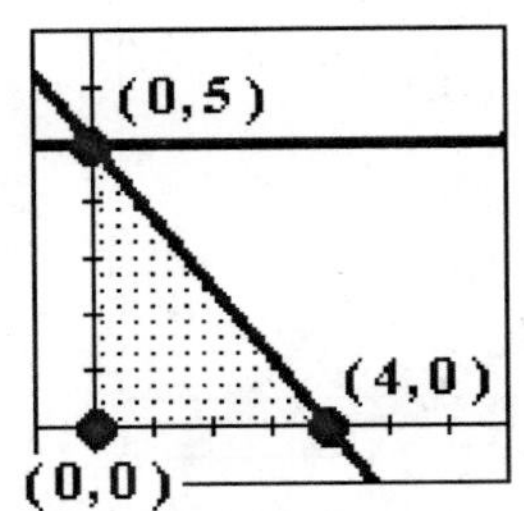

Point	$P = x - y$
$(0, 0)$	$= 0 - 0 = 0$
$(4, 0)$	$= 4 - 0 = 4$
$(0, 5)$	$= 0 - 5 = -5$

Max: $P = 4$ at $(4, 0)$

13.

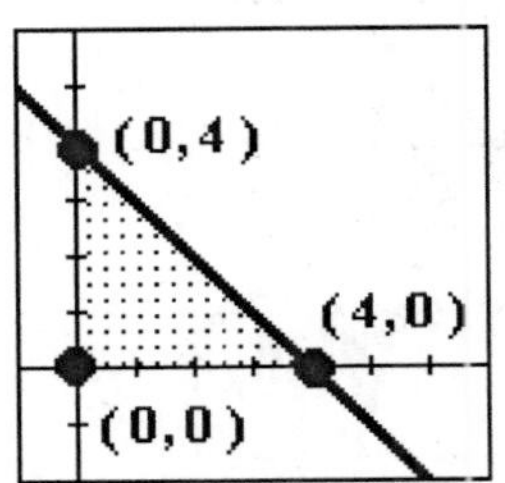

Point	$P = 5x + 12y$
$(0, 0)$	$= 5(0) + 12(0) = 0$
$(0, 4)$	$= 5(0) + 12(4) = 48$
$(4, 0)$	$= 5(4) + 12(0) = 20$

Min: $P = 0$ at $(0, 0)$

14.

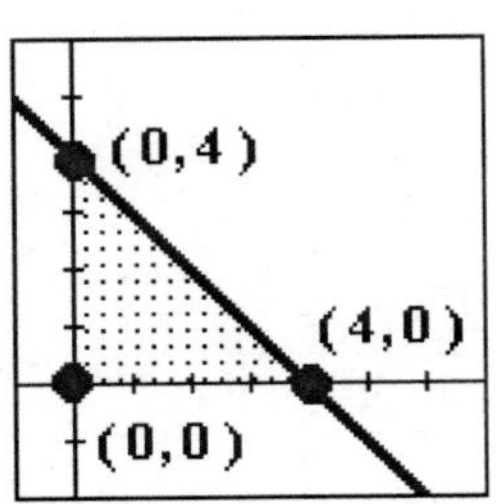

Point	$P = 3x + 6y$
$(0, 0)$	$= 3(0) + 6(0) = 0$
$(0, 4)$	$= 3(0) + 6(4) = 24$
$(4, 0)$	$= 3(4) + 6(0) = 12$

Min: $P = 0$ at $(0, 0)$

15.

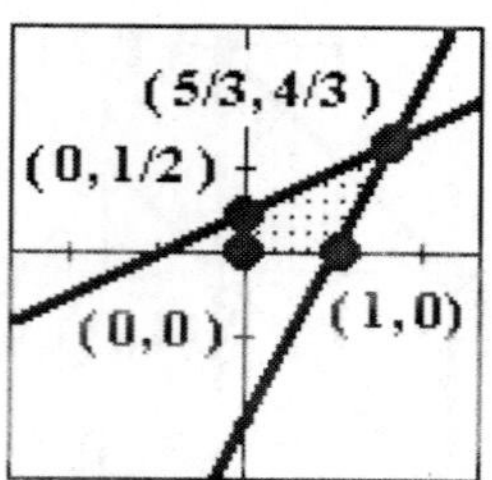

Point	$P = 3y + x$
$(0, 0)$	$= 3(0) + 0 = 0$
$(0, \frac{1}{2})$	$= 3(\frac{1}{2}) + 0 = \frac{3}{2}$
$(\frac{5}{3}, \frac{4}{3})$	$= 3(\frac{4}{3}) + \frac{5}{3} = \frac{17}{3}$
$(1, 0)$	$= 3(0) + 1 = 1$

Min: $P = 0$ at $(0, 0)$

16.

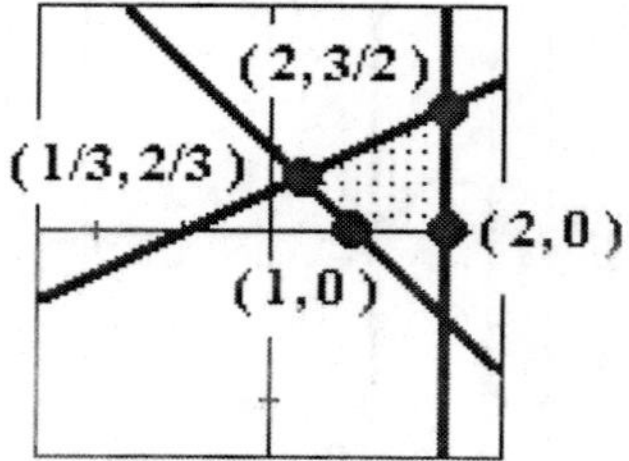

Point	$P = 5y + x$
$(1, 0)$	$= 5(0) + 1 = 1$
$(2, 0)$	$= 5(0) + 2 = 2$
$(2, \frac{3}{2})$	$= 5(\frac{3}{2}) + 2 = \frac{19}{2}$
$(\frac{1}{3}, \frac{2}{3})$	$= 5(\frac{2}{3}) + \frac{1}{3} = \frac{11}{3}$

Min: $P = 1$ at $(1, 0)$

17.

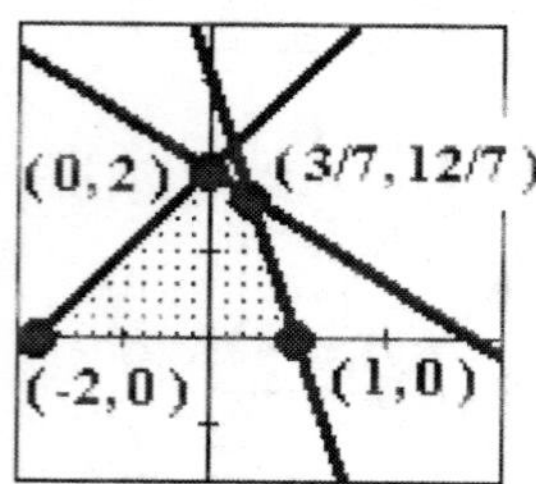

Point	$P = 6x + 2y$
$(-2, 0)$	$= 6(-2) + 2(0) = -12$
$(1, 0)$	$= 6(1) + 2(0) = 6$
$(\frac{3}{7}, \frac{12}{7})$	$= 6(\frac{3}{7}) + 2(\frac{12}{7}) = 6$
$(0, 2)$	$= 6(0) + 2(2) = 4$

Min: $P = -12$ at $(-2, 0)$

18.

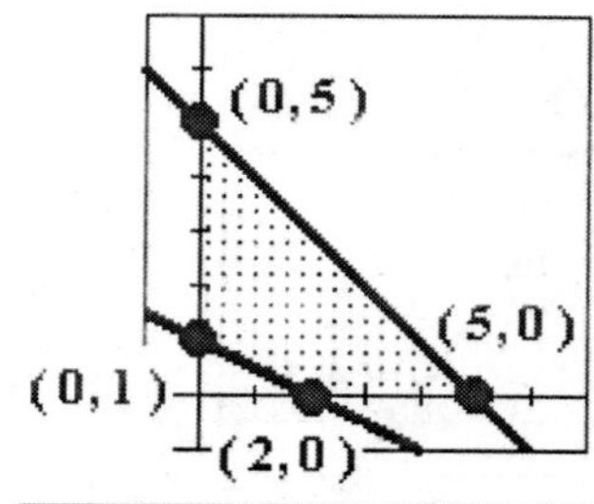

Point	$P = 2y - x$
$(0, 1)$	$= 2(1) - 0 = 2$
$(2, 0)$	$= 2(0) - 2 = -2$
$(5, 0)$	$= 2(0) - 5 = -5$
$(0, 5)$	$= 2(5) - 0 = 10$

Min: $P = -5$ at $(5, 0)$

19.

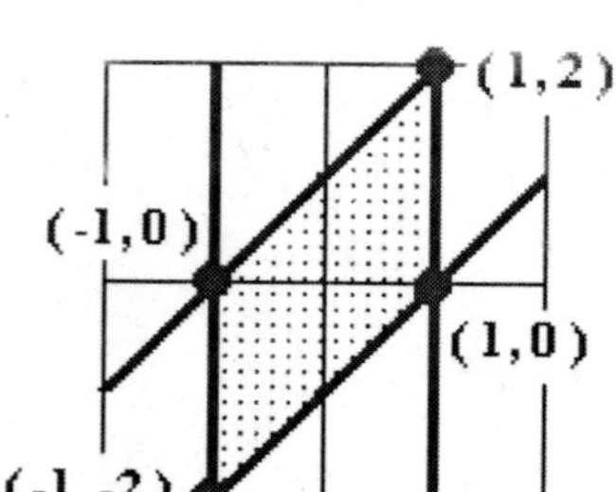

Point	$P = 2x - 2y$
$(1, 0)$	$= 2(1) - 2(0) = 2$
$(1, 2)$	$= 2(1) - 2(2) = -2$
$(-1, 0)$	$= 2(-1) - 2(0) = -2$
$(-1, -2)$	$= 2(-1) - 2(-2) = 2$

Min: $P = -2$ on the edge joining $(1, 2)$ and $(-1, 0)$

20.

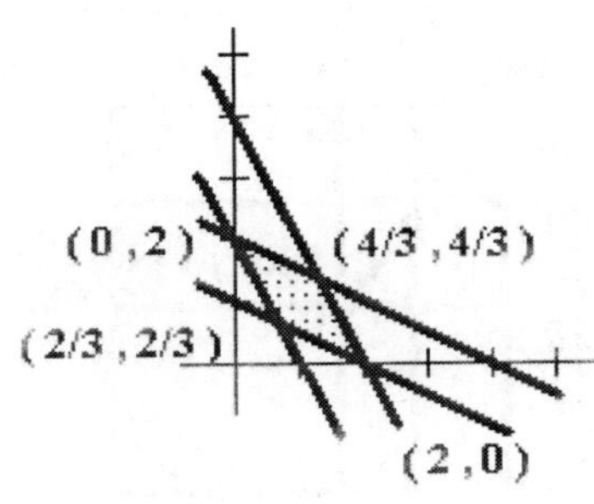

Point	$P = y - 2x$
$\left(\frac{2}{3}, \frac{2}{3}\right)$	$= \frac{2}{3} - 2\left(\frac{2}{3}\right) = -\frac{2}{3}$
$(2, 0)$	$= 0 - 2(2) = -4$
$\left(\frac{4}{3}, \frac{4}{3}\right)$	$= \frac{4}{3} - 2\left(\frac{4}{3}\right) = -\frac{4}{3}$
$(0, 2)$	$= 2 - 2(0) = 2$

Min: $P = -4$ at $(2, 0)$

21. Let $x = $ # tables and $y = $ # chairs.
Maximize $P = 100x + 80y$

subject to $\begin{cases} 2x + 3y \le 42 \\ 6x + 2y \le 42 \\ x \ge 0, y \ge 0 \end{cases}$

Point	$P = 100x + 80y$
$(7, 0)$	$= 100(7) + 80(0) = 700$
$(3, 12)$	$= 100(3) + 80(12) = 1260$
$(0, 14)$	$= 100(0) + 80(14) = 1120$

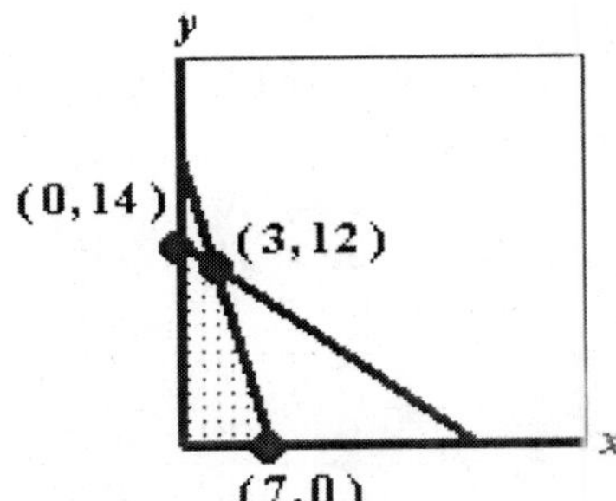

They should make 3 tables and 12 chairs, for a maximum profit of $1260.

22. Let $x = $ # snowman and $y = $ # Santa Claus ornaments.
Maximize $P = 80x + 64y$

subject to $\begin{cases} 4x + 3y \le 20 \\ 2x + 4y \le 20 \\ x \ge 0, y \ge 0 \end{cases}$

Point	$P = 80x + 64y$
$(5, 0)$	$= 80(5) + 64(0) = 400$
$(2, 4)$	$= 80(2) + 64(4) = 416$
$(0, 5)$	$= 80(0) + 64(5) = 320$

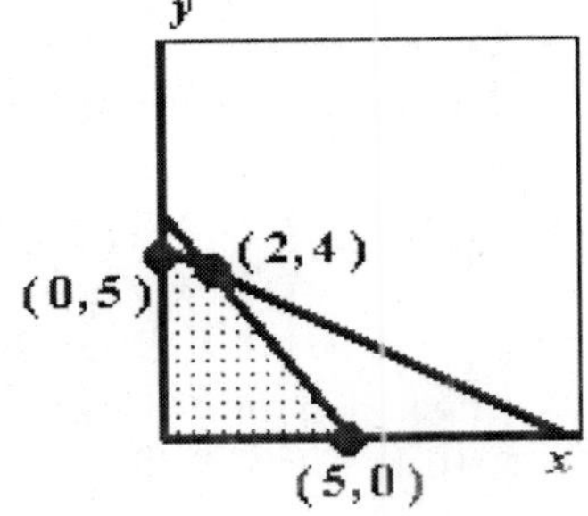

They should make 2 snowman and 4 Santa Claus ornaments, for a maximum profit of $416.

23. Let $x = \#$ IBM and $y = \#$ Apple.
Maximize $P = 50x + 40y$

subject to $\begin{cases} x + y \leq 60 \\ 20 \leq x \leq 30 \\ 30 \leq y \leq 50 \end{cases}$

Point	$P = 50x + 40y$
(20, 30)	$= 50(20) + 40(30) = 2200$
(30, 30)	$= 50(30) + 40(30) = 2700$
(20, 40)	$= 50(20) + 40(40) = 2600$

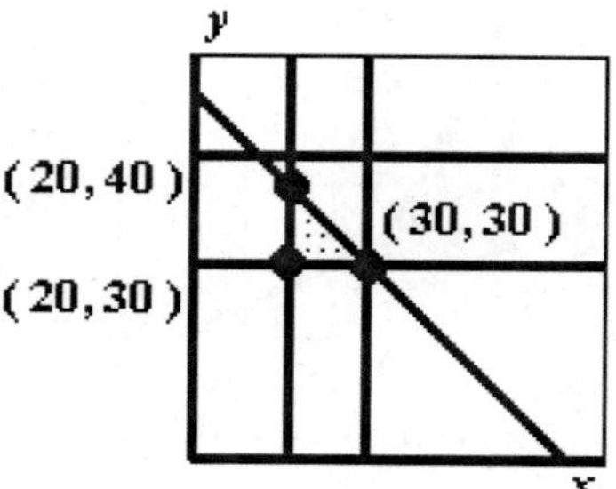

She should stock 30 IBM and 30 Apple computers, for a maximum commission of \$2700.

24. Let $x =$ grams of A and $y =$ grams of B.
Minimize $P = 3x + 4y$

subject to $\begin{cases} 3x + 2y \geq 16 \\ 2x + 6y \geq 34 \\ x \geq 0, y \geq 0 \end{cases}$

Point	$P = 3x + 4y$
(0, 8)	$= 3(0) + 4(8) = 32$
(2, 5)	$= 3(2) + 4(5) = 26$
(17, 0)	$= 3(17) + 4(0) = 51$

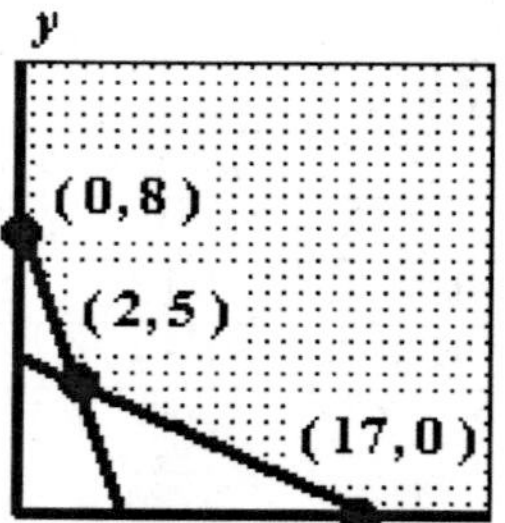

2 grams of A and 5 grams of B should be used, for a minimum cost of 26¢.

25. Let $x = \#$ DVRs and $y = \#$ TVs.
Maximize $P = 40x + 32y$

subject to $\begin{cases} 3x + 4y \leq 180 \\ 2x + 3y \leq 120 \\ 2x + y \leq 60 \\ x \geq 0, y \geq 0 \end{cases}$

Point	$P = 40x + 32y$
(0, 0)	$= 40(0) + 32(0) = 0$
(0, 40)	$= 40(0) + 32(40) = 1280$
(15, 30)	$= 40(15) + 32(30) = 1560$
(30, 0)	$= 40(30) + 32(0) = 1200$

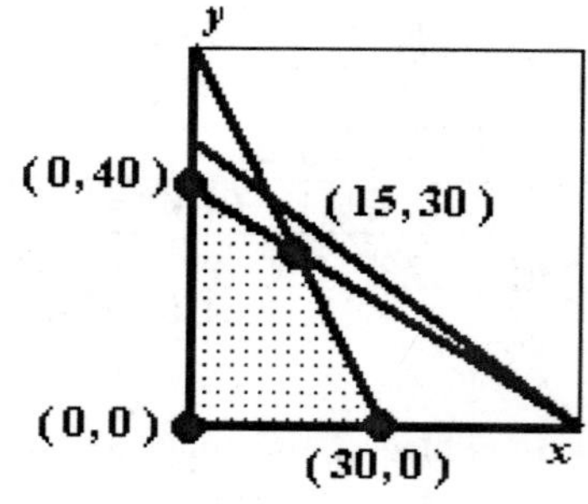

15 DVRs and 30 TVs should be made, for a maximum profit of \$1560.

26. Let x = # slow chips (2.0) and y = # fast chips (2.8).
Maximize $P = 27x + 20y$

subject to $\begin{cases} y \le 50, x \le 100 \\ 3x + 6y \le 360 \\ x \ge 0, y \ge 0 \end{cases}$

Point	$P = 27x + 20y$
(0, 0)	$= 27(0) + 20(0) = 0$
(100, 0)	$= 27(100) + 20(0) = 2700$
(100, 10)	$= 27(100) + 20(10) = 2900$
(20, 50)	$= 27(20) + 20(50) = 1540$
(0, 50)	$= 27(0) + 20(50) = 1000$

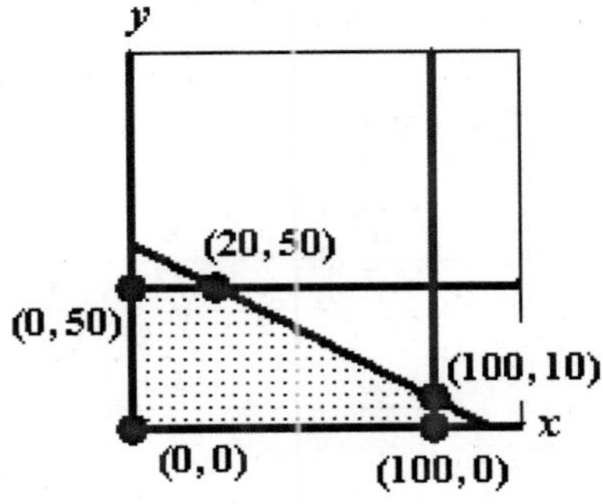

100 slow chips and 10 fast chips should be made, for a maximum profit of $2900.

27. Let x = \$ in stocks and y = \$ in bonds.
Maximize $P = 0.09x + 0.07y$

subject to $\begin{cases} x + y \le 200000 \\ x \ge 100000 \\ y \ge 50000 \end{cases}$

Point	$P = 0.09x + 0.07y$
(100000, 50000)	$= 12500$
(150000, 50000)	$= 17000$
(100000, 100000)	$= 16000$

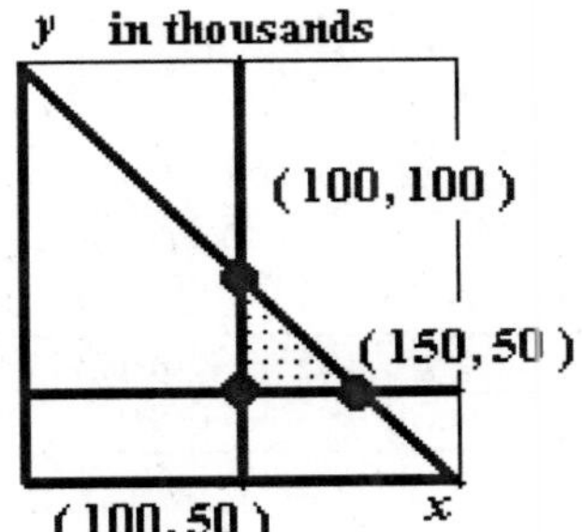

She should invest $150,000 in stocks and $50,000 in bonds, for a maximum return of $17,000.

28. Let x = acres of beans and y = acres of flowers.
Maximize $P = 1600x + 2000y$

subject to $\begin{cases} 8x + 12y \le 100{,}000 \\ x - 3y \ge 0 \\ 250x + 300y \le 3{,}000{,}000 \\ x \ge 0, y \ge 0 \end{cases}$

Point	$P = 1600x + 2000y$
(0, 0)	$= 0$
(12000, 0)	$= 19{,}200{,}000$
$\left(10000, \frac{5000}{3}\right)$	$= 19{,}333{,}333$
$\left(\frac{25000}{3}, \frac{25000}{9}\right)$	$= 18{,}888{,}889$

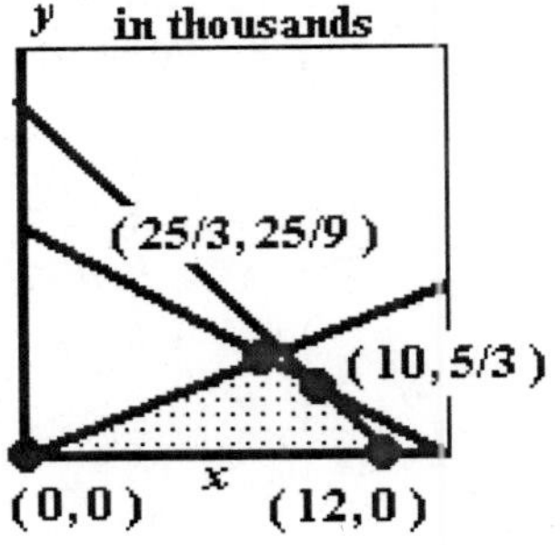

The country should plant 10,000 acres of beans and 1667 acres of flowers, for a maximum profit of $19,333,333.

29. Let x = # buses and y = # trucks.
Minimize $P = 350x + 200y$

subject to $\begin{cases} 40x + 10y \geq 100 \\ 3x + 6y \geq 18 \\ x \geq 0, y \geq 0 \end{cases}$

Point	$P = 350x + 200y$
(0, 10)	$= 350(0) + 200(10) = 2000$
(2, 2)	$= 350(2) + 200(2) = 1100$
(6, 0)	$= 350(6) + 200(0) = 2100$

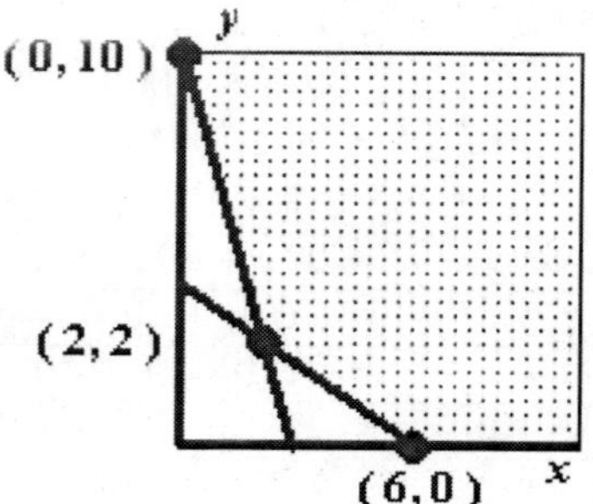

2 buses and 2 trucks should be rented, for a minimum cost of $1100.

30. Let x = barrels of Fantasy and y = barrels of Excess.
Maximize $P = 500x + 400y$

subject to $\begin{cases} 4x + 4y \leq 16 \\ 3x + 2y \leq 18 \\ x \geq 0, y \geq 0 \end{cases}$

Point	$P = 500x + 400y$
(0, 0)	$= 500(0) + 400(0) = 0$
(0, 4)	$= 500(0) + 400(4) = 1600$
(4, 0)	$= 500(4) + 400(0) = 2000$

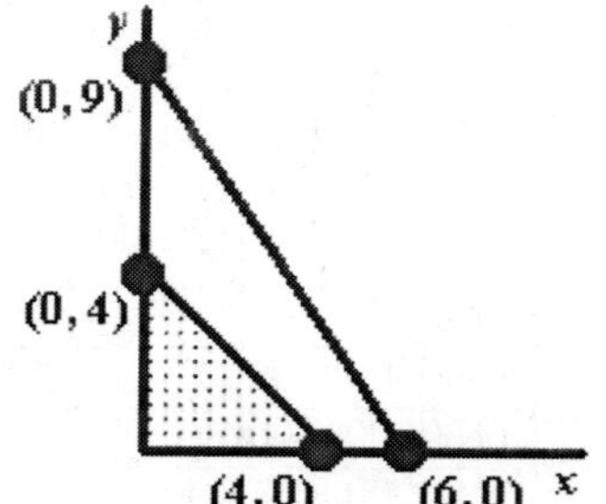

4 barrels of Fantasy and 0 barrels of Excess should be made, for a maximum profit of $2000.

31. **Answers may vary.**

32. **Answers may vary.**

33. $\begin{bmatrix} 1 & 2 & 3 \\ 1 & -2 & 3 \\ 0 & 2 & -3 \\ 2 & 0 & 6 \end{bmatrix} \Rightarrow \begin{bmatrix} 1 & 2 & 3 \\ 0 & -4 & 0 \\ 0 & 2 & -3 \\ 0 & -4 & 0 \end{bmatrix} \Rightarrow \begin{bmatrix} 1 & 2 & 3 \\ 0 & 1 & 0 \\ 0 & 2 & -3 \\ 0 & 0 & 0 \end{bmatrix} \Rightarrow \begin{bmatrix} 1 & 0 & 3 \\ 0 & 1 & 0 \\ 0 & 0 & -3 \\ 0 & 0 & 0 \end{bmatrix} \Rightarrow \begin{bmatrix} 1 & 0 & 0 \\ 0 & 1 & 0 \\ 0 & 0 & 1 \\ 0 & 0 & 0 \end{bmatrix}$

$-R_1 + R_2 \Rightarrow R_2$, $-2R_1 + R_4 \Rightarrow R_4$; $-\frac{1}{4}R_2 \Rightarrow R_2$, $-R_4 + R_2 \Rightarrow R_4$; $-2R_2 + R_1 \Rightarrow R_1$, $-2R_2 + R_3 \Rightarrow R_3$; $R_3 + R_1 \Rightarrow R_1$, $-\frac{1}{3}R_3 \Rightarrow R_3$

34. $\begin{bmatrix} 1 & 3 & -2 & 1 \\ 3 & 9 & -3 & 2 \end{bmatrix} \Rightarrow \begin{bmatrix} 1 & 3 & -2 & 1 \\ 0 & 0 & 3 & -1 \end{bmatrix} \Rightarrow \begin{bmatrix} 1 & 3 & -2 & 1 \\ 0 & 0 & 1 & -\frac{1}{3} \end{bmatrix} \Rightarrow \begin{bmatrix} 1 & 3 & 0 & \frac{1}{3} \\ 0 & 0 & 1 & -\frac{1}{3} \end{bmatrix}$

$-3R_1 + R_2 \Rightarrow R_2$; $\frac{1}{3}R_2 \Rightarrow R_2$; $2R_2 + R_1 \Rightarrow R_1$

35. $\left(\frac{1}{3} - 3y, y, -\frac{1}{3}\right)$

36. $\left[\begin{array}{ccc|ccc} 7 & 2 & 5 & 1 & 0 & 0 \\ 3 & 1 & 2 & 0 & 1 & 0 \\ 3 & 1 & 3 & 0 & 0 & 1 \end{array}\right] \Rightarrow \underset{-2R_2 + R_1 \Rightarrow R_1}{\left[\begin{array}{ccc|ccc} 1 & 0 & 1 & 1 & -2 & 0 \\ 3 & 1 & 2 & 0 & 1 & 0 \\ 3 & 1 & 3 & 0 & 0 & 1 \end{array}\right]} \Rightarrow \underset{\substack{-3R_1 + R_2 \Rightarrow R_2 \\ -3R_1 + R_3 \Rightarrow R_3}}{\left[\begin{array}{ccc|ccc} 1 & 0 & 1 & 1 & -2 & 0 \\ 0 & 1 & -1 & -3 & 7 & 0 \\ 0 & 1 & 0 & -3 & 6 & 1 \end{array}\right]} \Rightarrow$

$\underset{R_2 \Leftrightarrow R_3}{\left[\begin{array}{ccc|ccc} 1 & 0 & 1 & 1 & -2 & 0 \\ 0 & 1 & 0 & -3 & 6 & 1 \\ 0 & 1 & -1 & -3 & 7 & 0 \end{array}\right]} \Rightarrow \underset{-R_3 + R_2 \Rightarrow R_3}{\left[\begin{array}{ccc|ccc} 1 & 0 & 1 & 1 & -2 & 0 \\ 0 & 1 & 0 & -3 & 6 & 1 \\ 0 & 0 & 1 & 0 & -1 & 1 \end{array}\right]} \Rightarrow$

$\underset{-R_3 + R_1 \Rightarrow R_1}{\left[\begin{array}{ccc|ccc} 1 & 0 & 0 & 1 & -1 & -1 \\ 0 & 1 & 0 & -3 & 6 & 1 \\ 0 & 0 & 1 & 0 & -1 & 1 \end{array}\right]} \Rightarrow \text{Inverse} = \begin{bmatrix} 1 & -1 & -1 \\ -3 & 6 & 1 \\ 0 & -1 & 1 \end{bmatrix}$

Chapter 6 Review (page 642)

1. $\begin{cases} 2x - y = -1 \\ x + y = 7 \end{cases}$

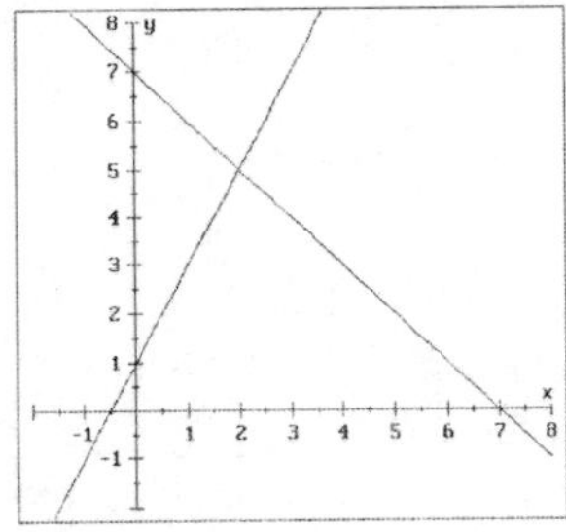

solution: $(2, 5)$

2. $\begin{cases} 5x + 2y = 1 \\ 2x - y = -5 \end{cases}$

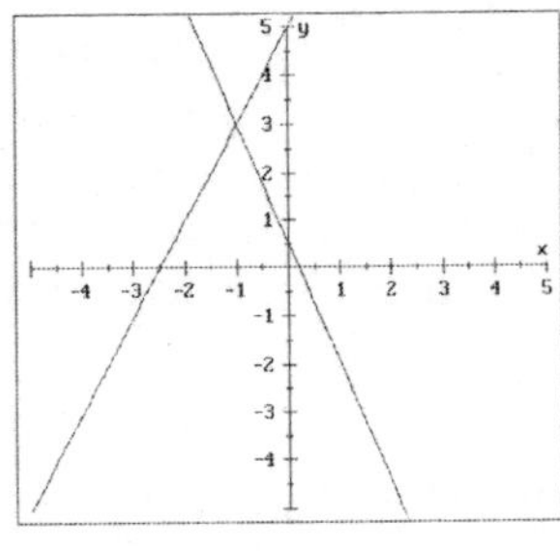

solution: $(-1, 3)$

3. $\begin{cases} y = 5x + 7 \\ x = y - 7 \end{cases}$

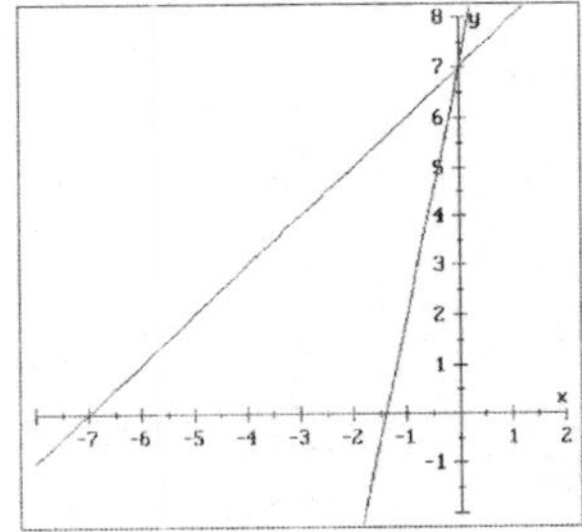

solution: $(0, 7)$

4. $\begin{cases} 3x + 2y = 6 \\ y = -\frac{3}{2}x + 3 \end{cases}$

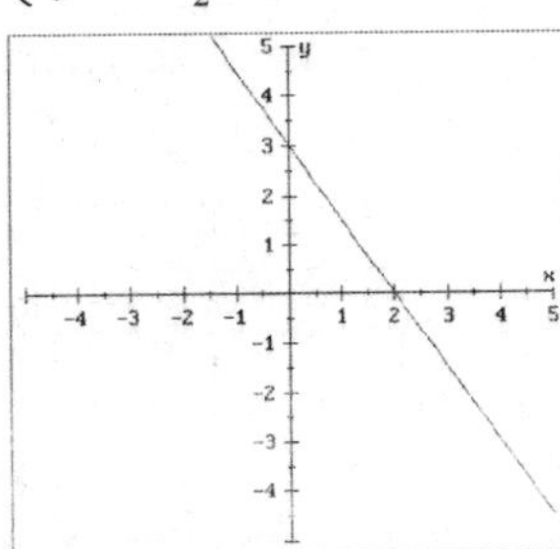

infinitely many solutions
dependent equations

5. 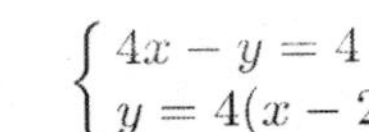
$\begin{cases} 4x - y = 4 \\ y = 4(x - 2) \end{cases}$

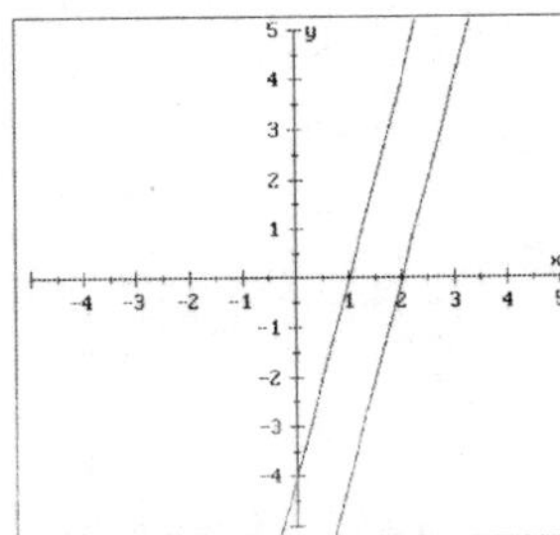

no solutions
inconsistent system

6. $\begin{cases} (1) & 2y + x = 0 \\ (2) & x = y + 3 \end{cases}$

Substitute $x = y + 3$ into (1):

$$\begin{aligned} 2y + x &= 0 \\ 2y + (y + 3) &= 0 \\ 3y + 3 &= 0 \\ 3y &= -3 \\ y &= -1 \end{aligned}$$

Substitute and solve for x:

$x = y + 3$

$x = -1 + 3 = 2$

$\boxed{x = 2, y = -1}$

7. $\begin{cases} (1) & 2x + y = -3 \\ (2) & x - y = 3 \end{cases}$

Substitute $x = y + 3$ into (1):

$$\begin{aligned} 2x + y &= -3 \\ 2(y + 3) + y &= -3 \\ 2y + 6 + y &= -3 \\ 3y &= -9 \\ y &= -3 \end{aligned}$$

Substitute and solve for x:

$x = y + 3$

$x = -3 + 3 = 0$

$\boxed{x = 0, y = -3}$

8. $\begin{cases} (1) & \dfrac{x + y}{2} + \dfrac{x - y}{3} = 1 \\ (2) & y = 3x - 2 \end{cases}$

Substitute $y = 3x - 2$ into (1):

$$\begin{aligned} \frac{x + 3x - 2}{2} + \frac{x - (3x - 2)}{3} &= 1 \\ \frac{4x - 2}{2} + \frac{-2x + 2}{3} &= 1 \end{aligned}$$

$$\begin{aligned} 3(4x - 2) + 2(-2x + 2) &= 6 \\ 12x - 6 - 4x + 4 &= 6 \\ 8x &= 8 \\ x &= 1 \end{aligned}$$

Substitute and solve for y:

$y = 3x - 2$

$y = 3(1) - 2 = 1$

$\boxed{x = 1, y = 1}$

9. $\begin{cases} (1) & y = 3x - 4 \\ (2) & 9x - 3y = 12 \end{cases}$

Substitute $y = 3x - 4$ into (2):

$$\begin{aligned} 9x - 3y &= 12 \\ 9x - 3(3x - 4) &= 12 \\ 9x - 9x + 12 &= 12 \\ 0 &= 0 \end{aligned}$$

Dependent equations

General solution: $(x, 3x - 4)$

10. $\begin{cases} (1) & x = -\frac{3}{2}y + 3 \\ (2) & 2x + 3y = 4 \end{cases}$

Substitute $x = -\frac{3}{2}y + 3$ into (2):

$$\begin{aligned} 2x + 3y &= 4 \\ 2\left(-\tfrac{3}{2}y + 3\right) + 3y &= 4 \\ -3y + 6 + 3y &= 4 \\ 6 &\neq 4 \end{aligned}$$

Inconsistent system $\Rightarrow$ No solution

11. $\begin{aligned} x + 5y &= 7 \\ 3x + y &= -7 \Rightarrow \times\ (-5) \end{aligned}$

$$\begin{aligned} x + 5y &= 7 \\ -15x - 5y &= 35 \\ \hline -14x &= 42 \\ x &= -3 \end{aligned}$$

$$\begin{aligned} x + 5y &= 7 \\ -3 + 5y &= 7 \\ 5y &= 10 \\ y &= 2 \end{aligned}$$

Solution: $\boxed{x = -3, y = 2}$

12. $\begin{aligned} 2x + 3y &= 11 \Rightarrow \times\ (3) \\ 3x - 7y &= -41 \Rightarrow \times\ (-2) \end{aligned}$

$$\begin{aligned} 6x + 9y &= 33 \\ -6x + 14y &= 82 \\ \hline 23y &= 115 \\ y &= 5 \end{aligned}$$

$$\begin{aligned} 2x + 3y &= 11 \\ 2x + 3(5) &= 11 \\ 2x &= -4 \\ x &= -2 \end{aligned}$$

Solution: $\boxed{x = -2, y = 5}$

13. $\underline{\begin{array}{l} 2(x+y)-x=0 \\ 3(x+y)+2y=1 \end{array}} \Rightarrow \underline{\begin{array}{l} x+2y=0 \\ 3x+5y=1 \end{array}} \Rightarrow \begin{array}{rl} -3x-6y= & 0 \\ 3x+5y= & 1 \\ \hline -y= & 1 \\ y= & -1 \end{array}$ $\quad \begin{array}{r} x+2y=0 \\ x+2(-1)=0 \\ x=2 \end{array}$

Solution: $\boxed{\begin{array}{l} x=2 \\ y=-1 \end{array}}$

14. $\underline{\begin{array}{l} 8x+12y=24 \\ 2x+\ \ 3y=\ \ 4 \end{array}} \begin{array}{l} \\ \Rightarrow \times\ (-4) \end{array} \quad \begin{array}{rl} 8x+12y= & 24 \\ -8x-12y= & -16 \\ \hline 0\neq & 8 \end{array} \Rightarrow$ Inconsistent system: No solution

15. $\underline{\begin{array}{l} 3x-\ \ y=\ \ 4 \\ 9x-3y=12 \end{array}} \begin{array}{l} \Rightarrow \times\ (-3) \\ \ \end{array} \quad \begin{array}{rl} -9x+3y= & -12 \\ 9x-3y= & 12 \\ \hline 0= & 0 \end{array} \quad \begin{array}{l} 3x-y=4 \\ 3x-4=y \end{array}$

Dependent equations, General Solution: $(x, 3x-4)$

16. $\begin{array}{ll} (1) & 3x+2y-z=2 \\ (2) & x+y-z=0 \\ (3) & 2x+3y-z=1 \end{array}$

Add (1) and $-(2)$:

$\begin{array}{rl} (1) & 3x+2y-z=2 \\ -(2) & -x-\ \ y+z=0 \\ \hline (4) & 2x+\ \ y\qquad =2 \end{array}$

Add equations (1) and $-(3)$:

$\begin{array}{rl} (1) & 3x+2y-z=\ \ 2 \\ -(3) & -2x-3y+z=-1 \\ \hline (5) & x-\ \ y\qquad =\ \ 1 \end{array}$

Solve the system of two equations and two unknowns formed by equations (4) and (5):

$\begin{array}{rl} 2x+y= & 2 \\ x-y= & 1 \\ \hline 3x\quad = & 3 \\ x\quad = & 1 \end{array} \quad \begin{array}{r} 2x+y=2 \\ 2(1)+y=2 \\ y=0 \end{array} \quad \begin{array}{r} x+y-z=0 \\ 1+0-z=0 \\ -z=-1 \\ z=1 \end{array}$

Solution: $\boxed{x=1, y=0, z=1}$

17. $\begin{array}{ll} (1) & 5x-y+z=3 \\ (2) & 3x+y+2z=2 \\ (3) & x+y=2 \end{array}$

Add (1) and (2):

$\begin{array}{rl} (1) & 5x-y+\ \ z=3 \\ (2) & 3x+y+2z=2 \\ \hline (4) & 8x\qquad +3z=5 \end{array}$

Add equations (1) and (3):

$\begin{array}{rl} (1) & 5x-y+z=3 \\ (3) & x+y\qquad =2 \\ \hline (5) & 6x\qquad +z=5 \end{array}$

Solve the system of two equations and two unknowns formed by equations (4) and (5):

$\underline{\begin{array}{l} 8x+3z=5 \\ 6x+\ \ z=5 \end{array}} \begin{array}{l} \\ \Rightarrow \times\ (-3) \end{array} \quad \begin{array}{rl} 8x+3z= & 5 \\ -18x-3z= & -15 \\ \hline -10x\quad = & -10 \\ x\quad = & 1 \end{array} \quad \begin{array}{r} 6x+z=5 \\ 6(1)+z=5 \\ z=-1 \end{array} \quad \begin{array}{r} x+y=2 \\ 1+y=2 \\ y=1 \end{array}$

Solution: $\boxed{x=1, y=1, z=-1}$

18. $\begin{array}{ll} (1) & 2x-y+z=1 \\ (2) & x-y+2z=3 \\ (3) & x-y+z=1 \end{array}$

Add (1) and $-(2)$:

$\begin{array}{rl} (1) & 2x-y+\ \ z=\ \ 1 \\ -(2) & -x+y-2z=-3 \\ \hline (4) & x\qquad -\ \ z=-2 \end{array}$

Add equations (1) and $-(3)$:

$\begin{array}{rl} (1) & 2x-y+z=\ \ 1 \\ -(3) & -x+y-z=-1 \\ \hline (5) & x\qquad\quad =\ \ 0 \end{array}$

Solve the system of two equations and two unknowns formed by equations (4) and (5):

$\begin{array}{r} x-z=-2 \\ 0-z=-2 \\ z=2 \end{array} \quad \begin{array}{r} x-y+z=1 \\ 0-y+2=1 \\ -y=-1 \\ y=1 \end{array}$

Solution: $\boxed{x=0, y=1, z=2}$

19. Let x = cost of fake fur and let y = cost of leather. Then $\begin{cases} (1) & 25x + 15y = 9300 \\ (2) & 10x + 30y = 12600 \end{cases}$

$$\begin{array}{l} 25x + 15y = 9300 \Rightarrow \times\ (-2) \\ \underline{10x + 30y = 12600} \end{array} \quad \begin{array}{rcl} -50x + 30y &=& -18600 \\ \underline{10x + 30y} &=& \underline{12600} \\ -40x &=& -6000 \\ x &=& 150 \end{array} \quad \begin{aligned} 25x + 15y &= 9300 \\ 25(150) + 15y &= 9300 \\ 15y &= 5550 \\ y &= 370 \end{aligned}$$

The fake fur coats cost \$150 while the leather coats cost \$370. The cost will be \$10,400.

20. Let x = # adult tickets, y = # senior tickets and z = # children tickets.

$$\begin{array}{ll} (1) & x + y + z = 1800 \\ (2) & 5x + 4y + 2.5z = 7425 \\ (3) & y + z = 900 \end{array}$$

Add $-4(1)$ and (2):

$$\begin{array}{lrcl} -4(1) & -4x - 4y - 4z &=& -7200 \\ (2) & 5x + 4y + 2.5z &=& 7425 \\ (4) & x \qquad - 1.5z &=& 225 \end{array}$$

Add equations (1) and $-(3)$:

$$\begin{array}{lrcl} (1) & x + y + z &=& 1800 \\ -(3) & -y - z &=& -900 \\ (5) & x &=& 900 \end{array}$$

Solve the system of two equations and two unknowns formed by equations (4) and (5):

$$\begin{aligned} x - 1.5z &= 225 \\ 900 - 1.5z &= 225 \\ -1.5z &= -675 \\ z &= 450 \end{aligned} \qquad \begin{aligned} y + z &= 900 \\ y + 450 &= 900 \\ y &= 450 \end{aligned}$$

There were 900 adult tickets, 450 senior tickets, and 450 children's tickets sold.

21. $\left[\begin{array}{cc|c} 2 & 5 & 7 \\ 3 & -1 & 2 \end{array}\right] \Rightarrow \underset{-R_1 + R_2 \Rightarrow R_1}{\left[\begin{array}{cc|c} 1 & -6 & -5 \\ 3 & -1 & 2 \end{array}\right]} \Rightarrow \underset{-3R_1 + R_2 \Rightarrow R_2}{\left[\begin{array}{cc|c} 1 & -6 & -5 \\ 0 & 17 & 17 \end{array}\right]} \Rightarrow \underset{\frac{1}{17}R_2 \Rightarrow R_2}{\left[\begin{array}{cc|c} 1 & -6 & -5 \\ 0 & 1 & 1 \end{array}\right]} \Rightarrow$

$\underset{6R_2 + R_1 \Rightarrow R_1}{\left[\begin{array}{cc|c} 1 & 0 & 1 \\ 0 & 1 & 1 \end{array}\right]}$ Solution: $\boxed{x = 1, y = 1}$

22. $\left[\begin{array}{cc|c} 3 & -1 & -4 \\ -6 & 2 & 8 \end{array}\right] \Rightarrow \underset{2R_1 + R_2 \Rightarrow R_2}{\left[\begin{array}{cc|c} 3 & -1 & -4 \\ 0 & 0 & 0 \end{array}\right]} \Rightarrow \begin{array}{l} 3x - y = -4 \\ 3x + 4 = y \end{array}$ Dependent equations

General Solution: $(x, 3x + 4)$

23. $\left[\begin{array}{ccc|c} 1 & 3 & -1 & 8 \\ 2 & 1 & -2 & 11 \\ 1 & -1 & 5 & -8 \end{array}\right] \Rightarrow \underset{\substack{-2R_1 + R_2 \Rightarrow R_2 \\ -R_1 + R_3 \Rightarrow R_3}}{\left[\begin{array}{ccc|c} 1 & 3 & -1 & 8 \\ 0 & -5 & 0 & -5 \\ 0 & -4 & 6 & -16 \end{array}\right]} \Rightarrow \underset{-\frac{1}{5}R_2 \Rightarrow R_2}{\left[\begin{array}{ccc|c} 1 & 3 & -1 & 8 \\ 0 & 1 & 0 & 1 \\ 0 & -4 & 6 & -16 \end{array}\right]} \Rightarrow$

$\underset{\substack{-3R_2 + R_1 \Rightarrow R_1 \\ 4R_2 + R_3 \Rightarrow R_3}}{\left[\begin{array}{ccc|c} 1 & 0 & -1 & 5 \\ 0 & 1 & 0 & 1 \\ 0 & 0 & 6 & -12 \end{array}\right]} \Rightarrow \underset{\substack{\frac{1}{6}R_3 + R_1 \Rightarrow R_1 \\ \frac{1}{6}R_3 \Rightarrow R_3}}{\left[\begin{array}{ccc|c} 1 & 0 & 0 & 3 \\ 0 & 1 & 0 & 1 \\ 0 & 0 & 1 & -2 \end{array}\right]}$ Solution: $\boxed{x = 3, y = 1, z = -2}$

24. $\left[\begin{array}{ccc|c} 1 & 3 & 1 & 3 \\ 2 & -1 & 1 & -11 \\ 3 & 2 & 3 & 2 \end{array}\right] \Rightarrow \left[\begin{array}{ccc|c} 1 & 3 & 1 & 3 \\ 0 & -7 & -1 & -17 \\ 0 & -7 & 0 & -7 \end{array}\right] \Rightarrow \left[\begin{array}{ccc|c} 1 & 3 & 1 & 3 \\ 0 & 1 & 0 & 1 \\ 0 & -7 & -1 & -17 \end{array}\right] \Rightarrow$

$-2R_1 + R_2 \Rightarrow R_2$, $-3R_1 + R_3 \Rightarrow R_3$; $R_2 \Leftrightarrow -\frac{1}{7}R_3$

$\left[\begin{array}{ccc|c} 1 & 0 & 1 & 0 \\ 0 & 1 & 0 & 1 \\ 0 & 0 & -1 & -10 \end{array}\right] \Rightarrow \left[\begin{array}{ccc|c} 1 & 0 & 0 & -10 \\ 0 & 1 & 0 & 1 \\ 0 & 0 & 1 & 10 \end{array}\right]$ Solution: $\boxed{x = -10, y = 1, z = 10}$

$-3R_2 + R_1 \Rightarrow R_1$, $7R_2 + R_3 \Rightarrow R_3$; $R_3 + R_1 \Rightarrow R_1$, $-R_3 \Rightarrow R_3$

25. $\left[\begin{array}{ccc|c} 1 & 1 & 1 & 4 \\ 3 & -2 & -2 & -3 \\ 4 & -1 & -1 & 0 \end{array}\right] \Rightarrow \left[\begin{array}{ccc|c} 1 & 1 & 1 & 4 \\ 0 & -5 & -5 & -15 \\ 0 & -5 & -5 & -16 \end{array}\right] \Rightarrow \left[\begin{array}{ccc|c} 1 & 1 & 1 & 4 \\ 0 & -5 & -5 & -15 \\ 0 & 0 & 0 & -1 \end{array}\right]$

$-3R_1 + R_2 \Rightarrow R_2$, $-4R_1 + R_3 \Rightarrow R_3$; $-R_2 + R_3 \Rightarrow R_3$

The last row indicates $0x + 0y + 0z = -1$. This is impossible. $\Rightarrow$ no solution

26. $-4 = x$, $x = -4$, $0 = x + 4$, $x + 7 = y \Rightarrow \boxed{x = -4, y = 3}$

27. $\begin{bmatrix} 3 & 2 & 1 \\ 3 & 2 & 1 \end{bmatrix} + \begin{bmatrix} -2 & 1 & 3 \\ 1 & -2 & 1 \end{bmatrix} = \begin{bmatrix} 1 & 3 & 4 \\ 4 & 0 & 2 \end{bmatrix}$

28. $\begin{bmatrix} 2 & 3 & 5 \\ 1 & -2 & 4 \\ 2 & 1 & -2 \end{bmatrix} - \begin{bmatrix} 0 & -2 & 1 \\ 3 & 4 & -2 \\ 6 & -4 & 1 \end{bmatrix} = \begin{bmatrix} 2 & 5 & 4 \\ -2 & -6 & 6 \\ -4 & 5 & -3 \end{bmatrix}$

29. $\begin{bmatrix} 1 & -2 \\ -3 & 1 \end{bmatrix} \begin{bmatrix} 2 & 3 \\ -1 & 2 \end{bmatrix} = \begin{bmatrix} 4 & -1 \\ -7 & -7 \end{bmatrix}$

30. $\begin{bmatrix} -2 & 3 & 5 \\ 1 & -2 & -3 \end{bmatrix} \begin{bmatrix} 2 & 1 \\ -1 & 2 \\ -2 & 3 \end{bmatrix} = \begin{bmatrix} -17 & 19 \\ 10 & -12 \end{bmatrix}$

31. $\begin{bmatrix} 1 & -3 & 2 \end{bmatrix} \begin{bmatrix} 2 \\ 1 \\ 3 \end{bmatrix} = \begin{bmatrix} 5 \end{bmatrix}$

32. $\begin{bmatrix} 1 \\ 2 \\ 1 \\ 5 \end{bmatrix} \begin{bmatrix} 2 & -1 & 1 & 3 \end{bmatrix} = \begin{bmatrix} 2 & -1 & 1 & 3 \\ 4 & -2 & 2 & 6 \\ 2 & -1 & 1 & 3 \\ 10 & -5 & 5 & 15 \end{bmatrix}$

33. $\begin{bmatrix} 1 & -5 & 3 \\ 2 & 1 & -1 \end{bmatrix} \begin{bmatrix} 2 \\ -2 \\ 3 \end{bmatrix} \begin{bmatrix} 1 & -1 \\ -1 & 3 \end{bmatrix} \begin{bmatrix} 1 \\ -2 \end{bmatrix} = \begin{bmatrix} 21 \\ -1 \end{bmatrix} \begin{bmatrix} 1 & -1 \\ -1 & 3 \end{bmatrix} \begin{bmatrix} 1 \\ -2 \end{bmatrix} \Rightarrow$ not possible

34. $\begin{bmatrix}1 & -3 & 2\end{bmatrix}\begin{bmatrix}2\\1\\-5\end{bmatrix}+\begin{bmatrix}1 & -3\end{bmatrix}\begin{bmatrix}2\\5\end{bmatrix}=\begin{bmatrix}-11\end{bmatrix}+\begin{bmatrix}-13\end{bmatrix}=\begin{bmatrix}-24\end{bmatrix}$

35. $\left(\begin{bmatrix}1 & -3\\3 & 1\end{bmatrix}+\begin{bmatrix}-1 & 3\\1 & 1\end{bmatrix}\right)\begin{bmatrix}1\\-5\end{bmatrix}=\begin{bmatrix}0 & 0\\4 & 2\end{bmatrix}\begin{bmatrix}1\\-5\end{bmatrix}=\begin{bmatrix}0\\-6\end{bmatrix}$

36. $\left[\begin{array}{cc|cc}2 & 3 & 1 & 0\\3 & 5 & 0 & 1\end{array}\right]\Rightarrow\underset{\frac{1}{2}R_1\Rightarrow R_1}{\left[\begin{array}{cc|cc}1 & \frac{3}{2} & \frac{1}{2} & 0\\3 & 5 & 0 & 1\end{array}\right]}\Rightarrow\underset{-3R_1+R_2\Rightarrow R_2}{\left[\begin{array}{cc|cc}1 & \frac{3}{2} & \frac{1}{2} & 0\\0 & \frac{1}{2} & -\frac{3}{2} & 1\end{array}\right]}\Rightarrow$

$\underset{-3R_2+R_1\Rightarrow R_1}{\left[\begin{array}{cc|cc}1 & 0 & 5 & -3\\0 & \frac{1}{2} & -\frac{3}{2} & 1\end{array}\right]}\Rightarrow\underset{2R_2\Rightarrow R_2}{\left[\begin{array}{cc|cc}1 & 0 & 5 & -3\\0 & 1 & -3 & 2\end{array}\right]}\Rightarrow$ Inverse: $\begin{bmatrix}5 & -3\\-3 & 2\end{bmatrix}$

37. $\left[\begin{array}{ccc|ccc}1 & 0 & 0 & 1 & 0 & 0\\2 & 0 & -2 & 0 & 1 & 0\\1 & 2 & 2 & 0 & 0 & 1\end{array}\right]\Rightarrow\underset{R_2\Leftrightarrow R_3}{\left[\begin{array}{ccc|ccc}1 & 0 & 0 & 1 & 0 & 0\\1 & 2 & 2 & 0 & 0 & 1\\2 & 0 & -2 & 0 & 1 & 0\end{array}\right]}\Rightarrow\underset{\substack{-R_1+R_2\Rightarrow R_2\\-2R_1+R_3\Rightarrow R_3}}{\left[\begin{array}{ccc|ccc}1 & 0 & 0 & 1 & 0 & 0\\0 & 2 & 2 & -1 & 0 & 1\\0 & 0 & -2 & -2 & 1 & 0\end{array}\right]}\Rightarrow$

$\underset{R_2+R_3\Rightarrow R_3}{\left[\begin{array}{ccc|ccc}1 & 0 & 0 & 1 & 0 & 0\\0 & 2 & 0 & -3 & 1 & 1\\0 & 0 & -2 & -2 & 1 & 0\end{array}\right]}\Rightarrow\underset{\substack{\frac{1}{2}R_2\Rightarrow R_2\\-\frac{1}{2}R_3\Rightarrow R_3}}{\left[\begin{array}{ccc|ccc}1 & 0 & 0 & 1 & 0 & 0\\0 & 1 & 0 & -\frac{3}{2} & \frac{1}{2} & \frac{1}{2}\\0 & 0 & 1 & 1 & -\frac{1}{2} & 0\end{array}\right]}$: Inverse $=\begin{bmatrix}1 & 0 & 0\\-\frac{3}{2} & \frac{1}{2} & \frac{1}{2}\\1 & -\frac{1}{2} & 0\end{bmatrix}$

38. $\left[\begin{array}{ccc|ccc}1 & 0 & 8 & 1 & 0 & 0\\3 & 7 & 6 & 0 & 1 & 0\\1 & 2 & 3 & 0 & 0 & 1\end{array}\right]\Rightarrow\underset{\substack{-3R_1+R_2\Rightarrow R_2\\-R_1+R_3\Rightarrow R_3}}{\left[\begin{array}{ccc|ccc}1 & 0 & 8 & 1 & 0 & 0\\0 & 7 & -18 & -3 & 1 & 0\\0 & 2 & -5 & -1 & 0 & 1\end{array}\right]}\Rightarrow\underset{\frac{1}{7}R_2\Rightarrow R_2}{\left[\begin{array}{ccc|ccc}1 & 0 & 8 & 1 & 0 & 0\\0 & 1 & -\frac{18}{7} & -\frac{3}{7} & \frac{1}{7} & 0\\0 & 2 & -5 & -1 & 0 & 1\end{array}\right]}\Rightarrow$

$\underset{-2R_2+R_3\Rightarrow R_3}{\left[\begin{array}{ccc|ccc}1 & 0 & 8 & 1 & 0 & 0\\0 & 1 & -\frac{18}{7} & -\frac{3}{7} & \frac{1}{7} & 0\\0 & 0 & \frac{1}{7} & -\frac{1}{7} & -\frac{2}{7} & 1\end{array}\right]}\Rightarrow\underset{\substack{-56R_3+R_1\Rightarrow R_1\\18R_3+R_2\Rightarrow R_2\\7R_3\Rightarrow R_3}}{\left[\begin{array}{ccc|ccc}1 & 0 & 0 & 9 & 16 & -56\\0 & 1 & 0 & -3 & -5 & 18\\0 & 0 & 1 & -1 & -2 & 7\end{array}\right]}\Rightarrow$ Inverse: $\begin{bmatrix}9 & 16 & -56\\-3 & -5 & 18\\-1 & -2 & 7\end{bmatrix}$

39. $\left[\begin{array}{cc|cc}-6 & 4 & 1 & 0\\-3 & 2 & 0 & 1\end{array}\right]\Rightarrow\underset{-\frac{1}{6}R_1\Rightarrow R_1}{\left[\begin{array}{cc|cc}1 & -\frac{2}{3} & -\frac{1}{6} & 0\\-3 & 2 & 0 & 1\end{array}\right]}\Rightarrow\underset{3R_1+R_2\Rightarrow R_2}{\left[\begin{array}{cc|cc}1 & -\frac{2}{3} & -\frac{1}{6} & 0\\0 & 0 & -\frac{1}{2} & 1\end{array}\right]}\Rightarrow$ No inverse exists.

40. $\left[\begin{array}{rrr|rrr} 4 & 4 & 1 & 1 & 0 & 0 \\ 1 & 1 & 1 & 0 & 1 & 0 \\ -1 & -1 & 0 & 0 & 0 & 1 \end{array}\right] \Rightarrow \left[\begin{array}{rrr|rrr} 1 & 1 & 1 & 0 & 1 & 0 \\ 4 & 4 & 1 & 1 & 0 & 0 \\ -1 & -1 & 0 & 0 & 0 & 1 \end{array}\right] \Rightarrow$

$R_1 \Leftrightarrow R_2$

$\left[\begin{array}{rrr|rrr} 1 & 1 & 1 & 0 & 1 & 0 \\ 0 & 0 & -3 & 1 & -4 & 0 \\ 0 & 0 & 1 & 0 & 1 & 1 \end{array}\right] \Rightarrow \left[\begin{array}{rrr|rrr} 1 & 1 & 1 & 0 & 1 & 0 \\ 0 & 0 & 0 & 1 & -1 & 3 \\ 0 & 0 & 1 & 0 & 1 & 1 \end{array}\right]$: No inverse exists.

$-4R_1 + R_2 \Rightarrow R_2$ $\quad 3R_3 + R_2 \Rightarrow R_2$

$R_1 + R_3 \Rightarrow R_3$

41. $\begin{bmatrix} 4 & -1 & 2 \\ 1 & 1 & 2 \\ 1 & 0 & 1 \end{bmatrix} \begin{bmatrix} x \\ y \\ z \end{bmatrix} = \begin{bmatrix} 0 \\ 1 \\ 0 \end{bmatrix}$

$$\begin{bmatrix} x \\ y \\ z \end{bmatrix} = \begin{bmatrix} 4 & -1 & 2 \\ 1 & 1 & 2 \\ 1 & 0 & 1 \end{bmatrix}^{-1} \begin{bmatrix} 0 \\ 1 \\ 0 \end{bmatrix} = \begin{bmatrix} 1 & 1 & -4 \\ 1 & 2 & -6 \\ -1 & -1 & 5 \end{bmatrix} \begin{bmatrix} 0 \\ 1 \\ 0 \end{bmatrix} = \begin{bmatrix} 1 \\ 2 \\ -1 \end{bmatrix}$$

42. $\begin{bmatrix} 1 & 3 & 1 & 3 \\ 1 & 4 & 1 & 3 \\ 0 & 1 & 1 & 0 \\ 1 & 2 & -1 & 2 \end{bmatrix} \begin{bmatrix} w \\ x \\ y \\ z \end{bmatrix} = \begin{bmatrix} 1 \\ 2 \\ 1 \\ 1 \end{bmatrix}$

$$\begin{bmatrix} w \\ x \\ y \\ z \end{bmatrix} = \begin{bmatrix} 1 & 3 & 1 & 3 \\ 1 & 4 & 1 & 3 \\ 0 & 1 & 1 & 0 \\ 1 & 2 & -1 & 2 \end{bmatrix}^{-1} \begin{bmatrix} 1 \\ 2 \\ 1 \\ 1 \end{bmatrix} = \begin{bmatrix} 3 & -5 & 5 & 3 \\ -1 & 1 & 0 & 0 \\ 1 & -1 & 1 & 0 \\ 0 & 1 & -2 & -1 \end{bmatrix} \begin{bmatrix} 1 \\ 2 \\ 1 \\ 1 \end{bmatrix} = \begin{bmatrix} 1 \\ 1 \\ 0 \\ -1 \end{bmatrix}$$

43. $\begin{vmatrix} 3 & -2 \\ 1 & -3 \end{vmatrix} = (3)(-3) - (-2)(1) = -9 + 2 = -7$

44. $\begin{vmatrix} 1 & -2 & 3 \\ 2 & -1 & 3 \\ 1 & -1 & 0 \end{vmatrix} = 1\begin{vmatrix} -1 & 3 \\ -1 & 0 \end{vmatrix} - (-2)\begin{vmatrix} 2 & 3 \\ 1 & 0 \end{vmatrix} + 3\begin{vmatrix} 2 & -1 \\ 1 & -1 \end{vmatrix}$

$= 1(3) + 2(-3) + 3(-1) = 3 - 6 - 3 = -6$

45. $\begin{vmatrix} 1 & 3 & -1 \\ 1 & 2 & 1 \\ 1 & 0 & 2 \end{vmatrix} = 1\begin{vmatrix} 2 & 1 \\ 0 & 2 \end{vmatrix} - 3\begin{vmatrix} 1 & 1 \\ 1 & 2 \end{vmatrix} + (-1)\begin{vmatrix} 1 & 2 \\ 1 & 0 \end{vmatrix}$

$= 1(4) - 3(1) - 1(-2) = 4 - 3 + 2 = 3$

46. Expand along 3rd row...

$$\begin{vmatrix} 1 & 2 & 3 & 4 \\ -1 & 3 & -3 & 2 \\ 0 & 0 & 0 & -1 \\ 3 & 3 & 4 & 3 \end{vmatrix} = 0(*) - 0(*) + 0(*) - (-1)\begin{vmatrix} 1 & 2 & 3 \\ -1 & 3 & -3 \\ 3 & 3 & 4 \end{vmatrix}$$

$$= 1\left(1\begin{vmatrix} 3 & -3 \\ 3 & 4 \end{vmatrix} - 2\begin{vmatrix} -1 & -3 \\ 3 & 4 \end{vmatrix} + 3\begin{vmatrix} -1 & 3 \\ 3 & 3 \end{vmatrix}\right)$$

$$= 1(21) - 2(5) + 3(-12) = -25$$

47. $x = \dfrac{\begin{vmatrix} -5 & 3 \\ -4 & 1 \end{vmatrix}}{\begin{vmatrix} 1 & 3 \\ -2 & 1 \end{vmatrix}} = \dfrac{7}{7} = 1 \quad y = \dfrac{\begin{vmatrix} 1 & -5 \\ -2 & -4 \end{vmatrix}}{\begin{vmatrix} 1 & 3 \\ -2 & 1 \end{vmatrix}} = \dfrac{-14}{7} = -2$

48. $x = \dfrac{\begin{vmatrix} -1 & -1 & 1 \\ -4 & -1 & 3 \\ -1 & -3 & 1 \end{vmatrix}}{\begin{vmatrix} 1 & -1 & 1 \\ 2 & -1 & 3 \\ 1 & -3 & 1 \end{vmatrix}} = \dfrac{2}{2} = 1 \quad y = \dfrac{\begin{vmatrix} 1 & -1 & 1 \\ 2 & -4 & 3 \\ 1 & -1 & 1 \end{vmatrix}}{\begin{vmatrix} 1 & -1 & 1 \\ 2 & -1 & 3 \\ 1 & -3 & 1 \end{vmatrix}} = \dfrac{0}{2} = 0 \quad z = \dfrac{\begin{vmatrix} 1 & -1 & -1 \\ 2 & -1 & -4 \\ 1 & -3 & -1 \end{vmatrix}}{\begin{vmatrix} 1 & -1 & 1 \\ 2 & -1 & 3 \\ 1 & -3 & 1 \end{vmatrix}} = \dfrac{-4}{2} = -2$

49. $x = \dfrac{\begin{vmatrix} 7 & -3 & 1 \\ -9 & 1 & -3 \\ 3 & 1 & 1 \end{vmatrix}}{\begin{vmatrix} 1 & -3 & 1 \\ 1 & 1 & -3 \\ 1 & 1 & 1 \end{vmatrix}} = \dfrac{16}{16} = 1 \quad y = \dfrac{\begin{vmatrix} 1 & 7 & 1 \\ 1 & -9 & -3 \\ 1 & 3 & 1 \end{vmatrix}}{\begin{vmatrix} 1 & -3 & 1 \\ 1 & 1 & -3 \\ 1 & 1 & 1 \end{vmatrix}} = \dfrac{-16}{16} = -1$

$z = \dfrac{\begin{vmatrix} 1 & -3 & 7 \\ 1 & 1 & -9 \\ 1 & 1 & 3 \end{vmatrix}}{\begin{vmatrix} 1 & -3 & 1 \\ 1 & 1 & -3 \\ 1 & 1 & 1 \end{vmatrix}} = \dfrac{48}{16} = 3$

50. $w = \dfrac{\begin{vmatrix} 4 & 1 & -1 & 1 \\ 4 & 1 & 0 & 1 \\ 0 & 1 & 2 & 1 \\ 2 & 0 & 1 & 1 \end{vmatrix}}{\begin{vmatrix} 1 & 1 & -1 & 1 \\ 2 & 1 & 0 & 1 \\ 0 & 1 & 2 & 1 \\ 1 & 0 & 1 & 1 \end{vmatrix}} = \dfrac{-4}{-4} = 1 \quad x = \dfrac{\begin{vmatrix} 1 & 4 & -1 & 1 \\ 2 & 4 & 0 & 1 \\ 0 & 0 & 2 & 1 \\ 1 & 2 & 1 & 1 \end{vmatrix}}{\begin{vmatrix} 1 & 1 & -1 & 1 \\ 2 & 1 & 0 & 1 \\ 0 & 1 & 2 & 1 \\ 1 & 0 & 1 & 1 \end{vmatrix}} = \dfrac{0}{-4} = 0$

continued on next page...

50. continued

$$y = \frac{\begin{vmatrix} 1 & 1 & 4 & 1 \\ 2 & 1 & 4 & 1 \\ 0 & 1 & 0 & 1 \\ 1 & 0 & 2 & 1 \end{vmatrix}}{\begin{vmatrix} 1 & 1 & -1 & 1 \\ 2 & 1 & 0 & 1 \\ 0 & 1 & 2 & 1 \\ 1 & 0 & 1 & 1 \end{vmatrix}} = \frac{4}{-4} = -1 \quad z = \frac{\begin{vmatrix} 1 & 1 & -1 & 4 \\ 2 & 1 & 0 & 4 \\ 0 & 1 & 2 & 0 \\ 1 & 0 & 1 & 2 \end{vmatrix}}{\begin{vmatrix} 1 & 1 & -1 & 1 \\ 2 & 1 & 0 & 1 \\ 0 & 1 & 2 & 1 \\ 1 & 0 & 1 & 1 \end{vmatrix}} = \frac{-8}{-4} = 2$$

51. $\begin{vmatrix} 3a & 3b & 3c \\ d & e & f \\ g & h & i \end{vmatrix} = 3\begin{vmatrix} a & b & c \\ d & e & f \\ g & h & i \end{vmatrix} = 21$

52. $\begin{vmatrix} a & b & c \\ d+g & e+h & f+i \\ g & h & i \end{vmatrix} = \begin{vmatrix} a & b & c \\ d & e & f \\ g & h & i \end{vmatrix} = 7$

53.
$$\begin{aligned} \frac{7x+3}{x^2+x} = \frac{7x+3}{x(x+1)} &= \frac{A}{x} + \frac{B}{x+1} \\ &= \frac{A(x+1)}{x(x+1)} + \frac{Bx}{x(x+1)} \\ &= \frac{Ax + A + Bx}{x(x+1)} \\ &= \frac{(A+B)x + A}{x(x+1)} \end{aligned}$$

$$\begin{cases} A + B = 7 \\ A = 3 \end{cases} \Rightarrow \begin{matrix} A = 3 \\ B = 4 \end{matrix} \quad \frac{7x+3}{x(x+1)} = \frac{3}{x} + \frac{4}{x+1}$$

54.
$$\begin{aligned} \frac{4x^3 + 3x + x^2 + 2}{x^4 + x^2} = \frac{4x^3 + x^2 + 3x + 2}{x^2(x^2+1)} &= \frac{A}{x} + \frac{B}{x^2} + \frac{Cx + D}{x^2+1} \\ &= \frac{Ax(x^2+1)}{x^2(x^2+1)} + \frac{B(x^2+1)}{x^2(x^2+1)} + \frac{(Cx+D)x^2}{x^2(x^2+1)} \\ &= \frac{Ax^3 + Ax + Bx^2 + B + Cx^3 + Dx^2}{x^2(x^2+1)} \\ &= \frac{(A+C)x^3 + (B+D)x^2 + Ax + B}{x^2(x^2+1)} \end{aligned}$$

$$\begin{cases} A + C = 4 \\ B + D = 1 \\ A = 3 \\ B = 2 \end{cases} \Rightarrow \begin{matrix} A = 3 \\ B = 2 \\ C = 1 \\ D = -1 \end{matrix} \quad \frac{4x^3 + x^2 + 3x + 2}{x^2(x^2+1)} = \frac{3}{x} + \frac{2}{x^2} + \frac{x-1}{x^2+1}$$

55. $\dfrac{x^2+5}{x^3+x^2+5x}=\dfrac{x^2+5}{x(x^2+x+5)}=\dfrac{A}{x}+\dfrac{Bx+C}{x^2+x+5}$

$$=\frac{A(x^2+x+5)}{x(x^2+x+5)}+\frac{(Bx+C)x}{x(x^2+x+5)}$$

$$=\frac{Ax^2+Ax+5A+Bx^2+Cx}{x(x^2+x+5)}$$

$$=\frac{(A+B)x^2+(A+C)x+(5A)}{x(x^2+x+5)}$$

$\begin{cases} A+B \quad\quad = 1 \\ A \quad\quad +C = 0 \\ 5A \quad\quad\quad = 5 \end{cases} \Rightarrow \begin{matrix} A=1 \\ B=0 \\ C=-1 \end{matrix}$ $\quad \dfrac{x^2+5}{x(x^2+x+5)}=\dfrac{1}{x}-\dfrac{1}{x^2+x+5}$

56. $\dfrac{x^2+1}{(x+1)^3}=\dfrac{A}{x+1}+\dfrac{B}{(x+1)^2}+\dfrac{C}{(x+1)^3}$

$$=\frac{A(x+1)^2}{(x+1)^3}+\frac{B(x+1)}{(x+1)^3}+\frac{C}{(x+1)^3}$$

$$=\frac{Ax^2+2Ax+A+Bx+B+C}{(x+1)^3}$$

$$=\frac{Ax^2+(2A+B)x+(A+B+C)}{(x+1)^3}$$

$\begin{cases} A \quad\quad\quad = 1 \\ 2A+B \quad = 0 \\ A+B+C=1 \end{cases} \Rightarrow \begin{matrix} A=1 \\ B=-2 \\ C=2 \end{matrix}$ $\quad \dfrac{x^2+1}{(x+1)^3}=\dfrac{1}{x+1}-\dfrac{2}{(x+1)^2}+\dfrac{2}{(x+1)^3}$

57. $y \geq -2x-1$

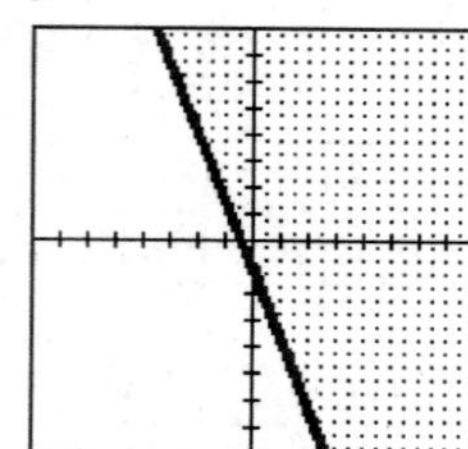

58. $x^2+y^2>4$

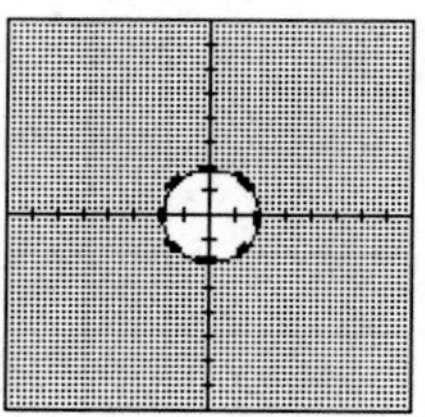

59. $\begin{cases} 3x+2y \leq 6 \\ x-y>3 \end{cases}$

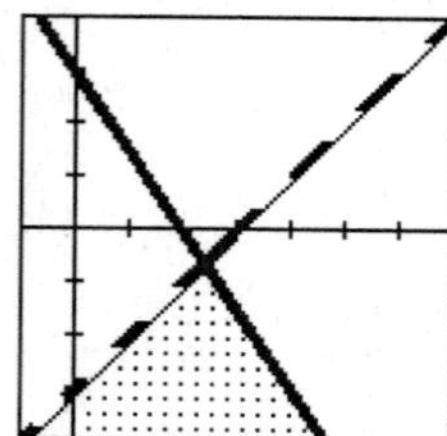

60. $\begin{cases} y \leq x^2+1 \\ y \geq x^2-1 \end{cases}$

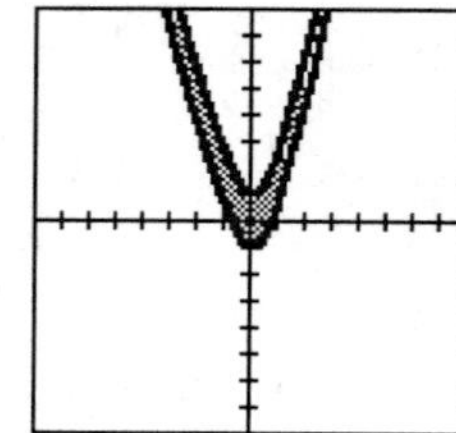

61.

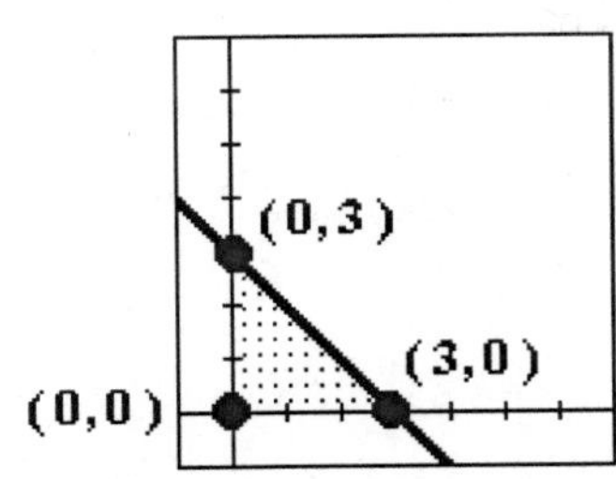

Point	$P = 2x + y$
$(0, 0)$	$= 2(0) + 0 = 0$
$(0, 3)$	$= 2(0) + 3 = 3$
$(3, 0)$	$= 2(3) + 0 = 6$

Max: $P = 6$ at $(3, 0)$

62.

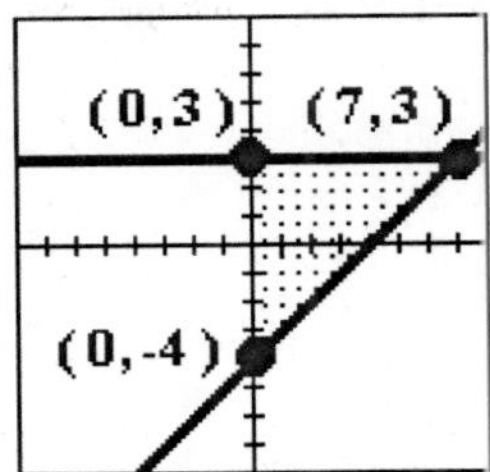

Point	$P = 2x - 3y$
$(0, 3)$	$= 2(0) - 3(3) = -9$
$(7, 3)$	$= 2(7) - 3(3) = 5$
$(0, -4)$	$= 2(0) - 3(-4) = 12$

Max: $P = 12$ at $(0, -4)$

63.

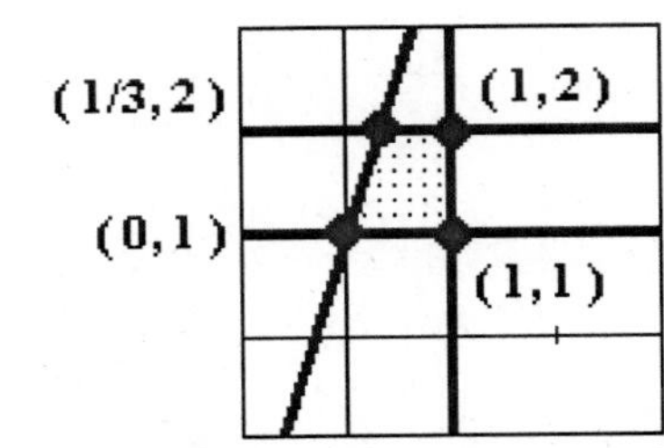

Point	$P = 3x - y$
$(0, 1)$	$= 3(0) - 1 = -1$
$(1, 1)$	$= 3(1) - 1 = 2$
$(1, 2)$	$= 3(1) - 2 = 1$
$(\frac{1}{3}, 2)$	$= 3(\frac{1}{3}) - 2 = -1$

Max: $P = 2$ at $(1, 1)$

64.

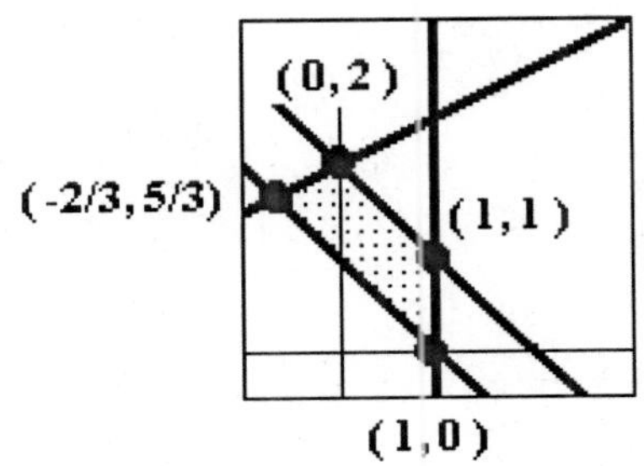

Point	$P = y - 2x$
$(0, 2)$	$= 2 - 2(0) = 2$
$(1, 1)$	$= 1 - 2(1) = -1$
$(1, 0)$	$= 0 - 2(1) = -2$
$(-\frac{2}{3}, \frac{5}{3})$	$= \frac{5}{3} - 2(-\frac{2}{3}) = 3$

Max: $P = 3$ at $(-\frac{2}{3}, \frac{5}{3})$

65. Let x = bags of Fertilizer x and y = bags of Fertilizer y.
Maximize $P = 6x + 5y$

$$\text{subject to} \begin{cases} 6x + 10y \leq 20000 \\ 8x + 6y \leq 16400 \\ 6x + 4y \leq 12000 \\ x \geq 0, y \geq 0 \end{cases}$$

Point	$P = 6x + 5y$
$(0, 0)$	$= 0$
$(0, 2000)$	$= 10000$
$(1000, 1400)$	$= 13000$
$(1600, 600)$	$= 6(1600) + 5(600) = 12600$
$(2000, 0)$	$= 6(2000) + 5(0) = 12000$

y
(1000,1400)
(0,2000)
(1600,600)
(0,0)
(2000,0)
x

1000 bags of x and 1400 bags of y should be made, for a maximum profit of \$12,600.

Chapter 6 Test (page 650)

1. $\begin{cases} x - 3y = -5 \\ 2x - y = 0 \end{cases}$

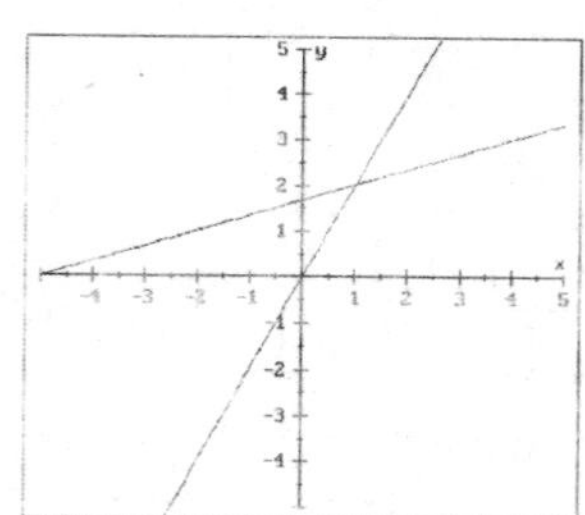

solution: (1, 2)

2. $\begin{cases} x = 2y + 5 \\ y = 2x - 4 \end{cases}$

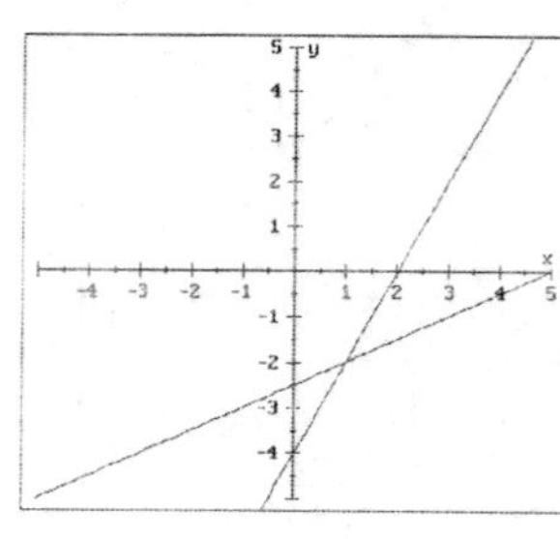

solution: (1, −2)

3.
$$\begin{aligned} 3x + y &= 0 \Rightarrow \times (5) & 15x + 5y &= 0 \\ 2x - 5y &= 17 & 2x - 5y &= 17 \\ & & 17x &= 17 \\ & & x &= 1 \end{aligned}$$
$$\begin{aligned} 3x + y &= 0 \\ 3(1) + y &= 0 \\ y &= -3 \end{aligned}$$
Solution: $\boxed{x = 1, y = -3}$

4.
$$\begin{aligned} \frac{x+y}{2} + x &= 7 \Rightarrow 3x + y = 14 \Rightarrow & 3x + y &= 14 \\ \frac{x-y}{2} - y &= -6 \Rightarrow x - 3y = -12 \Rightarrow & -3x + 9y &= 36 \\ & & 10y &= 50 \\ & & y &= 5 \end{aligned}$$
$$\begin{aligned} x - 3y &= -12 \\ x - 3(5) &= -12 \\ x &= 3 \end{aligned}$$
Solution: $\boxed{x = 3, \; y = 5}$

5. Let x = liters of 20% solution and y = liters of 45% solution. The following system applies:
$$\begin{aligned} x + y &= 10 \Rightarrow \times (-2) & -2x - 2y &= -20 \\ 0.2x + 0.45y &= 3 \Rightarrow \times (10) & 2x + 4.5y &= 30 \\ & & 2.5y &= 10 \\ & & y &= 4 \end{aligned}$$
She must use 4 liters of the 45% and 6 liters of the 20% solution.

6. Let x = # from Ace, y = # from Hi-Fi and z = # from CD World.

$$\begin{aligned} (1) \quad & x + y + z = 175 \\ (2) \quad & -x - y + z = 25 \\ (3) \quad & 170x + 165y + 160z = 28500 \end{aligned}$$

Add (1) and (2):
$$\begin{aligned} (1) \quad & x + y + z = 175 \\ (2) \quad & -x - y + z = 25 \\ (4) \quad & 2z = 200 \\ & z = 100 \end{aligned}$$

Add equations 170(2) and (3):
$$\begin{aligned} 170(2) \quad & -170x - 170y + 170z = 4250 \\ (3) \quad & 170x + 165y + 160z = 28500 \\ (5) \quad & -5y + 330z = 32750 \end{aligned}$$

continued on next page...

6. **continued**

Solve the system of two equations and two unknowns formed by equations (4) and (5):

$$\begin{aligned} -5y + 330z &= 32750 \\ -5y + 330(100) &= 32750 \\ -5y &= -250 \\ y &= 50 \end{aligned} \qquad \begin{aligned} x + y + z &= 175 \\ x + 50 + 100 &= 175 \\ y &= 25 \end{aligned}$$

Ace buys 25 units per month. Hi-Fi buys 50 units per month. CD World buys 100 units per month.

7. $\left[\begin{array}{cc|c} 3 & -2 & 4 \\ 2 & 3 & 7 \end{array}\right] \Rightarrow \left[\begin{array}{cc|c} 1 & -5 & -3 \\ 2 & 3 & 7 \end{array}\right] \Rightarrow \left[\begin{array}{cc|c} 1 & -5 & -3 \\ 0 & 13 & 13 \end{array}\right] \Rightarrow \left[\begin{array}{cc|c} 1 & -5 & -3 \\ 0 & 1 & 1 \end{array}\right]$

$-R_2 + R_1 \Rightarrow R_1$ $\quad -2R_1 + R_2 \Rightarrow R_2$ $\quad \frac{1}{13}R_2 \Rightarrow R_2$

From R_2: $y = 1$ From R_1: $x - 5y = -3$ Solution: $\boxed{x = 2, y = 1}$

$$\begin{aligned} x - 5(1) &= -3 \\ x &= 2 \end{aligned}$$

8. $\left[\begin{array}{ccc|c} 1 & 3 & -1 & 6 \\ 2 & -1 & -2 & -2 \\ 1 & 2 & 1 & 6 \end{array}\right] \Rightarrow \left[\begin{array}{ccc|c} 1 & 3 & -1 & 6 \\ 0 & -7 & 0 & -14 \\ 0 & 1 & -2 & 0 \end{array}\right] \Rightarrow \left[\begin{array}{ccc|c} 1 & 3 & -1 & 6 \\ 0 & 1 & 0 & 2 \\ 0 & 0 & -14 & -14 \end{array}\right] \Rightarrow$

$-2R_1 + R_2 \Rightarrow R_2$, $-R_3 + R_1 \Rightarrow R_3$ $\quad -\frac{1}{7}R_2 \Rightarrow R_2$, $7R_3 + R_2 \Rightarrow R_3$

$\left[\begin{array}{ccc|c} 1 & 3 & -1 & 6 \\ 0 & 1 & 0 & 2 \\ 0 & 0 & 1 & 1 \end{array}\right]$ $\quad -\frac{1}{14}R_3 \Rightarrow R_3$

From (3): $z = 1$
From (2): $y = 2$
From (1):
$$\begin{aligned} x + 3y - z &= 6 \\ x + 3(2) - (1) &= 6 \\ x &= 1 \end{aligned}$$

Solution: $\boxed{x = 1, y = 2, z = 1}$

9. $\left[\begin{array}{ccc|c} 1 & 2 & 3 & -5 \\ 3 & 1 & -2 & 7 \\ 0 & 1 & -1 & 2 \end{array}\right] \Rightarrow \left[\begin{array}{ccc|c} 1 & 2 & 3 & -5 \\ 0 & -5 & -11 & 22 \\ 0 & 1 & -1 & 2 \end{array}\right] \Rightarrow \left[\begin{array}{ccc|c} 1 & 2 & 3 & -5 \\ 0 & 1 & -1 & 2 \\ 0 & -5 & -11 & 22 \end{array}\right] \Rightarrow$

$-3R_1 + R_2 \Rightarrow R_2$ $\quad R_2 \Leftrightarrow R_3$

$\left[\begin{array}{ccc|c} 1 & 0 & 5 & -9 \\ 0 & 1 & -1 & 2 \\ 0 & 0 & -16 & 32 \end{array}\right] \Rightarrow \left[\begin{array}{ccc|c} 1 & 0 & 5 & -9 \\ 0 & 1 & -1 & 2 \\ 0 & 0 & 1 & -2 \end{array}\right] \Rightarrow \left[\begin{array}{ccc|c} 1 & 0 & 0 & 1 \\ 0 & 1 & 0 & 0 \\ 0 & 0 & 1 & -2 \end{array}\right]$ Solution: $\boxed{\begin{aligned} x &= 1 \\ y &= 0 \\ z &= -2 \end{aligned}}$

$-2R_2 + R_1 \Rightarrow R_1$, $5R_2 + R_3 \Rightarrow R_3$ $\quad -\frac{1}{16}R_3 \Rightarrow R_3$ $\quad -5R_3 + R_1 \Rightarrow R_1$, $R_2 + R_3 \Rightarrow R_2$

10. $\left[\begin{array}{ccc|c} 1 & 2 & 1 & 0 \\ 3 & -2 & -2 & 7 \\ 4 & 0 & -1 & 7 \end{array}\right] \Rightarrow \left[\begin{array}{ccc|c} 1 & 2 & 1 & 0 \\ 0 & -8 & -5 & 7 \\ 0 & -8 & -5 & 7 \end{array}\right] \Rightarrow \left[\begin{array}{ccc|c} 1 & 2 & 1 & 0 \\ 0 & 1 & \frac{5}{8} & -\frac{7}{8} \\ 0 & 0 & 0 & 0 \end{array}\right] \Rightarrow$

$-3R_1 + R_2 \Rightarrow R_2$, $-4R_1 + R_3 \Rightarrow R_3$ $\quad -R_2 + R_3 \Rightarrow R_3$, $-\frac{1}{8}R_2 \Rightarrow R_2$

continued on next page...

10. continued

$$\left[\begin{array}{ccc|c} 1 & 0 & -\frac{1}{4} & \frac{7}{4} \\ 0 & 1 & \frac{5}{8} & -\frac{7}{8} \\ 0 & 0 & 0 & 0 \end{array}\right] \Rightarrow \text{Solution: } \boxed{\begin{array}{l} x = \frac{7}{4} + \frac{1}{4}z \\ y = -\frac{7}{8} - \frac{5}{8}z \\ z = \text{any real number} \end{array}}$$
$-2R_2 + R_1 \Rightarrow R_1$

Note: This answer is equivalent to the answer provided in the textbook.

11. $$3\begin{bmatrix} 2 & -3 & 5 \\ 0 & 3 & -1 \end{bmatrix} - 5\begin{bmatrix} -2 & 1 & -1 \\ 0 & 3 & 2 \end{bmatrix} = \begin{bmatrix} 6 & -9 & 15 \\ 0 & 9 & -3 \end{bmatrix} - \begin{bmatrix} -10 & 5 & -5 \\ 0 & 15 & 10 \end{bmatrix} = \begin{bmatrix} 16 & -14 & 20 \\ 0 & -6 & -13 \end{bmatrix}$$

12. $$\begin{bmatrix} 1 & 2 & 3 \end{bmatrix}\begin{bmatrix} 2 & -2 \\ -2 & 2 \\ 1 & 0 \end{bmatrix}\begin{bmatrix} 3 \\ -2 \end{bmatrix} = \begin{bmatrix} 1 & 2 \end{bmatrix}\begin{bmatrix} 3 \\ -2 \end{bmatrix} = \begin{bmatrix} -1 \end{bmatrix}$$

13. $$\left[\begin{array}{cc|cc} 5 & 19 & 1 & 0 \\ 2 & 7 & 0 & 1 \end{array}\right] \Rightarrow \left[\begin{array}{cc|cc} 1 & \frac{19}{5} & \frac{1}{5} & 0 \\ 2 & 7 & 0 & 1 \end{array}\right] \Rightarrow \left[\begin{array}{cc|cc} 1 & \frac{19}{5} & \frac{1}{5} & 0 \\ 0 & -\frac{3}{5} & -\frac{2}{5} & 1 \end{array}\right] \Rightarrow$$
$\frac{1}{5}R_1 \Rightarrow R_1$ $\quad -2R_1 + R_2 \Rightarrow R_2$

$$\left[\begin{array}{cc|cc} 1 & \frac{19}{5} & \frac{1}{5} & 0 \\ 0 & 1 & \frac{2}{3} & -\frac{5}{3} \end{array}\right] \Rightarrow \left[\begin{array}{cc|cc} 1 & 0 & -\frac{7}{3} & \frac{19}{3} \\ 0 & 1 & \frac{2}{3} & -\frac{5}{3} \end{array}\right] \Rightarrow \text{Inverse: } \begin{bmatrix} -\frac{7}{3} & \frac{19}{3} \\ \frac{2}{3} & -\frac{5}{3} \end{bmatrix}$$
$-\frac{5}{3}R_2 \Rightarrow R_1$ $\quad -\frac{19}{5}R_2 + R_1 \Rightarrow R_1$

14. $$\left[\begin{array}{ccc|ccc} -1 & 3 & -2 & 1 & 0 & 0 \\ 4 & 1 & 4 & 0 & 1 & 0 \\ 0 & 3 & -1 & 0 & 0 & 1 \end{array}\right] \Rightarrow \left[\begin{array}{ccc|ccc} 1 & -3 & 2 & -1 & 0 & 0 \\ 0 & 13 & -4 & 4 & 1 & 0 \\ 0 & 3 & -1 & 0 & 0 & 1 \end{array}\right] \Rightarrow$$
$4R_1 + R_2 \Rightarrow R_2$
$-R_1 \Rightarrow R_1$

$$\left[\begin{array}{ccc|ccc} 1 & -3 & 2 & -1 & 0 & 0 \\ 0 & 1 & 0 & 4 & 1 & -4 \\ 0 & 3 & -1 & 0 & 0 & 1 \end{array}\right] \Rightarrow \left[\begin{array}{ccc|ccc} 1 & 0 & 2 & 11 & 3 & -12 \\ 0 & 1 & 0 & 4 & 1 & -4 \\ 0 & 0 & -1 & -12 & -3 & 13 \end{array}\right] \Rightarrow$$
$-4R_3 + R_2 \Rightarrow R_2$ $\quad 3R_2 + R_1 \Rightarrow R_1$
$-3R_2 + R_3 \Rightarrow R_3$

$$\left[\begin{array}{ccc|ccc} 1 & 0 & 0 & -13 & -3 & 14 \\ 0 & 1 & 0 & 4 & 1 & -4 \\ 0 & 0 & 1 & 12 & 3 & -13 \end{array}\right] \quad \text{Inverse: } \begin{bmatrix} -13 & -3 & 14 \\ 4 & 1 & -4 \\ 12 & 3 & -13 \end{bmatrix}$$
$2R_3 + R_1 \Rightarrow R_1$
$-R_3 \Rightarrow R_3$

15. $$\begin{bmatrix} 5 & 19 \\ 2 & 7 \end{bmatrix}\begin{bmatrix} x \\ y \end{bmatrix} = \begin{bmatrix} 3 \\ 2 \end{bmatrix}$$

$$\begin{bmatrix} x \\ y \end{bmatrix} = \begin{bmatrix} 5 & 19 \\ 2 & 7 \end{bmatrix}^{-1}\begin{bmatrix} 3 \\ 2 \end{bmatrix} = \begin{bmatrix} -\frac{7}{3} & \frac{19}{3} \\ \frac{2}{3} & -\frac{5}{3} \end{bmatrix}\begin{bmatrix} 3 \\ 2 \end{bmatrix} = \begin{bmatrix} \frac{17}{3} \\ -\frac{4}{3} \end{bmatrix}$$

16. $\begin{bmatrix} -1 & 3 & -2 \\ 4 & 1 & 4 \\ 0 & 3 & -1 \end{bmatrix} \begin{bmatrix} x \\ y \\ z \end{bmatrix} = \begin{bmatrix} 1 \\ 3 \\ -1 \end{bmatrix}$

$$\begin{bmatrix} x \\ y \\ z \end{bmatrix} = \begin{bmatrix} -1 & 3 & -2 \\ 4 & 1 & 4 \\ 0 & 3 & -1 \end{bmatrix}^{-1} \begin{bmatrix} 1 \\ 3 \\ -1 \end{bmatrix}$$

$$\begin{bmatrix} x \\ y \\ z \end{bmatrix} = \begin{bmatrix} -13 & -3 & 14 \\ 4 & 1 & -4 \\ 12 & 3 & -13 \end{bmatrix} \begin{bmatrix} 1 \\ 3 \\ -1 \end{bmatrix} = \begin{bmatrix} -36 \\ 11 \\ 34 \end{bmatrix}$$

17. $\begin{vmatrix} 3 & -5 \\ -3 & 1 \end{vmatrix} = (3)(1) - (-5)(-3) = 3 - 15 = -12$

18. $\begin{vmatrix} 3 & 5 & -1 \\ -2 & 3 & -2 \\ 1 & 5 & -3 \end{vmatrix} = 3\begin{vmatrix} 3 & -2 \\ 5 & -3 \end{vmatrix} - 5\begin{vmatrix} -2 & -2 \\ 1 & -3 \end{vmatrix} + (-1)\begin{vmatrix} -2 & 3 \\ 1 & 5 \end{vmatrix}$

$$= 3(1) - 5(8) - 1(-13) = 3 - 40 + 13 = -24$$

19. $y = \dfrac{\begin{vmatrix} 3 & 3 \\ -3 & 2 \end{vmatrix}}{\begin{vmatrix} 3 & -5 \\ -3 & 1 \end{vmatrix}} = \dfrac{15}{-12} = -\dfrac{5}{4}$

20. $y = \dfrac{\begin{vmatrix} 3 & 2 & -1 \\ -2 & 1 & -2 \\ 1 & 0 & -3 \end{vmatrix}}{\begin{vmatrix} 3 & 5 & -1 \\ -2 & 3 & -2 \\ 1 & 5 & -3 \end{vmatrix}} = \dfrac{-24}{-24} = 1$

21. $\dfrac{5x}{2x^2 - x - 3} = \dfrac{5x}{(2x-3)(x+1)} = \dfrac{A}{2x-3} + \dfrac{B}{x+1}$

$$= \frac{A(x+1)}{(2x-3)(x+1)} + \frac{B(2x-3)}{(2x-3)(x+1)}$$

$$= \frac{Ax + A + 2Bx - 3B}{(2x-3)(x+1)}$$

$$= \frac{(A+2B)x + (A-3B)}{(2x-3)(x+1)}$$

$\begin{cases} A + 2B = 5 \\ A - 3B = 0 \end{cases} \Rightarrow \begin{matrix} A = 3 \\ B = 1 \end{matrix} \quad \dfrac{5x}{(2x-3)(x+1)} = \dfrac{3}{2x-3} + \dfrac{1}{x+1}$

CHAPTER 6 TEST

22. $$\frac{3x^2+x+2}{x^3+2x} = \frac{3x^2+x+2}{x(x^2+2)} = \frac{A}{x} + \frac{Bx+C}{x^2+2}$$

$$= \frac{A(x^2+2)}{x(x^2+2)} + \frac{(Bx+C)x}{x(x^2+2)}$$

$$= \frac{Ax^2+2A+Bx^2+Cx}{x(x^2+2)}$$

$$= \frac{(A+B)x^2+Cx+2A}{x(x^2+2)}$$

$$\begin{cases} A+B \quad = 3 \\ \qquad C = 1 \\ 2A \quad\;\; = 2 \end{cases} \Rightarrow \begin{matrix} A = 1 \\ B = 2 \\ C = 1 \end{matrix} \qquad \frac{3x^2+x+2}{x(x^2+2)} = \frac{1}{x} + \frac{2x+1}{x^2+2}$$

23. $\begin{cases} x - 3y \geq 3 \\ x + 3y \leq 3 \end{cases}$

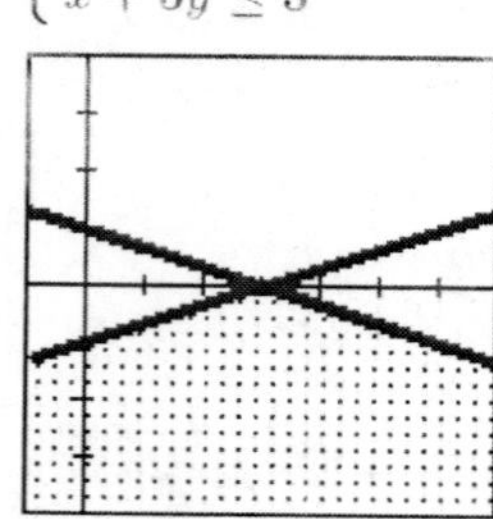

24. $\begin{cases} 3x + 4y \leq 12 \\ 3x + 4y \geq 6 \\ x \geq 0,\ y \geq 0 \end{cases}$

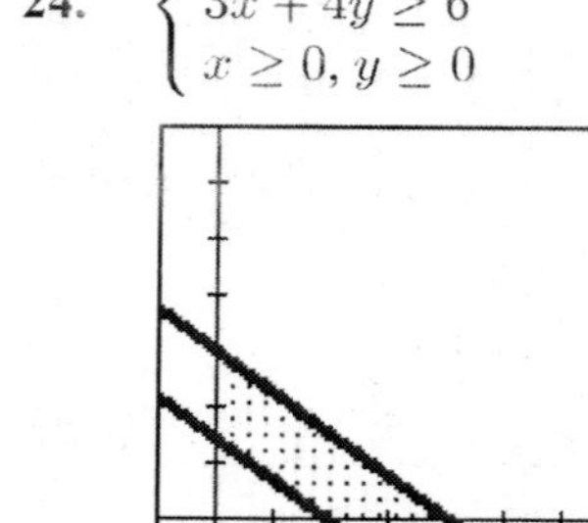

25.

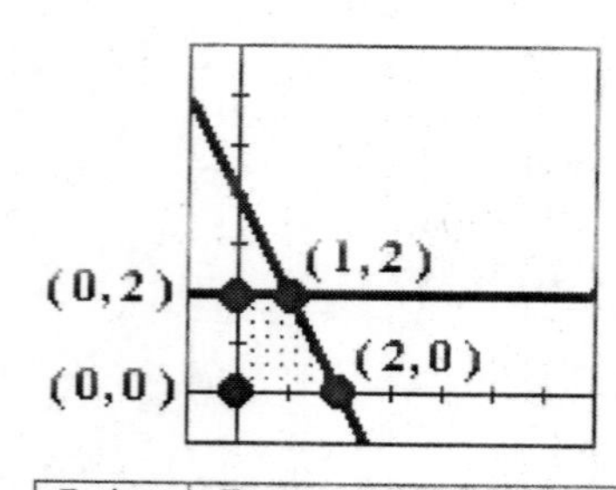

Point	$P = 3x + 2y$
(0, 2)	$= 3(0) + 2(2) = 4$
(1, 2)	$= 3(1) + 2(2) = 7$
(2, 0)	$= 3(2) + 2(0) = 6$
(0, 0)	$= 3(0) + 2(0) = 0$

Max: $P = 7$ at $(1, 2)$

26.

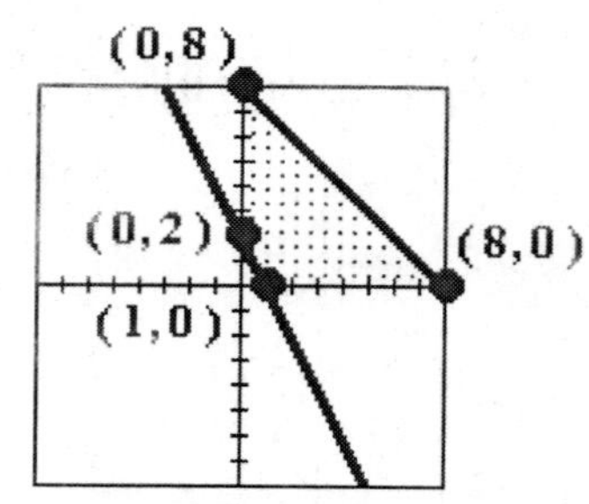

Point	$P = y - x$
(0, 2)	$= 2 - 0 = 2$
(0, 8)	$= 8 - 0 = 8$
(8, 0)	$= 0 - 8 = -8$
(1, 0)	$= 0 - 1 = -1$

Min: $P = -8$ at $(8, 0)$

Exercises 7.1 (page 666)

1. $(2, -5), 3$

2. $(0, 0), 6$

3. $(0, 0), \sqrt{5}$

4. $(9, 0), \sqrt{\frac{7}{2}}$, or $\frac{\sqrt{14}}{2}$

5. to the left

6. to the right

7. downward

8. upward

9. directrix, focus

10. $+ Bxy + Cy^2 + Dx + Ey + F$

11. Two squared variables: circle

12. Two squared variables: circle

13. One squared variable: parabola

14. One squared variable: parabola

15.
$$(x-h)^2 + (y-k)^2 = r^2$$
$$(x-0)^2 + (y-0)^2 = 7^2$$
$$\boxed{x^2 + y^2 = 49}$$
$$\boxed{x^2 + y^2 - 49 = 0}$$

16.
$$r = \sqrt{(-3-0)^2 + (2-0)^2} = \sqrt{13}$$
$$(x-h)^2 + (y-k)^2 = r^2$$
$$(x-0)^2 + (y-0)^2 = \left(\sqrt{13}\right)^2$$
$$\boxed{x^2 + y^2 = 13}$$
$$\boxed{x^2 + y^2 - 13 = 0}$$

17.
$$r = \sqrt{(3-2)^2 + (2-(-2))^2} = \sqrt{17}$$
$$(x-h)^2 + (y-k)^2 = r^2$$
$$(x-2)^2 + (y-(-2))^2 = \left(\sqrt{17}\right)^2$$
$$\boxed{(x-2)^2 + (y+2)^2 = 17}$$
$$x^2 - 4x + 4 + y^2 + 4y + 4 = 17$$
$$\boxed{x^2 + y^2 - 4x + 4y - 9 = 0}$$

18.
$$O\left(\frac{5+(-2)}{2}, \frac{4+(-3)}{2}\right) = O\left(\frac{3}{2}, \frac{1}{2}\right)$$
$$r = \sqrt{\left(5-\tfrac{3}{2}\right)^2 + \left(4-\tfrac{1}{2}\right)^2} = \sqrt{\tfrac{49}{2}}$$
$$(x-h)^2 + (y-k)^2 = r^2$$
$$\left(x-\tfrac{3}{2}\right)^2 + \left(y-\tfrac{1}{2}\right)^2 = \left(\sqrt{\tfrac{49}{2}}\right)^2$$
$$\boxed{\left(x-\tfrac{3}{2}\right)^2 + \left(y-\tfrac{1}{2}\right)^2 = \tfrac{49}{2}}$$
$$x^2 - 3x + \tfrac{9}{4} + y^2 - y + \tfrac{1}{4} = \tfrac{49}{2}$$
$$\boxed{x^2 + y^2 - 3x - y - 22 = 0}$$

19.
$$\begin{aligned} 3x + y &= 1 \Rightarrow \times (3) \\ -2x - 3y &= 4 \end{aligned} \qquad \begin{aligned} 9x + 3y &= 3 \\ -2x - 3y &= 4 \\ \hline 7x \quad &= 7 \\ x \quad &= 1 \end{aligned}$$
$$\begin{aligned} 3x + y &= 1 \\ 3(1) + y &= 1 \\ y &= -2 \end{aligned} \qquad \text{Center: } (1, -2)$$
$$(x-h)^2 + (y-k)^2 = r^2$$
$$(x-1)^2 + (y-(-2))^2 = 6^2$$
$$\boxed{(x-1)^2 + (y+2)^2 = 36}$$
$$x^2 - 2x + 1 + y^2 + 4y + 4 = 36$$
$$\boxed{x^2 + y^2 - 2x + 4y - 31 = 0}$$

20.
$$\begin{aligned} x + 2y &= 8 \Rightarrow \times (-2) \\ 2x - 3y &= -5 \end{aligned} \qquad \begin{aligned} -2x - 4y &= -16 \\ 2x - 3y &= -5 \\ \hline -7y &= -21 \\ y &= 3 \end{aligned}$$
$$\begin{aligned} x + 2y &= 8 \\ x + 2(3) &= 8 \\ x &= 2 \end{aligned} \qquad \text{Center: } (2, 3)$$
$$(x-h)^2 + (y-k)^2 = r^2$$
$$(x-2)^2 + (y-3)^2 = 8^2$$
$$\boxed{(x-2)^2 + (y-3)^2 = 64}$$
$$x^2 - 4x + 4 + y^2 - 6y + 9 = 64$$
$$\boxed{x^2 + y^2 - 4x - 6y - 51 = 0}$$

21.
$$x^2 + y^2 = 4$$
$$(x-0)^2 + (y-0)^2 = 2^2$$
$$C(0,0),\ r = 2$$

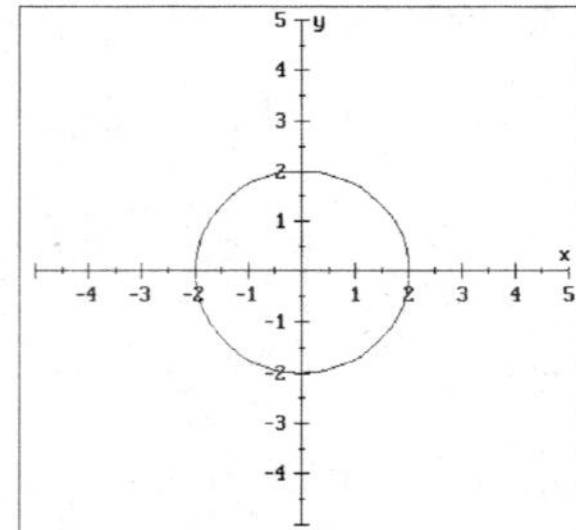

22.
$$x^2 - 2x + y^2 = 15$$
$$x^2 - 2x + 1 + y^2 = 15 + 1$$
$$(x-1)^2 + (y-0)^2 = 4^2$$
$$C(1,0),\ r = 4$$

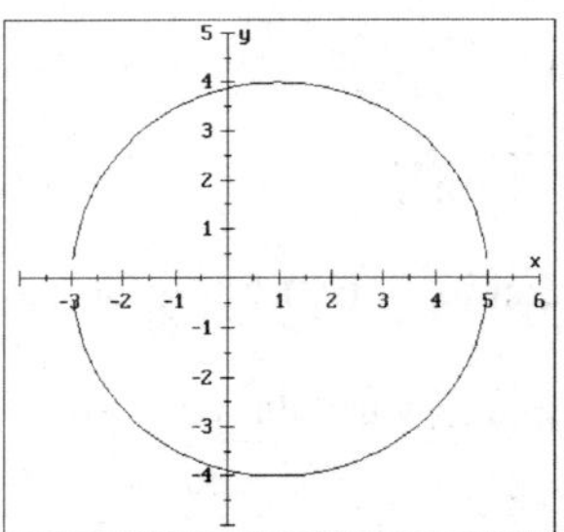

23.
$$3x^2 + 3y^2 - 12x - 6y = 12$$
$$x^2 - 4x + y^2 - 2y = 4$$
$$x^2 - 4x + 4 + y^2 - 2y + 1 = 4 + 4 + 1$$
$$(x-2)^2 + (y-1)^2 = 3^2$$
$$C(2,1),\ r = 3$$

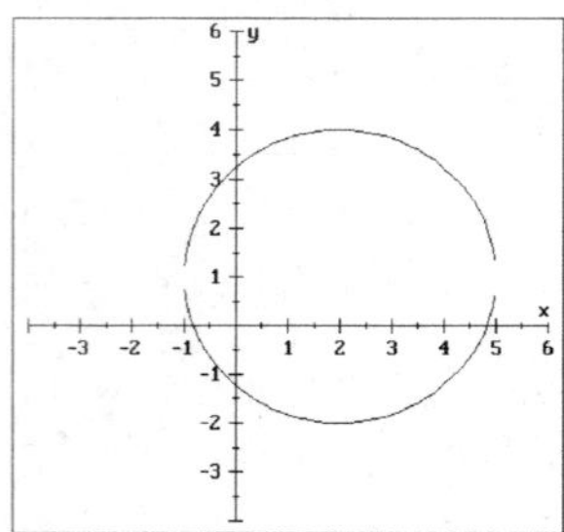

24.
$$2x^2 + 2y^2 + 4x - 8y + 2 = 0$$
$$x^2 + 2x + y^2 - 4y = -1$$
$$x^2 + 2x + 1 + y^2 - 4y + 4 = -1 + 1 + 4$$
$$(x+1)^2 + (y-2)^2 = 2^2$$
$$C(-1,2),\ r = 2$$

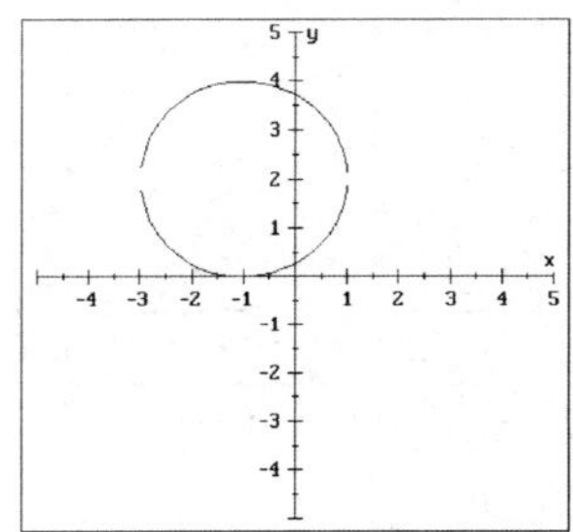

25.
$$x^2 = 12y$$
$$(x-0)^2 = 4 \cdot 3(y-0)$$
$p = 3$, opens up

V $(0,0)$, $F(0,3)$, D: $y = -3$

26.
$$y^2 = -12x$$
$$(y-0)^2 = 4 \cdot (-3)(x-0)$$
$p = -3$, opens left

V $(0,0)$, $F(-3,0)$, D: $x = 3$

27.
$$(y-3)^2 = 20x$$
$$(y-3)^2 = 4 \cdot 5(x-0)$$
$p = 5$, opens right

V $(0,3)$, $F(5,3)$, D: $x = -5$

28.
$$x^2 = -\tfrac{1}{2}(y+5)$$
$$(x-0)^2 = 4 \cdot \left(-\tfrac{1}{8}\right)(y-(-5))$$
$p = -\frac{1}{8}$, opens down

V $(0,-5)$, $F\left(0,-5\frac{1}{8}\right)$, D: $y = -4\frac{7}{8}$

29.
$$(x+2)^2 = -24(y-1)$$
$$(x-(-2))^2 = 4\cdot(-6)(y-1)$$
$p=-6$, opens down

V $(-2,1)$, $F(-2,-5)$, D: $y=7$

30.
$$(y+1)^2 = 28(x-2)$$
$$(y-(-1))^2 = 4\cdot 7(x-2)$$
$p=7$, opens right

V $(2,-1)$, $F(9,-1)$, D: $x=-5$

31. Vertical (up), $p=3$
$$(x-h)^2 = 4p(y-k)$$
$$(x-0)^2 = 4(3)(y-0)$$
$$x^2 = 12y$$

32. Vertical (down), $p=-3$
$$(x-h)^2 = 4p(y-k)$$
$$(x-0)^2 = 4(-3)(y-0)$$
$$x^2 = -12y$$

33. Horizontal (left), $p=-3$
$$(y-k)^2 = 4p(x-h)$$
$$(y-0)^2 = 4(-3)(x-0)$$
$$y^2 = -12x$$

34. Horizontal (right), $p=3$
$$(y-k)^2 = 4p(x-h)$$
$$(y-0)^2 = 4(3)(x-0)$$
$$y^2 = 12x$$

35. Vertical (down), $p=-3$
$$(x-h)^2 = 4p(y-k)$$
$$(x-3)^2 = 4(-3)(y-5)$$
$$(x-3)^2 = -12(y-5)$$

36. Horizontal (left), $p=-6$
$$(y-k)^2 = 4p(x-h)$$
$$(y-5)^2 = 4(-6)(x-3)$$
$$(y-5)^2 = -24(x-3)$$

37. Vertical (down), $p=-7$
$$(x-h)^2 = 4p(y-k)$$
$$(x-3)^2 = 4(-7)(y-5)$$
$$(x-3)^2 = -28(y-5)$$

38. Horizontal (right), $p=3$
$$(y-k)^2 = 4p(x-h)$$
$$(y-5)^2 = 4(3)(x-3)$$
$$(y-5)^2 = 12(x-3)$$

39. Vertical (down), $p=-1$
$$(x-h)^2 = 4p(y-k)$$
$$(x-0)^2 = 4(-1)(y-2)$$
$$x^2 = -4(y-2)$$

40. Vertical (up), $p=2$
$$(x-h)^2 = 4p(y-k)$$
$$(x-(-3))^2 = 4(2)(y-4)$$
$$(x+3)^2 = 8(y-4)$$

41. Horizontal (right), $p=2$
$$(y-k)^2 = 4p(x-h)$$
$$(y-(-5))^2 = 4(2)(x-1)$$
$$(y+5)^2 = 8(x-1)$$

42. Horizontal (left), $p=-3$
$$(y-k)^2 = 4p(x-h)$$
$$(y-5)^2 = 4(-3)(x-3)$$
$$(y-5)^2 = -12(x-3)$$

43.
$$(x-2)^2 = 4p(y-2)$$
$$(0-2)^2 = 4p(0-2)$$
$$4 = -8p$$
$$-\frac{1}{2} = p$$
$$-2 = 4p$$
$$(x-2)^2 = -2(y-2)$$

OR
$$(y-2)^2 = 4p(x-2)$$
$$(0-2)^2 = 4p(0-2)$$
$$4 = -8p$$
$$-\frac{1}{2} = p$$
$$-2 = 4p$$
$$(y-2)^2 = -2(x-2)$$

44.
$$(x-(-2))^2 = 4p(y-(-2))$$
$$(0+2)^2 = 4p(0+2)$$
$$4 = 8p$$
$$\frac{1}{2} = p$$
$$2 = 4p$$
$$(x+2)^2 = 2(y+2)$$

OR
$$(y-(-2))^2 = 4p(x-(-2))$$
$$(0+2)^2 = 4p(0+2)$$
$$4 = 8p$$
$$\frac{1}{2} = p$$
$$2 = 4p$$
$$(y+2)^2 = 2(x+2)$$

45. $(x-(-4))^2 = 4p(y-6)$ **OR** $(y-6)^2 = 4p(x-(-4))$

$$\begin{aligned}(0+4)^2 &= 4p(3-6)\\ 16 &= -12p\\ -\frac{4}{3} &= p\\ -\frac{16}{3} &= 4p\\ (x+4)^2 &= -\tfrac{16}{3}(y-6)\end{aligned} \qquad \begin{aligned}(3-6)^2 &= 4p(0+4)\\ 9 &= 16p\\ \frac{9}{16} &= p\\ \frac{9}{4} &= 4p\\ (y-6)^2 &= \tfrac{9}{4}(x+4)\end{aligned}$$

46. $(x-(-2))^2 = 4p(y-3)$ **OR** $(y-3)^2 = 4p(x-(-2))$

$$\begin{aligned}(0+2)^2 &= 4p(-3-3)\\ 4 &= -24p\\ -\frac{1}{6} &= p\\ -\frac{2}{3} &= 4p\\ (x+2)^2 &= -\tfrac{2}{3}(y-3)\end{aligned} \qquad \begin{aligned}(-3-3)^2 &= 4p(0+2)\\ 36 &= 8p\\ \frac{9}{2} &= p\\ 18 &= 4p\\ (y-3)^2 &= 18(x+2)\end{aligned}$$

47. $(x-6)^2 = 4p(y-8)$ **OR** $(y-8)^2 = 4p(x-6)$

$$\begin{aligned}(5-6)^2 &= 4p(10-8)\\ 1 &= 8p\\ \frac{1}{8} &= p\\ \frac{1}{2} &= 4p\\ (x-6)^2 &= \tfrac{1}{2}(y-8)\end{aligned} \qquad \begin{aligned}(10-8)^2 &= 4p(5-6)\\ 4 &= -4p\\ -1 &= p\\ -4 &= 4p\\ (y-8)^2 &= -4(x-6)\end{aligned}$$

Check to see which equation is satisfied by $(5, 6)$ as well. Answer: $(y-8)^2 = -4(x-6)$

48. $(x-2)^2 = 4p(y-3)$ **OR** $(y-3)^2 = 4p(x-2)$

$$\begin{aligned}(1-2)^2 &= 4p(\tfrac{13}{4}-3)\\ 1 &= p\\ 4 &= 4p\\ (x-2)^2 &= 4(y-3)\end{aligned} \qquad \begin{aligned}(\tfrac{13}{4}-3)^2 &= 4p(1-2)\\ \tfrac{1}{16} &= -4p\\ -\tfrac{1}{16} &= 4p\\ (y-3)^2 &= -\tfrac{1}{16}(x-2)\end{aligned}$$

Check to see which equation is satisfied by $\left(-1, \frac{21}{4}\right)$ as well. Answer: $(x-2)^2 = 4(y-3)$

49. $(x-3)^2 = 4p(y-1)$ **OR** $(y-1)^2 = 4p(x-3)$

$(4-3)^2 = 4p(3-1)$ $\qquad$ $(3-1)^2 = 4p(4-3)$

$1 = 8p$ $\qquad$ $4 = 4p$

$\frac{1}{8} = p$ $\qquad$ $(y-1)^2 = 4(x-3)$

$\frac{1}{2} = 4p$

$(x-3)^2 = \frac{1}{2}(y-1)$

Check to see which equation is satisfied by $(2, 3)$ as well. Answer: $(x-3)^2 = \frac{1}{2}(y-1)$

50. $(x-(-4))^2 = 4p(y-(-2))$ **OR** $(y-(-2))^2 = 4p(x-(-4))$

$(-3+4)^2 = 4p(0+2)$ $\qquad$ $(0+2)^2 = 4p(-3+4)$

$1 = 8p$ $\qquad$ $4 = 4p$

$\frac{1}{2} = 4p$ $\qquad$ $(y+2)^2 = 4(x+4)$

$(x+4)^2 = \frac{1}{2}(y+2)$

Check to see which equation is satisfied by $\left(\frac{9}{4}, 3\right)$ as well. Answer: $(y+2)^2 = 4(x+4)$

51.

$$y = x^2 + 4x + 5$$
$$y - 5 = x^2 + 4x$$
$$y - 5 + 4 = x^2 + 4x + 4$$
$$y - 1 = (x+2)^2$$

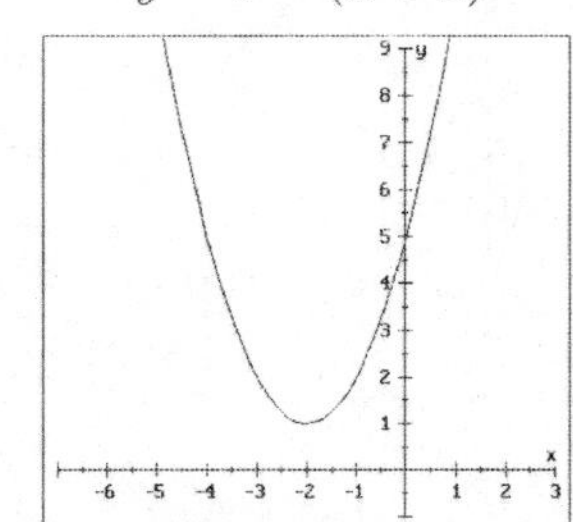

52.

$$2x^2 - 12x - 7y = 10$$
$$x^2 - 6x = \tfrac{7}{2}y + 5$$
$$x^2 - 6x + 9 = \tfrac{7}{2}y + 5 + 9$$
$$(x-3)^2 = \tfrac{7}{2}y + 14$$
$$(x-3)^2 = \tfrac{7}{2}(y+4)$$

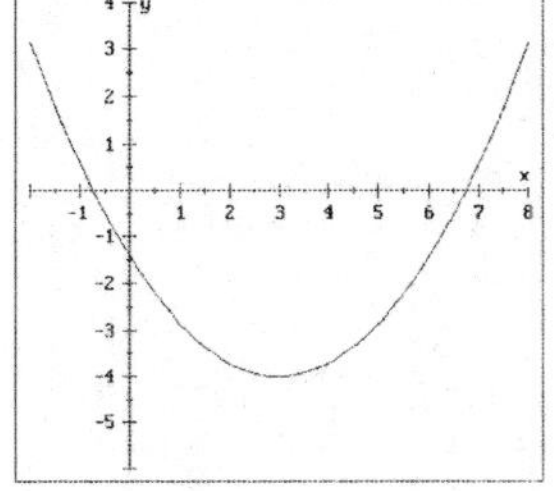

53.
$$\begin{aligned} y^2 + 4x - 6y &= -1 \\ y^2 - 6y &= -4x - 1 \\ y^2 - 6y + 9 &= -4x - 1 + 9 \\ (y-3)^2 &= -4x + 8 \\ (y-3)^2 &= -4(x-2) \end{aligned}$$

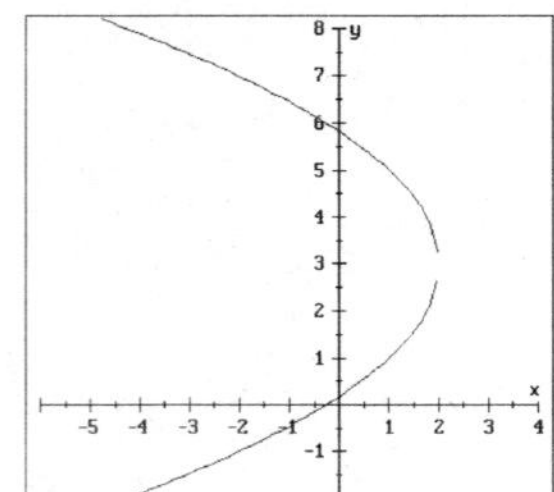

54.
$$\begin{aligned} x^2 - 2y - 2x &= -7 \\ x^2 - 2x &= 2y - 7 \\ x^2 - 2x + 1 &= 2y - 7 + 1 \\ (x-1)^2 &= 2y - 6 \\ (x-1)^2 &= 2(y-3) \end{aligned}$$

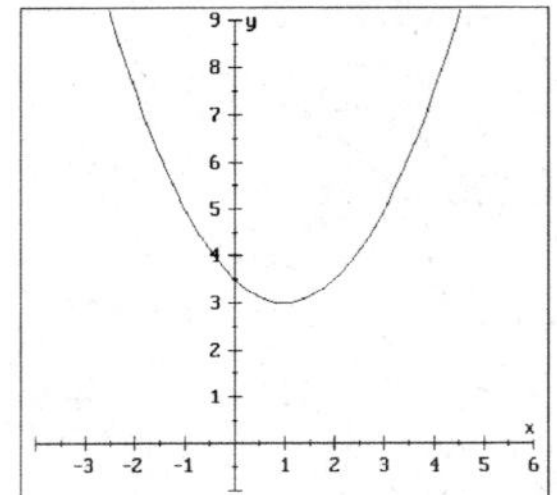

55.
$$\begin{aligned} y^2 - 4y &= 4x - 8 \\ y^2 - 4y + 4 &= 4x - 8 + 4 \\ (y-2)^2 &= 4x - 4 \\ (y-2)^2 &= 4(x-1) \end{aligned}$$

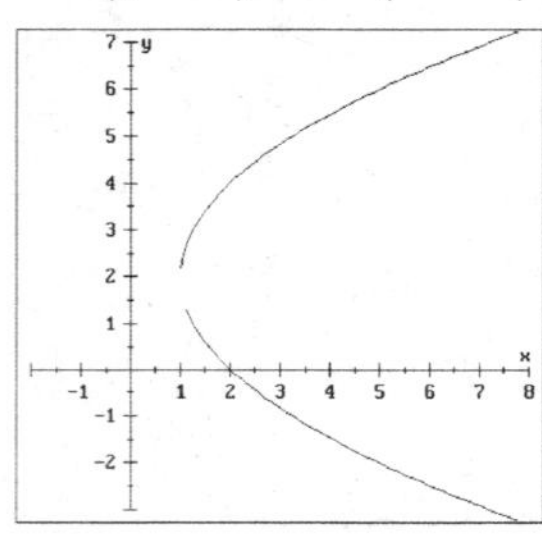

56.
$$\begin{aligned} y^2 + 2x - 2y &= 5 \\ y^2 - 2y &= -2x + 5 \\ y^2 - 2y + 1 &= -2x + 5 + 1 \\ (y-1)^2 &= -2x + 6 \\ (y-1)^2 &= -2(x-3) \end{aligned}$$

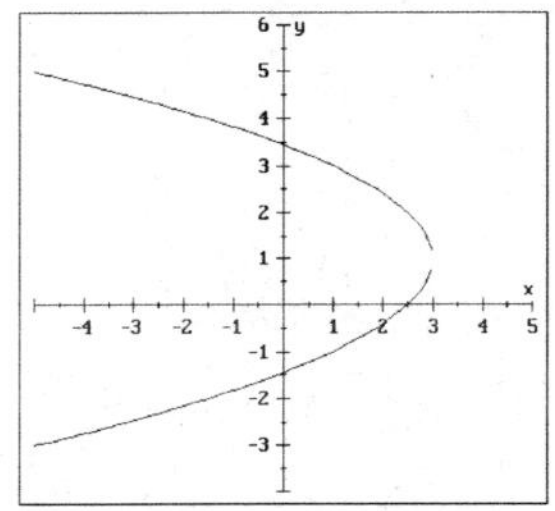

57.
$$\begin{aligned} y^2 - 4y &= -8x + 20 \\ y^2 - 4y + 4 &= -8x + 20 + 4 \\ (y-2)^2 &= -8x + 24 \\ (y-2)^2 &= -8(x-3) \end{aligned}$$

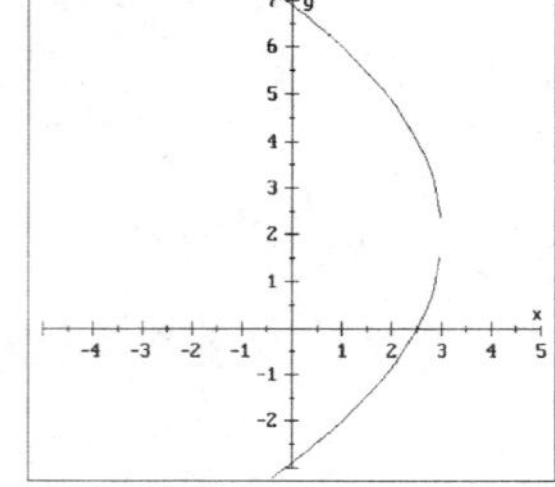

58.
$$\begin{aligned} y^2 - 2y &= 9x + 17 \\ y^2 - 2y + 1 &= 9x + 17 + 1 \\ (y-1)^2 &= 9x + 18 \\ (y-1)^2 &= 9(x+2) \end{aligned}$$

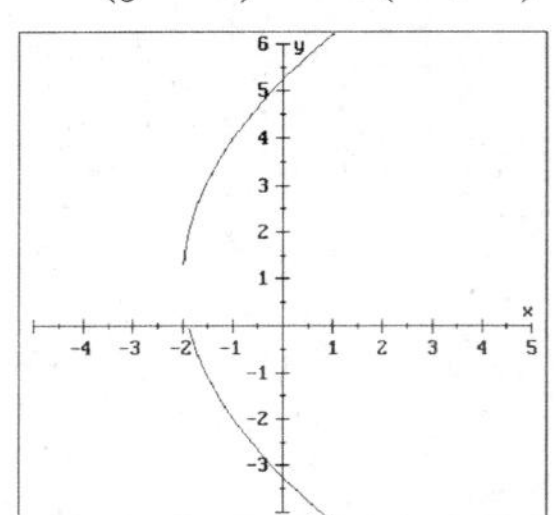

59.

$$\begin{aligned} x^2 - 6y + 22 &= -4x \\ x^2 + 4x &= 6y - 22 \\ x^2 + 4x + 4 &= 6y - 22 + 4 \\ (x+2)^2 &= 6y - 18 \\ (x+2)^2 &= 6(y-3) \end{aligned}$$

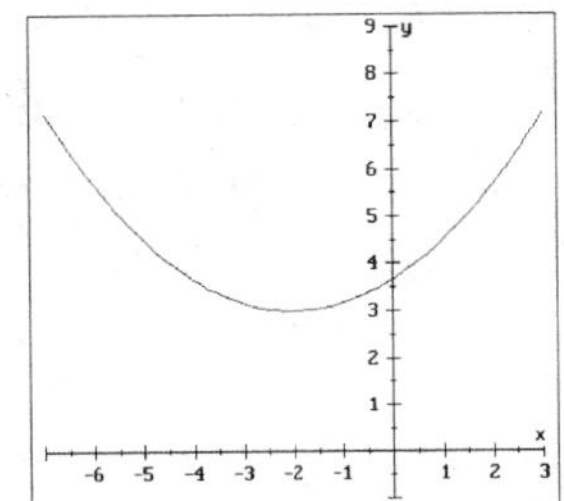

60.

$$\begin{aligned} 4y^2 - 4y + 16x &= 7 \\ y^2 - y &= -4x + \tfrac{7}{4} \\ y^2 - y + \tfrac{1}{4} &= -4x + \tfrac{7}{4} + \tfrac{1}{4} \\ \left(y - \tfrac{1}{2}\right)^2 &= -4x + 2 \\ \left(y - \tfrac{1}{2}\right)^2 &= -4\left(x - \tfrac{1}{2}\right) \end{aligned}$$

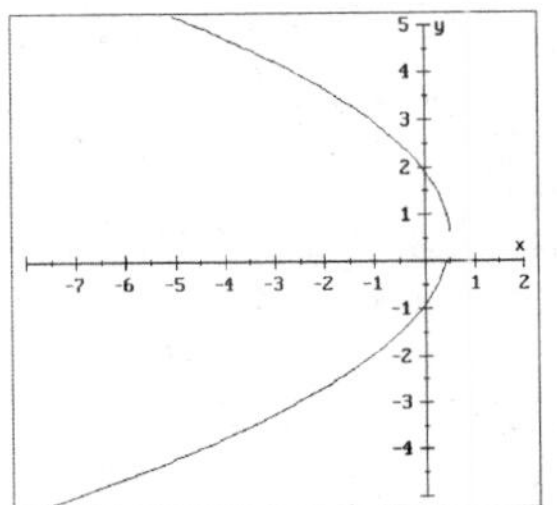

61.

$$\begin{aligned} 4x^2 - 4x + 32y &= 47 \\ x^2 - x &= -8y + \tfrac{47}{4} \\ x^2 - x + \tfrac{1}{4} &= -8y + \tfrac{47}{4} + \tfrac{1}{4} \\ \left(x - \tfrac{1}{2}\right)^2 &= -8y + 12 \\ \left(x - \tfrac{1}{2}\right)^2 &= -8\left(y - \tfrac{3}{2}\right) \end{aligned}$$

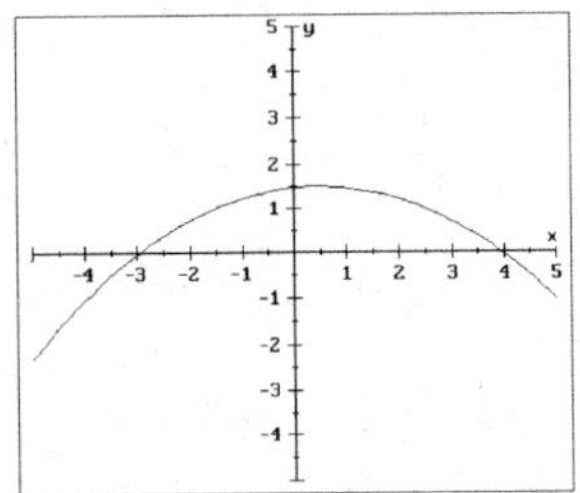

62.

$$\begin{aligned} 4y^2 - 16x + 17 &= 20y \\ y^2 - 5y &= 4x - \tfrac{17}{4} \\ y^2 - 5y + \tfrac{25}{4} &= 4x - \tfrac{17}{4} + \tfrac{25}{4} \\ \left(y - \tfrac{5}{2}\right)^2 &= 4x + 2 \\ \left(y - \tfrac{5}{2}\right)^2 &= 4\left(x + \tfrac{1}{2}\right) \end{aligned}$$

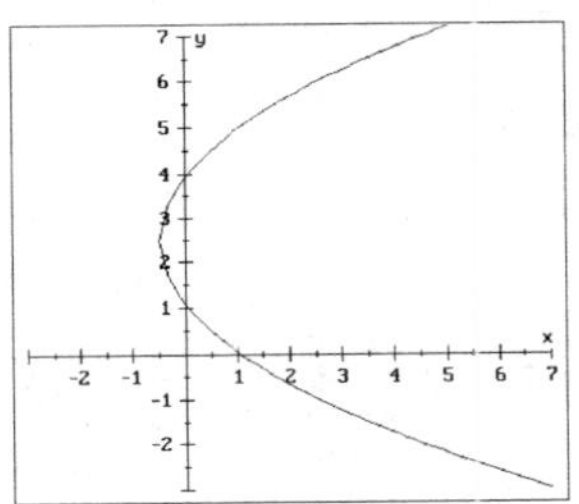

63.

$$\begin{aligned} y^2 &= 4x - 12 \\ y &= \pm\sqrt{4x - 12} \end{aligned}$$

64.

$$\begin{aligned} y^2 + 8x - 24 &= 0 \\ y^2 &= -8x + 24 \\ y &= \pm\sqrt{-8x + 24} \end{aligned}$$

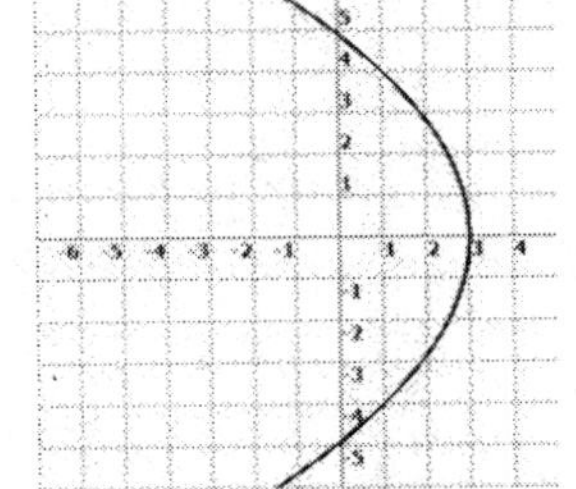

65. Check the coordinates:

$$x^2 + y^2 = 50^2 + 70^2 = 2500 + 4900 = 7400$$

$7400 < 8100$, so the city can receive.

66. Check the coordinates:

$$x^2 + y^2 = (-4)^2 + (-5)^2 = 16 + 25 = 41$$

Since $41 > 36$, the siren cannot be heard.

67. Graph both circles: $\begin{cases} x^2 + y^2 = 1600 \\ x^2 + (y-35)^2 = 625 \end{cases}$

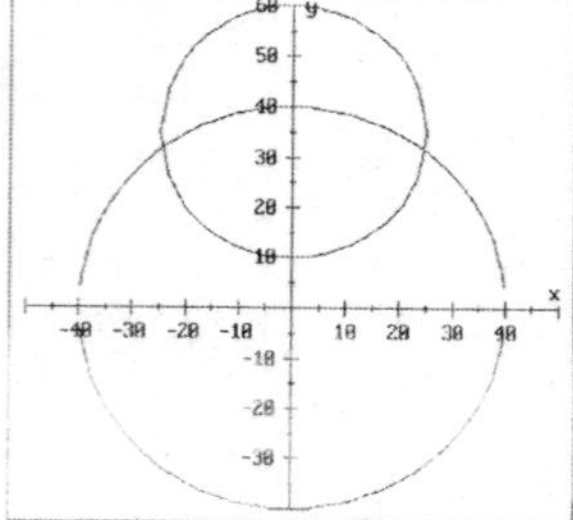

The point farthest from the transmitter $(0, 0)$ is the point $(0, 60)$. The greatest distance is 60 miles.

68. $$\text{distance} = \sqrt{(15-0)^2 + (36-0)^2} = \sqrt{225 + 1296} = \sqrt{1521} = 39$$

Since the distance is 39 feet, the ripples will reach the seagull in 13 seconds.

69. $C(4, 0), r = 4$

$$(x-h)^2 + (y-k)^2 = r^2$$
$$(x-4)^2 + (y-0)^2 = 4^2$$
$$(x-4)^2 + y^2 = 16$$

70. $C(5, 14), r = 5$

$$(x-h)^2 + (y-k)^2 = r^2$$
$$(x-5)^2 + (y-14)^2 = 5^2$$
$$(x-5)^2 + (y-14)^2 = 25$$

71. $x^2 + y^2 = 16$: $C(0, 0), r = 4$

Small gear: $C(7, 0), r = 3$

$$(x-h)^2 + (y-k)^2 = r^2$$
$$(x-7)^2 + (y-0)^2 = 3^2$$
$$(x-7)^2 + y^2 = 9$$

72.

$x^2 + y^2 = 2500$	$(x-10)^2 + y^2 = 900$
$C(0, 0), r = 50$	$C(10, 0), r = 30$
Endpoints on x:	Endpoints on x:
$(-50, 0), (50, 0)$	$(-20, 0), (40, 0)$

Smallest width $= 50 - 40 = 10$ ft

Largest width $= -20 - (-50) = 30$ ft

73. Find the distance to the focus:

$4p = 8 \Rightarrow p = 2$

It will be hottest 2 feet from the vertex.

74. Find the distance to the focus:

$4p = 12 \Rightarrow p = 3$

The light should be 3 feet from the vertex.

75. The vertex is $(0, 0)$, while $(15, -10)$ is on the curve (vertical parabola):

$$(x-h)^2 = 4p(y-k)$$
$$(15-0)^2 = 4p(-10-0)$$
$$225 = -40p$$
$$-\tfrac{45}{2} = 4p \Rightarrow x^2 = -\tfrac{45}{2}y$$

76. $$y = 30x - x^2$$
$$0 = 30x - x^2$$
$$0 = x(30 - x)$$
$$x = 0 \quad \textbf{or} \quad 30 - x = 0$$
$$30 = x$$

Hits at $(30, 0) \Rightarrow$ 5 feet short

77. The depth is the y-coordinate when $x = 4$. [4 feet on each side of the vertex]
$y = \frac{1}{16}x^2$
$y = \frac{1}{16}(4)^2 = 1$
The depth is 1 foot.

78. The vertex is $(0, 0)$, while $(1, 3)$ is on the curve (horizontal parabola):
$(y-k)^2 = 4p(x-h)$
$(3-0)^2 = 4p(1-0)$
$9 = 4p$
$\frac{9}{4} = p \Rightarrow d = \frac{9}{4}$ feet

79.
$$s = -16t^2 + 80\sqrt{3}t$$
$$-\tfrac{1}{16}s = t^2 - 5\sqrt{3}t$$
$$-\tfrac{1}{16}s + \tfrac{75}{4} = t^2 - 5\sqrt{3}t + \tfrac{75}{4}$$
$$-\tfrac{1}{16}(s-300) = \left(t - \tfrac{5\sqrt{3}}{2}\right)^2$$
The maximum height is 300 feet.

80. $\boxed{\text{Income}} = \boxed{\text{Price}} \cdot \boxed{\text{\# rented}}$
$$y = -45\left(\tfrac{n}{32} - \tfrac{1}{2}\right)n$$
$$y = -\tfrac{45}{32}n^2 + \tfrac{45}{2}n$$
$$-\tfrac{32}{45}y = n^2 - 16n$$
$$-\tfrac{32}{45}y + 64 = n^2 - 16n + 64$$
$$-\tfrac{32}{45}y + 64 = (n-8)^2$$
She should build 8 cabins.

81. Place the vertex at $(0, 0)$, with the focus at $(1, 0) \Rightarrow p = 1, 4p = 4$.
$(y-k)^2 = 4p(x-h)$
$y^2 = 4x$
Let $x = 10$: $y^2 = 4x$
$y^2 = 4(10) \Rightarrow y = \pm\sqrt{40}$
The width $= 2\sqrt{40} \approx 12.6$ cm.

82. The vertex is $(0, 15)$, while $(450, 120)$ is on the curve (vertical parabola):
$(x-h)^2 = 4p(y-k)$
$(450-0)^2 = 4p(120-15)$
$202{,}500 = 420p$
$\frac{13{,}500}{7} = 4p \Rightarrow x^2 = \frac{13{,}500}{7}(y-15)$

83. The vertex is $(0, 0)$, while $(315, -630)$ is on the curve (vertical parabola):
$(x-h)^2 = 4p(y-k)$
$(315-0)^2 = 4p(-630-0)$
$99{,}225 = -2520p$
$-\frac{19845}{504} = p \Rightarrow 4p = -\frac{19845}{126}$
Let $y = -430$:
$x^2 = -\frac{19845}{126}y$
$x^2 = -\frac{19845}{126}(-430)$
$x = \pm\sqrt{-\frac{19845}{126}(-430)}$
$x \approx \pm 260$
The width is about 520 feet.

84. The equation is $(x-h)^2 = 4p(y-k)$. From the figure, $h = 0$. Also, the points $(4, 0)$ and $(3, 5)$ are on the graph:
$x^2 = 4p(y-k) \qquad x^2 = 4p(y-k)$
$4^2 = 4p(0-k) \qquad 3^2 = 4p(5-k)$
$16 = -4pk \qquad 9 = 20p - 4pk$
$-4 = pk$
Substituting: $9 = 20p - 4pk$
$9 = 20p - 4(-4)$
$-\frac{7}{20} = p \Rightarrow k = \frac{80}{7}$
The maximum height is $\dfrac{80}{7}$ meters.

85.

$$\begin{aligned} (y-2)^2 &= 8(x-1) \\ y^2 - 4y + 4 &= 8x - 8 \\ y^2 - 8x - 4y + 12 &= 0 \\ 0x^2 + 0xy + y^2 - 8x - 4y + 12 &= 0 \end{aligned}$$

86.

$$\begin{aligned} (x+2)^2 + (y-5)^2 &= 36 \\ x^2 + 4x + 4 + y^2 - 10y + 25 &= 36 \\ x^2 + 0xy + y^2 + 4x - 10y - 7 &= 0 \end{aligned}$$

87.

$$\begin{aligned} (x-h)^2 + (y-k)^2 &= r^2 \\ (0-h)^2 + (8-k)^2 &= r^2 \\ h^2 + 64 - 16k + k^2 &= r^2 \\ h^2 + k^2 - r^2 &= 16k - 64 \end{aligned}$$

$$\begin{aligned} (x-h)^2 + (y-k)^2 &= r^2 \\ (5-h)^2 + (3-k)^2 &= r^2 \\ 25 - 10h + h^2 + 9 - 6k + k^2 &= r^2 \\ h^2 + k^2 - r^2 &= 10h + 6k - 34 \end{aligned}$$

$$\begin{aligned} (x-h)^2 + (y-k)^2 &= r^2 \\ (4-h)^2 + (6-k)^2 &= r^2 \\ 16 - 8h + h^2 + 36 - 12k + k^2 &= r^2 \\ h^2 + k^2 - r^2 &= 8h + 12k - 52 \end{aligned}$$

$$\begin{cases} 16k - 64 = 10h + 6k - 34 & \Rightarrow \quad 10k - 10h = 30 \\ 16k - 64 = 8h + 12k - 52 & \Rightarrow \quad 4k - 8h = 12 \end{cases} \Rightarrow k = 3, h = 0$$

Substitute into one of the above equations to get $r = 5$. Circle: $x^2 + (y-3)^2 = 25$

88.

$$\begin{aligned} (x-h)^2 + (y-k)^2 &= r^2 \\ (-2-h)^2 + (0-k)^2 &= r^2 \\ 4 + 4h + h^2 + k^2 &= r^2 \\ h^2 + k^2 - r^2 &= -4h - 4 \end{aligned}$$

$$\begin{aligned} (x-h)^2 + (y-k)^2 &= r^2 \\ (2-h)^2 + (8-k)^2 &= r^2 \\ 4 - 4h + h^2 + 64 - 16k + k^2 &= r^2 \\ h^2 + k^2 - r^2 &= 4h + 16k - 68 \end{aligned}$$

$$\begin{aligned} (x-h)^2 + (y-k)^2 &= r^2 \\ (5-h)^2 + (-1-k)^2 &= r^2 \\ 25 - 10h + h^2 + 1 + 2k + k^2 &= r^2 \\ h^2 + k^2 - r^2 &= 10h - 2k - 26 \end{aligned}$$

$$\begin{cases} -4h - 4 = 4h + 16k - 68 & \Rightarrow \quad -8h - 16k = -64 \\ -4h - 4 = 10h - 2k - 26 & \Rightarrow \quad -14h + 2k = -22 \end{cases} \Rightarrow h = 2, k = 3$$

Substitute into one of the above equations to get $r = 5$. Circle: $(x-2)^2 + (y-3)^2 = 25$

89.

$$\begin{aligned} y &= ax^2 + bx + c \\ 8 &= a(1)^2 + b(1) + c \\ 8 &= a + b + c \end{aligned}$$

$$\begin{aligned} y &= ax^2 + bx + c \\ -1 &= a(-2)^2 + b(-2) + c \\ -1 &= 4a - 2b + c \end{aligned}$$

$$\begin{aligned} y &= ax^2 + bx + c \\ 15 &= a(2)^2 + b(2) + c \\ 15 &= 4a + 2b + c \end{aligned}$$

$$\begin{cases} a + b + c = 8 \\ 4a - 2b + c = -1 \\ 4a + 2b + c = 15 \end{cases} \Rightarrow a = 1, b = 4, c = 3 \Rightarrow y = x^2 + 4x + 3$$

90.
$$y = ax^2 + bx + c \qquad y = ax^2 + bx + c \qquad y = ax^2 + bx + c$$
$$-3 = a(1)^2 + b(1) + c \qquad 12 = a(-2)^2 + b(-2) + c \qquad 3 = a(-1)^2 + b(-1) + c$$
$$-3 = a + b + c \qquad 12 = 4a - 2b + c \qquad 3 = a - b + c$$

$$\begin{cases} a + b + c = -3 \\ 4a - 2b + c = 12 \\ a - b + c = 3 \end{cases} \Rightarrow a = 2, b = -3, c = -2 \Rightarrow y = 2x^2 - 3x - 2$$

91. The stone hits the ground when $s = 0$:
$$0 = -16t^2 + 128t$$
$$0 = -16t(t - 8)$$
It hits the ground after 8 seconds.
Find s when $t = x$:
$$s = -16x^2 + 128x$$
Find s when $t = 8 - x$:
$$\begin{aligned} s &= -16(8 - x)^2 + 128(8 - x) \\ &= -16(64 - 16x + x^2) + 1024 - 128x \\ &= -1024 + 256x - 16x^2 + 1024 - 128x \\ &= -16x^2 + 128x \end{aligned}$$

92. The maximum height occurs at the vertex:
$$\begin{aligned} s &= -16t^2 + 128t \\ -\tfrac{1}{16}s &= t^2 - 8t \\ -\tfrac{1}{16}s + 16 &= t^2 - 8t + 16 \\ -\tfrac{1}{16}s + 16 &= (t - 4)^2 \end{aligned}$$
The maximum height occurs after 4 seconds, which is half the time of 8 seconds (found in **#91**) it takes the stone to hit the ground.

93. $x^2 + 4x + \boxed{4}$

94. $y^2 - 12y + \boxed{36}$

95. $x^2 - 7x + \boxed{\frac{49}{4}}$

96. $y^2 + 11y + \boxed{\frac{121}{4}}$

97.
$$\begin{aligned} x^2 + 4x &= 5 \\ x^2 + 4x - 5 &= 0 \\ (x + 5)(x - 1) &= 0 \\ x = -5 \text{ or } x &= 1 \end{aligned}$$

98.
$$\begin{aligned} y^2 - 12y &= 13 \\ y^2 - 12y - 13 &= 0 \\ (y + 1)(y - 13) &= 0 \\ y = -1 \text{ or } y &= 13 \end{aligned}$$

99.
$$\begin{aligned} x^2 - 7x - 18 &= 0 \\ (x + 2)(x - 9) &= 0 \\ x = -2 \text{ or } x &= 9 \end{aligned}$$

100.
$$\begin{aligned} y^2 + 11y &= -18 \\ y^2 + 11y + 18 &= 0 \\ (y + 2)(y + 9) &= 0 \\ y = -2 \text{ or } y &= -9 \end{aligned}$$

Exercises 7.2 (page 684)

1. sum, constant

2. focus

3. vertices

4. minor

5. $(a, 0), (-a, 0)$

6. $b^2 = a^2 - c^2$

7. $2a = 26 \Rightarrow$ String: 26 inches long
$2b = 10 \Rightarrow b = 5$
$b^2 = a^2 - c^2$
$5^2 = 13^2 - c^2 \Rightarrow c = 12$
Thumbtacks: $2c = 24$ inches apart

8. $2a = 20 \Rightarrow$ String: 20 cm long
$2b = 12 \Rightarrow b = 6$
$b^2 = a^2 - c^2$
$6^2 = 10^2 - c^2 \Rightarrow c = 8$
Thumbtacks: $2c = 16$ cm apart

9. Both variables squared with equal coefficients: circle

10. Both variables squared with equal coefficients: circle

11. One variable squared: parabola

12. One variable squared: parabola

13. Both variables squared with unequal coefficients: ellipse

14. Both variables squared with unequal coefficients: ellipse

15. $a = 4, b = 3$; horizontal
$C(0,0)$
$\frac{x^2}{16} + \frac{y^2}{9} = 1$

16. $a = 7, b = 5$; vertical
$C(0,0)$
$\frac{x^2}{25} + \frac{y^2}{49} = 1$

17. $c = 3, a = 5$; horizontal
$b^2 = a^2 - c^2$
$= 25 - 9 = 16$
$\frac{x^2}{25} + \frac{y^2}{16} = 1$

18. $c = 4, a = 7$; vertical
$b^2 = a^2 - c^2$
$= 49 - 16 = 33$
$\frac{x^2}{33} + \frac{y^2}{49} = 1$

19. $c = 1, b = \frac{4}{3}$; vertical
$a^2 = b^2 + c^2$
$= \frac{16}{9} + 1 = \frac{25}{9}$
$\frac{x^2}{16/9} + \frac{y^2}{25/9} = 1$
$\frac{9x^2}{16} + \frac{9y^2}{25} = 1$

20. $c = 1, b = \frac{4}{3}$; horizontal
$a^2 = b^2 + c^2$
$= \frac{16}{9} + 1 = \frac{25}{9}$
$\frac{x^2}{25/9} + \frac{y^2}{16/9} = 1$
$\frac{9x^2}{25} + \frac{9y^2}{16} = 1$

21. $c = 3, a = 4$; vertical
$b^2 = a^2 - c^2$
$= 16 - 9 = 7$
$\frac{x^2}{7} + \frac{y^2}{16} = 1$

22. $c = 5, a = 6$; horizontal
$b^2 = a^2 - c^2$
$= 36 - 25 = 11$
$\frac{x^2}{36} + \frac{y^2}{11} = 1$

23. vertical
$\frac{(x-3)^2}{4} + \frac{(y-4)^2}{9} = 1$

24. $a = 6$, vertical
$\frac{(x-3)^2}{4} + \frac{(y-4)^2}{36} = 1$

25. horizontal
$\frac{(x-3)^2}{9} + \frac{(y-4)^2}{4} = 1$

26. $a = 5$, horizontal
$\frac{(x-3)^2}{25} + \frac{(y-4)^2}{4} = 1$

27. Center: $(3, 4)$, $b = 4$, $c = 5$, horizontal

$a^2 = b^2 + c^2 = 16 + 25 = 41$

$$\frac{(x-3)^2}{41} + \frac{(y-4)^2}{16} = 1$$

28. Center: $(6, 5)$, $b = 3$, $c = 2$, horizontal

$a^2 = b^2 + c^2 = 9 + 4 = 13$

$$\frac{(x-6)^2}{13} + \frac{(y-5)^2}{9} = 1$$

29. Center: $(0, 4)$, $c = 4$, $a = 6$, horizontal

$b^2 = a^2 - c^2 = 36 - 16 = 20$

$$\frac{x^2}{36} + \frac{(y-4)^2}{20} = 1$$

30. $a = 6$, $c = 2$, vertical

$b^2 = a^2 - c^2 = 36 - 4 = 32$

$$\frac{(x+4)^2}{32} + \frac{(y-5)^2}{36} = 1$$

31. Center: $(0, 0)$, $c = 6$, $a = 10$, horizontal

$b^2 = a^2 - c^2 = 100 - 36 = 64$

$$\frac{x^2}{100} + \frac{y^2}{64} = 1$$

32. Center: $(0, 0)$, $a = 2$, $b^2 = 2$, horizontal

$$\frac{x^2}{4} + \frac{y^2}{2} = 1$$

33. $$\frac{x^2}{25} + \frac{y^2}{9} = 1$$

Center: $(0, 0)$, $a = 5$, $b = 3$, horizontal

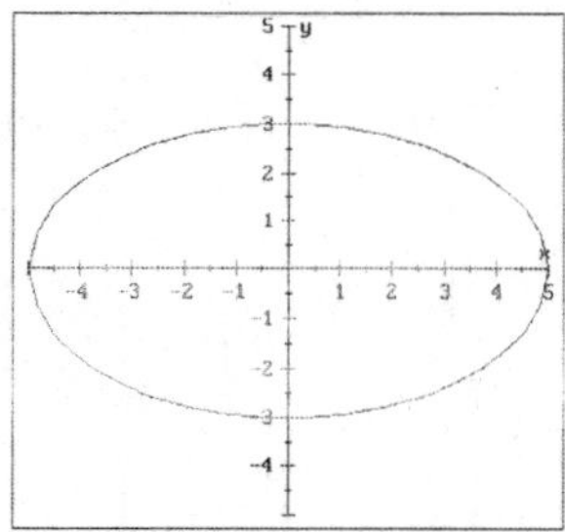

34. $$\frac{x^2}{36} + \frac{y^2}{25} = 1$$

Center: $(0, 0)$, $a = 6$, $b = 5$, horizontal

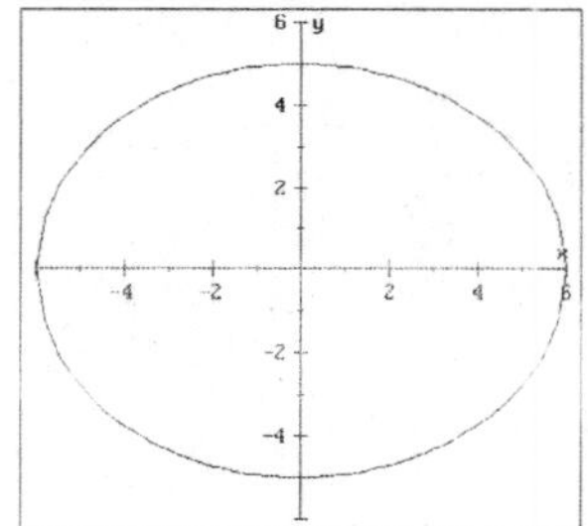

35. $$\frac{x^2}{25} + \frac{y^2}{49} = 1$$

Center: $(0, 0)$, $a = 7$, $b = 5$, vertical

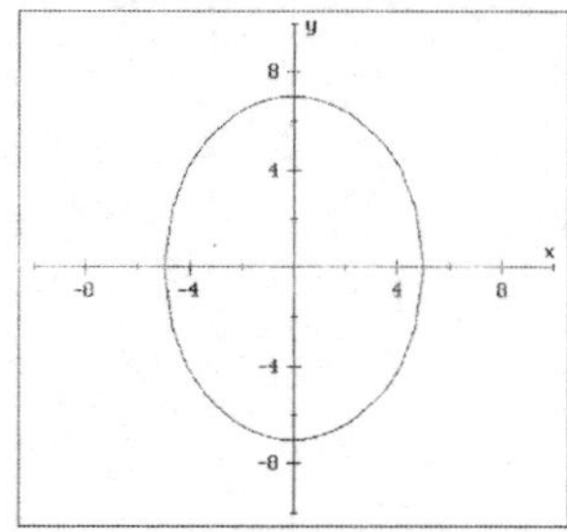

36. $4x^2 + y^2 = 4$

$$\frac{4x^2}{4} + \frac{y^2}{4} = \frac{4}{4}$$

$$\frac{x^2}{1} + \frac{y^2}{4} = 1$$

Center: $(0, 0)$, $a = 2$, $b = 1$, vertical

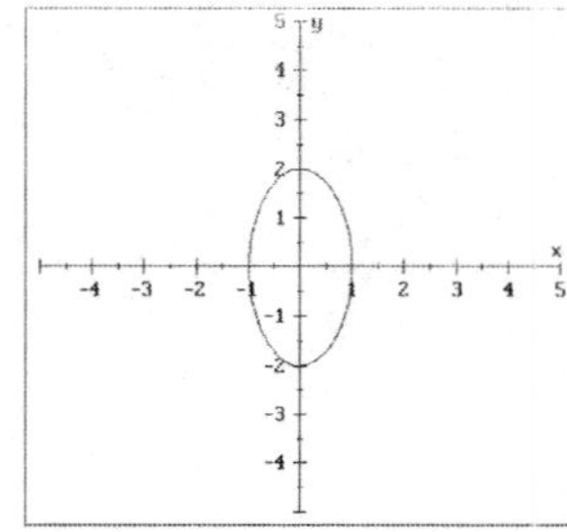

37. $\dfrac{x^2}{16}+\dfrac{(y+2)^2}{36}=1$

Center: $(0,-2)$, $a=6$, $b=4$, vertical

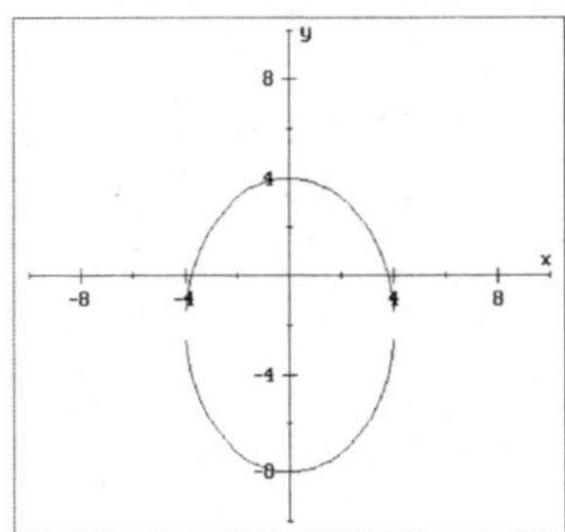

38. $$(x-1)^2+\frac{4y^2}{25}=4$$
$$\frac{(x-1)^2}{4}+\frac{4y^2}{4(25)}=\frac{4}{4}$$
$$\frac{(x-1)^2}{4}+\frac{y^2}{25}=1$$

Center: $(1,0)$, $a=5$, $b=2$, vertical

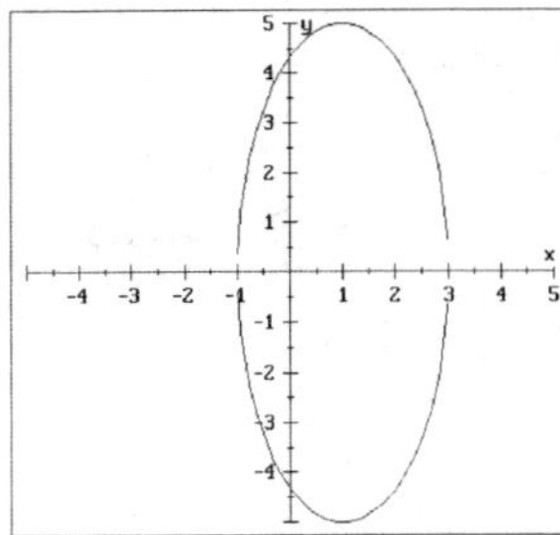

39. $\dfrac{(x-4)^2}{49}+\dfrac{(y-2)^2}{9}=1$

Center: $(4,2)$, $a=7$, $b=3$, horizontal

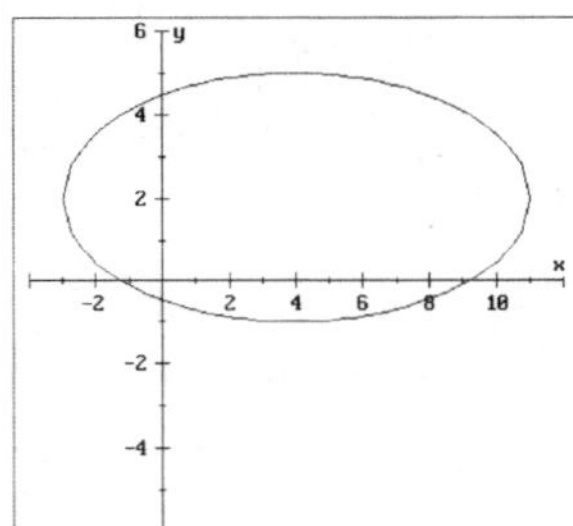

40. $\dfrac{(x-1)^2}{25}+\dfrac{y^2}{4}=1$

Center: $(1,0)$, $a=5$, $b=2$, horizontal

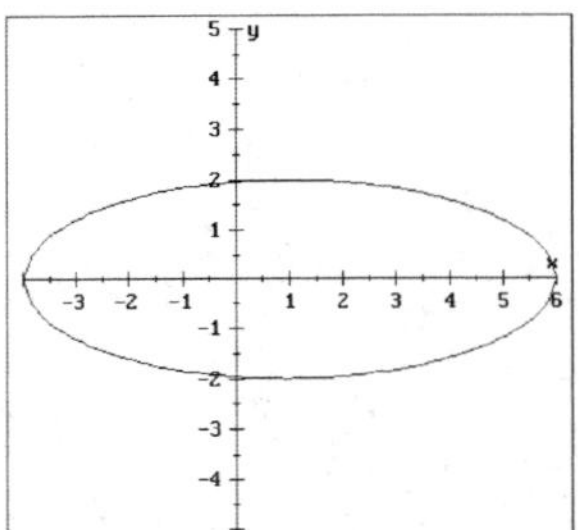

41. $$4x^2+y^2-2y=15$$
$$4x^2+y^2-2y+1=15+1$$
$$4x^2+(y-1)^2=16$$
$$\frac{4x^2}{16}+\frac{(y-1)^2}{16}=\frac{16}{16}$$
$$\frac{x^2}{4}+\frac{(y-1)^2}{16}=1$$

42. $$4x^2+25y^2+8x-96=0$$
$$4\left(x^2+2x\right)+25y^2=96$$
$$4\left(x^2+2x+1\right)+25y^2=96+4$$
$$4(x+1)^2+25y^2=100$$
$$\frac{4(x+1)^2}{100}+\frac{25y^2}{100}=\frac{100}{100}$$
$$\frac{(x+1)^2}{25}+\frac{y^2}{4}=1$$

43.

$$
\begin{aligned}
9x^2 + 4y^2 + 18x + 16y - 11 &= 0 \\
9(x^2 + 2x) + 4(y^2 + 4y) &= 11 \\
9(x^2 + 2x + 1) + 4(y^2 + 4y + 4) &= 11 + 9 + 16 \\
9(x+1)^2 + 4(y+2)^2 &= 36 \\
\frac{9(x+1)^2}{36} + \frac{4(y+2)^2}{36} &= \frac{36}{36} \\
\frac{(x+1)^2}{4} + \frac{(y+2)^2}{9} &= 1
\end{aligned}
$$

44.

$$
\begin{aligned}
x^2 + 4y^2 - 10x - 8y &= -13 \\
x^2 - 10x + 4(y^2 - 2y) &= -13 \\
x^2 - 10x + 25 + 4(y^2 - 2y + 1) &= -13 + 25 + 4 \\
(x-5)^2 + 4(y-1)^2 &= 16 \\
\frac{(x-5)^2}{16} + \frac{4(y-1)^2}{16} &= \frac{16}{16} \\
\frac{(x-5)^2}{16} + \frac{(y-1)^2}{4} &= 1
\end{aligned}
$$

45.

$$
\begin{aligned}
x^2 + 4y^2 - 4x + 8y + 4 &= 0 \\
x^2 - 4x + 4(y^2 + 2y) &= -4 \\
x^2 - 4x + 4 + 4(y^2 + 2y + 1) &= -4 + 4 + 4 \\
(x-2)^2 + 4(y+1)^2 &= 4 \\
\frac{(x-2)^2}{4} + \frac{(y+1)^2}{1} &= 1
\end{aligned}
$$

Center: $(2, -1)$, $a = 2$, $b = 1$, horizontal

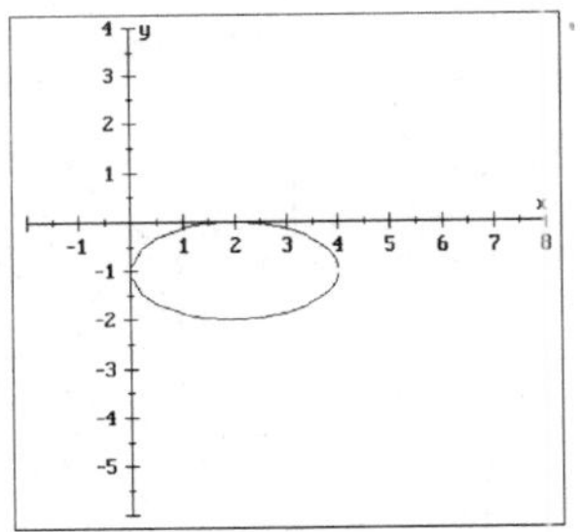

46.

$$
\begin{aligned}
x^2 + 4y^2 - 2x - 16y &= -13 \\
x^2 - 2x + 4(y^2 - 4y) &= -13 \\
x^2 - 2x + 1 + 4(y^2 - 4y + 4) &= -13 + 1 + 16 \\
(x-1)^2 + 4(y-2)^2 &= 4
\end{aligned}
$$

$\frac{(x-1)^2}{4} + \frac{(y-2)^2}{1} = 1$

Center: $(1, 2)$, $a = 2$, $b = 1$, horizontal

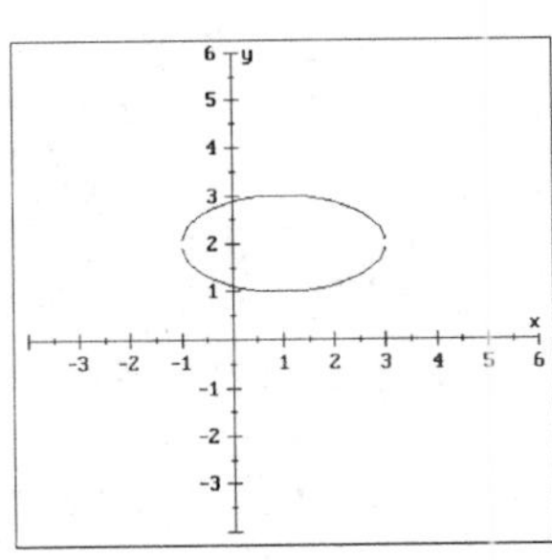

47.

$$16x^2 + 25y^2 - 160x - 200y + 400 = 0$$
$$16(x^2 - 10x) + 25(y^2 - 8y) = -400$$
$$16(x^2 - 10x + 25) + 25(y^2 - 8y + 16) = -400 + 400 + 400$$
$$16(x-5)^2 + 25(y-4)^2 = 400$$
$$\frac{(x-5)^2}{25} + \frac{(y-4)^2}{16} = 1$$

Center: $(5, 4)$, $a = 5$, $b = 4$, horizontal

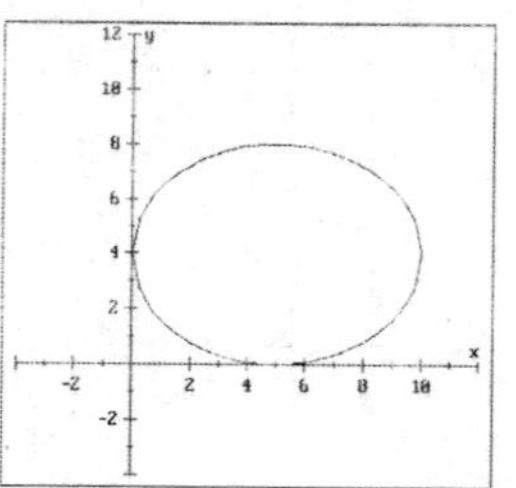

48.

$$3x^2 + 2y^2 + 7x - 6y = -1$$
$$3(x^2 + \tfrac{7}{3}x) + 2(y^2 - 3y) = -1$$
$$3(x^2 + \tfrac{7}{3}x + \tfrac{49}{36}) + 2(y^2 - 3y + \tfrac{9}{4}) = -1 + \tfrac{49}{12} + \tfrac{9}{2}$$
$$3(x + \tfrac{7}{6})^2 + 2(y - \tfrac{3}{2})^2 = \tfrac{91}{12}$$
$$\frac{(x + \frac{7}{6})^2}{91/36} + \frac{(y - \frac{3}{2})^2}{91/24} = 1$$

Center: $(-\frac{7}{6}, \frac{3}{2})$, $a = \sqrt{\frac{91}{36}}$, $b = \sqrt{\frac{91}{24}}$, vertical

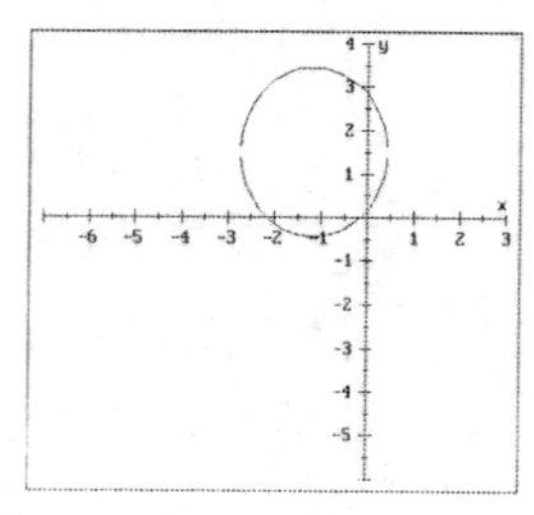

49.

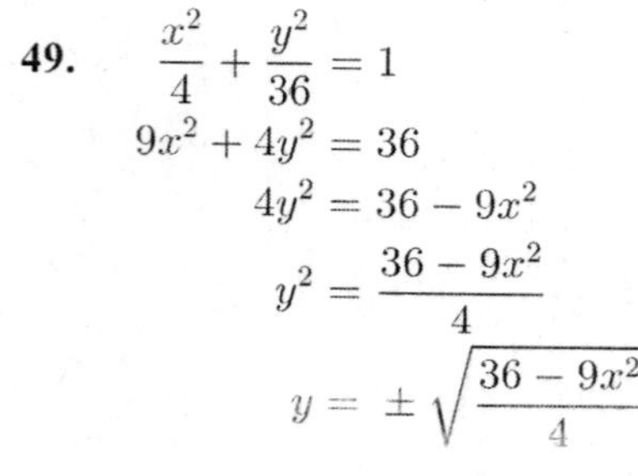

$$\frac{x^2}{4} + \frac{y^2}{36} = 1$$
$$9x^2 + 4y^2 = 36$$
$$4y^2 = 36 - 9x^2$$
$$y^2 = \frac{36 - 9x^2}{4}$$
$$y = \pm\sqrt{\frac{36 - 9x^2}{4}}$$

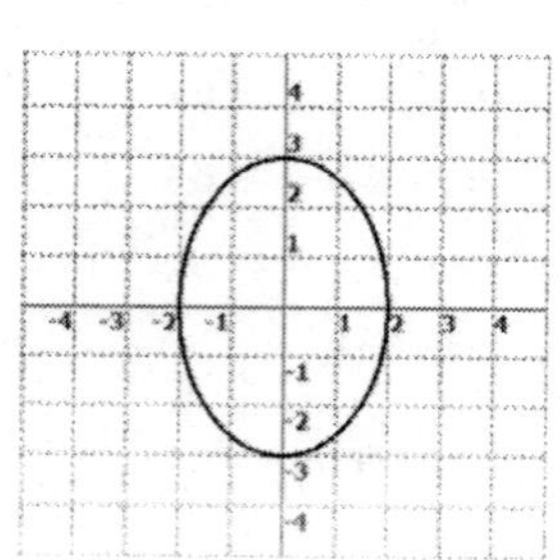

50.

$$\frac{(x+3)^2}{4} + \frac{(y-2)^2}{25} = 1$$
$$25(x+3)^2 + 4(y-2)^2 = 100$$
$$4(y-2)^2 = 100 - 25(x+3)^2$$
$$\sqrt{4(y-2)^2} = \pm\sqrt{100 - 25(x+3)^2}$$
$$2(y-2) = \pm\sqrt{100 - 25(x+3)^2}$$
$$y - 2 = \pm\frac{\sqrt{100-25(x+3)^2}}{2}$$
$$y = 2 \pm \frac{\sqrt{100-25(x+3)^2}}{2}$$

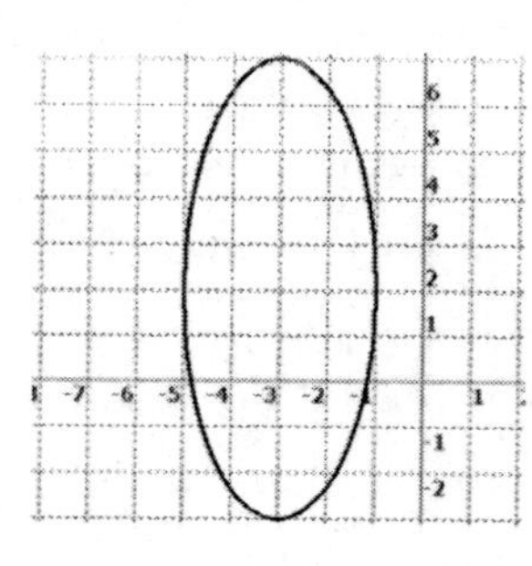

51. $C(0,0)$, $a = 30$, $b = 20$, horizontal

$$\frac{(x-0)^2}{30^2} + \frac{(y-0)^2}{20^2} = 1$$

$$\frac{x^2}{900} + \frac{y^2}{400} = 1$$

52. $a = 6$, $b = 5$

5 m
6 m 6 m

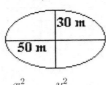

$$\frac{x^2}{36} + \frac{y^2}{25} = 1$$

53. $a = 50$, $b = 30$

30 m
50 m

$$\frac{x^2}{2500} + \frac{y^2}{900} = 1$$

$$\begin{aligned} c^2 &= a^2 - b^2 \\ &= 2500 - 900 \\ &= 1600 \\ c &= 40 \end{aligned}$$

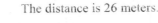

$$\begin{aligned} \frac{40^2}{2500} + \frac{y^2}{900} &= 1 \\ \frac{y^2}{900} &= \frac{900}{2500} \\ \frac{y}{30} &= \pm\frac{30}{50} \\ y &= \pm 18 \end{aligned}$$

The focal width is 36 meters.

54. Using the Pythagorean Theorem:

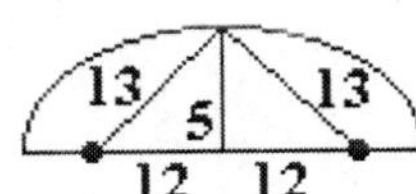

The distance is 26 meters.

55. $a = 24$, $b = 12$

$$\begin{aligned} \frac{x^2}{144} + \frac{y^2}{576} &= 1 \\ \frac{x^2}{144} + \frac{(-12)^2}{576} &= 1 \\ \frac{x^2}{144} &= \pm\frac{432}{576} \\ x &\approx \pm 10.4 \end{aligned}$$

The width is about 20.8 inches.

56. $a = 36$, $b = 30$

$$\begin{aligned} \frac{x^2}{1296} + \frac{y^2}{900} &= 1 \\ \frac{16^2}{1296} + \frac{y^2}{900} &= 1 \\ \frac{y^2}{900} &= \pm\frac{1040}{1296} \\ y &\approx \pm 13.45 \end{aligned}$$

The width is about 26.9 inches.

57. The farthest distance $= a + c$:

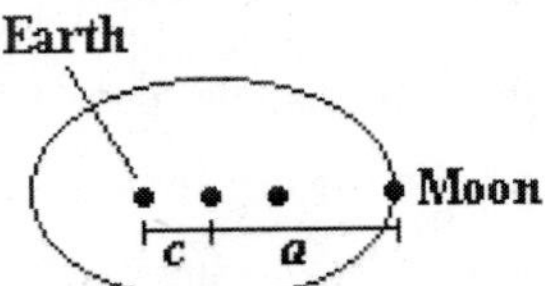

$$a = \frac{378000}{2} = 189000$$

$$\frac{c}{a} = \frac{11}{200}$$

$$c = \frac{11a}{200} = 10395$$

distance $= a + c = 199{,}395$ miles

58.

$$\begin{aligned} 9x^2 + 16y^2 &= 144 \\ \frac{9x^2}{144} + \frac{16y^2}{144} &= \frac{144}{144} \\ \frac{x^2}{16} + \frac{y^2}{9} &= 1 \end{aligned}$$

$a = 4$, $b = 3$

$$\begin{aligned} A &= \pi ab \\ &= \pi(4)(3) \\ &= 12\pi \text{ square units,} \end{aligned}$$

or about 37.7 square units

59. $FB = \sqrt{(c-0)^2 + (0-b)^2} = \sqrt{c^2+b^2} = \sqrt{a^2} = |a| = a\ (a \geq 0)$

60. The equation of the ellipse is $\dfrac{x^2}{a^2} + \dfrac{y^2}{b^2} = 1$.
P is a point on the ellipse, so solve for y^2:

$$\frac{x^2}{a^2} + \frac{y^2}{b^2} = 1$$
$$\frac{y^2}{b^2} = 1 - \frac{x^2}{a^2}$$
$$y^2 = b^2\left(1 - \frac{x^2}{a^2}\right)$$

$$\begin{aligned} FP &= \sqrt{(c-x)^2 + (0-y)^2} \\ &= \sqrt{(c-x)^2 + y^2} \\ &= \sqrt{(c-x)^2 + b^2\left(1 - \frac{x^2}{a^2}\right)} \\ &= \sqrt{(c-x)^2 + (a^2-c^2)\left(1 - \frac{x^2}{a^2}\right)} \\ &= \sqrt{c^2 - 2cx + x^2 + a^2 - x^2 - c^2 + \frac{c^2}{a^2}x^2} \\ &= \sqrt{a^2 - 2cx + \frac{c^2}{a^2}x^2} \\ &= \sqrt{\left(a - \frac{c}{a}x\right)^2} = a - \frac{c}{a}x \end{aligned}$$

61. The equation of the ellipse is $\dfrac{x^2}{a^2} + \dfrac{y^2}{b^2} = 1$.
Let $x = c$ and solve for y^2:

$$\frac{x^2}{a^2} + \frac{y^2}{b^2} = 1$$
$$\frac{c^2}{a^2} + \frac{y^2}{b^2} = 1$$
$$\begin{aligned} y^2 &= b^2\left(1 - \frac{c^2}{a^2}\right) \\ &= b^2\left(1 - \frac{a^2-b^2}{a^2}\right) \\ &= b^2\left(1 - 1 + \frac{b^2}{a^2}\right) = \frac{b^4}{a^2} \end{aligned}$$

Thus, $y = \pm\sqrt{\dfrac{b^4}{a^2}} = \pm\dfrac{b^2}{a}$.
The coordinates of A' and A are $\left(c, \dfrac{b^2}{a}\right)$ and $\left(c, -\dfrac{b^2}{a}\right)$. Therefore, the focal width is $\dfrac{2b^2}{a}$.

62. By the result of **#60**, the distance between a point $P(x, y)$ on the ellipse and a focus $F(c, 0)$ is $D = a - \dfrac{c}{a}x$. Since P is a point on the ellipse, x must take on values from $-a$ to a. To make D as small as possible, x must be positive and as large as possible. This occurs when $x = a$. If $x = a$, then point P is actually at point V.

63. Let the origin be at the midpoint of the line segment between the two thumbtacks and let the x-axis be parallel to that segment. Then $2a = 6$, so $a = 3$. Also, $2c = 2$, so $c = 1$. Find b:
$b^2 = a^2 - c^2 = 3^2 - 1^2 = 8$. The equation is $\dfrac{x^2}{a^2} + \dfrac{y^2}{b^2} = 1$, or $\dfrac{x^2}{9} + \dfrac{y^2}{8} = 1$.

64. Consider the following diagram:

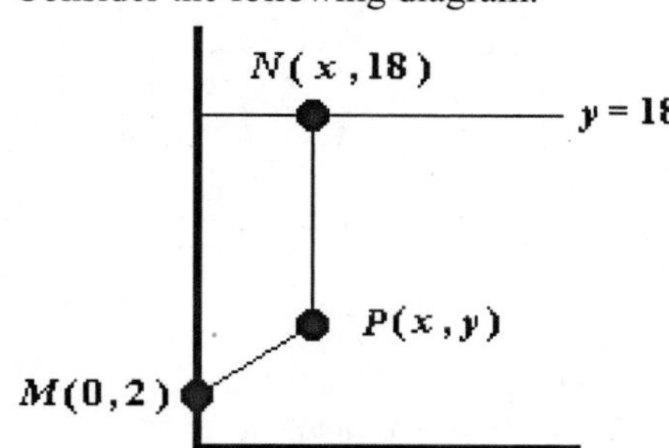

$$PM = \tfrac{1}{3}PN$$
$$\sqrt{(x-0)^2+(y-2)^2} = \tfrac{1}{3}\sqrt{(x-x)^2+(y-18)^2}$$
$$x^2+(y-2)^2 = \tfrac{1}{9}\left[0+(y-18)^2\right]$$
$$x^2+y^2-4y+4 = \tfrac{1}{9}(y-18)^2$$
$$9x^2+9y^2-36y+36 = y^2-36y+324$$
$$9x^2+8y^2 = 288$$
$$\frac{x^2}{32}+\frac{y^2}{36} = 1$$

65-67. Answers may vary.

68. $AB = \begin{bmatrix} 3 & -1 & 2 \\ 0 & 2 & -1 \\ 3 & 1 & 1 \end{bmatrix}\begin{bmatrix} 1 & 2 \\ 2 & 0 \\ -1 & 1 \end{bmatrix} = \begin{bmatrix} -1 & 8 \\ 5 & -1 \\ 4 & 7 \end{bmatrix}$

69. $B + C = \begin{bmatrix} 1 & 2 \\ 2 & 0 \\ -1 & 1 \end{bmatrix} + \begin{bmatrix} 0 & 1 \\ -1 & 1 \\ -2 & 0 \end{bmatrix} = \begin{bmatrix} 1 & 3 \\ 1 & 1 \\ -3 & 1 \end{bmatrix}$

70. $5B - 2C = 5\begin{bmatrix} 1 & 2 \\ 2 & 0 \\ -1 & 1 \end{bmatrix} - 2\begin{bmatrix} 0 & 1 \\ -1 & 1 \\ -2 & 0 \end{bmatrix} = \begin{bmatrix} 5 & 10 \\ 10 & 0 \\ -5 & 5 \end{bmatrix} - \begin{bmatrix} 0 & 2 \\ -2 & 2 \\ -4 & 0 \end{bmatrix} = \begin{bmatrix} 5 & 8 \\ 12 & -2 \\ --1 & 5 \end{bmatrix}$

71. $AC + B = \begin{bmatrix} 3 & -1 & 2 \\ 0 & 2 & -1 \\ 3 & 1 & 1 \end{bmatrix}\begin{bmatrix} 0 & 1 \\ -1 & 1 \\ -2 & 0 \end{bmatrix} + \begin{bmatrix} 1 & 2 \\ 2 & 0 \\ -1 & 1 \end{bmatrix} = \begin{bmatrix} -3 & 2 \\ 0 & 2 \\ -3 & 4 \end{bmatrix} + \begin{bmatrix} 1 & 2 \\ 2 & 0 \\ -1 & 1 \end{bmatrix} = \begin{bmatrix} -2 & 4 \\ 2 & 2 \\ -4 & 5 \end{bmatrix}$

72. The inverse does not exist.

Exercises 7.3 (page 698)

1. difference, constant

2. focus

3. $(a, 0), (-a, 0)$

4. $(0, a), (0, -a)$

5. transverse axis

6. $a^2 + b^2 = c^2$

7. Both variables squared with equal coefficients and same sign: circle

8. Both variables squared with equal coefficients and same sign: circle

9. One variable squared: parabola

10. One variable squared: parabola

11. Both variables squared with unequal coefficients and same sign: ellipse

12. Both variables squared with unequal coefficients and same sign: ellipse

13. Both variables squared with opposite signs: hyperbola

14. Both variables squared with opposite signs: hyperbola

15. $a = 5$, $c = 7$; horizontal
$$b^2 = c^2 - a^2$$
$$= 49 - 25 = 24$$
$$\frac{x^2}{25} - \frac{y^2}{24} = 1$$

16. $a = 2$, $c = 3$; horizontal
$$b^2 = c^2 - a^2$$
$$= 9 - 4 = 5$$
$$\frac{x^2}{4} - \frac{y^2}{5} = 1$$

17. $a = 2$, $b = 3$; horizontal
$$\frac{(x-2)^2}{4} - \frac{(y-4)^2}{9} = 1$$

18. $a = 2$, $c = 3$; horizontal
$$b^2 = c^2 - a^2$$
$$= 9 - 4 = 5$$
$$\frac{(x+1)^2}{4} - \frac{(y-3)^2}{5} = 1$$

19. $a = 3$; vertical
$$\frac{(y-3)^2}{9} - \frac{(x-5)^2}{b^2} = 1$$
$$\frac{(8-3)^2}{9} - \frac{(1-5)^2}{b^2} = 1$$
$$\frac{25}{9} - \frac{16}{b^2} = 1$$
$$-\frac{16}{b^2} = -\frac{16}{9}$$
$$b^2 = 9$$
$$\frac{(y-3)^2}{9} - \frac{(x-5)^2}{9} = 1$$

20. Center: $(0, 0)$, $c = 10$, $a = 8$; vertical
$$b^2 = c^2 - a^2$$
$$= 100 - 64 = 36$$
$$\frac{y^2}{64} - \frac{x^2}{36} = 1$$

21. Center: $(0, 0)$, $a = 3$, $c = 5$; vertical
$$b^2 = c^2 - a^2$$
$$= 25 - 9 = 16$$
$$\frac{y^2}{9} - \frac{x^2}{16} = 1$$

22. $c = 4$, $a = 2$; horizontal
$$b^2 = c^2 - a^2$$
$$= 16 - 4 = 12$$
$$\frac{x^2}{4} - \frac{y^2}{12} = 1$$

23. $c = 6$, $a = 2$; horizontal
$$b^2 = c^2 - a^2$$
$$= 36 - 4 = 32$$
$$\frac{(x-1)^2}{4} - \frac{(y-4)^2}{32} = 1$$

24.
$$\frac{(x-1)^2}{4} - \frac{(y+3)^2}{16} = 1$$

OR

$$\frac{(y+3)^2}{4} - \frac{(x-1)^2}{16} = 1$$

25.
$$\frac{x^2}{a^2} - \frac{y^2}{b^2} = 1$$
$$\frac{4^2}{a^2} - \frac{2^2}{b^2} = 1$$
$$\frac{16}{a^2} - \frac{4}{b^2} = 1$$
$$\frac{16}{a^2} = 1 + \frac{4}{b^2}$$
$$\frac{64}{a^2} = 4 + \frac{16}{b^2}$$

$$\frac{x^2}{a^2} - \frac{y^2}{b^2} = 1$$
$$\frac{8^2}{a^2} - \frac{(-6)^2}{b^2} = 1$$
$$\frac{64}{a^2} - \frac{36}{b^2} = 1$$

$$\frac{64}{a^2} - \frac{36}{b^2} = 1$$
$$4 + \frac{16}{b^2} - \frac{36}{b^2} = 1$$
$$3 = \frac{20}{b^2}$$
$$b^2 = \frac{20}{3}$$
$$a^2 = 10$$

$$\frac{x^2}{10} - \frac{3y^2}{20} = 1$$

26.

$$\frac{(x-3)^2}{a^2}-\frac{(y+1)^2}{b^2}=1$$
$$\frac{(0-3)^2}{a^2}-\frac{(-1+1)^2}{b^2}=1$$
$$\frac{9}{a^2}=1$$
$$9=a^2$$

$$\frac{(x-3)^2}{9}-\frac{(y+1)^2}{b^2}=1$$
$$\frac{\left(3+\frac{3\sqrt{5}}{2}-3\right)^2}{9}-\frac{(0+1)^2}{b^2}=1$$
$$\frac{5}{4}-\frac{1}{b^2}=1$$
$$\frac{1}{4}=\frac{1}{b^2}$$
$$4=b^2$$

$$\frac{(x-3)^2}{9}-\frac{(y+1)^2}{4}=1$$

27.

$$4(x-1)^2-9(y+2)^2=36$$
$$\frac{4(x-1)^2}{36}-\frac{9(y+2)^2}{36}=\frac{36}{36}$$
$$\frac{(x-1)^2}{9}-\frac{(y+2)^2}{4}=1$$

$a=3, b=2$

Area $=(2a)(2b)=(6)(4)=24$ sq. units

28.

$$x^2-y^2-4x-6y=6$$
$$x^2-4x-(y^2+6y)=6$$
$$x^2-4x+4-(y^2+6y+9)=6+4-9$$
$$(x-2)^2-(y+3)^2=1$$
$$\frac{(x-2)^2}{1}-\frac{(y+3)^2}{1}=1$$

$a=1, b=1$

Area $=(2a)(2b)=(2)(2)=4$ sq. units

29.

$$x^2+6x-y^2+2y=-11$$
$$x^2+6x-(y^2-2y)=-11$$
$$x^2+6x+9-(y^2-2y+1)=-11+9-1$$
$$(x+3)^2-(y-1)^2=-3$$
$$\frac{(x+3)^2}{-3}-\frac{(y-1)^2}{-3}=1$$
$$\frac{(y-1)^2}{3}-\frac{(x+3)^2}{3}=1\Rightarrow a=\sqrt{3}, b=\sqrt{3};$$

Area $=(2a)(2b)=\left(2\sqrt{3}\right)\left(2\sqrt{3}\right)=12$ sq. units

30.

$$9x^2-4y^2=18x+24y+63$$
$$9(x^2-2x)-4(y^2+6y)=63$$
$$9(x^2-2x+1)-4(y^2+6y+9)=63+9-36$$
$$9(x-1)^2-4(y+3)^2=36$$
$$\frac{9(x-1)^2}{36}-\frac{4(y+3)^2}{36}=\frac{36}{36}$$
$$\frac{(x-1)^2}{4}-\frac{(y+3)^2}{9}=1\Rightarrow a=2, b=3;$$

Area $=(2a)(2b)=(4)(6)=24$ sq. units

31. $(2a)(2b) = 36$
$4(2b) = 36$
$b = \frac{9}{2}$
$$\frac{(x+2)^2}{4} - \frac{4(y+4)^2}{81} = 1$$
OR
$$\frac{(y+4)^2}{4} - \frac{4(x+2)^2}{81} = 1$$

32. $(2a)(2b) = 24$
$(2a)(12) = 24$
$a = 1$
$$\frac{(x-3)^2}{1} - \frac{(y+5)^2}{36} = 1$$
OR
$$\frac{(y+5)^2}{1} - \frac{(x-3)^2}{36} = 1$$

33. Center: $(0, 0)$, $a = 6$, $b = \frac{5}{4}$
$$\frac{x^2}{6^2} - \frac{y^2}{\left(\frac{5}{4}\right)^2} = 1$$
$$\frac{x^2}{36} - \frac{16y^2}{25} = 1$$

34. $a = 3$, $c = 5$; horizontal
$b^2 = c^2 - a^2$
$= 25 - 9 = 16$
$$\frac{x^2}{9} - \frac{y^2}{16} = 1$$

35. $\frac{x^2}{9} - \frac{y^2}{4} = 1$
Center: $(0, 0)$, $a = 3$, $b = 2$, horizontal

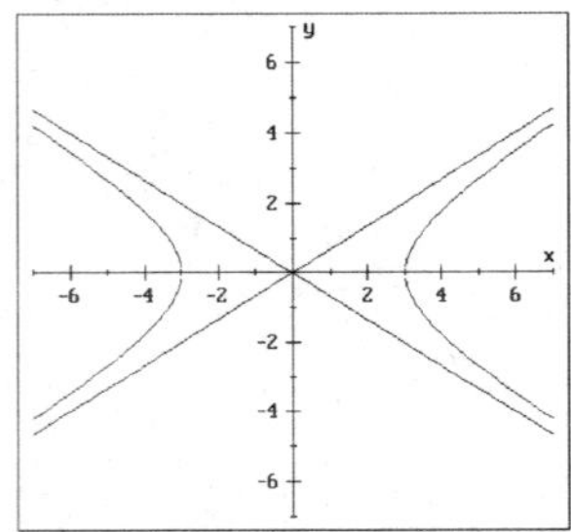

36. $\frac{y^2}{4} - \frac{x^2}{9} = 1$
Center: $(0, 0)$, $a = 2$, $b = 3$, vertical

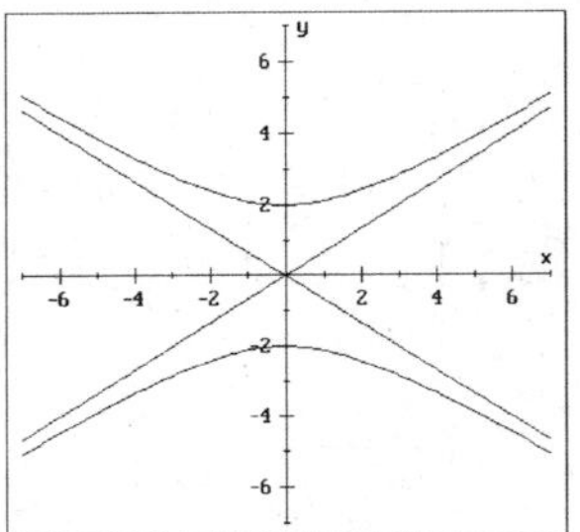

37. $4x^2 - 3y^2 = 36$
$$\frac{4x^2}{36} - \frac{3y^2}{36} = \frac{36}{36}$$
$$\frac{x^2}{9} - \frac{y^2}{12} = 1$$
Center: $(0, 0)$, $a = 3$, $b = 2\sqrt{3}$, horizontal

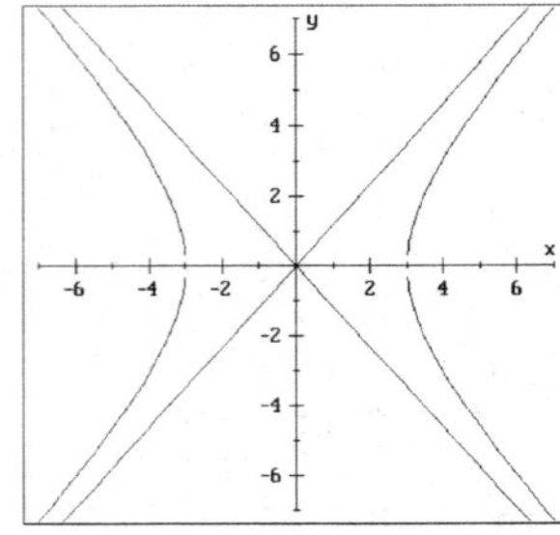

38. $3x^2 - 4y^2 = 36$
$$\frac{3x^2}{36} - \frac{4y^2}{36} = \frac{36}{36}$$
$$\frac{x^2}{12} - \frac{y^2}{9} = 1$$
Center: $(0, 0)$, $a = 2\sqrt{3}$, $b = 3$, horizontal

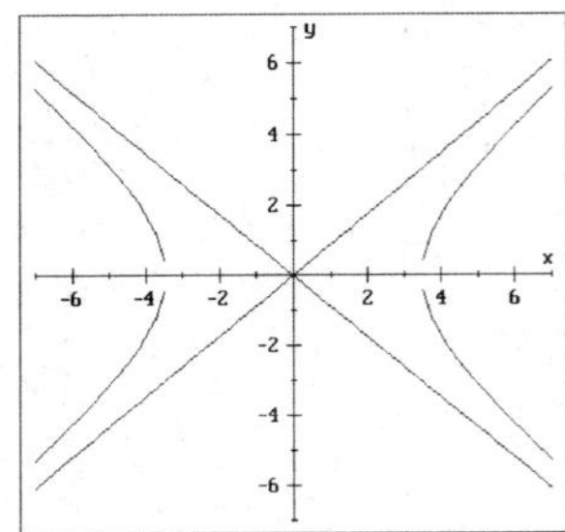

39. $y^2 - x^2 = 1$

$\frac{y^2}{1} - \frac{x^2}{1} = 1$

Center: $(0, 0)$, $a = 1$, $b = 1$, vertical

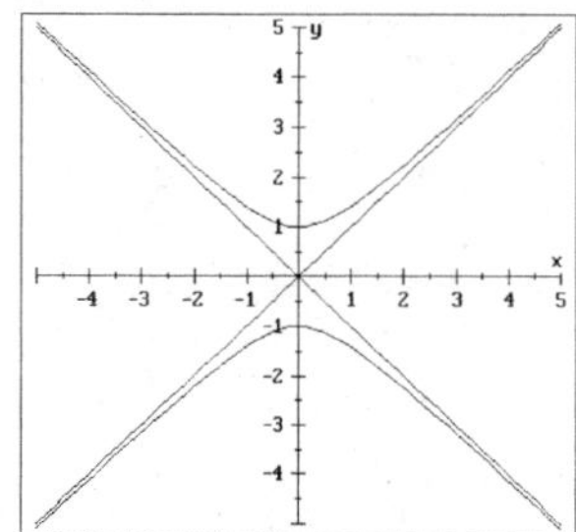

40. $x^2 - \frac{y^2}{4} = 1$

$\frac{x^2}{1} - \frac{y^2}{4} = 1$

Center: $(0, 0)$, $a = 1$, $b = 2$, horizontal

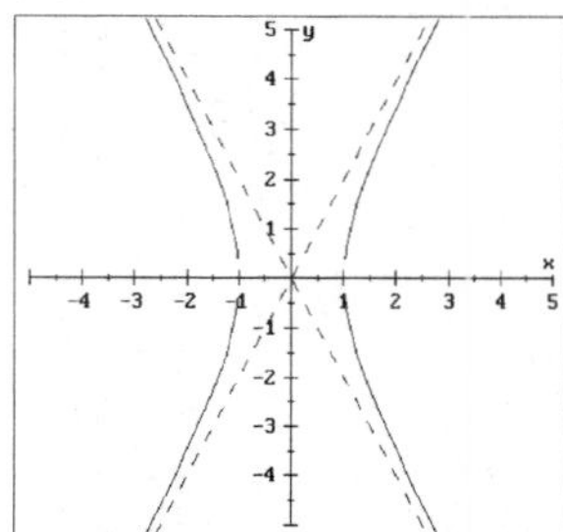

41. $\frac{(x+2)^2}{9} - \frac{y^2}{4} = 1$

Center: $(-2, 0)$, $a = 3$, $b = 2$, horizontal

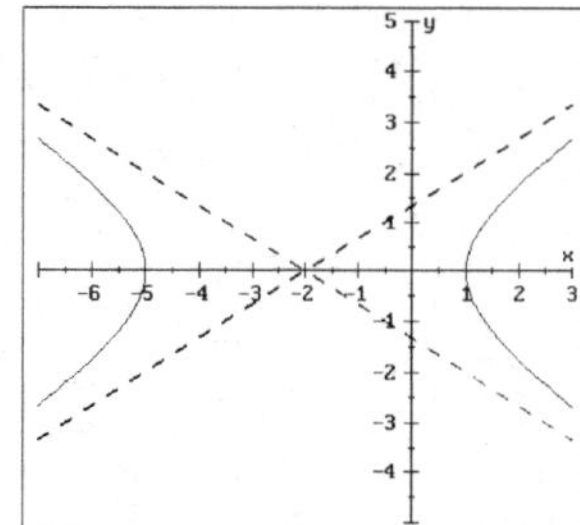

42. $\frac{y^2}{9} - \frac{(x-2)^2}{36} = 1$

Center: $(2, 0)$, $a = 3$, $b = 6$, vertical

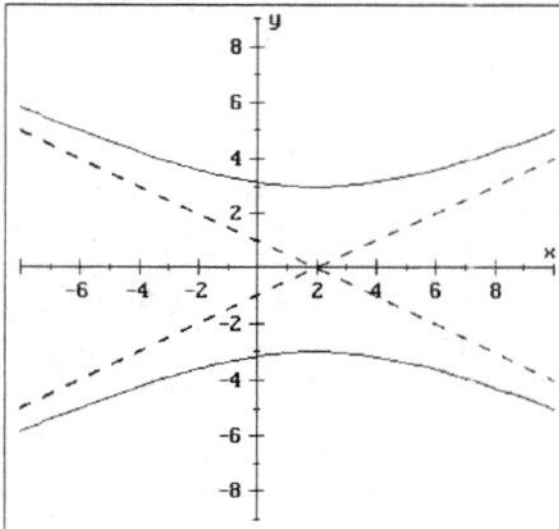

43. $4(y-2)^2 - 9(x+1)^2 = 36$

$\frac{4(y-2)^2}{36} - \frac{9(x+1)^2}{36} = \frac{36}{36}$

$\frac{(y-2)^2}{9} - \frac{(x+1)^2}{4} = 1$

Center: $(-1, 2)$, $a = 3$, $b = 2$, vertical

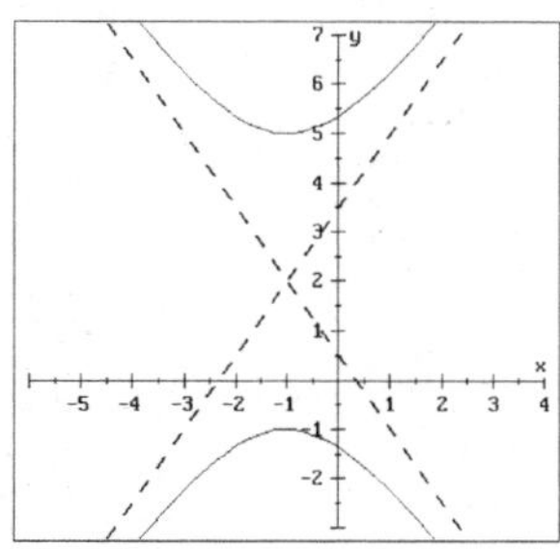

44. $9(y+2)^2 - 4(x-1)^2 = 36$

$\frac{9(y+2)^2}{36} - \frac{4(x-1)^2}{36} = \frac{36}{36}$

$\frac{(y+2)^2}{4} - \frac{(x-1)^2}{9} = 1$

Center: $(1, -2)$, $a = 2$, $b = 3$, vertical

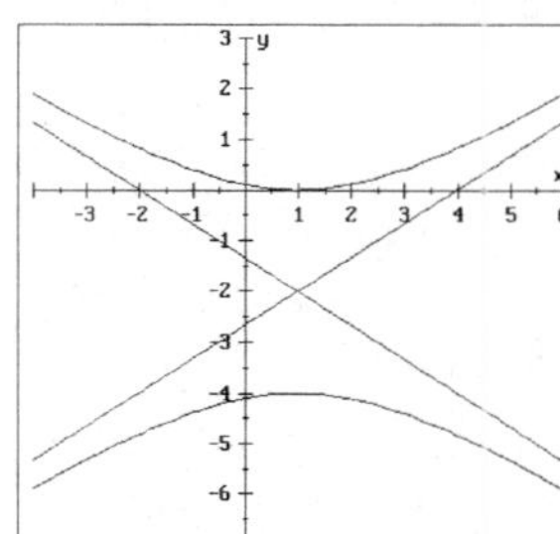

45.

$$\begin{aligned} 4x^2 - 2y^2 + 8x - 8y &= 8 \\ 4(x^2 + 2x) - 2(y^2 + 4y) &= 8 \\ 4(x^2 + 2x + 1) - 2(y^2 + 4y + 4) &= 8 + 4 - 8 \\ 4(x + 1)^2 - 2(y + 2)^2 &= 4 \\ \frac{4(x+1)^2}{4} - \frac{2(y+2)^2}{4} &= \frac{4}{4} \\ \frac{(x+1)^2}{1} - \frac{(y+2)^2}{2} &= 1 \end{aligned}$$

Center: $(-1, -2)$, $a = 1$, $b = \sqrt{2}$, horizontal

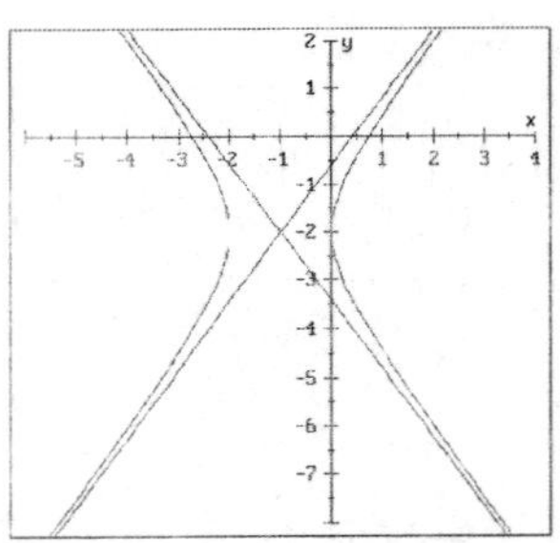

46.

$$\begin{aligned} x^2 - y^2 - 4x - 6y &= 6 \\ x^2 - 4x - (y^2 + 6y) &= 6 \\ x^2 - 4x + 4 - (y^2 + 6y + 9) &= 6 + 4 - 9 \\ (x - 2)^2 - (y + 3)^2 &= 1 \\ \frac{(x-2)^2}{1} - \frac{(y+3)^2}{1} &= 1 \end{aligned}$$

Center: $(2, -3)$, $a = 1$, $b = 1$, horizontal

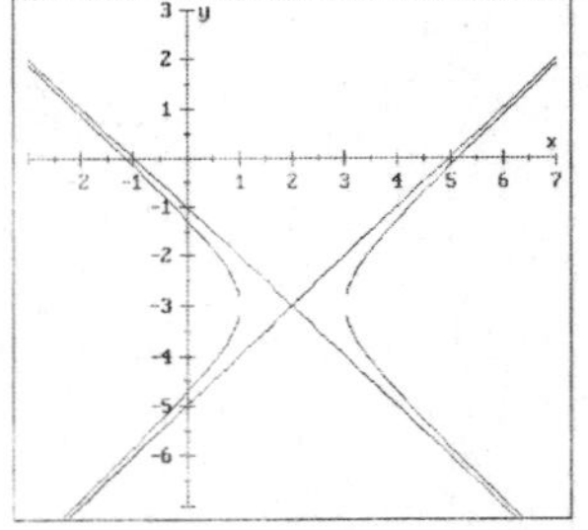

47.

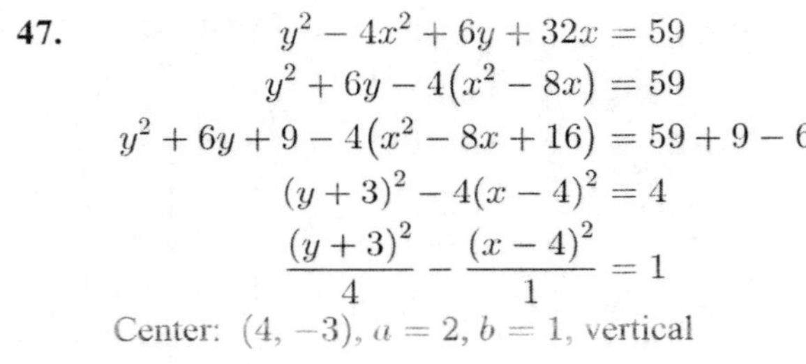

$$\begin{aligned} y^2 - 4x^2 + 6y + 32x &= 59 \\ y^2 + 6y - 4(x^2 - 8x) &= 59 \\ y^2 + 6y + 9 - 4(x^2 - 8x + 16) &= 59 + 9 - 64 \\ (y + 3)^2 - 4(x - 4)^2 &= 4 \\ \frac{(y+3)^2}{4} - \frac{(x-4)^2}{1} &= 1 \end{aligned}$$

Center: $(4, -3)$, $a = 2$, $b = 1$, vertical

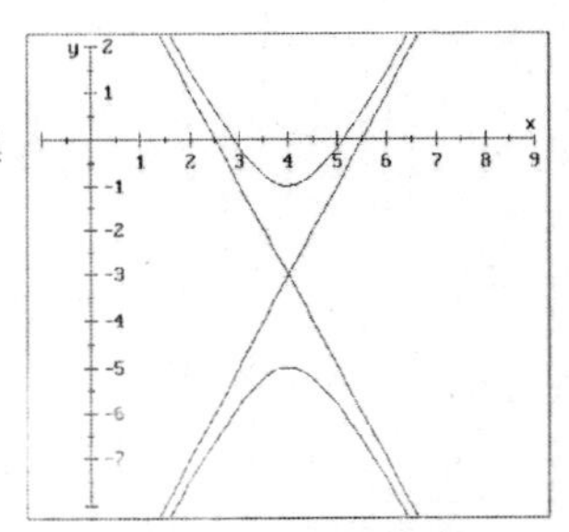

48.

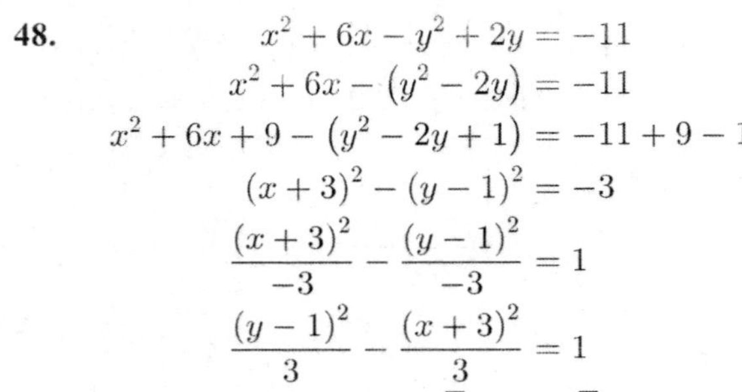

$$\begin{aligned} x^2 + 6x - y^2 + 2y &= -11 \\ x^2 + 6x - (y^2 - 2y) &= -11 \\ x^2 + 6x + 9 - (y^2 - 2y + 1) &= -11 + 9 - 1 \\ (x + 3)^2 - (y - 1)^2 &= -3 \\ \frac{(x+3)^2}{-3} - \frac{(y-1)^2}{-3} &= 1 \\ \frac{(y-1)^2}{3} - \frac{(x+3)^2}{3} &= 1 \end{aligned}$$

Center: $(-3, 1)$, $a = \sqrt{3}$, $b = \sqrt{3}$, vertical

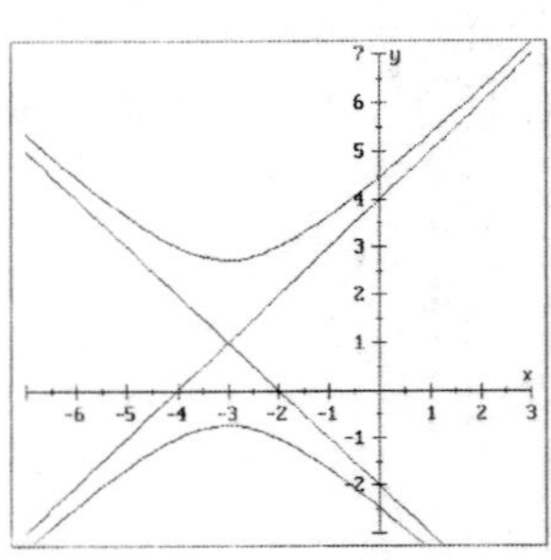

49. $-xy = 6$

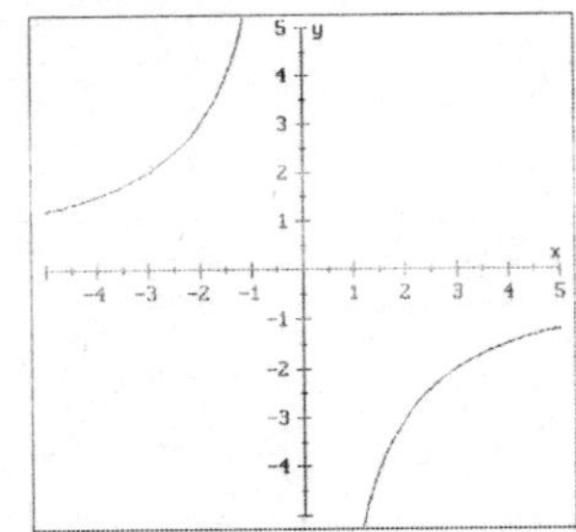

50. $xy = 20$

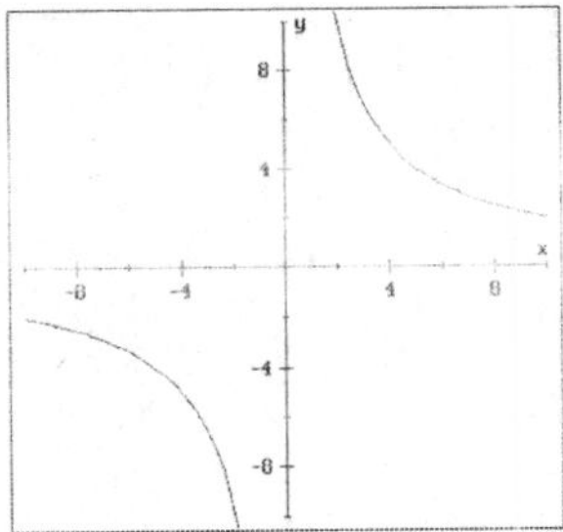

51. Foci: $(-2, 1), (8, 1)$
Center: $(3, 1), c = 5$
$2a = 6 \Rightarrow a = 3, b = 4$
$$\frac{(x-3)^2}{9} - \frac{(y-1)^2}{16} = 1$$

52. Foci: $(3, -1), (3, 5)$
Center: $(3, 2), c = 3$
$2a = 5 \Rightarrow a = \frac{5}{2}, b = \frac{\sqrt{11}}{2}$
$$\frac{4(y-2)^2}{25} - \frac{4(x-3)^2}{11} = 1$$

53. The distance between the point (x, y) and the line $x = -2$ is the difference between the y-coordinates, or $y - (-2) = y + 2$.
$$\begin{aligned}\sqrt{(x-0)^2 + (y-3)^2} &= \frac{3}{2}(y+2)\\ x^2 + (y-3)^2 &= \frac{9}{4}(y+2)^2\\ 4x^2 + 4(y-3)^2 &= 9(y+2)^2\\ 4x^2 + 4(y^2 - 6y + 9) &= 9(y^2 + 4y + 4)\\ 4x^2 - 5y^2 - 60y &= 0\end{aligned}$$

54. The distance between the point (x, y) and the line $y = -3$ is the difference between the x-coordinates, or $x - (-3) = x + 3$.
$$\begin{aligned}\sqrt{(x-5)^2 + (y-4)^2} &= \frac{5}{3}(x+3)\\ (x-5)^2 + (y-4)^2 &= \frac{25}{9}(x+3)^2\\ 9(x-5)^2 + 9(y-4)^2 &= 25(x+3)^2\\ 9(x^2 - 10x + 25) + 9(y^2 - 8y + 16) &= 25(x^2 + 6x + 9)\\ 9x^2 - 90x + 225 + 9y^2 - 72y + 144 &= 25x^2 + 150x + 225\\ 9y^2 - 72y - 16x^2 - 240x + 144 &= 0\\ 9(y^2 - 8y) - 16(x^2 + 15x) &= -144\\ 9(y^2 - 8y + 16) - 16\left(x^2 + 15x + \frac{225}{4}\right) &= -144 + 144 - 900\end{aligned}$$

continued on next page.

54. continued

$$9(y^2 - 8y + 16) - 16\left(x^2 + 15x + \frac{225}{4}\right) = -144 + 144 - 900$$
$$9(y-4)^2 - 16\left(x + \tfrac{15}{2}\right)^2 = -900$$
$$16\left(x + \tfrac{15}{2}\right)^2 - 9(y-4)^2 = 900$$
$$\frac{4\left(x + \frac{15}{2}\right)^2}{225} - \frac{(y-4)^2}{100} = 1$$

55. $x^2 - \dfrac{y^2}{4} = 1$

$$-\frac{y^2}{4} = -x^2 + 1$$
$$y^2 = 4x^2 - 4$$
$$y = \pm\sqrt{4x^2 - 4}$$

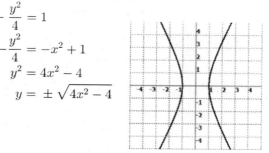

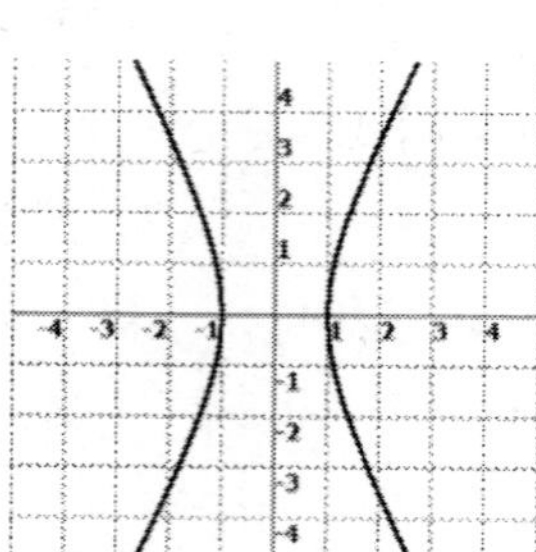

56. $\dfrac{(x+3)^2}{4} - \dfrac{(y-2)^2}{25} = 1$

$$-\frac{(y-2)^2}{25} = -\frac{(x+3)^2}{4} + 1$$
$$\frac{(y-2)^2}{25} = \frac{(x+3)^2}{4} - 1$$
$$(y-2)^2 = \frac{25(x+3)^2}{4} - 25$$
$$y - 2 = \pm\sqrt{\frac{25(x+3)^2}{4} - 25}$$
$$y = 2 \pm \sqrt{\frac{25(x+3)^2}{4} - 25}$$

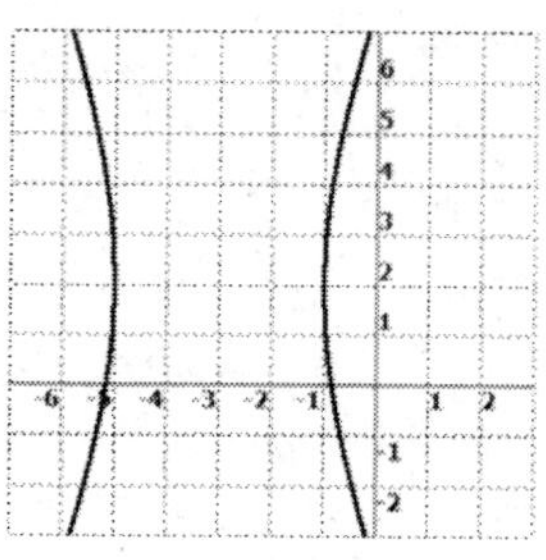

57.
$$xy = k$$
$$(12)(2) = k$$
$$24 = k$$

58.
$$a = 100{,}000{,}000$$
$$c = 200{,}000{,}000$$
$$\frac{x^2}{100{,}000{,}000^2} - \frac{y^2}{200{,}000{,}000^2} = 1$$

59.
$$9y^2 - x^2 = 81$$
$$\frac{9y^2}{81} - \frac{x^2}{81} = \frac{81}{81}$$
$$\frac{y^2}{9} - \frac{x^2}{81} = 1$$
$a = 3 \Rightarrow 3$ units

60. The point $(10, 1 \times 10^{-4})$ is on the graph.
$$y = \frac{k}{x}$$
$$1 \times 10^{-4} = \frac{k}{10}$$
$$1 \times 10^{-3} = k$$

61.
$$2a = 24 \Rightarrow a = 12$$
$$c = 13 \Rightarrow b = 5$$
$$\frac{x^2}{144} - \frac{y^2}{25} = 1$$

62.
$$x^2 - 4y^2 = 576$$
$$x^2 - 4(5)^2 = 576$$
$$x^2 - 100 = 576$$
$$x^2 = 676$$
$$x = \pm\sqrt{676}$$
$$= \pm 26$$
$$(26, 5)$$

63.
$$2a = 12 \Rightarrow a = 6$$
$$c = 10 \Rightarrow b = 8$$
$$\frac{x^2}{36} - \frac{y^2}{64} = 1$$

64.
$$y^2 - x^2 = 25$$
$$\frac{y^2}{25} - \frac{x^2}{25} = 1$$
$$C(0,0), V(0,5)$$
$$y^2 - x^2 = 25$$
$$10^2 - x^2 = 25$$
$$75 = x^2$$
$$x = \sqrt{75} = 5\sqrt{3}$$
$2\left(5\sqrt{3}\right) = 10\sqrt{3}$ miles

65-68. Answers may vary.

69.
$$f(x) = 3x - 2$$
$$y = 3x - 2$$
$$x = 3y - 2$$
$$x + 2 = 3y$$
$$\frac{x+2}{3} = y \Rightarrow f^{-1}(x) = \frac{x+2}{3}$$

70.
$$f(x) = \frac{x+1}{x}$$
$$y = \frac{x+1}{x}$$
$$x = \frac{y+1}{y}$$
$$xy = y + 1$$
$$xy - y = 1$$
$$y(x-1) = 1$$
$$y = \frac{1}{x-1} \Rightarrow f^{-1}(x) = \frac{1}{x-1}$$

71.
$$f(x) = \frac{5x}{x+2}$$
$$y = \frac{5x}{x+2}$$
$$x = \frac{5y}{y+2}$$
$$x(y+2) = 5y$$
$$xy + 2x = 5y$$
$$2x = 5y - xy$$
$$2x = y(5 - x)$$
$$\frac{2x}{5-x} = y \Rightarrow f^{-1}(x) = \frac{2x}{5-x}$$

72.
$$f(x) = x$$
$$y = x$$
$$x = y \Rightarrow f^{-1}(x) = x$$

73. $f(g(x)) = f\left((x+1)^2\right) = \left((x+1)^2\right)^2 + 1 = (x+1)^4 + 1$

74. $g(f(x)) = g(x^2+1) = (x^2+1+1)^2 = (x^2+2)^2$

75. $f(f(x)) = f(x^2+1) = (x^2+1)^2 + 1$

76. $g(g(x)) = g\left((x+1)^2\right) = \left((x+1)^2+1\right)^2$

Exercises 7.4 (page 707)

1. graphs

2. graphically, substitution, adding

3. $\begin{cases} 8x^2 + 32y^2 = 256 \\ x = 2y \end{cases}$

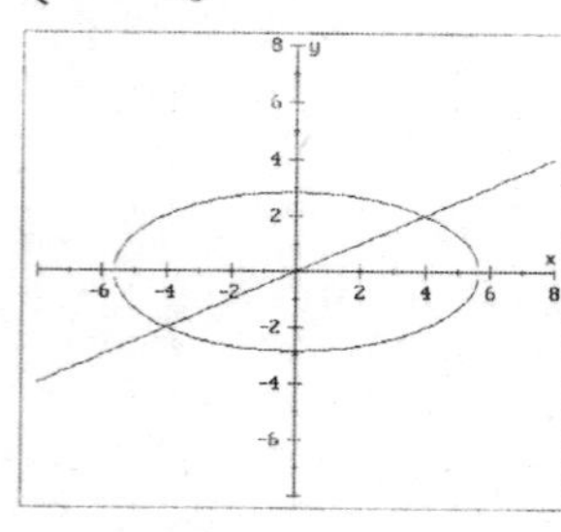

$(4, 2), (-4, -2)$

4. $\begin{cases} x^2 + y^2 = 2 \\ x + y = 2 \end{cases}$

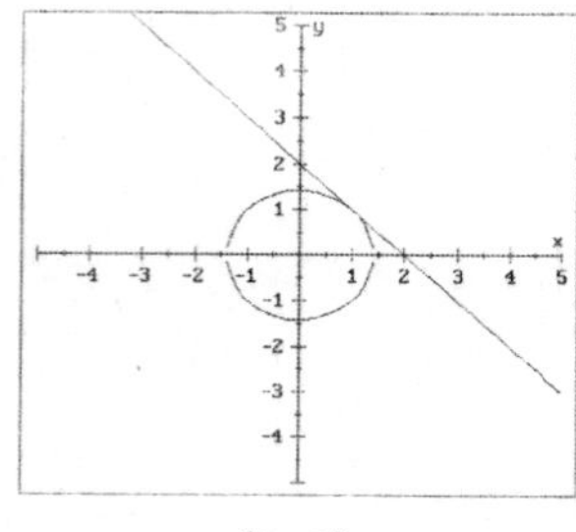

$(1, 1)$

5. $\begin{cases} x^2 + y^2 = 90 \\ y = x^2 \end{cases}$

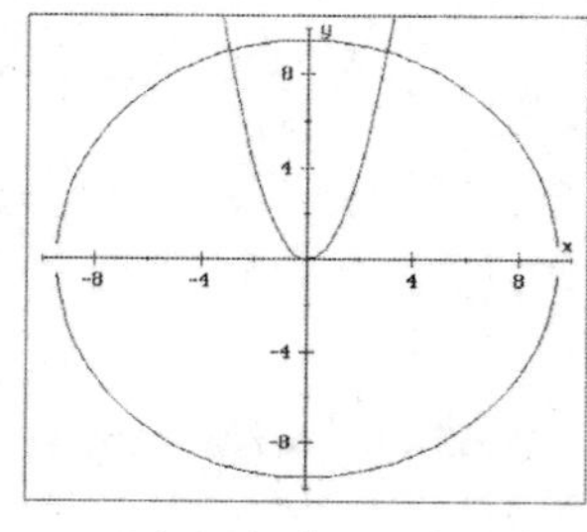

$(3, 9), (-3, 9)$

6. $\begin{cases} x^2 + y^2 = 5 \\ x + y = 3 \end{cases}$

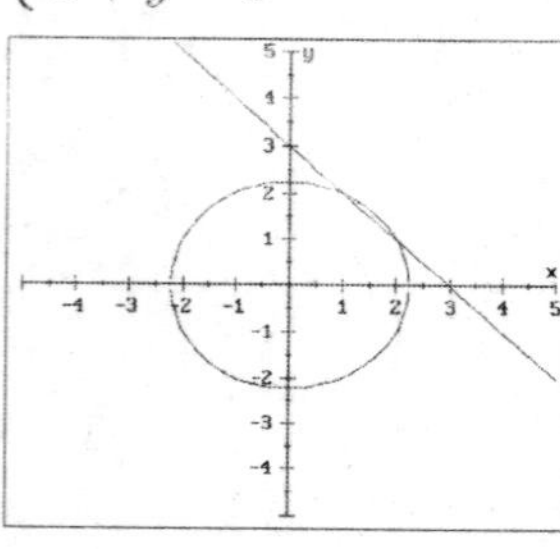

$(1, 2), (2, 1)$

7. $\begin{cases} x^2 + y^2 = 25 \\ 12x^2 + 64y^2 = 768 \end{cases}$

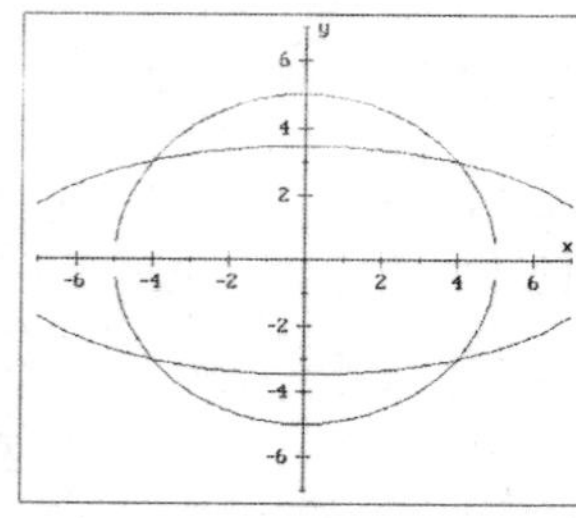

$(-4, 3), (4, 3)$
$(-4, -3), (4, -3)$

8. $\begin{cases} x^2 + y^2 = 13 \\ y = x^2 - 1 \end{cases}$

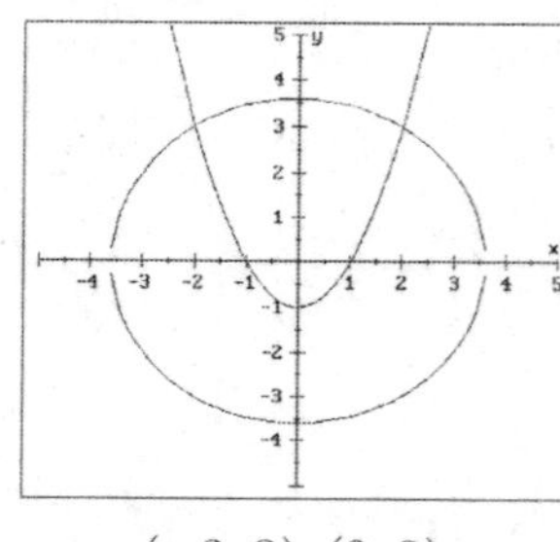

$(-2, 3), (2, 3)$

9. $\begin{cases} x^2 - 13 = -y^2 \\ y = 2x - 4 \end{cases}$

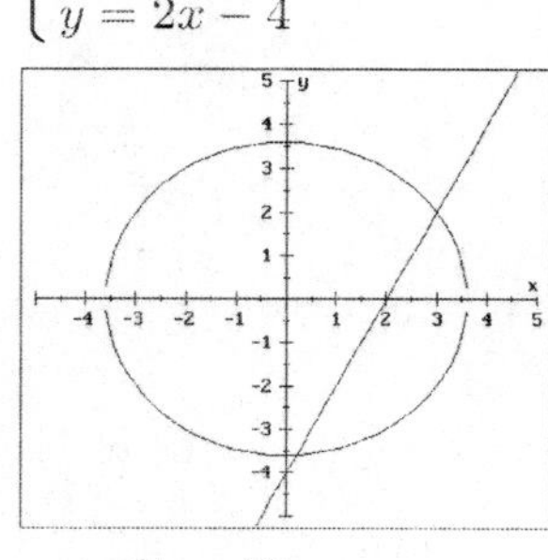

$\left(\frac{1}{5}, -\frac{18}{5}\right)$, $(3, 2)$

10. $\begin{cases} x^2 + y^2 = 20 \\ y = x^2 \end{cases}$

$(2, 4)$, $(-2, 4)$

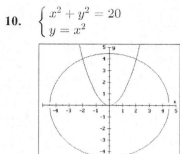

11. $\begin{cases} x^2 - 6x - y = -5 \\ x^2 - 6x + y = -5 \end{cases}$

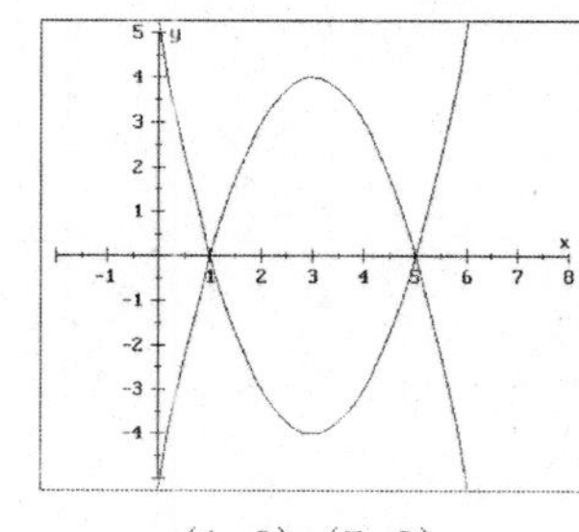

$(1, 0)$, $(5, 0)$

12. $\begin{cases} x^2 - y^2 = -5 \\ 3x^2 + 2y^2 = 30 \end{cases}$

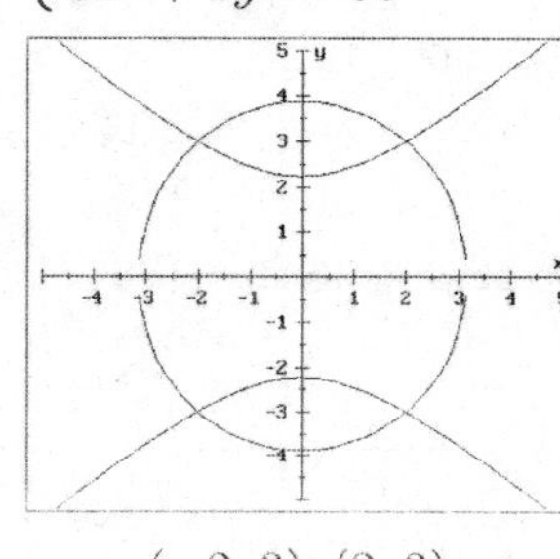

$(-2, 3)$, $(2, 3)$
$(-2, -3)$, $(2, -3)$

13. $\begin{cases} y = x + 1 \\ y = x^2 + x \end{cases}$

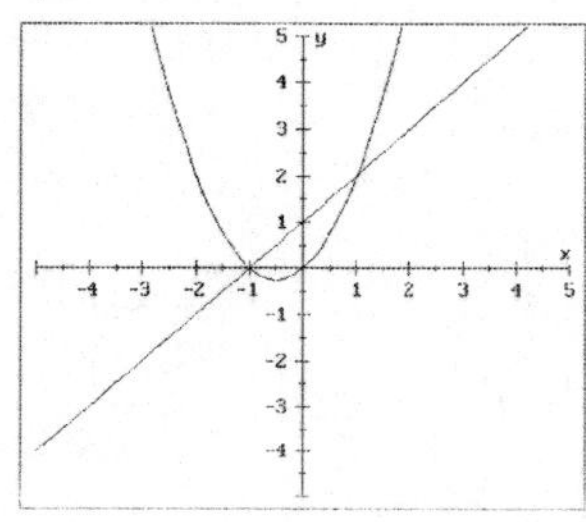

$(1, 2)$, $(-1, 0)$

14. $\begin{cases} y = 6 - x^2 \\ y = x^2 - x \end{cases}$

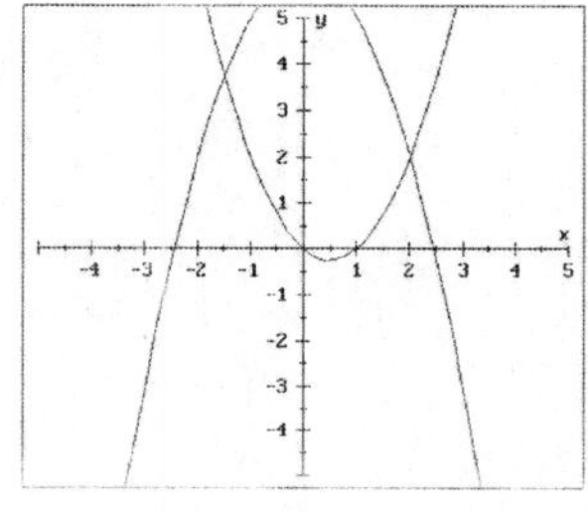

$(2, 2)$, $(-1.5, 3.75)$

15. $\begin{cases} 6x^2 + 9y^2 = 10 & \Rightarrow \ y = \pm\sqrt{\frac{10-6x^2}{9}} \\ 3y - 2x = 0 & \Rightarrow \ y = \frac{2}{3}x \end{cases}$

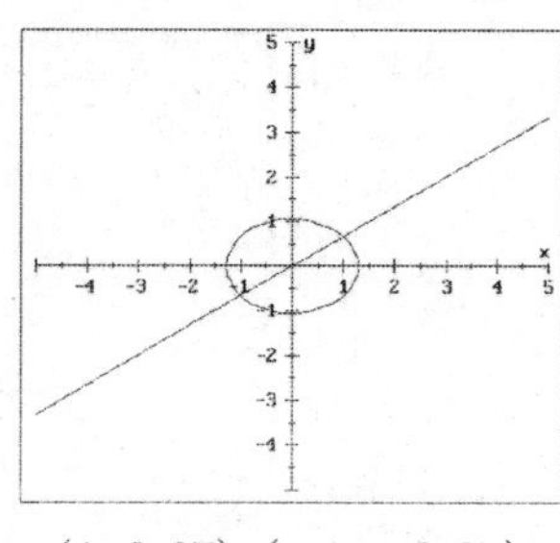

$(1, 0.67)$, $(-1, -0.67)$

16. $\begin{cases} x^2 + y^2 = 68 & \Rightarrow \ y = \pm\sqrt{68 - x^2} \\ y^2 - 3x^2 = 4 & \Rightarrow \ y = \pm\sqrt{4 + 3x^2} \end{cases}$

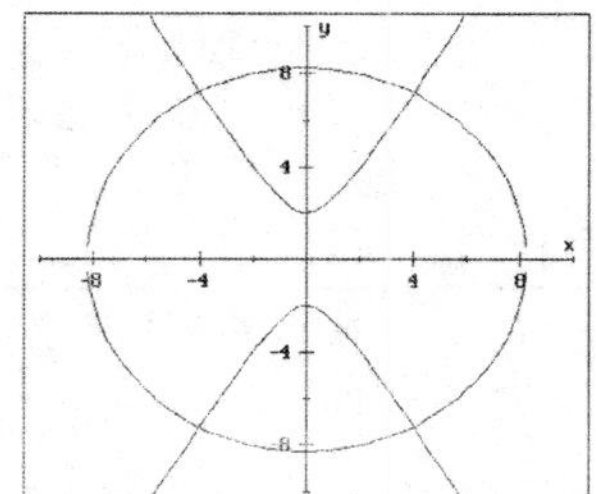

$(4, 7.2)$, $(4, -7.2)$, $(-4, 7.2)$, $(-4, -7.2)$

17.
$$5x + 3y = 15 \Rightarrow y = \frac{15 - 5x}{3}$$
$$25x^2 + 9y^2 = 225$$
$$25x^2 + 9\left(\frac{15 - 5x}{3}\right)^2 = 225$$
$$25x^2 + (15 - 5x)^2 = 225$$
$$25x^2 + 225 - 150x + 25x^2 = 225$$
$$50x^2 - 150x = 0$$
$$50x(x - 3) = 0$$

$x = 0$	$x = 3$
$y = \frac{15 - 5(0)}{3} = 5$	$y = \frac{15 - 5(3)}{3} = 0$
$(0, 5)$	$(3, 0)$

18.
$$y = x^2 \Rightarrow x^2 = y$$
$$x^2 + y^2 = 20$$
$$y + y^2 = 20$$
$$y^2 + y - 20 = 0$$
$$(y - 4)(y + 5) = 0$$

$y = 4$	$y = -5$
$4 = x^2 \Rightarrow x = \pm 2$	$-5 = x^2$
$(2, 4)$, $(-2, 4)$	no real solutions

19.
$$x + y = 2 \Rightarrow y = 2 - x$$
$$x^2 + y^2 = 2$$
$$x^2 + (2 - x)^2 = 2$$
$$x^2 + 4 - 4x + x^2 = 2$$
$$2x^2 - 4x + 2 = 0$$
$$2(x - 1)(x - 1) = 0$$

$x = 1$
$y = 2 - 1 = 1$
$(1, 1)$

20.
$$x^2 + y^2 = 36 \Rightarrow x^2 = 36 - y^2$$
$$49x^2 + 36y^2 = 1764$$
$$49(36 - y^2) + 36y^2 = 1764$$
$$1764 - 49y^2 + 36y^2 = 1764$$
$$-13y^2 = 0$$

$y = 0$
$x^2 = 36 - 0^2 \Rightarrow x = \pm 6$
$(6, 0)$, $(-6, 0)$

21.
$$x + y = 3 \Rightarrow y = 3 - x$$
$$x^2 + y^2 = 5$$
$$x^2 + (3 - x)^2 = 5$$
$$x^2 + 9 - 6x + x^2 = 5$$
$$2x^2 - 6x + 4 = 0$$
$$2(x - 1)(x - 2) = 0$$

$x = 1$	$x = 2$
$y = 3 - 1 = 2$	$y = 3 - 2 = 1$
$(1, 2)$	$(2, 1)$

22.
$$x^2 - x - y = 2 \Rightarrow y = x^2 - x - 2$$
$$4x - 3y = 0$$
$$4x - 3(x^2 - x - 2) = 0$$
$$4x - 3x^2 + 3x + 6 = 0$$
$$3x^2 - 7x - 6 = 0$$
$$(3x + 2)(x - 3) = 0$$

$x = -\frac{2}{3}$	$x = 3$
$y = \left(-\frac{2}{3}\right)^2 - \left(-\frac{2}{3}\right) - 2$	$y = 3^2 - 3 - 2$
$= -\frac{8}{9}$	$= 4$
$\left(-\frac{2}{3}, -\frac{8}{9}\right)$	$(3, 4)$

23.
$$y = x^2 - 1 \Rightarrow x^2 = y + 1$$
$$x^2 + y^2 = 13$$
$$y + 1 + y^2 = 13$$
$$y^2 + y - 12 = 0$$
$$(y - 3)(y + 4) = 0$$

$y = 3$	$y = -4$
$3 + 1 = x^2 \Rightarrow x = \pm 2$	$-4 + 1 = x^2$
$(2, 3)$, $(-2, 3)$	no real solutions

24. $x^2 + y^2 = 25 \Rightarrow x^2 = 25 - y^2$

$$2x^2 - 3y^2 = 5$$
$$2(25 - y^2) - 3y^2 = 5$$
$$50 - 2y^2 - 3y^2 = 5$$
$$45 = 5y^2$$
$$9 = y^2$$

$y = 3$: $x^2 = 25 - 3^2 \Rightarrow x = \pm 4$; $(4, 3), (-4, 3)$

$y = -3$: $x^2 = 25 - (-3)^2 \Rightarrow x = \pm 4$; $(4, -3), (-4, -3)$

25.

$$y = x^2 \Rightarrow x^2 = y$$
$$x^2 + y^2 = 30$$
$$y + y^2 = 30$$
$$y^2 + y - 30 = 0$$
$$(y - 5)(y + 6) = 0$$

$y = 5$: $5 = x^2 \Rightarrow x = \pm\sqrt{5}$; $\left(\sqrt{5}, 5\right), \left(-\sqrt{5}, 5\right)$

$y = -6$: $-6 = x^2$; no real solutions

26. $x^2 + y^2 = 9 \Rightarrow x^2 = 9 - y^2$

$$9x^2 - 7y^2 = 81$$
$$9(9 - y^2) - 7y^2 = 81$$
$$81 - 9y^2 - 7y^2 = 81$$
$$-16y^2 = 0$$

$y = 0$: $x^2 = 9 - 0^2 \Rightarrow x = \pm 3$; $(3, 0), (-3, 0)$

27.

$$\begin{aligned} 2x^2 + y^2 &= 6 \\ x^2 - y^2 &= 3 \\ \hline 3x^2 &= 9 \\ x^2 &= 3 \\ x &= \pm\sqrt{3} \end{aligned} \qquad \begin{aligned} 2x^2 + y^2 &= 6 \\ 2(3) + y^2 &= 6 \\ y^2 &= 0 \\ y &= 0 \end{aligned}$$

$\left(\sqrt{3}, 0\right), \left(-\sqrt{3}, 0\right)$

28.

$$\begin{aligned} x^2 + y^2 &= 13 \\ x^2 - y^2 &= 5 \\ \hline 2x^2 &= 18 \\ x^2 &= 9 \\ x &= \pm 3 \end{aligned} \qquad \begin{aligned} x^2 + y^2 &= 13 \\ 9 + y^2 &= 13 \\ y^2 &= 4 \\ y &= \pm 2 \end{aligned}$$

$(3, 2), (-3, 2), (3, -2), (-3, -2)$

29.

$$\begin{aligned} x^2 + y^2 &= 20 \\ x^2 - y^2 &= -12 \\ \hline 2x^2 &= 8 \\ x^2 &= 4 \\ x &= \pm 2 \end{aligned} \qquad \begin{aligned} x^2 + y^2 &= 20 \\ 4 + y^2 &= 20 \\ y^2 &= 16 \\ y &= \pm 4 \end{aligned}$$

$(2, 4), (-2, 4), (2, -4), (-2, -4)$

30.

$$xy = -\tfrac{9}{2} \Rightarrow y = -\tfrac{9}{2x}$$
$$3x + 2y = 6$$
$$3x + 2\left(-\frac{9}{2x}\right) = 6$$
$$3x - \frac{9}{x} = 6$$
$$3x^2 - 6x - 9 = 0$$
$$3(x - 3)(x + 1) = 0$$

$x = 3$: $y = -\frac{9}{2(3)} = -\frac{3}{2}$; $\left(3, -\frac{3}{2}\right)$

$x = -1$: $y = -\frac{9}{2(-1)} = \frac{9}{2}$; $\left(-1, \frac{9}{2}\right)$

31. $y = x^2 - 10 \Rightarrow x^2 = y + 10$

$$y^2 = 40 - x^2$$
$$y^2 = 40 - y - 10$$
$$y^2 + y - 30 = 0$$
$$(y - 5)(y + 6) = 0$$

$y = 5$: $x^2 = 5 + 10 \Rightarrow x = \pm\sqrt{15}$; $\left(\sqrt{15}, 5\right), \left(-\sqrt{15}, 5\right)$

$y = -6$: $x^2 = -6 + 10 \Rightarrow x = \pm 2$; $(2, -6), (-2, -6)$

32.
$$\begin{aligned} x^2 - 6x - y &= -5 \\ x^2 - 6x + y &= -5 \\ \hline 2x^2 - 12x &= -10 \\ 2(x-1)(x-5) &= 0 \end{aligned}$$
$$\frac{x=1}{y = x^2 - 6x + 5 = 0} \quad (1, 0)$$
$$\frac{x=5}{y = x^2 - 6x + 5 = 0} \quad (5, 0)$$

33.
$$\begin{aligned} y = x^2 - 4 &\Rightarrow x^2 = y + 4 \\ x^2 - y^2 &= -16 \\ y + 4 - y^2 &= -16 \\ y^2 - y - 20 &= 0 \\ (y-5)(y+4) &= 0 \end{aligned}$$
$$\frac{y = 5}{x^2 = 5 + 4 \Rightarrow x = \pm 3} \quad (3, 5), (-3, 5)$$
$$\frac{y = -4}{x^2 = -4 + 4 \Rightarrow x = 0} \quad (0, -4)$$

34.
$$\begin{aligned} 6x^2 + 8y^2 &= 182 \\ 8x^2 - 3y^2 &= 24 \\ \hline 18x^2 + 24y^2 &= 546 \\ 64x^2 - 24y^2 &= 192 \\ \hline 82x^2 &= 738 \\ x^2 &= 9 \\ x &= \pm 3 \end{aligned}$$
$$\begin{aligned} 6x^2 + 8y^2 &= 182 \\ 6(9) + 8y^2 &= 182 \\ 8y^2 &= 128 \\ y^2 &= 16 \\ y &= \pm 4 \end{aligned}$$
$(3, 4), (-3, 4), (3, -4), (-3, -4)$

35.
$$\begin{aligned} x^2 - y^2 &= -5 \\ 3x^2 + 2y^2 &= 30 \\ \hline 2x^2 - 2y^2 &= -10 \\ 3x^2 + 2y^2 &= 30 \\ \hline 5x^2 &= 20 \\ x^2 &= 4 \\ x &= \pm 2 \end{aligned}$$
$$\begin{aligned} 3x^2 + 2y^2 &= 30 \\ 3(4) + 2y^2 &= 30 \\ 2y^2 &= 18 \\ y^2 &= 9 \\ y &= \pm 3 \end{aligned}$$
$(2, 3), (-2, 3), (2, -3), (-2, -3)$

36.
$$\begin{aligned} \tfrac{1}{x} + \tfrac{1}{y} &= 5 \\ \tfrac{1}{x} - \tfrac{1}{y} &= -3 \\ \hline \tfrac{2}{x} &= 2 \\ x &= 1 \end{aligned}$$
$$\begin{aligned} \tfrac{1}{x} + \tfrac{1}{y} &= 5 \\ \tfrac{1}{1} + \tfrac{1}{y} &= 5 \\ \tfrac{1}{y} &= 4 \\ y &= \tfrac{1}{4} \end{aligned}$$
$\left(1, \tfrac{1}{4}\right)$

37.
$$\begin{aligned} \tfrac{1}{x} + \tfrac{2}{y} &= 1 \\ \tfrac{2}{x} - \tfrac{1}{y} &= \tfrac{1}{3} \\ \hline \end{aligned}$$
$$\begin{aligned} \tfrac{1}{x} + \tfrac{2}{y} &= 1 \\ \tfrac{4}{x} - \tfrac{2}{y} &= \tfrac{2}{3} \\ \hline \tfrac{5}{x} &= \tfrac{5}{3} \\ x &= 3 \end{aligned}$$
$$\begin{aligned} \tfrac{1}{x} + \tfrac{2}{y} &= 1 \\ \tfrac{1}{3} + \tfrac{2}{y} &= 1 \\ \tfrac{2}{y} &= \tfrac{2}{3} \\ y &= 3 \end{aligned}$$
$(3, 3)$

38.
$$\begin{aligned} \tfrac{1}{x} + \tfrac{3}{y} &= 4 \\ \tfrac{2}{x} - \tfrac{1}{y} &= 7 \\ \hline \end{aligned}$$
$$\begin{aligned} \tfrac{1}{x} + \tfrac{3}{y} &= 4 \\ \tfrac{6}{x} - \tfrac{3}{y} &= 21 \\ \hline \tfrac{7}{x} &= 25 \\ x &= \tfrac{7}{25} \end{aligned}$$
$$\begin{aligned} \tfrac{1}{x} + \tfrac{3}{y} &= 4 \\ \tfrac{1}{7/25} + \tfrac{3}{y} &= 4 \\ \tfrac{3}{y} &= \tfrac{3}{7} \\ y = 7 &\Rightarrow \left(\tfrac{7}{25}, 7\right) \end{aligned}$$

39.
$$\begin{aligned} 3y^2 &= xy \\ 3y^2 - xy &= 0 \\ y(3y - x) &= 0 \\ y = 0 &\text{ or } x = 3y \end{aligned}$$
$$\begin{aligned} &y = 0 \\ \hline 2x^2 + xy - 84 &= 0 \\ 2x^2 + x(0) - 84 &= 0 \\ 2x^2 &= 84 \\ x^2 &= 42 \\ x &= \pm\sqrt{42} \end{aligned}$$
$\left(\sqrt{42}, 0\right), \left(-\sqrt{42}, 0\right)$
$$\begin{aligned} &x = 3y \\ \hline 2x^2 + xy - 84 &= 0 \\ 2(3y)^2 + (3y)y - 84 &= 0 \\ 18y^2 + 3y^2 - 84 &= 0 \\ 21y^2 &= 84 \\ y^2 = 4 &\Rightarrow y = \pm 2 \end{aligned}$$
$(6, 2), (-6, -2)$

40. $x^2 + y^2 = 10 \Rightarrow x^2 = 10 - y^2$

$$\begin{aligned} 2x^2 - 3y^2 &= 5 \\ 2(10 - y^2) - 3y^2 &= 5 \\ 20 - 2y^2 - 3y^2 &= 5 \\ 15 &= 5y^2 \\ 3 &= y^2 \end{aligned}$$

$y = \sqrt{3}$

$$\begin{aligned} x^2 &= 10 - \left(\sqrt{3}\right)^2 \\ x^2 &= 7 \\ x &= \pm\sqrt{7} \end{aligned}$$

$\left(\sqrt{7}, \sqrt{3}\right), \left(-\sqrt{7}, \sqrt{3}\right)$

$y = -\sqrt{3}$

$$\begin{aligned} x^2 &= 10 - \left(-\sqrt{3}\right)^2 \\ x^2 &= 7 \\ x &= \pm\sqrt{7} \end{aligned}$$

$\left(\sqrt{7}, -\sqrt{3}\right), \left(-\sqrt{7}, -\sqrt{3}\right)$

41. $xy = \frac{1}{6} \Rightarrow y = \frac{1}{6x}$

$$\begin{aligned} y + x &= 5xy \\ \frac{1}{6x} + x &= \frac{5x}{6x} \\ 1 + 6x^2 &= 5x \\ 6x^2 - 5x + 1 &= 0 \\ (2x - 1)(3x - 1) &= 0 \end{aligned}$$

$x = \frac{1}{2}$: $y = \dfrac{1}{6(1/2)} = \dfrac{1}{3}$, $\left(\frac{1}{2}, \frac{1}{3}\right)$

$x = \frac{1}{3}$: $y = \dfrac{1}{6(1/3)} = \dfrac{1}{2}$, $\left(\frac{1}{3}, \frac{1}{2}\right)$

42. $xy = \frac{1}{12} \Rightarrow y = \frac{1}{12x}$

$$\begin{aligned} y + x &= 7xy \\ \frac{1}{12x} + x &= \frac{7x}{12x} \\ 1 + 12x^2 &= 7x \\ 12x^2 - 7x + 1 &= 0 \\ (4x - 1)(3x - 1) &= 0 \end{aligned}$$

$x = \frac{1}{4}$: $y = \dfrac{1}{12(1/4)} = \dfrac{1}{3}$, $\left(\frac{1}{4}, \frac{1}{3}\right)$

$x = \frac{1}{3}$: $y = \dfrac{1}{12(1/3)} = \dfrac{1}{4}$, $\left(\frac{1}{3}, \frac{1}{4}\right)$

43. Let x = width and y = length.

$$\begin{cases} xy = 63 \\ 2x + 2y = 32 \end{cases}$$

$xy = 63 \Rightarrow y = \frac{63}{x}$

$$\begin{aligned} 2x + 2y &= 32 \\ 2x + 2\left(\frac{63}{x}\right) &= 32 \\ 2x^2 + 126 &= 32x \\ 2x^2 - 32x + 126 &= 0 \\ 2(x - 9)(x - 7) &= 0 \end{aligned}$$

$x = 9$: $y = \frac{63}{9} = 7$

$x = 7$: $y = \frac{63}{7} = 9$

The dimensions are 9 cm by 7 cm.

44. Let x = width and y = length.

$$\begin{cases} xy = 2880 \\ 2x + 2y = 216 \end{cases}$$

$xy = 2880 \Rightarrow y = \frac{2880}{x}$

$$\begin{aligned} 2x + 2y &= 216 \\ 2x + 2\left(\frac{2880}{x}\right) &= 216 \\ 2x^2 + 5760 &= 216x \\ 2x^2 - 216x + 5760 &= 0 \\ 2(x - 60)(x - 48) &= 0 \end{aligned}$$

$x = 60$: $y = \frac{2880}{60} = 48$

$x = 48$: $y = \frac{2880}{48} = 60$

The dimensions are 48 in. by 60 in.

45. Let x = width and y = length.

$$\begin{cases} xy = 8000 \\ 2x + y = 260 \end{cases}$$

$xy = 8000 \Rightarrow y = \frac{8000}{x}$

$$\begin{aligned} 2x + y &= 260 \\ 2x + \left(\frac{8000}{x}\right) &= 260 \\ 2x^2 + 8000 &= 260x \\ 2x^2 - 260x + 8000 &= 0 \\ 2(x - 50)(x - 80) &= 0 \end{aligned}$$

$x = 50$: $y = \frac{8000}{50} = 160$

$x = 80$: $y = \frac{8000}{80} = 100$

The dimensions are 50 ft by 160 ft or 80 ft by 100 ft.

46. Let $x =$ Grant's principal.

	I	P	r
Grant	225	x	$\frac{225}{x}$
Jeff	240	$x+500$	$\frac{240}{x+500}$

$$\boxed{\text{Jeff's rate}} = \boxed{\text{Grant's rate}} - 0.01$$

$$\frac{240}{x+500} = \frac{225}{x} - 0.01$$

$$240x = 225(x+500) - 0.01x(x+500)$$

$$0.01x^2 + 20x - 112{,}500 = 0$$

$$x^2 + 2000x - 11{,}250{,}000 = 0$$

$$(x-2500)(x+4500) = 0$$

$x - 2500 = 0$ **or** $x + 4500 = 0$

$x = 2500$ $\qquad x = -4500 \Rightarrow$ Grant invested \$2500 at 9% interest.

47. Let $x =$ Carol's principal.

	I	P	r
Carol	67.50	x	$\frac{67.50}{x}$
John	94.50	$x+150$	$\frac{94.50}{x+150}$

$$\boxed{\text{John's rate}} = \boxed{\text{Carol's rate}} + 0.015$$

$$\frac{94.50}{x+150} = \frac{67.50}{x} + 0.015$$

$$94.5x = 67.5(x+150) + 0.015x(x+150)$$

$$0.015x^2 - 24.75x + 10{,}125 = 0$$

$$x^2 - 1650x + 675{,}000 = 0$$

$$(x-750)(x-900) = 0$$

$x - 750 = 0$ **or** $x - 900 = 0$ $\qquad$ Carol invested either \$750 at 9% or

$x = 750$ $\qquad x = 900 \Rightarrow$ she invested \$900 at 7.5% interest.

48. Let $r =$ Jim's rate. Then his brother's rate is $r - 17$.

	Rate	Time	Dist.
Jim's trip	r	$\frac{306}{r}$	306
Brother's trip	$r-17$	$\frac{306}{r-17}$	306

$$\boxed{\text{Jim's time}} = \boxed{\text{Brother's time}} - 1.5$$

$$\frac{306}{r} = \frac{306}{r-17} - 1.5$$

$$306(r-17) = 306r - 1.5r(r-17)$$

$$1.5r^2 - 25.5r - 5202 = 0$$

$$r^2 - 17r - 3468 = 0$$

$$(r-68)(r+51) = 0$$

$r - 68 = 0$ **or** $r + 51 = 0$

$r = 68$ $\qquad r = -51$ $\quad$ Jim drove 68 miles per hour for 4.5 hours.

49. $\begin{cases} y = \frac{1}{10}x \\ y = -\frac{1}{300}x^2 + \frac{1}{5}x \end{cases}$

$$\frac{1}{10}x = -\frac{1}{300}x^2 + \frac{1}{5}x$$
$$30x = -x^2 + 60x$$
$$x^2 - 30x = 0$$
$$x(x - 30) = 0$$
$$x = 0 \quad \textbf{or} \quad x - 30 = 0$$
$$x = 30$$
$$x = 30 \Rightarrow y = \tfrac{1}{10}(30) = 3 \quad \boxed{(30, 3)}$$

50. $\begin{cases} y = \frac{1}{3}x \\ y = -\frac{1}{6}x^2 + 2x \end{cases}$

$$\frac{1}{3}x = -\frac{1}{6}x^2 + 2x$$
$$2x = -x^2 + 12x$$
$$x^2 - 10x = 0$$
$$x(x - 10) = 0$$
$$x = 0 \quad \textbf{or} \quad x - 10 = 0$$
$$x = 10$$
$$x = 10 \Rightarrow y = \tfrac{1}{3}(10) = \tfrac{10}{3}$$
$$\sqrt{(10-0)^2 + \left(\tfrac{10}{3} - 0\right)^2} = \sqrt{100 + \frac{100}{9}}$$
$$= \sqrt{\frac{1000}{9}}$$
$$= \frac{10\sqrt{10}}{3} \text{ mi}$$

51. $\begin{cases} y = x^2 \\ x + y = 2 \end{cases}$

$$x + y = 2$$
$$x + x^2 = 2$$
$$x^2 + x - 2 = 0$$
$$(x + 2)(x - 1) = 0$$
$$x + 2 = 0 \quad \textbf{or} \quad x - 1 = 0$$
$$x = -2 \qquad\qquad x = 1$$
$$x = -2 \Rightarrow y = (-2)^2 = 4$$
$$x = 1 \Rightarrow y = 1^2 = 1$$

There are potential collision points at $(-2, 4)$ and $(1, 1)$.

52. $\begin{cases} y = x^2 + 1 \\ x + y = -4 \end{cases}$

$$x + y = -4$$
$$x + x^2 + 1 = -4$$
$$x^2 + x + 5 = 0$$

The two solutions to this equation are not real, so there is no danger of collision.

53. $\begin{cases} x = 2y \\ (x-120)^2 + y^2 = 100^2 \end{cases}$

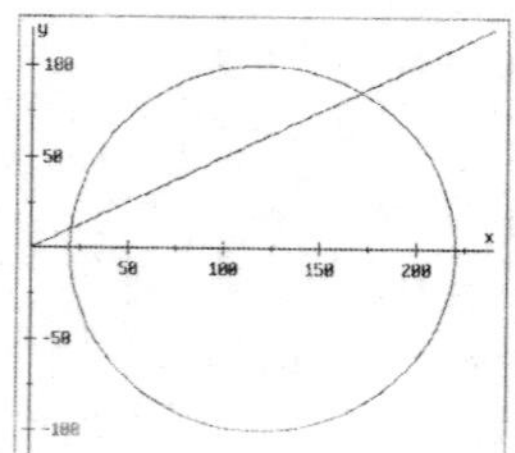

The x-coordinate of the point where the line crosses the circle closest to the origin has the approximate coordinates $(20.5, 10.25)$. The distance to the origin is about 23 miles.

54. $\begin{cases} x = 2y \\ (x-120)^2 + y^2 = 100^2 \end{cases}$

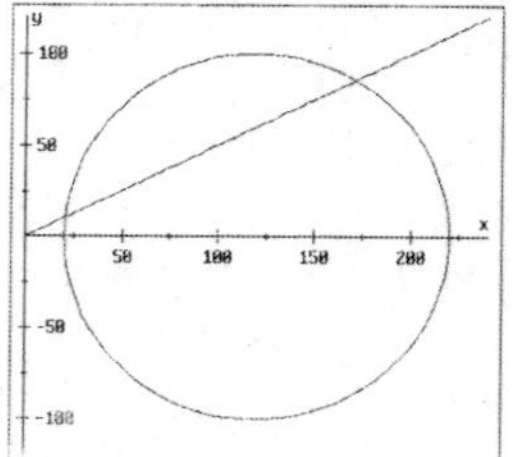

The x-coordinate of the point where the line crosses the circle farthest from the origin has the approximate coordinates $(171.5, 85.7)$. The distance to the point found in **#53** is about 169 miles.

55-60. Answers may vary.

61. $y = \dfrac{3x+1}{x-1}$
Vertical: $x = 1$; Horizontal: $y = \frac{3}{1} = 3$
Slant: none

62. $y = \dfrac{x^2+3}{x-1} = x + 1 + \dfrac{4}{x-1}$
Vertical: $x = 1$; Horizontal: none
Slant: $y = x + 1$

63. $y = \dfrac{3x+1}{x^2-1} = \dfrac{3x+1}{(x-1)(x+1)}$
Vertical: $x = 1, x = -1$
Horizontal: $y = 0$; Slant: none

64. $y = \dfrac{x^2+3}{x^2+1}$
Vertical: none; Horizontal: $y = \frac{1}{1} = 1$
Slant: none

65. $f(x) = \dfrac{3x^2+5}{5x^2+3}$; Replace x with $-x$:
Identical $\Rightarrow$ symmetric about y-axis

66. $f(x) = \dfrac{3x^3+5}{5x^2+3}$; Replace x with $-x$:
No special result $\Rightarrow$ no symmetry

67. $f(x) = \dfrac{3x^3}{5x^2+3}$; Replace x with $-x$:
Opposite $\Rightarrow$ symmetric about origin

68. $f(x) = \dfrac{3x^4+8}{2x^2-5}$; Replace x with $-x$:
Identical $\Rightarrow$ symmetric about y-axis

Chapter 7 Review (page 711)

1. $$\begin{aligned} (x-h)^2 + (y-k)^2 &= r^2 \\ (x-0)^2 + (y-0)^2 &= 4^2 \\ x^2 + y^2 &= 16 \end{aligned}$$

2. $r = \sqrt{(6-0)^2 + (8-0)^2} = 10$
$$\begin{aligned} (x-h)^2 + (y-k)^2 &= r^2 \\ (x-0)^2 + (y-0)^2 &= 10^2 \\ x^2 + y^2 &= 100 \end{aligned}$$

3.
$$(x-h)^2+(y-k)^2=r^2$$
$$(x-3)^2+(y-(-2))^2=5^2$$
$$(x-3)^2+(y+2)^2=25$$

4.
$$r=\sqrt{(-2-1)^2+(4-0)^2}=5$$
$$(x-h)^2+(y-k)^2=r^2$$
$$(x-(-2))^2+(y-4)^2=5^2$$
$$(x+2)^2+(y-4)^2=25$$

5.
$$C\left(\frac{-2+12}{2},\frac{4+16}{2}\right)=C(5,10)$$
$$r=\sqrt{(12-5)^2+(16-10)^2}=\sqrt{85}$$
$$(x-h)^2+(y-k)^2=r^2$$
$$(x-5)^2+(y-10)^2=\left(\sqrt{85}\right)^2$$
$$(x-5)^2+(y-10)^2=85$$

6.
$$C\left(\frac{-3+7}{2},\frac{-6+10}{2}\right)=C(2,2)$$
$$r=\sqrt{(7-2)^2+(10-2)^2}=\sqrt{89}$$
$$(x-h)^2+(y-k)^2=r^2$$
$$(x-2)^2+(y-2)^2=\left(\sqrt{89}\right)^2$$
$$(x-2)^2+(y-2)^2=89$$

7.
$$x^2+y^2-6x+4y=3$$
$$x^2-6x+y^2+4y=3$$
$$x^2-6x+9+y^2+4y+4=3+9+4$$
$$(x-3)^2+(y+2)^2=16$$

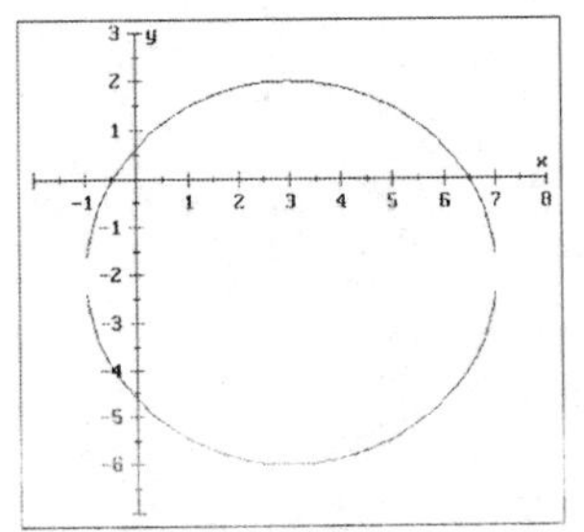

8.
$$x^2+4x+y^2-10y=-13$$
$$x^2+4x+4+y^2-10y+25=-13+4+25$$
$$(x+2)^2+(y-5)^2=16$$

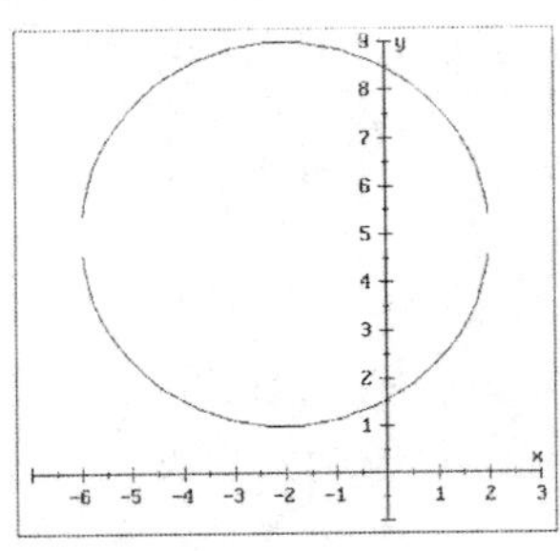

9. Horizontal
$$(y-0)^2=4p(x-0)$$
$$(4-0)^2=4p(-8-0)$$
$$16=-32p$$
$$-2=4p$$
$$y^2=-2x$$

10. Vertical
$$(x-0)^2=4p(y-0)$$
$$(-8-0)^2=4p(4-0)$$
$$64=16p$$
$$16=4p$$
$$x^2=16y$$

11. Vertical
$$(x+2)^2=4p(y-3)$$
$$(-4+2)^2=4p(-8-3)$$
$$4=4p(-11)$$
$$-\frac{4}{11}=4p$$
$$(x+2)^2=-\frac{4}{11}(y-3)$$

12.
$$x^2 - 4y - 2x + 9 = 0$$
$$x^2 - 2x = 4y - 9$$
$$x^2 - 2x + 1 = 4y - 9 + 1$$
$$(x - 1)^2 = 4(y - 2)$$

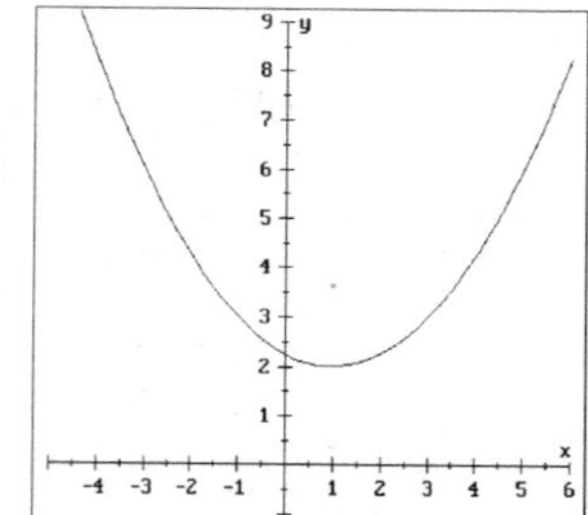

13.
$$y^2 - 6y = 4x - 13$$
$$y^2 - 6y + 9 = 4x - 13 + 9$$
$$(y - 3)^2 = 4(x - 1)$$

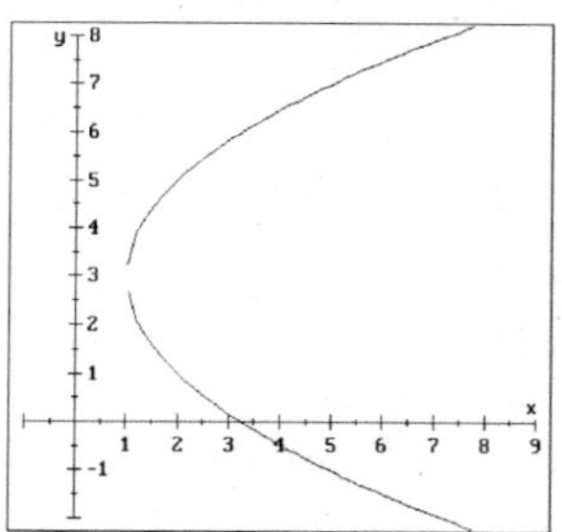

14. $a = 6, b = 4$, horizontal

$$\frac{x^2}{36} + \frac{y^2}{16} = 1$$

15. $a = 5, b = 2$, vertical

$$\frac{x^2}{4} + \frac{y^2}{25} = 1$$

16. $a = 4, b = 3$, horizontal $\Rightarrow \dfrac{(x + 2)^2}{16} + \dfrac{(y - 3)^2}{9} = 1$

17.
$$4x^2 + y^2 - 16x + 2y = -13$$
$$4(x^2 - 4x) + y^2 + 2y = -13$$
$$4(x^2 - 4x + 4) + y^2 + 2y + 1 = -13 + 16 + 1$$
$$4(x - 2)^2 + (y + 1)^2 = 4$$
$$\frac{(x - 2)^2}{1} + \frac{(y + 1)^2}{4} = 1$$

Center: $(2, -1)$, $a = 2$, $b = 1$, vertical

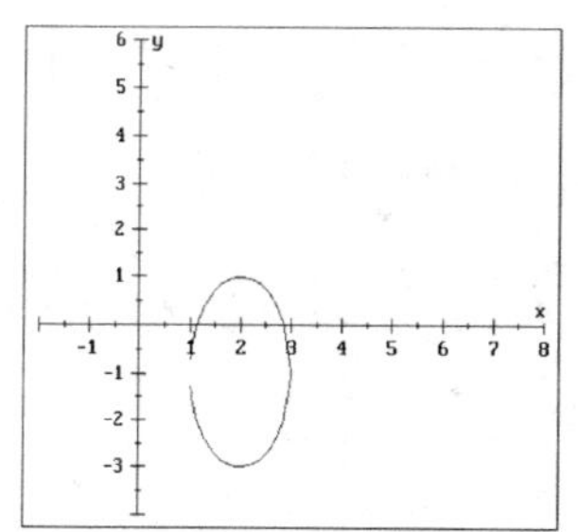

18. $a = 2, c = 4$; horizontal

$b^2 = c^2 - a^2 = 16 - 4 = 12$

$$\frac{x^2}{4} - \frac{y^2}{12} = 1$$

19. $a = 3, c = 5$; vertical

$b^2 = c^2 - a^2 = 25 - 9 = 16$

$$\frac{y^2}{9} - \frac{x^2}{16} = 1$$

20. $C(0, 3)$, $a = 3, c = 5$; horizontal

$b^2 = c^2 - a^2 = 25 - 9 = 16$

$$\frac{x^2}{9} - \frac{(y - 3)^2}{16} = 1$$

21. $C(3, 0)$, $a = 3, c = 5$; vertical

$b^2 = c^2 - a^2 = 25 - 9 = 16$

$$\frac{y^2}{9} - \frac{(x - 3)^2}{16} = 1$$

22. $y = \pm \dfrac{b}{a} x \Rightarrow y = \pm \dfrac{4}{5} x$

23.
$$9x^2 - 4y^2 - 16y - 18x = 43$$
$$9(x^2 - 2x) - 4(y^2 + 4y) = 43$$
$$9(x^2 - 2x + 1) - 4(y^2 + 4y + 4) = 43 + 9 - 16$$
$$9(x-1)^2 - 4(y+2)^2 = 36$$
$$\frac{(x-1)^2}{4} - \frac{(y+2)^2}{9} = 1$$
Center: $(1, -2)$, $a = 2$, $b = 3$, horizontal

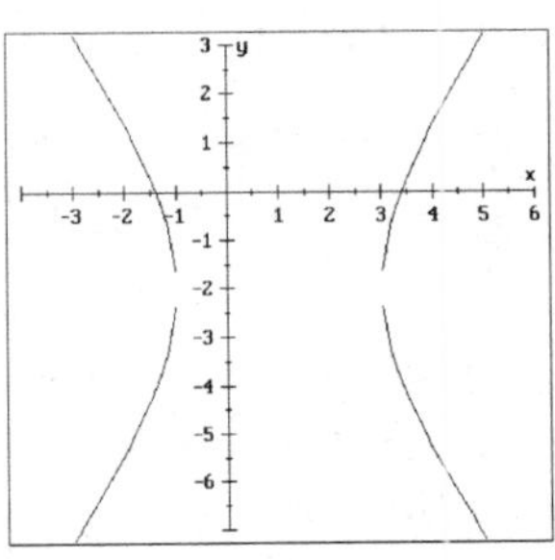

24. $4xy = 1$

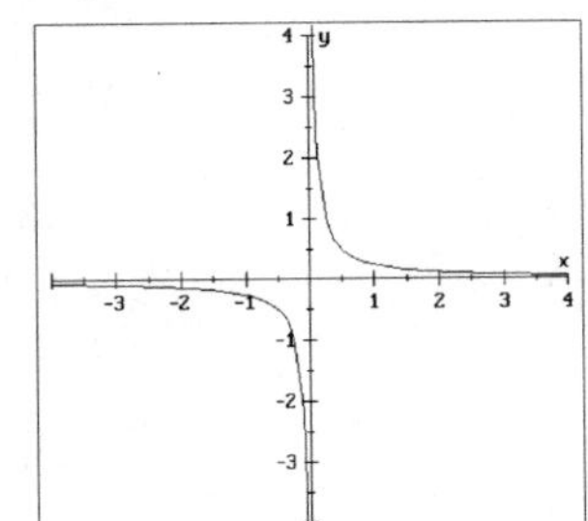

25. $\begin{cases} x^2 + y^2 = 16 \\ y = x + 4 \end{cases}$

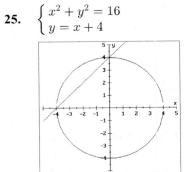

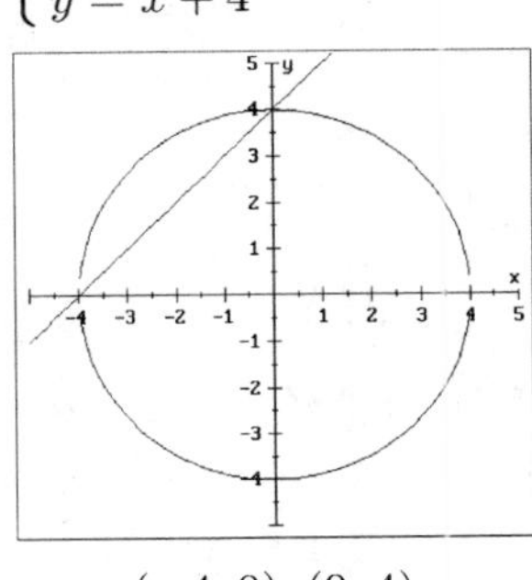

$(-4, 0)$, $(0, 4)$

26. $\begin{cases} 3x^2 + y^2 = 52 \\ x^2 - y^2 = 12 \end{cases}$

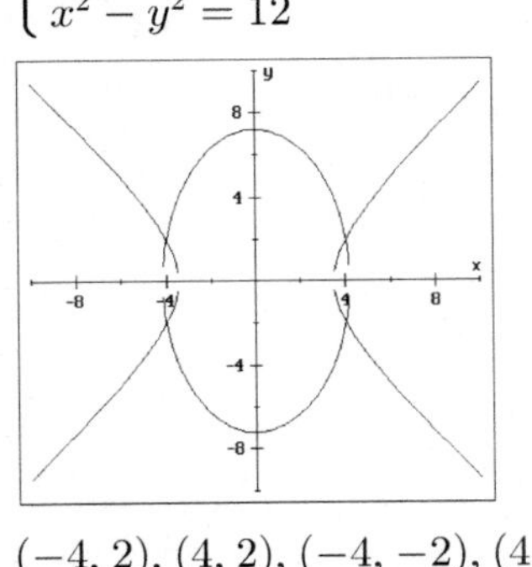

$(-4, 2)$, $(4, 2)$, $(-4, -2)$, $(4, -2)$

27. $\begin{cases} \dfrac{x^2}{16} + \dfrac{y^2}{12} = 1 \\ x^2 - \dfrac{y^2}{3} = 1 \end{cases}$

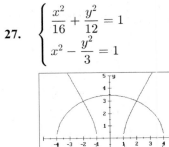

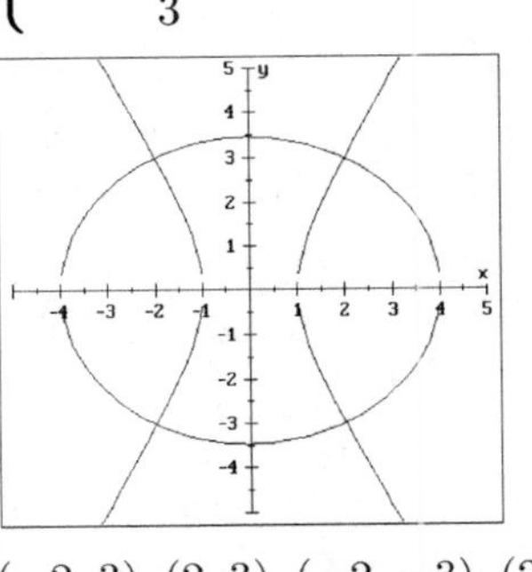

$(-2, 3)$, $(2, 3)$, $(-2, -3)$, $(2, -3)$

28.
$$\begin{aligned} 3x^2 + y^2 &= 52 \\ x^2 - y^2 &= 12 \\ \hline 4x^2 &= 64 \\ x^2 &= 16 \\ x &= \pm 4 \end{aligned} \qquad \begin{aligned} 3x^2 + y^2 &= 52 \\ 3(16) + y^2 &= 52 \\ y^2 &= 4 \\ y &= \pm 2 \end{aligned}$$
$(4, 2)$, $(-4, 2)$, $(4, -2)$, $(-4, -2)$

29. $-\sqrt{3}y + 4\sqrt{3} = 3x \Rightarrow x = \dfrac{-\sqrt{3}y + 4\sqrt{3}}{3}$

$$x^2 + y^2 = 16$$
$$\left(\frac{-\sqrt{3}y + 4\sqrt{3}}{3}\right)^2 + y^2 = 16$$
$$3y^2 - 24y + 48 + 9y^2 = 144$$
$$12y^2 - 24y - 96 = 0$$
$$12(y-4)(y+2) = 0$$

$$\frac{y = 4}{x = \dfrac{-\sqrt{3}(4) + 4\sqrt{3}}{3} = 0 \Rightarrow (0, 4)}$$

$$\frac{y = -2}{x = \dfrac{-\sqrt{3}(-2) + 4\sqrt{3}}{3} = 2\sqrt{3} \Rightarrow \left(2\sqrt{3}, -2\right)}$$

30. $\frac{x^2}{16} + \frac{y^2}{12} = 1$, $x^2 - \frac{y^2}{3} = 1$

$$3x^2 + 4y^2 = 48$$
$$3x^2 - y^2 = 3$$
$$5y^2 = 45$$

$5y^2 = 45$, $y^2 = 9$, $y = \pm 3$

$3x^2 - y^2 = 3$, $3x^2 - 9 = 3$, $3x^2 = 12$, $x^2 = 4$, $x = \pm 2 \Rightarrow (2, 3), (-2, 3), (2, -3), (-2, -3)$

Chapter 7 Test (page 719)

1.
$$(x-h)^2 + (y-k)^2 = r^2$$
$$(x-2)^2 + (y-3)^2 = 3^2$$
$$(x-2)^2 + (y-3)^2 = 9$$

2. $C\left(\dfrac{-2+6}{2}, \dfrac{-2+8}{2}\right) = C(2, 3)$
$$r = \sqrt{(6-2)^2 + (8-3)^2} = \sqrt{41}$$
$$(x-h)^2 + (y-k)^2 = r^2$$
$$(x-2)^2 + (y-3)^2 = \left(\sqrt{41}\right)^2$$
$$(x-2)^2 + (y-3)^2 = 41$$

3. $r = \sqrt{(7-2)^2 + (7-(-5))^2} = 13$
$$(x-h)^2 + (y-k)^2 = r^2$$
$$(x-2)^2 + (y-(-5))^2 = 13^2$$
$$(x-2)^2 + (y+5)^2 = 169$$

4.
$$x^2 + y^2 - 4x + 6y + 4 = 0$$
$$x^2 - 4x + y^2 + 6y = -4$$
$$x^2 - 4x + 4 + y^2 + 6y + 9 = -4 + 4 + 9$$
$$(x-2)^2 + (y+3)^2 = 9$$
$$C(2, -3),\ r = 3$$

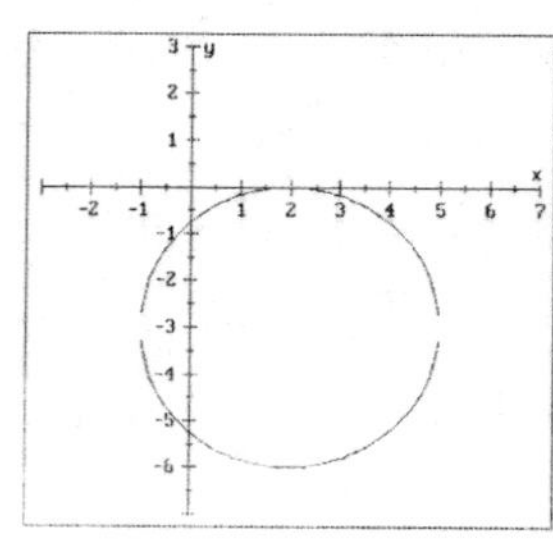

5. Vertical (up), $p = 4$

$$(x-h)^2 = 4p(y-k)$$
$$(x-3)^2 = 4(4)(y-2)$$
$$(x-3)^2 = 16(y-2)$$

6. Horizontal

$$(y+6)^2 = 4p(x-4)$$
$$(-4+6)^2 = 4p(3-4)$$
$$4 = -4p$$
$$-4 = 4p$$
$$(y+6)^2 = -4(x-4)$$

7. $(x-2)^2 = 4p(y+3)$ **OR** $(y+3)^2 = 4p(x-2)$

$$(0-2)^2 = 4p(0+3) \qquad (0+3)^2 = 4p(0-2)$$
$$4 = 4p(3) \qquad 9 = 4p(-2)$$
$$\frac{4}{3} = 4p \qquad -\frac{9}{2} = 4p$$
$$(x-2)^2 = \tfrac{4}{3}(y+3) \qquad (y+3)^2 = -\tfrac{9}{2}(x-2)$$

8.

$$x^2 - 6x - 8y = 7$$
$$x^2 - 6x = 8y + 7$$
$$x^2 - 6x + 9 = 8y + 7 + 9$$
$$(x-3)^2 = 8(y+2)$$

Vertex: $(3, -2)$, vertical

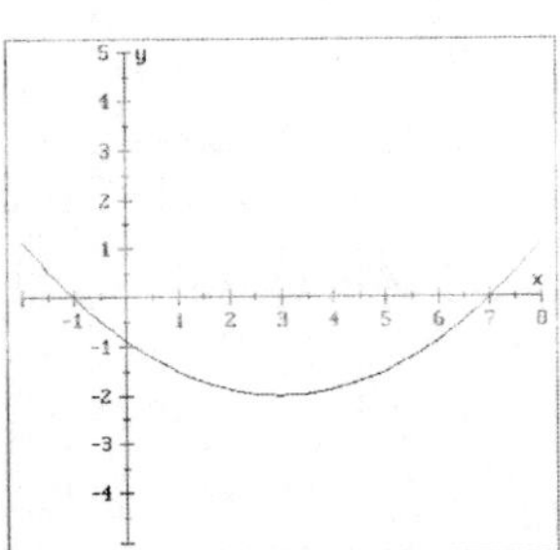

9. $a = 10$, $c = 6$, horizontal

$$b^2 = a^2 - c^2$$
$$= 100 - 36 = 64$$
$$\frac{x^2}{100} + \frac{y^2}{64} = 1$$

10. $b = 12$, $c = 5$, horizontal

$$a^2 = b^2 + c^2$$
$$= 144 + 25 = 169$$
$$\frac{x^2}{169} + \frac{y^2}{144} = 1$$

11. $a = 6$, $b = 2$, vertical

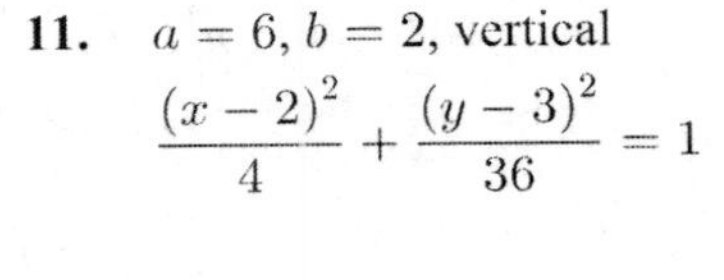

$$\frac{(x-2)^2}{4} + \frac{(y-3)^2}{36} = 1$$

12.

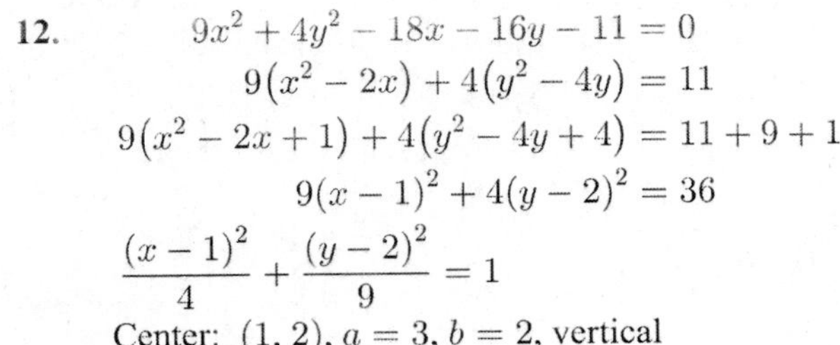

$$9x^2 + 4y^2 - 18x - 16y - 11 = 0$$
$$9(x^2 - 2x) + 4(y^2 - 4y) = 11$$
$$9(x^2 - 2x + 1) + 4(y^2 - 4y + 4) = 11 + 9 + 16$$
$$9(x-1)^2 + 4(y-2)^2 = 36$$
$$\frac{(x-1)^2}{4} + \frac{(y-2)^2}{9} = 1$$

Center: $(1, 2)$, $a = 3$, $b = 2$, vertical

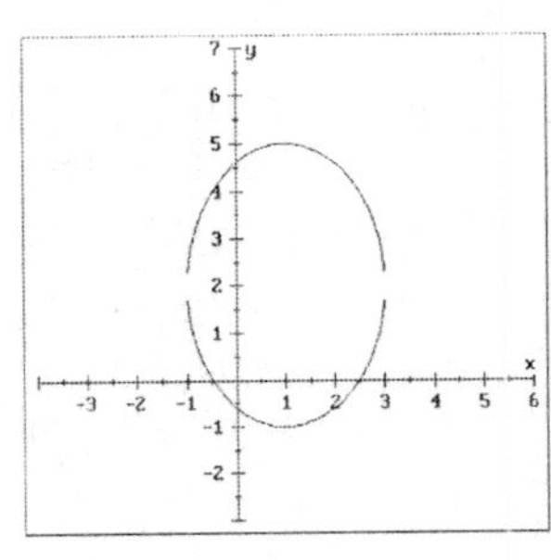

13. $a = 5, c = 13$; horizontal
$$b^2 = c^2 - a^2 = 169 - 25 = 144$$
$$\frac{x^2}{25} - \frac{y^2}{144} = 1$$

14. $C(0, 0), a = 6, c = \frac{13}{2}$
horizontal
$$b^2 = c^2 - a^2 = \frac{169}{4} - 36 = \frac{25}{4}$$
$$\frac{x^2}{36} - \frac{4y^2}{25} = 1$$

15. $a = 8, c = 10$; horizontal
$$b^2 = c^2 - a^2 = 100 - 64 = 36$$
$$\frac{(x-2)^2}{64} - \frac{(y+1)^2}{36} = 1$$

16.
$$\begin{aligned} x^2 - 4y^2 + 16y &= 8 \\ x^2 - 4(y^2 - 4y) &= 8 \\ x^2 - 4(y^2 - 4y + 4) &= 8 - 16 \\ x^2 - 4(y-2)^2 &= -8 \\ \frac{(y-2)^2}{2} - \frac{x^2}{8} &= 1 \end{aligned}$$
Center: $(0, 2)$, $a = \sqrt{2}$, $b = \sqrt{8}$, vertical

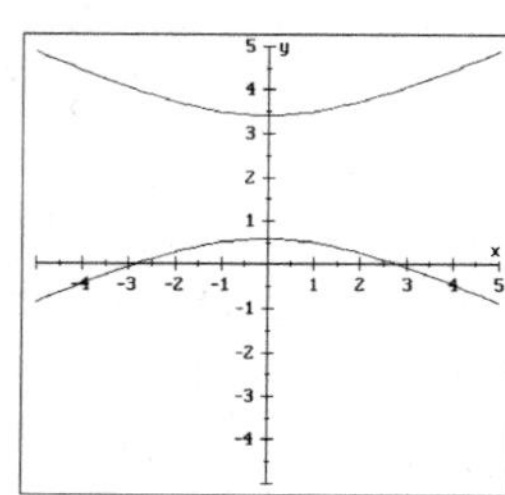

17.
$$\begin{aligned} y = x^2 - 3 \Rightarrow x^2 &= y + 3 \\ x^2 + y^2 &= 23 \\ y + 3 + y^2 &= 23 \\ y^2 + y - 20 &= 0 \\ (y-4)(y+5) &= 0 \end{aligned}$$

$y = 4$: $4 + 3 = x^2 \Rightarrow x = \pm\sqrt{7}$; $(\sqrt{7}, 4), (-\sqrt{7}, 4)$

$y = -5$: $-5 + 3 = x^2$; no real solutions

18.
$$\begin{aligned} x^2 + y^2 = 27 \Rightarrow x^2 &= 27 - y^2 \\ 2x^2 - 3y^2 &= 9 \\ 2(27 - y^2) - 3y^2 &= 9 \\ 54 - 2y^2 - 3y^2 &= 9 \\ 45 &= 5y^2 \\ 9 &= y^2 \end{aligned}$$

$y = 3$: $x^2 = 27 - 3^2 \Rightarrow x = \pm 3\sqrt{2}$; $(3\sqrt{2}, 3), (-3\sqrt{2}, 3)$

$y = -3$: $x^2 = 27 - (-3)^2 \Rightarrow x = \pm 3\sqrt{2}$; $(3\sqrt{2}, -3), (-3\sqrt{2}, -3)$

19.
$$\begin{aligned} y^2 - 4y - 6x - 14 &= 0 \\ y^2 - 4y &= 6x + 14 \\ y^2 - 4x + 4 &= 6x + 14 + 4 \\ (y-2)^2 &= 6(x+3) \Rightarrow \text{Parabola} \end{aligned}$$

20.
$$\begin{aligned} 2x^2 + 3y^2 - 4x + 12y + 8 &= 0 \\ 2(x^2 - 2x) + 3(y^2 + 4y) &= -8 \\ 2(x^2 - 2x + 1) + 3(y^2 + 4y + 4) &= -8 + 2 + 12 \\ 2(x-1)^2 + 3(y+2)^2 &= 6 \\ \frac{(x-1)^2}{3} + \frac{(y+2)^2}{2} &= 1 \Rightarrow \text{ellipse} \end{aligned}$$

Cumulative Review Exercises (page 720)

1. $64^{2/3} = \left(64^{1/3}\right)^2 = 4^2 = 16$

2. $8^{-1/3} = \dfrac{1}{8^{1/3}} = \dfrac{1}{2}$

3. $\dfrac{y^{2/3}y^{5/3}}{y^{1/3}} = \dfrac{y^{7/3}}{y^{1/3}} = y^{6/3} = y^2$

4. $\dfrac{\left(x^{5/3}\right)\left(x^{1/2}\right)}{x^{3/4}} = \dfrac{x^{13/6}}{x^{3/4}} = x^{34/24} = x^{17/12}$

5. $\left(x^{2/3} - x^{1/3}\right)\left(x^{2/3} + x^{1/3}\right) = x^{4/3} + x^{3/3} - x^{3/3} - x^{2/3} = x^{4/3} - x^{2/3}$

6. $\left(x^{-1/2} + x^{1/2}\right)^2 = \left(x^{-1/2} + x^{1/2}\right)\left(x^{-1/2} + x^{1/2}\right) = x^{-2/2} + x^0 + x^0 + x^{2/2} = \dfrac{1}{x} + 2 + x$

7. $\sqrt[3]{-27x^3} = \sqrt[3]{(-3x)^3} = -3x$

8. $\sqrt{48t^3} = \sqrt{16t^2}\sqrt{3t} = 4t\sqrt{3t}$

9. $\sqrt[3]{\dfrac{128x^4}{2x}} = \sqrt[3]{64x^3} = 4x$

10. $\sqrt{x^2 + 6x + 9} = \sqrt{(x+3)^2} = x + 3$

11. $\sqrt{50} - \sqrt{8} + \sqrt{32} = 5\sqrt{2} - 2\sqrt{2} + 4\sqrt{2} = 7\sqrt{2}$

12. $-3\sqrt[4]{32} - 2\sqrt[4]{162} + 5\sqrt[4]{48} = -3 \cdot 2\sqrt[4]{2} - 2 \cdot 3\sqrt[4]{2} + 5 \cdot 2\sqrt[4]{3} = -12\sqrt[4]{2} + 10\sqrt[4]{3}$

13. $3\sqrt{2}\left(2\sqrt{3} - 4\sqrt{12}\right) = 6\sqrt{6} - 12\sqrt{24} = 6\sqrt{6} - 12 \cdot 2\sqrt{6} = -18\sqrt{6}$

14. $\dfrac{5}{\sqrt[3]{x}} = \dfrac{5\sqrt[3]{x^2}}{\sqrt[3]{x}\sqrt[3]{x^2}} = \dfrac{5\sqrt[3]{x^2}}{x}$

15.
$$\begin{aligned}\frac{\sqrt{x}+2}{\sqrt{x}-1} &= \frac{\left(\sqrt{x}+2\right)\left(\sqrt{x}+1\right)}{\left(\sqrt{x}-1\right)\left(\sqrt{x}+1\right)}\\ &= \frac{x + 3\sqrt{x} + 2}{x - 1}\end{aligned}$$

16. $\sqrt[6]{x^3y^3} = \left(x^3y^3\right)^{1/6} = x^{3/6}y^{3/6} = x^{1/2}y^{1/2} = (xy)^{1/2} = \sqrt{xy}$

17.
$$\begin{aligned}5\sqrt{x+2} &= x + 8\\ \left(5\sqrt{x+2}\right)^2 &= (x+8)^2\\ 25(x+2) &= x^2 + 16x + 64\\ 25x + 50 &= x^2 + 16x + 64\\ 0 &= x^2 - 9x + 14\\ 0 &= (x-2)(x-7)\end{aligned}$$
$x = 2$ or $x = 7$ (both check)

18.
$$\begin{aligned}\sqrt{x} + \sqrt{x+2} &= 2\\ \sqrt{x+2} &= 2 - \sqrt{x}\\ \left(\sqrt{x+2}\right)^2 &= \left(2 - \sqrt{x}\right)^2\\ x + 2 &= 4 - 4\sqrt{x} + x\\ 4\sqrt{x} &= 2\\ \left(4\sqrt{x}\right)^2 &= 2^2\\ 16x &= 4\\ x &= \frac{1}{4}\end{aligned}$$

19.
$$\begin{aligned} 2x^2 + x - 3 &= 0 \\ x^2 + \frac{1}{2}x &= \frac{3}{2} \\ x^2 + \frac{1}{2}x + \frac{1}{16} &= \frac{24}{16} + \frac{1}{16} \\ \left(x + \tfrac{1}{4}\right)^2 &= \tfrac{25}{16} \\ x + \tfrac{1}{4} &= \pm\tfrac{5}{4} \\ x &= -\tfrac{1}{4} \pm \tfrac{5}{4} \\ x = 1 \text{ or } x &= -\tfrac{3}{2} \end{aligned}$$

20. $3x^2 + 4x - 1 = 0 \Rightarrow a = 3, b = 4, c = -1$
$$\begin{aligned} x &= \frac{-b \pm \sqrt{b^2 - 4ac}}{2a} \\ &= \frac{-4 \pm \sqrt{4^2 - 4(3)(-1)}}{2(3)} \\ &= \frac{-4 \pm \sqrt{16 + 12}}{6} \\ &= \frac{-4 \pm \sqrt{28}}{6} = \frac{-2 \pm \sqrt{7}}{3} \end{aligned}$$

21. $(3 + 5i) + (4 - 3i) = 3 + 5i + 4 - 3i = 7 + 2i$

22. $(7 - 4i) - (12 + 3i) = 7 - 4i - 12 - 3i = -5 - 7i$

23. $(2 - 3i)(2 + 3i) = 4 + 6i - 6i - 9i^2 = 4 - 9(-1) = 4 + 9 = 13 + 0i$

24. $(3 + i)(3 - 3i) = 9 - 9i + 3i - 3i^2 = 9 - 6i - 3(-1) = 9 - 6i + 3 = 12 - 6i$

25. $(3 - 2i) - (4 + i)^2 = 3 - 2i - \left(16 + 8i + i^2\right) = 3 - 2i - (15 + 8i) = 3 - 2i - 15 - 8i$
$= -12 - 10i$

26. $\dfrac{5}{3 - i} = \dfrac{5(3 + i)}{(3 - i)(3 + i)} = \dfrac{5(3 + i)}{9 - i^2} = \dfrac{5(3 + i)}{10} = \dfrac{3 + i}{2} = \dfrac{3}{2} + \dfrac{1}{2}i$

27. $|3 + 2i| = \sqrt{3^2 + 2^2} = \sqrt{13}$

28. $|5 - 6i| = \sqrt{5^2 + (-6)^2} = \sqrt{61}$

29. $2x^2 + 4x = k \Rightarrow 2x^2 + 4x - k = 0$

$a = 2, b = 4, c = -k$: Set $b^2 - 4ac = 0$.
$$\begin{aligned} b^2 - 4ac &= 0 \\ 4^2 - 4(2)(-k) &= 0 \\ 16 + 8k &= 0 \\ k &= -2 \end{aligned}$$

30. $y = \frac{1}{2}x^2 - x + 1$: $a = \frac{1}{2}, b = -1, c = 1$
$$x = -\frac{b}{2a} = -\frac{-1}{2\left(\frac{1}{2}\right)} = 1$$
$$y = \frac{1}{2}(1)^2 - 1 + 1 = \frac{1}{2}$$

31.
$$\begin{aligned} x^2 - x - 6 &> 0 \\ (x + 2)(x - 3) &> 0 \end{aligned}$$
factors $= 0$: $x = -2, x = 3$

intervals: $(-\infty, -2), (-2, 3), (3, \infty)$

interval	test number	value of $x^2 - x - 6$
$(-\infty, -2)$	-3	$+6$
$(-2, 3)$	0	-6
$(3, \infty)$	4	$+6$

Solution: $(-\infty, -2) \cup (3, \infty)$

32.
$$\begin{aligned} x^2 - x - 6 &\le 0 \\ (x + 2)(x - 3) &\le 0 \end{aligned}$$
factors $= 0$: $x = -2, x = 3$

intervals: $(-\infty, -2), (-2, 3), (3, \infty)$

interval	test number	value of $x^2 - x - 6$
$(-\infty, -2)$	-3	$+6$
$(-2, 3)$	0	-6
$(3, \infty)$	4	$+6$

Solution: $[-2, 3]$

CUMULATIVE REVIEW EXERCISES

33. $f(-1) = 3(-1)^2 + 2 = 3 + 2 = 5$

34. $(g \circ f)(2) = g(f(2)) = g(3(2)^2 + 2)$
$= g(14)$
$= 2(14) - 1 = 27$

35. $(f \circ g)(x) = f(g(x))$
$= f(2x - 1)$
$= 3(2x - 1)^2 + 2$
$= 3(4x^2 - 4x + 1) + 2$
$= 12x^2 - 12x + 3 + 2$
$= 12x^2 - 12x + 5$

36. $(g \circ f)(x) = g(f(x))$
$= g(3x^2 + 2)$
$= 2(3x^2 + 2) - 1$
$= 6x^2 + 4 - 1$
$= 6x^2 + 3$

37. $y = \log_2 x \Rightarrow 2^y = x$

38. $3^b = a \Rightarrow \log_3 a = b$

39. $\log_x 25 = 2 \Rightarrow x^2 = 25 \Rightarrow x = 5$

40. $\log_5 125 = x \Rightarrow 5^x = 125 \Rightarrow x = 3$

41. $\log_3 x = -3 \Rightarrow 3^{-3} = x \Rightarrow x = \dfrac{1}{27}$

42. $\log_5 x = 0 \Rightarrow 5^0 = x \Rightarrow x = 1$

43. $y = \log_2 x$; inverse: $y = 2^x$

44. $\log_{10} 10^x = x$, so $y = x$.

45. $\log 98 = \log(14 \cdot 7) = \log 14 + \log 7 = 1.1461 + 0.8451 = 1.9912$

46. $\log 2 = \log \dfrac{14}{7} = \log 14 - \log 7 = 1.1461 - 0.8451 = 0.3010$

47. $\log 49 = \log 7^2 = 2 \log 7 = 2(0.8451) = 1.6902$

48. $\log \dfrac{7}{5} = \log \dfrac{7}{10/2} = \log 7 - \log \dfrac{10}{2} = \log 7 - (\log 10 - \log 2) = \log 7 - \log 10 + \log 2$
$= 0.8451 - 1 + 0.3010 = 0.1461$

49.
$$\begin{aligned} 2^{x+2} &= 3^x \\ \log 2^{x+2} &= \log 3^x \\ (x+2)\log 2 &= x \log 3 \\ x\log 2 + 2\log 2 &= x\log 3 \\ 2\log 2 &= x\log 3 - x\log 2 \\ 2\log 2 &= x(\log 3 - \log 2) \\ \frac{2\log 2}{\log 3 - \log 2} &= x \end{aligned}$$

50.
$$\begin{aligned} 2\log 5 + \log x - \log 4 &= 2 \\ \log 5^2 + \log x - \log 4 &= 2 \\ \log \frac{25x}{4} &= 2 \\ 10^2 &= \frac{25x}{4} \\ 400 &= 25x \\ 16 &= x \end{aligned}$$

51.
$$\begin{aligned} A &= A_0\left(1 + \frac{r}{k}\right)^{kt} \\ &= 9000\left(1 + \frac{-0.12}{1}\right)^{1(9)} \\ &\approx \$2848.31 \end{aligned}$$

52. $\log_6 8 = \dfrac{\log 8}{\log 6} \approx 1.16056$

53. $\begin{cases} 2x + y = 5 \\ x - 2y = 0 \end{cases}$

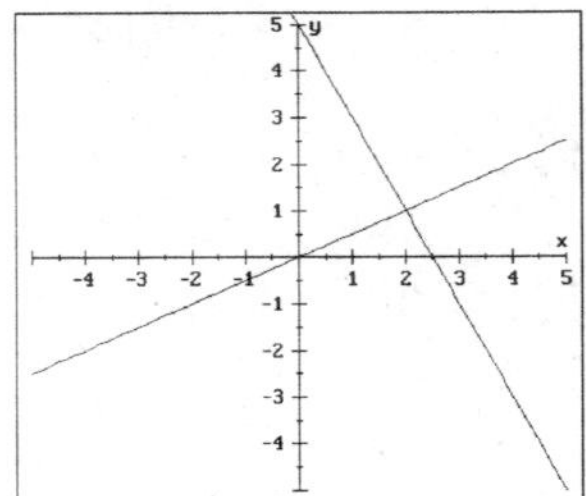

solution: (2, 1)

54. $\begin{cases} (1) & 3x + y = 4 \\ (2) & 2x - 3y = -1 \end{cases}$

Substitute $y = -3x + 4$ from (1) into (2):

$$\begin{aligned} 2x - 3y &= -1 \\ 2x - 3(-3x + 4) &= -1 \\ 2x + 9x - 12 &= -1 \\ 11x &= 11 \\ x &= 1 \end{aligned}$$

Substitute and solve for y:

$y = -3x + 4 = -3(1) + 4 = 1$

$\boxed{x = 1, y = 1}$

55.

$$\begin{aligned} x + 2y &= -2 \\ 2x - y &= 6 \Rightarrow \times 2 \end{aligned} \qquad \begin{aligned} x + 2y &= -2 \\ 4x - 2y &= 12 \\ \hline 5x &= 10 \\ x &= 2 \end{aligned} \qquad \begin{aligned} 2x - y &= 6 \\ 2(2) - y &= 6 \\ -y &= 2 \\ y &= -2 \end{aligned}$$

Solution: $\boxed{x = 2, y = -2}$

56.

$$\begin{aligned} \frac{x}{10} + \frac{y}{5} &= \frac{1}{2} \Rightarrow \times 10 \\ \frac{x}{2} - \frac{y}{5} &= \frac{13}{10} \Rightarrow \times 10 \end{aligned} \qquad \begin{aligned} x + 2y &= 5 \\ 5x - 2y &= 13 \\ \hline 6x &= 18 \\ x &= 3 \end{aligned} \qquad \begin{aligned} x + 2y &= 5 \\ 3 + 2y &= 5 \\ 2y &= 2 \\ y &= 1 \end{aligned}$$

Solution: $\boxed{x = 3, y = 1}$

57. $\begin{vmatrix} 3 & -2 \\ 1 & -1 \end{vmatrix} = 3(-1) - (-2)1 = -3 + 2 = -1$

58. $y = \dfrac{\begin{vmatrix} 4 & -1 \\ 3 & -7 \end{vmatrix}}{\begin{vmatrix} 4 & -3 \\ 3 & 4 \end{vmatrix}} = \dfrac{-25}{25} = -1$

59. $\begin{bmatrix} x \\ y \\ z \end{bmatrix} = \begin{bmatrix} 1 & 1 & 1 \\ 2 & -1 & -1 \\ 1 & -2 & 1 \end{bmatrix}^{-1} \begin{bmatrix} 1 \\ -4 \\ 4 \end{bmatrix} = \begin{bmatrix} \frac{1}{3} & \frac{1}{3} & 0 \\ \frac{1}{3} & 0 & -\frac{1}{3} \\ \frac{1}{3} & -\frac{1}{3} & \frac{1}{3} \end{bmatrix} \begin{bmatrix} 1 \\ -4 \\ 4 \end{bmatrix} = \begin{bmatrix} -1 \\ -1 \\ 3 \end{bmatrix}$

60. $\begin{bmatrix} x \\ y \\ z \end{bmatrix} = \begin{bmatrix} 1 & 2 & 3 \\ 3 & 2 & 1 \\ 2 & 3 & 1 \end{bmatrix}^{-1} \begin{bmatrix} 6 \\ 6 \\ 6 \end{bmatrix} = \begin{bmatrix} -\frac{1}{12} & \frac{7}{12} & -\frac{1}{3} \\ -\frac{1}{12} & -\frac{5}{12} & \frac{2}{3} \\ \frac{5}{12} & \frac{1}{12} & -\frac{1}{3} \end{bmatrix} \begin{bmatrix} 6 \\ 6 \\ 6 \end{bmatrix} = \begin{bmatrix} 1 \\ 1 \\ 1 \end{bmatrix}$

Exercises 8.1 (page 729)

1. power

2. degree

3. first

4. exponents

5. $7 \cdot 6 \cdot 5 \cdot 4 \cdot 3 \cdot 2 \cdot 1$

6. 1

7. $(n-1)!$

8. $11 - 7 + 1 = 5$

9. $5! = 5 \cdot 4 \cdot 3 \cdot 2 \cdot 1 = 120$

10. $-5! = -(5 \cdot 4 \cdot 3 \cdot 2 \cdot 1) = -120$

11. $3! \cdot 6! = 6 \cdot 720 = 4320$

12. $0! \cdot 7! = 1 \cdot 5040 = 5040$

13. $6! + 6! = 720 + 720 = 1440$

14. $5! - 2! = 120 - 2 = 118$

15. $\dfrac{9!}{12!} = \dfrac{9!}{12 \cdot 11 \cdot 10 \cdot 9!} = \dfrac{1}{1320}$

16. $\dfrac{8!}{5!} = \dfrac{8 \cdot 7 \cdot 6 \cdot 5!}{5!} = 8 \cdot 7 \cdot 6 = 336$

17. $\dfrac{5! \cdot 7!}{9!} = \dfrac{5! \cdot 7!}{9 \cdot 8 \cdot 7!} = \dfrac{120}{72} = \dfrac{5}{3}$

18. $\dfrac{3! \cdot 5! \cdot 7!}{1!8!} = \dfrac{3! \cdot 5! \cdot 7!}{8 \cdot 7!} = \dfrac{720}{8} = 90$

19. $\dfrac{18!}{6!(18-6)!} = \dfrac{18!}{6! \cdot 12!} = \dfrac{18 \cdot 17 \cdot 16 \cdot 15 \cdot 14 \cdot 13 \cdot 12!}{6! \cdot 12!} = \dfrac{13{,}366{,}080}{720} = 18{,}564$

20. $\dfrac{15!}{9!(15-9)!} = \dfrac{15!}{9! \cdot 6!} = \dfrac{15 \cdot 14 \cdot 13 \cdot 12 \cdot 11 \cdot 10 \cdot 9!}{9! \cdot 6!} = \dfrac{3{,}603{,}600}{720} = 5005$

21. Row 5 of Pascal's triangle: 1 5 10 10 5 1
$(a+b)^5 = a^5 + 5a^4b + 10a^3b^2 + 10a^2b^3 + 5ab^4 + b^5$

22. Row 7 of Pascal's triangle: 1 7 21 35 35 21 7 1
$(a+b)^7 = a^7 + 7a^6b + 21a^5b^2 + 35a^4b^3 + 35a^3b^4 + 21a^2b^5 + 7ab^6 + b^7$

23. Row 3 of Pascal's triangle: 1 3 3 1
$(x-y)^3 = x^3 + 3x^2(-y) + 3x(-y)^2 + (-y)^3 = x^3 - 3x^2y + 3xy^2 - y^3$

24. Row 7 of Pascal's triangle: 1 7 21 35 35 21 7 1
$(x-y)^7$
$= x^7 + 7x^6(-y) + 21x^5(-y)^2 + 35x^4(-y)^3 + 35x^3(-y)^4 + 21x^2(-y)^5 + 7x(-y)^6 + (-y)^7$
$= x^7 - 7x^6y + 21x^5y^2 - 35x^4y^3 + 35x^3y^4 - 21x^2y^5 + 7xy^6 - y^7$

25. $(a+b)^3 = a^3 + \dfrac{3!}{1!2!}a^2b + \dfrac{3!}{2!1!}ab^2 + b^3 = a^3 + 3a^2b + 3ab^2 + b^3$

26. $(a+b)^4 = a^4 + \dfrac{4!}{1!3!}a^3b + \dfrac{4!}{2!2!}a^2b^2 + \dfrac{4!}{3!1!}ab^3 + b^4 = a^4 + 4a^3b + 6a^2b^2 + 4ab^3 + b^4$

27. $(a-b)^5 = a^5 + \frac{5!}{1!4!}a^4(-b) + \frac{5!}{2!3!}a^3(-b)^2 + \frac{5!}{3!2!}a^2(-b)^3 + \frac{5!}{4!1!}a(-b)^4 + (-b)^5$
$= a^5 - 5a^4b + 10a^3b^2 - 10a^2b^3 + 5ab^4 - b^5$

28. $(x-y)^4 = x^4 + \frac{4!}{1!3!}x^3(-y) + \frac{4!}{2!2!}x^2(-y)^2 + \frac{4!}{3!1!}x(-y)^3 + (-y)^4$
$= x^4 - 4x^3y + 6x^2y^2 - 4xy^3 + y^4$

29. $(2x+y)^3 = (2x)^3 + \frac{3!}{1!2!}(2x)^2y + \frac{3!}{2!1!}(2x)y^2 + y^3 = 8x^3 + 12x^2y + 6xy^2 + y^3$

30. $(x+2y)^3 = x^3 + \frac{3!}{1!2!}x^2(2y) + \frac{3!}{2!1!}x(2y)^2 + (2y)^3 = x^3 + 6x^2y + 12xy^2 + 8y^3$

31. $(x-2y)^3 = x^3 + \frac{3!}{1!2!}x^2(-2y) + \frac{3!}{2!1!}x(-2y)^2 + (-2y)^3 = x^3 - 6x^2y + 12xy^2 - 8y^3$

32. $(2x-y)^3 = (2x)^3 + \frac{3!}{1!2!}(2x)^2(-y) + \frac{3!}{2!1!}(2x)(-y)^2 + (-y)^3 = 8x^3 - 12x^2y + 6xy^2 - y^3$

33. $(2x+3y)^4 = (2x)^4 + \frac{4!}{1!3!}(2x)^3(3y) + \frac{4!}{2!2!}(2x)^2(3y)^2 + \frac{4!}{3!1!}(2x)(3y)^3 + (3y)^4$
$= 16x^4 + 96x^3y + 216x^2y^2 + 216xy^3 + 81y^4$

34. $(2x-3y)^4 = (2x)^4 + \frac{4!}{1!3!}(2x)^3(-3y) + \frac{4!}{2!2!}(2x)^2(-3y)^2 + \frac{4!}{3!1!}(2x)(-3y)^3 + (-3y)^4$
$= 16x^4 - 96x^3y + 216x^2y^2 - 216xy^3 + 81y^4$

35. $(x-2y)^4 = x^4 + \frac{4!}{1!3!}x^3(-2y) + \frac{4!}{2!2!}x^2(-2y)^2 + \frac{4!}{3!1!}x(-2y)^3 + (-2y)^4$
$= x^4 - 8x^3y + 24x^2y^2 - 32xy^3 + 16y^4$

36. $(x+2y)^4 = x^4 + \frac{4!}{1!3!}x^3(2y) + \frac{4!}{2!2!}x^2(2y)^2 + \frac{4!}{3!1!}x(2y)^3 + (2y)^4$
$= x^4 + 8x^3y + 24x^2y^2 + 32xy^3 + 16y^4$

37. $(x-3y)^5 = x^5 + \frac{5!}{1!4!}x^4(-3y) + \frac{5!}{2!3!}x^3(-3y)^2 + \frac{5!}{3!2!}x^2(-3y)^3 + \frac{5!}{4!1!}x(-3y)^4 + (-3y)^5$
$= x^5 - 15x^4y + 90x^3y^2 - 270x^2y^3 + 405xy^4 - 243y^5$

38. $(3x-y)^5$
$= (3x)^5 + \frac{5!}{1!4!}(3x)^4(-y) + \frac{5!}{2!3!}(3x)^3(-y)^2 + \frac{5!}{3!2!}(3x)^2(-y)^3 + \frac{5!}{4!1!}(3x)(-y)^4 + (-y)^5$
$= 243x^5 - 405x^4y + 270x^3y^2 - 90x^2y^3 + 15xy^4 - y^5$

39. $$\left(\frac{x}{2}+y\right)^4=\left(\frac{x}{2}\right)^4+\frac{4!}{1!3!}\left(\frac{x}{2}\right)^3y+\frac{4!}{2!2!}\left(\frac{x}{2}\right)^2y^2+\frac{4!}{3!1!}\left(\frac{x}{2}\right)y^3+y^4$$
$$=\frac{1}{16}x^4+\frac{1}{2}x^3y+\frac{3}{2}x^2y^2+2xy^3+y^4$$

40. $$\left(x+\frac{y}{2}\right)^4=x^4+\frac{4!}{1!3!}x^3\left(\frac{y}{2}\right)+\frac{4!}{2!2!}x^2\left(\frac{y}{2}\right)^2+\frac{4!}{3!1!}x\left(\frac{y}{2}\right)^3+\left(\frac{y}{2}\right)^4$$
$$=x^4+2x^3y+\frac{3}{2}x^2y^2+\frac{1}{2}xy^3+\frac{1}{16}y^4$$

41. The 3rd term will involve b^2.
$$\frac{4!}{2!2!}a^2b^2=6a^2b^2$$

42. The 2nd term will involve $(-b)^1$.
$$\frac{4!}{3!1!}a^3(-b)=-4a^3b$$

43. The 5th term will involve b^4.
$$\frac{7!}{3!4!}a^3b^4=35a^3b^4$$

44. The 4th term will involve b^3.
$$\frac{5!}{2!3!}a^2b^3=10a^2b^3$$

45. The 6th term will involve $(-b)^5$.
$$\frac{5!}{0!5!}a^0(-b)^5=-b^5$$

46. The 7th term will involve $(-b)^6$.
$$\frac{8!}{2!6!}a^2(-b)^6=28a^2b^6$$

47. The 5th term will involve b^4.
$$\frac{17!}{13!4!}a^{13}b^4=2380a^{13}b^4$$

48. The 3rd term will involve $(-b)^2$.
$$\frac{12!}{10!2!}a^{10}(-b)^2=66a^{10}b^2$$

49. The 2nd term will involve $\left(-\sqrt{2}\right)^1$.
$$\frac{4!}{3!1!}a^3\left(-\sqrt{2}\right)^1=-4\sqrt{2}\,a^3$$

50. The 3rd term will involve $\left(-\sqrt{3}\right)^2$.
$$\frac{8!}{6!2!}a^6\left(-\sqrt{3}\right)^2=84\,a^6$$

51. The 5th term will involve $\left(\sqrt{3}b\right)^4$.
$$\frac{9!}{5!4!}a^5\left(\sqrt{3}b\right)^4=1134a^5b^4$$

52. The 4th term will involve $(-b)^3$.
$$\frac{7!}{4!3!}\left(\sqrt{2}a\right)^4(-b)^3=-140\,a^4b^3$$

53. The 3rd term will involve y^2.
$$\frac{4!}{2!2!}\left(\frac{x}{2}\right)^2y^2=\frac{3}{2}x^2y^2$$

54. The 3rd term will involve $\left(\frac{n}{2}\right)^2$.
$$\frac{8!}{6!2!}m^6\left(\frac{n}{2}\right)^2=7m^6n^2$$

55. The 10th term will involve $\left(-\frac{s}{2}\right)^9$.
$$\frac{11!}{2!9!}\left(\frac{r}{2}\right)^2\left(-\frac{s}{2}\right)^9=-\frac{55}{2048}r^2s^9$$

56. The 6th term will involve $\left(-\frac{q}{2}\right)^5$.
$$\frac{9!}{4!5!}\left(\frac{p}{2}\right)^4\left(-\frac{q}{2}\right)^5=-\frac{63}{256}p^4q^5$$

57. The 4th term will involve b^3.
$$\frac{n!}{(n-3)!3!}a^{n-3}b^3$$

58. The 5th term will involve $(-b)^4$.
$$\frac{n!}{(n-4)!4!}a^{n-4}(-b)^4 = \frac{n!}{(n-4)!4!}a^{n-4}b^4$$

59. The rth term will involve b^{r-1}.
$$\frac{n!}{(n-r+1)!(r-1)!}a^{n-r+1}b^{r-1}$$

60. The $(r+1)$th term will involve b^r.
$$\frac{n!}{(n-r)!(r)!}a^{n-r}b^r$$

61. **Answers may vary.**

62. **Answers may vary.**

63. Each term will contain $a^n\left(-\frac{1}{a}\right)^{10-n}$, or $a^n\left(-a^{n-10}\right)$. The constant term will occur when this product is equal to 1, or when the sum of the exponents equals 0.
$n + n - 10 = 0 \Rightarrow n = 5$
$$\frac{10!}{5!5!}a^5\left(-\frac{1}{a}\right)^5 = -252$$

64. Each term will contain $x^n\left(\frac{1}{x}\right)^{9-n}$, or $x^n\left(x^{n-9}\right)$. The x^5 term will occur when the sum of the exponents equals 5.
$n + n - 9 = 5 \Rightarrow n = 7$
$$\frac{9!}{7!2!}x^7\left(\frac{1}{x}\right)^2 = 36x^5\text{; coefficient} = 36$$

65. $\dfrac{n!}{0!(n-0)!} = \dfrac{n!}{0!n!} = \dfrac{n!}{1 \cdot n!} = 1$

66. $\dfrac{n!}{n!(n-n)!} = \dfrac{n!}{n!0!} = \dfrac{n!}{n! \cdot 1} = 1$

67-70. Answers may vary.

71. $3x^3y^2z^4 - 6xyz^5 + 15x^2yz^2 = 3xyz^2(x^2yz^2 - 2z^3 + 5x)$

72. $3z^2 - 15tz + 12t^2 = 3(z^2 - 5tz + 4t^2) = 3(z-4t)(z-t)$

73. $a^4 - b^4 = (a^2+b^2)(a^2-b^2) = (a^2+b^2)(a+b)(a-b)$

74. $3r^4 - 36r^3 - 135r^2 = 3r^2(r^2 - 12r - 45) = 3r^2(r-15)(r+3)$

75. $\dfrac{\frac{1}{x}+\frac{1}{3}}{\frac{1}{x}-\frac{1}{3}} = \dfrac{3x\left(\frac{1}{x}+\frac{1}{3}\right)}{3x\left(\frac{1}{x}-\frac{1}{3}\right)} = \dfrac{3+x}{3-x}$

76. $\dfrac{x-\frac{1}{y}}{y-\frac{1}{x}} = \dfrac{xy\left(x-\frac{1}{y}\right)}{xy\left(y-\frac{1}{x}\right)} = \dfrac{x^2y-x}{xy^2-y} = \dfrac{x(xy-1)}{y(xy-1)} = \dfrac{x}{y}$

Exercises 8.2 (page 738)

1. domain

2. domain

3. series

4. finite

SECTION 8.2

5. infinite

6. alternating

7. Summation notation

8. sum

9. 6

10. $\sum_{k=1}^{5}(3k) = 3\sum_{k=1}^{5}k$

11. $5c$

12. sum

13. $f(1) = 5(1)(1-1) = 0$ $\quad f(2) = 5(2)(2-1) = 10$ $\quad f(3) = 5(3)(3-1) = 30$
$f(4) = 5(4)(4-1) = 60$ $\quad f(5) = 5(5)(5-1) = 100$ $\quad f(6) = 5(6)(6-1) = 150$

14. $f(1) = 1\left(\frac{1-1}{2}\right)\left(\frac{1-2}{3}\right) = 0$ $\quad f(2) = 2\left(\frac{2-1}{2}\right)\left(\frac{2-2}{3}\right) = 0$ $\quad f(3) = 3\left(\frac{3-1}{2}\right)\left(\frac{3-2}{3}\right) = 1$
$f(4) = 4\left(\frac{4-1}{2}\right)\left(\frac{4-2}{3}\right) = 4$ $\quad f(5) = 5\left(\frac{5-1}{2}\right)\left(\frac{5-2}{3}\right) = 10$ $\quad f(6) = 6\left(\frac{6-1}{2}\right)\left(\frac{6-2}{3}\right) = 20$

15. 1, 6, 11, 16, ... Add 5 to get the next term. The next term is 21.

16. 1, 8, 27, 64, ... Each term is a perfect cube. The next term is $5^3 = 125$.

17. a, $a+d$, $a+2d$, $a+3d$, ... Add d to get the next term. The next term is $a+4d$.

18. a, ar, ar^2, ar^3, ... Multiply by r to get the next term. The next term is ar^4.

19. 1, 3, 6, 10, ... The difference between terms increases by 1 each time. The next term is $10+5=15$.

20. 20, 17, 13, 8, ... The difference between terms increases 1 each time. The next term is $8-6=2$.

21. $1+2+3+4+5=15$

22. $2+4+6+8+10=30$

23. $3+3+3+3+3=15$

24. $4+4+4+4+4=20$

25. $2\left(\frac{1}{3}\right)^1 + 2\left(\frac{1}{3}\right)^2 + 2\left(\frac{1}{3}\right)^3 + 2\left(\frac{1}{3}\right)^4 + 2\left(\frac{1}{3}\right)^5 = \frac{2}{3} + \frac{2}{9} + \frac{2}{27} + \frac{2}{81} + \frac{2}{243} = \frac{242}{243}$

26. $(-1)^n = -1 + 1 + (-1) + 1 + (-1) = -1$

27. $[3(1)-2] + [3(2)-2] + [3(3)-2] + [3(4)-2] + [3(5)-2] = 1+4+7+10+13 = 35$

28. $[2(1)+1] + [2(2)+1] + [2(3)+1] + [2(4)+1] + [2(5)+1] = 3+5+7+9+11 = 35$

29. $a_1 = 3$
$a_2 = 2a_1 + 1 = 2(3) + 1 = 7$
$a_3 = 2a_2 + 1 = 2(7) + 1 = 15$
$a_4 = 2a_3 + 1 = 2(15) + 1 = 31$

30. $a_1 = -5$
$a_2 = -a_1 - 3 = -(-5) - 3 = 2$
$a_3 = -a_2 - 3 = -(2) - 3 = -5$
$a_4 = -a_3 - 3 = -(-5) - 3 = 2$

31. $a_1 = -4$
$a_2 = \frac{a_1}{2} = \frac{-4}{2} = -2$
$a_3 = \frac{a_2}{2} = \frac{-2}{2} = -1$
$a_4 = \frac{a_3}{2} = \frac{-1}{2} = -\frac{1}{2}$

32. $a_1 = 0$
$a_2 = 2a_1^2 = 2(0)^2 = 0$
$a_3 = 2a_2^2 = 2(0)^2 = 0$
$a_4 = 2a_3^2 = 2(0)^2 = 0$

33. $a_1 = k$
$a_2 = a_1^2 = k^2$
$a_3 = a_2^2 = (k^2)^2 = k^4$
$a_4 = a_3^2 = (k^4)^2 = k^8$

34. $a_1 = 3$
$a_2 = ka_1 = 3k$
$a_3 = ka_2 = k(3k) = 3k^2$
$a_4 = ka_3 = k(3k^2) = 3k^3$

35. $a_1 = 8$
$a_2 = \frac{2a_1}{k} = \frac{2(8)}{k} = \frac{16}{k}$
$a_3 = \frac{2a_2}{k} = \frac{2\left(\frac{16}{k}\right)}{k} = \frac{32}{k^2}$
$a_4 = \frac{2a_3}{k} = \frac{2\left(\frac{32}{k^2}\right)}{k} = \frac{64}{k^3}$

36. $a_1 = m$
$a_2 = \frac{a_1^2}{m} = \frac{m^2}{m} = m$
$a_3 = \frac{a_2^2}{m} = \frac{m^2}{m} = m$
$a_4 = \frac{a_3^2}{m} = \frac{m^2}{m} = m$

37. alternating **38.** not alternating **39.** not alternating **40.** alternating

41. $\sum_{k=1}^{5} 2k = 2\sum_{k=1}^{5} k = 2(1+2+3+4+5) = 2(15) = 30$

42. $\sum_{k=3}^{6} 3k = 3\sum_{k=3}^{6} k = 3(3+4+5+6) = 3(18) = 54$

43. $\sum_{k=3}^{4} (-2k^2) = -2\sum_{k=3}^{4} k^2 = -2(3^2+4^2) = -2(25) = -50$

44. $\sum_{k=1}^{100} 5 = 100(5) = 500$

45. $\sum_{k=1}^{5} (3k-1) = 3\sum_{k=1}^{5} k - \sum_{k=1}^{5} 1 = 3(1+2+3+4+5) - 5(1) = 3(15) - 5 = 40$

46. $\sum_{n=2}^{5} (n^2+3n) = \sum_{n=2}^{5} n^2 + 3\sum_{n=2}^{5} n = (2^2+3^2+4^2+5^2) + 3(2+3+4+5)$
$= (4+9+16+25) + 3(14) = 54 + 42 = 96$

47. $\sum_{k=1}^{1000} \frac{1}{2} = 1000\left(\frac{1}{2}\right) = 500$

48. $\sum_{x=4}^{5} \frac{2}{x} = \frac{2}{4} + \frac{2}{5} = \frac{1}{2} + \frac{2}{5} = \frac{5}{10} + \frac{4}{10} = \frac{9}{10}$

49. $\sum_{x=3}^{4} \frac{1}{x} = \frac{1}{3} + \frac{1}{4} = \frac{4}{12} + \frac{3}{12} = \frac{7}{12}$

50. $$\sum_{x=2}^{6}(3x^2+2x)-3\sum_{x=2}^{6}x^2=\sum_{x=2}^{6}(3x^2+2x)-\sum_{x=2}^{6}3x^2$$
$$=\sum_{x=2}^{6}2x=2\sum_{x=2}^{6}x=2(2+3+4+5+6)=2(20)=40$$

51. $$\sum_{x=1}^{4}(4x+1)^2-\sum_{x=1}^{4}(4x-1)^2=\sum_{x=1}^{4}(16x^2+8x+1)-\sum_{x=1}^{4}(16x^2-8x+1)$$
$$=\sum_{x=1}^{4}16x=16\sum_{x=1}^{4}x=16(1+2+3+4)=16(10)=160$$

52. $$\sum_{x=0}^{10}(2x-1)^2+4\sum_{x=0}^{10}x(1-x)=\sum_{x=0}^{10}(4x^2-4x+1)+4\sum_{x=0}^{10}(x-x^2)$$
$$=\sum_{x=0}^{10}(4x^2-4x+1)+\sum_{x=0}^{10}(4x-4x^2)=\sum_{x=0}^{10}1=11(1)=11$$

53. $$\sum_{x=6}^{8}(5x-1)^2+\sum_{x=6}^{8}(10x-1)=\sum_{x=6}^{8}(25x^2-10x+1)+\sum_{x=6}^{8}(10x-1)$$
$$=\sum_{x=6}^{8}(25x^2)=25\sum_{x=6}^{8}x^2=25(6^2+7^2+8^2)=3725$$

54. $$\sum_{x=2}^{7}(3x+1)^2-3\sum_{x=2}^{7}x(3x+2)=\sum_{x=2}^{7}(9x^2+6x+1)-3\sum_{x=2}^{7}(3x^2+2x)$$
$$=\sum_{x=2}^{7}(9x^2+6x+1)-\sum_{x=2}^{7}(9x^2+6x)=\sum_{x=2}^{7}1=1(6)=6$$

55-58. Answers may vary.

59. $\dfrac{8}{12}=\dfrac{4}{x}$
$8x=48$
$x=6$ cm

60. $\dfrac{9}{21}=\dfrac{12}{x}$
$9x=252$
$x=28$ m

61. $AB^2+BC^2=AC^2$
$24^2+10^2=AC^2$
$676=AC^2$
$26\text{ ft}=AC$

62. $AB^2+BC^2=AC^2$
$3^2+x^2=7^2$
$9+x^2=49$
$x^2=40$
$x=\sqrt{40}=2\sqrt{10}$ in.

Exercises 8.3 (page 744)

1. $(n-1)d$

2. d

3. infinite

4. first, difference, number

5. $a_n = a + (n-1)d$

6. $S_n = \dfrac{n(a+a_n)}{2}$

7. Arithmetic means

8. $s = 16t^2$

9. 1, 3, 5, 7, 9, 11

10. $-12, -17, -22, -27, -32, -37$

11.
$$\begin{aligned} a_n &= a + (n-1)d \\ a_3 &= 5 + (3-1)d \\ 2 &= 5 + 2d \\ -3 &= 2d \\ -\frac{3}{2} &= d \Rightarrow 5, \frac{7}{2}, 2, \frac{1}{2}, -1, -\frac{5}{2} \end{aligned}$$

12.
$$\begin{aligned} a_n &= a + (n-1)d \\ a_5 &= 4 + (5-1)d \\ 12 &= 4 + 4d \\ 8 &= 4d \\ 2 &= d \Rightarrow 4, 6, 8, 10, 12, 14 \end{aligned}$$

13.
$$\begin{aligned} a_n &= a + (n-1)d \\ a_7 &= a + (7-1)\frac{5}{2} \\ 24 &= a + 6\left(\frac{5}{2}\right) \\ 24 &= a + 15 \\ 9 &= a \Rightarrow 9, \frac{23}{2}, 14, \frac{33}{2}, 19, \frac{43}{2} \end{aligned}$$

14.
$$\begin{aligned} a_n &= a + (n-1)d \\ a_{20} &= a + (20-1)(-3) \\ -49 &= a + 19(-3) \\ -49 &= a - 57 \\ 8 &= a \Rightarrow 8, 5, 2, -1, -4, -7 \end{aligned}$$

15.
$$\begin{aligned} a_n &= a + (n-1)d \\ a_{40} &= 6 + (40-1)8 \\ &= 6 + 39(8) = 6 + 312 = 318 \end{aligned}$$

16.
$$\begin{aligned} a_n &= a + (n-1)d \\ a_{35} &= 50 + (35-1)(-6) \\ &= 50 + 34(-6) = 50 - 204 = -154 \end{aligned}$$

17.
$$\begin{aligned} a_n &= a + (n-1)d \\ a_6 &= -2 + (6-1)d \\ 28 &= -2 + 5d \\ 30 &= 5d \Rightarrow d = 6 \end{aligned}$$

18.
$$\begin{aligned} a_n &= a + (n-1)d \\ a_7 &= a + (7-1)(-6) \\ -42 &= a + 6(-6) \\ -42 &= a - 36 \Rightarrow a = -6 \end{aligned}$$

19.
$$\begin{aligned} a_n &= a + (n-1)d \\ a_{55} &= -8 + (55-1)7 \\ &= -8 + 54(7) = -8 + 378 = 370 \end{aligned}$$

20. 2nd term: $-4 = a + d$ 3rd term: $6 = a + 2d$

Solve the system: $\begin{cases} a + d = -4 \\ a + 2d = 6 \end{cases}$

$a = -14,\ d = 10$

$a_{37} = -14 + 36(10) = 346$

21. 5th term $\quad$ 2nd term

$14 = a + 4d \quad 5 = a + d$

Solve the system: $\begin{cases} a + 4d = 14 \\ a + d = 5 \end{cases}$

$a = 2,\, d = 3$

$a_{15} = 2 + 14(3) = 44$

22. 4th term $\quad$ 2nd term

$13 = a + 3d \quad 3 = a + d$

Solve the system: $\begin{cases} a + 3d = 13 \\ a + d = 3 \end{cases}$

$a = -2,\, d = 5$

$a_{24} = -2 + 23(5) = 113$

23. $a = 10,\, a_5 = 20$

$20 = 10 + 4d$

$10 = 4d$

$\frac{5}{2} = d \Rightarrow 10, \boxed{\frac{25}{2}, 15, \frac{35}{2}}, 20$

24. $a = 5,\, a_7 = 15$

$15 = 5 + 6d$

$10 = 6d$

$\frac{5}{3} = d \Rightarrow 5, \boxed{\frac{20}{3}, \frac{25}{3}, 10, \frac{35}{3}, \frac{40}{3}}, 15$

25. $a = -7,\, a_6 = \frac{2}{3}$

$\frac{2}{3} = -7 + 5d$

$\frac{23}{3} = 5d$

$\frac{23}{15} = d$

$-7, \boxed{-\frac{82}{15}, -\frac{59}{15}, -\frac{12}{5}, -\frac{13}{15}}, \frac{2}{3}$

26. $a = -11,\, a_5 = -2$

$-2 = -11 + 4d$

$9 = 4d$

$\frac{9}{4} = d \Rightarrow -11, \boxed{-\frac{35}{4}, -\frac{13}{2}, -\frac{17}{4}}, -2$

27. $a = 5,\, d = 2$

$a_{15} = a + (n-1)d = 5 + 14(2) = 33$

$S_{15} = \frac{n(a + a_{15})}{2} = \frac{15(5 + 33)}{2} = 285$

28. $a = -3,\, d = -1$

$a_{10} = a + (n-1)d = -3 + 9(-1) = -12$

$S_{10} = \frac{n(a + a_{10})}{2} = \frac{10(-3 + (-12))}{2} = -75$

29. $a = \frac{27}{2},\, d = \frac{3}{2}$

$a_{20} = a + (n-1)d = \frac{27}{2} + 19\left(\frac{3}{2}\right) = 42$

$S_{20} = \frac{n(a + a_{20})}{2} = \frac{20\left(\frac{27}{2} + 42\right)}{2} = 555$

30. $a = 1,\, d = \frac{2}{3}$

$a_{10} = a + (n-1)d = 1 + 9\left(\frac{2}{3}\right) = 7$

$S_{10} = \frac{n(a + a_{10})}{2} = \frac{10(1 + 7)}{2} = 40$

31. $d = \frac{1}{2},\, a_{25} = 10$

$10 = a + 24\left(\frac{1}{2}\right)$

$10 = a + 12 \Rightarrow a = -2$

$a_{30} = a + (n-1)d = -2 + 29\left(\frac{1}{2}\right) = \frac{25}{2}$

$S_{30} = \frac{n(a + a_{30})}{2} = \frac{30\left(-2 + \frac{25}{2}\right)}{2} = 157\frac{1}{2}$

32. $a = 2,\, a_{15} = 86$

$86 = 2 + 14d$

$84 = 14d \Rightarrow d = 6$

$a_{100} = a + (n-1)d = 2 + 99(6) = 596$

$S_{100} = \frac{n(a + a_{100})}{2} = \frac{100(2 + 596)}{2} = 29{,}900$

SECTION 8.3

33. $a = 1,\ d = 1,\ n = a_{200} = 200;\ S_{200} = \dfrac{n(a + a_{200})}{2} = \dfrac{200(1 + 200)}{2} = 20{,}100$

34. $a = 1,\ d = 1,\ n = a_{1000} = 1000;\ S_{1000} = \dfrac{n(a + a_{1000})}{2} = \dfrac{1000(1 + 1000)}{2} = 500{,}500$

35. $a = 180,\ d = 180,\ n = 8 - 2 = 6$

$a_6 = a + (n - 1)d = 180 + 5(180)$

$= 1080°$

$a = 180,\ d = 180,\ n = 12 - 2 = 10$

$a_{10} = a + (n - 1)d = 180 + 9(180)$

$= 1800°$

36. $a = 5000,\ d = -200,\ n = 13$

Note: $n = 13$ occurs at the <u>beginning</u> of the 13th month, right after the 12th payment has been made

13th term $= a + (n - 1)d$

$= 5000 + 12(-200)$

$= \$2600$

37. $a = 5500,\ d = -105,\ n = 49$

Note: $n = 49$ occurs at the <u>beginning</u> of the 49th month, right after the 48th payment has been made

49th term $= a + (n - 1)d$

$= 5500 + 48(-105)$

$= \$460$

38. $a = \dfrac{1}{2},\ a_{51} = 6\dfrac{3}{4} = \dfrac{27}{4}$

$a_{51} = a + (n - 1)d$

$\dfrac{27}{4} = \dfrac{1}{2} + 50d$

$\dfrac{25}{4} = 50d \Rightarrow d = \dfrac{1}{8}$

The distance increased $\frac{1}{8}$ mile per day.

39. $a = 237{,}500;\ d = 150{,}000;$

$a_{10} = a + (n - 1)d$

$= 237{,}500 + 9(150{,}000)$

$= \$1{,}587{,}500$

40. $a_{10} = a + (n - 1)d$

$= 16 + 9(32) = 304$ feet

41. $a_3 = a + (n - 1)d$

$= 16 + 2(32) = 80$ feet

42. $a = 1,\ d = 1,\ n = 150,\ a_{150} = 150$

$S_{150} = \dfrac{n(a + a_{150})}{2} = \dfrac{150(1 + 150)}{2}$

$= 11{,}325$ bricks

43. $a = 1,\ d = 1,\ n = 20,\ a_{20} = 20$

$S = \dfrac{n(a + a_{20})}{2} = \dfrac{20(1 + 20)}{2} = 210$ logs

44. $24 + 25 + 26 + \cdots \Rightarrow a = 24,\ d = 1,\ n = 30$

$a_{30} = a + (n - 1)d = 24 + 29(1) = 53;\ S_{30} = \dfrac{n(a + a_{30})}{2} = \dfrac{30(24 + 53)}{2} = 1155$ seats

7

45-48. Answers may vary.

49.
$$\begin{aligned} x + \sqrt{x+3} &= 9 \\ \sqrt{x+3} &= 9 - x \\ \left(\sqrt{x+3}\right)^2 &= (9-x)^2 \\ x + 3 &= 81 - 18x + x^2 \\ 0 &= x^2 - 19x + 78 \\ 0 &= (x-6)(x-13) \\ x = 6 &\text{ or } x = 13 \end{aligned}$$
$x = 13$ does not check and is extraneous.

50.
$$\begin{aligned} \frac{x+3}{x} + \frac{x-3}{5} &= 2 \\ 5x\left(\frac{x+3}{x} + \frac{x-3}{5}\right) &= 5x(2) \\ 5(x+3) + x(x-3) &= 10x \\ 5x + 15 + x^2 - 3x &= 10x \\ x^2 - 8x + 15 &= 0 \\ (x-3)(x-5) &= 0 \\ x = 3 \quad &\text{or} \quad x = 5 \end{aligned}$$

51.
$$\begin{aligned} \frac{1}{x} + \frac{2}{x^2} + \frac{1}{x^3} &= 0 \\ x^3\left(\frac{1}{x} + \frac{2}{x^2} + \frac{1}{x^3}\right) &= x^3(0) \\ x^2 + 2x + 1 &= 0 \\ (x+1)(x+1) &= 0 \\ x &= -1 \end{aligned}$$

52.
$$\begin{aligned} x + 3\sqrt{x} - 10 &= 0 \\ 3\sqrt{x} &= 10 - x \\ \left(3\sqrt{x}\right)^2 &= (10-x)^2 \\ 9x &= 100 - 20x + x^2 \\ 0 &= x^2 - 29x + 100 \\ 0 &= (x-25)(x-4) \\ x = 25 &\text{ or } x = 4 \end{aligned}$$
$x = 25$ does not check and is extraneous.

53.
$$\begin{aligned} x^4 - 1 &= 0 \\ \left(x^2+1\right)\left(x^2-1\right) &= 0 \end{aligned}$$
$$\begin{aligned} x^2 + 1 &= 0 & &\textbf{OR} & x^2 - 1 &= 0 \\ x^2 &= -1 & & & x^2 &= 1 \\ x &= \pm\sqrt{-1} & & & x &= \pm\sqrt{1} \\ x &= \pm i & & & x &= \pm 1 \end{aligned}$$

54.
$$\begin{aligned} x^4 - 29x^2 + 100 &= 0 \\ \left(x^2-25\right)\left(x^2-4\right) &= 0 \\ (x+5)(x-5)(x+2)(x-2) &= 0 \\ x = \pm 5, x &= \pm 2 \end{aligned}$$

Exercises 8.4 (page 753)

1. r^{n-1}

2. first, ratio, number

3. ar^{n-1}

4. series

5. infinite

6. $S_n = \dfrac{a - ar^n}{1 - r}$, $r \neq 1$

7. Geometric means

8. $S_\infty = \dfrac{a}{1-r}$

9. 10, 20, 40, 80

10. −3, −6, −12, −24

11. −2, −6, −18, −54

12. 64, 32, 16, 8

13. $3, 3\sqrt{2}, 6, 6\sqrt{2}$

14. $2, 2\sqrt{3}, 6, 6\sqrt{3}$

15.
$$a_4 = ar^{4-1}$$
$$54 = 2r^3$$
$$27 = r^3$$
$$3 = r \Rightarrow 2, 6, 18, 54$$

16.
$$a_3 = ar^{3-1}$$
$$4 = a\left(\frac{1}{2}\right)^2$$
$$4 = \frac{1}{4}a$$
$$16 = a \Rightarrow 16, 8, 4, 2$$

17. $a = \frac{1}{4}, r = 4;\ a_6 = ar^{6-1} = \left(\frac{1}{4}\right)4^5 = 256$

18.
$$a_2 = ar^1 \qquad ar^3 = 5 \qquad r = 5:\ a = \frac{0.2}{r} = \frac{0.2}{5} = \frac{1}{25}$$
$$0.2 = ar^1 \qquad ar \cdot r^2 = 5 \qquad r = -5:\ a = \frac{0.2}{r} = \frac{0.2}{-5} = -\frac{1}{25}$$
$$a_4 = ar^3 \qquad 0.2r^2 = 5$$
$$5 = ar^3 \qquad r^2 = 25 \qquad a_8 = ar^7 \qquad a_8 = ar^7$$
$$r = \pm 5 \qquad = \frac{1}{25}(5)^7 \qquad = -\frac{1}{25}(-5)^7$$
$$= 3125 \qquad = 3125$$

19.
$$a_2 = ar^1 \qquad ar^2 = -18 \qquad r = -3:\ a = \frac{6}{r} = \frac{6}{-3} = -2$$
$$6 = ar^1 \qquad ar \cdot r = -18 \qquad a_5 = ar^4 = -2(-3)^4 = -162$$
$$a_3 = ar^2 \qquad 6r = -18$$
$$-18 = ar^2 \qquad r = -3$$

20.
$$a_2 = ar^1 \qquad ar^3 = \frac{1}{3} \qquad r = \frac{1}{3}:\ a = \frac{3}{r} = \frac{3}{1/3} = 9$$
$$3 = ar^1 \qquad ar \cdot r^2 = \frac{1}{3} \qquad r = -\frac{1}{3}:\ a = \frac{3}{r} = \frac{3}{-1/3} = -9$$
$$a_4 = ar^3 \qquad 3r^2 = \frac{1}{3} \qquad a_6 = ar^5 \qquad a_6 = ar^5$$
$$\frac{1}{3} = ar^3 \qquad r^2 = \frac{1}{9} \qquad = 9\left(\frac{1}{3}\right)^5 \qquad = -9\left(-\frac{1}{3}\right)^5$$
$$r = \pm\frac{1}{3} \qquad = \frac{1}{27} \qquad = \frac{1}{27}$$

21.
$$a_5 = ar^4$$
$$20 = 10r^4$$
$$2 = r^4$$
$\sqrt[4]{2} = r$ (problem specifies positive)

$10, \boxed{10\sqrt[4]{2}, 10\sqrt{2}, 10\sqrt[4]{8}}, 20$

22.
$$a_7 = ar^6$$
$$5 = -5r^6$$
$$-1 = r^6$$
r is not a real number $\Rightarrow$ not possible

SECTION 8.4

23. $a_6 = ar^5$
$2048 = 2r^5$
$1024 = r^5$
$4 = r$
2, $\boxed{8, 32, 128, 512}$, 2048

24. $a_5 = ar^4$
$2 = 162r^4$
$\frac{1}{81} = r^4$
$\pm\frac{1}{3} = r$
162, $\boxed{-54, 18, -6}$, 2 or 162, $\boxed{54, 18, 6}$, 2

25. $a = 4, r = 2, n = 5$

$$S_5 = \frac{a - ar^n}{1 - r} = \frac{4 - 4(2)^5}{1 - 2} = \frac{-124}{-1} = 124$$

26. $a = 9, r = 3, n = 6$

$$S_6 = \frac{a - ar^n}{1 - r} = \frac{9 - 9(3)^6}{1 - 3} = \frac{-6552}{-2} = 3276$$

27. $a = 2, r = -3, n = 10$

$$S_{10} = \frac{a - ar^n}{1 - r} = \frac{2 - 2(-3)^{10}}{1 - (-3)} = \frac{-118{,}096}{4} = -29{,}524$$

28. $a = \frac{1}{8}, r = 2, n = 12$

$$S_{12} = \frac{a - ar^n}{1 - r} = \frac{\frac{1}{8} - \frac{1}{8}(2)^{12}}{1 - 2} = \frac{-\frac{4095}{8}}{-1} = \frac{4095}{8}$$

29. $a = 3, r = \frac{3}{2}, n = 6$

$$S_6 = \frac{a - ar^n}{1 - r} = \frac{3 - 3\left(\frac{3}{2}\right)^6}{1 - \frac{3}{2}} = \frac{-\frac{1995}{64}}{-\frac{1}{2}} = \frac{1995}{32}$$

30. $a = 12, r = -\frac{1}{2}, n = 6$

$$S_6 = \frac{a - ar^n}{1 - r} = \frac{12 - 12\left(-\frac{1}{2}\right)^6}{1 - \left(-\frac{1}{2}\right)} = \frac{\frac{189}{16}}{\frac{3}{2}} = \frac{63}{8}$$

31. $a = 6, r = \frac{2}{3}$

$$S_\infty = \frac{a}{1 - r} = \frac{6}{1 - \frac{2}{3}} = \frac{6}{\frac{1}{3}} = 18$$

32. $a = 8, r = \frac{1}{2}$

$$S_\infty = \frac{a}{1 - r} = \frac{8}{1 - \frac{1}{2}} = \frac{8}{\frac{1}{2}} = 16$$

33. $a = 12, r = -\frac{1}{2}$

$$S_\infty = \frac{a}{1 - r} = \frac{12}{1 - \left(-\frac{1}{2}\right)} = \frac{12}{\frac{3}{2}} = 8$$

34. $a = 1, r = \frac{1}{3}$

$$S_\infty = \frac{a}{1 - r} = \frac{1}{1 - \frac{1}{3}} = \frac{1}{\frac{2}{3}} = \frac{3}{2}$$

35. $a = \frac{5}{10} = \frac{1}{2}, r = \frac{1}{10}$

$$S_\infty = \frac{a}{1 - r} = \frac{\frac{1}{2}}{1 - \frac{1}{10}} = \frac{\frac{1}{2}}{\frac{9}{10}} = \frac{5}{9}$$

36. $a = \frac{6}{10} = \frac{3}{5}, r = \frac{1}{10}$

$$S_\infty = \frac{a}{1 - r} = \frac{\frac{3}{5}}{1 - \frac{1}{10}} = \frac{\frac{3}{5}}{\frac{9}{10}} = \frac{2}{3}$$

37. $a = \frac{25}{100} = \frac{1}{4}, r = \frac{1}{100}$

$S_\infty = \frac{a}{1-r} = \frac{\frac{1}{4}}{1 - \frac{1}{100}} = \frac{\frac{1}{4}}{\frac{99}{100}} = \frac{25}{99}$

38. $a = \frac{37}{100}, r = \frac{1}{100}$

$S_\infty = \frac{a}{1-r} = \frac{\frac{37}{100}}{1 - \frac{1}{100}} = \frac{\frac{37}{100}}{\frac{99}{100}} = \frac{37}{99}$

39. $a = 623, r = 1.10$

$a_9 = ar^8 = 623(1.1)^8$

≈ 1335 students

$\#\text{ professors} = \frac{1335}{60} \approx 22.25$

23 professors will be needed.

40.

Down	Up
$a = 10, r = \frac{1}{2}$	$a = 5, r = \frac{1}{2}$
$S_\infty = \frac{a}{1-r}$	$S_\infty = \frac{a}{1-r}$
$= \frac{10}{1 - \frac{1}{2}}$	$= \frac{5}{1 - \frac{1}{2}}$
$= 20$	$= 10$

Total vertical distance: 30 m

41. $a = 100, r = 0.6, a_5 = 100(0.6)^4$

$= 12.96$ ft

Down	Up
$a = 100, r = 0.6$	$a = 60, r = 0.6$
$S_\infty = \frac{a}{1-r}$	$S_\infty = \frac{a}{1-r}$
$= \frac{100}{1 - 0.6}$	$= \frac{60}{1 - 0.6}$
$= 250$	$= 150$

Total vertical distance: 400 ft

42. $a = 70, r = 0.7, a_5 = 70(0.7)^4$

$= 16.807$ ft

Down	Up
$a = 100, r = 0.7$	$a = 70, r = 0.7$
$S_\infty = \frac{a}{1-r}$	$S_\infty = \frac{a}{1-r}$
$= \frac{100}{1 - 0.7}$	$= \frac{70}{1 - 0.7}$
$= 333\frac{1}{3}$	$= 233\frac{1}{3}$

Total vertical distance: $566\frac{2}{3}$ ft

43. $a = 10, r = 0.95$

$a_{14} = ar^{13} = 10(0.95)^{13}$

≈ 5.13 meters

44. $a = 1, r = 2, n = 10$

$S_{10} = \frac{a - ar^n}{1 - r} = \frac{1 - 1 \cdot 2^{10}}{1 - 2} = 1023$ names

45. $a = 1000, r = 1 + \frac{0.0675}{365}, n = 365$

$ar^{365} = 1000\left(1 + \frac{0.0675}{365}\right)^{365}$

$\approx \$1069.82$

The interest will be \$69.82.

46. $a = 1, r = 2, n = 10 \cdot 2 = 20$

$ar^{20} = 1(2)^{20} = 1{,}048{,}576$

47. $a = c, r = 0.80, n = 5 \Rightarrow ar^5 = c(0.80)^5 = 0.32768c$, or about $\frac{1}{3}c$

48.

$7\frac{1}{2}\%$ compounded annually	$7\frac{1}{4}\%$ compounded daily
$a = 1000,\ r = 1 + \frac{0.075}{1},\ n = 1$	$a = 1000,\ r = 1 + \frac{0.0725}{365},\ n = 365$
$ar^1 = 1000(1.075)^1 = \$1075$	$ar^1 = 1000\left(1 + \frac{0.0725}{365}\right)^{365} \approx \$1075.19 \Rightarrow$ Better investment

49. $a = 5 \times 10^9,\ r = 2$

$n = (3010 - 1990)/30 = 34$

$ar^{34} = 5 \times 10^9(2)^{34} \approx 8.6 \times 10^{19}$

50. $a = 1300,\ r = 1 + \frac{0.07}{1},\ n = 17$

$ar^{17} = 1300(1.07)^{17} \approx \$4106.46$

51. $a = 50{,}000;\ r = 1.06,\ n = 22$

$ar^{22} = 50{,}000(1.06)^{22} \approx \$180{,}176.87$

52. $a = 1000,\ r = 1 + \frac{0.07}{1},\ n = 10$

$ar^{10} = 1000(1.07)^{10} \approx \$1967.15$

53. $a = 1000,\ r = 1 + \frac{0.07}{4},\ n = 40$

$ar^{40} = 1000\left(1 + \frac{0.07}{4}\right)^{40} \approx \$2001.60$

54. $a = 1000,\ r = 1 + \frac{0.07}{12},\ n = 120$

$ar^{120} = 1000\left(1 + \frac{0.07}{12}\right)^{120} \approx \$2009.66$

55. $a = 1000,\ r = 1 + \frac{0.07}{365},\ n = 3650$

$ar^{3650} = 1000\left(1 + \frac{0.07}{365}\right)^{3650} \approx \$2013.62$

56. $a = 1000,\ r = 1 + \frac{0.07}{8760},\ n = 87600$

$ar^{87600} = 1000\left(1 + \frac{0.07}{8760}\right)^{87600} \approx \$2013.75$

57. $a = 2000,\ r = 1 + \frac{0.11}{4},\ n = 180$

$ar^{180} = 2000\left(1 + \frac{0.11}{4}\right)^{180} \approx \$264{,}094.58$

58. Since the bacteria double in 5 minutes, it will take 5 minutes for one bacterium to become two bacteria. It will then take 2 hours for the two bacteria to fill the dish, for a total of 2 hours and 5 minutes.

59. $a = 1000,\ r = 0.8$

$S_\infty = \frac{a}{1 - r} = \frac{1000}{1 - 0.8} = 5000$

60. $a = 1000,\ r = 0.9$

$S_\infty = \frac{a}{1 - r} = \frac{1000}{1 - 0.9} = 10{,}000$

61. $a = 1,\ r = 2,\ n = 64$

$S = \frac{a - ar^n}{1 - r} = \frac{1 - 1(2)^{64}}{1 - 2} \approx 1.8447 \times 10^{19}$ grains

62. $\frac{1.8447 \times 10^{19}}{500,000} = 3.689 \times 10^{13}$ bushels

63. no

64. yes

65. $(3+2i)+(2-5i)=3+2i+2-5i=5-3i$

66. $(7+8i)-(2-5i)=7+8i-2+5i=5+13i$

67. $(3+i)(3-i)=9-3i+3i-i^2=9-(-1)=10+0i$

68. $\left(3+\sqrt{3}i\right)\left(3-\sqrt{3}i\right)=9-3\sqrt{3}i+3\sqrt{3}i-3i^2=9-3(-1)=12+0i$

69. $\dfrac{2+3i}{2-i}=\dfrac{(2+3i)(2+i)}{(2-i)(2+i)}=\dfrac{4+2i+6i+3i^2}{4-i^2}=\dfrac{4+8i+3(-1)}{4-(-1)}=\dfrac{1+8i}{5}=\dfrac{1}{5}+\dfrac{8}{5}i$

70. $(7+3i)^2=(7+3i)(7+3i)=49+21i+21i+9i^2=49+42i+9(-1)=40+42i$

71. $i^{127}=i^{124}i^3=\left(i^4\right)^{31}i^3=1^{31}i^3=i^3=-i$

72. $i^{-127}=\dfrac{1}{i^{127}}=\dfrac{1\cdot i}{i^{127}\cdot i}=\dfrac{i}{i^{128}}=\dfrac{i}{\left(i^4\right)^{42}}=\dfrac{i}{1^{42}}=\dfrac{i}{1}=i$

Exercises 8.5 (page 759)

1. two

2. $n=1$

3. $n=k+1$

4. hypothesis

5.

$n=1$:
$$5(1)\stackrel{?}{=}\frac{5(1)(1+1)}{2}$$
$$5=5$$

$n=2$:
$$5+5(2)\stackrel{?}{=}\frac{5(2)(2+1)}{2}$$
$$15\stackrel{?}{=}\frac{10(3)}{2}$$
$$15=15$$

$n=3$:
$$5+10+5(3)\stackrel{?}{=}\frac{5(3)(3+1)}{2}$$
$$30\stackrel{?}{=}\frac{15(4)}{2}$$
$$30=30$$

$n=4$:
$$5+10+15+5(4)\stackrel{?}{=}\frac{5(4)(4+1)}{2}$$
$$50\stackrel{?}{=}\frac{20(5)}{2}$$
$$50=50$$

SECTION 8.5

6.

$n = 1$

$$1^2 \stackrel{?}{=} \frac{1(1+1)(2(1)+1)}{6}$$
$$1 \stackrel{?}{=} \frac{1(2)(3)}{6}$$
$$1 = 1$$

$n = 2$

$$1^2 + 2^2 \stackrel{?}{=} \frac{2(2+1)(2(2)+1)}{6}$$
$$5 \stackrel{?}{=} \frac{2(3)(5)}{6}$$
$$5 = 5$$

$n = 3$

$$1^2 + 2^2 + 3^2 \stackrel{?}{=} \frac{3(3+1)(2(3)+1)}{6}$$
$$14 \stackrel{?}{=} \frac{3(4)(7)}{6}$$
$$14 = 14$$

$n = 4$

$$1^2 + 2^2 + 3^2 + 4^2 \stackrel{?}{=} \frac{4(4+1)(2(4)+1)}{6}$$
$$30 \stackrel{?}{=} \frac{4(5)(9)}{6}$$
$$30 = 30$$

7.

$n = 1$

$$3(1) + 4 \stackrel{?}{=} \frac{1(3(1)+11)}{2}$$
$$7 \stackrel{?}{=} \frac{1(14)}{2}$$
$$7 = 7$$

$n = 2$

$$7 + 3(2) + 4 \stackrel{?}{=} \frac{2(3(2)+11)}{2}$$
$$17 \stackrel{?}{=} \frac{2(17)}{2}$$
$$17 = 17$$

$n = 3$

$$7 + 10 + 3(3) + 4 \stackrel{?}{=} \frac{3(3(3)+11)}{2}$$
$$30 \stackrel{?}{=} \frac{3(20)}{2}$$
$$30 = 30$$

$n = 4$

$$7 + 10 + 13 + 3(4) + 4 \stackrel{?}{=} \frac{4(3(4)+11)}{2}$$
$$46 \stackrel{?}{=} \frac{4(23)}{2}$$
$$46 = 46$$

8.

$n = 1$

$$1(1+2) \stackrel{?}{=} \frac{1}{6}(1+1)(2(1)+7)$$
$$3 \stackrel{?}{=} \frac{1}{6}(2)(9)$$
$$3 = 3$$

$n = 2$

$$3 + 2(2+2) \stackrel{?}{=} \frac{2}{6}(2+1)(2(2)+7)$$
$$11 \stackrel{?}{=} \frac{2}{6}(3)(11)$$
$$11 = 11$$

$n = 3$

$$3 + 8 + 3(3+2) \stackrel{?}{=} \frac{3}{6}(3+1)(2(3)+7)$$
$$26 \stackrel{?}{=} \frac{3}{6}(4)(13)$$
$$26 = 26$$

$n = 4$

$$3 + 8 + 15 + 4(4+2) \stackrel{?}{=} \frac{4}{6}(4+1)(2(4)+7)$$
$$50 \stackrel{?}{=} \frac{4}{6}(5)(15)$$
$$50 = 50$$

9.

Check $n = 1$: $2 \stackrel{?}{=} 1(1+1)$ True for $n = 1$

$2 = 2$

Assume for $n = k$: $2 + 4 + 6 + \cdots + 2k = k(k+1)$

Show for $n = k + 1$: $\boxed{2 + 4 + 6 + \cdots + 2k} + 2(k+1) = \boxed{k(k+1)} + 2(k+1)$

$$2 + 4 + 6 + \cdots + 2(k+1) = k^2 + k + 2k + 2$$

$$2 + 4 + 6 + \cdots + 2(k+1) = k^2 + 3k + 2$$

$$2 + 4 + 6 + \cdots + 2(k+1) = (k+1)(k+2)$$

Since this is what results when $n = k + 1$ is in the formula, we have shown that the formula works for $n = k + 1$ if it works for $n = k$.

10.

Check $n = 1$: $2(1) - 1 \stackrel{?}{=} 1^2$ True for $n = 1$

$1 = 1$

Assume for $n = k$: $1 + 3 + 5 + \cdots + (2k-1) = k^2$

Show for $n = k + 1$: $\boxed{1 + 3 + 5 + \cdots + (2k-1)} + 2(k+1) - 1 = \boxed{k^2} + 2(k+1) - 1$

$$1 + 3 + 5 + \cdots + [2(k+1) - 1] = k^2 + 2k + 2 - 1$$

$$1 + 3 + 5 + \cdots + [2(k+1) - 1] = k^2 + 2k + 1$$

$$1 + 3 + 5 + \cdots + [2(k+1) - 1] = (k+1)^2$$

Since this is what results when $n = k + 1$ in the formula, we have shown that the formula works for $n = k + 1$ if it works for $n = k$.

11.

Check $n = 1$: $4(1) - 1 \stackrel{?}{=} 1(2(1) + 1)$ True for $n = 1$

$3 = 3$

Assume for $n = k$ and show for $n = k + 1$:

$$3 + 7 + 11 + \cdots + (4k - 1) = k(2k+1)$$

$$\boxed{3 + 7 + 11 + \cdots + (4k-1)} + 4(k+1) - 1 = \boxed{k(2k+1)} + 4(k+1) - 1$$

$$3 + 7 + 11 + \cdots + [4(k+1) - 1] = 2k^2 + k + 4k + 4 - 1$$

$$3 + 7 + 11 + \cdots + [4(k+1) - 1] = 2k^2 + 5k + 3$$

$$3 + 7 + 11 + \cdots + [4(k+1) - 1] = (k+1)(2k+3)$$

$$3 + 7 + 11 + \cdots + [4(k+1) - 1] = (k+1)(2(k+1)+1)$$

Since this is what results when $n = k + 1$ is in the formula, we have shown that the formula works for $n = k + 1$ if it works for $n = k$.

12.

Check $n = 1$: $4(1) \stackrel{?}{=} 2(1)(1+1)$ True for $n = 1$ $4 = 4$
Assume for $n = k$ and show for $n = k + 1$: $4 + 8 + 12 + \cdots + 4k = 2k(k+1)$ $\boxed{4 + 8 + 12 + \cdots + 4k} + 4(k+1) = \boxed{2k(k+1)} + 4(k+1)$ $4 + 8 + 12 + \cdots + 4(k+1) = 2k^2 + 2k + 4k + 4$ $4 + 8 + 12 + \cdots + 4(k+1) = 2k^2 + 6k + 4$ $4 + 8 + 12 + \cdots + 4(k+1) = (2k+2)(k+2)$ $4 + 8 + 12 + \cdots + 4(k+1) = 2(k+1)(k+2)$
Since this is what results when $n = k + 1$ in the formula, we have shown that the formula works for $n = k + 1$ if it works for $n = k$.

13.

Check $n = 1$: $14 - 4(1) \stackrel{?}{=} 12(1) - 2(1)^2$ True for $n = 1$ $10 = 10$
Assume for $n = k$ and show for $n = k + 1$: $10 + 6 + 2 + \cdots + (14 - 4k) = 12k - 2k^2$ $\boxed{10 + 6 + 2 + \cdots + (14 - 4k)} + 14 - 4(k+1) = \boxed{12k - 2k^2} + 14 - 4(k+1)$ $10 + 6 + 2 + \cdots + (14 - 4(k+1)) = 12k - 2k^2 + 14 - 4k - 4$ $10 + 6 + 2 + \cdots + (14 - 4(k+1)) = 12k + 12 - 2k^2 - 4k - 2$ $10 + 6 + 2 + \cdots + (14 - 4(k+1)) = 12(k+1) - 2(k^2 + 2k + 1)$ $10 + 6 + 2 + \cdots + (14 - 4(k+1)) = 12(k+1) - 2(k+1)^2$
Since this is what results when $n = k + 1$ is in the formula, we have shown that the formula works for $n = k + 1$ if it works for $n = k$.

14.

Check $n = 1$: $10 - 2(1) \stackrel{?}{=} 9(1) - (1)^2$ True for $n = 1$ $8 = 8$
Assume for $n = k$ and show for $n = k + 1$: $8 + 6 + 4 + \cdots + (10 - 2k) = 9k - k^2$ $\boxed{8 + 6 + 4 + \cdots + (10 - 2k)} + 10 - 2(k+1) = \boxed{9k - k^2} + 10 - 2(k+1)$ $8 + 6 + 4 + \cdots + (10 - 2(k+1)) = 9k - k^2 + 10 - 2k - 2$ $8 + 6 + 4 + \cdots + (10 - 2(k+1)) = 9k + 9 - k^2 - 2k - 1$ $8 + 6 + 4 + \cdots + (10 - 2(k+1)) = 9(k+1) - (k^2 + 2k + 1)$ $8 + 6 + 4 + \cdots + (10 - 2(k+1)) = 9(k+1) - (k+1)^2$
Since this is what results when $n = k + 1$ is in the formula, we have shown that the formula works for $n = k + 1$ if it works for $n = k$.

15.

Check $n = 1$: $3(1) - 1 \stackrel{?}{=} \frac{1(3(1)+1)}{2}$ True for $n = 1$

$2 = 2$

Assume for $n = k$ and show for $n = k + 1$:

$$2 + 5 + 8 + \cdots + (3k - 1) = \frac{k(3k+1)}{2}$$

$$\boxed{2 + 5 + 8 + \cdots + (3k - 1)} + 3(k+1) - 1 = \boxed{\frac{k(3k+1)}{2}} + 3(k+1) - 1$$

$$2 + 5 + 8 + \cdots + (3(k+1) - 1) = \frac{k(3k+1)}{2} + \frac{2 \cdot (3(k+1) - 1)}{2}$$

$$2 + 5 + 8 + \cdots + (3(k+1) - 1) = \frac{3k^2 + k + 6k + 6 - 2}{2}$$

$$2 + 5 + 8 + \cdots + (3(k+1) - 1) = \frac{3k^2 + 7k + 4}{2}$$

$$2 + 5 + 8 + \cdots + (3(k+1) - 1) = \frac{(k+1)(3k+4)}{2}$$

$$2 + 5 + 8 + \cdots + (3(k+1) - 1) = \frac{(k+1)(3(k+1)+1)}{2}$$

Since this is what results when $n = k + 1$ is in the formula, we have shown that the formula works for $n = k + 1$ if it works for $n = k$.

16.

Check $n = 1$: $3(1) \stackrel{?}{=} \frac{3(1)(1+1)}{2}$ True for $n = 1$

$3 = 3$

Assume for $n = k$ and show for $n = k + 1$:

$$3 + 6 + 9 + \cdots + 3k = \frac{3k(k+1)}{2}$$

$$\boxed{3 + 6 + 9 + \cdots + 3k} + 3(k+1) = \boxed{\frac{3k(k+1)}{2}} + 3(k+1)$$

$$3 + 6 + 9 + \cdots + 3(k+1) = \frac{3k(k+1)}{2} + \frac{2 \cdot 3(k+1)}{2}$$

$$3 + 6 + 9 + \cdots + 3(k+1) = \frac{3(k+1)k + 3(k+1) \cdot 2}{2}$$

$$3 + 6 + 9 + \cdots + 3(k+1) = \frac{3(k+1)(k+2)}{2}$$

Since this is what results when $n = k + 1$ is in the formula, we have shown that the formula works for $n = k + 1$ if it works for $n = k$.

17.

Check $n=1$: $1^2 \stackrel{?}{=} \frac{1(1+1)(2(1)+1)}{6}$ True for $n=1$ $1=1$
Assume for $n=k$ and show for $n=k+1$: $1^2+2^2+3^2+\cdots+k^2=\frac{k(k+1)(2k+1)}{6}$ $\boxed{1^2+2^2+3^2+\cdots+k^2}+(k+1)^2=\boxed{\frac{k(k+1)(2k+1)}{6}}+(k+1)^2$ $1^2+2^2+3^2+\cdots+(k+1)^2=\frac{(2k^2+k)(k+1)}{6}+\frac{6(k+1)(k+1)}{6}$ $1^2+2^2+3^2+\cdots+(k+1)^2=\frac{(2k^2+k+6(k+1))(k+1)}{6}$ $1^2+2^2+3^2+\cdots+(k+1)^2=\frac{(2k^2+7k+6)(k+1)}{6}$ $1^2+2^2+3^2+\cdots+(k+1)^2=\frac{(2k+3)(k+2)(k+1)}{6}$ $1^2+2^2+3^2+\cdots+(k+1)^2=\frac{(k+1)(k+2)(2k+3)}{6}$
Since this is what results when $n=k+1$ is in the formula, we have shown that the formula works for $n=k+1$ if it works for $n=k$.

18.

Check $n=1$: $1 \stackrel{?}{=} 1^2$ True for $n=1$
Assume for $n=k$ and show for $n=k+1$: $1+2+3+\cdots+(k-1)+k+(k-1)+\cdots+1=k^2$ $\boxed{1+2+3+\cdots+k}+(k+1)+k+\boxed{(k-1)+\cdots+1}=\boxed{k^2}+k+k+1$ $1+2+3+\cdots+k+(k+1)+k+\cdots+1=k^2+2k+1$ $1+2+3+\cdots+k+(k+1)+k+\cdots+1=(k+1)^2$
Since this is what results when $n=k+1$ is in the formula, we have shown that the formula works for $n=k+1$ if it works for $n=k$.

19. Check $n = 1$: $\frac{5}{3}(1) - \frac{4}{3} \stackrel{?}{=} 1\left(\frac{5}{6}(1) - \frac{1}{2}\right)$ True for $n = 1$

$\frac{1}{3} = \frac{1}{3}$

Assume for $n = k$ and show for $n = k + 1$:

$$\frac{1}{3} + 2 + \frac{11}{3} + \cdots + \left(\frac{5}{3}k - \frac{4}{3}\right) = k\left(\frac{5}{6}k - \frac{1}{2}\right)$$

$$\boxed{\frac{1}{3} + 2 + \frac{11}{3} + \cdots + \left(\frac{5}{3}k - \frac{4}{3}\right)} + \left(\frac{5}{3}(k+1) - \frac{4}{3}\right) = \boxed{k\left(\frac{5}{6}k - \frac{1}{2}\right)} + \left(\frac{5}{3}(k+1) - \frac{4}{3}\right)$$

$$\frac{1}{3} + 2 + \frac{11}{3} + \cdots + \left(\frac{5}{3}(k+1) - \frac{4}{3}\right) = \frac{5}{6}k^2 - \frac{1}{2}k + \frac{5}{3}k + \frac{5}{3} - \frac{4}{3}$$

$$\frac{1}{3} + 2 + \frac{11}{3} + \cdots + \left(\frac{5}{3}(k+1) - \frac{4}{3}\right) = \frac{5}{6}k^2 + \frac{7}{6}k + \frac{1}{3}$$

$$\frac{1}{3} + 2 + \frac{11}{3} + \cdots + \left(\frac{5}{3}(k+1) - \frac{4}{3}\right) = (k+1)\left(\frac{5}{6}k + \frac{1}{3}\right)$$

$$\frac{1}{3} + 2 + \frac{11}{3} + \cdots + \left(\frac{5}{3}(k+1) - \frac{4}{3}\right) = (k+1)\left(\frac{5}{6}k + \frac{5}{6} - \frac{1}{2}\right)$$

$$\frac{1}{3} + 2 + \frac{11}{3} + \cdots + \left(\frac{5}{3}(k+1) - \frac{4}{3}\right) = (k+1)\left(\frac{5}{6}(k+1) - \frac{1}{2}\right)$$

Since this is what results when $n = k + 1$ is in the formula, we have shown that the formula works for $n = k + 1$ if it works for $n = k$.

20. Check $n = 1$: $\frac{1}{1 \cdot 2} \stackrel{?}{=} \frac{1}{1+1}$ True for $n = 1$

$\frac{1}{2} = \frac{1}{2}$

Assume for $n = k$ and show for $n = k + 1$:

$$\frac{1}{1 \cdot 2} + \frac{1}{2 \cdot 3} + \frac{1}{3 \cdot 4} + \cdots + \frac{1}{k(k+1)} = \frac{k}{k+1}$$

$$\boxed{\frac{1}{1 \cdot 2} + \frac{1}{2 \cdot 3} + \frac{1}{3 \cdot 4} + \cdots + \frac{1}{k(k+1)}} + \frac{1}{(k+1)(k+2)} = \boxed{\frac{k}{k+1}} + \frac{1}{(k+1)(k+2)}$$

$$\frac{1}{1 \cdot 2} + \frac{1}{2 \cdot 3} + \frac{1}{3 \cdot 4} + \cdots + \frac{1}{(k+1)(k+2)} = \frac{k(k+2) + 1}{(k+1)(k+2)}$$

$$\frac{1}{1 \cdot 2} + \frac{1}{2 \cdot 3} + \frac{1}{3 \cdot 4} + \cdots + \frac{1}{(k+1)(k+2)} = \frac{k^2 + 2k + 1}{(k+1)(k+2)}$$

$$\frac{1}{1 \cdot 2} + \frac{1}{2 \cdot 3} + \frac{1}{3 \cdot 4} + \cdots + \frac{1}{(k+1)(k+2)} = \frac{(k+1)^2}{(k+1)(k+2)}$$

$$\frac{1}{1 \cdot 2} + \frac{1}{2 \cdot 3} + \frac{1}{3 \cdot 4} + \cdots + \frac{1}{(k+1)(k+2)} = \frac{k+1}{k+2}$$

Since this is what results when $n = k + 1$ is in the formula, we have shown that the formula works for $n = k + 1$ if it works for $n = k$.

21.

Check $n = 1$: $\left(\frac{1}{2}\right)^1 \stackrel{?}{=} 1 - \left(\frac{1}{2}\right)^1$ True for $n = 1$

$\frac{1}{2} = \frac{1}{2}$

Assume for $n = k$ and show for $n = k + 1$:

$$\frac{1}{2} + \frac{1}{4} + \frac{1}{8} + \cdots + \left(\frac{1}{2}\right)^k = 1 - \left(\frac{1}{2}\right)^k$$

$$\boxed{\frac{1}{2} + \frac{1}{4} + \frac{1}{8} + \cdots + \left(\frac{1}{2}\right)^k} + \left(\frac{1}{2}\right)^{k+1} = \boxed{1 - \left(\frac{1}{2}\right)^k} + \left(\frac{1}{2}\right)^{k+1}$$

$$\frac{1}{2} + \frac{1}{4} + \frac{1}{8} + \cdots + \left(\frac{1}{2}\right)^{k+1} = 1 - 2\left(\frac{1}{2}\right)\left(\frac{1}{2}\right)^k + \left(\frac{1}{2}\right)^{k+1}$$

$$\frac{1}{2} + \frac{1}{4} + \frac{1}{8} + \cdots + \left(\frac{1}{2}\right)^{k+1} = 1 - 2\left(\frac{1}{2}\right)^{k+1} + \left(\frac{1}{2}\right)^{k+1}$$

$$\frac{1}{2} + \frac{1}{4} + \frac{1}{8} + \cdots + \left(\frac{1}{2}\right)^{k+1} = 1 - \left(\frac{1}{2}\right)^{k+1}$$

Since this is what results when $n = k + 1$ is in the formula, we have shown that the formula works for $n = k + 1$ if it works for $n = k$.

22.

Check $n = 1$: $\frac{1}{3}\left(\frac{2}{3}\right)^{1-1} \stackrel{?}{=} 1 - \left(\frac{2}{3}\right)^1$ True for $n = 1$

$\frac{1}{3} = \frac{1}{3}$

Assume for $n = k$ and show for $n = k + 1$:

$$\frac{1}{3} + \frac{2}{9} + \frac{4}{27} + \cdots + \frac{1}{3}\left(\frac{2}{3}\right)^{k-1} = 1 - \left(\frac{2}{3}\right)^k$$

$$\boxed{\frac{1}{3} + \frac{2}{9} + \frac{4}{27} + \cdots + \frac{1}{3}\left(\frac{2}{3}\right)^{k-1}} + \frac{1}{3}\left(\frac{2}{3}\right)^k = \boxed{1 - \left(\frac{2}{3}\right)^k} + \frac{1}{3}\left(\frac{2}{3}\right)^k$$

$$\frac{1}{3} + \frac{2}{9} + \frac{4}{27} + \cdots + \frac{1}{3}\left(\frac{2}{3}\right)^k = 1 - \frac{3}{2}\left(\frac{2}{3}\right)\left(\frac{2}{3}\right)^k + \frac{3}{2}\left(\frac{2}{3}\right)\left(\frac{1}{3}\right)\left(\frac{2}{3}\right)^k$$

$$\frac{1}{3} + \frac{2}{9} + \frac{4}{27} + \cdots + \frac{1}{3}\left(\frac{2}{3}\right)^k = 1 - \frac{3}{2}\left(\frac{2}{3}\right)^{k+1} + \frac{1}{2}\left(\frac{2}{3}\right)^{k+1}$$

$$\frac{1}{3} + \frac{2}{9} + \frac{4}{27} + \cdots + \frac{1}{3}\left(\frac{2}{3}\right)^k = 1 - \left(\frac{2}{3}\right)^{k+1}$$

Since this is what results when $n = k + 1$ is in the formula, we have shown that the formula works for $n = k + 1$ if it works for $n = k$.

23.

Check $n = 1$: $2^{1-1} \stackrel{?}{=} 2^1 - 1$ True for $n = 1$

$1 = 1$

Assume for $n = k$ and show for $n = k + 1$:

$$2^0 + 2^1 + 2^2 + \cdots + 2^{k-1} = 2^k - 1$$

$$\boxed{2^0 + 2^1 + 2^2 + \cdots + 2^{k-1}} + 2^k = \boxed{2^k - 1} + 2^k$$

$$2^0 + 2^1 + 2^2 + \cdots + 2^k = 2 \cdot 2^k - 1$$

$$2^0 + 2^1 + 2^2 + \cdots + 2^k = 2^{k+1} - 1$$

Since this is what results when $n = k + 1$ is in the formula, we have shown that the formula works for $n = k + 1$ if it works for $n = k$.

24.

Check $n = 1$: $1^3 \stackrel{?}{=} \left[\dfrac{1(1+1)}{2}\right]^2$ True for $n = 1$

$1 = 1$

Assume for $n = k$ and show for $n = k + 1$:

$$1^3 + 2^3 + 3^3 + \cdots + k^3 = \left[\frac{k(k+1)}{2}\right]^2$$

$$\boxed{1^3 + 2^3 + 3^3 + \cdots + k^3} + (k+1)^3 = \boxed{\left[\frac{k(k+1)}{2}\right]^2} + (k+1)^3$$

$$1^3 + 2^3 + 3^3 + \cdots + (k+1)^3 = \frac{k^2(k+1)^2 + 4(k+1)^3}{4}$$

$$1^2 + 2^2 + 3^2 + \cdots + (k+1)^2 = \frac{(k+1)^2[k^2 + 4(k+1)]}{4}$$

$$1^2 + 2^2 + 3^2 + \cdots + (k+1)^2 = \frac{(k+1)^2(k+2)^2}{4}$$

Since this is what results when $n = k + 1$ is in the formula, we have shown that the formula works for $n = k + 1$ if it works for $n = k$.

25.

Check $n = 1$: $x - y$ is a factor of $x^1 - y^1$. True for $n = 1$

Assume for $n = k$ and show for $n = k + 1$:

Thus, we assume that $x^k - y^k = (x - y)(\text{SOMETHING})$.

$$\begin{aligned} x^{k+1} - y^{k+1} &= x^{k+1} - xy^k + xy^k - y^{k+1} \\ &= x(x^k - y^k) + y^k(x - y) \\ &= x(x - y)(\text{SOMETHING}) + y^k(x - y) \\ &= (x - y)\left[x(\text{SOMETHING}) + y^k\right] \end{aligned}$$

We have shown that $x - y$ is a factor of $x^{k+1} - y^{k+1}$ if it is a factor of $x^k - y^k$.

26.

Check $n = 1$: $1 < 2^1$ True for $n = 1$
Assume for $n = k$ and show for $n = k + 1$: Certainly, $2^k + 1 < 2^k + 2 < 2^k + 2^k$. $k < 2^k$ $k + 1 < 2^k + 1 < 2^k + 2^k = 2 \cdot 2^k = 2^{k+1}$ $k + 1 < 2^{k+1}$
We have shown that $k + 1 < 2^{k+1}$ if $k < 2^k$.

27. The formula is true for $n = 3$, since a triangle has $180° = (3 - 2) \cdot 180°$. Next, assume that a polygon with k sides has an angle sum of $(k - 2) \cdot 180°$. Take a polygon with $k + 1$ sides. Consider two adjacent sides with a common endpoint. Connect the endpoints which are NOT common to both sides. The figure is now a polygon with k sides with a triangle adjacent to it.

$$\boxed{\begin{array}{c}\text{Sum of angles of}\\(k+1)\text{-sided polygon}\end{array}} = \boxed{\begin{array}{c}\text{Sum of angles of}\\k\text{-sided polygon}\end{array}} + \boxed{\begin{array}{c}\text{Sum of angles of}\\\text{triangle}\end{array}}$$

$$= (k - 2) \cdot 180° + 180° = (k - 1) \cdot 180° = [(k + 1) - 2] \cdot 180°$$

Thus, the formula works for $n = k + 1$ if it works for $n = k$.

28. The formula works for $n = 1$ and $n = 2$, but it does not work for $n = 3$. Therefore, it does not work for all natural numbers.

29. Assume for $n = k$ and show for $n = k + 1$:

$$1 + 2 + 3 + \cdots + k = \tfrac{k}{2}(k + 1) + 1$$

$$\boxed{1 + 2 + 3 + \cdots + k} + (k + 1) = \boxed{\tfrac{k}{2}(k + 1) + 1} + (k + 1)$$

$$1 + 2 + 3 + \cdots + (k + 1) = \tfrac{1}{2}k(k + 1) + (k + 1) + 2$$

$$1 + 2 + 3 + \cdots + (k + 1) = \tfrac{1}{2}(k + 1)(k + 2)$$

$$1 + 2 + 3 + \cdots + (k + 1) = \tfrac{(k+1)}{2}(k + 2)$$

The formula works for $n = k + 1$ if it works for $n = k$. However, the formula does not work for $n = 1$. Thus, the formula does not work for all natural numbers.

30.

Check $n = 1$: $1 + 1 = 1 + 1$ True for $n = 1$
Assume for $n = k$ and show for $n = k + 1$: $k + 1 = 1 + k$ $k + 1 + 1 = 1 + k + 1$ $k + 1 + 1 = 1 + 1 + k$ $(k + 1) + 1 = 1 + (1 + k)$
We have shown that the formula works for $n = k + 1$ if it works for $n = k$.

31.

Check $n = 1$: $7^1 - 1 = 7 - 1 = 6$ True for $n = 1$ Thus, $7^1 - 1$ is divisible by 6.
Assume for $n = k$ and show for $n = k + 1$: $7^k - 1$ is divisible by 6, so $7^k - 1 = 6 \cdot x$, where x is some natural number. Then $7^{k+1} - 1 = 7^k \cdot 7 - 1 = (6x + 1) \cdot 7 - 1 = 42x + 6 = 6(7x + 1)$ Thus, $7^{k+1} - 1$ is divisible by 6.
We have shown that $7^{k+1} - 1$ is divisible by 6 if $7^k - 1$ is divisible by 6.

32.

Check $n = 2$: $1 + 2(2) < 3^2$ True for $n = 2$ $5 < 9$
Assume for $n = k$ and show for $n = k + 1$: Certainly, $3^k + 2 = 3^k + 1 + 1 < 3^k + 3^k + 3^k$. $1 + 2k < 3^k$ $1 + 2k + 2 < 3^k + 2 < 3^k + 3^k + 3^k = 3 \cdot 3^k = 3^{k+1}$ $1 + 2(k + 1) < 3^{k+1}$
We have shown that $1 + 2(k + 1) < 3^{k+1}$ if $1 + 2k < 3^k$.

33.

Check $n = 1$: True for $n = 1$

$$1 + r^1 \stackrel{?}{=} \frac{1 - r^2}{1 - r}$$

$$1 + r \stackrel{?}{=} \frac{(1 + r)(1 - r)}{1 - r}$$

$$1 + r = 1 + r$$

Assume for $n = k$ and show for $n = k + 1$:

$$1 + r + r^2 + r^3 + \cdots + r^k = \frac{1 - r^{k+1}}{1 - r}$$

$$\boxed{1 + r + r^2 + r^3 + \cdots + r^k} + r^{k+1} = \boxed{\frac{1 - r^{k+1}}{1 - r}} + r^{k+1}$$

$$1 + r + r^2 + r^3 + \cdots + r^{k+1} = \frac{1 - r^{k+1} + r^{k+1}(1 - r)}{1 - r}$$

$$1 + r + r^2 + r^3 + \cdots + r^{k+1} = \frac{1 - r^{k+1} + r^{k+1} - r^{k+2}}{1 - r}$$

$$1 + r + r^2 + r^3 + \cdots + r^{k+1} = \frac{1 - r^{(k+1)+1}}{1 - r}$$

Since this is what results when $n = k + 1$ is in the formula, we have shown that the formula works for $n = k + 1$ if it works for $n = k$.

34.

Check $n=1$: $a+(1-1)d \stackrel{?}{=} \dfrac{1(a+(a+(1-1)d))}{2}$ True for $n=1$

$a=a$

Assume for $n=k$ and show for $n=k+1$:

$$a+(a+d)+(a+2d)+\cdots+a+(k-1)d = \frac{k(a+(a+(k-1)d))}{2}$$
$$= \frac{2ak+k^2d-kd}{2}$$
$$\boxed{a+(a+d)+(a+2d)+\cdots+a+(k-1)d} + a + kd = \boxed{\frac{2ak+k^2d-kd}{2}} + a + kd$$
$$a+(a+d)+(a+2d)+\cdots+(a+kd) = \frac{2ak+k^2d-kd+2a+2kd}{2}$$
$$a+(a+d)+(a+2d)+\cdots+(a+kd) = \frac{2a(k+1)+k^2d+kd}{2}$$
$$a+(a+d)+(a+2d)+\cdots+(a+kd) = \frac{2a(k+1)+kd(k+1)}{2}$$
$$a+(a+d)+(a+2d)+\cdots+(a+kd) = \frac{(k+1)(2a+kd)}{2}$$
$$a+(a+d)+(a+2d)+\cdots+(a+kd) = \frac{(k+1)(a+(a+kd))}{2}$$

Since this is what results when $n=k+1$ is in the formula, we have shown that the formula works for $n=k+1$ if it works for $n=k$.

35.

Check $n=1$: $a^m a^1 = a^m \cdot a = a^{m+1}$, by definition True for $n=1$

Assume for $n=k$ and show for $n=k+1$:

$$a^m a^k = a^{m+k}$$
$$a^m a^k a = a^{m+k} a$$
$$a^m a^{k+1} = a^{m+k+1}$$
$$a^m a^{k+1} = a^{m+(k+1)}$$

We have shown that the formula works for $n=k+1$ if it works for $n=k$.

36.

Check $n=1$: $(a^m)^1 = a^m = a^{m\cdot 1}$ True for $n=1$

Assume for $n=k$ and show for $n=k+1$:

$$(a^m)^k = a^{mk}$$
$$(a^m)^k a^m = a^{mk} a^m$$
$$(a^m)^{k+1} = a^{mk+m}$$
$$(a^m)^{k+1} = a^{m(k+1)}$$

We have shown that the formula works for $n=k+1$ if it works for $n=k$.

37. **a.** 1 **b.** 3 **c.** 7 **d.** 15

38. **a.** Number of moves for 1 disk: $2^{n-1} = 2^{1-1} = 2^0 = 1$ move

b. It takes $2^k - 1$ moves to transfer k disks.

c. All but the largest $\Rightarrow k$ disks $\Rightarrow 2^k - 1$ moves

d. 1

e. $2^k - 1$ to transfer back

f. $2^k - 1 + 1 + 2^k - 1$

g. $2^k - 1 + 1 + 2^k - 1 = 2^k + 2^k - 1 = 2 \cdot 2^k - 1 = 2^{k+1} - 1$

h. Since the number of moves works for $k + 1$ disks when it works for k disks, and since it works for 1 disks, it works for any number of disks.

39. $3x + 4y \le 12$

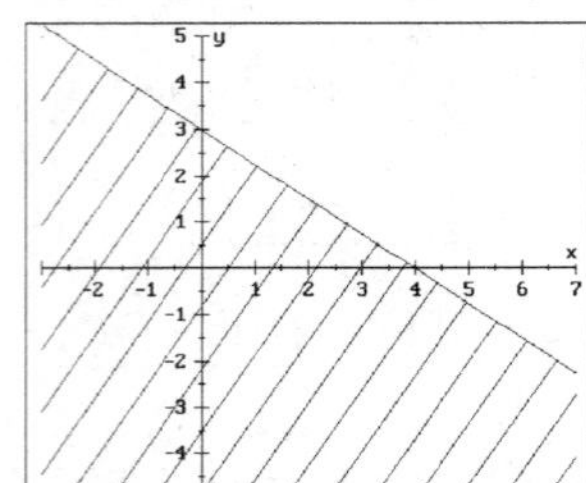

40. $4x - 3y < 12$

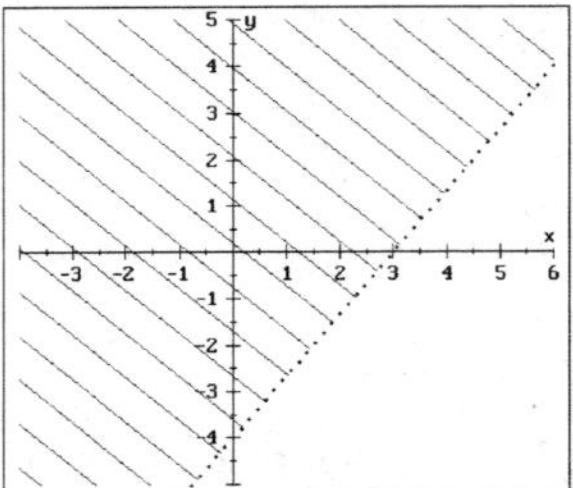

41. $2x + y > 5$

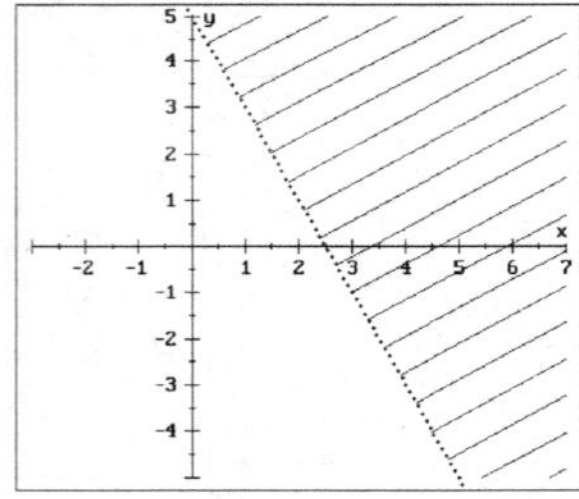

42. $x + 3y \ge 7$

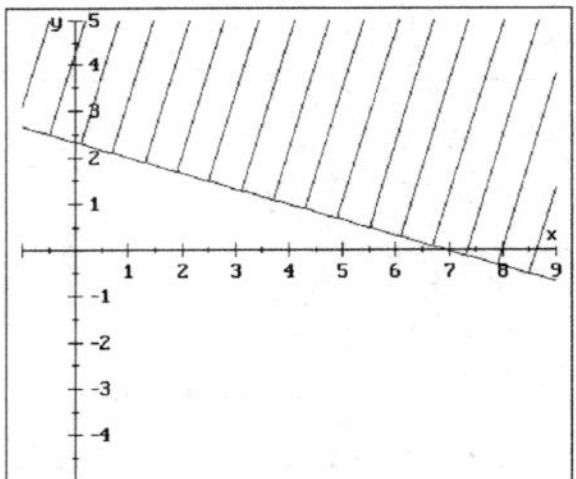

Exercises 8.6 (page 769)

1. $6 \cdot 4 = 24$

2. permutation

3. $\dfrac{n!}{(n-r)!}$

4. $n!$

5. 1

6. $(n-1)!$

7. $\dfrac{n!}{r!(n-r)!}$

8. $\binom{n}{r}$

9. 1

10. 1

11. $\dfrac{n!}{a! \cdot b! \cdots}$

12. combinations, permutations

SECTION 8.6

13. $P(7, 4) = \dfrac{7!}{(7-4)!} = \dfrac{7!}{3!} = \dfrac{7 \cdot 6 \cdot 5 \cdot 4 \cdot 3!}{3!} = 7 \cdot 6 \cdot 5 \cdot 4 = 840$

14. $P(8, 3) = \dfrac{8!}{(8-3)!} = \dfrac{8!}{5!} = \dfrac{8 \cdot 7 \cdot 6 \cdot 5!}{5!} = 8 \cdot 7 \cdot 6 = 336$

15. $C(7, 4) = \dfrac{7!}{4!(7-4)!} = \dfrac{7!}{4!3!} = \dfrac{7 \cdot 6 \cdot 5 \cdot 4!}{4!3!} = \dfrac{7 \cdot 6 \cdot 5}{3 \cdot 2 \cdot 1} = 35$

16. $C(8, 3) = \dfrac{8!}{3!(8-3)!} = \dfrac{8!}{3!5!} = \dfrac{8 \cdot 7 \cdot 6 \cdot 5!}{3!5!} = \dfrac{8 \cdot 7 \cdot 6}{3 \cdot 2 \cdot 1} = 56$

17. $P(5, 5) = \dfrac{5!}{(5-5)!} = \dfrac{5!}{0!} = \dfrac{5!}{1} = 5 \cdot 4 \cdot 3 \cdot 2 \cdot 1 = 120$

18. $P(5, 0) = \dfrac{5!}{(5-0)!} = \dfrac{5!}{5!} = 1$

19. $\dbinom{5}{4} = \dfrac{5!}{4!(5-4)!} = \dfrac{5 \cdot 4!}{4!1!} = \dfrac{5}{1} = 5$

20. $\dbinom{8}{4} = \dfrac{8!}{4!(8-4)!} = \dfrac{8 \cdot 7 \cdot 6 \cdot 5 \cdot 4!}{4!4!} = \dfrac{8 \cdot 7 \cdot 6 \cdot 5}{4 \cdot 3 \cdot 2 \cdot 1} = 70$

21. $\dbinom{5}{0} = \dfrac{5!}{0!(5-0)!} = \dfrac{5!}{0!5!} = \dfrac{1}{1} = 1$

22. $\dbinom{5}{5} = \dfrac{5!}{5!(5-5)!} = \dfrac{5!}{5!0!} = \dfrac{1}{1} = 1$

23. $P(5, 4) \cdot C(5, 3) = \dfrac{5!}{(5-4)!} \cdot \dfrac{5!}{3!(5-3)!} = \dfrac{5!}{1!} \cdot \dfrac{5!}{3!2!} = 120 \cdot 10 = 1200$

24. $P(3, 2) \cdot C(4, 3) = \dfrac{3!}{(3-2)!} \cdot \dfrac{4!}{3!(4-3)!} = \dfrac{3!}{1!} \cdot \dfrac{4!}{3!1!} = 6 \cdot 4 = 24$

25. $\dbinom{5}{3}\dbinom{4}{3}\dbinom{3}{3} = \dfrac{5!}{3!(5-3)!} \cdot \dfrac{4!}{3!(4-3)!} \cdot \dfrac{3!}{3!(3-3)!} = 10 \cdot 4 \cdot 1 = 40$

26. $\dbinom{5}{5}\dbinom{6}{6}\dbinom{7}{7}\dbinom{8}{8} = 1 \cdot 1 \cdot 1 \cdot 1 = 1$

27. $\dbinom{68}{66} = \dfrac{68!}{66!(68-66)!} = \dfrac{68 \cdot 67 \cdot 66!}{66!2!} = \dfrac{68 \cdot 67}{2 \cdot 1} = 2278$

28. $\dbinom{100}{99} = \dfrac{100!}{99!(100-99)!} = \dfrac{100 \cdot 99!}{99!1!} = 100$

29. $8 \cdot 6 \cdot 3 = 144$

30. $9 \cdot 10 \cdot 10 \cdot 10 \cdot 10 \cdot 10 = 900{,}000$

31. $8 \cdot 10 \cdot 10 \cdot 10 \cdot 10 \cdot 10 \cdot 10 = 8{,}000{,}000$

32. $6! = 720$

33. Consider the e and the r to be a block that cannot be divided, say x. Then the problem becomes finding the number of ways to rearrange the letters in the word $numbx$. This can be done in 5!, or 120 ways. For each of these possibilities, the e and the r could be reversed, doubling the number of possibilities. The answer is $2 \cdot 120$, or 240 ways.

34. The total number of ways, without restrictions, of rearranging the letters is 6!, or 720. Since there are 240 ways of rearranging the letters so that the e and the r ARE next to each other (see **#33**), then there are $720 - 240$, or 480 ways of rearranging the letters so that the e and the r are NOT next to each other.

35. The word must appear as $\square\, L\, U\, \square\, \square$, where one of the Fs must appear in each box. This can be done in 3!, or 6 ways.

36. The word must appear as $F\, \square\, \square\, B\, L\, \square$, where one of the Es must appear in each box. This can be done in 3!, or 6 ways.

37. $8! = 40{,}320$

38. The line might look like this:

5	5	4	4	3	3	2	2	1	1
W	M	W	M	W	M	W	M	W	M

Then there would be $5 \cdot 5 \cdot 4 \cdot 4 \cdot 3 \cdot 3 \cdot 2 \cdot 2 \cdot 1 \cdot 1 = 14{,}400$ ways. However, the line could start with a man instead of a woman, so there are $2 \cdot 14{,}400 = 28{,}800$ possible arrangements.

39. The line will look like this:

5	4	3	2	1	5	4	3	2	1
M	M	M	M	M	W	W	W	W	W

Then there are $5 \cdot 4 \cdot 3 \cdot 2 \cdot 1 \cdot 5 \cdot 4 \cdot 3 \cdot 2 \cdot 1 = 14{,}400$ arrangements.

40. The line will look like this:

5	4	3	2	1	5	4	3	2	1
W	W	W	W	W	M	M	M	M	M

Then there are $5 \cdot 4 \cdot 3 \cdot 2 \cdot 1 \cdot 5 \cdot 4 \cdot 3 \cdot 2 \cdot 1 = 14{,}400$ arrangements.

41. $P(30, 3) = \dfrac{30!}{27!} = 24{,}360$

42. $P(100, 3) = \dfrac{100!}{97!} = 970{,}200$

43. $(8 - 1)! = 7! = 5040$

44. $(7 - 1)! = 6! = 720$

45. Consider the two people who must sit together as a single person, so that there are 5 "people" who must be arranged in a circle. This can be done in $(5 - 1)! = 4! = 24$ ways. However, the two people who have been seated next to each other could be switched, so that the number of arrangements is doubled. There are $2 \cdot 24 = 48$ possible arrangements.

SECTION 8.6

46. Without restrictions, 6 people can be seated at a round table in $(6-1)! = 5! = 120$ ways. Since there are 48 ways to sit the 6 people so that 2 MUST be together (see **#45**), there are $120 - 48$, or 72 ways of seating the people so that the 2 are NOT seated next to each other.

47. Consider Sally and John as a single person and Martha and Peter as a single person, so that there are 5 "people" who must be arranged in a circle. This can be done in $(5-1)! = 4! = 24$ ways. However, each group of 2 people could be switched, so that the number of arrangements will equal $2 \cdot 2 \cdot 24$, or 96.

48. Consider the three people as a single person, so that there are 6 "people" who must be arranged in a circle. This can be done in $(6-1)! = 5! = 120$ ways. However, the group of three people can be rearranged in 3!, or 6 ways, so the total number of arrangements is $6 \cdot 120$, or 720.

49. $\binom{10}{4} = \dfrac{10!}{4!6!} = 210$

50. $\binom{24}{6} = \dfrac{24!}{6!18!} = 134{,}596$

51. $4! = 24$

52. $\binom{20}{7} = \dfrac{20!}{7!13!} = 77{,}520$

53. $7! = 5040$

54. $8! = 40{,}320$

55. $\dfrac{6!}{3!2!1!} = 60$

56. $\dfrac{6!}{2!1!1!1!} = 360$

57. $25 \cdot 24 \cdot 9 \cdot 9 \cdot 8 \cdot 7 = 2{,}721{,}600$

58. $\binom{7}{5} = 21$

59. $\binom{6}{3}\binom{8}{3} = 20 \cdot 56 = 1120$

60. $\binom{11}{3}\binom{18}{3} = 165 \cdot 816 = 134{,}640$

61. $\binom{12}{4}\binom{10}{3} = 495 \cdot 120 = 59{,}400$

62. $\binom{10}{5}\binom{8}{2} = 252 \cdot 28 = 7056$

63. $\underset{\text{H}}{\underline{17}} \cdot \underset{\text{W}}{\underline{16}} = 272$

64. There are a total of 7!, or 5040 ways to arrange the people without restrictions. Count the number of arrangements with the two people together. To do this, consider them as one person, so that there are 6!, or 720 arrangements. This needs to be doubled, since the two people considered as a group can switch places. Then there are 1440 arrangements with the two people together. The number of arrangements in which they are NOT together is $5040 - 1440 = 3600$.

65. $\binom{8}{2} = 28$

66. $\binom{10}{2} = 45$

67. $\binom{10}{5} = 252$

68. $\binom{25}{9} = 2{,}042{,}975$

69. $\binom{30}{5} = 142{,}506$

70. $\binom{20}{3}\binom{30}{3} = 1140 \cdot 4060$
$= 4{,}628{,}400$

71. $\binom{12}{10} = 66$

72. Pick 5 of the 10 as true: $\binom{10}{5} = 252$

73. For each topping, you have two choices, select or do not select:
$\frac{2}{T_1}\ \frac{2}{T_2}\ \frac{2}{T_3}\ \frac{2}{T_4}\ \frac{2}{T_5}\ \frac{2}{T_6}\ \frac{2}{T_7}\ \frac{2}{T_8}$
$2 \cdot 2 \cdot 2 \cdot 2 \cdot 2 \cdot 2 \cdot 2 \cdot 2 = 256$

74. For each topping, you have two choices, select or do not select:
$\frac{2}{T_1}\ \frac{2}{T_2}\ \frac{2}{T_3}\ \frac{2}{T_4}\ \frac{2}{T_5}\ \frac{2}{T_6}\ \frac{2}{T_7}\ \frac{2}{T_8}\ \frac{2}{T_9}\ \frac{2}{T_{10}}$
$2 \cdot 2 \cdot 2 \cdot 2 \cdot 2 \cdot 2 \cdot 2 \cdot 2 \cdot 2 \cdot 2 = 1024$

75. 9th row of triangle: 1 8 28 56 70 56 28 8 1; 4th number in row: $\boxed{56}$

76. 8th row of triangle: 1 7 21 35 35 21 7 1; 5th number in row: $\boxed{35}$

77. $C(n, n) = \dfrac{n!}{n!(n-n)!} = \dfrac{n!}{n!0!} = \dfrac{n!}{n!} = 1$

78. $C(n, 0) = \dfrac{n!}{0!n!} = \dfrac{n!}{n!} = 1$

79. $\binom{n}{n-r} = \dfrac{n!}{(n-r)!(n-(n-r))!} = \dfrac{n!}{(n-r)!r!} = \dfrac{n!}{r!(n-r)!} = \binom{n}{r}$

80. **Answers may vary.**

81. **Answers may vary.**

82. **Answers may vary.**

83. $\log_x 16 = 4$
$x^4 = 16 \Rightarrow x = 2$

84. $\log_\pi x = \dfrac{1}{2}$
$x = \pi^{1/2} = \sqrt{\pi}$

85. $\log_{\sqrt{7}} 49 = x$
$\left(\sqrt{7}\right)^x = 49 \Rightarrow x = 4$

86. $\log_x \dfrac{1}{2} = -\dfrac{1}{3} \Rightarrow x^{-1/3} = \dfrac{1}{2} \Rightarrow x = 8$

87. true

88. false

89. true

90. false

Exercises 8.7 (page 776)

1. experiment

2. sample space

3. $\dfrac{n(E)}{n(S)}$

4. $P(A) \cdot P(B|A)$

5. $\{(1, H), (2, H), (3, H), (4, H), (5, H), (6, H), (1, T), (2, T), (3, T), (4, T), (5, T), (6, T)\}$

SECTION 8.7

6. $\{(H,H,H),(H,H,T),(H,T,H),(H,T,T),(T,H,H),(T,H,T),(T,T,H),(T,T,T)\}$

7. $\{A,B,C,D,E,F,G,H,I,J,K,L,M,N,O,P,Q,R,S,T,U,V,W,X,Y,Z\}$

8. $\{0, 1, 2, 3, 4, 5, 6, 7, 8, 9\}$

9. $\frac{1}{6}$

10. $\frac{2}{6}=\frac{1}{3}$

11. $\frac{4}{6}=\frac{2}{3}$

12. $\frac{3}{6}=\frac{1}{2}$

13. $\frac{19}{42}$

14. $\frac{42}{42}=1$

15. $\frac{13}{42}$

16. $\frac{9+2}{42}=\frac{11}{42}$

17. $\frac{3}{8}$

18. $\frac{2}{8}=\frac{1}{4}$

19. $\frac{0}{8}=0$

20. $\frac{1}{8}$

21. rolls of 4: $\{(1,3),(2,2),(3,1)\}$
Probability $=\frac{3}{36}=\frac{1}{12}$

22. $\frac{\#\text{ diamonds}}{\#\text{ cards}}=\frac{13}{52}=\frac{1}{4}$

23. $\frac{\#\text{ aces}}{\#\text{ cards}}\cdot\frac{\#\text{ aces}}{\#\text{ cards}}=\frac{4}{52}\cdot\frac{4}{52}=\frac{1}{169}$

24. $\frac{\#\text{ aces}}{\#\text{ cards}}\cdot\frac{\#\text{ aces}}{\#\text{ cards}}=\frac{4}{52}\cdot\frac{3}{51}=\frac{1}{221}$

25. $\frac{\#\text{ red}}{\#\text{ eggs}}=\frac{5}{12}$

26. $\frac{\#\text{ ways to get 2 red eggs}}{\text{total }\#\text{ ways to get 2 eggs}}=\frac{\binom{5}{2}}{\binom{12}{2}}=\frac{10}{66}=\frac{5}{33}$

27. $\frac{\#\text{ ways to get 13 cards of the same suit}}{\#\text{ ways to get 13 cards from the deck of 52}}=\frac{4\cdot\binom{13}{13}}{\binom{52}{13}}$
$=\frac{4}{6.350136\times10^{11}}$
$\approx 6.3\times10^{-12}$

28. $\frac{\#\text{ ways to get 6 diamonds}}{\#\text{ ways to get 6 cards from the deck of 52}}=\frac{\binom{13}{6}}{\binom{52}{6}}=\frac{1716}{20{,}358{,}520}$
$=\frac{33}{391{,}510}$

29. impossible $\Rightarrow 0$

30. $\frac{\#\text{ ways to get 5 clubs}}{\#\text{ ways to get 5 cards from the 26 black cards}}=\frac{\binom{13}{5}}{\binom{26}{5}}=\frac{1287}{65780}=\frac{9}{460}$

31. $\frac{\#\text{ face cards}}{\#\text{ cards in deck}}=\frac{12}{52}=\frac{3}{13}$

32. $\frac{\#\text{ ways to get 6 cards from the 12 face cards}}{\#\text{ ways to get 6 cards from the deck of 52}}=\frac{\binom{12}{6}}{\binom{52}{6}}=\frac{924}{20{,}358{,}520}$
$=\frac{33}{727{,}090}$

33. $\frac{\#\text{ ways to get 5 orange}}{\#\text{ ways to get 5 cubes}}=\frac{\binom{5}{5}}{\binom{6}{5}}=\frac{1}{6}$

34. rolls of 4: $\{(1,1,2),(1,2,1),(2,1,1)\}$
Probability $=\frac{3}{216}=\frac{1}{72}$

35. rolls of 11: (1, 4, 6), (1, 5, 5), (1, 6, 4), (2, 3, 6), (2, 4, 5), (2, 5, 4), (2, 6, 3), (3, 2, 6), (3, 3, 5) (3, 4, 4), (3, 5, 3), (3, 6, 2), (4, 1, 6), (4, 2, 5), (4, 3, 4), (4, 4, 3), (4, 5, 2), (4, 6, 1), (5, 1, 5), (5, 2, 4), (5, 3, 3), (5, 4, 2), (5, 5, 1), (6, 1, 4), (6, 2, 3), (6, 3, 2), (6, 4, 1)

Probability $= \dfrac{27}{216} = \dfrac{1}{8}$

36. $\dfrac{\binom{8}{5}}{\binom{18}{5}} = \dfrac{56}{8568} = \dfrac{1}{153}$

37. $\dfrac{\binom{5}{3}}{2^5} = \dfrac{10}{32} = \dfrac{5}{16}$

38. $\dfrac{\binom{5}{5}}{2^5} = \dfrac{1}{32}$

39. $SSSS, SSSF, SSFS, SSFF, SFSS, SFSF, SFFS, SFFF,$
$FSSS, FSSF, FSFS, FSFF, FFSS, FFSF, FFFS, FFFF$

40. $\dfrac{1}{16}$

41. $\dfrac{4}{16} = \dfrac{1}{4}$

42. $\dfrac{6}{16} = \dfrac{3}{8}$

43. $\dfrac{4}{16} = \dfrac{1}{4}$

44. $\dfrac{1}{16}$

45. $\dfrac{16}{16} = 1$

46. $\dfrac{176}{282} = \dfrac{88}{141}$

47. $\dfrac{32}{119}$

48. $\dfrac{15}{71}$

49. $\dfrac{\binom{8}{4}}{\binom{10}{4}} = \dfrac{70}{210} = \dfrac{1}{3}$

50. $\dfrac{\binom{5}{3}}{\binom{9}{3}} = \dfrac{10}{84} = \dfrac{5}{42}$

51. $$\begin{aligned} P(A \cap B) &= P(A) \cdot P(B|A) \\ &= 0.3(0.6) = 0.18 \end{aligned}$$

52. $$\begin{aligned} P(A \cap B) &= P(A) \cdot P(B|A) \\ 0.3 &= P(A)(0.6) \\ 0.5 &= P(A) \end{aligned}$$

53. $$\begin{aligned} P(A \cap B) &= P(A) \cdot P(B|A) \\ &= 0.2(0.7) = 0.14 \end{aligned}$$

54. $$\begin{aligned} P(A \cap B) &= P(A) \cdot P(B|A) \\ &= 0.40(0.85) \\ &= 0.34 = 34\% \end{aligned}$$

55. $$\begin{aligned} P(A \cap B) &= P(A) \cdot P(B|A) \\ 0.25 &= 0.75P(B|A) \\ 0.33 &\approx P(B|A) \\ 33\% &\approx P(B|A) \end{aligned}$$

56. $$\begin{aligned} P(A \cap B) &= P(A) \cdot P(B|A) \\ &= 0.4(0.7) = 0.28 \end{aligned}$$

57. no

58. yes

59. $$|x+3| = 7$$
$x + 3 = 7$ **OR** $x + 3 = -7$
$x = 4$ $\qquad x = -10$

60. $$|3x-2| = |2x-3|$$
$3x - 2 = 2x - 3$ **OR** $3x - 2 = -(2x - 3)$
$x = -1$ $\qquad 3x - 2 = -2x + 3$
$5x = 5$
$x = 1$

61. $|x-3|<7$
$-7<x-3<7$
$-4<x<10$
$(-4,10)$

62. $|3x-2|\ge|2x-3|$
$\sqrt{(3x-2)^2}\ge\sqrt{(2x-3)^2}$
$9x^2-12x+4\ge4x^2-12x+9$
$5x^2-5\ge0$
$5(x+1)(x-1)\ge0$
$(-\infty,-1]\cup[1,\infty)$

Chapter 8 Review (page 779)

1. $6!=6\cdot5\cdot4\cdot3\cdot2\cdot1=720$

2. $7!\cdot0!\cdot1!\cdot3!=5040\cdot1\cdot1\cdot6=30{,}240$

3. $\frac{8!}{7!}=\frac{8\cdot7!}{7!}=8$

4. $\frac{5!\cdot7!\cdot8!}{6!\cdot9!}=\frac{5!\cdot7\cdot6!\cdot8!}{6!\cdot9\cdot8!}=\frac{5!\cdot7}{9}=\frac{280}{3}$

5. $(x+y)^3=x^3+\frac{3!}{1!2!}x^2y+\frac{3!}{2!1!}xy^2+y^3=x^3+3x^2y+3xy^2+y^3$

6. $(p+q)^4=p^4+\frac{4!}{1!3!}p^3q+\frac{4!}{2!2!}p^2q^2+\frac{4!}{3!1!}pq^3+q^4=p^4+4p^3q+6p^2q^2+4pq^3+q^4$

7. $(a-b)^5=a^5+\frac{5!}{1!4!}a^4(-b)+\frac{5!}{2!3!}a^3(-b)^2+\frac{5!}{3!2!}a^2(-b)^3+\frac{5!}{4!1!}a(-b)^4+(-b)^5$
$=a^5-5a^4b+10a^3b^2-10a^2b^3+5ab^4-b^5$

8. $(2a-b)^3=(2a)^3+\frac{3!}{1!2!}(2a)^2(-b)+\frac{3!}{2!1!}(2a)(-b)^2+(-b)^3=8a^3-12a^2b+6ab^2-b^3$

9. The 4th term will involve b^3.
$\frac{8!}{5!3!}a^5b^3=56a^5b^3$

10. The 3rd term will involve $(-y)^2$.
$\frac{5!}{3!2!}(2x)^3(-y)^2=80x^3y^2$

11. The 7th term will involve $(-y)^6$.
$\frac{9!}{3!6!}x^3(-y)^6=84x^3y^6$

12. The 4th term will involve 7^3.
$\frac{6!}{3!3!}(4x)^37^3=439{,}040x^3$

13. $4^3-1=63$

14. $\frac{4^2+2}{2}=\frac{18}{2}=9$

15. $a_1=5$
$a_2=3a_1+2=3(5)+2=17$
$a_3=3a_2+2=3(17)+2=53$
$a_4=3a_3+2=3(53)+2=161$

16. $a_1=-2$
$a_2=2a_1^2=2(-2)^2=8$
$a_3=2a_2^2=2(8)^2=128$
$a_4=2a_3^2=2(128)^2=32{,}768$

17. $\sum_{k=1}^{4} 3k^2 = 3\sum_{k=1}^{4} k^2 = 3\left(1^2 + 2^2 + 3^2 + 4^2\right) = 3(30) = 90$

18. $\sum_{k=1}^{10} 6 = 10(6) = 60$

19. $\sum_{k=5}^{8} (k^3 + 3k^2) = \sum_{k=5}^{8} k^3 + 3\sum_{k=5}^{8} k^2 = \left(5^3 + 6^3 + 7^3 + 8^3\right) + 3\left(5^2 + 6^2 + 7^2 + 8^2\right)$
$= 1718$

20. $\sum_{k=1}^{30} \left(\frac{3}{2}k - 12\right) - \frac{3}{2}\sum_{k=1}^{30} k = \frac{3}{2}\sum_{k=1}^{30} k - \sum_{k=1}^{30} 12 - \frac{3}{2}\sum_{k=1}^{30} k = -\sum_{k=1}^{30} 12 = -360$

21. $a = 5, d = 4$
$a_{29} = a + (n-1)d$
$= 5 + (29-1)4 = 117$

22. $a = 8, d = 7$
$a_{40} = a + (n-1)d$
$= 8 + (40-1)7 = 281$

23. $a = 6, d = -7$
$a_{15} = a + (n-1)d$
$= 6 + (15-1)(-7) = -92$

24. $a = \frac{1}{2}, d = -2$
$a_{35} = a + (n-1)d$
$= \frac{1}{2} + (35-1)(-2) = -\frac{135}{2}$

25. $a = 2, a_5 = 8$
$8 = 2 + 4d$
$6 = 4d$
$\frac{3}{2} = d \Rightarrow 2, \boxed{\frac{7}{2}, 5, \frac{13}{2}}, 8$

26. $a = 10, a_7 = 100$
$100 = 10 + 6d$
$90 = 6d$
$15 = d \Rightarrow 10, \boxed{25, 40, 55, 70, 85}, 100$

27. $a = 5, d = 4$
$a_{40} = a + (n-1)d = 5 + 39(4) = 161$
$S_{40} = \frac{n(a + a_{40})}{2} = \frac{40(5 + 161)}{2} = 3320$

28. $a = 8, d = 7$
$a_{40} = a + (n-1)d = 8 + 39(7) = 281$
$S_{40} = \frac{n(a + a_{40})}{2} = \frac{40(8 + 281)}{2} = 5780$

29. $a = 6, d = -7$

$a_{40} = a + (n-1)d = 6 + 39(-7) = -267;\ S_{40} = \frac{n(a + a_{40})}{2} = \frac{40(6 - 267)}{2} = -5220$

30. $a = \frac{1}{2}, d = -2$

$a_{40} = a + (n-1)d = \frac{1}{2} + 39(-2) = -\frac{155}{2};\ S_{40} = \frac{n(a + a_{40})}{2} = \frac{40\left(\frac{1}{2} - \frac{155}{2}\right)}{2} = -1540$

31. $a = 81, r = \frac{1}{3}$
$a_{11} = ar^{n-1} = 81\left(\frac{1}{3}\right)^{10} = \frac{1}{729}$

32. $a = 2, r = 3$
$a_9 = ar^{n-1} = 2(3)^8 = 13{,}122$

33. $a = 9, r = \frac{1}{2}$

$$a_{15} = ar^{n-1} = 9\left(\frac{1}{2}\right)^{14} = \frac{9}{16{,}384}$$

34. $a = 8, r = -\frac{1}{5}$

$$a_7 = ar^{n-1} = 8\left(-\frac{1}{5}\right)^6 = \frac{8}{15{,}625}$$

35.

$$\begin{aligned} a_5 &= ar^4 \\ 8 &= 2r^4 \\ 4 &= r^4 \\ \pm\sqrt[4]{4} &= r \Rightarrow r = \pm\sqrt{2} \end{aligned}$$

Use $r = +\sqrt{2}$:

$2, \boxed{2\sqrt{2}, 4, 4\sqrt{2}}, 8$

36.

$$\begin{aligned} a_6 &= ar^5 \\ 64 &= -2r^5 \\ -32 &= r^5 \\ -2 &= r \end{aligned}$$

$-2, \boxed{4, -8, 16, -32}, 64$

37. $a_3 = ar^2$

$64 = 4r^2$

$16 = r^2 \Rightarrow r = 4$ (problem specifies positive) $\Rightarrow 4, \boxed{16}, 64$

38. $a = 81, r = \frac{1}{3}, n = 8$

$$S_8 = \frac{a - ar^n}{1 - r} = \frac{81 - 81\left(\frac{1}{3}\right)^8}{1 - \frac{1}{3}} = \frac{81 - \frac{1}{81}}{\frac{2}{3}} = \frac{3280}{27}$$

39. $a = 2, r = 3, n = 8$

$$S_8 = \frac{a - ar^n}{1 - r} = \frac{2 - 2(3)^8}{1 - 3} = \frac{-13{,}120}{-2} = 6560$$

40. $a = 9, r = \frac{1}{2}, n = 8$

$$S_8 = \frac{a - ar^n}{1 - r} = \frac{9 - 9\left(\frac{1}{2}\right)^8}{1 - \frac{1}{2}} = \frac{\frac{2295}{256}}{\frac{1}{2}} = \frac{2295}{128}$$

41. $a = 8, r = -\frac{1}{5}, n = 8$

$$S_8 = \frac{a - ar^n}{1 - r} = \frac{8 - 8\left(-\frac{1}{5}\right)^8}{1 - \left(-\frac{1}{5}\right)} = \frac{\frac{3{,}124{,}992}{390{,}625}}{\frac{6}{5}} = \frac{520{,}832}{78{,}125}$$

42. $a = \frac{1}{3}, r = 3, n = 8$

$$S_8 = \frac{a - ar^n}{1 - r} = \frac{\frac{1}{3} - \frac{1}{3}(3)^8}{1 - 3} = \frac{-\frac{6560}{3}}{-2} = \frac{3280}{3}$$

43.

$$\begin{aligned} a_7 &= ar^6 \\ &= 2\sqrt{2}\left(\sqrt{2}\right)^6 \\ &= 16\sqrt{2} \end{aligned}$$

44. $a = \dfrac{1}{3}, r = \dfrac{1}{2}$

$$S_\infty = \frac{a}{1 - r} = \frac{\frac{1}{3}}{1 - \frac{1}{2}} = \frac{\frac{1}{3}}{\frac{1}{2}} = \frac{2}{3}$$

45. $a = \dfrac{1}{5}, r = -\dfrac{2}{3}$

$$S_\infty = \frac{a}{1 - r} = \frac{\frac{1}{5}}{1 - \left(-\frac{2}{3}\right)} = \frac{\frac{1}{5}}{\frac{5}{3}} = \frac{3}{25}$$

46. $a = \frac{1}{3}, r = \frac{3}{2} > 1 \Rightarrow$ no sum

47. $a = \frac{1}{2}, r = \frac{1}{2}$

$$S_\infty = \frac{a}{1-r} = \frac{\frac{1}{2}}{1-\frac{1}{2}} = \frac{\frac{1}{2}}{\frac{1}{2}} = 1$$

48. $a = \frac{3}{10}, r = \frac{1}{10}$

$$S_\infty = \frac{a}{1-r} = \frac{\frac{3}{10}}{1-\frac{1}{10}} = \frac{\frac{3}{10}}{\frac{9}{10}} = \frac{1}{3}$$

49. $a = \frac{9}{10}, r = \frac{1}{10}$

$$S_\infty = \frac{a}{1-r} = \frac{\frac{9}{10}}{1-\frac{1}{10}} = \frac{\frac{9}{10}}{\frac{9}{10}} = 1$$

50. $a = \frac{17}{100}, r = \frac{1}{100}$

$$S_\infty = \frac{a}{1-r} = \frac{\frac{17}{100}}{1-\frac{1}{100}} = \frac{\frac{17}{100}}{\frac{99}{100}} = \frac{17}{99}$$

51. $a = \frac{45}{100}, r = \frac{1}{100}$

$$S_\infty = \frac{a}{1-r} = \frac{\frac{45}{100}}{1-\frac{1}{100}} = \frac{\frac{45}{100}}{\frac{99}{100}} = \frac{5}{11}$$

52. $a = 3000, r = 1 + \frac{0.0775}{365}, n = 2190$

$$ar^{365} = 3000\left(1 + \frac{0.0775}{365}\right)^{2190}$$
$$\approx \$4775.81$$

The amount will be \$4775.81.

53. $a = 4000, r = 1.05, n = 10$

$ar^{10} = 4000(1.05)^{10} \approx 6516$ in 10 years

$ar^{-5} = 4000(1.05)^{-5} \approx 3134$ 5 years ago

54. $a = 10{,}000;\ r = 0.90;\ ar^{10} = 10{,}000(0.90)^{10} \approx \$3486.78$ in 10 years

55.

$n = 1$

$$1^3 \stackrel{?}{=} \frac{1^2(1+1)^2}{4}$$
$$1 = 1$$

$n = 2$

$$1^3 + 2^3 \stackrel{?}{=} \frac{2^2(2+1)^2}{4}$$
$$9 \stackrel{?}{=} \frac{4(9)}{4}$$
$$9 = 9$$

$n = 3$

$$1^3 + 2^3 + 3^3 \stackrel{?}{=} \frac{3^2(3+1)^2}{4}$$
$$36 \stackrel{?}{=} \frac{9(16)}{4}$$
$$36 = 36$$

$n = 4$

$$1^3 + 2^3 + 3^3 + 4^3 \stackrel{?}{=} \frac{4^2(4+1)^2}{4}$$
$$100 \stackrel{?}{=} \frac{16(25)}{4}$$
$$100 = 100$$

CHAPTER 8 REVIEW

56. Check $n = 1$: $1^3 = \dfrac{1^2(1+1)^2}{4}$ True for $n = 1$

$1 = 1$

Assume for $n = k$ and show for $n = k + 1$:

$$1^3 + 2^3 + 3^3 + \cdots + k^3 = \frac{k^2(k+1)^2}{4}$$

$$\boxed{1^3 + 2^3 + 3^3 + \cdots + k^3} + (k+1)^3 = \boxed{\frac{k^2(k+1)^2}{4}} + (k+1)^3$$

$$1^3 + 2^3 + 3^3 + \cdots + (k+1)^3 = \frac{k^2(k+1)^2 + 4(k+1)^3}{4}$$

$$1^2 + 2^2 + 3^2 + \cdots + (k+1)^2 = \frac{(k+1)^2[k^2 + 4(k+1)]}{4}$$

$$1^2 + 2^2 + 3^2 + \cdots + (k+1)^2 = \frac{(k+1)^2(k+2)^2}{4}$$

Since this is what results when $n = k + 1$ is in the formula, we have shown that the formula works for $n = k + 1$ if it works for $n = k$.

57. $P(8, 5) = \dfrac{8!}{(8-5)!} = \dfrac{8!}{3!} = 8 \cdot 7 \cdot 6 \cdot 5 \cdot 4 = 6720$

58. $C(7, 4) = \dfrac{7!}{4!(7-4)!} = \dfrac{7!}{4!3!} = \dfrac{7 \cdot 6 \cdot 5 \cdot 4!}{4! \cdot 3 \cdot 2 \cdot 1} = 35$

59. $0! \cdot 1! = 1 \cdot 1 = 1$

60. $P(10, 2) \cdot C(10, 2) = \dfrac{10!}{8!} \cdot \dfrac{10!}{2!8!} = 90 \cdot 45 = 4050$

61. $P(8, 6) \cdot C(8, 6) = \dfrac{8!}{2!} \cdot \dfrac{8!}{6!2!} = 20{,}160 \cdot 28 = 564{,}480$

62. $C(8, 5) \cdot C(6, 2) = \dfrac{8!}{5!3!} \cdot \dfrac{6!}{2!4!} = 56 \cdot 15 = 840$

63. $C(7, 5) \cdot P(4, 0) = \dfrac{7!}{5!2!} \cdot \dfrac{4!}{4!} = 21 \cdot 1 = 21$

64. $C(12, 10) \cdot C(11, 0) = \dfrac{12!}{10!2!} \cdot \dfrac{11!}{0!11!} = 66 \cdot 1 = 66$

65. $\dfrac{P(8, 5)}{C(8, 5)} = \dfrac{6720}{56} = 120$

66. $\dfrac{C(8, 5)}{C(13, 5)} = \dfrac{56}{1287}$

67. $\dfrac{C(6, 3)}{C(10, 3)} = \dfrac{20}{120} = \dfrac{1}{6}$

68. $\dfrac{C(13, 5)}{C(52, 5)} = \dfrac{1287}{2{,}598{,}960} = \dfrac{33}{66{,}640}$

69. Consider each set of two people who must sit together as a single person, so that there are 8 "people" who must be arranged in a circle. This can be done in $(8-1)! = 7! = 5040$ ways. However, each pair seated next to each other could be switched, so that the number of arrangements is multiplied by 4. There are $4 \cdot 5040 = 20{,}160$ possible arrangements.

70. $\frac{9!}{2!2!} = 90{,}720$

71.

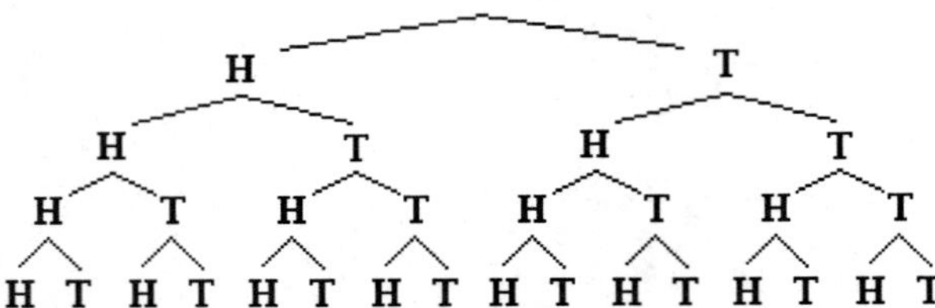

72. $\binom{4}{3}\binom{4}{2} = 4 \cdot 6 = 24$

73. $\frac{\binom{4}{3}\binom{4}{2}}{\binom{52}{5}} = \frac{24}{2{,}598{,}960} = \frac{1}{108{,}290}$

74. $1 - \frac{1}{108{,}290} = \frac{108{,}289}{108{,}290}$

75. $\frac{\binom{4}{4}\binom{4}{4}\binom{4}{4}\binom{4}{1}}{\binom{52}{13}} \approx \frac{4}{6.35 \times 10^{11}} \approx 6.3 \times 10^{-12}$

76. $\frac{\binom{8}{3}\binom{6}{2}}{\binom{14}{5}} = \frac{840}{2002} = \frac{60}{143}$

77. $\frac{13+13}{52} = \frac{1}{2}$

78. $\frac{26+4-2}{52} = \frac{7}{13}$

79. $\frac{1}{\binom{52}{5}} = \frac{1}{2{,}598{,}960}$

80. $\frac{4\binom{13}{5}}{\binom{52}{5}} = \frac{5148}{2{,}598{,}960} = \frac{33}{16{,}660}$

81. Use the tree diagram in **#71**. $\Rightarrow \frac{15}{16}$

Chapter 8 Test (page 786)

1. $3! \cdot 0! \cdot 4! \cdot 1! = 6 \cdot 1 \cdot 24 \cdot 1 = 144$

2. $\frac{2! \cdot 4! \cdot 6! \cdot 8!}{3! \cdot 5! \cdot 7!} = 2! \cdot \frac{4!}{3!} \cdot \frac{6!}{5!} \cdot \frac{8!}{7!}$
$= 2 \cdot 4 \cdot 6 \cdot 8 = 384$

3. The 2nd term will involve $(2y)^1$.
$\frac{5!}{4!1!}x^4(2y)^1 = 10x^4y$

4. The 7th term will involve $(-b)^6$.
$\frac{8!}{2!6!}(2a)^2(-b)^6 = 112a^2b^6$

5. $\sum_{k=1}^{3}(4k+1) = 4\sum_{k=1}^{3}k + \sum_{k=1}^{3}1 = 4(1+2+3) + 3(1) = 24 + 3 = 27$

CHAPTER 8 TEST

6. $\sum_{k=2}^{4}(3k-21) = 3\sum_{k=2}^{4}k - \sum_{k=2}^{4}21 = 3(2+3+4) - 3(21) = 27 - 63 = -36$

7. $a = 2, d = 3$

$a_{10} = a + (n-1)d = 2 + 9(3) = 29$

$S_{10} = \dfrac{n(a + a_{10})}{2} = \dfrac{10(2+29)}{2} = 155$

8. $a = 5, d = -4$

$a_{10} = a + (n-1)d = 5 + 9(-4) = -31$

$S_{10} = \dfrac{n(a + a_{10})}{2} = \dfrac{10(5-31)}{2} = -130$

9. $a = 4, a_5 = 24$

$24 = 4 + 4d$

$20 = 4d$

$5 = d \Rightarrow 4, \boxed{9, 14, 19}, 24$

10. $a_4 = ar^3$

$-54 = -2r^3$

$27 = r^3$

$3 = r \Rightarrow -2, \boxed{-6, -18}, -54$

11. $a = \frac{1}{4}, r = 2, n = 10$

$S_{10} = \dfrac{a - ar^n}{1-r} = \dfrac{\frac{1}{4} - \frac{1}{4}(2)^{10}}{1-2} = \dfrac{-\frac{1023}{4}}{-1} = \dfrac{1023}{4} = 255.75$

12. $a = 6, r = \frac{1}{3}, n = 10$

$S_{10} = \dfrac{a - ar^n}{1-r} = \dfrac{6 - 6\left(\frac{1}{3}\right)^{10}}{1 - \frac{1}{3}} = \dfrac{\frac{354,288}{59,049}}{\frac{2}{3}} = \dfrac{177,144}{19,683} \approx 9$

13. $a = c;\ r = 0.75$

$ar^3 = c(0.75)^3 \approx \$0.42c$ in 3 years

14. $a = c;\ r = 1.10$

$ar^4 = c(1.10)^4 \approx \$1.46c$ in 4 years

15.

Check $n = 1$: $3 = \frac{1}{2}(1)(1+5)$ True for $n = 1$

$3 = 3$

Assume for $n = k$ and show for $n = k+1$:

$$3 + 4 + 5 + \cdots + (k+2) = \frac{1}{2}k(k+5)$$

$$\boxed{3 + 4 + 5 + \cdots + (k+2)} + ((k+1)+2) = \boxed{\frac{1}{2}k(k+5)} + ((k+1)+2)$$

$$3 + 4 + 5 + \cdots + ((k+1)+2) = \frac{1}{2}k^2 + \frac{7}{2}k + 3$$

$$3 + 4 + 5 + \cdots + ((k+1)+2) = \frac{1}{2}(k^2 + 7k + 6)$$

$$3 + 4 + 5 + \cdots + ((k+1)+2) = \frac{1}{2}(k+1)(k+6) = \frac{1}{2}(k+1)((k+1)+5)$$

Since this is what results when $n = k+1$ is in the formula, we have shown that the formula works for $n = k+1$ if it works for $n = k$.

16. $8 \cdot 10 \cdot 10 \cdot 10 \cdot 10 \cdot 10 = 800{,}000$

17. $P(7, 2) = \dfrac{7!}{5!} = 42$

18. $P(4, 4) = \dfrac{4!}{0!} = 24$

19. $C(8, 2) = \dfrac{8!}{2!6!} = 28$

20. $C(12, 0) = \dfrac{12!}{0!12!} = 1$

21. $4!4! = 576$

22. $(6 - 1)! = 5! = 120$

23. $\dfrac{5!}{2!} = 60$

24. $\{(H, H, H), (H, H, T), (H, T, H), (H, T, T), (T, H, H), (T, H, T), (T, T, H), (T, T, T)\}$

25. $\dfrac{1}{6}$

26. $\dfrac{4 + 4}{52} = \dfrac{2}{13}$

27. $\dfrac{\binom{13}{5}}{\binom{52}{5}} = \dfrac{33}{66{,}640}$

28. rolls of 9: $\{(3, 6), (4, 5), (5, 4), (6, 3)\}$
Probability $= \dfrac{4}{36} = \dfrac{1}{9}$

29. $\dfrac{\#\text{ blue}}{\#\text{ all}} \cdot \dfrac{\#\text{ blue}}{\#\text{ all}} = \dfrac{30}{50} \cdot \dfrac{29}{49} = \dfrac{87}{245}$

30. $\dfrac{\binom{18}{4}}{\binom{20}{4}} = \dfrac{3060}{4845} = \dfrac{12}{19}$

Exercise 9.1

1. interest

2. compound

3. annual

4. principal, present

5. future

6. percent

7. interest

8. nominal

9. periodic rate

10. conversion

11. principal, periodic rate,
frequency of compounding, number of years

12. future value, periodic rate,
frequency of compounding, number of years

13. effective

14. 10

15. $I = Prt = 4500(0.0325)(4)$
$= \$585$

16. $I = Prt = 12{,}400(0.045)(8.25)$
$= \$4603.50$

17.
$$I = Prt$$
$$814 = P(0.055)(4)$$
$$\frac{814}{(0.055)(4)} = P$$
$$\$3700 = P$$

18.
$$I = Prt$$
$$3450 = (11{,}500)(0.0375)t$$
$$\frac{3450}{(11{,}500)(0.0375)} = t$$
$$8 = t \Rightarrow 8 \text{ years}$$

19.
$$I = Prt$$
$$7500 = (50{,}000)(r)(2.5)$$
$$\frac{7500}{(50{,}000)(2.5)} = r$$
$$0.06 = r \Rightarrow 6\%$$

20.
$$I = Prt$$
$$5000 = (5000)(0.0625)t$$
$$\frac{5000}{(5000)(0.0625)} = t$$
$$16 = t \Rightarrow 16 \text{ years}$$

21. $A_0 = 1200, i = 0.08, k = 1, n = 1$
$A_n = A_0(1+i)^{kn}$
$A_1 = 1200(1+0.08)^{1\cdot 1} = \$1296$

22. $A_0 = 1200, i = 0.08, k = 1, n = 3$
$A_n = A_0(1+i)^{kn}$
$A_3 = 1200(1+0.08)^{1\cdot 3} \approx \$1511.65$

23. $A_0 = 1200, i = 0.08, k = 1, n = 5$
$A_n = A_0(1+i)^{kn}$
$A_5 = 1200(1+0.08)^{1\cdot 5} \approx \$1763.19$

24. $A_0 = 1200, i = 0.08, k = 1, n = 20$
$A_n = A_0(1+i)^{kn}$
$A_{20} = 1200(1+0.08)^{1\cdot 20} \approx \$5593.15$

25. $A_0 = 1200, i = 0.03, k = 1, n = 10$
$A_n = A_0(1+i)^{kn}$
$A_{10} = 1200(1+0.03)^{1\cdot 10} \approx \$1612.70$

26. $A_0 = 1200, i = 0.05, k = 1, n = 10$
$A_n = A_0(1+i)^{kn}$
$A_{10} = 1200(1+0.05)^{1\cdot 10} \approx \$1954.67$

27. $A_0 = 1200, i = 0.09, k = 1, n = 10$
$A_n = A_0(1+i)^{kn}$
$A_{10} = 1200(1+0.09)^{1\cdot 10} \approx \$2840.84$

28. $A_0 = 1200, i = 0.12, k = 1, n = 10$
$A_n = A_0(1+i)^{kn}$
$A_{10} = 1200(1+0.12)^{1\cdot 10} \approx \$3727.02$

29. $A_0 = 1200, i = \frac{0.06}{2}, k = 2, n = 15$
$A_n = A_0(1+i)^{kn}$
$A_{15} = 1200\left(1+\frac{0.06}{2}\right)^{2\cdot 15} \approx \$2912.71$

30. $A_0 = 1200, i = \frac{0.06}{4}, k = 4, n = 15$
$A_n = A_0(1+i)^{kn}$
$A_{15} = 1200\left(1+\frac{0.06}{4}\right)^{4\cdot 15} \approx \$2931.86$

31. $A_0 = 1200, i = \frac{0.06}{12}, k = 12, n = 15$
$A_n = A_0(1+i)^{kn}$
$A_{15} = 1200\left(1+\frac{0.06}{12}\right)^{12\cdot 15} \approx \$2944.91$

32. $A_0 = 1200, i = \frac{0.06}{365}, k = 365, n = 15$
$A_n = A_0(1+i)^{kn}$
$A_{15} = 1200\left(1+\frac{0.06}{365}\right)^{365\cdot 15} \approx \$2951.31$

33. $k = 4, i = \frac{0.06}{4}$
$R = (1+i)^k - 1$
$= \left(1+\frac{0.06}{4}\right)^4 - 1$
$\approx 0.0614 = 6.14\%$

34. $k = 12, i = \frac{0.08}{12}$
$R = (1+i)^k - 1$
$= \left(1+\frac{0.08}{12}\right)^{12} - 1$
$\approx 0.0830 = 8.30\%$

35. $k = 2, i = \frac{0.095}{2}$
$R = (1+i)^k - 1$
$= \left(1+\frac{0.095}{2}\right)^2 - 1$
$\approx 0.0973 = 9.73\%$

36. $k = 360, i = \frac{0.10}{360}$
$R = (1+i)^k - 1$
$= \left(1+\frac{0.10}{360}\right)^{360} - 1$
$\approx 0.1052 = 10.52\%$

37. $A_6 = 20{,}000;\ i = \frac{0.06}{2},\ k = 2,\ n = 6$
$$A_0 = A_n(1+i)^{-kn} = 20{,}000\left(1 + \tfrac{0.06}{2}\right)^{-2\cdot 6} \approx \$14{,}027.60$$

38. $A_6 = 20{,}000;\ i = \frac{0.08}{4},\ k = 4,\ n = 6$
$$A_0 = A_n(1+i)^{-kn} = 20{,}000\left(1 + \tfrac{0.08}{4}\right)^{-4\cdot 6} \approx \$12{,}434.43$$

39. $A_6 = 20{,}000;\ i = \frac{0.09}{12},\ k = 12,\ n = 6$
$$A_0 = A_n(1+i)^{-kn} = 20{,}000\left(1 + \tfrac{0.09}{12}\right)^{-12\cdot 6} \approx \$11{,}678.47$$

40. $A_6 = 20{,}000;\ i = \frac{0.07}{360},\ k = 360,\ n = 6$
$$A_0 = A_n(1+i)^{-kn} = 20{,}000\left(1 + \tfrac{0.07}{360}\right)^{-360\cdot 6} \approx \$13{,}141.47$$

41.
$$I = Prt$$
$$175 = (2500)(r)(2)$$
$$\frac{175}{(2500)(2)} = r$$
$$0.035 = r \Rightarrow 3.5\%, \text{ or } 3\tfrac{1}{2}\%$$

42.
$$I = Prt$$
$$3483 = P(0.0645)(3)$$
$$\frac{3483}{(0.0645)(3)} = P$$
$$\$18{,}000 = P$$

43. $A_0 = 7000,\ i = \frac{0.06}{4},\ k = 4,\ n = 18$
$$A_n = A_0(1+i)^{kn}$$
$$A_{18} = 7000\left(1 + \tfrac{0.06}{4}\right)^{4\cdot 18} \approx \$20{,}448.11$$

44. $A_0 = 5700,\ i = \frac{0.08}{12},\ k = 12,\ n = 6$
$$A_n = A_0(1+i)^{kn}$$
$$A_6 = 5700\left(1 + \tfrac{0.08}{12}\right)^{12\cdot 6} \approx \$9196.96$$

45. $A_0 = 147{,}500;\ i = \frac{0.075}{2},\ k = 2,\ n = 12$
$$A_n = A_0(1+i)^{kn}$$
$$A_{12} = 147500\left(1 + \tfrac{0.075}{2}\right)^{2\cdot 12} \approx \$356{,}867.13$$

46. $A_0 = 3,\ i = \frac{0.0873}{2},\ k = 2,\ n = 8$
$$A_n = A_0(1+i)^{kn}$$
$$A_8 = 3\left(1 + \tfrac{0.0873}{2}\right)^{2\cdot 8} \approx \$5.943 \text{ million}$$

47. $A_0 = 137{,}000;\ i = \frac{0.11}{1},\ k = 1,\ n = 4$
$$A_n = A_0(1+i)^{kn}$$
$$A_4 = 137{,}000\left(1 + \tfrac{0.11}{1}\right)^{1\cdot 4} \approx \$207{,}976$$

48. $A_0 = 47{,}000;\ i = \frac{0.085}{1},\ k = 1,\ n = 5$
$$A_n = A_0(1+i)^{kn}$$
$$A_5 = 47{,}000\left(1 + \tfrac{0.085}{1}\right)^{1\cdot 5} \approx \$70{,}672$$

49. $A_0 = 4.3,\ i = \frac{0.072}{1},\ k = 1,\ n = 10$
$$A_n = A_0(1+i)^{kn}$$
$$A_{10} = 4.3\left(1 + \tfrac{0.072}{1}\right)^{1\cdot 10} \approx \$8.62 \text{ million ft}^3$$

50.

Bank One	Bank Two
$k = 4,\ i = \frac{0.0435}{4}$	$k = 12,\ i = \frac{0.043}{12}$
$R = (1+i)^k - 1$	$R = (1+i)^k - 1$
$= \left(1 + \frac{0.0435}{4}\right)^4 - 1$	$= \left(1 + \frac{0.043}{12}\right)^{12} - 1$
$\approx 0.0442 = 4.42\%$	$\approx 0.0439 = 4.39\%$

Bank One provides the better growth.

51. NOW account

$k = 4,\ i = \frac{0.072}{4}$

$R = (1+i)^k - 1$

$= \left(1 + \frac{0.072}{4}\right)^4 - 1$

$\approx 0.0740 = 7.40\%$

Money Market

$k = 12,\ i = \frac{0.069}{12}$

$R = (1+i)^k - 1$

$= \left(1 + \frac{0.069}{12}\right)^{12} - 1$

$\approx 0.0712 = 7.12\%$

52. CD

$k = 2,\ i = \frac{0.062}{2}$

$R = (1+i)^k - 1$

$= \left(1 + \frac{0.062}{2}\right)^2 - 1$

$\approx 0.0630 = 6.30\%$

Passbook

$k = 4,\ i = \frac{0.0525}{4}$

$R = (1+i)^k - 1$

$= \left(1 + \frac{0.0525}{4}\right)^4 - 1$

$\approx 0.0535 = 5.35\%$

53. $A_0 = 1230,\ i = \frac{0.12}{360},\ k = 360,\ n = 0.25$

$A_n = A_0(1+i)^{kn}$

$A_{0.25} = 1230\left(1 + \frac{0.12}{360}\right)^{360(0.25)} \approx \$1267.45$

54. $A_0 = 2570,\ i = \frac{0.114}{12},\ k = 12,\ n = 0.75$

$A_n = A_0(1+i)^{kn}$

$A_{0.75} = 2570\left(1 + \frac{0.114}{12}\right)^{12(0.75)} \approx \$2798.27$

55. $A_{1.5} = 4200;\ i = \frac{0.0575}{12},\ k = 12,\ n = 1.5$

$A_0 = A_n(1+i)^{-kn} = 4200\left(1 + \frac{0.0575}{12}\right)^{-12(1.5)}$

$\approx \$3853.73$

56. $A_{1.5} = 2780;\ i = \frac{0.076}{4},\ k = 4,\ n = 1.5$

$A_0 = A_n(1+i)^{-kn} = 2780\left(1 + \frac{0.076}{4}\right)^{-4(1.5)}$

$\approx \$2483.13$

57. First ten years

$A_0 = 12{,}000;\ i = \frac{0.075}{12},\ k = 12,\ n = 10$

$A_n = A_0(1+i)^{kn} = 12{,}000\left(1 + \frac{0.075}{12}\right)^{12(10)}$

$\approx \$25{,}344.78$

Next four years

$A_0 = 37{,}344.78;\ i = \frac{0.075}{12},\ k = 12,\ n = 4$

$A_n = A_0(1+i)^{kn} = 37{,}344.78\left(1 + \frac{0.075}{12}\right)^{12(4)}$

$\approx \$50{,}363.14$

58. First five years

$A_0 = 1100;\ i = \frac{0.10}{12},\ k = 12,\ n = 5$

$A_n = A_0(1+i)^{kn} = 1100\left(1 + \frac{0.10}{12}\right)^{12(5)}$

$\approx \$1809.84$

Next five years

$A_0 = 1809.84;\ i = \frac{0.08}{2},\ k = 2,\ n = 5$

$A_n = A_0(1+i)^{kn} = 1809.84\left(1 + \frac{0.08}{2}\right)^{2(5)}$

$\approx \$2679.01$

59-62. Answers may vary.

63. $\dfrac{x^2 - 2x - 15}{2x^2 - 9x - 5} = \dfrac{(x-5)(x+3)}{(2x+1)(x-5)} = \dfrac{x+3}{2x+1}$

64. $3x(x^2 - 5) - (x^3 - 2x) = 3x^3 - 15x - x^3 + 2x = 2x^3 - 13x$

65. $\dfrac{(3-x)(x+3)}{-x^2+9} = \dfrac{(3-x)(x+3)}{9-x^2} = \dfrac{(3-x)(x+3)}{(3+x)(3-x)} = 1$

66. $-\sqrt{x^2 - 6x + 9} = -\sqrt{(x-3)^2} = -(x-3) = -x + 3$

Exercise 9.2

1. annuities

2. end

3. payments, interest

4. term

5. regular deposit, periodic rate, frequency of compounding, number of years

6. sinking

7. $P = 100, i = \frac{0.06}{1}, k = 1, n = 10$

$$A_n = \frac{P\left[(1+i)^{kn} - 1\right]}{i} = \frac{100\left[\left(1+\frac{0.06}{1}\right)^{1\cdot 10} - 1\right]}{\frac{0.06}{1}} \approx \$1318.08$$

8. $P = 100, i = \frac{0.06}{1}, k = 1, n = 5$

$$A_n = \frac{P\left[(1+i)^{kn} - 1\right]}{i} = \frac{100\left[\left(1+\frac{0.06}{1}\right)^{1\cdot 5} - 1\right]}{\frac{0.06}{1}} \approx \$563.71$$

9. $P = 100, i = \frac{0.06}{1}, k = 1, n = 3$

$$A_n = \frac{P\left[(1+i)^{kn} - 1\right]}{i} = \frac{100\left[\left(1+\frac{0.06}{1}\right)^{1\cdot 3} - 1\right]}{\frac{0.06}{1}} \approx \$318.36$$

10. $P = 100, i = \frac{0.06}{1}, k = 1, n = 20$

$$A_n = \frac{P\left[(1+i)^{kn} - 1\right]}{i} = \frac{100\left[\left(1+\frac{0.06}{1}\right)^{1\cdot 20} - 1\right]}{\frac{0.06}{1}} \approx \$3678.56$$

11. $P = 100, i = \frac{0.04}{1}, k = 1, n = 10$

$$A_n = \frac{P\left[(1+i)^{kn} - 1\right]}{i} = \frac{100\left[\left(1+\frac{0.04}{1}\right)^{1\cdot 10} - 1\right]}{\frac{0.04}{1}} \approx \$1200.61$$

12. $P = 100, i = \frac{0.07}{1}, k = 1, n = 10$

$$A_n = \frac{P\left[(1+i)^{kn} - 1\right]}{i} = \frac{100\left[\left(1+\frac{0.07}{1}\right)^{1\cdot 10} - 1\right]}{\frac{0.07}{1}} \approx \$1381.64$$

13. $P = 100, i = \frac{0.095}{1}, k = 1, n = 10$

$$A_n = \frac{P\left[(1+i)^{kn} - 1\right]}{i} = \frac{100\left[\left(1+\frac{0.095}{1}\right)^{1\cdot 10} - 1\right]}{\frac{0.095}{1}} \approx \$1556.03$$

14. $P = 100, i = \frac{0.085}{1}, k = 1, n = 10$

$$A_n = \frac{P\left[(1+i)^{kn} - 1\right]}{i} = \frac{100\left[\left(1+\frac{0.085}{1}\right)^{1\cdot 10} - 1\right]}{\frac{0.085}{1}} \approx \$1483.51$$

SECTION 9.2

15. $P = 100,\ i = \frac{0.08}{2},\ k = 2,\ n = 15$

$$A_n = \frac{P\left[(1+i)^{kn} - 1\right]}{i} = \frac{100\left[\left(1+\frac{0.08}{2}\right)^{2\cdot 15} - 1\right]}{\frac{0.08}{2}} \approx \$5608.49$$

16. $P = 100,\ i = \frac{0.08}{4},\ k = 4,\ n = 15$

$$A_n = \frac{P\left[(1+i)^{kn} - 1\right]}{i} = \frac{100\left[\left(1+\frac{0.08}{4}\right)^{4\cdot 15} - 1\right]}{\frac{0.08}{4}} \approx \$11{,}405.15$$

17. $P = 100,\ i = \frac{0.08}{12},\ k = 12,\ n = 15$

$$A_n = \frac{P\left[(1+i)^{kn} - 1\right]}{i} = \frac{100\left[\left(1+\frac{0.08}{12}\right)^{12\cdot 15} - 1\right]}{\frac{0.08}{12}} \approx \$34{,}603.82$$

18. $P = 100,\ i = \frac{0.08}{1},\ k = 1,\ n = 15$

$$A_n = \frac{P\left[(1+i)^{kn} - 1\right]}{i} = \frac{100\left[\left(1+\frac{0.08}{1}\right)^{1\cdot 15} - 1\right]}{\frac{0.08}{1}} \approx \$2715.21$$

19. $A_n = 20{,}000;\ i = \frac{0.04}{1},\ k = 1,\ n = 10$

$$P = \frac{A_n i}{(1+i)^{kn} - 1} = \frac{20{,}000\left(\frac{0.04}{1}\right)}{\left(1+\frac{0.04}{1}\right)^{1\cdot 10} - 1} \approx \$1665.81$$

20. $A_n = 20{,}000;\ i = \frac{0.06}{4},\ k = 4,\ n = 10$

$$P = \frac{A_n i}{(1+i)^{kn} - 1} = \frac{20{,}000\left(\frac{0.06}{4}\right)}{\left(1+\frac{0.06}{4}\right)^{4\cdot 10} - 1} \approx \$368.54$$

21. $A_n = 20{,}000;\ i = \frac{0.09}{2},\ k = 2,\ n = 10$

$$P = \frac{A_n i}{(1+i)^{kn} - 1} = \frac{20{,}000\left(\frac{0.09}{2}\right)}{\left(1+\frac{0.09}{2}\right)^{2\cdot 10} - 1} \approx \$637.52$$

22. $A_n = 20{,}000;\ i = \frac{0.08}{12},\ k = 12,\ n = 10$

$$P = \frac{A_n i}{(1+i)^{kn} - 1} = \frac{20{,}000\left(\frac{0.08}{12}\right)}{\left(1+\frac{0.08}{12}\right)^{12\cdot 10} - 1} \approx \$109.32$$

23. $P = 200,\ i = \frac{0.06}{12},\ k = 12,\ n = 1$

$$A_n = \frac{P\left[(1+i)^{kn} - 1\right]}{i} = \frac{200\left[\left(1+\frac{0.06}{12}\right)^{12\cdot 1} - 1\right]}{\frac{0.06}{12}} \approx \$2467.11$$

24. $P = 1300,\ i = \frac{0.065}{4},\ k = 4,\ n = 21$

$$A_n = \frac{P\left[(1+i)^{kn} - 1\right]}{i} = \frac{1300\left[\left(1+\frac{0.065}{4}\right)^{4\cdot 21} - 1\right]}{\frac{0.065}{4}} \approx \$229{,}839.59$$

25. $P = 135{,}000;\ i = \frac{0.087}{12},\ k = 12,\ n = 20$

$$A_n = \frac{P\left[(1+i)^{kn} - 1\right]}{i} = \frac{135{,}000\left[\left(1 + \frac{0.087}{12}\right)^{12\cdot 20} - 1\right]}{\frac{0.087}{12}} \approx \$86{,}803{,}923.58$$

26. $P = 25,\ i = \frac{0.075}{12},\ k = 12,\ n = 11$

$$A_n = \frac{P\left[(1+i)^{kn} - 1\right]}{i} = \frac{25\left[\left(1 + \frac{0.075}{12}\right)^{12\cdot 11} - 1\right]}{\frac{0.075}{12}} \approx \$5104.12$$

27. $A_n = 750{,}000;\ i = \frac{0.0975}{12},\ k = 12,\ n = 2.5$

$$P = \frac{A_n i}{(1+i)^{kn} - 1} = \frac{750{,}000\left(\frac{0.0975}{12}\right)}{\left(1 + \frac{0.0975}{12}\right)^{12\cdot 2.5} - 1} \approx \$22{,}177.71$$

28. $A_n = 500{,}000;\ i = \frac{0.085}{12},\ k = 12,\ n = 25$

$$P = \frac{A_n i}{(1+i)^{kn} - 1} = \frac{500{,}000\left(\frac{0.085}{12}\right)}{\left(1 + \frac{0.085}{12}\right)^{12\cdot 25} - 1} \approx \$484.47$$

29.

Bank A

$A_n = 10{,}000;\ i = \frac{0.055}{1},\ k = 1,\ n = 20$

$$P = \frac{A_n i}{(1+i)^{kn} - 1} = \frac{10{,}000\left(\frac{0.055}{1}\right)}{\left(1 + \frac{0.055}{1}\right)^{1\cdot 20} - 1} \approx \$286.79 \text{ per year}$$

Bank B

$A_n = 10{,}000;\ i = \frac{0.0535}{12},\ k = 12,\ n = 20$

$$P = \frac{A_n i}{(1+i)^{kn} - 1} = \frac{10{,}000\left(\frac{0.0535}{12}\right)}{\left(1 + \frac{0.0535}{12}\right)^{12\cdot 20} - 1} \approx \$23.36 \text{ per month, or } \$280.32 \text{ per year}$$

Bank B requires the lower annual contributions.

30. $A_n = 47{,}000;\ i = \frac{0.102}{12},\ k = 12,\ n = 12$

$$P = \frac{A_n i}{(1+i)^{kn} - 1} = \frac{47{,}000\left(\frac{0.102}{12}\right)}{\left(1 + \frac{0.102}{12}\right)^{12\cdot 12} - 1} \approx \$167.63$$

31.

First 15 years

$P = 100,\ i = \frac{0.08}{12},\ k = 12,\ n = 15$

$$A_n = \frac{P\left[(1+i)^{kn} - 1\right]}{i} = \frac{100\left[\left(1 + \frac{0.08}{12}\right)^{12\cdot 15} - 1\right]}{\frac{0.08}{12}} \approx \$34.603.82$$

Next 15 years

$P = 34{,}603.82,\ i = \frac{0.08}{12},\ k = 12,\ n = 15$

$$A_n = P(1+i)^{kn} = 34{,}603.82\left(1 + \frac{0.08}{12}\right)^{12\cdot 15} \approx \$114{,}432.12$$

32. $P = 200,\ i = \frac{0.08}{12},\ k = 12,\ n = 15$

$$A_n = \frac{P\left[(1+i)^{kn} - 1\right]}{i} = \frac{200\left[\left(1 + \frac{0.08}{12}\right)^{12\cdot 15} - 1\right]}{\frac{0.08}{12}} \approx \$69{,}207.64$$

33.

Last 5 years	First 5 years
$A_n = 13{,}500;\ i = \frac{0.09}{1},\ k = 1,\ n = 5$	$A_n = 8774.07;\ i = \frac{0.09}{1},\ k = 1,\ n = 5$
$PV = A_n(1+i)^{-kn}$	$P = \dfrac{A_n i}{(1+i)^{kn} - 1}$
$= 13{,}500\left(1 + \dfrac{0.09}{1}\right)^{-1(5)}$	$= \dfrac{8774.07\left(\frac{0.09}{1}\right)}{\left(1 + \frac{0.09}{1}\right)^{1\cdot 5} - 1}$
$\approx \$8774.07$	$\approx \$1466.08$ per year

34. **Answers may vary.**

35.
$$\begin{aligned} \frac{2(5x-12)}{x} &= 8 \\ 2(5x-12) &= 8x \\ 10x - 24 &= 8x \\ 2x &= 24 \\ x &= 12 \end{aligned}$$

36.
$$\begin{aligned} \frac{2(5x-12)}{x} &= x \\ 2(5x-12) &= x^2 \\ 0 &= x^2 - 10x + 24 \\ 0 &= (x-4)(x-6) \\ x = 4 \quad &\text{or} \quad x = 6 \end{aligned}$$

37.
$$\begin{aligned} \sqrt{2x+3} &= 3 \\ \left(\sqrt{2x+3}\right)^2 &= 3^2 \\ 2x + 3 &= 9 \\ 2x &= 6 \\ x &= 3 \end{aligned}$$

38.
$$\begin{aligned} \sqrt{2x+3} &= x \\ \left(\sqrt{2x+3}\right)^2 &= x^2 \\ 2x + 3 &= x^2 \\ 0 &= x^2 - 2x - 3 \\ 0 &= (x-3)(x+1) \\ \boxed{x = 3} \quad &\text{or} \quad x = -1 \text{ (extraneous)} \end{aligned}$$

Exercise 9.3

1. present value

2. present value

3. promissory note

4. installments

5. amortizing

6. mortgage

7. $P = 3500,\ k = 1,\ i = \dfrac{0.0525}{1},\ n = 25$

$$\begin{aligned} A_0 &= \frac{P\left[1 - (1+i)^{-kn}\right]}{i} \\ &= \frac{3500\left[1 - \left(1 + \frac{0.0525}{1}\right)^{-1\cdot 25}\right]}{\frac{0.0525}{1}} \\ &\approx \$48{,}116.14 \end{aligned}$$

8. $P = 375,\ k = 2,\ i = \dfrac{0.0492}{2},\ n = 10$

$$\begin{aligned} A_0 &= \frac{P\left[1 - (1+i)^{-kn}\right]}{i} \\ &= \frac{375\left[1 - \left(1 + \frac{0.0492}{2}\right)^{-2\cdot 10}\right]}{\frac{0.0492}{2}} \\ &\approx \$5868.09 \end{aligned}$$

9. $A = 25{,}000;\ k = 12, i = \dfrac{0.12}{12}, n = 15$

$$P = \frac{Ai}{1-(1+i)^{-kn}} = \frac{25{,}000\left(\frac{0.12}{12}\right)}{1-\left(1+\frac{0.12}{12}\right)^{-12\cdot 15}} \approx \$300.04$$

10. $A = 1750;\ k = 12, i = \dfrac{0.19}{12}, n = 1.5$

$$P = \frac{Ai}{1-(1+i)^{-kn}} = \frac{1750\left(\frac{0.19}{12}\right)}{1-\left(1+\frac{0.19}{12}\right)^{-12\cdot 1.5}} \approx \$112.50$$

11. $P = 700, k = 4, i = \dfrac{0.0625}{4}, n = 15$

$$A_0 = \frac{P\left[1-(1+i)^{-kn}\right]}{i} = \frac{700\left[1-\left(1+\frac{0.0625}{4}\right)^{-4\cdot 15}\right]}{\frac{0.0625}{4}} \approx \$27{,}128.43$$

12. $P = 15{,}000;\ k = 12, i = \dfrac{0.092}{12}, n = 20$

$$A_0 = \frac{P\left[1-(1+i)^{-kn}\right]}{i} = \frac{15{,}000\left[1-\left(1+\frac{0.092}{12}\right)^{-12\cdot 20}\right]}{\frac{0.092}{12}} \approx \$1{,}643{,}603.78$$

13. $P = 12{,}000;\ k = 1, i = \dfrac{0.085}{1}, n = 15$

$$A_0 = \frac{P\left[1-(1+i)^{-kn}\right]}{i} = \frac{12{,}000\left[1-\left(1+\frac{0.085}{1}\right)^{-1\cdot 15}\right]}{\frac{0.085}{1}} \approx \$99{,}650.84$$

14. $P = 5000, k = 4, i = \dfrac{0.0766666667}{4}, n = 25$

$$A_0 = \frac{P\left[1-(1+i)^{-kn}\right]}{i} = \frac{5000\left[1-\left(1+\frac{0.0766666667}{4}\right)^{-4\cdot 25}\right]}{\frac{0.0766666667}{4}} \approx \$221{,}794.27$$

15. $A = 21{,}700;\ k = 12, i = \dfrac{0.084}{12}, n = 4$

$$P = \frac{Ai}{1-(1+i)^{-kn}} = \frac{21{,}700\left(\frac{0.084}{12}\right)}{1-\left(1+\frac{0.084}{12}\right)^{-12\cdot 4}} \approx \$533.84$$

16. Refer to **#15**. Total payments $= 48 \cdot 533.84 = \$25{,}624.32$

17.

15-year

$A = 130{,}000;\ k = 12, i = \dfrac{0.12}{12}, n = 15$

$$P = \frac{Ai}{1-(1+i)^{-kn}} = \frac{130{,}000\left(\frac{0.12}{12}\right)}{1-\left(1+\frac{0.12}{12}\right)^{-12\cdot 15}} \approx \$1560.22$$

20-year

$A = 130{,}000;\ k = 12, i = \dfrac{0.11}{12}, n = 20$

$$P = \frac{Ai}{1-(1+i)^{-kn}} = \frac{130{,}000\left(\frac{0.11}{12}\right)}{1-\left(1+\frac{0.11}{12}\right)^{-12\cdot 20}} \approx \$1341.84$$

18. Refer to **#17**

15-year

Total $= 180 \cdot 1560.22 = \$280{,}839.60$

20-year

Total $= 240 \cdot 1341.84 = \$322{,}041.60$

19.

From 55 to 80	From 20 to 55
$P = 5000;\ k = 12,\ i = \frac{0.0875}{12},\ n = 25$	$A_n = 608{,}166.24;\ i = \frac{0.0875}{12},\ k = 12,\ n = 35$

$$A_0 = \frac{P\left[1-(1+i)^{-kn}\right]}{i} = \frac{5000\left[1-\left(1+\frac{0.0875}{12}\right)^{-12\cdot 25}\right]}{\frac{0.0875}{12}} \approx \$608{,}166.24$$

$$P = \frac{A_n i}{(1+i)^{kn}-1} = \frac{608{,}166.24\left(\frac{0.0875}{12}\right)}{\left(1+\frac{0.0875}{12}\right)^{12\cdot 35}-1} \approx \$220.13$$

20. **a.** $$A_n = \frac{1000\left[\left(1+\frac{0.08}{1}\right)^{1\cdot 10}-1\right]}{\frac{0.08}{1}} \approx \$14{,}486.56$$

$$A_n = 14{,}486.56\left(1+\frac{0.08}{1}\right)^{1(10)} \approx 31{,}275.40$$

b. $$A_n = \frac{500\left[\left(1+\frac{0.08}{1}\right)^{1\cdot 20}-1\right]}{\frac{0.08}{1}} \approx \$22{,}880.98$$

c. $$A_n = \frac{2000\left[\left(1+\frac{0.08}{1}\right)^{1\cdot 10}-1\right]}{\frac{0.08}{1}} \approx \$28{,}973.12$$

d. $$A_n = 8000\left(1+\frac{0.08}{1}\right)^{1(20)} \approx \$37{,}287.66 \Leftarrow \text{Best } A_n\text{, so best option}$$

21.

First ten years

$$A_n = \frac{500\left[\left(1+\frac{0.0725}{4}\right)^{4\cdot 10}-1\right]}{\frac{0.0725}{4}} \approx \$29{,}003.32$$

Next ten years (2 parts)

$$A_n = \frac{1500\left[\left(1+\frac{0.0725}{4}\right)^{4\cdot 10}-1\right]}{\frac{0.0725}{4}} \approx \$87{,}009.96$$

$$A_n = 29{,}003.32\left(1+\frac{0.0725}{4}\right)^{4(10)} \approx \$59{,}496.55$$

Total = \$87,009.96 + \$59,496.55 = \$146,506.51

22.

First five years

$$A_n = \frac{150\left[\left(1+\frac{0.05}{12}\right)^{12\cdot 5}-1\right]}{\frac{0.05}{12}} \approx \$10{,}200.91$$

Next five years (2 parts)

$$A_n = \frac{150\left[\left(1+\frac{0.065}{12}\right)^{12\cdot 5}-1\right]}{\frac{0.065}{12}} \approx \$10{,}601.10$$

$$A_n = 10{,}200.91\left(1+\frac{0.065}{12}\right)^{12(5)} \approx \$14{,}106.00$$

Total = \$10,601.10 + \$14,106.00 = \$24,707.10

23. $$\frac{6\sqrt{30}}{3\sqrt{5}} = \frac{6}{3}\cdot\frac{\sqrt{30}}{\sqrt{5}} = 2\sqrt{\frac{30}{5}} = 2\sqrt{6}$$

24. $\dfrac{6}{\sqrt{7}-2} = \dfrac{6\left(\sqrt{7}+2\right)}{\left(\sqrt{7}-2\right)\left(\sqrt{7}+2\right)} = \dfrac{6\left(\sqrt{7}+2\right)}{7-4} = \dfrac{6\left(\sqrt{7}+2\right)}{3} = 2\left(\sqrt{7}+2\right)$

25. $3\sqrt{5x}+5\sqrt{20x} = 3\sqrt{5x}+5\sqrt{4}\sqrt{5x} = 3\sqrt{5x}+10\sqrt{5x} = 13\sqrt{5x}$

26. $\sqrt{\dfrac{x^3y^5}{x^5y^6}} = \sqrt{\dfrac{1}{x^2y}} = \dfrac{1}{x\sqrt{y}} = \dfrac{1\sqrt{y}}{x\sqrt{y}\sqrt{y}} = \dfrac{\sqrt{y}}{xy}$

Chapter 9 Review

1. $I = Prt = 2000(0.09)(5) = 900$
$2000 + 900 = \$2900$

2. $A_n = 2000\left(1+\dfrac{0.09}{1}\right)^{1\cdot 5} \approx \$3077.25$

3. $A_n = 2350\left(1+\frac{0.14}{360}\right)^{360(1/6)} \approx \$2405.47$

4. $A_n = 2000\left(1+\dfrac{0.076}{4}\right)^{4\cdot 16} \approx \$6670.80$

5. BigBank: $R = \left(1+\dfrac{0.063}{4}\right)^4 - 1 = 0.0645$

BestBank: $R = \left(1+\dfrac{0.0621}{365}\right)^{365} - 1 = 0.0641$

BigBank has the better return.

6. $A_6 = 7900;\ i = \frac{0.0575}{2},\ k=2,\ n=6$
$A_0 = A_n(1+i)^{-kn}$
$= 7900\left(1+\frac{0.0575}{2}\right)^{-2\cdot 6} \approx \$5622.23$

7. $A_n = \dfrac{500\left[\left(1+\frac{0.05}{1}\right)^{1\cdot 13}-1\right]}{\frac{0.05}{1}}$
$\approx \$8856.49$

8. $A_n = \dfrac{150\left[\left(1+\frac{0.08}{12}\right)^{12\cdot 20}-1\right]}{\frac{0.08}{12}}$
$\approx \$88{,}353.06$

9. $P = \dfrac{40{,}700\left(\frac{0.075}{12}\right)}{\left(1+\frac{0.075}{12}\right)^{12\cdot 7}-1} \approx \$369.89$

10. $A_0 = \dfrac{250\left[1-\left(1+\frac{0.065}{2}\right)^{-2\cdot 20}\right]}{\frac{0.065}{2}}$
$\approx \$5552.11$

11. $A_0 = \dfrac{50{,}000\left[1-\left(1+\frac{0.096}{1}\right)^{-1\cdot 20}\right]}{\frac{0.096}{1}}$
$\approx \$437{,}563.50$

12. $P = \dfrac{150{,}500\left(\frac{0.1075}{12}\right)}{1-\left(1+\frac{0.1075}{12}\right)^{-12\cdot 15}} \approx \$1687.03$; Total paid $= 1687.03\cdot 180 = \$303{,}665.40$

13. $P = \dfrac{150{,}500\left(\frac{0.1075}{12}\right)}{1-\left(1+\frac{0.1075}{12}\right)^{-12\cdot 30}} \approx \$1404.89$; Total paid $= 1404.89\cdot 360 = \$505{,}760.40$

Chapter 9 Test

1. compound **2.** periodic **3.** effective **4.** annual

5. annuities **6.** sinking fund **7.** present value **8.** amortizing

9. $I = Prt = 1300(0.05)(10) = 650$
$1300 + 650 = \$1950$

10. $A_n = 1300\left(1 + \frac{0.05}{1}\right)^{1 \cdot 10} \approx \$2117.56$

11. $A_n = 1300\left(1 + \frac{0.05}{12}\right)^{12 \cdot 10} \approx \$2141.11$

12. $R = \left(1 + \frac{0.05}{12}\right)^{12} - 1 = 0.05116$
$= 5.116\%$

13. $A_0 = 5000\left(1 + \frac{0.07}{4}\right)^{-4 \cdot 10} \approx \$2498.00$

14. $A_n = \dfrac{700\left[\left(1 + \frac{0.073}{12}\right)^{12 \cdot 5} - 1\right]}{\frac{0.073}{12}}$
$\approx \$50{,}506.10$

15. $P = \dfrac{8000\left(\frac{0.065}{12}\right)}{\left(1 + \frac{0.065}{12}\right)^{12 \cdot 5} - 1} \approx \$113.20$

16. $A_0 = \dfrac{1000\left[1 - \left(1 + \frac{0.068}{12}\right)^{-12 \cdot 15}\right]}{\frac{0.068}{12}}$
$\approx \$112{,}652.71$

17. $P = \dfrac{90{,}000\left(\frac{0.0895}{12}\right)}{1 - \left(1 + \frac{0.0895}{12}\right)^{-12 \cdot 15}} \approx \$910.16$

Cumulative Review Exercises

1. $\begin{cases} 2x + y = 8 \\ x - 2y = -1 \end{cases}$

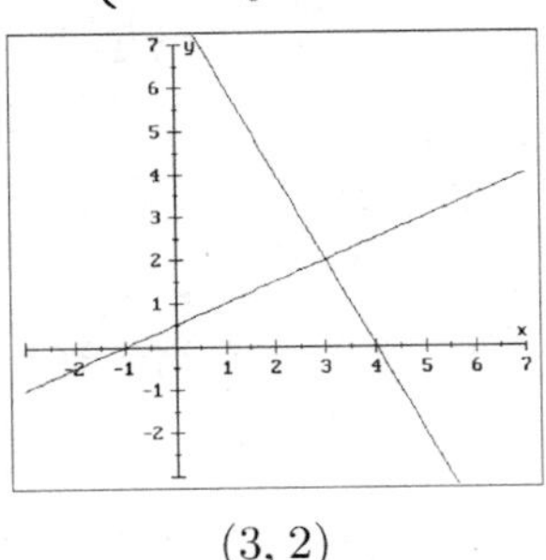

(3, 2)

2. $\begin{cases} 3x = -y + 2 \\ y + x - 4 = -2x \end{cases}$

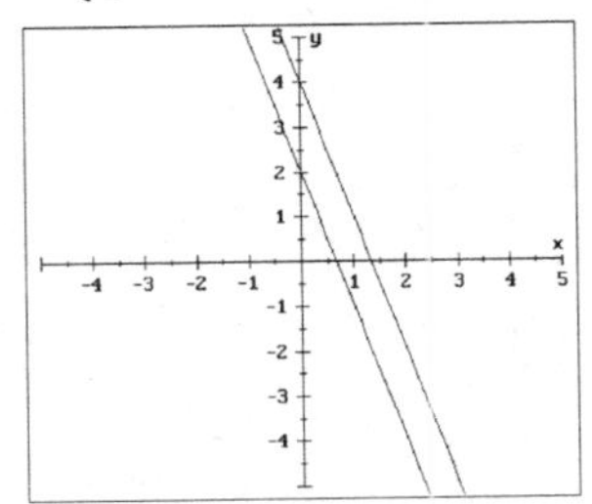

no solution, inconsistent system

3.
$$\begin{aligned} 5x &= 3y + 12 \Rightarrow 5x - 3y = 12 \Rightarrow \quad 5x - 3y = 12 \\ 2x - 3y &= 3 \quad\;\; \Rightarrow 2x - 3y = 3 \;\;\Rightarrow -2x + 3y = -3 \\ &\qquad\qquad\qquad\qquad\qquad\quad 3x = 9 \\ &\qquad\qquad\qquad\qquad\qquad\quad x = 3 \end{aligned}$$

$2x - 3y = 3$
$2(3) - 3y = 3$
$-3y = -3$
$y = 1$

Solution: $\boxed{x = 3, y = 1}$

CUMULATIVE REVIEW EXERCISES

4. $$\begin{bmatrix} x \\ y \\ z \end{bmatrix} = \begin{bmatrix} 2 & 1 & -1 \\ 1 & -1 & 1 \\ 1 & 1 & -3 \end{bmatrix}^{-1} \begin{bmatrix} 7 \\ 2 \\ 2 \end{bmatrix} = \begin{bmatrix} 3 \\ 2 \\ 1 \end{bmatrix}$$

5. $$\left[\begin{array}{ccc|c} 2 & 1 & -1 & 0 \\ 1 & -1 & 1 & 3 \\ 1 & 1 & -3 & -5 \end{array}\right] \Rightarrow \underset{R_1 \Leftrightarrow R_3}{\left[\begin{array}{ccc|c} 1 & 1 & -3 & -5 \\ 1 & -1 & 1 & 3 \\ 2 & 1 & -1 & 0 \end{array}\right]} \Rightarrow \underset{\substack{-R_1 + R_2 \Rightarrow R_2 \\ -2R_1 + R_3 \Rightarrow R_3}}{\left[\begin{array}{ccc|c} 1 & 1 & -3 & -5 \\ 0 & -2 & 4 & 8 \\ 0 & -1 & 5 & 10 \end{array}\right]} \Rightarrow$$

$$\underset{\substack{\frac{1}{2}R_2 + R_1 \Rightarrow R_1 \\ -\frac{1}{2}R_2 + R_3 \Rightarrow R_3 \\ -\frac{1}{2}R_2 \Rightarrow R_2}}{\left[\begin{array}{ccc|c} 1 & 0 & -1 & -1 \\ 0 & 1 & -2 & -4 \\ 0 & 0 & 3 & 6 \end{array}\right]} \Rightarrow \underset{\substack{\frac{1}{3}R_3 + R_1 \Rightarrow R_1 \\ \frac{2}{3}R_3 + R_2 \Rightarrow R_2 \\ \frac{1}{3}R_3 \Rightarrow R_3}}{\left[\begin{array}{ccc|c} 1 & 0 & 0 & 1 \\ 0 & 1 & 0 & 0 \\ 0 & 0 & 1 & 2 \end{array}\right]}$$

Solution: $\boxed{x = 1, y = 0, z = 2}$

6. $$\left[\begin{array}{cccc|c} 2 & -2 & 3 & 1 & 2 \\ 1 & 1 & 1 & 1 & 5 \\ -1 & 2 & -3 & 2 & 2 \\ 1 & 1 & 2 & -1 & 4 \end{array}\right] \Rightarrow \underset{\substack{-2R_2 + R_1 \Rightarrow R_2 \\ 2R_3 + R_1 \Rightarrow R_3 \\ -2R_4 + R_1 \Rightarrow R_4}}{\left[\begin{array}{cccc|c} 2 & -2 & 3 & 1 & 2 \\ 0 & -4 & 1 & -1 & -8 \\ 0 & 2 & -3 & 5 & 6 \\ 0 & -4 & -1 & 3 & -6 \end{array}\right]} \Rightarrow \underset{\substack{-2R_1 + R_2 \Rightarrow R_1 \\ 2R_3 + R_2 \Rightarrow R_3 \\ -R_4 + R_2 \Rightarrow R_4}}{\left[\begin{array}{cccc|c} -4 & 0 & -5 & -3 & -12 \\ 0 & -4 & 1 & -1 & -8 \\ 0 & 0 & -5 & 9 & 4 \\ 0 & 0 & 2 & -4 & -2 \end{array}\right]}$$

$$\underset{\frac{1}{2}R_4 \Rightarrow R_4}{\left[\begin{array}{cccc|c} -4 & 0 & -5 & -3 & -12 \\ 0 & -4 & 1 & -1 & -8 \\ 0 & 0 & -5 & 9 & 4 \\ 0 & 0 & 1 & -2 & -1 \end{array}\right]} \Rightarrow \underset{\substack{-R_1 + R_3 \Rightarrow R_1 \\ 5R_2 + R_3 \Rightarrow R_2 \\ 5R_4 + R_3 \Rightarrow R_4}}{\left[\begin{array}{cccc|c} 4 & 0 & 0 & 12 & 16 \\ 0 & -20 & 0 & 4 & -36 \\ 0 & 0 & -5 & 9 & 4 \\ 0 & 0 & 0 & -1 & -1 \end{array}\right]} \Rightarrow \underset{\substack{\frac{1}{4}R_1 \Rightarrow R_1 \\ \frac{1}{4}R_2 \Rightarrow R_2 \\ -R_4 \Rightarrow R_4}}{\left[\begin{array}{cccc|c} 1 & 0 & 0 & 3 & 4 \\ 0 & -5 & 0 & 1 & -9 \\ 0 & 0 & -5 & 9 & 4 \\ 0 & 0 & 0 & 1 & 1 \end{array}\right]}$$

$$\Rightarrow \underset{\substack{-3R_4 + R_1 \Rightarrow R_1 \\ -R_4 + R_2 \Rightarrow R_2 \\ -9R_4 + R_3 \Rightarrow R_3}}{\left[\begin{array}{cccc|c} 1 & 0 & 0 & 0 & 1 \\ 0 & -5 & 0 & 0 & -10 \\ 0 & 0 & -5 & 0 & -5 \\ 0 & 0 & 0 & 1 & 1 \end{array}\right]} \Rightarrow \underset{\substack{-\frac{1}{5}R_2 \Rightarrow R_2 \\ -\frac{1}{5}R_3 \Rightarrow R_3}}{\left[\begin{array}{cccc|c} 1 & 0 & 0 & 0 & 1 \\ 0 & 1 & 0 & 0 & 2 \\ 0 & 0 & 1 & 0 & 1 \\ 0 & 0 & 0 & 1 & 1 \end{array}\right]}$$

Solution: $\boxed{x = 1, y = 2, z = 1, t = 1}$

7. $$\begin{bmatrix} 2 & 1 \\ 1 & 4 \end{bmatrix} + \begin{bmatrix} -1 & 2 \\ 2 & 3 \end{bmatrix} = \begin{bmatrix} 1 & 3 \\ 3 & 7 \end{bmatrix}$$

8. $$\begin{bmatrix} -1 & 2 \\ 2 & 3 \end{bmatrix} - \begin{bmatrix} 2 & 1 \\ 1 & 4 \end{bmatrix} = \begin{bmatrix} -3 & 1 \\ 1 & -1 \end{bmatrix}$$

9. $$\begin{bmatrix} 2 & 1 \\ 1 & 4 \end{bmatrix} \begin{bmatrix} 2 & 0 & -1 \\ -1 & 2 & 2 \end{bmatrix} = \begin{bmatrix} 3 & 2 & 0 \\ -2 & 8 & 7 \end{bmatrix}$$

10. $\begin{bmatrix} -1 & 2 \\ 2 & 3 \end{bmatrix}^2 + 2\begin{bmatrix} 2 & 1 \\ 1 & 4 \end{bmatrix} = \begin{bmatrix} -1 & 2 \\ 2 & 3 \end{bmatrix}\begin{bmatrix} -1 & 2 \\ 2 & 3 \end{bmatrix} + \begin{bmatrix} 4 & 2 \\ 2 & 8 \end{bmatrix} = \begin{bmatrix} 5 & 4 \\ 4 & 13 \end{bmatrix} + \begin{bmatrix} 4 & 2 \\ 2 & 8 \end{bmatrix} = \begin{bmatrix} 9 & 6 \\ 6 & 21 \end{bmatrix}$

11. $\left[\begin{array}{cc|cc} 2 & 6 & 1 & 0 \\ 2 & 4 & 0 & 1 \end{array}\right] \Rightarrow \underset{\frac{1}{2}R_1 \Rightarrow R_1}{\left[\begin{array}{cc|cc} 1 & 3 & \frac{1}{2} & 0 \\ 2 & 4 & 0 & 1 \end{array}\right]} \Rightarrow \underset{-2R_1 + R_2 \Rightarrow R_2}{\left[\begin{array}{cc|cc} 1 & 3 & \frac{1}{2} & 0 \\ 0 & -2 & -1 & 1 \end{array}\right]} \Rightarrow$

$\underset{-\frac{1}{2}R_2 \Rightarrow R_2}{\left[\begin{array}{cc|cc} 1 & 3 & \frac{1}{2} & 0 \\ 0 & 1 & \frac{1}{2} & -\frac{1}{2} \end{array}\right]} \Rightarrow \underset{-3R_2 + R_1 \Rightarrow R_1}{\left[\begin{array}{cc|cc} 1 & 0 & -1 & \frac{3}{2} \\ 0 & 1 & \frac{1}{2} & -\frac{1}{2} \end{array}\right]} \Rightarrow \text{Inverse: } \begin{bmatrix} -1 & \frac{3}{2} \\ \frac{1}{2} & -\frac{1}{2} \end{bmatrix}$

12. $\left[\begin{array}{ccc|ccc} 1 & -1 & 1 & 1 & 0 & 0 \\ 1 & 4 & 0 & 0 & 1 & 0 \\ 2 & 4 & 1 & 0 & 0 & 1 \end{array}\right] \Rightarrow \underset{\substack{-R_1 + R_2 \Rightarrow R_2 \\ -2R_2 + R_3 \Rightarrow R_3}}{\left[\begin{array}{ccc|ccc} 1 & -1 & 1 & 1 & 0 & 0 \\ 0 & 5 & -1 & -1 & 1 & 0 \\ 0 & 6 & -1 & -2 & 0 & 1 \end{array}\right]} \Rightarrow \underset{-R_2 + R_3 \Rightarrow R_2}{\left[\begin{array}{ccc|ccc} 1 & -1 & 1 & 1 & 0 & 0 \\ 0 & 1 & 0 & -1 & -1 & 1 \\ 0 & 6 & -1 & -2 & 0 & 1 \end{array}\right]}$

$\Rightarrow \underset{\substack{R_2 + R_1 \Rightarrow R_1 \\ -6R_2 + R_3 \Rightarrow R_3}}{\left[\begin{array}{ccc|ccc} 1 & 0 & 1 & 0 & -1 & 1 \\ 0 & 1 & 0 & -1 & -1 & 1 \\ 0 & 0 & -1 & 4 & 6 & -5 \end{array}\right]} \Rightarrow \underset{\substack{R_3 + R_1 \Rightarrow R_1 \\ -R_3 \Rightarrow R_3}}{\left[\begin{array}{ccc|ccc} 1 & 0 & 0 & 4 & 5 & -4 \\ 0 & 1 & 0 & -1 & -1 & 1 \\ 0 & 0 & 1 & -4 & -6 & 5 \end{array}\right]} \Rightarrow \text{Inv} = \begin{bmatrix} 4 & 5 & -4 \\ -1 & -1 & 1 \\ -4 & -6 & 5 \end{bmatrix}$

13. $\begin{vmatrix} -3 & 5 \\ 4 & 7 \end{vmatrix} = (-3)(7) - (5)(4) = -21 - 20 = -41$

14. $\begin{vmatrix} 2 & -3 & 2 \\ 0 & 1 & -1 \\ 1 & -2 & 1 \end{vmatrix} = 2\begin{vmatrix} 1 & -1 \\ -2 & 1 \end{vmatrix} - (-3)\begin{vmatrix} 0 & -1 \\ 1 & 1 \end{vmatrix} + 2\begin{vmatrix} 0 & 1 \\ 1 & -2 \end{vmatrix}$

$= 2(-1) + 3(1) + 2(-1) = -2 + 3 - 2 = -1$

15. $x = \dfrac{\begin{vmatrix} 11 & 3 \\ 24 & 5 \end{vmatrix}}{\begin{vmatrix} 4 & 3 \\ -2 & 5 \end{vmatrix}}$

16. $y = \dfrac{\begin{vmatrix} 4 & 11 \\ -2 & 24 \end{vmatrix}}{\begin{vmatrix} 4 & 3 \\ -2 & 5 \end{vmatrix}}$

17. $\dfrac{-x+1}{(x+1)(x+2)} = \dfrac{A}{x+1} + \dfrac{B}{x+2}$

$= \dfrac{A(x+2)}{(x+1)(x+2)} + \dfrac{B(x+1)}{(x+1)(x+2)}$

$= \dfrac{Ax + 2A + Bx + B}{(x+1)(x+2)}$

$= \dfrac{(A+B)x + (2A+B)}{(x+1)(x+2)}$

$\begin{cases} A + B = -1 \\ 2A + B = 1 \end{cases} \Rightarrow A = 2,\ B = -3$

$\dfrac{-x+1}{(x+1)(x+2)} = \dfrac{2}{x+1} - \dfrac{3}{x+2}$

18.
$$\begin{aligned}\frac{x-4}{(2x-5)^2} &= \frac{A}{2x-5} + \frac{B}{(2x-5)^2}\\ &= \frac{A(2x-5)}{(2x-5)^2} + \frac{B}{(2x-5)^2}\\ &= \frac{2Ax-5A+B}{(2x-5)^2}\\ &= \frac{2Ax+(-5A+B)}{(2x-5)^2}\end{aligned}$$

$$\begin{cases} 2A = 1 \\ -5A + B = -4 \end{cases} \Rightarrow \begin{array}{l} A = \frac{1}{2} \\ B = -\frac{3}{2} \end{array}$$

$$\frac{x-4}{(2x-5)^2} = \frac{\frac{1}{2}}{2x-5} - \frac{\frac{3}{2}}{(2x-5)^2}$$

19. $y \le 2x + 6$

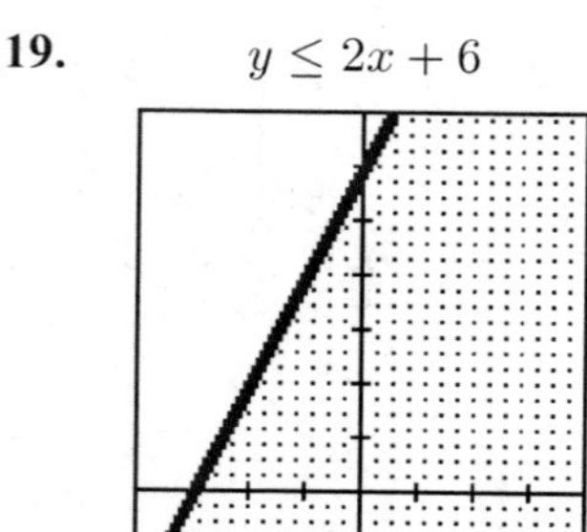

20. $\begin{cases} 2x + 3y \ge 6 \\ 2x - 3y \le 6 \end{cases}$

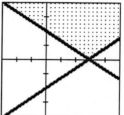

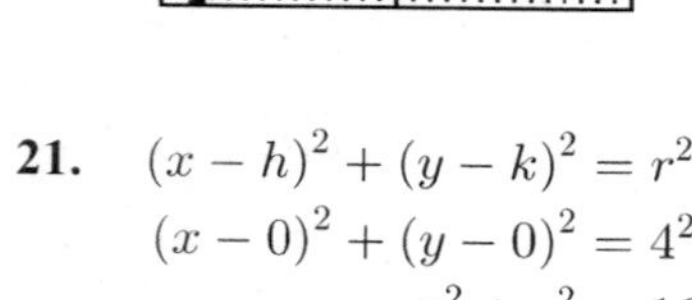

21.
$$\begin{aligned}(x-h)^2 + (y-k)^2 &= r^2\\ (x-0)^2 + (y-0)^2 &= 4^2\\ x^2 + y^2 &= 16\end{aligned}$$

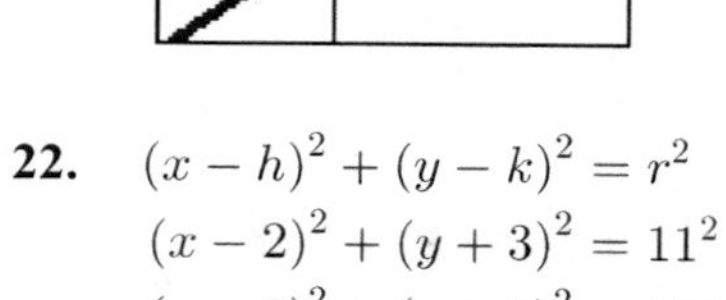

22.
$$\begin{aligned}(x-h)^2 + (y-k)^2 &= r^2\\ (x-2)^2 + (y+3)^2 &= 11^2\\ (x-2)^2 + (y+3)^2 &= 121\end{aligned}$$

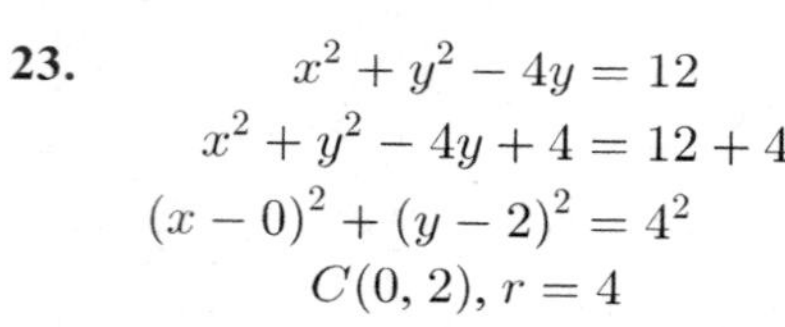

23.
$$\begin{aligned}x^2 + y^2 - 4y &= 12\\ x^2 + y^2 - 4y + 4 &= 12 + 4\\ (x-0)^2 + (y-2)^2 &= 4^2\end{aligned}$$
$C(0, 2),\ r = 4$

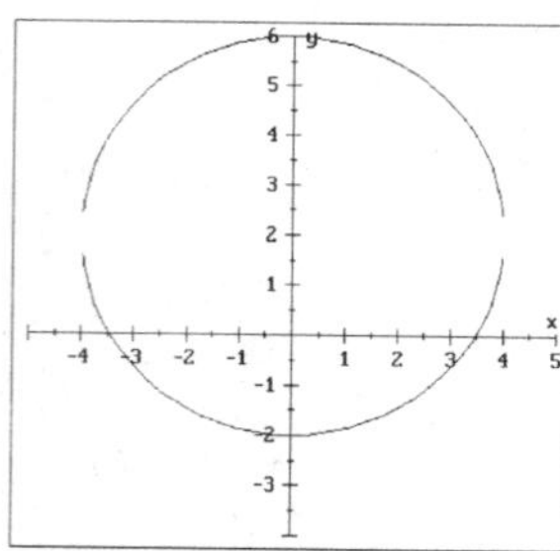

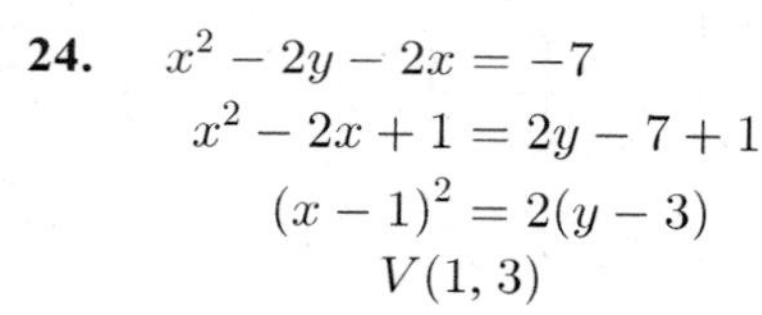

24.
$$\begin{aligned}x^2 - 2y - 2x &= -7\\ x^2 - 2x + 1 &= 2y - 7 + 1\\ (x-1)^2 &= 2(y-3)\end{aligned}$$
$V(1, 3)$

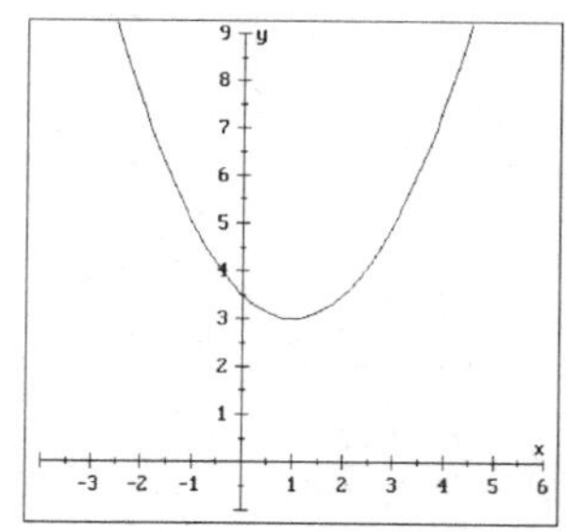

25.
$$x^2 + 4y^2 + 2x = 3$$
$$x^2 + 2x + 1 + 4y^2 = 3 + 1$$
$$(x+1)^2 + 4y^2 = 4$$
$$\frac{(x+1)^2}{4} + \frac{y^2}{1} = 1$$

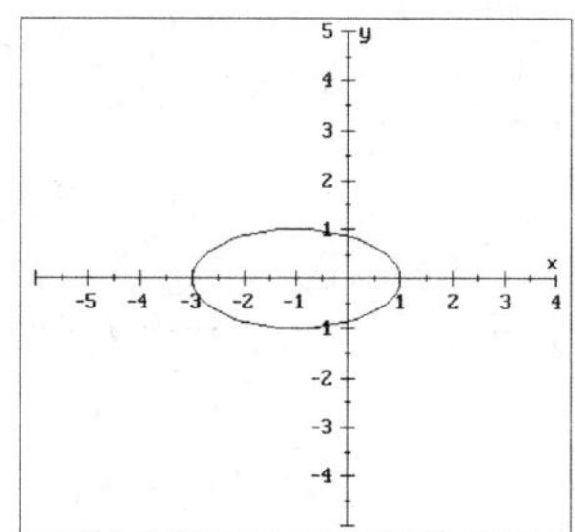

26.
$$x^2 - 9y^2 - 4x = 5$$
$$x^2 - 4x + 4 - 9y^2 = 5 + 4$$
$$(x-2)^2 - 9y^2 = 9$$
$$\frac{(x-2)^2}{9} - \frac{y^2}{1} = 1$$

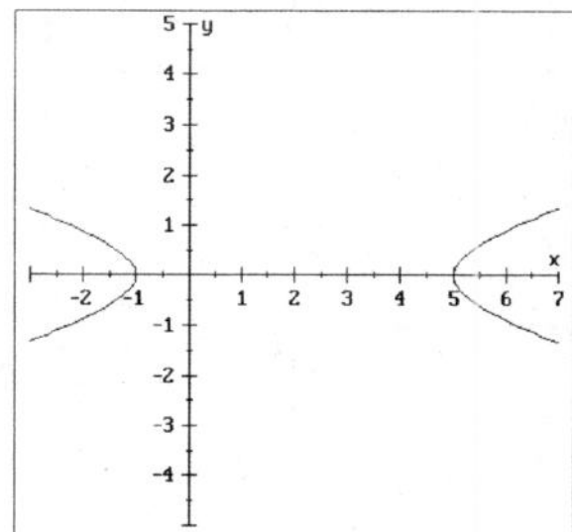

27. $a = 6, b = 4$
$$\frac{x^2}{36} + \frac{y^2}{16} = 1$$

28. $a = 5, c = 2$
$$b^2 = a^2 - c^2 = 25 - 4 = 21$$
$$\frac{(x-2)^2}{21} + \frac{(y-3)^2}{25} = 1$$

29. $a = 2, c = 3$
$$b^2 = c^2 - a^2 = 9 - 4 = 5$$
$$\frac{x^2}{4} - \frac{y^2}{5} = 1$$

30. $2a = 6, 2b = 6 \Rightarrow a = 3, b = 3$
$$\frac{(y-4)^2}{9} - \frac{(x-2)^2}{9} = 1$$

31. The 2nd term will involve $(2y)^1$.
$$\frac{8!}{7!1!}x^7(2y)^1 = 16x^7y$$

32. The 6th term will involve $(2y)^5$.
$$\frac{8!}{3!5!}x^3(2y)^5 = 1792x^3y^5$$

33. $\displaystyle\sum_{k=1}^{5} 2 = 5(2) = 10$

34. $\displaystyle\sum_{k=2}^{6}(3k+1) = 3\sum_{k=2}^{6}k + \sum_{k=2}^{6}1 = 3(2+3+4+5+6) + 5(1) = 60 + 5 = 65$

35. $a = -2, d = 3$
$$a_6 = a + (n-1)d = -2 + 5(3) = 13$$
$$S_6 = \frac{n(a + a_6)}{2} = \frac{6(-2+13)}{2} = 33$$

36. $a = \frac{1}{9}, r = 3, n = 6$
$$S_6 = \frac{a - ar^n}{1 - r} = \frac{\frac{1}{9} - \frac{1}{9}(3)^6}{1-3} = \frac{-\frac{728}{9}}{-2} = \frac{364}{9}$$

37. $P(8,4) = \dfrac{8!}{(8-4)!} = \dfrac{8!}{4!} = 1680$

38. $P(24,0) = \dfrac{24!}{(24-0)!} = \dfrac{24!}{24!} = 1$

CUMULATIVE REVIEW EXERCISES

39. $C(12, 10) = \dfrac{12!}{10!2!} = 66$

40. $P(4, 4) \cdot C(6, 6) = 24 \cdot 1 = 24$

41. $4! \cdot 6! = 17{,}280$

42. $\binom{12}{4} = \dfrac{12!}{4!8!} = 495$

43. $\dfrac{2}{36} = \dfrac{1}{18}$

44. $\dfrac{\binom{26}{5}}{\binom{52}{5}} = \dfrac{65{,}780}{2{,}598{,}960} = \dfrac{253}{9996}$

45. $(0.6)(0.8) = 0.48$

46.

Check $n = 1$: $3(1) + 1 \stackrel{?}{=} \dfrac{1(3(1)+5)}{2}$ True for $n = 1$

$4 = 4$

Assume for $n = k$ and show for $n = k + 1$:

$$4 + 7 + 10 + \cdots + (3k+1) = \frac{k(3k+5)}{2}$$

$$\boxed{4 + 7 + 10 + \cdots + (3k+1)} + 3(k+1) + 1 = \boxed{\frac{k(3k+5)}{2}} + 3(k+1) + 1$$

$$4 + 7 + 10 + \cdots + (3(k+1)+1) = \frac{k(3k+5)}{2} + \frac{2 \cdot (3(k+1)+1)}{2}$$

$$4 + 7 + 10 + \cdots + (3(k+1)+1) = \frac{3k^2 + 5k + 6k + 6 + 2}{2}$$

$$4 + 7 + 10 + \cdots + (3(k+1)+1) = \frac{3k^2 + 11k + 8}{2}$$

$$4 + 7 + 10 + \cdots + (3(k+1)+1) = \frac{(k+1)(3k+8)}{2}$$

$$4 + 7 + 10 + \cdots + (3(k+1)+1) = \frac{(k+1)(3(k+1)+5)}{2}$$

Since this is what results when $n = k + 1$ in the formula, we have shown that the formula works for $n = k + 1$ if it works for $n = k$.

47. $A_0 = 10{,}000\left(1 + \dfrac{0.085}{1}\right)^{-1 \cdot 12}$

$\approx \$3757.02$

48. $P = \dfrac{110{,}000\left(\frac{0.0875}{12}\right)}{1 - \left(1 + \frac{0.0875}{12}\right)^{-12 \cdot 20}} \approx \$972.08$